Goodheart-Willcox
automotive
encyclopedia

fundamental principles, construction,
operation, service, repairs

Edited by

WILLIAM K. TOBOLDT

Author of Fix Your Ford, Fix Your Chevrolet, Auto Body
Repairing and Repainting. Formerly, Editor of Motor
Service. Member, Society of Automotive Engineers.

LARRY JOHNSON

Executive Technical Editor, Motor Service and Service
Station Management. Co-author of Fix Your Volks-
wagen. Affiliate Member, Society of Automotive
Engineers.

South Holland, Illinois

THE GOODHEART-WILLCOX CO., INC.
Publishers

INTRODUCTION

The automotive service field offers excellent opportunities for men with the necessary educational background and practical training. A good mechanic is well paid, and his work is always in demand.

The AUTOMOTIVE ENCYCLOPEDIA is a book of Fundamentals and Basic Service Procedures -- the foundation on which a sound, thorough knowledge of auto mechanics is based. The mechanic with a knowledge of these important fundamentals is not "tied" to a shop manual; he has the know-how which will enable him to quickly diagnose trouble and provide the service or repair needed on any make of car -- any model -- at any time.

The ENCYCLOPEDIA tells, and shows by clear illustrations, what happens when you turn on an ignition key and "step on the gas" -- how energy in fuel is converted into power, and the power is transmitted to the driving wheels of a car. This book describes the accessory parts that contribute to the development and utilization of that power. It covers the sciences involved in the repair and maintenance of the modern car -- Internal Combustion, Electricity, Hydraulics and Pneumatics.

The AUTOMOTIVE ENCYCLOPEDIA provides instruction in Automotive Mechanics, as recommended by the standards for Automotive Service Instruction in Schools prepared by the Automotive Industry -- Vocational Educational Conference. It covers, also, numerous other topics of interest and practical value to the auto mechanic.

This book is intended, too, as a guide for car owners and prospective owners who want to learn about cars so they can achieve reliable, economical operation of their own cars, and better handle any emergencies that might arise on the highway.

William K. Toboldt

Larry Johnson

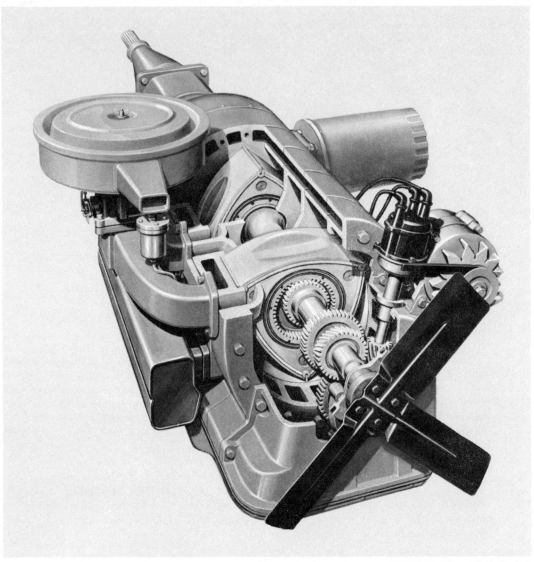

Wankel rotary engine, as used on the cover, showing two triangular shaped rotors which rotate in a figure eight-shaped chamber, and operate on the conventional four-stroke cycle of intake, compression, power, and exhaust strokes. Conventional pistons, valves, and connecting rods are eliminated.

CONTENTS

Contents

AUTOMOTIVE TOOLS

Hand tools, measuring devices, and fastening methods form a most important part of every automotive repair job.

Hand tools are used on every job to remove, disassemble or adjust parts and units. Measuring devices are a must for checking sizes and clearances. Various types of fasteners such as bolts and nuts, are used to hold the parts together.

It is therefore essential that every mechanic be thoroughly familiar with the tools, measuring devices, and fastening methods that are used in the automotive industry. In addition, it is important to know the correct methods of using tools and measuring devices, not only to be able to complete the work as quickly as possible, but also with maximum accuracy and safety.

Fig. 1-1. Example of typical open-end wrench.

Open-End Wrenches

Probably the most important tool in a mechanic's kit is the open-end wrench. These are used for loosening or tightening bolts and nuts, and an example of one of these wrenches is illustrated in Fig. 1-1.

Wrench sizes are designated by the width of the opening. And a set of standard open-end wrenches usually has the smallest opening of 3/8 in. and increases in size in 1/16 in. steps with the largest opening of 1 in. Larger openings are also available, but are not always included in a set.

In order to be able to turn a nut in a restricted space, the end of the wrench is placed at an angle to the handle. Usually this is 15 deg. By having first one side of the wrench up, and then the other, it is possible to turn nuts in very restricted spaces.

Wrenches are also made with openings at 22 1/2 deg., 30 deg., 60 deg. and 90 deg. to the handle.

While the smallest opening of a standard wrench set is usually 3/8 in., smaller wrenches known as

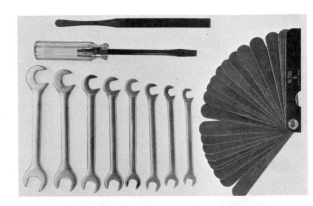

Fig. 1-2. Set of special open-end wrenches with other tools comprising a set for ignition work.

miniature, Fig. 1-2, are also available. Such wrenches are needed for work on ignition systems, etc. The openings range in size in 1/32 in. steps from 3/16 in. to 15/32 in.

Special open-end wrenches designed specifically for adjusting valve tappets on L-head engines, are also available. These wrenches are thinner and longer than the conventional open-end wrench, and five sizes from 3/8 in. to 5/8 in. are the openings usually provided.

Box Wrenches

In order to reduce the possibility of a wrench slipping from the nut, the box-type wrench, Fig. 1-3, was designed. Usually the box is a double hexagon (12

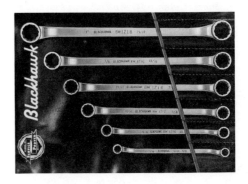

Fig. 1-3. Set of box-type wrenches.

grooves). These grooves engage the corners of the nut. This permits moving the handle of the wrench through an arc of as little as 30 deg. The wrench can then be repositioned on the nut. This is an extremely important advantage, as the movement of the wrench handle is often restricted because of space limitations. Furthermore, as the walls of the box are relatively thin, less space surrounding the nut is required than is the case with the conventional open-end wrench. The disadvantage of the box wrench is that it cannot be used on copper tubing fittings. However, a box-type wrench, Fig. 1-4, with a section of the box cut away, is available for such work.

In addition to the regular box wrenches with the straight handles, some have the heads set at angles of 15 deg. to the handle, Fig. 1-5. This tips the end of the wrench which is not on the nut upward, and provides clearance for the mechanic's knuckles. There are also many wrenches designed for specific jobs. Fig. 1-6, shows a special wrench designed especially for work on manifold units.

Fig. 1-4. Special wrench for working on copper tubing fittings.

Fig. 1-5. Box-type wrench with head at 15 deg. to handle. The off-set provides clearance for mechanic's knuckles.

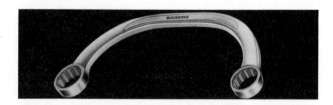

Fig. 1-6. Special wrench for working on exhaust manifolds.

Socket Wrenches

Socket wrenches, Fig. 1-7, like the box wrench, completely surround the nut to be tightened or loosened, and in that way there is little chance of the wrench slipping from the nut. With assorted handles they greatly reduce the time for removing nuts. Usually the socket wrench used in automotive work has 12 grooves to engage the corners of the nut. Socket wrenches come in sizes from approximately 3/16 in.

Fig. 1-7. Conventional socket on left and deep socket on right. When used for spark plug removal, the deep type is provided with a rubber insert which grasps the plug for easy removal.

to 1 5/8 in. Socket wrenches as used in automotive service work have detachable handles of various types, Fig. 1-8. The drive opening of the socket, that is the opening in the socket in which the wrench handle is placed is 1/4 in., 3/8 in., 1/2 in., or 3/4 in. square. This is known as the "drive." In addition, one manufacturer has a socket wrench with 7/16 in. drive, which is designed to take the place of both the 3/8 in. and 1/2 in. drive socket sets.

Mechanics usually have a set of 1/4 in., 3/8 in., and 1/2 in. drive socket wrenches in their kits. The 1/4 in. square drive socket set usually includes sockets ranging in size from 1/4 in. to 7/8 in. And the 1/2 in. square drive socket set is designed for use on nuts ranging in size from 3/8 in. to 1 5/16 in.

In addition to the various size sockets of standard depth which are used for loosening and tightening conventional nuts, extra deep sockets are also available, and are used primarily for removing spark plugs.

A socket wrench set also includes various types of handles, which are so designed that nuts in normally inaccessible positions can be reached, and as a result the time for their removal and replacement is greatly reduced. The following types are usually included: reversible ratchet handle, extensions of various lengths, speeder, cross handle, hinge or flex handle, Fig. 1-8.

Inside the head of the ratchet handle, Fig. 1-8, is a pawl or dog which engages or fits into one or more of the ratchet teeth. Pulling on the handle in one direction, the dog holds in the ratchet piece and turns the socket. Moving the handle in the opposite direc-

Fig. 1-8. Assorted socket wrench handles. From front to rear: Ratchet, extension, flex handle and spinner.

tion, the dog ratchets over the teeth, permitting the handle to be backed up without moving the socket. As the teeth of the ratchet are relatively fine, the ratchet handle can be swung through a very small angle or arc in order to get a new grip. By using a ratchet handle, it is not necessary to disengage the socket from the nut, and in that way the nut can be quickly removed.

The speed handle, which is shaped like a carpenter's brace, Fig. 1-8, is also designed for quick removal of the nut, and is used primarily after the nut has once been loosened by means of another wrench providing greater leverage.

In many cases it is not possible to get a direct pull on a nut, and then a universal joint, Fig. 1-9, is used between the handle and socket.

Fig. 1-9. A universal joint is used to provide an angle drive.

Torque Wrenches

In many cases it is essential that a nut be tightened to a specified amount. If overtightened, the part on which the nut is mounted may be distorted and leakage of some sort may occur. This is particularly true in the case of cylinder head and bearing nuts and bolts. So that such nuts or bolts can be tightened to the specified amount, a torque wrench, Fig. 1-10, is used. Torque wrenches are provided with an indicator which will show the amount of torque in either foot pounds or inch pounds. When using a torque wrench, it is imperative that the threads of the nut to be tightened be clean and oiled, so that no additional friction will be present.

Torque wrenches are used with the socket of the size to fit the nut which is to be tightened.

Adjustable Wrenches

There are three general types of adjustable wrenches. These include the adjustable-end wrench, Fig. 1-11, the monkey wrench, Fig. 1-12, and the pipe or Stillson wrench, Fig. 1-13.

The adjustable-end wrench and the monkey wrench are convenient to have in a mechanic's kit, as they will fit any nut which is within the range of their adjustment. They are available in various sizes, and are specified according to their length. The main dis-

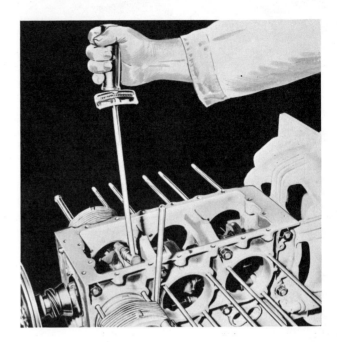

Fig. 1-10. Using a torque wrench on a connecting rod bolt.

advantage of these two adjustable wrenches is that they do not hold their adjustment. Consequently they are apt to slip on the nut.

The pipe or Stillson wrench, as the name implies, is designed specifically for tightening and loosening pipes or other circular items.

Pipe wrenches are seldom needed in automotive work, but occasionally they are found necessary on nuts which have been so damaged that conventional wrenches will not hold on them.

Fig. 1-11. Adjustable-end wrench.

Fig. 1-12. Monkey wrench.

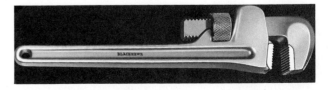

Fig. 1-13. Stillson wrench which is used for pipe work.

Fig. 1-14. Left. Care must be taken to select wrenches that fit the nut exactly. Fig. 1-15. Right. If wrong size wrench is used, corners of the nut will become rounded, then even the correct wrench will no longer fit.

Regardless of what type of wrench is being used, be sure that it fits the nut or bolt head, Fig. 1-14. If the wrench opening is too large for the particular nut, Fig. 1-15, it will slip and round off the corners of the nut. In addition, when the wrench slips, the mechanic may receive a skinned knuckle. It is always much safer to pull on a wrench than to push on it.

Pliers

There are many different types of pliers used in automotive work. One of the most commonly used pliers in the automotive field is the 6 in. combination slip-joint pliers, Fig. 1-16. The slip-joint permits the jaws to be opened wider at the hinge for gripping larger diameters.

The diagonal cutting pliers, Fig. 1-17, are needed not only for cutting wire but are also used extensively for removing cotter pins.

Long nose pliers, Fig. 1-18, either the flat nose or duck bill type, are needed frequently in recovering a washer or a nut which has dropped into an inaccessible place, and are also used frequently to aid in positioning small parts.

The channel-lock pliers, Fig. 1-19, is a variation of the slip-joint pliers in that it is adjustable. The opening of the pliers can be adjusted to several different sizes, by means of a dog which engages any one of the circular channels. In that way the jaws of the pliers remain approximately parallel regardless of the size of the opening.

One of the most versatile tools in the mechanic's

Fig. 1-16. Combination slip-joint pliers.

Fig. 1-17. Diagonal cutting pliers are used not only for cutting wire, but also for pulling cotter pins.

Fig. 1-18. There are many different types of long nose pliers. These are used frequently for positioning small parts.

Fig. 1-19. Channel-lock pliers are not so apt to lose their adjustment and their jaws remain approximately parallel throughout their range.

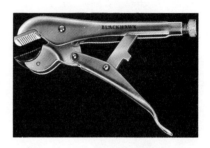

Fig. 1-20. Locking or vise-grip pliers are one of the most important tools in a mechanic's kit.

Fig. 1-20a. Snap ring pliers.

Fig. 1-20b. Special pliers used to disconnect non-metallic ignition cable from spark plugs.

Fig. 1-21. Pliers should not be used for loosening or tightening nuts.

kit is the vise-grip or locking pliers, Fig. 1-20. When locked in position on a part, it will grip it firmly even though the area contacted by the jaws of the pliers is extremely small. It has an infinite number of uses ranging from holding two parts together while they are being worked on, to gripping the end of a broken stud and turning it out of its threaded hole.

Snap ring pliers, Fig. 1-20a, are important tools in every repair kit. They are used to remove snap rings, Fig. 2-9, from various parts such as hydraulic valve lifters and transmissions.

Ignition Cable Pliers

Non-metallic conductors in radiation suppression ignition cable can be broken easily. To avoid breakage pull should be applied only on the rubber boot covering the spark plug insulator. This can be simplified by using special pliers as shown in Fig. 1-20b.

Pliers and Stillson wrenches should never be used for loosening or tightening nuts, Fig. 1-21.

Screwdrivers

Many different types and sizes of screwdrivers are needed by the automotive mechanic. The conventional screwdriver, Fig. 1-22, has a flat blade designed to engage a straight groove in the head of the screw.

The Phillips-type screwdriver, Fig. 1-23, has a pointed end with four grooves which are designed to engage corresponding slots in the head of the Phillips-type screw.

Another type screwdriver is the clutch-type screwdriver, Fig. 1-24, with a fluted end designed to engage a corresponding opening in the head of the screw.

Fig. 1-22. Conventional screwdriver.

Fig. 1-23. Phillips head screwdriver.

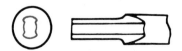

Fig. 1-24. Clutch-type screwdriver.

The usual length of screwdrivers is 3, 4, 6, 8, 10 and 12 inches. A complete set is essential.

When the space over the head of a screw is limited,

an offset screwdriver, Fig. 1-25, is needed to remove or tighten the screw. These are available in different sizes, and can also be obtained with ratchet heads.

Screwdrivers should only be used on screws. The blade of the screwdriver should fit the slot in the screw, Fig. 1-26, and the blade of the screwdriver should always be held vertical to the screw head.

Screwdrivers are not designed to be used as levers or pry bars. If a pry bar is not immediately available and a screwdriver must be used, be sure that the screwdriver selected is strong enough to stand the strain without bending. Screwdrivers should fit the screw slot snugly, as a loose fit will not only damage the screw head but also the screwdriver blade.

Fig. 1-25. Offset-type screwdriver is needed when there is little clearance over the screw head.

Fig. 1-26. The screwdriver blade must always fit the slot in the screw.

Setscrew Wrenches

Setscrew wrenches, or Allen wrenches, Fig. 1-27, are used on setscrews with hexagonal recesses in the screw heads. These wrenches are L-shaped bars of steel. A typical set comprises eleven wrenches ranging in size from .050 to 3/8 in., and are designed to

Fig. 1-27. Set of setscrew wrenches, also known as Allen wrenches, with setscrews on left.

fit setscrew sizes No. 4 to 3/4 in. Spanner wrenches, Fig. 1-28, are used to tighten and loosen round nuts which have a series of notches cut into the outer edge. For the most part, these are special wrenches furnished by the manufacturer to service special parts.

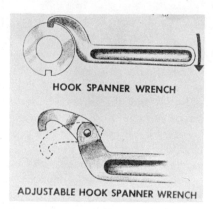

Fig. 1-28. *Two types of spanner wrenches which are used on radial nuts.*

Hammers

Automotive mechanics require hammers of various types and sizes. The most important is the ball peen hammer, Fig. 1-29. The flat portion of the head used for most hammering is called the face, and the other end the peen. When the peen is ball-shaped it is known as a ball peen, and is used primarily for riveting work.

Fig. 1-29. *A hammer should be gripped close to the end of the handle, and the full face of the hammer should strike the work.*

Fig. 1-30. *Never strike the work with the edge of the hammer face.*

Ball peen hammers are usually classed according to the weight of the head without the handle. A good combination hammer set for automotive work would include 12 oz., 1/2 lb., and 4 oz. hammers. A small hammer is very handy for light work, especially when cutting gaskets out of sheet stock.

Simple as the hammer is, there are right and wrong ways to use it. The beginner usually has a tendency to grip the handle too close to the head. This is known as choking a hammer, and reduces the force of the blow. The hammer should be gripped close to the end of the handle, Fig. 1-29. In this way a heavier blow can be struck with less effort. Be careful not to strike the work with the edge of the hammer face, Fig. 1-30. In other words, the full face of the hammer should contact the head of the chisel or other work.

Never work with a hammer having a loose head. This is dangerous because the head of the hammer may fly off and cause an injury.

The end of the hammer handle should not be used for bumping purposes, as this will quickly split and ruin the handle. Neither should hammer handles be used as levers.

If there is any danger of damaging the surface or work, a "soft" hammer, Fig. 1-31, should be used. Such special hammers are provided with faces of rawhide, plastic or lead.

Fig. 1-31. *Typical soft face hammer which is used when there is any danger of damaging the work.*

For straightening sheet metal on automotive bodies there is a large variety of hammers known as dinging hammers. These are discussed in another chapter.

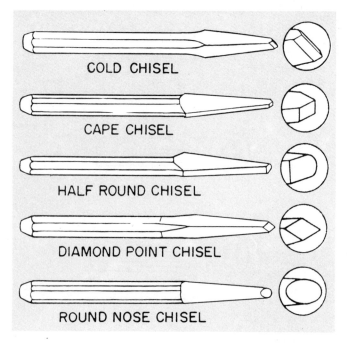

Fig. 1-32. *Note the cutting edge of these different types of cold chisels.*

Tools

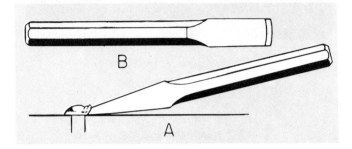

Fig. 1-33. A rivet buster is used to cut the heads from rivets.

Chisels

Cold chisels, Fig. 1-32, are used for cutting metal, to cut the heads from rivets, chip metal, and to split nuts which have become rusted and cannot be loosened by means of a wrench.

The cape chisel, Fig. 1-32, has a narrow cutting edge, and is used primarily for cutting keyways and narrow grooves.

In general, automotive mechanics will use only the flat chisel, and the sizes most frequently used are 3/8 in., 1/2 in. and 3/4 in.

A rivet buster, Fig. 1-33, is a special form of chisel and is designed specifically for cutting the heads from rivets. It differs from the conventional cold or flat chisel, in that only one side of the cutting edge is ground.

When using a chisel, a right handed person should hold the tool in his left hand, and wield the hammer with his right. The chisel should be held rather loosely

with fingers curled around the chisel about one inch from the head of the chisel.

When chipping metal, the depth of the cut is controlled by the angle of the chisel, Fig. 1-34. Deeper cuts are taken as the angle of the chisel approaches the vertical. When chipping, the mechanic should keep his eye on the cutting edge, and not the head of the chisel.

Goggles should be worn when chipping and grinding, and precautions should be taken so that chips will not strike anyone who is nearby. Never use a chisel on which the head has mushroomed, as portions of the "mushroom" will fly off when struck by a hammer. The battered end should be ground off on a grinding wheel.

Fig. 1-35. Sharpening chisel on power grinder.

When sharpening a flat chisel, Fig. 1-35, the two ground surfaces should form an angle of 60 deg., as shown in Fig. 1-36. Rivet busters, Fig. 1-33, are ground on one surface only, and at an angle of approximately 30 deg.

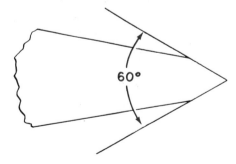

Fig. 1-36. Flat chisels should be sharpened to an angle of 60 deg.

A variety of punches, Fig. 1-37, are required in automotive work. The starting punch, or drift as it is sometimes known, is designed to punch out rivets after the heads have been cut off. These punches are also

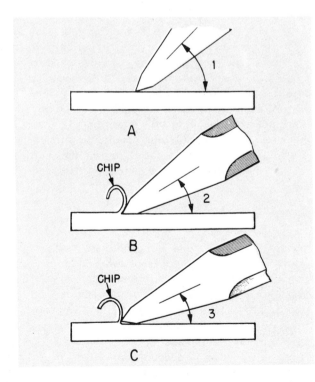

Fig. 1-34. The depth of cut is controlled by the angle of the chisel.

Fig. 1-37. A variety of punches are required in automotive service.

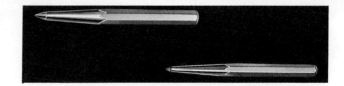

Fig. 1-39. Two types of center punches.

used to start driving out straight or tapered pins, Fig. 1-38. After the pin has been driven partly from the hole, the starting punch can no longer be used because of its taper. A pin punch is then used to complete the job of punching out the pin. Pin punches should not be used to start such work because a hard blow on the punch would bend the slender shank.

A lining-up punch has a long taper, and is used to shift parts to bring corresponding holes into alignment.

Fig. 1-38. When punching out a pin, use starting punch first and follow through with a pin punch.

The center punch, Fig. 1-39, is ground to a fine point, and is used to mark the location of a hole that is to be drilled. Without such a mark the drill will wander over the surface and the hole will be drilled at the wrong position.

Screw Extractors

Screw extractors, Fig. 1-40, are used for removing screws and studs which have broken off so that they cannot be turned by conventional or vise-grip pliers. The screw extractor is made with a tapered left hand thread. After drilling a hole in the broken screw, the screw extractor is screwed into the hole. Continued turning of the extractor causes the tapered threads of the extractor to jam in the hole so that the broken screw (right hand thread) can be screwed out.

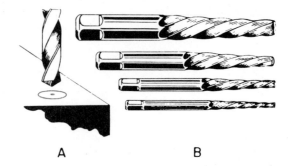

Fig. 1-40. After drilling a hole in broken stud, the screw extractor is turned in, which in turn will screw out the broken stud.

Metal Shears

For cutting sheet metal and gasket material, heavy tin shears, Fig. 1-41, are needed. The straight blade shear is the type most usually needed, however the curved blade shear and the scroll pivoter snips are also convenient to have available. The curved blade shears are used for making curved cuts, and the scroll pivoter snips to follow an irregular line easily.

Power Wrenches

Power wrenches (often called impact tools), Fig. 1-42, are designed for loosening and tightening nuts, quickly. Their use results not only in a material saving of time, but also considerable reduction in fatigue on the part of the mechanic. They are designed for use with heavy-duty socket wrenches. Both electrical and pneumatic types are available.

As an example of the time that can be saved by using a power wrench, a valve job on an automotive engine required 4 hr. 20 min. when conventional hand tools were used. When the same job was done with the aid of a power wrench, only 3 hr. 14 min. were required.

Files

Files, Fig. 1-43, are hardened steel tools with diagonal rows of cutting edges or teeth which are used for smoothing, polishing and removing metal. There are more than 20 types of files with sizes of each type ranging from 3 to 18 in. A file with a single row of parallel teeth is called a single-cut file. Files which have one row of teeth crossing another row in a criss-cross pattern are called double-cut files, Fig. 1-43.

Files are graded according to the tooth spacing. The terms used to indicate the coarseness or fineness of a file are: rough coarse, bastard, second-cut, smooth, and dead smooth. And the file may be either single-cut or double-cut.

There are many different shapes in which files are available, Fig. 1-43. The mill file is single-cut, tapering in thickness and width for one-third of its length. It is used primarily for fine work and is available with either square or round edges or with one safe edge. A safe edge is one without teeth.

Fig. 1-43. In order from the top: double-cut mill bastard, single-cut flat bastard, square, round tapered, half-round.

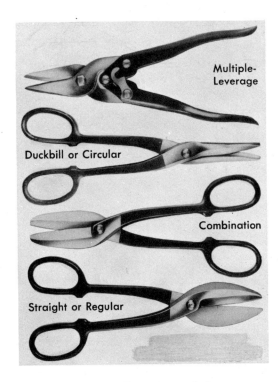

Fig. 1-41. Different types of shears.

Multiple-Leverage

Duckbill or Circular

Combination

Straight or Regular

A double-cut file, tapering in thickness and width is known as a flat file. It is used when a faster cut is desired. The hand file is single-cut and similar in shape to a flat file, with parallel sides and a slight taper in thickness. It has square edges one of which is a safe edge. For rough filing, the bastard file is used.

The round file is tapered and usually single cut. In larger sizes, it is also available in double-cut. For enlarging large holes, a round 12 in. bastard file is usually used. If the hole is of small diameter, a round 6 in. file, usually known as a rat-tail is used. In addition to the tapered round file, there are also untapered round files available. The principal use of round files is to enlarge circular openings and file concave surfaces.

The half-round file is a double-cut file tapering in thickness and width, and with one flat and one oval side. It is used mainly for rough filing on concave surfaces.

The triangular file is useful for filing small notches, square or cornered holes. In addition, it is frequently used for recutting mashed and damaged threads on bolts and other parts.

As previously pointed out, files with coarse teeth are used when it is desired to remove a lot of metal as quickly as possible. Files with fine teeth remove less metal, but produce a smoother surface. In addition, the type of metal must be considered when selecting a file.

When filing cast iron, a bastard file should first be used and a second-cut file for finishing. On soft steel, a second-cut file is used first, and a smooth-cut for finishing. On hard steel, filing is started with a smooth-cut and finished with a dead-smooth file.

For truing ignition breaker points a file of the type shown in Fig. 1-44 is used.

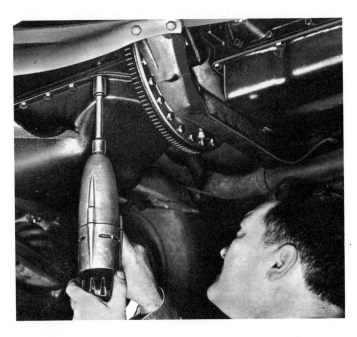

Fig. 1-42. Power wrenches or impact tools save a lot of time and effort.

BLACKHAWK

Fig. 1-44. Type of file used to true ignition breaker points.

On soft metals such as brass or bronze, use a bastard-cut first and then a second-cut. On aluminum, babbitt or lead, a Vixen-cut file, Fig. 1-45, similar to those used by automotive body repairmen is preferred. If that type file is not available, a bastard file may be used.

Fig. 1-45. A Vixen cut file is used by auto body man and for soft metals such as lead and babbitt.

Files should never be used without a handle, as the pointed tang may be driven into the palm of the mechanic's hand, inflicting a bad wound. Whenever possible, the work to be filed should be clamped in the jaws of a vise and if the work is of soft metal, the jaws of the vise should be covered with soft caps so that the work will not be marked or otherwise damaged.

Another precaution regarding files is that they should never be used as levers. Files are brittle and will quickly break, if hammered on or used as levers.

File teeth are designed to cut only when the tool is pushed forward. So the preferred method of filing is to raise the file from the work before drawing it back to start the next stroke.

Only enough pressure should be applied to the file to keep it cutting. Excessive pressure only results in increased effort being required to move the file forward.

The correct way to hold a file is shown in Fig. 1-46.

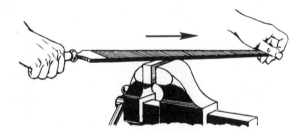

Fig. 1-46. Illustrating the correct method of holding a file.

A right-handed mechanic will grasp the file handle in his right hand. The end of the file is held in the left hand with the fingers curled over the end. His feet should be spread apart and his body should lean slightly forward so that his left shoulder will tend to be over the work. In order that a flat surface is filed, the forward movement of the file must be perfectly horizontal. Any rocking of the file will result in a convex surface.

When filing a round surface, the file should be rocked as shown in Fig. 1-47.

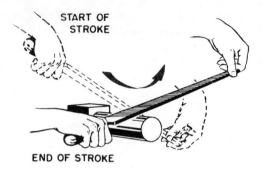

Fig. 1-47. When filing a round surface, the file should be rocked.

File teeth will tend to become clogged, particularly when soft metals are being filed. As a result such material between the file teeth will tend to scratch the surface being filed. This can be overcome to a degree by first rubbing chalk on the file. To clean the teeth of a file, the teeth should be brushed with a file card or other wire bristled brush.

Files should be hung on a rack when not in use, as placing them in a drawer with other tools will quickly dull the teeth.

How to Solder

Soldering is a method of joining two metals together. In addition, on automotive body repair work, it is used to fill dents to form a smooth surface. One of the major uses of soldering is in connecting electric wires to instruments, and other electrical equipment. This keeps the wires from becoming loose or disconnected, as the result of vibration.

Solder is an alloy of lead and tin. By varying the proportions of the lead and tin, solder of different melting points can be secured. Solders that melt readily are known as soft solder, while those which require greater heat are known as hard solder.

The process of soldering consists of first cleaning the surfaces to be soldered. The joint is then heated and a flux is applied. The flux is a chemical designed to keep oxides from forming, and permit the solder to adhere to the surfaces. After the flux is applied, the solder is then melted into the joint, Fig. 1-48. This can be done by means of a soldering copper or the flame of a torch.

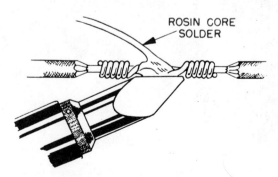

Fig. 1-48. Method of soldering splice in electric wires.

Soldering coppers, Fig. 1-49, often called soldering irons, are used mostly for soldering small pieces and when there is danger of an open flame damaging nearby parts. Made of copper, the tips of these tools

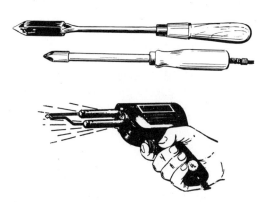

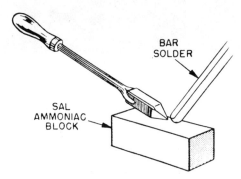

Fig. 1-50. One method of tinning a soldering copper.

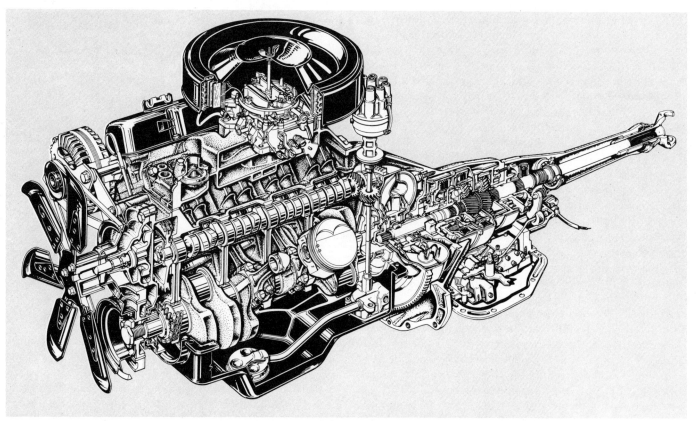

Fig. 1-49. Different sizes of soldering coppers are needed. Electric coppers are shown at the bottom.

must be given a coating of solder before they are used, Fig. 1-50. This is known as tinning, and the process is to first file the tip of the copper so that it is clean and smooth. It is then heated, dipped in flux and solder applied. Some mechanics prefer to melt the solder on the surface of a building brick, and then rub the tip of the copper on the solder. Another method is to use a block of sal ammoniac.

After the iron has been tinned, the mechanic should take care that it is not overheated. That would burn the copper and it would be necessary to re-tin it.

On some soldering jobs, it is desirable to first tin the surfaces to be joined, and then solder them together. That process is usually followed on larger areas where a strong joint is to be made. It is also used when solder is to be applied to sheet iron.

Soldering coppers may be heated in a flame or special oven. Or soldering irons with electric heating elements may be used, Fig. 1-49.

There are many different types of fluxes available. It is important to select the type best suited for the metals to be joined. For electrical connections a rosin type flux is recommended. An acid type is used when soldering sheet iron.

New, 340 cu. in. V-8 power plant used in Plymouth Barracuda. Bore and stroke are 4.04 x 3.31. The engine develops 275 hp at 5,000 rpm.

Fig. 1-51. Different types of adjustable hacksaw frames.

How to use a Hacksaw

Hacksaws are used to cut metal. As shown in Fig. 1-51, the detachable cutting blade is mounted in a metal frame. Different length frames are available. Some frames are made adjustable so that various size blades can be used. The usual lengths of hacksaw blades are 8, 10, and 12. in. The 10 and 12 in. sizes are most frequently used. For power-driven hacksaws, blades of 12, 14, 17, 18, 21, 24 and 30 in. lengths are available.

Hacksaw blades are made of high grade tool steel, hardened and tempered. There are two types, the all-hard and the flexible. All-hard blades are hardened throughout, while only the teeth of flexible blades are hardened. So that the blades can be attached to the frame, the blades are provided with holes at both ends. These holes are then slipped on the pins on the frame. To adjust the tension of the blade, and also to secure it tightly to the frame, the position of one of the pins is adjustable. This adjustment is made by either a wing nut or by turning the handle.

The "set" in a saw refers to the amount the teeth are pushed out in opposite directions from the sides of the blade. The teeth of all hacksaw blades are set to provide clearance for the blade. The usual types of set are alternate, raker and undulated. In addition, there is a double alternate set.

Blades for hand-operated hacksaws come with 14, 18, 24 and 32 teeth per inch. It is important that the teeth per inch be considered when selecting a hacksaw blade for a particular job, Fig. 1-52. Also, thought must be given to whether the all-hard or flexible blade is more suitable for a particular job.

In general, an all-hard blade is considered best for sawing brass, cast iron, steel and other stock of heavy cross section. For cutting hollow shapes, and metals of light section such as channel iron, tubing tin, copper, aluminum or babbitt, a flexible blade is preferable.

Hacksaw blade manufacturers recommend that 14-tooth saws be used for cutting soft steel, brass, cast-iron and stock of heavy cross section. For cutting drill rod, light angles, high speed steel, tool steel and small solids, 18-tooth blades are recommended. Use 24-tooth blades for cutting brass tubing, heavy B-X cable, iron pipe, metal conduit and drill rod. For cutting thin tubing, sheet metal, light B-X cable, channels, etc., 32-tooth blades are suggested.

After selecting the correct blade for the material, it is placed on the pins on the hacksaw frame, with the teeth pointing toward the front of the frame. The blade is then stretched tightly in the frame.

If an accurate cut is to be made, it is advisable to mark the stock with a scriber, and nick the work with a file. The nick will make it easier for the saw to start cutting and also insure accuracy. Make sure the work is held securely in a vise, with the line to be cut as close to the vise jaws as possible. Use sufficient pressure on the saw when starting the cut,

14 TEETH PER INCH

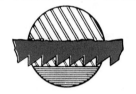

FOR LARGE SECTIONS OF MILD MATERIAL

18 TEETH PER INCH

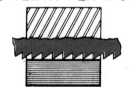

FOR LARGE SECTIONS OF TOUGH STEEL

24 TEETH PER INCH

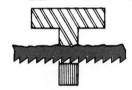

FOR ANGLE IRON, HEAVY PIPE, BRASS, COPPER

32 TEETH PER INCH

FOR THIN TUBING

KEEP AT LEAST TWO TEETH CUTTING TO AVOID THIS ➝

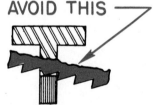

Fig. 1-52. Hacksaw blades must be selected in accordance with the type of metal that is to be cut.

so that the saw teeth immediately begin to bite into the metal. The hacksaw blade should be held vertically and moved forward with a light steady stroke. At the end of the forward stroke, relieve the pressure and draw the saw straight back. See Fig. 1-53.

The most effective cutting speed is about one stroke per second. When the material is nearly cut through, the pressure on the blade should be reduced to prevent the teeth from catching. When cutting thin

Tools

stock, it is advisable to clamp it between two pieces of wood or soft metal, and saw through all three pieces. This will prevent the saw from sticking, and also prevent possible damage to the work.

For cutting round holes in metal, a hole saw is advisable. The hole saw is driven by an electric drill, and is used for drilling large diameter holes in instrument panels and fire walls, for the installation of instruments and other accessories. It is provided with a centering or pilot drill for starting and centering the cut.

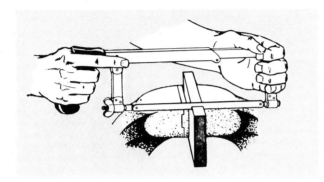

Fig. 1-53. Illustrating the correct method of using a hacksaw.

Drilling, Reaming and Tapping

The automotive mechanic frequently finds it necessary to drill holes in order to install additional accessories and equipment on various types of automotive vehicles, such as passenger cars, trucks and tractors.

While holes are occasionally drilled with a hand or breast drill, the usual method is to use an electric drill, Fig. 1-54. The electric drills used in most automotive shops are 1/4 in., 1/2 in., and 3/4 in. The

Fig. 1-54. Electric drills have many uses and are a "must" for every mechanic's tool kit.

size designations indicate the largest size drill that should be inserted in the chuck. If drills larger than the specified size are used, the electric drill may be overloaded and may overheat. Premature failure can then be expected. It should be pointed out, however, that a well-made electric drill can stand a certain degree of overload for a short period without harm.

Twist Drills

The tool used to do the actual cutting is known as a twist drill, Fig. 1-55. A twist drill has two cutting edges.

Twist drills are made of either carbon steel, or high speed steel. However, the former quickly becomes dull and if heated excessively, it will lose its hardness. High speed steel will retain its temper when red hot and twist drills of that material are therefore preferred.

While there are other types of drills, the straight shank drill is used almost entirely in automotive maintenance shops.

Fig. 1-55. Small set of twist drills. These, ranging up to 1/2 in. diameter, all have 1/4 in. shanks for use in a 1/4 in. drill.

Sharpening Drills

Before a drill is used, it is important that it be correctly ground and sharpened. Unless the drill is in good condition it may drill an oversize hole, possibly break or at least cut slowly.

A correctly sharpened drill will have: (1) equal and correctly sized drill point angles, (2) equal length cutting lips, (3) correct clearance behind the cutting lips, and (4) correct chisel edge angle. All four are equally important and are illustrated in Fig. 1-56. For general drilling, the angles shown in the upper part of Fig. 1-56 are used, while if very hard and tough materials are to be drilled the angles shown in the center of the illustration are used. The lower portion of the illustration shows what is meant by the two halves, A-1 and A-2 of the drill point angle, as well as the two equal-length cutting lips, L-1 and L-2.

Lip clearance behind the cutting lip at the margin is determined by inspection, while the cutting edge or lip is measured by a gauge. The lip clearance angle may be within certain limits, as shown in Fig. 1-56, but must be the same on both sides of the drill. The margin, shown at the top of Fig. 1-56, is the narrow strip which extends the entire length of the flutes, and is practically the full diameter of the drill. The portion back of the margin is slightly less in diameter and is the body clearance.

Both lips of a twist drill must be the same length. For most materials they should be ground to an angle of 59 deg. If the cutting edges are ground at different angles, and the point is in the center, only one lip will cut. The angle of 59 deg. for the lip is correct when the drill is to be used on aluminum, steel and cast iron. For brass and copper the angle should be 50 deg.; while 45 deg. is preferred for Bakelite, plastic, wood or fibre.

The heel of the drill, that is the surface of the point back of the cutting lips, should be at an angle of 12 to 15 deg., as shown in Fig. 1-56. Incorrect grinding of the lip clearance will result in drilling holes larger than the diameter of the drill, drill breakage and slow cutting.

The rake angle of the drill is the angle of the flutes in relation to the axis. This is usually 22 to 30 deg., and is, of course, built into the drill by the manufacturers.

Drills should be placed in a grinding jig or attachment for sharpening. This will insure accuracy.

Reamers

When it is desired to have a hole with particularly smooth surface or have the hole finished to an exact diameter, a reamer, Fig. 1-57, should be used. The hole is first drilled to a diameter slightly smaller than the desired finished size, and then finished with the reamer.

A reamer consists of three parts; the body, shank and cutting blades. The reamer can be rotated by hand, and a suitable wrench or handle; or it can be power driven. When power driven, the speed is approximately 50 rpm.

The blades of a reamer are made of steel, and hardened to such an extent that they are extremely brittle. They must, therefore, be carefully handled. The usual method of storing reamers is to provide a wooden rack with a separate division for each reamer.

When reaming a hole, the reamer should be turned in the cutting direction only. Also only a very little metal should be removed by the reamer, as it is a finishing operation and it is not designed to make heavy cuts. Usually .002 in. is the limit of the amount of metal to be removed by reaming.

By steady even rotation of the reamer, "shattering" is reduced or eliminated.

In Fig. 1-57, are shown two solid reamers, a spiral flute reamer, and a straight flute reamer. The

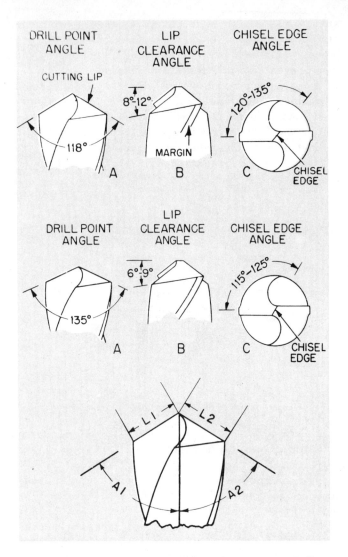

Fig. 1-56. Indicating the various angles on a twist drill.

spiral flute is more expensive but has a reduced tendency toward chattering. Reamers of the types shown in Fig. 1-57 are available in standard sizes and are also available in size variations of .001 in. for special work.

Where only occasional reaming is to be done, some shops will secure several expansion or adjustable reamers, embracing the required range of sizes. Care must of course be taken when adjusting the size of the reamer, to be sure it is correctly set. In setting adjustable reamers, the usual method is to use a micrometer.

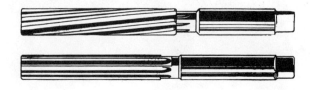

Fig. 1-57. The upper view is of a spiral flute reamer, while the lower is a straight flute reamer.

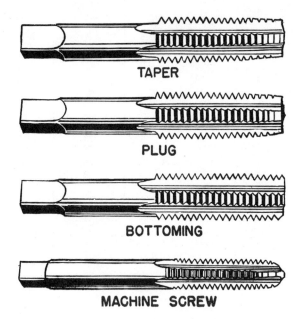

Fig. 1-58. *Illustrating four different types of taps.*

Expansion reamers are usually available in standard sizes from 1/4 in. to 1 in. by 32nds. They are designed to allow the blades to expand 1/32 in. For example, the 1/4 in. expansion reamers will cover sizes ranging from 1/4 in. to 9/32 in.

In automotive service work, reamers are used for fitting such parts as kingpins and piston pins. However, a power-driven hone is now used extensively for fitting piston pins.

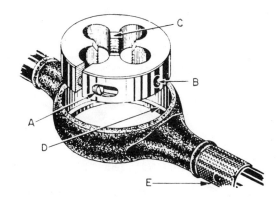

Fig. 1-59. *Adjustable round split die for cutting external threads. A-Adjusting screw. B-Drive hole. C-Cutting teeth. D-Shoulder for die. E-Die holder handle.*

Taps and Dies

Taps, Fig. 1-58, and dies, Fig. 1-59, are thread-cutting tools. A tap is used to cut internal threads on such parts as nuts, while a die cuts external threads on bolts and studs. As shown on page 26, there are many different types of bolts and nuts.

There is special terminology used when discussing threads, bolts and nuts, Fig. 1-60, and, to avoid con-fusion, it is important that such terms be understood.

The major diameter, formerly known as the outside diameter, is the largest diameter of the thread. The minor diameter is the diameter taken at the base of the thread. The pitch of a thread is the distance measured parallel to its axis, between corresponding points on adjacent thread forms, in the same axial plane and on the same side of the axis. The number of threads per inch is the reciprocal of the pitch in inches.

When it is desired to drill and tap a hole, it is necessary that the hole be of the correct diameter for the particular tap. That is known as the tap drill. The different tap and drill sizes are given in Fig. 1-61.

When it is desired to drill a hole into which a bolt is to be inserted, the drill is known as a clearance or body drill.

Taps and dies are marked according to the type and diameter thread they will cut. For example, an 8-32 is designed to cut 32 threads per inch on No. 8 stock.

When tapping a hole with a tap or cutting a thread with a die, considerable care is required. Taps are easily broken. When using a tap or die, it is important that the direction the tool is turned be reversed frequently. This is done to free the tool of chips and also recut the threads. Forcing the tool will result in tool breakage, ruined parts and poor threads.

When threading steel parts, a lubricant such as lard oil should be used. Kerosene is preferred for use with aluminum. No lubricant is required for threading brass or cast iron.

Fabricating Tubing

Tubing is used extensively in automobiles, trucks and tractors for oil, fuel and brake lines. Great care must be exercised in fitting tubing for specific jobs.

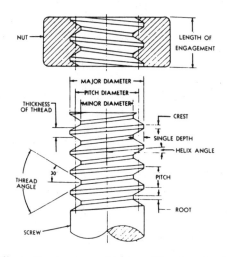

Fig. 1-60. *Illustrating terms used in describing American Standard screw threads.*

Carelessness in fabrication, or the selection of the wrong material, may result in accidents and harm to the occupants of the vehicle.

Soft copper tubing is usually considered satisfactory for gasoline lines. However, it should never be used for hydraulic brake lines as it is not strong enough to withstand the pressures developed in such lines. For hydraulic brake lines, only special tubing designed for the purpose should be used. Such tubing is of seamless steel.

Dimensions of copper and steel tubing are given in the accompanying table. Note that the outside diameter of tubing is used to indicate its size, whereas pipe sizes are determined by their inside diameter.

Size or O.D.	Wall Thickness Copper Tube	Wall Thickness Single Wall Steel Tubing	Wall Thickness Double Wall Steel Tubing
1/8	.030	.025	.025
3/16	.030	.025	.025
1/4	.030	.028	.028
5/16	.032	.028	.028
3/8	.032	.028	.028
7/16		.030	.032
1/2	.032	.030	
1/2		.035	
9/16		.030	
5/8	.035	.035	.035

When making a line of tubing the first step, after selecting the size and material of which the line is to be made, is to cut it to the length desired, Fig. 1-62. In cutting tubing only a special tubing cutter should be used, as it is imperative that the tubing be cut smoothly and at right angles to the center line of the tubing. Unless the end of the tubing is smooth, and at right angles to the center line of the tubing, it will be impossible to make a leakproof joint. Tubing can be connected to equipment by either flare-type or flareless-type fittings. The latter type, Fig. 1-63, is known as a compression fitting, and requires only that the end of the tubing be smooth and true. The connection can be quickly made, but has the disadvantage that it cannot be taken apart many times without the probability of leaks occurring.

The flare-type connection, Fig. 1-64, as the name implies, requires that the end of the tubing be flared, Fig. 1-65. This type of fitting can be disassembled many times with but little possibility of leaks occurring.

A tube cutting tool is shown in Fig. 1-62. Such a tool will make a clean cut, square with the sides of the tubing. In addition, there is little possibilty of filings getting into the tubing, and subsequently causing trouble in the system. With a tubing cutter the position of the cutting wheel is adjusted until it contacts the surface lightly. The complete tool is then swung completely around the tubing, after which the cutting

Nominal size	Thr'd series	Major diameter, inches	Root diameter, inches	Tap drill to produce approx. 75% full thread	Decimal equivalent of tap drill
0-80	N. F.	.0600	.0438	3/64	.0469
1-64	N. C.	.0730	.0527	53	.0595
72	N. F.	.0730	.0550	53	.0595
2-56	N. C.	.0860	.0628	50	.0700
64	N. F.	.0860	.0657	50	.0700
3-48	N. C.	.0990	.0719	47	.0785
56	N. F.	.0990	.0758	45	.0820
4-40	N. C.	.1120	.0795	43	.0890
48	N. F.	.1120	.0849	42	.0935
5-40	N. C.	.1250	.0925	38	.1015
44	N. F.	.1250	.0955	37	.1040
6-32	N. C.	.1380	.0974	36	.1065
40	N. F.	.1380	.1055	33	.1130
8-32	N. C.	.1640	.1234	29	.1360
36	N. F.	.1640	.1279	29	.1360
10-24	N. C.	.1900	.1359	25	.1495
32	N. F.	.1900	.1494	21	.1590
12-24	N. C.	.2160	.1619	16	.1770
28	N. F.	.2160	.1696	14	.1820
1/4-20	N. C.	.2500	.1850	7	.2010
28	N. F.	.2500	.2036	3	.2130
5/16-18	N. C.	.3125	.2403	F	.2570
24	N. F.	.3125	.2584	I	.2720
3/8-16	N. C.	.3750	.2938	5/16	.3125
24	N. F.	.3750	.3209	Q	.3320
7/16-14	N. C.	.4375	.3447	U	.3680
20	N. F.	.4375	.3726	25/64	.3906
1/2-13	N. C.	.5000	.4001	27/64	.4219
20	N. F.	.5000	.4351	29/64	.4531
9/16-12	N. C.	.5625	.4542	31/64	.4844
18	N. F.	.5625	.4903	33/64	.5156
5/8-11	N. C.	.6250	.5069	17/32	.5312
18	N. F.	.6250	.5528	37/64	.5781
3/4-10	N. C.	.7500	.6201	21/32	.6562
16	N. F.	.7500	.6688	11/16	.6875
7/8-9	N. C.	.8750	.7307	49/64	.7656
14	N. F.	.8750	.7822	13/16	.8125
1-8	N. C.	1.0000	8376	7/8	.8750
14	N. F.	1.0000	9072	15/16	.9375

Fig. 1-61. Table of thread sizes, together with tap drill and clearance drill sizes.

STEP ①

SCREW THE CUTTING WHEEL LIGHTLY AGAINST THE TUBING

STEP ②

ROTATE THE CUTTER KEEPING A SLIGHT PRESSURE AGAINST THE CUTTING WHEEL WITH THE SCREW ADJUSTMENT

Fig. 1-62. Showing the procedure for cutting copper tubing with a special cutter.

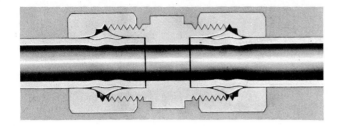

Fig. 1-63. Flareless type tubing connector.

wheel is again adjusted. The procedure is repeated until the cut is completed.

After the tubing has been cut to the desired length, the ends should be reamed or burred to remove any burrs at the end of the tubing. One method of doing this is to use the reamer provided on one end of the tubing cutter. When reaming tubing, it is always important to hold the end of the tubing pointed down, so metal chips will not drop into the tubing.

One type of reaming tool is an "inner and outer" reamer. This is a cylindrically shaped tool that reams both the inside and outside edges of the tubing.

With the tubing cleanly and squarely cut, reamed and with burrs removed, it is then ready for either a tight joint with a compression (flareless) type fitting, Fig. 1-63, or for flaring for use with a flare-type fitting, Fig. 1-64.

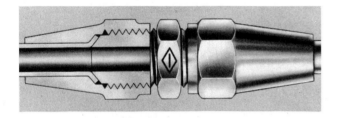

Fig. 1-64. Note how end of tubing is flared for this flare-type tubing connector.

Flaring

There are several different types of flaring tools available. One type consists of a flaring bar and screw feed flaring yoke, Fig. 1-65. When making a flare with a tool of this type, the tubing is placed in the flaring bar with the end protruding slightly above the face of the bar. Care must be taken that the tubing is clamped in the bar, so pressure of the flaring cone will not force the tubing through the bar.

Before slipping the yoke over the bar to start flaring, a little oil should be placed on the cone or spreader. Particular care must be taken when the flared connection is to be used on units subject to vibration. It is not wise to work the tubing any more than is necessary, because the working will tend to make the metal hard and brittle so it is more subject to breakage.

On tubes flared too short, the full clamping area of the fitting is not used and consequently the joint

may leak or suffer early failure. Tubing flared too long will stick and jam on the threads during assembly. Flares that are not straight usually result from the fact that the tubing was cut on an angle.

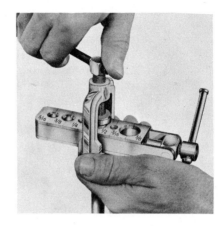

Fig. 1-65. Using a flaring tool on a piece of copper tubing.

Brazed steel tubing, such as used for hydraulic brake lines, must be double flared. If only single flared, it will invariably crack or split. Double flaring is similar to single flaring except that an additional operation is introduced. To make a double flare with the tool shown in Fig. 1-66, two operations are involved. In the first operation, the tubing is belled through the use of an adapter. In the second operation, the adapter is removed and the flaring cone

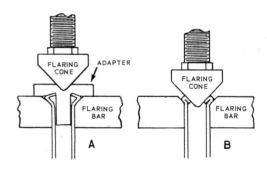

Fig. 1-66. Procedure for making a double flare in tubing.

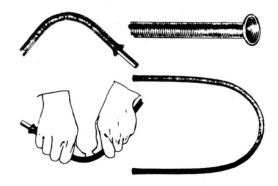

Fig. 1-67. This spring type bender is slipped over the tubing so that the tubing can be bent without kinking.

screwed down.. This folds the tubing down on itself and forms an accurate 45 deg. double flare without cracking or splitting the tubing.

It is frequently necessary to bend tubing. This should be done only with special tube benders. Only soft temper tubing should be bent. On smaller size tubing a simple outside bending spring, Fig. 1-67, is usually satisfactory. This bender is slipped over the outside of the tubing and prevents the tubing from kinking when it is bent. When using a spring-type tube bender, it must be remembered that the tubing must be bent somewhat further than required, and then backed up to the desired angle. In that way the spring is loosened in the bender and can be easily removed.

On larger sizes of tubing or where precise and uniform bends are required, the use of a lever type or gear type bender, Fig. 1-68, should be used. These benders can be slipped on the tubing at the exact point the bend is desired, and are particularly advantageous when the tubing has been partly connected, or is lo-

cated in hard-to-get-at places. Bulk tubing is sold in coils. When removing a piece of copper tubing from a coil, first place the coil on the bench. Hold down

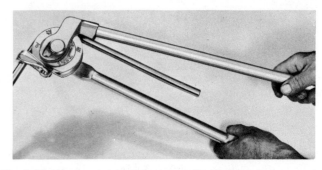

Fig. 1-68. For larger size tubing a mechanical bender is required.

the free end of the tubing, and then roll the coil of tubing along the bench until the desired length is obtained. In this way kinking the tubing will be avoided.

Quiz - Automotive Tools

Write answers on a separate sheet of paper. Do not write in this book.

1. The size of open-end wrenches increase in:
   a. 1/16 in. steps.
   b. 1/32 in. steps.
   c. 1/8 in. steps.
   d. 1/4 in. steps.
2. What is the main reason for using a box type wrench?
   a. Greater strength.
   b. Used on rounded nuts.
   c. Less liable to slip from nut.
3. List the three standard size drives for socket wrenches.
4. Why are torque wrenches needed?
5. A Stillson wrench is used to tighten:
   a. Square nuts.
   b. Hexagonal nuts.
   c. Pipe connections.
6. The channel-lock pliers are designed to:
   a. Lock channels.
   b. Have adjustable openings of different sizes and at the same time have the jaws remain parallel.
7. The end of a Phillips-type screwdriver is:
   a. A flat blade.
   b. Pointed end with four grooves.
   c. Fluted end.
8. A set screw wrench has:
   a. Four sides.
   b. Six sides.
   c. Eight sides.

9. The rounded end of a machinists hammer is known as the:
   a. Face.
   b. Peen.
   c. Riveter.
10. A cape chisel is used to cut:
    a. Narrow grooves.
    b. Rivet heads.
    c. Tool steel.
11. When using a chisel it should be held:
    a. Tightly in the hand.
    b. With a pair of slip-joint pliers.
    c. Loosely in the hand.
12. A screw extractor has:
    a. Tapered right-hand threads.
    b. Tapered left-hand threads.
13. A file with a single row of parallel teeth is called:
    a. A bastard file.
    b. A singleton file.
    c. A single-cut file.
14. A file with one row of teeth crossing the other is called:
    a. A criss-cross file.
    b. A double-cut file.
    c. A Vixen-cut file.
15. When filing soft steel, which type file should be used first?
    a. A bastard file.
    b. A smooth-cut file.
    c. A second-cut file.
16. Solder is an alloy of:
    a. Lead and tin.
    b. Lead and zinc.
    c. Tin and zinc.
    d. Lead and cadmium.

17. Hacksaw blades are made of:
    a. High grade tool steel.
    b. Chilled cast iron.
    c. Carbaloy.
18. List the usual lengths of blades used in manually operated hacksaws.
19. What tooth saw blade is recommended to cut soft steel, cast iron and stock of heavy cross section?
    a. 16 tooth.
    b. 32 tooth.
    c. 24 tooth.
    d. 14 tooth.

20. What is the usual cutting lip angle on a twist drill?
    a. 45 deg.
    b. 59 deg.
    c. 60 deg.
    d. 75 deg.
21. A tap is used to cut external threads. True or False?
22. After cutting a piece of tubing, why should it be reamed?
    a. To increase its size.
    b. To restore it to its original size.
    c. To remove any burrs from the cut edge.

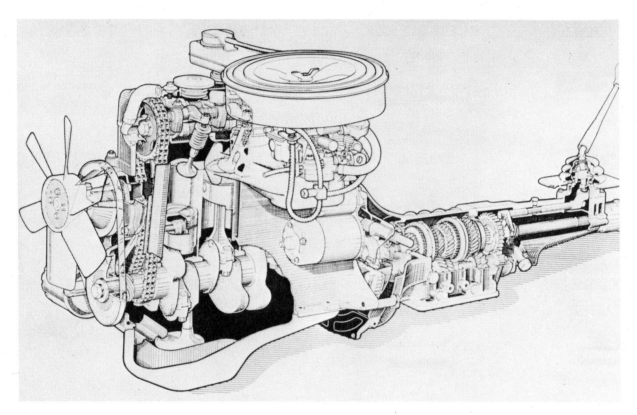

Dodge Colt engine showing overhead camshaft, chain driven.

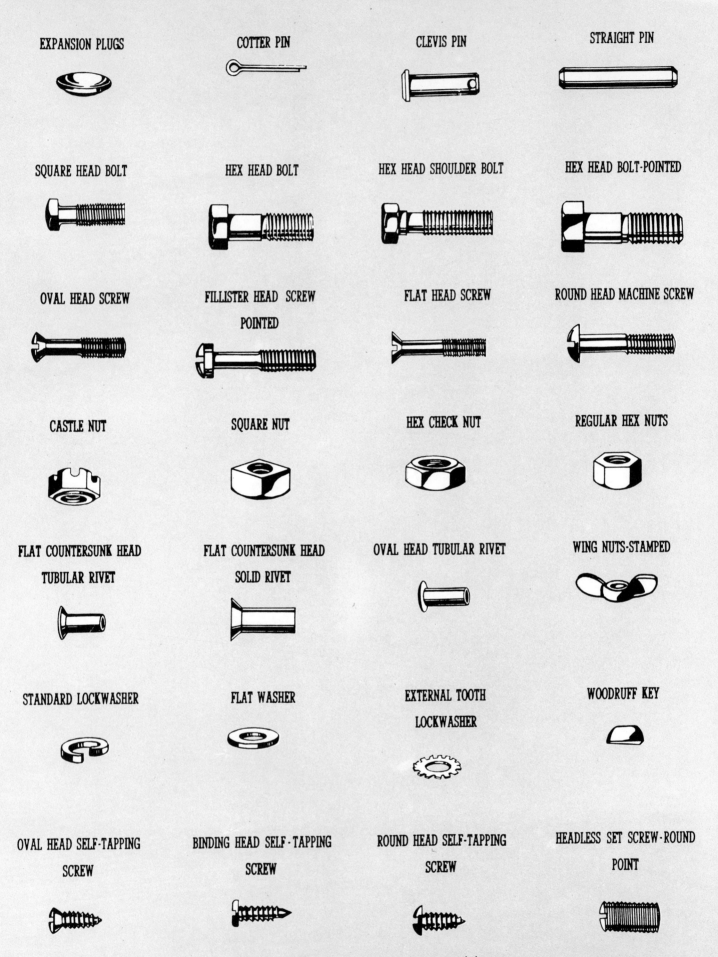

Fig. 2-1. *Illustrating fasteners used on automobiles.*

FASTENING DEVICES

There are many different devices used for fastening different parts together in the modern automobile. These devices range all the way from the familiar bolt and nut to spring clips, and sheet metal screws.

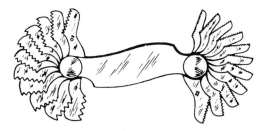

Fig. 2-2. *Type of gauge used for measuring the pitch of threads.*

A number of the different fastening devices are illustrated in Fig. 2-1. It is important to know the difference between and to be able to identify these various types of fastening devices.

The term machine screw is applied to that type of threaded screw which is turned into threaded holes in metal parts.

Bolts require nuts, and the bolts are inserted through holes in parts so that the threaded end of the bolt protrudes. The nut is then turned on the exposed end of the bolt.

Both ends of a stud are threaded, one end is screwed into a threaded hole of a part such as an engine cylinder. After another part with a suitable hole is placed in position on the stud, a nut is placed on the exposed end of the stud and tightened. And in that way the parts are held together.

Threads on bolts are known as external threads, while threads in nuts are known as internal threads The major terms used in connection with threads include major diameter, minor diameter, pitch, pitch diameter and lead, Fig. 1-60. The major diameter is the largest diameter of the thread on the screw. The minor diameter is the smallest diameter of the thread on the screw. The pitch is the distance from a given point on a thread, to the corresponding point on the next thread, and is measured parallel to the axis of the screw. The pitch diameter is that of an imaginary cylinder, the surface of which would pass through the threads at such point as to make equal the width

of the threads, and the width of the spaces cut by the cylinder.

Bolts and screws are usually designated by their length, major diameter, and by the number of threads per inch. In Fig. 1-61, the threads of various types and sizes as listed in the Society of Automotive Engineers Handbook are given. It will be noted that sizes up to 1/4 in. are designated by number and over 1/4 in. are designated in fractions of an inch.

In order to measure the pitch of a thread, a special gauge, Fig. 2-2, should be used.

As pointed out previously, one method of designating screws and bolts is by the type of head. Most bolts have hexagonal heads, while machine screws will have heads ranging from the conventional hexagon to straight slots, and are installed by means of a screwdriver. In addition, some screws will have special recesses requiring special tools for their installation. These special recesses include the Phillips, Fig. 2-3, fluted and the internal hexagon or Allen type.

Fig. 2-3. *Character of opening in head of Phillips screw.*

Sheet Metal Screws

One special type of screw is known as a sheet metal or self-tapping screw, Fig. 2-4. Because of its fluted and tapered point it will cut its own threads as it is screwed into the sheet metal.

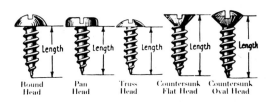

Fig. 2-4. *Types of sheet metal screws.*

To join two thicknesses of light gauge sheet metal, drill or clean punch both sheets.

Stronger fastenings are made by piercing both sheets together so that burrs are nested.

Holes in light gauge sheet metal should be burred when fastening part with holes provided.

Fig. 2-5. Different methods of using sheet metal screws.

Sheet metal screws are used extensively in holding sheet metal parts together, Fig. 2-5. A hole is first punched or drilled into the sheet metal, and then the screw is turned into the hole.

Nuts

There are two broad classifications of nuts: square and hexagon. See Fig. 2-1. The hexagon is further divided into plain hex and slotted or castellated. The square-headed nut is used occasionally in body construction. The plain hex nut is generally used in connection with some type of lock washer, Fig. 2-1. The slotted or castellated nut is designed for use with a cotter pin, which of course necessitates a hole through the end of the bolt or stud, through which the cotter pin can pass.

Another type of nut which is coming into extensive use, incorporates in its design a self-locking device, Fig. 2-6. There are several different designs of these self-locking nuts which are used extensively in such places as valve tappet screws, and connecting rod bolts.

Fig. 2-6. This type of self-locking nut has a composition plug, which is forced against the threads, to prevent the nut from turning.

Speed-Nuts

In order to reduce the time of assembly of parts, the speed-nut was developed. There are many different types of speed-nuts and clips. A speed-nut, Fig. 2-7, is simply pressed onto the bolt or stud and it takes the place of the conventional threaded nut and lock washer. Speed clip nuts, Fig. 2-8, are snapped onto the sheet metal, are self-aligning, and are used in blind locations such as radiator grilles.

Lock Washers

Lock washers are installed under the head of a screw, or under a nut, so that they will not become loose as the result of vibration. There are three major types of lock washers: the plain, external and internal. See Fig. 2-1. In addition there is one with both internal and external teeth, but it is used infrequently.

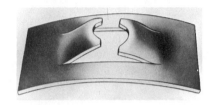

Fig. 2-7. Flat type speed nut, or self-locking nut. These take less time to apply and provide maximum holding power.

Fig. 2-8. Speed clip nuts are used in blind locations such as radiator grilles. They are self-aligning and are snapped onto the sheet metal.

Snap Rings

Snap rings, Fig. 2-9, are employed to prevent endwise movement of cylindrical parts and shafts. There are both internal and external snap rings. The internal type snap ring is used in a groove cut in a housing, while the external type snap ring is designed to fit in a groove cut on the outside of a cylindrical piece such as a shaft. They are used extensively in manual shift and automatic transmissions, and also in hydraulic valve lifters.

Keys and Splines

Keys and splines are used to lock gears, and other parts to shafts so that they will rotate as a single unit. The keys used most frequently in automotive design include the Woodruff key, sunk key and gib-head key. The keys fit into slots known as keyways, Fig. 2-10, which are cut into both the shaft and the mating part. The design is such that the key will extend into both parts so that they will rotate as one.

Splines are external teeth cut on a shaft, Fig. 2-11,

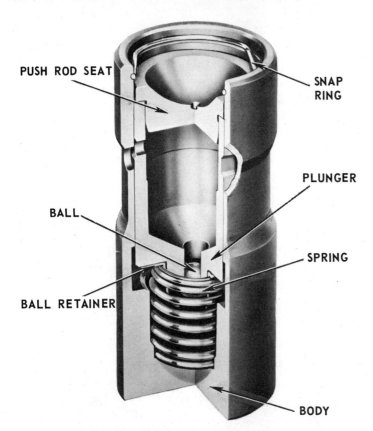

PUSH ROD SEAT

SNAP RING

BALL

PLUNGER

BALL RETAINER

SPRING

BODY

Fig. 2-9. Showing how a snap ring is used to hold an assembly together.

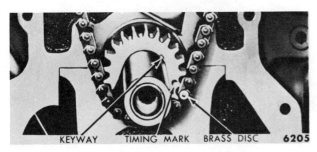

KEYWAY   TIMING MARK   BRASS DISC   6205

Fig. 2-10. Note the keyway on the timing gear.

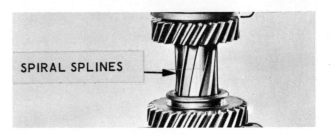

SPIRAL SPLINES

Fig. 2-11. Note the spiral splines on this transmission main shaft.

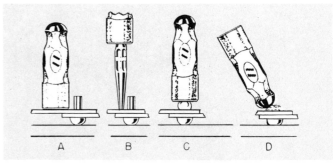

A   B   C   D

Fig. 2-12. When a rivet set is not available, first drive the two parts together and onto the rivet head as in A and B. Then rivet over the rivet head as in C and D.

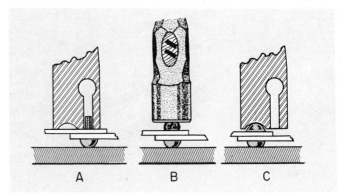

A   B   C

Fig. 2-13. Procedure when using a rivet set.

and corresponding internal teeth cut on the mating part. In effect, they are mating internal and external gears with a 1 to 1 ratio. Splines are used in the design of transmission, propeller shafts, and rear axle assemblies.

Rivets

A rivet is a metal pin with a head at one end, and is designed to fasten two parts together. After the rivet is passed through the holes in the parts to be joined, the small end of the rivet is formed into a head by means of a rivet set, or by using the peen end of a ball peen hammer, Fig. 2-12.

In addition to using rivets for holding pieces of metal together, rivets are also used extensively for fastening brake lining to brake shoes.

When a rivet set is available, the steps A, B and C, Fig. 2-13 are followed.

Quiz - Fastening Devices

1. What is the major difference between a machine screw and a bolt?
2. A stud has threads on one end. True or False?
3. The largest diameter on a screw is known as the:
   a. Pitch diameter.
   b. Major diameter.
   c. Minor diameter.
4. Most bolts have what shape head?
   a. Square head.
   b. Octagonal head.
   c. Hexagonal head.
   d. Round head.
5. What type of nut is used with a cotter pin?
6. Name two methods used to keep nuts from becoming loose on a bolt.
7. What is the purpose of a spline?

Experimental electric vehicle engineered by Ford of Great Britian, for short range urban use. This vehicle has four 12V, lead-acid batteries, and uses two series-wound 24V electric motors to drive the rear wheels.

MEASURING INSTRUMENTS

Fig. 3-1. Using an inside micrometer to measure a diameter. The size can be extended by means of the measuring rod.

A micrometer is an instrument designed for linear measurement with accuracy of .001 in. or better. One type, known as the inside micrometer, Fig. 3-1, is used for measuring the distance between two parallel surfaces, and for measuring the inside diameter of cylinders. The outside micrometer, Fig. 3-2, is designed to measure the outside diameter of cylindrical forms and also the thickness of materials. On the outside micrometer, the spindle is attached to the thimble on the inside, at the point of adjustment which is often provided with a ratchet stop. The part of the spindle which is concealed within the sleeve and thimble is

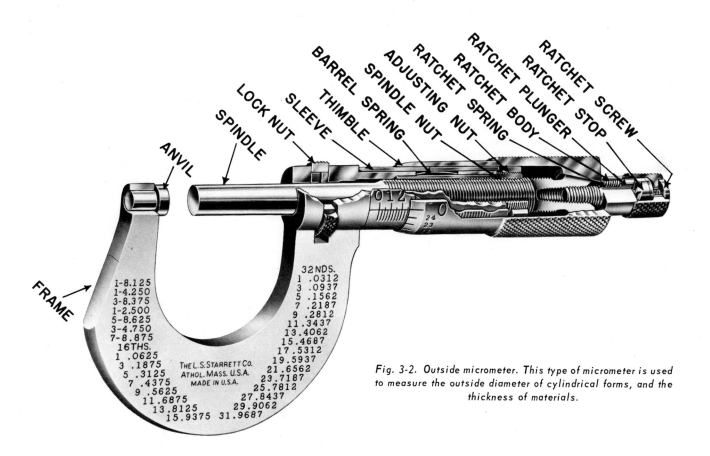

Fig. 3-2. Outside micrometer. This type of micrometer is used to measure the outside diameter of cylindrical forms, and the thickness of materials.

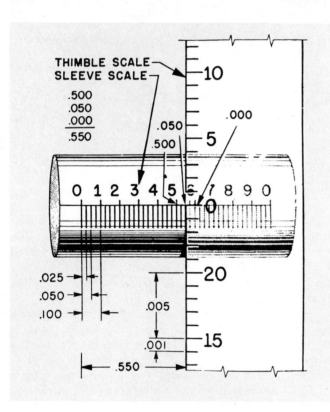

THIMBLE SCALE
SLEEVE SCALE

.500
.050
.000
─────
.550

.050
.500

.000

0 1 2 3 4 5 6 7 8 9 0

.025
.050
.100

.005

.001

.550

Fig. 3-3. Enlarged micrometer scales. In this case the reading is .550 in.

threaded to fit a nut in the frame. The frame being stationary, the thimble is revolved by the thumb and finger, and the spindle being attached to the thimble, revolves with it and moves through the nut in the frame, approaching or receding from the anvil.

The measurement of the opening between the anvil and the spindle is indicated by the line and figures on the sleeve and the thimble.

The pitch of the screw threads on the concealed part of the spindle is 40 to an inch. One complete revolution of the spindle, therefore, moves it longitudinally 1/40th or .025 in. The sleeve is marked with 40 lines to the inch, corresponding to the number of threads on the spindle. When the micrometer is closed, the bevelled end of the thimble coincides with the line marked 0 on the sleeve, and the 0 mark on the thimble also coincides with the horizontal line on the sleeve.

Opening the micrometer by revolving the thimble one full revolution will make the 0 line of the thimble coincide with the horizontal line of the sleeve. The distance between the anvil and spindle is therefore .025 in. The bevelled edge of the thimble is marked in 25 divisions. Rotating the thimble from one of these divisions to the next moves the spindle longitudinally 1/25th of .025, or .001 in.

To read the micrometer, multiply the number of vertical divisions visual on the sleeve by 25, and add the number of divisions on the bevel of the thimble from 0 to the line which coincides with the horizontal line on the sleeve. In the enlarged portion of the mi-

crometer shown in Fig. 3-3, the reading would be .550 in. Fig. 3-4 shows the correct method of holding a micrometer. The reading on the micrometer, shown in Fig. 3-4, is .260 in.

When using a micrometer, care must be exercised so that when turning the thimble it is not turned too tight. This will not only result in distortion of the frame and consequent inaccuracy of the readings but will also result in wear of the screw threads. Only gentle pressure should be used. To overcome this difficulty, some micrometers are provided with a ratchet drive on the thimble so that regardless of who uses the micrometer the same pressure will be exerted on the thimble.

Inside micrometers, Fig. 3-1, are read in the same manner as described for outside micrometers. However, the actual use of the inside micrometer is more difficult. To make a measurement with an inside micrometer, it is absolutely necessary that the instrument be held so that it is perpendicular to the two surfaces.

For automotive work, micrometers reading up to 5 in. are needed. Most micrometers have a range of reading of only 1 in. However, other types are available which have interchangeable anvils so that one instrument will have a wide range of reading.

Special micrometers for measuring the diameters of crankshaft main bearing journals (after removing the bearing cap, but without removing the crankshaft) are available.

Another type of micrometer is designed to measure the thickness of engine bearing shells, and in that way determine the extent of wear. The anvil of such

.200
.050
.010
─────
.260

Fig. 3-4. Correct method of holding a micrometer.

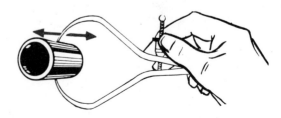

Fig. 3-5. Using a pair of outside calipers for measuring a diameter.

micrometers is rounded, so that point contact is made on the inner surface of the bearing, while the spindle contacts the outer surface.

When the accuracy of the micrometer is not needed, the conventional caliper, Fig. 3-5, is used. Calipers of both inside and outside measurements are available, and with care, accuracy in measurement of .01 in. can be easily attained.

For measuring the diameter of small holes, telescoping gauges are available, Fig. 3-6.

After adjusting the gauge in the hole so that it fits snugly, the gauge is removed, and the diameter of the gauge is then measured with a conventional micrometer.

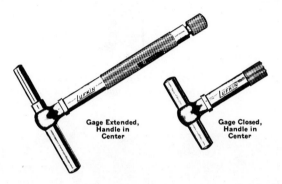

Fig. 3-6. A telescoping gauge is used to measure small internal diameters or the inside size of slots.

Metric Micrometers are used in the same manner as the English type previously described except that graduations are in the Metric System and readings are obtained as follows:

Since the pitch of the spindle screw in Metric micrometers is 0.5 millimeters, one complete revolution of the thimble advances the spindle toward or away from the anvil exactly 0.5 millimeters.

The longitudinal line on the sleeve is graduated in millimeters from 0 to 25 mm and each millimeter is subdivided in 0.5 mm. Therefore it requires two revolutions of the thimble to advance the spindle a distance equal to 1 millimeter.

The beveled edge of the thimble is graduated in 50 divisions, every fifth line being numbered from 0 to 50.

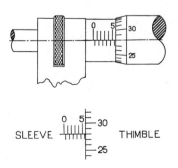

SLEEVE ‖‖‖‖ THIMBLE

Fig. 3-6a. Reading metric micrometer. In this example, the reading is 5.78 millimeters. (L. S. Starrett Co.)

Since a complete revolution of the thimble advances the spindle 0.5 mm, each graduation on the thimble is equal to 1/50 of 0.5 mm or 0.01 mm, two graduations equal 0.02 mm, etc.

To read a Metric micrometer, add the total reading in millimeters visible on the sleeve to the reading in hundredths of a millimeter indicated by the graduation on the thimble which coincides with the longitudinal line on the sleeve.

Example: Refer to Fig. 3-6a.

The "5" mm graduation is visible, representing. . . . . 5 mm
There is one additional 0.5 mm line visible, representing . . . . 0.5 mm
Line "28" on the thimble coincides with the longitudinal line on the sleeve, each line representing .01 mm . . . . 28 x .01 mm = 0.28 mm
The Micrometer Reading is . . . . 5.78 mm

Dial Gauges

To measure the amount of out-of-round and taper in an engine cylinder, a dial gauge, Fig. 3-7, is usually used. Such gauges are inserted in the cylinder bore, and as the gauge is moved up and down in the cylin-

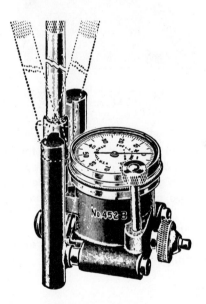

Fig. 3-7. Dial gauges are used extensively to measure the diameter and wear of engine cylinders.

der, movement of the indicating needle of the gauge will show the variation in measurement. Similarly, the amount of out-of-round is measured by rotating the gauge in the cylinder. Such gauges are calibrated to read in .001 in.

By means of a special fixture, dial gauges are also used extensively for measuring the backlash of gears. This is particularly important to the adjustment of the rear axle, pinion and ring gear.

Thickness Gauge

The thickness or feeler gauge is used extensively for measuring the distance between two surfaces, when those surfaces are only a few thousandths of an inch apart. As shown in Fig. 3-8, a feeler gauge consists of an assortment of steel strips of graduated thickness. Each blade of the gauge is marked with its thickness in thousandths of an inch. To use such a gauge, a blade is inserted in the space to be measured, and the gauge blade that fits snugly in the space, is then equal to that space in thousandths of an inch. Thickness or feeler gauges are used extensively for measuring valve tappet clearance, ignition breaker point spacing, and the gap of spark plugs.

When used to measure the clearance between a piston and a cylinder, the force required to withdraw the gauge is measured by a spring balance, Fig. 3-9.

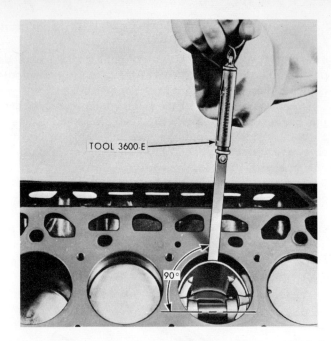

Fig. 3-9. Using a feeler gauge and a spring balance to check the clearance between a piston and the cylinder.

Fig. 3-8. Typical thickness or feeler gauge used for measuring the width of small spaces.

Fig. 3-10. The wire type of thickness gauge is usually used to measure spark plug gaps. Note bending lever on right.

In addition to the flat blade type of thickness gauge, gauges made of different diameter wire, Fig. 3-10, are also used. Such gauges are used particularly for measuring the gaps of ignition breaker points, and spark plug gaps.

Other gauges used frequently in the automotive service field include wire gauges, screw pitch gauges, and vernier calipers.

Straightedge

A straightedge is used frequently to check the trueness of a surface. In Fig. 3-11, a cylinder head is being checked for warpage with a straightedge and the amount of warpage is measured by means of a feeler gauge.

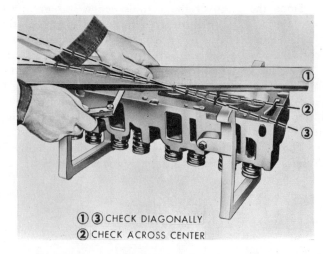

Fig. 3-11. Using a straightedge and a feeler gauge to measure the warpage of a cylinder head.

Quiz - Measuring Instruments

1. For what purpose are inside micrometers frequently used in automotive service work?
2. When the thimble of a micrometer is turned one division as indicated by the lines on the beveled edge of the thimble, how far has the spindle moved?
   a. .025 in.
   b. .0025 in.
   c. .001 in.
   d. .005 in.
3. When the thimble of a micrometer is turned one division as indicated by the lines on the beveled edge of the thimble, how far has the spindle moved?
   a. 5.0mm
   b. .5mm
   c. .05mm
   d. .25mm
   e. .1mm
4. For what purposes is a dial gauge frequently used in automotive service work?
5. A thickness gauge is used:
   a. To measure the thickness of sheet metal.
   b. To measure the diameter of car engine cylinders.
   c. To measure the space between two surfaces.
6. For what purpose is a straighedge frequently used in the auto shop?

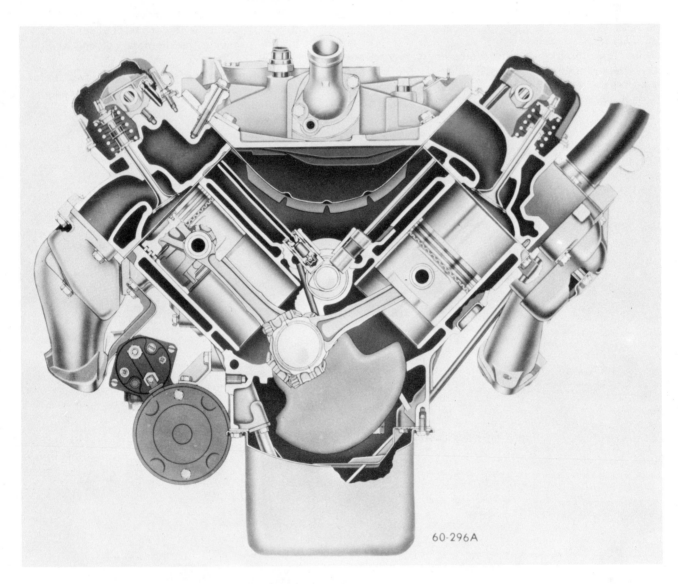

60-296A

Details of Buick 350 cu. in. V-8 engine.

ENGINE
FUNDAMENTALS

Automobiles have been operated successfully by electric motors, steam engines, and internal combustion engines. The internal combustion engine burns fuel within the cylinders, and converts the expanding force of the combustion or "explosion" into rotary mechanical force used to propel the vehicle.

There are several types of internal combustion engines; two and four cycle reciprocating engines,

Engine Fuels

These engines can be made to operate on almost anything that can be converted into a gas that will burn. For example; wood, coal, alcohol, vegetable oils, mineral oils, etc. Some form of petroleum product is almost universally used however because of convenience.

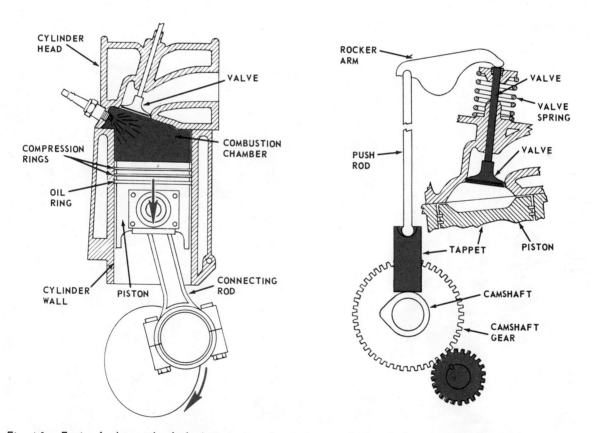

Fig. 4-1a. Engine fundamentals. Left. Arrangement of parts in one cylinder. Right. Camshaft drive and valve linkage.

gas turbines, free piston and rotary engines. However, the four cycle, Fig. 4-2, and to a lesser degree the two cycle, Fig. 4-3, reciprocating engines have been developed to such a degree that they have almost complete dominance of the automotive field. The other types of engines will be described in a later chapter.

A wide variety of petroleum products are used as fuel: gasoline, kerosene, fuel oil, liquefied petroleum gas (LPG), etc. When kerosene, fuel oil, or LPG is used, it is necessary to alter the design or equipment of the engine to other than standard gasoline engine practice.

Engine Design

Gasoline engines as used in automotive vehicles are of two basic types, four cycle and two cycle. Either type may be either water or air-cooled. In the United States, four, six and eight cylinder engines are available and in the not distant past, twelve and sixteen cylinder engines were available.

The typical automobile engine, standard for a great many years, has been a reciprocating piston, four cycle, water cooled, poppet valve, gasoline engine.

Reciprocating Engines

Each "cylinder" of the typical automobile engine has a "piston" which reciprocates -- or moves back and forth -- within the cylinder and is connected to the "crankshaft" by means of a link known as a "connecting rod." See Figs. 4-1a, 4-1b, and 4-1c.

Other types of reciprocating engines substitute an eccentric, an inclined plate, or a cam mechanism for the crankshaft. The "free piston" engine has no crankshaft or connecting rods.

Rotary Engines

Rotary types of engines are not as yet widely used in automobiles. As they are somewhat similar to turbines, they are described herein under that heading.

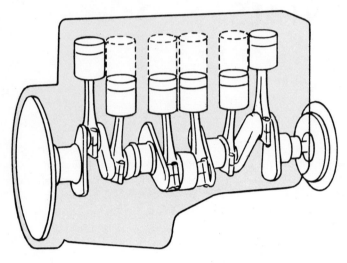

Fig. 4-1b. Arrangement of six cylinders on crankshaft.

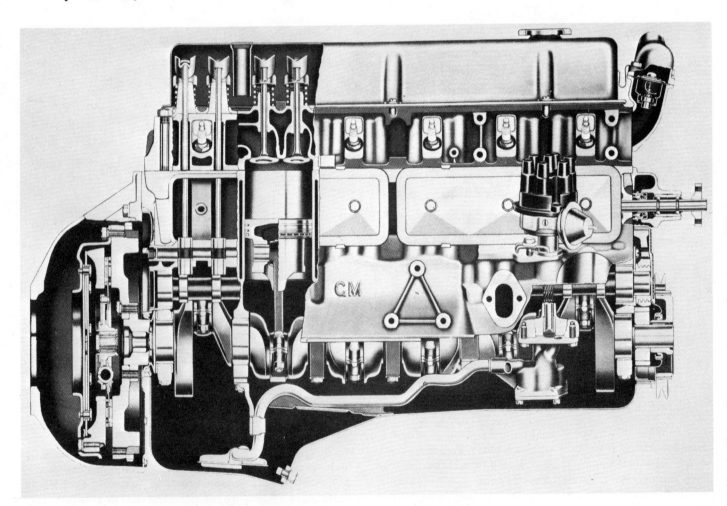

Fig. 4-1c. Pontiac in-line six cylinder engine.

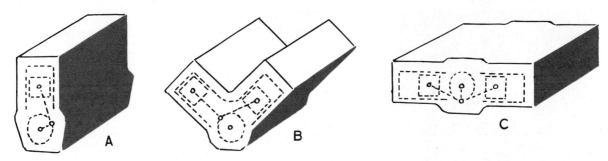

Fig. 4-5. Types of cylinder blocks. (A) In-line block, (B) V-type block, (C) Opposed or "flat" block.

ciprocating engine—one inward in the cylinder and one outward—in each of the two revolutions of the crankshaft required to complete the cycle. See Fig. 4-2.

In order to fulfill the first requisite, it is necessary to fill the cylinder with an explosive mixture. This is accomplished by the atmospheric pressure

Two-Stroke Cycle

In the two-cycle engine, the piston takes over some of the valve function in order to obtain a power stroke each revolution of the crankshaft. This involves the use of ports in the cylinders, shown in Fig. 4-3. These ports are covered and uncovered by the move-

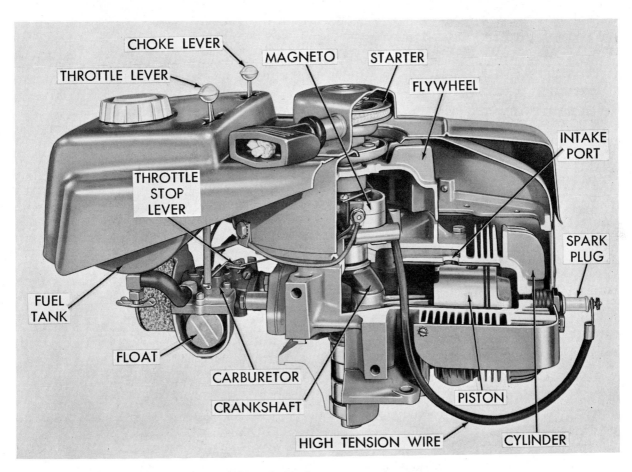

Two stroke cycle Jacobsen engine, cutaway view.

pushing the mixture into the cylinder, after the piston has created a vacuum in the cylinder by moving toward the crankshaft. The mixture is conducted from the carburetor through a pipe known as a manifold, and is regulated by the opening and closing of a valve. These valves will be studied in detail later.

ments of the piston, and thus act as a valve in controlling the filling and emptying of the cylinder.

It must be understood that both inlet and exhaust ports are covered by the piston, except for a short time at the extreme end of the stroke. A deflector is placed on top of the piston on the inlet side, to divert

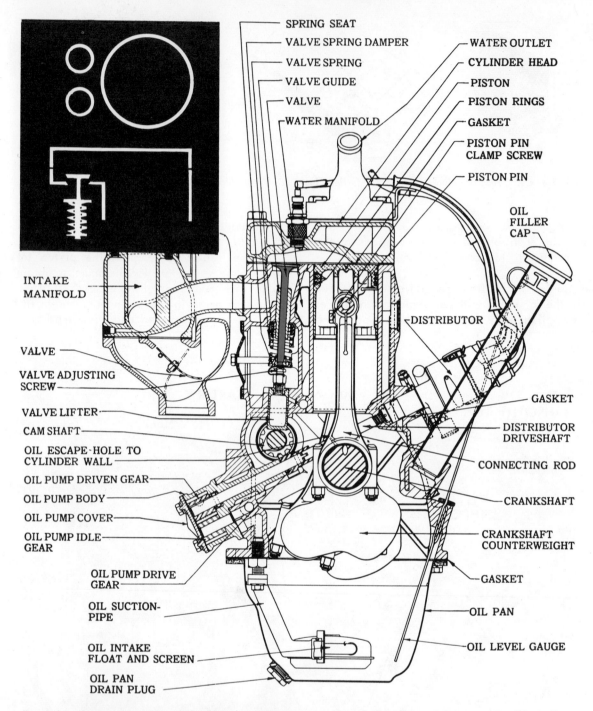

Fig. 4-6a. Cross section of an L-head, or side valve engine, where both valves are on one side of the cylinder. In the T-head, exhaust valves are on one side of the cylinder, inlet valves on the other side. The engine parts are named here and corresponding parts can be identified in the other forms.

the fresh mixture up into the cylinder while the exhaust is leaving the cylinder on the opposite side.

Alternate phases of vacuum and compression in the crankcase can be avoided by using a blower or "supercharger" to push air into the cylinder as illustrated in Fig. 4-4. In this particular design (used in the GM Diesel), a row of ports around the bottom of the cylinder serves for the inlet. In this case the piston acts as an inlet valve, and cam-operated exhaust valves, are placed in the cylinder head In this

design the blower pumps air into the cylinder, and the fuel is pumped in under pressure as explained in the section of this text devoted to diesel engines.

Multi-Cylinder Engines

Almost all automobile engines -- water cooled or air cooled -- four cycle or two cycle -- have more than one cylinder. These multiple cylinders are arranged in-line, opposed or in V form as shown in Fig. 4-5.

Engines for other purposes, such as airplanes, utilize additional arrangements such as radial, inverted in-line, inverted V, X-shaped, and other forms.

Cylinder Types

The location of the valves in four-cycle engines, either water or air cooled, is one of the basic elements of design. There are four basic designs: three of which are in current use. These three are the "L head," the "I head," and the "F head," as shown in Fig. 4-6a, Fig. 4-6b and Fig. 4-6c respectively. The "T head," along with sleeve valves, rotary valves and other variations is not in current use.

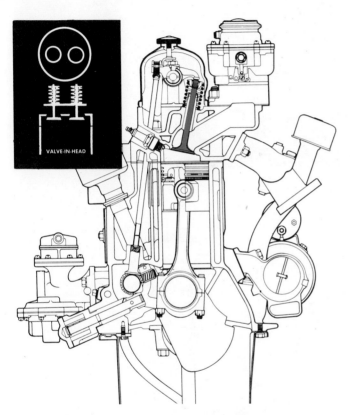

Fig. 4-6b. In the I-head, also known as overhead valve or valve-in-head engine, both valves are placed directly over the piston. This design must not be confused with "overhead camshaft" engines described later.

It should be noted that in the L-head design, the valve ports and gas passages are built in the cylinder block. In the I-head engine, these passages are built in the detachable cylinder head. The F-head engine has one valve in the head, and one in the block, with the necessary passages built into both head and block.

Cylinder Blocks

The engine crankcase and cylinder block, or blocks, are often cast in one piece, which is ordinarily the largest and most intricate single piece of

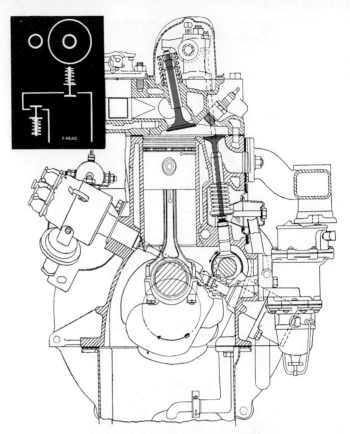

Fig. 4-6c. The F-head design is a combination of the L-head and I-head forms, as it has one valve in the head and one at the side of the cylinder. Note that each of these three designs uses a single camshaft to operate all valves.

metal in the automobile. Even when the cylinders, cylinder heads or cylinder sleeves are separate pieces, the crankcase is still the largest single part in the engine. Practically all of the engine parts are attached to the crankcase directly or indirectly. See Figs. 4-7 and 4-8.

Fig. 4-7. Crankcase and cylinder block casting of Pontiac V-8 engine.

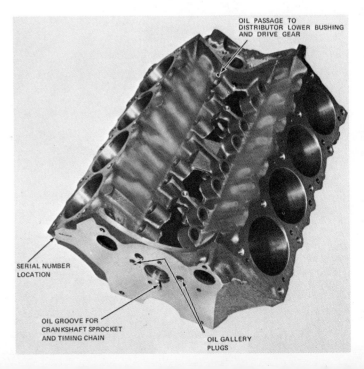

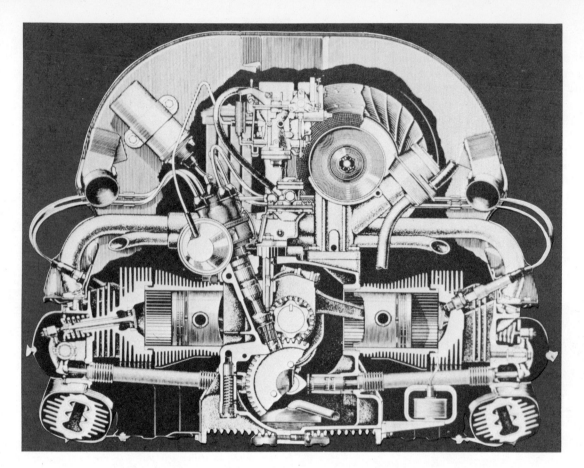

Four cylinder opposed, air-cooled Volkswagen engine.

The crankcase houses the crankshaft and in most cases the camshaft also. With the oil pan, which goes on the lower surface of the crankcase, it forms an oil-tight housing in which the rotating and reciprocating parts operate. The cylinder block contains the pistons which are attached to the crankshaft by means of the connecting rods, Fig. 4-6a.

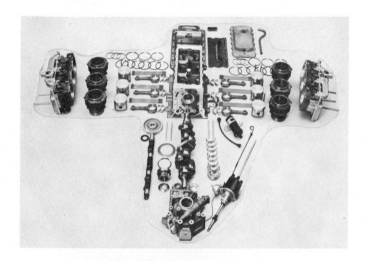

Fig. 4-8. Parts of air-cooled Corvair engine. The cylinders, which are individually formed, are separate from the crankcase and cylinder heads. The cylinders are attached to the crankcase by means of long studs.

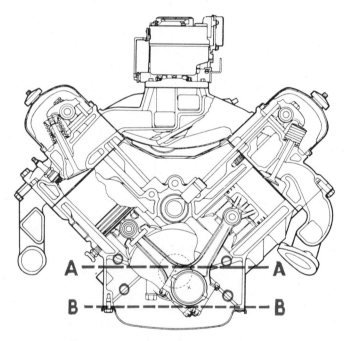

Fig. 4-9. The line A-A is on a plane with the center of the crankshaft while the crankcase extends to the line B-B. Note stiffening webs or ribs at 0-0-0-0 in crankcase.

The crankcase and cylinder block are usually made of high grade cast iron with alloys to improve the wearing characteristics of the cylinders.

It is thus readily understood that this major unit

44

must be extremely strong and rigid to avoid any bending or distortion. As this intricate casting varies in thickness, it does not always cool uniformly and internal stresses are created. These stresses sometimes cause warpage, but much has been done in the way of design to minimize the effects of warpage, by causing it to occur in such directions that it does not

shaft rather than having the oil pan surface in the same plane as the crankshaft. See Fig. 4-9.

While the metal used for these castings is ordinarily termed "cast iron" or "aluminum" as the case might be, the terminology is rather loose because these metals in most cases are alloys. In the case of cast iron, small amounts of chromium, molybdenum

Fig. 4-10. This typical crankshaft is for a six cylinder engine and has a main bearing journal between each of the cylinders.

cause the cylinder bores to warp to any great extent or become excessively out-of-round. Distortion may occur from incorrect placing of the metal masses around the cylinders, from expansion and contraction due to the heat of operation, or from excessive mechanical stresses placed upon it, such as unequal or extreme tightening of bolts, etc.

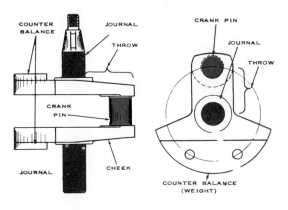

Fig. 4-11. Single throw crankshaft as used in single cylinder engine. Main bearing journals are in solid black, connecting rod journals in color.

Cylinder Distortion

This warpage or distortion can occur in several directions. The cylinder head surface can warp or twist, the cylinder bore may warp longitudinally or become out-of-round, the crankshaft or camshaft bearing bores may be warped out of line, etc.

To stiffen engine block and crankcase castings, webs or ribs are often added to the casting at the points of greatest stress. In some cases the crankcase is extended below the center line of the crank-

or other metals may be added. In the case of aluminum castings, it is customary to add other materials to create an alloy which along with heat and chemical treatment increases the strength and wear resisting ability of the metal. In some cases sleeves are inserted in the cylinder blocks to resist wear, minimize distortion, etc. These sleeves will be discussed later.

Engine Crankshafts

The engine crankshaft is often regarded as the "backbone" of the engine. It serves to change the reciprocating motion of the piston into rotary motion and handles the entire power output. It revolves in bearings located in the engine crankcase, must be free to revolve with as little friction as possible, yet must not have any appreciable looseness in the bearings.

For these reasons, the crankshaft is large in diameter, very accurately machined, and the bearings which support it are of generous size and length. The number of bearings used will depend upon the number of cylinders in the engine, and the design of the engine. By locating a main bearing journal between each cylinder, it is possible to use a lighter crankshaft than if two cylinders are placed between each main bearing journal. See Fig. 4-10.

While engine crankshafts are in general quite similar there is latitude for variation, depending upon the design of the engine. A single-cylinder engine will have one throw on the crankshaft, as shown in Fig. 4-11. A two-cylinder engine will have two throws spaced 180 deg. apart. A three-cylinder engine will have three throws spaced 120 deg. apart. A four-cylinder engine will normally have cylinders 1 and 4 on the same side, and cylinders 2 and 3 on the other side, 180 deg. apart as shown in Fig. 4-12.

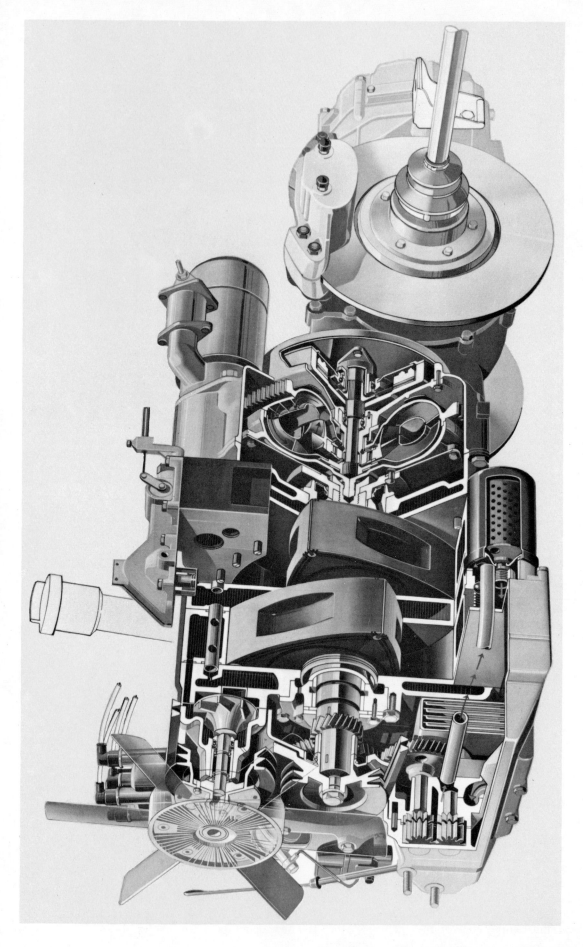

Twin-rotor rotary combustion Wankel engine used on NSU Ro 80 front wheel drive cars. Compression ratio: 9:1. This engine has two cross-draft carburetors, dual ignition system with two spark plugs per rotor. Engine is coupled to hydrokinetic torque converter. Clutch is dry, single plate.

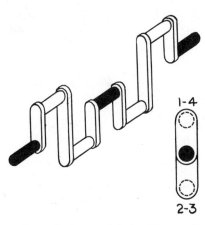

Fig. 4-12. A four cylinder crankshaft will normally have the throws spaced 180 degs. apart with cylinders 1 and 4 on the same side. Some V-8's use a similar construction.

Six Cylinder Crankshafts

A six cylinder engine may have a left-hand crankshaft or a right-hand crankshaft, depending on the firing order of the cylinders. (Firing orders will be covered later.) The crank throws are spaced 120 deg. apart in both cases as shown in Fig. 4-13, and cylinders 1 and 6 are on the same side in each case. Like-

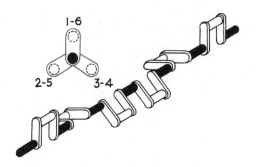

Fig. 4-13. A right-hand crankshaft for a six cylinder engine will have the cranks arranged as shown.

wise, cylinders 2 and 5 are in the same plane, and cylinders 3 and 4 are in the same plane. On the right-hand crankshaft, cylinders 3 and 4 are to the right of the No. 1 crank throw, while on the left-hand crankshaft, cylinders 3 and 4 are on the left side of the No. 1 crank throw. See Fig. 4-14.

Eight Cylinder Crankshafts

An eight cylinder V-type engine normally has a four-throw crankshaft with two cylinders attached to each throw. An in-line eight will have eight throws on the crankshaft.

In the V-8, variation of the location of the crank pins is possible. In one case, all four throws may be in the same plane, two on each side of the crankshaft, the same as a four cylinder crankshaft, or the throws

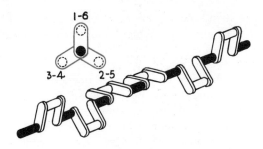

Fig. 4-14. A left-hand crankshaft for a six cylinder engine will have the same spacing of crank throws, but No. 3 and 4 throws will be to the left of No. 1 and 6.

may be in two planes each 90 deg. apart as shown in Fig. 4-15.

Variation is also possible in the in-line eight. One crankshaft is known as the 4-4 type, and the construction may be obtained by placing two four-cylin-

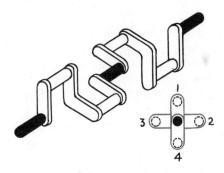

Fig. 4-15. While normally a V-8 crankshaft has the throws arranged the same as a four cylinder engine, a variation is possible as shown herewith.

der crankshafts end to end with the crank arms of one crankshaft in a horizontal position, and the crank arms of the other in a vertical position as shown in Fig. 4-16.

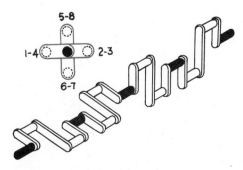

Fig. 4-16. A straight eight crankshaft of the 4-4 type resembles two four-cylinder crankshafts connected end to end.

The other design is known as the 2-4-2 type, and may be obtained by sawing one four-cylinder crankshaft in two in the middle, placing half of it on each end of the other four-cylinder crankshaft. In this case, the two crank arms on each end would be at right angles to the center four crank arms. See Fig. 4-17.

The foregoing covers in brief form the basic construction and operation of the major units of the engine. Some study may be required for a thorough understanding of these fundamentals. This complete understanding is essential in order to be able to grasp the details of operation and service procedures that are to follow. It will be found that the difference between poor work and truly expert work is that the expert understands WHY something needs to be done, as well as WHAT to do, and HOW to do it.

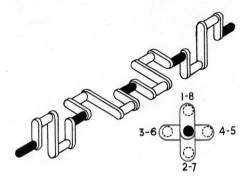

Fig. 4-17. The 2-4-2 type of crankshaft for a straight eight engine is arranged as shown.

Quiz - Engine Fundamentals

Write answers on separate sheet of paper. DO NOT write in this book.

1. All automobiles have either six or eight cylinders. True or False?
2. The majority of automobile engines are of the water cooled type. True or False?
3. Is a "flat" engine the same as an "in-line" engine? Yes or No?
4. Name the largest single part of the engine.
5. Do all reciprocating engines have a crankshaft? Yes or No?
6. List in proper sequence the events that occur in a four-cycle internal combustion engine.
7. A "valve" and a "port" are the same thing. True or False?

8. How does the mixture get into the cylinder?
9. The "I-head," "valve-in-head," and "overhead valve," engines are identical. True or False?
10. How is the explosive mixture in the cylinder ignited?
11. What is the basic difference between a four-cycle engine and a two-cycle engine?
12. How many "throws" are on the crankshaft of a V-8 engine? Two, Four or Eight?
13. Could two four-cylinder crankshafts be used for an in-line eight cylinder engine? Yes or No?
14. What causes distortion of engine blocks?
15. All four cylinder crankshafts are alike. True or False?
16. Six cylinder crankshafts may be of more than one design. True or False?

ENGINE CONSTRUCTION

Many things are demanded of an engine used to propel an automobile. Some of them are:

A. Power to climb steep grades.
B. Speed to go as fast as desired.
C. Economy in the use of fuel and oil.
D. Flexibility for ease of handling.
E. Quietness in operation.
F. Freedom from frequent adjustments.
G. Reliability to go anywhere -- any time.

Some of these requirements are conflicting. For example: any amount of power can be had from an engine of sufficient size, but a supersize engine is not economical to operate. Other conflicts exist, so all automobile engines are a compromise in several ways, in order to obtain the most desirable combination of performance characteristics.

The size of an engine is determined by the bore, stroke and number of cylinders. The bore is the diameter of the cylinders; the stroke is the length of piston travel. See Fig. 5-1. The bore area multiplied by the stroke will give the displacement of one cylinder; which multiplied by the number of cylinders, will give the engine displacement or size.

Size alone however is not a definite measure of the power developed by the engine. Many other things need to be taken into consideration. Some of them are:

1. Engine rotating speed.
2. Compression ratio.
3. Valve size, lift and timing.
4. Internal engine friction.
5. Mechanical condition of parts.

Many other things enter into this, which will be dealt with later in detail. It might seem that items 1, 2, 3 and 4 are inbuilt and not subject to alternation by service procedures. However, each can be altered by the mechanic and must be understood by him.

Possibly the most important of these items is the mechanical condition of the parts and units. Certainly it is the item most directly under the control of the serviceman. An example of this is the cylinders, rings and pistons. If an engine is badly worn or damaged so that there is little or no compression in the cylinders, the mechanic can do little in any direction until compression has been restored.

It is of such importance that the cylinders be round and true that they are machined and finished

to an accuracy of a fraction of a thousandth of an inch. This is in order that the piston and rings, which are finished with equal accuracy, will have a true mating surface. Otherwise the compression may leak between the pistons and cylinders on the power and compression strokes, and little power would be developed. Also the oil might leak through between piston and cylinder wall on the suction stroke, and be burned and wasted.

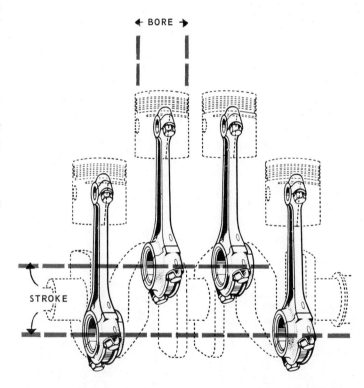

Fig. 5-1. While the diameter of the cylinder determines the bore of an engine, the length of the crank arm determines the distance the piston will travel.

Cylinder Wall Wear

Cylinder walls do wear regardless of the material of which they are made and how carefully they are designed and finished. This wear is due to many causes, including: the pressure of the piston rings against the cylinder walls, the amount of water condensed in the cylinder, temperature of operation, degree of lubrication, kind of lubricant, type of fuel being used, type of service in which the engine is operated, the amount of abrasive in the lubricant and in the combustible fuel drawn into the cylinder from the carburetor, and the

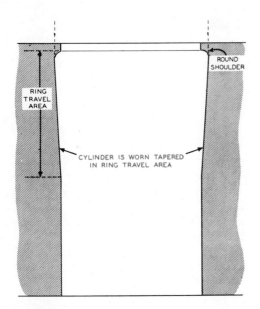

Fig. 5-2. Grit from the air plus heat and less lubrication, causes this pattern of wear on cylinder walls.

length of time since the engine was last in operation.

Cylinders wear to a taper, as shown in Fig. 5-2, and also out-of-round, as shown in Fig. 5-3.

The taper wear is largely due to insufficient lubrication in the upper area of the cylinder, the effects of condensation and consequent corrosion, greater amount of abrasives present and the type of fuel used.

The out-of-round wear results primarily from greater side pressure exerted by the piston on its pow-

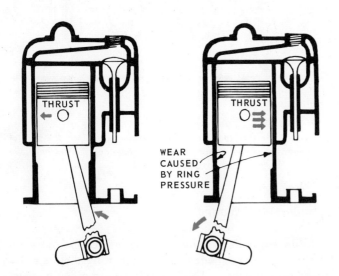

Fig. 5-3. The side thrust on the piston is greater on the explosion stroke than on the compression stroke due to the greater pressures on the piston head.

er stroke than on the other strokes. Design features will also have an effect on cylinder wear, as short stroke engines will tend to wear faster than long stroke engines, and high speeds will also tend to increase cylinder wear because of increased cylinder wall pressure. The design of the water jackets surrounding the cylinder walls is also an important factor, as is the accumulation of rust and other sediment in the water jackets.

Most cylinder wear occurs during the first few miles of operation as the engine has not reached full operating temperature. During that period there is a maximum amount of condensation in the cylinders which is a major factor in causing wear. In addition, there is little oil on the cylinder walls when the engine is first started.

This cylinder and ring wear will be given additional consideration later in this text.

In some engines the cylinders are fitted with sleeves upon the inner surface of which the piston rings bear. These sleeves are of two types "dry" and "wet." The dry type is simply a sleeve or barrel which is pressed into an oversize bore in the cylinder block. The wet type is a cylinder barrel which replaces the cylinder wall and the cooling water circulates in contact with the outside of this barrel. In this case, a sealing gasket is required at both ends of the cylinder barrel. See Fig. 5-4.

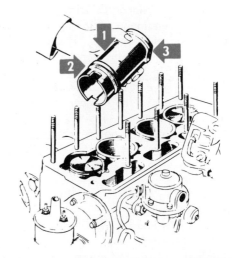

Fig. 5-4. Arrow 1-Inserted wet sleeve. Arrow 2-Bottom sealing gasket. Arrow 3-Top sealing surface for head gasket.

There is a certain service advantage to either the wet or dry type of cylinder sleeve, or the separate barrel-type cylinder in some cases. If one cylinder wall becomes damaged, it may be more economical to replace the sleeve or barrel, than to rebore the cylinder and fit oversize pistons and rings. Furthermore, if the cylinder had to be oversized very much the engine would be out of balance unless all the cylinders were oversized the same.

Another method of reducing the wear on the inside of the cylinder, is to chrome plate the surface where the rings bear. It is customary in such cases to provide very small indentations in the plated surface to encourage the retention of an oil film.

Cylinder Head Gaskets

There are several different types of cylinder head gaskets, Fig. 5-6. Each has its own particular advantages. The major types are:
1. Steel clad asbestos.
2. Composition.
3. Embossed steel.
4. Steel plate.
5. Load cell.

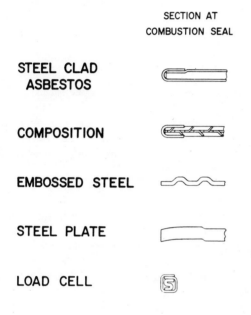

SECTION AT
COMBUSTION SEAL

STEEL CLAD
ASBESTOS

COMPOSITION

EMBOSSED STEEL

STEEL PLATE

LOAD CELL

Fig. 5-6. Major types of cylinder head gaskets.

The steel clad asbestos cylinder head gasket is the most familiar as it has been in use for many years, Fig. 5-6. In general, it is made of a sheet of asbestos approximately 0.030 in. thick covered on both sides with a sheet of steel about 0.010 in. thick. In addition the entire gasket is given a coat of special lacquer or varnish. At openings of the gasket, the ends are flanged over, keeping the asbestos from direct exposure to the combustion gases and coolant.

The composition gasket has a steel core with a soft rubber-asbestos coating on each side. This type gasket has a wide application and provides a particularly effective seal for the coolant. Condition of the head and cylinder block surface is not critical.

The embossed steel gasket has wide acceptance in the passenger car engine field. It is made of cold rolled steel 0.015 to 0.020 in. thick. It has raised sections called embossments around the cylinder openings and water passages. The design provides an effective seal as the clamping action results in sealing pressure of approximately 10,000 psi. It also provides excellent

heat transfer qualities and a rigid support for the cylinder head. However, it cannot compensate for irregularities or dirt on the mating surface of the head and cylinder block.

The steel plate gasket is used extensively on diesel engines and is made of sheet steel about 0.090 in. thick. It has slight embossments around the cylinder bore openings. In addition, rubber grommets are provided for sealing coolant openings. These grommets are glued in place in some cases and in others are installed in position when the engine is assembled.

The load cell is essentially a sealing ring which is fitted one per cylinder when the engine is assembled. Rubber O-rings are placed at each coolant opening. To prevent these rings from shifting, cylinder head and block surfaces are grooved to correctly position the loose parts.

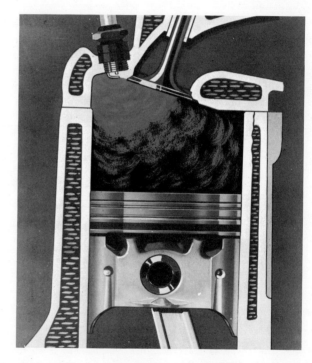

Fig. 5-7. Combustion chambers vary widely in shape, and are sometimes partially in the cylinder, piston head and valve head as well as the cylinder head.

Combustion Chamber

The combustion chamber is the space within the cylinder, above the piston, where the burning of the gas occurs. See Fig. 5-7. Since the early days of the industry, research has continued and is still continuing, perhaps more rapid than ever before, on the design characteristics of the combustion chamber itself. This text is not an engineering design book but is intended as a service text. We will therefore not get into combustion chamber design any deeper than is necessary for our purpose.

The trend in design has been, and is, to concentrate

as much of the expansion force as possible on the head of the piston and avoid dissipation of the expansive force in directions that do not produce power. It may be seen by reference to preceding illustrations of cylinder types that the overhead valve type comes nearer to accomplishing this objective than any of the others.

Another trend is toward the creation and control of turbulence or movement of the air and gasoline mixture within the cylinder to create a more uniform and better mixture of the gasoline and air. One design was developed by an engineer named Ricardo and was used extensively in L-head engines. The principle of this design is shown in Fig. 5-8. In the case of extremely high compression engines, some very involved shapes have been used for cylinder heads and pistons. Such designs are characteristic of diesel engines which will be studied as this text progresses.

It has long been recognized that the more the explosive mixture is compressed within the cylinder before it is ignited, the more power will be developed by the explosion stroke. A limiting factor other than the strength of the engine parts is imposed, however, by the characteristics of the fuel used. One of these characteristics is the tendency of the fuel to

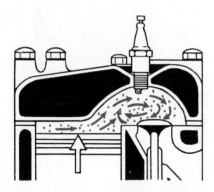

Fig. 5-8. The shape of the combustion chamber has much to do with the proper mixing of the gasoline and air to obtain maximum benefit from the combustion.

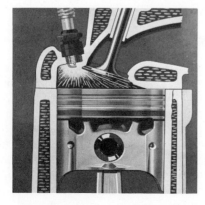

Fig. 5-9. This particular piston is of the aluminum "skeleton" type and is used with an aluminum connecting rod.

"ping" or "knock" as the compression pressure is raised. Much research and study have been expended on this phenomenon which is known as detonation. This is ordinarily attributed to irregular and too rapid expansion or explosion of the gasoline and air mixture. The noise comes from vibration of the walls of the combustion chamber.

The material of which the combustion chamber is made, and the efficiency of the cooling system also have a distinct bearing on the compression ratio that can be used in a given engine. For example, aluminum cylinder heads and aluminum pistons can operate at higher compression ratios than cast iron or steel. One reason for this is perhaps that the heat of combustion is dissipated more rapidly to the cooling water or air due to the superior heat conducting ability of aluminum.

Engine Pistons

Engine pistons serve several purposes: they transmit the force of the explosion to the crankshaft through the connecting rod; they act as a guide for the upper end of the connecting rod; they also serve as a carrier for the piston rings used to seal the piston in the cylinder. See Fig. 5-9.

Pistons operate under exceedingly difficult mechanical and thermal (heat) conditions, and must therefore be made and installed with the utmost care. They must be strong enough to stand the force of the explosion, and yet be as light as possible to avoid excessive inertia forces when their direction of travel is reversed twice each revolution. They must be able to withstand the heat from the burning gas, plus the heat generated by friction. As they must slide freely within the cylinder, they cannot be fitted too tightly. If too loosely fitted in the cylinder, they will knock and rattle.

Piston Materials

Cast iron or semi-steel has been used extensively as a piston material. It is strong enough for the stresses imposed; has a melting point above the cylinder operating temperature; expands at the same rate as cast iron cylinders, and does not generate excessive friction when properly lubricated. The principal objection is that of weight. This objection has increased in importance as engine speeds have been increased.

Aluminum alloy is also used as a material for pistons. It is lighter than cast iron, is readily cast and machined, and does not generate excessive friction in the cylinder. Aluminum expands more rapidly than cast iron when subjected to the heat of operation, and also has a much lower melting point. In material and design, the aluminum piston has been developed to a point where its advantages apparently outweigh its disadvantages, because it is almost universally used in automobile engines.

Fig. 5-10. *This is typical of piston damage when the top of the piston becomes overheated.*

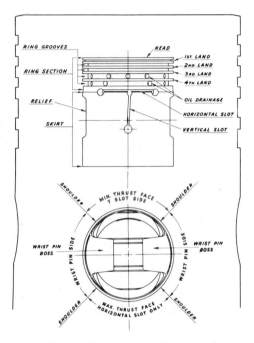

Fig. 5-11. *Note that the T slot is on the minor thrust side. The major thrust side has horizontal slot only.*

The lighter weight means less inertia for the reciprocating parts and thus higher speed for the engine along with better acceleration. This lessened inertia also decreases bearing loads at high speeds and reduces side thrust on the cylinder walls. Due to the greater heat conductivity of aluminum, the piston head runs cooler and in general, it is possible to use higher compression ratios.

Early aluminum pistons were noisy because they had to be fitted in the cylinder with considerably more clearance than cast iron pistons. This resulted in piston slap and rattle when the engine was cold, and until the piston expanded in the cylinder. This difficulty has been largely overcome by designing the piston skirt so it is flexible, by use of special alloys and by means of steel struts, Fig. 5-15.

Aluminum pistons possess the desirable characteristic of conducting the heat away from the combustion chamber more rapidly than cast iron, but they also melt at a much lower temperature. Aluminum pistons seldom melt entirely, but their strength decreases rapidly as the temperature increases. In

many cases of stuck or broken rings, the top edge of the piston or the aluminum lands between the rings, may soften and melt or be blown away by the hot gas as shown in Fig. 5-10.

Severe and continued detonation is also responsible for broken piston heads and wedged piston rings. The aluminum is said to become soft and plastic enough when overheated, to allow the ring grooves to deform. The strength of aluminum pistons can be increased by alloying the aluminum with other metals and also by heat treatment processes. Some of the materials added to the aluminum are copper, magnesium, nickel, silicon, etc.

Piston Construction

The piston head or "crown," Fig. 5-11, is the top surface against which the explosive force is exerted. It may be flat, concave, convex, or a great variety of shapes to promote turbulence or help control combustion. See Fig. 5-12. A narrow groove is sometimes cut into the piston above the top ring to serve

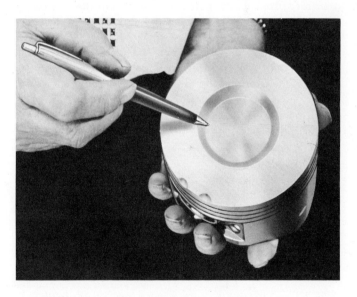

Fig. 5-12a. *Part of the combustion chamber is in this piston head.*

Fig. 5-12b. *Indentations in top are for valve head clearance.*

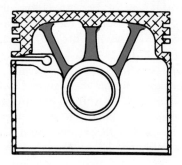

Fig. 5-13. *Ribs are cast into the inside of the piston to strengthen it between the crown and the piston boss.*

as a "heat dam" to reduce the amount of heat reaching the top ring.

The piston rings which are carried in the ring grooves are of two basic types: "compression" rings and "oil control" rings. Both types are made in a wide variety of designs. The upper ring or rings are to prevent compression leakage, and the lower ring or rings are to control oil. The lower groove or grooves often have holes or slots in the bottom of the grooves to permit oil drainage from behind the rings.

The piston ring lands are the parts of the piston between the ring grooves, and provide a seating surface for the sides of the piston rings.

The main section of the piston is known as the skirt and forms a bearing area in contact with the cylinder wall which takes the thrust caused by the crankshaft as previously described. There is some thrust on both sides. The "major" thrust side is the side opposite the crank throw, as it goes down on the power stroke. The "minor" thrust is of course the other side, which is opposite the crank throw as the piston goes up on the compression stroke. Pistons are internally braced to make them as strong as possible. See Fig. 5-13.

The piston or wrist pin hole in the piston bosses may also serve as a bearing for the piston pin, and may not be located in the exact middle of the piston. It may be placed as much as 1/16 in. to one side, in an effort to lessen the side thrust on the cylinder wall.

In some cases the piston skirt is extended downward on the thrust sides to form what is known as a "slipper" piston. This design may be seen in Figs. 5-9 and 5-12b. The purpose of this design is to increase the area of piston contact with the cylinder walls on the thrust faces.

Some pistons are also cut away, or partially cut away around the piston pin holes as may be seen in Figs. 5-9, 5-11, and 5-12a. This is known as a "relief" and is intended to provide additional clearance to avoid "seizing" if the piston should become overheated and expand excessively.

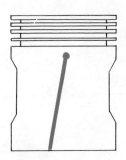 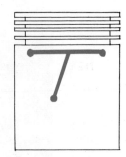 

Fig. 5-14. *Left. Aluminum pistons may have a diagonal slot cut through the skirt on the minor thrust side. Center. In some cases, a slot shaped something like a T is cut in the piston skirt. Right. Two slots may be connected by a third slot to form a U-shaped slot design.*

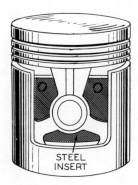

Fig. 5-15. *A steel insert may be cast into an aluminum piston to help control the expansion rate.*

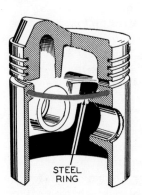

Fig. 5-16. *Instead of a vertical insert, a steel ring may be cast into the piston to help control the expansion.*

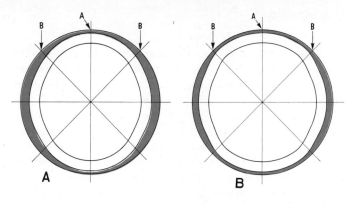

Fig. 5-17. (A) When the piston is cold, there is also more clearance at the shoulders (B) than at (A). (Clearances are exaggerated for emphasis.) (B) As the temperature of the piston increases, it becomes more nearly round and the clearance more nearly uniform.

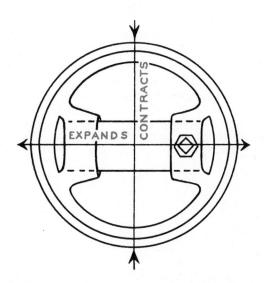

Fig. 5-18. Expansion of the piston occurs parallel with the piston pin.

Piston Design

Alloy pistons may have the skirts split in a variety of ways. Some typical piston slots are shown in Fig. 5-14. These slots are placed on the thrust sides to provide flexibility in the piston skirt. By this means the piston can be fitted more closely when cold and can expand when hot, without damage.

Other pistons are of the "strut" type as shown in Fig. 5-15. In this case, an alloy steel insert is cast into the aluminum piston to control the expansion of the aluminum, and thus maintain more constant clearance. Such pistons are usually skeleton like and do not contact the cylinder walls around the piston pin holes.

Still another design is known as the "steel belted" type and has a steel ring cast into the aluminum piston above the piston pin holes to help control expansion. See Fig. 5-16.

Most aluminum pistons are "cam-ground" -- that is, they are purposely machined with the skirts oval as shown in Fig. 5-17. The reason for this is that while the skirts will be out-of-round when cold in

such fashion that the thrust faces will have the greater diameter, the skirt will become more nearly round when the piston expands at operating temperature. See Fig. 5-18. In this case the piston contact surface is something like the pattern shown in Fig. 5-19.

Pistons are also slightly tapered in many cases. The top of the piston runs much hotter than the bottom or skirt so the top is smaller in diameter. This is particularly true of the piston above the top ring. When the entire piston is not tapered, the top lands are at least smaller in diameter than the skirt which needs less clearance.

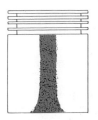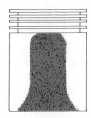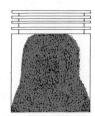

Fig. 5-19. As a cam ground piston expands, the pattern of contact with the cylinder wall progresses from the cold piston at left to the warm piston at right.

Fig. 5-20. Inserted iron bands are sometimes used in heavy-duty pistons to strengthen the ring grooves.

Another thing that is often done in the case of heavy-duty engines to compensate for the tendency of pistons to get soft from the excess heat at the top, is to insert an iron band for the top ring or rings as shown in Fig. 5-20.

The top surfaces of pistons are often contoured to provide turbulence to the explosive mixture and thereby provide more efficient combustion. This is particularly true in the case of diesel engines.

One type of such pistons is known as the Mexican Hat design, Fig. 5-21. This is a feature of the Allis Chalmers diesel. In this design the fuel injector is centrally located over the cylinder and piston and the fuel is directed downward in a conical shaped spray.

Fig. 5-21. Mexican hat type piston for use in diesel engines.

The spray will strike the top and rim of the piston rather than the relatively cool cylinder wall. It is claimed the fuel will be mixed with a greater percentage of air and will result in improved combustion.

The piston used in the Mercedes-Benz diesel is shown in Fig. 5-22. This provides what is known as an open combustion chamber. In this design turbulence is provided by injecting fuel at an angle.

Another type of piston provides a spherical chamber in which combustion takes place. This is known as the M-system, and is shown in Fig. 5-23. Fuel is injected so it strikes the surface of the spherical chamber. In addition to wide application in the commercial transport field and industrial field, it is used extensively in engines designed for multi-fuel uses, particularly engines intended for military use.

Detroit Diesel Crosshead Piston

To increase piston life and provide greater load factor capability, the Detroit Diesel Div. of General Motors Corp., has developed a crosshead-type piston, Fig. 5-24. This is a two-piece piston which separates the crown of the piston from the skirt. Each part carries out its prescribed function without being forced

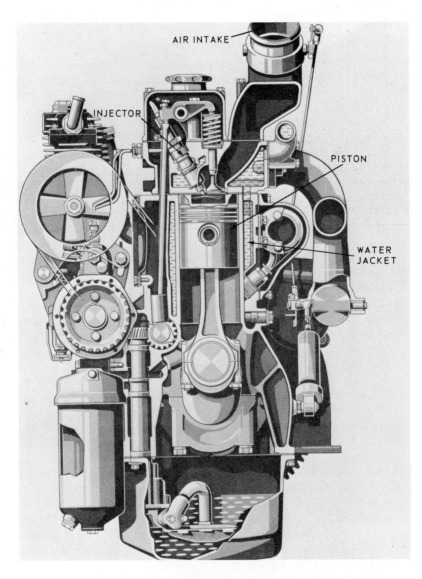

Fig. 5-22. Note rim around top of piston to form open combustion chamber.

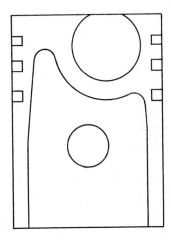

Fig. 5-23. Piston with almost hemispherical cavity which provides combustion chamber of the M-type for diesel engines.

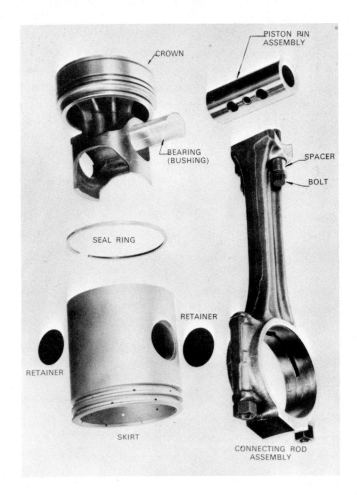

Fig. 5-24. Sectional view of Detroit Diesel Crosshead piston.

to react to unnecessary mechanical or thermal loads. The crown and skirt are free to rock on the piston pin axis independently of each other. As a result the vertical forces of combustion and compression are separated from the side thrust. Side thrust load on the piston due to various positions of the connecting rod cannot be transmitted to the crown of the piston as this is not solidly connected to the piston pin.

As a result of this construction, wear of the piston rings is reduced and thermal loads are confined to the crown.

Pressure lubrication is provided for the piston pin which has a heavy-duty type bearing with a tin-lead overlay.

Superior cooling of the piston crown is provided by supplying oil to chambers under the crown. A standpipe in the chamber maintains oil level at the desired height.

Quiz - Engine Construction

1. The power of an automobile engine is determined by the number of cylinders. True or False?
2. The stroke of the engine is determined by the length of the cylinder_____, crankshaft throw _____, displacement of the cylinder_____.
3. How can the displacement of an engine be found?
4. Explain why cylinders wear out-of-round.
5. A wet cylinder sleeve is lubricated, a dry sleeve is not. True or False?
6. Cylinder head gaskets for a V-8 engine are interchangeable and may be used on either side. True or False?
7. The combustion chamber is usually: above the piston_____, below the piston_____, in the crankcase_____.
8. Name three things required of the piston.
9. Which material is used most for pistons: steel _____, aluminum_____, cast iron_____?
10. What is a heat dam in a piston?
11. Which side of the piston is the major thrust side?
12. What is meant by piston relief?
13. Pistons are slotted so that they can be more readily inserted in the cylinders. True or False?
14. Describe a cam-ground piston.
15. How many major types of cylinder head gaskets are there?
    Three
    Four
    Five
    Six
    Seven
16. The tops of pistons are often contoured to provide turbulence. True or False?

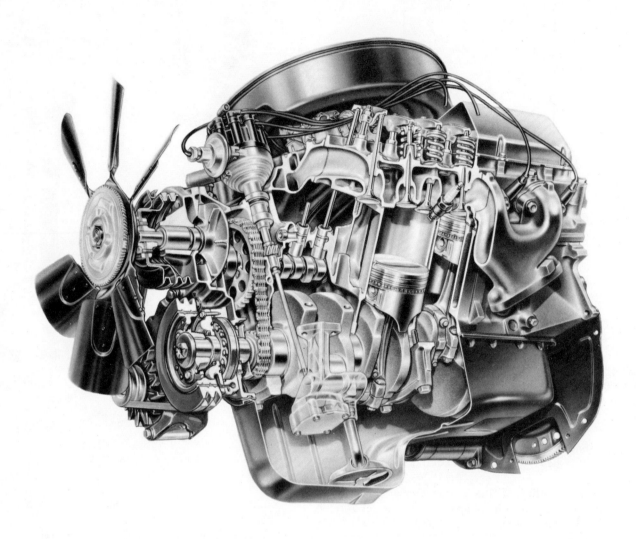

Ford light weight engine. Development for this engine centered on need for larger engine to accommodate extra accessories and to reduce exhaust emissions. Engine evolved in two displacement sizes--429 and 460 cu. in. V-8's with common bore size diameter, but longer stroke on the ''460.''

ENGINE PISTONS, RINGS AND PINS

Piston rings have been designed with such a multitude of variations as to be almost unbelievable. Originally they were a simple split ring made of cast iron. As engine power output has constantly increased and oiling requirements have steadily become more complicated, more and more has been demanded of piston rings.

Modern piston rings are made of steel as well as cast iron and are often of multiple sections instead of a single piece. They are often quite complicated in design, are heat treated in various ways and plated with other metals. Furthermore there are two distinct classifications: compression rings and oil control rings. A typical piston ring installation is shown in Fig. 6-1.

Piston rings would not present much of a problem if cylinders and pistons did not expand, distort out-of-round, and warp when at operating temperatures. But they DO expand and may also distort and warp, so the

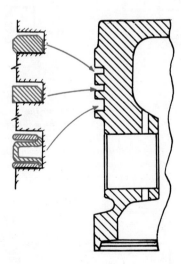

Fig. 6-1. This cross section shows two compression rings in the upper grooves, and an oil control ring in the lower groove.

rings must be capable of conforming to these changing conditions. Furthermore, the ring itself is exposed to heat and to alternating pressure and vacuum. It is expected to prevent the passage of pressure in one direction and to control the flow of oil in the other direction.

Piston Ring Blow-By

The compression pressure and explosion pressure can go past the ring in several ways. This is known as "blow-by." The pressure can go through the ring gap which changes in width according to the expansion and contraction of the cylinder and ring. If it were fitted so precisely that the ring ends touched to seal the gap, it would score the cylinder when the ring expanded from the heat of operation.

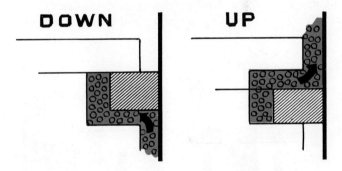

Fig. 6-2. Oil can creep around in back of the rings to find its way into the combustion chamber, and gases can creep down into the crankcase from the combustion chamber in a similar manner, but in the opposite direction.

Blow-by can also occur by going behind the ring as shown in Fig. 6-2. If the ring were fitted tightly enough sidewise in the groove to avoid possible leakage, there would be danger of sticking when the piston and rings expand.

Blow-by is a serious problem when the cylinder walls distort out-of-round when at operating temperature. This can be caused by improper cylinder or cylinder head design, improper cooling or unequal tightening of adjacent bolts. This distortion may occur in more than one spot on the cylinder wall and the different spots are often of different size and shape. See Fig. 6-3.

In the same ways that compression leaks down past the ring, oil can also pass upward into the cylinder and the result is known as "oil-pumping." This causes fouling of the spark plugs, excessive deposits of carbon in the combustion chamber, and smoking at the exhaust as well as waste of oil.

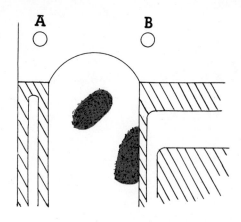

Fig. 6-3. Distortion of cylinder walls can cause the cylinders to be out-of-round or to distort in spots as indicated here.

Oil-Pumping

It is easier for oil to pass upward in some cases, than it is for compression to leak down past the rings. Therefore, it is possible to have an engine with good compression and power, which is also an oil-pumper. The oil might act to seal excessive side clearance in the ring grooves, and prevent leaks of

rings and fitting them to the pistons and cylinders. Many other things which enter into the matter will be considered in this text.

Compression Rings

The top compression ring is usually rectangular in cross section or with a bevel cut on the inner top corner, Fig. 6-5. Often the ring is chrome plated, Fig. 6-6, or is molybdenum filled cast iron to provide better wearing qualities. The second compression ring is often a coated cast iron ring. Some compression rings have a taper on the face and may or may not have an inside bevel.

The idea of the bevel on the inside upper corner of the ring is to cause the ring to twist in the groove in such manner that the outside lower edge presses on the cylinder wall more tightly than the rest of the ring face. The tapered outer face does the same thing. In both cases, the limited area in contact with the cylinder wall offers a higher pressure at that point, to effect a better seal. Such rings must be installed right side up and are usually stamped "top" on the side to be installed on top. See Fig. 6-7.

The second ring is also usually a compression ring, but may be slightly different in design as it

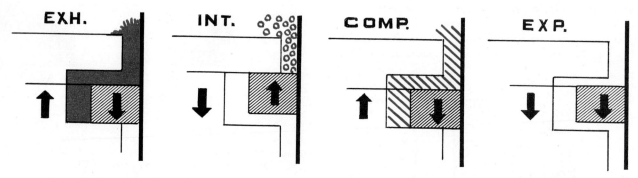

Fig. 6-4. There must be some clearance between the ring and the bottom of the groove, and also on the sides of the ring. The result is that a ring can act as a pump in the manner shown. On the exhaust stroke, the exhaust gas tends to hold the rings in the bottom of the groove as the piston travels up. On the intake stroke, the vacuum in the combustion chamber tends to hold the ring against the top of the groove while the piston goes down. On the compression stroke, the pressure in the combustion chamber again tends to hold the ring against the bottom of the groove. On the explosion stroke, the expanding gases tend to push both piston and ring in the same direction, thus permitting the ring to float in the groove.

compression. At the same time, the alternating vacuum and pressure in the cylinder may cause the ring to act as a pump. See Fig. 6-4.

This condition is aggravated if the walls of the ring grooves, and the sides of the rings, are not flat and true. The volume of leakage past the back of the ring can be much greater than through the tiny gap at the ends of the ring.

It may be seen from the foregoing that great care is required in reconditioning cylinders to make sure that they are round and true when new rings are fitted. Equal care is required in selecting the new

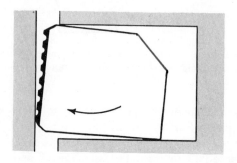

Fig. 6-5. A ring beveled in this manner has a tendency to tilt in the ring groove.

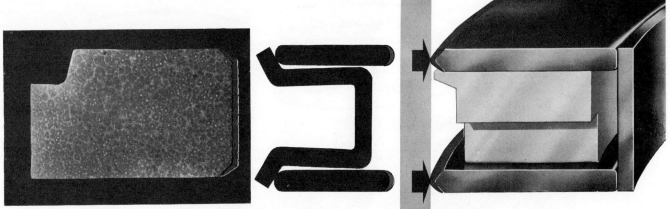

Fig. 6-6. Three different types of chrome plated piston rings.

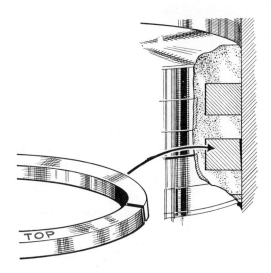

Fig. 6-7. Tapered rings are usually marked. If not, they should be installed as shown here.

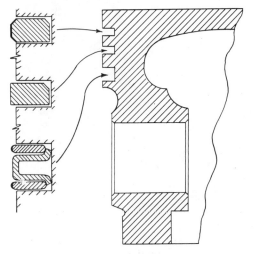

Fig. 6-8. In this installation, the top and bottom rings are chrome plated. The second ring is of the "twist" type.

helps in oil control. This difference might be a bevel cut on the inner or outer corner, which might be combined with a taper on either the inside or outside. A typical installation is shown in Fig. 6-8.

Oil Control Rings

The third ring from the top, and the fourth if four are used, are of the oil-control type, and vary all the way from simple to extremely complicated types. Several varieties are shown in Fig. 6-9. In any case, it must be remembered that the oil scraped from the cylinder wall by the oil ring must have a free passage to the inside of the piston. For this reason, holes or slots are cut in the lower ring grooves. When an inner ring or expander is used, these openings must be kept open if the oil ring is to function as intended. See Fig. 6-10.

Another typical ring installation is shown in Fig. 6-11. Note that the No. 1 ring, has a full face contact on the cylinder wall and the ring expansive pressure is therefore distributed over a wide area. Ring No. 2, is also a compression ring but has a narrower contact surface and therefore a higher pressure on that area, because the entire expansive force of the ring is concentrated on the narrow area in contact with the cylinder wall. The result is that the top ring will show less tendency to wear the cylinder in the driest and hottest part, and the second ring will seat more quickly to the cylinder wall even though it has more lubrication than the top ring.

Ring No. 3, is an oil control ring and has two narrow edges in contact with the cylinder wall. Having slots cut between the two edges, the oil will be scraped from the cylinder wall into the channel or slots of the ring. Ring No. 4, in this case is of the extremely flexible type which follows closely the contour of the cylinder walls even when they are slightly out-of-round.

In this connection, it is well to remember that the piston ring moves in the groove. Due to the constant reversing of direction of piston travel, and the necessity of sidewise clearance between ring and groove, it may be seen that the rings move up and down in the ring grooves as shown previously. A film of oil cushions this movement.

Likewise it will be understood that if the cylinder is worn tapered, the rings will expand and con-

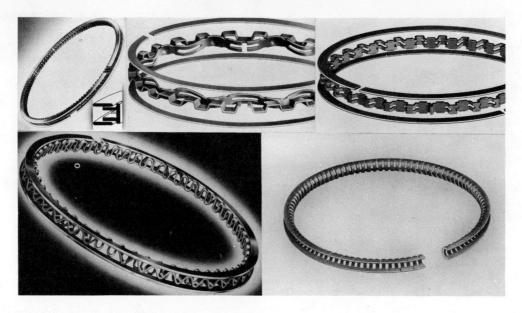

Fig. 6-9. Oil control rings are made in wide variety.

tract as they move up and down in a bore that is larger at one end than the other. Similarly if the cylinder is out-of-round in spots, the rings will be pumping in and out of the groove as they try to follow the cylinder wall.

panding stainless steel spring expander and is designed specifically to prevent oil clogging in heavy duty service. Note that the expander is located above the drainage slots so oil flow will not be restricted. In addition, drainage slots at the bottom of the ring are curved to eliminate sharp corners. The face of the ring is faced with chrome to reduce wear.

Fig. 6-10. A typical slotted steel expander as used with a slotted oil control ring.

Another type of oil control ring is shown in Fig. 6-10a. This ring is a cast iron ring with a self ex-

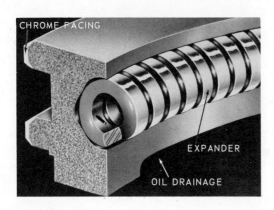

Fig. 6-10a. Chrome faced oil ring with stainless steel coiled spring expander. (Sealed Power)

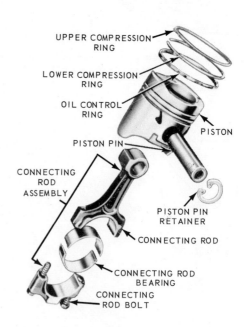

Fig. 6-10b. Piston, rod, pin and ring assembly. Note piston pin retainer. (Ford)

Piston Pins

Piston pins, also known as "wrist pins," are the connection between the upper end of the connecting rod and the piston, Fig. 6-10b. There are three main types:

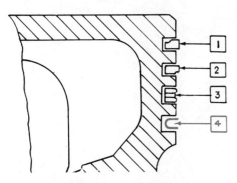

Fig. 6-11. *A typical piston ring installation with an extremely flexible oil control ring in the bottom groove.*

A. Pins anchored in the piston with the bushing in the upper end of the connecting rod oscillating on the pin, Fig. 6-12.

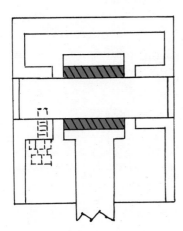

Fig. 6-12. *Where the pin is anchored in the piston, the bearing is located in the upper end of the connecting rod.*

B. Pins clamped in the rod with the pin oscillating in the piston, Fig. 6-13.

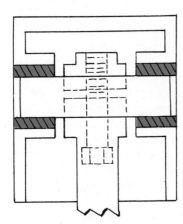

Fig. 6-13. *Where the piston pin is anchored in the connecting rod, there is a bearing in each of the piston bosses.*

C. Pins which are full floating in both connecting rod and piston with lock rings or soft metal plugs in both piston bosses, to prevent endwise movement of the piston pin. See Fig. 6-14.

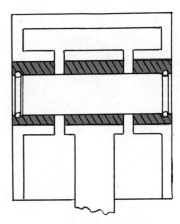

Fig. 6-14. *Where the pin is held in place by snap rings or plugs, the pin "floats" and bears in the piston bosses and also in the rod end. This illustration shows the principle involved, but actually the pin would bear directly in the piston bosses of an aluminum piston, and the retaining ring grooves would be cut into the piston.*

Other than the type of bearing and the provision for holding the pins in place, all three types are quite similar. They are ordinarily hollow steel pins, case-hardened on the outside surface. They are subjected to extremely heavy loads and are not adjustable for wear. When worn, they must be replaced. As they have an oscillating motion in the bearing surface, rather than the high surface speed between the crankshaft and the connecting rod bearings, the steel pin can bear directly in the aluminum piston, or in bronze bushings in either cast iron or aluminum pistons, or a bronze bushing in the upper end of the connecting rod.

Other variations found in design include "needle" or roller bearings in hardened bushings, an "interference fit" in the connecting rod which requires the pin to be pressed into a hole slightly smaller than the pin. In the case of an aluminum connecting rod, there may be no bushing required.

The proper size for a piston pin presents a problem. If the pin is large enough in diameter to provide a long wearing bearing surface, the reciprocating weight will be increased and the bearing loads correspondingly increased. If it is as small as permissible to hold down bearing loads, it will be smaller in diameter, and thus have less bearing surface to carry the load.

If the pin is fastened in the piston with a small screw, the assembly will be lighter than where a bolt is used in the connecting rod. However, if it is clamped in the rod, it will have double the bearing surface as there will be a bearing in each piston boss. If it floats in both piston and rod, it will have the greatest bearing surface along with the lightest weight.

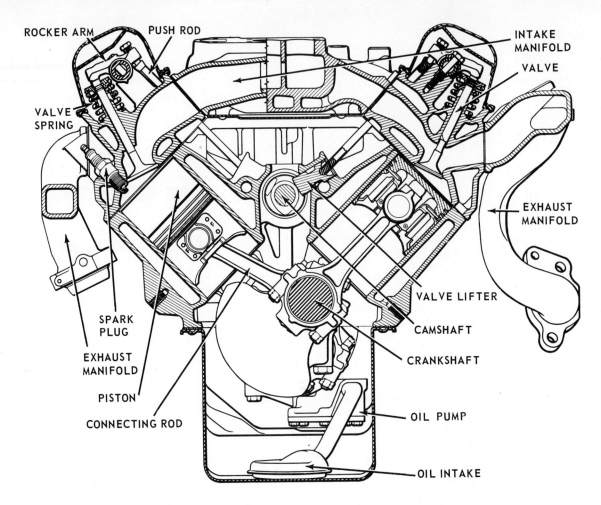

Fig. 6-15. The exhaust manifolds on Dodge Dart 273 cu. in. V-8 engine are unusual. The right manifold is of the low-runner design with a center outlet. The left manifold has a high-runner that extends to the rear of the engine.

One problem with this construction is that if the locking ring or retaining plug should fail to stay in place, the pin will probably score the cylinder quickly and deeply.

One ever present complication is the fact that all three metals in contact; steel, bronze and aluminum, have a different rate of heat expansion. Obviously, being attached to the piston, the pins and bushings will run hot. In general, heat in any bearing promotes wear. Very little wear in a piston pin or bushing will create noise.

It will then be understood that all piston pin designs are a compromise in some direction and none of them appear to be ideal. Of course the repairman can do little about the design of the engine parts, but if he has a thorough understanding of some of the problems involved in a case of this kind, he will be sure to do the best possible job and thus avoid having to do it over again. Fitting of piston pins will be explained in detail later herein.

Quiz - Engine Piston Rings and Pins

1. Name two results of oil pumping.
2. Blow-by may be a serious problem after the engine warms up to operating temperature. True or False?
3. Do piston rings move up and down in the grooves? Yes or No?
4. Why must piston rings be flexible?
5. A piston ring may act as a pump. True or False?
6. Give two reasons for cylinder wall distortion.
7. Do piston rings move in and out in the grooves? Yes or No?
8. More oil leakage occurs at the ring gap than around behind the ring. True or False?
9. If an engine has good compression it will not pump oil. True or False?
10. Name four ways of holding the piston pin in place.
11. Describe an "interference fit."
12. Bronze bushings can be used with aluminum pistons. True or False?
13. In order to obtain the greatest wearing surface, the piston pin should be clamped in the connecting rod _____, the piston _____, neither _____.
14. A hardened steel pin can be used in an aluminum piston without any bushings. True or False?
15. Aluminum and bronze have about the same rate of heat expansion. True or False?
16. Piston pins are not adjustable for wear. True or False?

ENGINE CRANKSHAFTS AND CAMSHAFTS

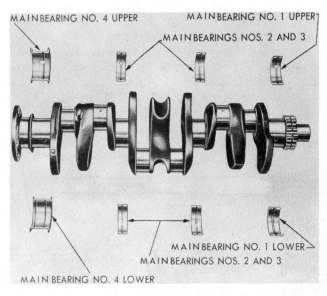

Fig. 7-1. Forged steel crankshaft with bearing inserts.

Automobile engine crankshafts may be forged out of steel, or they may be made out of cast steel by a special process. Examples are shown in Figs. 7-1, and 7-2. They are usually in one piece, although they are sometimes built up of more than one piece. In this case, all pieces must be carefully and rigidly connected. The bearing journals are all finished in precise alignment one with the other, and great care is exercised to see that the journals are absolutely round,

and not tapered longitudinally. A high degree of accuracy is necessary in any work that is done with an engine crankshaft or any of the bearings. This will be covered more fully later.

Fig. 7-2. Typical cast steel crankshaft.

In automobile engines, it is customary to attach a gear or sprocket at the end of the crankshaft opposite the flywheel end, to drive the camshaft either by chain or gear. Also, a torsional vibration dampener is usually attached near the camshaft drive gear or sprocket, to help smooth out the vibration set up in the crankshaft due to the power impulses which have a tendency to twist the crankshaft. See Fig. 7-3.

Engine Flywheels

A flywheel is ordinarily mounted near the rear main bearing. This is usually the longest and heaviest of the main bearings, as it must support the weight of the flywheel. The purpose of the flywheel is to assist

Fig. 7-3. A counter-balanced crankshaft complete with flywheel and vibration damper.

Fig. 7-4. Special equipment is utilized to check the running balance of an engine with the rotating and reciprocating parts in place.

the engine to idle smoothly by carrying the pistons through those parts of the operating cycle when power is not being produced. The heavier the engine flywheel, the smoother the engine will idle. However, because of its inertia an excessively heavy flywheel will cause the engine to accelerate and decelerate slowly. For these reasons heavy duty or truck engines have large and heavy flywheels and racing car or high speed engines have light flywheels.

The rear surface of the flywheel is usually machined flat and used for one surface of the clutch. In the case of automatic transmissions where no clutch is used, part of the fluid flywheel or torque converter is attached to and becomes a part of the flywheel.

Crankshaft Balance

Because of the forces acting on the flywheel and crankshaft and the speed at which it revolves, it is necessary to balance it with great care. The assembly is first balanced statically and then balanced dynamically. To obtain static balance, the weight must be equal in all directions from the center when the crankshaft is at rest. Dynamic balance means balance while the crankshaft is turning. Dynamic balance is attained when the centrifugal forces of rotation are equal in all directions at any point. This balancing operation requires special machinery and involves removal of metal at the heavy points or addition of metal at the light points.

In order to obtain rotating balance, crankshafts are equipped with counterweights which are usually forged or cast integrally with the crankshaft, but in some cases have been bolted rigidly to the crankshaft. These counterweights are located on the opposite side of the crankshaft from the connecting rod in order to balance the weight of the rod.

In addition to balancing the crankshaft proper, the entire rotating assembly is balanced dynamically. This assembly includes the fan pulley, vibration damper, timing gears, crankshaft, flywheel and the clutch or converter parts attached to it. In addition, the connecting rod assemblies including piston pins, pistons, bearings, etc. are all very carefully balanced one with another so that the rotating mass will have as little vibration as possible. See Fig. 7-4.

Torsional Vibration

The explosive forces acting on the pistons and the inertia forces of the reciprocating parts vary in intensity as the pistons move up and down in the cylinders. This variation in force, or torque, causes the crankshaft to twist or vibrate and this is known as torsional vibration. It is more noticeable at certain speeds than others and is of greater intensity on long shafts than on short ones. For example, a straight eight shaft will have greater vibration than a four cylincer crankshaft.

For example, when the No. 1 cylinder fires, it tends to turn the front end of the crankshaft instantly. This force is transmitted through the length of the crankshaft to the flywheel which has considerable inertia. The crankshaft then momentarily "winds up" or twists lengthwise to a small degree, but which is enough to create vibration. Any piece of steel--no matter how heavy--can be twisted slightly by torque applied to it. This twisting of the crankshaft depends upon the forces operating in the engine, and is more severe at some speeds than others. Vibration dampers have been found helpful in controlling this crankshaft twist.

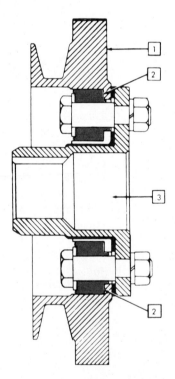

Fig. 7-5. 1. Pulley.
2. Rubber blocks.
3. Pulley hub.

Vibration Dampers

Regardless of the type of vibration damper used, the principle of operation is similar. They add mass or inertia to the end of the crankshaft opposite the flywheel in order to minimize the twisting of the

66

crankshaft. Perhaps the simplest of all such devices was the use of a flywheel at each end of the crankshaft. In such case the weight of both flywheels would be about the same as the weight of a single normal flywheel.

In other words the flywheel was divided--half on each end of the crankshaft. It has been found better to use a smaller flywheel on the front end and mount it so that it floats. In one type, as shown in Fig. 7-5, rubber is used between the small flywheel and its hub to permit limited circumferential movement between the crankshaft and small flywheel.

In another type of vibration damper, Fig. 7-6, which resembles a miniature clutch, there is a friction facing mounted between the hub face and small flywheel face. This friction is regulated and adjusted by means of spring tension.

Still another type has the flywheel floating or suspended in fluid such as heavy oil. In any case, the small flywheel because of its mass and inertia, resists sudden twisting of the shaft and thus minimizes torsional vibration.

Critical Speeds

No matter how carefully the crankshaft and the parts attached to it are balanced, there will be certain speeds at which some vibration will occur. These are known as critical speeds and will often cause other parts near them to vibrate also. By means of careful

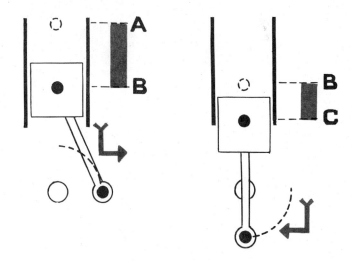

Fig. 7-7. During the first quarter revolution of the crankshaft from top dead center, the piston moves the distance from A to B. During the second quarter revolution the distance moved by the piston is less as shown from B to C.

design and balancing, these critical periods are caused to occur at speeds outside the ordinary working speeds of the engine.

In this connection, it is not too difficult to balance rotating parts, but when reciprocating parts are attached to them the problem becomes much more complicated. We have already given consideration to the fact that each one of the heavy connecting rod and piston assemblies must be started, speeded up, slowed down and stopped twice during each revolution. There are further unbalancing factors that enter into this matter.

Other Causes Of Vibration

For example, the piston does not accelerate and decelerate uniformly during each quarter of a revolution. During the first quarter revolution from top dead center (t.d.c.), the connecting rod moves down a distance according to the length of the crank throw and also moves out away from the center of the cylinder. Both the downward and outward motions cause the piston to travel downward. During the second quarter of a revolution, we have a downward motion equal to the crank throw, but the end of the rod is now moving back toward the center line of the cylinder and during the last portion of the movement, the piston is no longer moving downward. As a result, the actual movement of the piston is less than during the first quarter revolution, Fig. 7-7.

It may be seen from the foregoing that all of these forces acting on the crankshaft give it a tremendous job to do. For this reason it is important for the repairman to understand that he cannot add or subtract a fraction of an ounce of weight to any of these parts during a repair operation. Furthermore the crankshaft, bearings, bearing journals, etc. must be in excellent mechanical condition at all times.

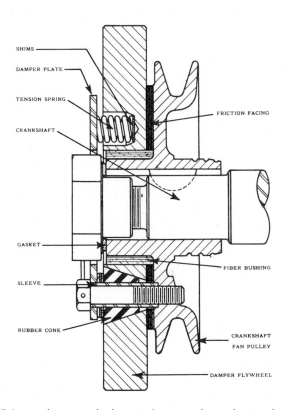

SHIMS

DAMPER PLATE

TENSION SPRING

CRANKSHAFT

FRICTION FACING

GASKET

FIBER BUSHING

SLEEVE

RUBBER CONE

CRANKSHAFT FAN PULLEY

DAMPER FLYWHEEL

Fig. 7-6. Another typical vibration damper utilizing friction facings as well as rubber bushings.

Fig. 7-8. Typical eight cylinder (V-8) camshaft.

Engine Camshafts

A camshaft in its simplest form is a straight shaft with an eccentric lobe or cam on it. Two such camshafts would be used on a one cylinder, T-head, four cycle, poppet valve engine. One shaft for the inlet valve, another for the exhaust valve. If the engine is of the L-head, I-head or F-head design, both cams would ordinarily be on the same shaft. These cams would be located at different places around the perimeter of the shaft as the valves need to be opened at different times in the operating cycle.

For a multiple-cylinder engine, there are ordinarily as many cams as there are valves to be operated. See Fig. 7-8. This is not always the case however as some V-type engines have had one cam so arranged as to operate one valve in each block. This is usually the case in opposed cylinders or "pancake" engines as shown in Fig. 7-9. In four-cycle engines, each valve is opened once every other revolution of the engine crankshaft so the camshaft is geared to run at half the crankshaft speed.

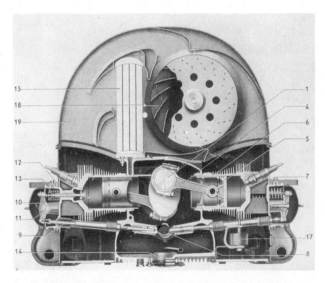

Fig. 7-9. The camshaft (8) is below the crankshaft (1) in this Volkswagen pancake engine and each cam operates two valves -- one on each side.

As the camshaft is not subjected to such severe reciprocating forces and runs at slower speed than the crankshaft, it is much smaller and has smaller bearings. The camshaft is made of steel and the cams are hardened to avoid rapid wear on the cam surface.

These cams appear to have a simple shape, but actually the exact shape of the cam is a meticulous job of design. See Fig. 7-10. The design is worked out after a painstaking and detailed program of mathematical calculation, and checked by lengthy experimentation. If the shape of the cams is altered by wear, the efficiency of the engine deteriorates with great rapidity. There is much more to the matter than just opening and closing a valve.

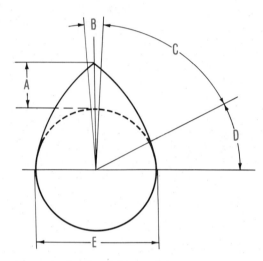

Fig. 7-10. A is the height of lift, B the toe section, C the flank area, D the ramp, and E the heel diameter of the cam.

Cam Functions

The cam is designed to lift the valve at precisely the correct instant of piston travel and hold it open long enough to obtain the most efficient filling and emptying of the cylinder. It exerts considerable control over the volumetric efficiency of the engine. This will be discussed fully later in this text.

In a passenger car engine, ramps on the cams are designed to open the valves smoothly and gradually. This avoids shock to the valves, valve springs, etc., and makes for quietness of operation. The final design is usually a compromise between efficiency and quietness of operation.

On racing engines where noise is not important and utmost efficiency is desired, the cams are often shaped with more abrupt ramps, higher lift, flatter flank and wider toe. The cam is intended to "bat" the valve open quickly, open it wider, hold it open longer and close it rapidly. Such engines are noisy, idle roughly and wear more quickly.

If the camshaft is chain driven, it rotates in the same direction as the crankshaft which is clockwise from the front of the engine. If the camshaft is driven by a gear meshed with a mating gear on the crankshaft, the camshaft rotation is counterclockwise, or opposite from the crankshaft.

Camshaft Location

On an L, F or I-head, in-line engine, the camshaft is usually located to one side and above the crankshaft, Fig. 7-11. On V-type engines, the camshaft is usually located above the crankshaft as shown in Fig. 6-15.

Fig. 7-11. Sectional valve train and lifters of 230 cu. in. Chevrolet, I-head, in-line engine.

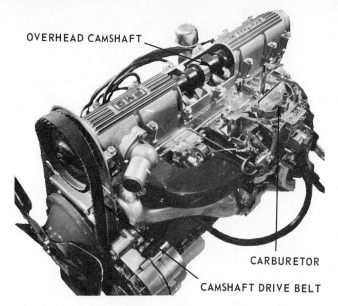

OVERHEAD CAMSHAFT

CARBURETOR

CAMSHAFT DRIVE BELT

Fig. 7-12. Showing flexible camshaft drive belt and overhead camshaft on Pontiac six-cylinder engine.

On the overhead camshaft engine--not to be confused with overhead valve engines--the camshaft is located above the cylinder head. See Figs. 7-12, 7-13 and 7-14. The overhead camshaft may be driven by

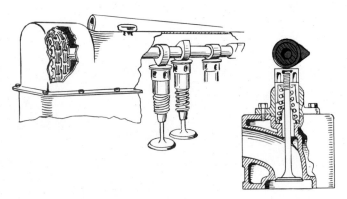

Fig. 7-13. Typical valve layout for overhead camshaft engine.

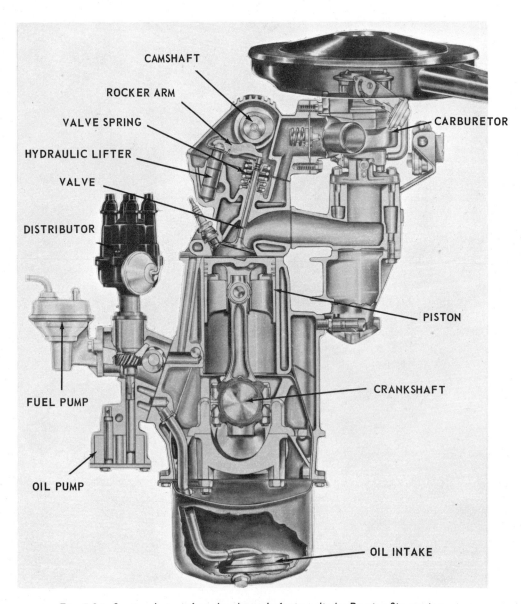

CAMSHAFT

ROCKER ARM

VALVE SPRING

HYDRAULIC LIFTER

VALVE

DISTRIBUTOR

CARBURETOR

PISTON

FUEL PUMP

CRANKSHAFT

OIL PUMP

OIL INTAKE

Fig. 7-14. Sectional view of overhead camshaft six-cylinder Pontiac Six engine.

means of a vertical shaft and bevel gears, by chain, Fig. 19-4, by means of a cog belt, Figs. 7-12, 7-13 and 7-14. Race engines have their overhead camshaft driven either by a shaft or by a series of gears, Fig. 12-10. The cog belt as used on the Pontiac 230 cu. in. engine is made of Neoprene reinforced with fiber glass and among the advantages claimed for this construction are heat and oil resistance, and its ability to absorb shock and constant flexing. In addition, it is inherently quiet and needs no lubrication.

The overhead camshaft construction eliminates the use of push rods and permits excellent valve action at high speeds as there is little inertia of moving parts.

As with the crankshaft, it is necessary that the camshaft journals be round and true, and the camshaft

Fig. 7-15. With the four cylinder engine, a power impulse is obtained every half revolution as shown by the diagram at the left. The space between O and X indicates the time the exhaust valve is open during the power stroke and no power is obtained. With the six-cylinder, four-cycle engine, (or the three-cylinder, two cycle engine) there is a power impulse being exerted at all times with three impulses per revolution. There is also a slight overlap period when two cylinders are exerting power. With the eight cylinder in-line engine as shown at the right, there is considerable overlap of the power impulses as they occur each quarter revolution.

be straight and true. There should be no measurable wear on the cam surfaces. There must be no appreciable looseness in the bearings, as any radial movement or vibration of the cams would affect the operation of the valves.

The location of the cams around the camshaft along with the design of the crankshaft determines the firing order of the engine.

Firing Order

A one-cylinder, two-cycle engine fires once each revolution. A one-cylinder, four-cycle engine fires once every other revolution. A two-cylinder, two-cycle engine fires twice each revolution, while a two-cylinder, four-cycle engine fires once every revolution so there is no question about firing order.

In a four-cylinder, four-cycle engine, the No. 1 piston moves downward on the power stroke, while No. 4 is also moving down on the intake stroke. While No. 1 and 4 are going down, 2 and 3 are, of course going up. One is on the exhaust stroke; the other on

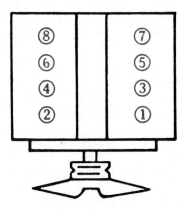

Fig. 7-16. One popular V-8 firing order is 1, 4, 5, 2, 7, 6, 3, 8.

the compression stroke. There are therefore two possible firing orders, 1, 2, 4, 3 or 1, 3, 4, 2. In either case, one power impulse is obtained every one-half revolution of the crankshaft, giving two power impulses per revolution. See Fig. 7-15.

The six-cylinder, four-cycle engine (and a three-cylinder, two-cycle engine) has the crank throws spaced 120 deg. apart, rather than 180 deg., and gets a power impulse every one-third revolution of the crankshaft. The firing order of a right-hand crankshaft can be 1, 5, 3, 6, 2, 4, or it can be 1, 2, 4, 6, 5, 3. With the left-hand crankshaft, the firing order can be 1, 4, 2, 6, 3, 5, or it can be 1, 3, 5, 6, 4, 2.

With an eight-cylinder, in-line, four-cycle engine, there will be a power impulse every one-quarter revolution (90 deg.) of crankshaft rotation. There are several possible firing order combinations.

While different firing orders are used, the general idea of an in-line engine firing order is to fire cylinders as nearly as possible at alternate ends of the crankshaft.

On a V-type engine the objective is to alternate between the ends of the crankshaft and the cylinder blocks on each side, to distribute the forces around over the engine and avoid concentrating subsequent explosions near one point of the crankshaft. This reduces vibration, and makes for a smoother running engine. A popular firing order is shown in Fig. 7-16.

QUIZ-ENGINE CRANKSHAFTS AND CAMSHAFTS

1. What is the purpose of a flywheel?
2. What is the difference between static and dynamic balance?
3. Torsional vibration is more noticeable in an in-line eight crankshaft than in a V-eight crankshaft. True or False?
4. Give a description of the most simple type of vibration damper.
5. When the crankshaft rotational speed is constant,

is the distance travelled by the piston during each quarter revolution the same? Yes or No?

6. How many possible firing orders are there for a four-cylinder, four-cycle engine? One____, Two ____, Four____.

7. A six-cylinder, four-cycle, in-line engine camshaft has how many lobes on it? Six____, Twelve ____, Eighteen____.

8. Is more than one valve ever operated by one cam? Yes or No?

9. A worn cam flank will cause: Noise____, Loss of power____, Oil pumping____.

10. What is the difference between an I-head engine and an overhead camshaft engine?

11. Name one advantage and one disadvantage of overhead camshaft engines.

12. How many power impulses per revolution occur in an eight-cylinder, four-cycle engine? Four____, Eight____, Sixteen____.

13. How many power impulses per revolution occur in a three-cylinder, two-cycle engine? Three____, Six____, Twelve____.

14. Why is the firing order of V-type engines arranged differently than on in-line engines?

The crankshaft counterweight in this Ford engine, is forged as an integral part of the crankshaft.

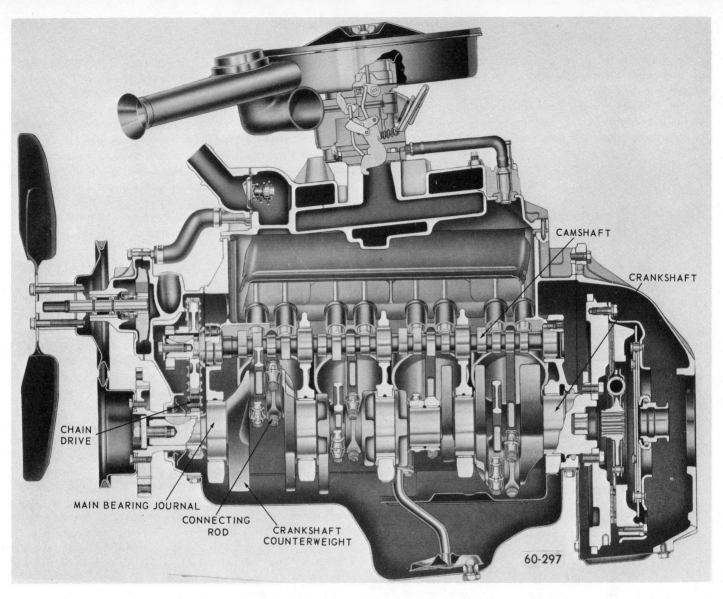

CAMSHAFT

CRANKSHAFT

CHAIN DRIVE

MAIN BEARING JOURNAL

CONNECTING ROD

CRANKSHAFT COUNTERWEIGHT

60-297

Fig. 8-1. Sectional view of Buick V-8 350 cu. in. engine.

ENGINE
BEARINGS, VALVES

A one or two-cylinder engine will usually have two main bearings, a front main bearing and a rear main bearing. The rear main bearing is always adjacent to the flywheel. A four-cylinder engine normally has three mains, one at the front, one between cylinders No. 2 and No. 3, and one at the rear. However, some four-cylinder engines have five main bearings, one between each cylinder. An eight-cylinder V-type engine may have three but usually has five main bearings. See Fig. 8-1.

In a previous chapter, reference was made to cylinder block distortion. This can be serious if the crankcase distorts to throw the engine main bearings out of alignment with each other. An example of this is shown in Fig. 8-2.

On engines having less than eight-cylinders and on in-line eights, it is customary to provide a throw on the crankshaft for each cylinder. On V-type en-

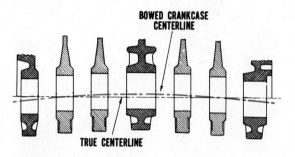

Fig. 8-2. Bearing bores in the crankcase can warp out of alignment and cause serious trouble.

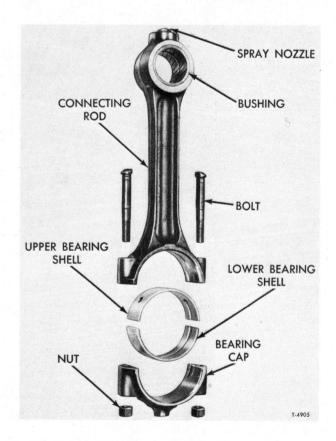

Fig. 8-3. This connecting rod has an integral type of bearing.

Fig. 8-4. Details of modern connecting rod assembly. Note precision type bearing inserts.

gines, however, the rods are usually placed side by side, two on each throw. This is shown in Fig. 8-1.

There are two types of bearings used on automobile engine crankshafts. One is known as the poured, cast-in or integral type, and the other is known as the precision or slip-in type. The bearing surface is, in all cases, a soft metal with good heat conducting qualities and which will possess a low coefficient of friction in contact with the steel crankshaft journal. The metal must be soft to allow any abrasive material to become imbedded in the bearing, rather than remain between bearing and journal surfaces and damage the journal.

Integral Bearings

Integral or poured bearings are made by pouring molten babbitt or bearing metal into the bearing seats. The seats are first tinned and the bearing metal adheres permanently until melted out, Fig. 8-3. This type of bearing is no longer used in automotive engines.

Precision Bearings

The precision or slip-in type of bearing as shown in Fig. 8-4, has become increasingly popular since engine speeds and loads have been increased so much that a material stronger than babbitt became necessary. It is now used in the majority of automobile engines for both main and connecting rod bearings. The bearing material is an alloy of several metals and may include lead, tin, copper, silver, cadmium, etc. The proportion of the various metals varies considerably, and the development is the result of much experience and experimentation.

The bearing insert or shell, consists of a hard shell of steel or bronze, perhaps with additional metal linings or laminations, and a thin lining of anti-friction metal or bearing alloy to form the inner surface. These inserts are manufactured to extremely close dimensions and must be handled carefully to avoid damage. When properly installed they are very durable. When they do wear from continued use, they are discarded and replaced with new inserts.

Precision type bearing inserts, being made to such close dimensions, must be used under closely controlled conditions. Fitting and installing them properly involves measurement in fractions of thousandths of an inch. Careless workmanship in installation cannot be tolerated, as they are not adjustable. We will consider fitting them later in this text.

Main Bearing Caps and Seals

An exploded view of a typical V-8 crankshaft together with its bearings, caps and seals is shown in Fig. 8-4a. Note that there are two bolts for each cap. In larger engines four bolts are often used. The center main bearing in the illustration is designed to take the end thrust as indicated by the flanges on the side. To

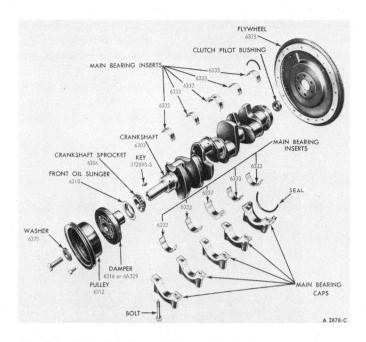

Fig. 8-4a. Exploded view of V-8 crankshaft, bearings and seals.

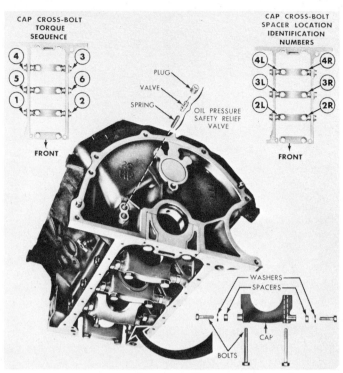

Fig. 8-4b. Note side bolts used on this high performance Ford engine.

prevent oil leakage, the rear main bearing is provided with a seal. Seals are either of the wick type or are made of neoprene. In some designs (Chevrolet for example) the lower seal will be extended into the bolt area of the cap.

The upper seal can be removed in most cases, without removing the crankshaft, by first loosening the main bearing cap bolts to lower the crankshaft slightly. Then remove the rear bearing cap, after which the upper seal can be pushed around the shaft until one end protrudes. The end can then be grasped with pliers and pulled out the rest of the way.

In the case of high performance engines, the main bearing caps are provided with cross bolts, in addition to the usual vertical bolts, Fig. 8-4b.

Camshaft Bearings

Camshaft bearings are usually made of bronze, and are bushings rather than in the form of split bearings. See Fig. 8-5. Sometimes the camshaft bears directly in a hole bored in the crankcase without any

bushing. Camshaft bushings are not adjustable for wear and are replaced when worn. The degree of wear dictating replacement is more a matter of oil clearance than any tendency toward noise. This will be considered fully in the chapter devoted to lubrication.

Engine Valves

Internal combustion engine valves have a tremendous task to perform and under the very best conditions they are not all that could be desired. The conditions under which the valves operate would seem to impose an impossible task upon them, but they have been developed to a point where they are fairly efficient. A great amount of ingenuity has been expended upon sleeve valves, rotary valves, slide valves and poppet valves. The poppet valve despite all its shortcomings is used almost universally.

Fig. 8-5. The holes in these camshaft bushings are for lubrication purposes.

Fig. 8-6. This hollow valve stem is partially filled with sodium which melts when the valve gets hot and bounces back and forth between head and stem to assist the heat to flow from head to stem.

Poppet valves are noisy and it is difficult to cool them, but they are simple and do provide an effective seal under operating conditions.

These operating conditions are brutal. The valves are in the combustion chamber and are exposed to the burning gas, but are not surrounded with cooling water as is the combustion chamber. Neither are they cooled by the oil as is the piston. The explosion temperature within an engine combustion chamber may momentarily approach 5,000 degs. F. and the exhaust valve must then open and permit these hot gases to go between the valve head and the cylinder block at high velocity.

It may be readily seen that the exhaust valve head may attain a temperature of 1,000 degs. or more under these conditions. The valve cannot readily be cooled directly by the cooling water in the engine and the only cooling comes from contact with the valve guides and with the cylinder block during the short space of time it is in contact with the valve seat. How short this space of time is may be realized if thought is given to the speed at which the engine operates.

If the engine is operating at 3,000 rpm that means that any one cylinder will fire 1,500 times in that minute and that every time the cylinder fires, the exhaust must open to let the burned gas out. In spite of the fact, that the valve is lifted off its seat 1,500 times each minute, a large portion of the heat passes from the valve head and into the valve seat and then into the water jacket.

Valve Temperatures

It is not difficult to understand why exhaust valves are prone to cause trouble. In normal operation the valve head around the seating surface will operate at a temperature of 1,000 to 1,200 degs. F. The central portion of the valve head will run somewhat hotter, 1,200 to 1,400 degs. and the stem adjacent to the head perhaps 800 to 1,000 degs. Running thus at a red heat under normal conditions, it may be seen

that the steel valve may melt under abnormal conditions such as a leaking valve or a cooling disorder.

The inlet valve has a somewhat easier task as it is not exposed to the burning gas while it is off its seat. The inlet valve is also cooled by the incoming gas mixture which is at below atmospheric temperature.

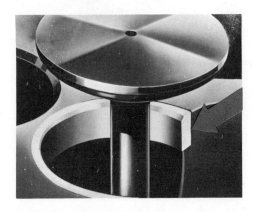

Fig. 8-7. These alloy inserts are often pressed or shrunk in place.

Valve and Seat Materials

Exhaust valves are usually made of heat resistant alloy steel. Quite often they are partially filled with mineral salts to help them get rid of the heat. See Fig. 8-6. The valve seat is often also made of heat resistant alloy in the form of an insert which is set into the cylinder head or block under the exhaust valve. See the alloy inserts in Fig. 8-7. These inserts are used in cast iron blocks or heads as well as

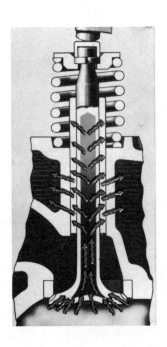

Fig. 8-8. Showing the heat path from valve to the water jacket.

aluminum heads or blocks.

The particular construction shown in Fig. 8-8 has a special heat resistant alloy on the valve face and also bears on a heat resistant valve seat insert. Such construction is used in heavy-duty engines.

Induction Hardened Seats

One of the results of the new low-lead and lead free fuel (not to be confused with the lead free premium fuel which has been available in some areas for years) is higher valve temperatures and attendant valve and seat burning.

In the past the lead in the fuel has acted as a lubricant, at least between the valve face and its seat. When there is no lead in the fuel, the cast iron seats become oxidized by the hot exhaust gases. These oxides abrade the valve face and seat, so there is metal transfer from the seat to the valve. Valve seat wear increases rapidly as valve lash becomes greater. When lash increases from 0.001 to 0.040 in. the impact loads increase up to 30 times which still further valve and seat wear.

To overcome this situation, several methods are available. One method is to use alloys for the valve seats or hard noncorrosive inserts. Instead of ethyl lead in the fuel, boron oxide or iron phosphate can be used, but these materials have an adverse effect on catalytic mufflers which are being installed on some vehicles. Another method is to aluminize the valve face or chrome plate the valve head, which has been adopted by Buick, for example. Valve stems are also being chrome plated in order to reduce wear in that area.

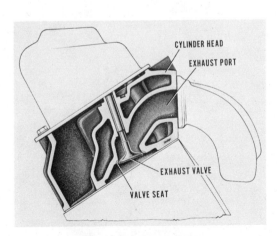

Fig. 8-8a. Induction hardened valve seats have been adopted by Dodge to increase durability.

Internally cooled valves such as shown in Fig. 8-6 are also being more widely used and extensive research on water filled valve stems is promising, showing temperature reduction up to 600 deg. F. To further aid in the dissipation of heat valve stem diameter is being increased in many cases.

Induction hardening of valve seats has been adopted by Dodge, Fig. 8-8a. This process heats the valve seats to 1700 deg. and hardens them to a depth of 0.05 to 0.08 in. This gives the seats approximately the same durability as is obtained with leaded fuel.

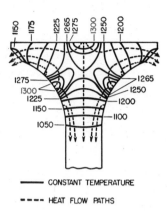

Fig. 8-8b. Temperature measurements made on exhaust valve. Note location of hottest areas.

Valve Cooling

The heat flows from the valve head to the cooling water as shown in Fig. 8-8. Recent tests made by Thompson Ramo Wooldridge, Inc., engineers show that the popular conception that solid exhaust valves are cooled primarily by conduction down the stem is not true. Fig. 8-8b shows the temperature measurements made at the cross section of a valve to determine the path of the heat flow. The solid lines are paths of equal temperature and the dotted lines are heat flow paths.

Many of the heat flow paths leave the valve at the face. In fact, the engineers state that over half of the total heat absorbed by the valve leaves through the face.

It will also be noted that the heat flows from the valve stem to the valve guide and from the guide to the head or block, Fig. 8-8. As heat will flow more readily through one piece of metal than from one piece to another, the separate valve guide on most passenger car engines have been dispensed with and instead the cylinder block or head is reamed and acts as the guide. When that construction is used, replacement valves are provided with oversize stems and the guides are then reamed to the desired size when it becomes necessary to install new valves.

Valve Seat Contact Area

From the foregoing, it should be realized that anything that reduces the area of contact between the valve and the cylinder head or block will hamper the escape of heat from the valve. Thus if valve seat is too narrow or valve guide worn excessively, the area of contact will be reduced and valve will overheat.

The area of contact could be increased by widening the valve seat, but it has been found that a wider seat also encourages flakes of carbon to adhere, hold the valve off the seat and cause burning of the valve face. Another method of increasing the contact area would be to increase the diameter of the valve head or the valve stem or both by installing oversize valves, oversize or longer guides, etc.

There are of course mechanical limitations to the amount of increase in these dimensions. Of more importance however, would be the increase of weight in the valve. The valve is required to move endwise with such rapidity that it must be kept as light in weight as possible. Any excess weight would add to the inertia and slow down the valve action. So here again a compromise must be made and a reasonable limitation in size imposed.

Fig. 8-9. If the valve has a thin edge as shown at the left or if the valve head is warped as shown at the right, the thin edges thus created will become excessively hot.

Fig. 8-10. An exhaust valve may be properly seated as at the left when cold, but may expand rapidly and climb off the seat as shown at the right.

Valve Heat Dissipation

This matter of valve heat dissipation must be thoroughly understood if automobile engines are to be serviced properly. There are several things to be considered in this connection. Some of them are similar to problems previously discussed in connection with pistons and rings.

For example, the heat of operation causes distortion of cylinder heads, blocks, etc. The same conditions cause distortion of valve and valve seat. Any hot spots in the cylinder head or block near the valves or any unequal tightening of the cylinder head bolts will aggravate distortion and cause valve difficulties. The valve and seat may be round and true when the engine is cold, but may not be round and true when the engine gets to operating temperature.

The valve head is liable to warp due to the difference in temperature at different points. This warpage will be aggravated if the rim of the valve head is thin

or uneven. See Fig. 8-9. Furthermore, the temperature may vary around the rim of the valve head in some cases due to the difference in volume and velocity of the gas going between the valve and seat as determined by combustion chamber design and valve port shape.

In addition to changes in valve and valve seat shape, the diameter of both may change. The valve head runs hotter than the valve seat because the seat is nearer the cooling water. Therefore the valve head may expand more than the seat and as a result the valve may rise on the seat as shown in Fig. 8-10. This action results in a change in the valve seat area location.

It will be apparent that the dimension between the valve seat and the valve lifter will be lengthened by such expansion. The length of the valve itself between the seat surface and the end of the stem, will be altered by lengthwise expansion of the valve and valve stem.

One of the most important factors affecting valves temperatures is that of valve lash or tappet clearance. Insufficient clearance will result in the valves contacting the seats for a shorter time and consequently operate at higher temperatures. Excessive clearance will result in noisy operation and loss of power. Great accuracy should therefore be used when adjusting valve lash.

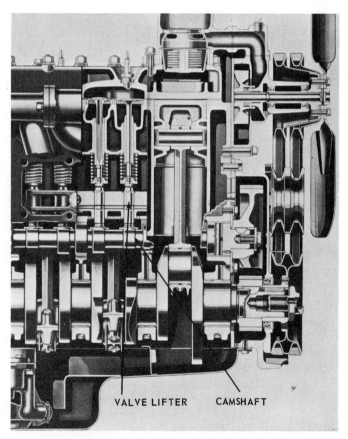

VALVE LIFTER   CAMSHAFT

Fig. 8-11. Valves in L-head engines are raised by means of short valve lifters which are usually adjustable as to length.

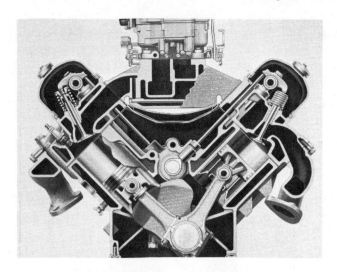

Fig. 8-12. *Overhead valves require push rods and rocker arms which are mounted on a rocker shaft.*

Valve Operating Mechanism

The camshaft, Figs. 7-8 and 8-1, is designed to raise the valves from their seats and is rotated by means of gears or chains, meshing with a gear on the crankshaft. In four-cycle engines, the camshaft must operate at half the speed of the crankshaft and consequently the camshaft gear must be twice the diameter as the gear on the crankshaft, Fig. 8-13.

In the L-head engine, where both valves are on the same side of the cylinder, it is customary to place the camshaft directly under the valves and operate the valves with short valve lifters. See Fig. 8-11.

In the overhead valve engine design, a single camshaft is usual with a cam for each valve. In many designs the camshaft is located in the crankcase and operates the valves by means of long push rods and rocker arms, Figs. 8-12 and 8-19. Because of the weight of the push rod, appreciable power is required to move it. To overcome this problem, some engines are designed with the camshaft placed over the valves, Fig. 8-12a. This design eliminates the push rod and power is saved. Still other designs have the cams operating directly on caps on the ends of the valve

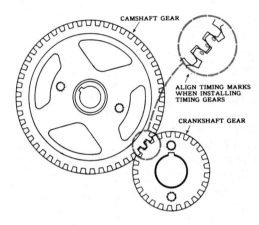

Fig. 8-13. *Timing gears are usually marked as shown to insure that the valves will be correctly timed.*

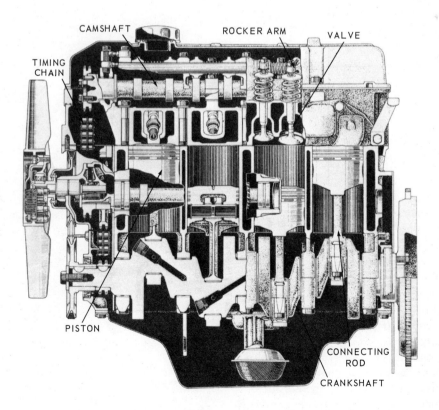

Fig. 8-12a. *Toyota engine with overhead camshaft with rocker arms.*

stems with further saving in power.

On the F-head engine, a single camshaft is ordinarily used, one valve being operated directly by means of a short push rod, and the other valve being operated by a long push rod and a rocker arm.

As the valves must be precisely opened and closed with relation to the piston travel, any wear in the camshaft driving chain or gear will result in the valve not being opened and closed at the exact instant desired and a loss in engine efficiency will be incurred. For this reason, it is usual to avoid long chains or multiple gears in the camshaft drive arrangement.

Worn Cams

We have already considered the accuracy with which the cam shape or contour is formed in order to provide the proper operating characteristics for the valves. Ordinarily the surface of the cam is so hard that the exact shape remains substantially unaltered for many thousand miles of operation. There is of course some friction between the cam and the valve lifter that rides on it, and some wear is bound to occur in time. This wear is usually on the highest part of the cam, and will decrease the height or "lift" of the valve. The result is that the valve does not open as wide as it should, and the "breathing" ability of the engine suffers.

Fig. 8-14a. Details of cogged type fiberglass-reinforced belt used to drive overhead camshaft on Chevrolet Vega 2300 engine.

Fig. 8-14. Timing chain sprockets are usually marked so that when a line drawn through the center of both shafts bisects the timing marks, the timing is correct. Flywheels are also usually marked to facilitate checking the valve timing.

If the wear on the cam is at the sides or on the ramp, the valve action will become noisy, and also the valve will open late or close early, or both. Excessive wear in the valve lifters will have the same results: noise and faulty valve timing.

Usually the wear on cams is so slow and the loss of engine performance so gradual that it goes unnoticed unless the valve lift is checked against factory specifications. In rare cases a defective camshaft has been found, and the loss of engine performance

BACKLASH
.003"–.005"
ALL GEARS EXCEPT
BLOWER GEARS
.0005"–.0025"

Fig. 8-14b. Gear train and timing marks on two cycle, three cylinder GMC diesel engine. 1–Balance shaft L. H. Helix. 2–Governor drive. 3–Crankshaft gear. 4–Idler gear. 5–Blower rotor gear. 6–Blower rotor gear upper. 7–Camshaft gear, R. H. Helix. Note particularly the balancer gear to drive the balance shaft and weights.

so rapid as to be noticed. In some cases the entire camshaft was not properly hardened, and in other cases it has been one or more individual cams that were soft enough to wear quickly.

Types of Camshaft Drives

There are three basic types of drives for camshafts; time gears, timing chains and the cogged belt. The timing gear method, Fig. 8-13, is used where long life and hard service are expected, as in commercial vehicles and race cars. Timing chains, Fig. 8-14, are used extensively in the passenger car field and in general are quieter than timing gears. The cogged belt, Fig. 8-14a, is a more recent development and is made of fiber glass reenforced rubber. It eliminates a long series of gears and is used primarily on engines with overhead camshafts. In this case (Chevrolet Vega) adjustment is provided by means of slotted water pump housing.

In the case of diesel engines it is necessary to provide a drive for the injection pump as well as the camshaft. This involves additional gearing, Figs. 8-14b

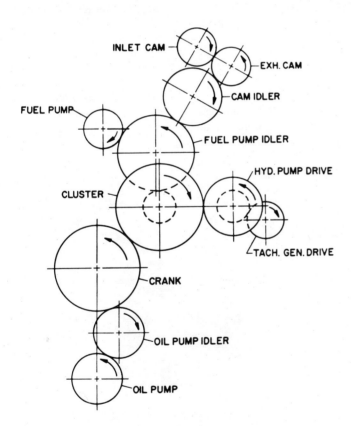

Fig. 8-14c. Gear train on Caterpillar vehicular 5.4 bore, V-12 engine.

and 8-14c. The former shows the gear train of a two cycle GMC three cylinder diesel engine. Note that in addition to the camshaft and crankshaft gears there is an idler gear, a balance shaft gear, upper and lower

blower gears and a governor drive gear. A particularly long gear train is used on the Caterpillar V-12 engine shown in Fig. 8-14c. In all there are eleven gears in the train on the double camshaft engine.

Valve Timing

Anything that occurs to change the time that the valve opens, the duration of the time it is held open, the size of the opening, or the time that it closes, will have a decided effect on the engine performance. This fact is seldom fully realized. Many engines run constantly below par, because mechanics in general have too little knowledge of the necessity of proper valve clearance adjustment.

A full realization of the need for accurate adjustment can come only from a study of valve action and requirements. This study starts with the relation between the crankshaft and camshaft. Due to the difference in the diameter of the circles described by the crank throw, and the cam nose and the difference in the comparative speed of rotation, the crank throw may travel many times as fast as the cam nose. While the cam nose is moving 1/4 in., the crank throw may move 1-1/2 in. If the cam is a few thousandths late in opening the valve, the crank throw and the piston attached to it will move a considerable distance farther than it should before the valve opens.

In this manner the motion of the piston is partially lost, and the power output suffers. Obviously, therefore, a worn timing chain or gears should be replaced as soon as the wear exceeds the specifications rather than run them until they become noisy or break, which is all too often the case.

In a few cases, adjustment is provided for timing chains such as an eccentric mounting for an accessory shaft, automatic slack adjusters, etc. In most cases it is necessary to install a new chain when the old one becomes worn and stretched. In general, a deflection of 1/2 in. is permitted for timing chains installed on passenger car engines which are used to drive a single camshaft.

In a gear-driven camshaft, the crankshaft gear is usually made of steel but the camshaft gear is often made of nonmetallic composition. This nonmetallic substance is quite durable and also makes for quieter operation. These gears are not adjustable and must be replaced when worn.

The car manufacturers set up specifications as to the amount of wear permissible in the chain or between the gear teeth. They also mark the gears or chains to facilitate correct timing. See Figs. 8-13 and 8-14. In addition, they also furnish timing charts by means of which valve timing can be readily checked.

The extreme accuracy with which it is desired to open and close the valves may be understood when thought is given to the speed at which the valve parts operate. This timing becomes more important as engine speeds are increased. This is the reason for what is known as valve "overlap." Valve overlap means that the intake and exhaust valves may both be open at the same time in any one cylinder. This, however, is to compensate for the time required by the air or gas to flow through the manifolds.

Many things have to be considered when designing the timing of an engine. In order that the engine may operate satisfactorily at high speeds, it is necessary that the exhaust valve open before the end of the power stroke and close after the completion of the exhaust stroke; also that the inlet valve open before the end of the exhaust stroke and close after the completion of the inlet stroke. This involves an overlapping of the exhaust and inlet periods which is made necessary by the inertia of the gases in the manifold and in part by the slow opening and closing motions of the valves made necessary by the demands for quiet operation. See Fig. 8-15.

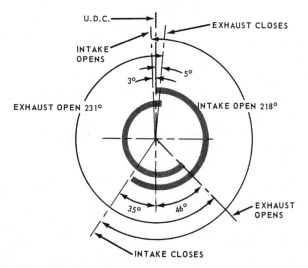

Fig. 8-15. *This diagram illustrates the overlap or time during which both valves are open in the same cylinder. This is necessary in a high speed engine to compensate for the inertia of the gas moving into and out of the cylinders.*

Valve Springs

Valve springs, Fig. 8-16, are required to close the valve after it has been opened by the action of the cam. Valve springs are of the coil type and are made of special high grade steel designed to withstand the high rate of stress applications, temperature and also to keep the valve from bouncing on its seat.

On some engines a single valve spring is used for each valve. On many high performance engines, two valves springs, Fig. 16-27, one within the other, are required in order to obtain the desired pressure characteristics. Usually the end turns of the springs are closer together than the other turns in order to reduce spring surge, Fig. 8-16. Valve springs are

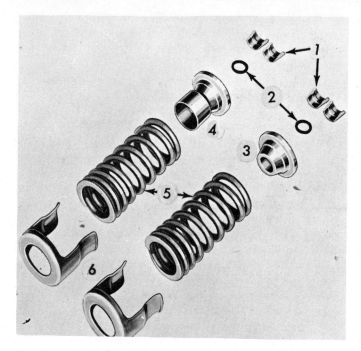

Fig. 8-16. *Typical valve springs with accessory parts. 1-Cone type valve spring keepers. 2-"O" ring oil seals. 3-Valve spring retainer. 4-Valve spring retainer with oil deflector. 5-Valve springs. 6-Valve spring surge dampers.*

also provided with dampers which help to reduce surging, Fig. 8-16.

Valve spring pressure varies with the type of engine. Stronger springs are required on high speed engines and also on engines with heavier push rods, valves, rocker arms, etc.

Valve Lifters

The valve lifter is a device interposed in the valve system and transmits the action of the cam to the valve or push rod as the case may be.

Fig. 8-17. *Mechanical type valve lifter.*

There are two types of valve lifters; mechanical, and hydraulic.

The solid or mechanical lifter, Fig. 8-17, is usually of the mushroom type and is provided with an adjusting screw so that the clearance or lash between the valve stem and the lifter is adjustable. This is necessary as engine heat will expand and lengthen the valve stem to such a degree that the valve would not close, with the further result that the combustible charge in the cylinder would not be compressed.

Instead of the mushroom type lifter some engines are equipped with roller type lifters. In this design the engine cam strikes a roller mounted on the lower face of the lifter. This has the advantage of reducing friction as compared to the mushroom type lifter.

Hydraulic lifters are designed to automatically take up the clearance that exists between the valve and the lifter, Fig. 8-18. The great advantage of this type of valve lifter is that it is quiet in operation as it has zero valve lash.

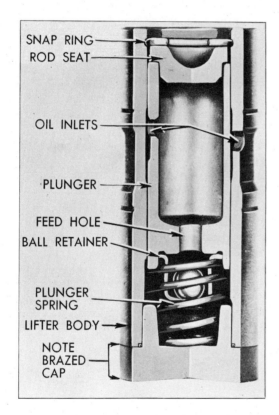

Fig. 8-18. Hydraulic type valve lifter.

Oil enters each lifter through grooves and oil holes in the lifter body and plunger, flows down into the chamber below the plunger through the feed hole and around the ball check. At the start of the cycle the plunger spring holds all lash clearances out of the valve linkage. As the engine cam starts raising the valve lifter body, oil in the lower chamber and the check ball spring firmly seat the check ball to prevent loss of oil from the lower chamber. The lifting force is then transmitted through the entrapped oil to the check ball and plunger, so that the plunger and push rod seat move upward with the body to operate the valve linkage which opens the engine valve.

Then as the engine valve seats, the linkage parts and lifter plunger stop, but the plunger spring forces the body of the lifter to follow the cam downward until it again rests on the cam base circle. Oil pressure against the ball check from the lower chamber ceases when the plunger movement stops and allows passage of oil past the ball check into the lower chamber to replace the slight amount of oil lost through "leak down," which is the oil that escapes through the clearance between the plunger and the body.

When valve linkage expands due to engine temperature increases, the plunger must move to a slightly lower position in the lifter body to assure full closing of the engine valve. Similarly, when engine temperature drops, the plunger must move to a slightly higher position. In either case, the capacity of the lower chamber changes, and the volume of oil present is automatically controlled by passage of oil through the plunger feed hole.

To provide for variations in size of parts due to servicing, some systems are provided with adjustable rocker arms, while other manufacturers provide push rods of varying lengths.

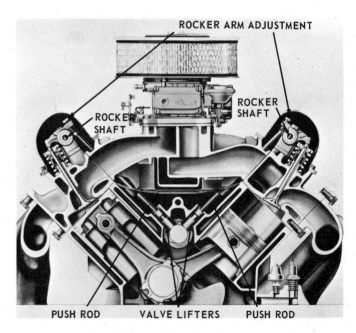

Fig. 8-19. Note rocker arm shaft and rocker arm with adjusting nut.

Rocker Arms

Two methods of adjusting valve lash on overhead valve engines are shown in Figs. 8-19 and 8-20.

In Fig. 8-19, the rocker arms are mounted on a rocker shaft and adjustment of the valve lash is made by turning the adjusting screw at the end of the rocker

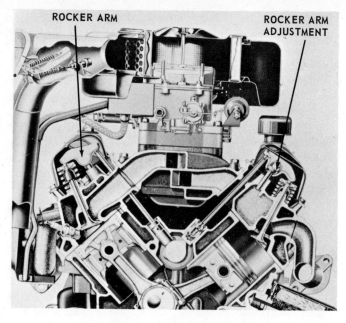

Fig. 8-20. Note semispherical depression in rocker arm and adjusting nut.

arm and which contacts the upper end of the push rod.

In the design shown in Fig. 8-20, the rocker shaft has been dispensed with. Instead each rocker arm is mounted on an individual stud. The rocker arm has a semispherical depression and a corresponding fulcrum seat rides in the depression and is held down by the adjusting nut. Turning the adjusting screw will move the rocker arm closer to the valve end and push rod end, thus decreasing the valve lash.

Some engines are provided with nonadjustable rocker arms, so that it is necessary to install new push rods of the desired length in order to adjust valve lash.

Quiz - Engine Bearings, Valves

1. Is an integral bearing and a precision bearing the same thing? Yes or No?
2. Why is bearing metal comparatively soft?
3. Bushings are always used on all camshaft journals. True or False?
4. Slip-in bearings are not adjustable for wear. True or False?
5. Name four metals used in bearing metal alloys.
6. Valve seats can be too wide. True or False?
7. Valves are sometimes hollow to make them lighter in weight. True or False?
8. Excessive heat gets out of valve by flowing to the valve seat_____, the valve guide_____, both _____.
9. Why are valves not made larger?
10. An exhaust valve may reach a temperature of 500 deg. F.____, 1,000 deg. F.____, 3,000 deg. F. ____.
11. Valve length is not constant. True or False?
12. At what speed does the camshaft operate? Half crankshaft speed____, the same speed____, twice the crankshaft speed____.
13. What is the objection to a long chain in a camshaft drive?
14. The cam nose travels faster than the crank throw. True or False?
15. Are timing chains adjustable for wear? Yes____, No____, Sometimes____.
16. What is valve overlap?
17. Are stronger or weaker valve springs used on high performance engines? Stronger____, Weaker ____.
18. How many types of valve lifters are there? 1.____, 2.____, 3.____, 4.____.
19. What is the great advantage of a hydraulic valve lifter?
    1. Better valve action.
    2. Closes the valves faster.
    3. Quieter valve action.
    4. More accurate valve timing.
20. The new low-lead fuel increases valve seat temperatures. True or False?
21. Lead in the fuel acts as a lubricant. True or False?
22. The cogged belt is used primarily on what type engine?
    1. L-head engine.
    2. F-head engine.
    3. Overhead valve engine with push rods.
    4. Overhead camshaft engine.

ENGINE PERFORMANCE

Fig. 9-1. Torque is exerted when pulling on the end of a wrench.

This chapter will deal with ways in which engines are measured dimensionally and in the power developed. Before discussing these subjects it is first necessary to define some of the terms that are used.

Inertia

Inertia is defined as the inability of matter to move or stop itself. Another definition is that an object will tend to move in the same direction or speed until acted on by another force.

Work

When an object is moved from one position to another, work is said to be performed. Work is measured in units of foot pounds, (ft. lbs.). For example; if a three pound weight is lifted 2 ft., the work performed would be 3 lbs. x 2 ft. = 6 ft. lbs. In other words, work equals the force in pounds required to move the object times the distance moved in feet. Work is performed when weights are lifted, springs compressed, shafts rotated.

The ability or capacity to do work is known as energy. A lump of coal, or a quart of gasoline, has energy stored in it, which when released will perform work. A valve spring can do the work of closing a valve when it is released after having been compressed.

Power

Power is defined as the rate or speed at which work is performed. One horsepower is defined as the amount doing 33,000 ft. lbs. of work in one minute. The unit of measurement was originated by an engineer by the name of Watt, who found that a strong horse could hoist 366 lbs. of coal up a mine shaft at the rate of one foot per second. In one minute, the horse would have raised the 366 lbs. 60 feet. This would be equivalent to raising 21,960 lbs., one foot in one minute. Arbitrarily, Mr. Watt raised this figure to 33,000 lbs. one foot in one minute.

Expressed as a formula:

$$HP = \frac{ft.lb. \ per \ min.}{33,000} = \frac{DW}{33,000 \ t}$$

where D = the distance the weight is to be moved.
W = Force in pounds required to move the weight through that distance.
t = time in minutes required to move the weight through the distance D.

For example:

How many horsepower would be required to move a weight of 5,000 lbs. a distance of 60 ft. across a level floor in three minutes?

$$HP = \frac{DW}{33,000 \ t} = \frac{60 \times 5000}{33,000 \times 3} = 3.03 \ hp$$

Torque

Torque is defined as turning or twisting effort. While torque is measured in pound feet, it differs from work or power as torque does not necessarily produce motion. For example; if a 50 pound force was applied at the end of a 3 ft. lever, there would be 150 lbs. ft. of torque. Whether the lever moved or not would be beside the point, Fig. 9-1.

In the case of the automotive engine, torque is low at low engine speeds and increases rapidly with the speed. Automotive engineers make every effort to increase the torque at low speeds and to remain as nearly constant as possible. Note the variation in torque and horsepower, as shown in Fig. 9-2.

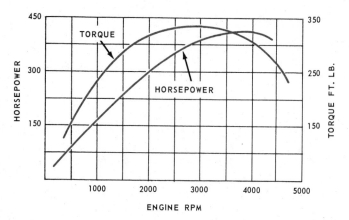

Fig. 9-2. Note the variation in torque and horsepower as the engine speed changes.

Friction

Friction is the resistance to relative motion between two bodies in contact with each other, or separated only by a lubricant.

Friction varies not only with different materials, but also with the surface condition of the materials. Friction was originally attributed to the interlocking of projections and depressions on the surfaces, but present day theory is that molecular attraction is the explanation.

The amount of friction is proportional to the pressure between the two surfaces is contact and is independent of the area of the surfaces in contact, Fig. 9-3. It also depends on the relative velocity of the moving surfaces.

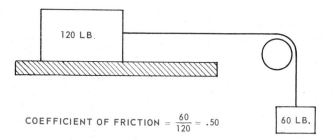

Fig. 9-3. One method of determining the coefficient of friction.

In the case of viscous friction such as that which occurs when solids move through liquids or gases, (an automobile moving through air for example) the force of friction varies directly with the relative velocity and rises very rapidly when the velocity becomes very great.

The friction of lubricated surfaces is much less

than that of dry surfaces. It is also greatly reduced when rolling friction (ball and roller bearings) is substituted for sliding friction.

Experiments show that dividing the force required to slide one object over the other at a constant speed, by the pressure holding them together, is a constant which is known as the coefficient of friction. The coefficient of friction is always the same for those materials and surfaces, Fig. 9-3.

For example: If a pull of 60 lbs. is required to keep a weight of 120 lbs. sliding over a surface at a constant speed, the coefficient of sliding friction would be:

$$\frac{60}{120} = 0.5$$

It must be emphasized that more force is required for initial movement than to keep the object moving. Sliding friction is therefore measured after motion has started.

A lubricant is a substance placed or injected between two surfaces to reduce friction. The thin layer of lubricant, adhering to the two surfaces is then sheared by the movement. The friction within the lubricant being less than that between the two surfaces, less force is required to produce movement.

A simple experiment to determine the coefficient of friction can be easily performed by means of a flat board and a weight. The weight is placed on one end of the board and that end is then raised until the weight starts to slide. At that point, the height of the end of the board is measured and also the base of the triangle formed by the tilted board. Dividing the height by the base equals the coefficient of friction, Fig. 9-4.

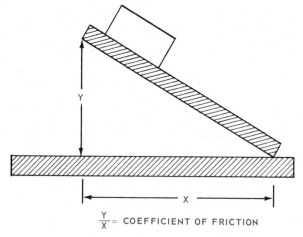

$\frac{Y}{X}$ = COEFFICIENT OF FRICTION

Fig. 9-4. Coefficient of friction equals $\frac{Y}{X}$.

Bore-Stroke-Displacement

The diameter of an engine cylinder is referred to as the bore and the distance the piston moves from bottom dead center to top dead center is called the stroke, Fig. 5-1.

Displacement of an engine is a measurement of its size and is equal to the number of cubic inches the piston displaces as it moves from bottom dead center to top dead center. In other words it is equal to the area of the piston times the stroke. In the case of a multi-cylinder engine it is also necessary to multiply by the number of cylinders.

Displacement = A x S x N

Where A is the area of the piston in square inches, S is the length of stroke in inches and N the number of cylinders. Assuming you have a six cylinder engine with a 4 in. bore and a 4-1/4 in. stroke, the procedure is to first calculate the piston area:

Area = 4 x 4 x .7854 = 12.56 sq. in.

Then the displacement equals
= 12.56 x 4.25 x 6 = 320.28 cu. in.

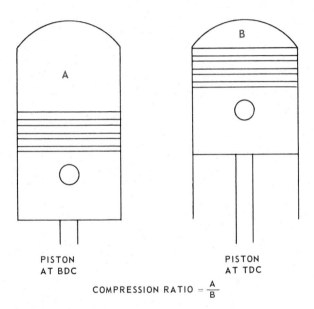

COMPRESSION RATIO = $\frac{A}{B}$

Fig. 9-5. Compression ratio is equal to the volume of A divided by the volume of B.

Compression Ratio

Compression ratio of an engine is the extent to which the combustible gases are compressed within the cylinder, Fig. 9-5. It is calculated by dividing the volume existing within the cylinder with the piston at BDC, with the volume in the cylinder with the piston at TDC. For example; if the volume with the piston at BDC is 45 cu. in. and at TDC is 5 cu. in. the compression ratio is

$$\frac{45}{5} = 9 \text{ to } 1$$

In other words the gas is compressed to one-ninth its original volume.

Up to a certain point, the more the fuel charge is compressed, the more power will be obtained. Experiments made by General Motors engineers, indicate that 17 to 1 compression ratio is the peak efficiency for gasoline engines.

In the service field, the compression ratio of an engine can be increased by planing material from the cylinder head, installing thinner gaskets, by increasing the stroke by regrinding the crankshaft or by increasing the bore of the engine. However, consideration must be given to the possibility of the valves striking the piston.

In case it is desired to increase the compression ratio of an engine, the following formula may be used:

$$\frac{B}{C-1} = A$$

Where A equals the volume of the combustion chamber, B is the displacement of the cylinder, and C is the desired compression ratio. For example; if the displacement is 36 cu. in. and the desired compression ratio is 10 to 1, then

$$\frac{36}{10-1} = 4 \text{ cu. in.}$$

In other words, for that particular engine, the combustion chamber would have to have a volume of 4 cu. in. to obtain a compression ratio of 10 : 1.

Volumetric Efficiency

No engine is 100 percent efficient. One of the factors affecting the efficiency of a gasoline engine is the difficulty of getting a full charge of combustible mixture into the cylinder. Because of restrictions of the intake manifold, atmospheric temperature, valve timing and similar factors, a theoretically full charge does not reach the cylinder. The ratio of the amount of charge actually taken in per cycle to a complete charge is known as the volumetric efficiency.

After a certain engine speed is reached, the volumetric efficiency drops rapidly. In general, maximum volumetric efficiency is reached at approximately the same point where maximum torque is reached. For example; one engine had maximum efficiency 82 percent at 1,500 rpm, but at 2,500 rpm it had dropped to 65 percent.

One method of increasing volumetric efficiency is to use a supercharger.

As atmospheric pressure drops with increase in altitude, volumetric efficiency will also decrease as it is the difference in pressure between the pressure outside the cylinder and the pressure inside the cylinder that determined the amount of mixture which will enter the cylinder, Fig. 9-6.

Brake Horsepower

Brake horsepower may be defined as the power that is available for propelling the vehicle. It is the power that remains after the effects of friction and the power that is required to drive the fan, water pump, oil pump and generator is subtracted from the power developed within the cylinder, i.e., the indicated horsepower.

The term brake horsepower is derived from the equipment first used to determine the power developed by an engine, which is known as the Prony brake, Fig. 9-7.

It will be noted that the prony brake consists of a large drum and a band type brake which operates on the outer surface of the drum. Attached to the brake is a lever, with its free end bearing on a weighing scale.

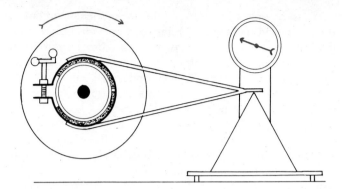

Fig. 9-7. Schematic drawing of a Prony brake used in measuring brake horsepower.

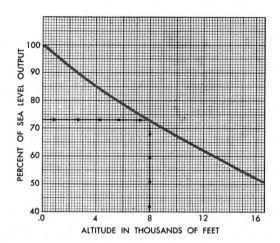

Fig. 9-6. Note how the power of an engine drops as the altitude and therefore the atmospheric pressure drop.

the engines are usually directly connected to the shaft of the dynamometer. When used in service stations, the dynamometer is provided with rollers which are then driven by the wheels of the vehicle, Figs. 9-9 and 9-10.

The drive-on type of dynamometer is now used extensively in diagnostic centers to supply factual information of the improvement in performance of the vehicle, Fig. 9-11.

Engine Torque

As previously described, torque is turning effort and in the case of an automotive engine, the pressure on the piston provides torque. As shown in Fig. 9-12, the torque at idling speed is relatively low, but increases rapidly as the engine speed rises. The torque maintains a high level, but decreases as higher speeds are reached.

In designing the engine, engineers try to have the engine maintain as high a torque as possible through-

The drum is directly connected to the engine crankshaft to be tested. As the drum is rotated, the brake is tightened, imposing a load on the engine, which in turn causes the lever to be pressed against the scale.

When making a Prony brake test, the throttle is first set to operate the engine at some specific speed. The brake is then tightened until the speed drops off. The weight on the scale is then noted. This procedure is repeated, each time at a higher speed, (usually in increments of 100 rpm). The following formula is then used to calculate the brake horsepower developed at each speed:

$$BHP = \frac{2\pi LRW}{33,000} = \frac{LRW}{5252}$$

Where L = Length of lever arm in feet.
R = Engine speed in rpm.
W = Load in pounds on scale.

The data thus produced can then be plotted to scale, as shown in Fig. 9-8, which is typical of the horsepower developed by a gasoline engine.

Brake horsepower can also be measured on a dynamometer. Such equipment consists of a resistance creating device, such as an electric generator, or a paddle wheel revolving in a fluid, which is so arranged as to absorb and dissipate the power produced by the engine. Suitable gauges are provided to indicate the amount of power absorbed.

In automotive manufacturers' testing laboratories

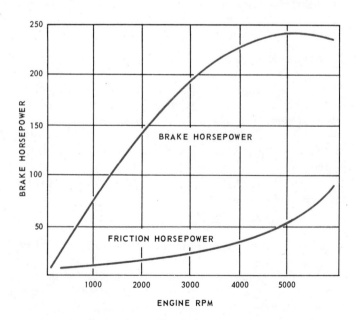

Fig. 9-8. Brake horsepower as determined by a Prony brake or a dynamometer.

out the speed range of the engine. Assisting in this are large carburetors, large section manifolds, large valves and exhaust systems with minimum back pressure. However, as engine speed increases, there is less time for the fuel mixture to fill the cylinders

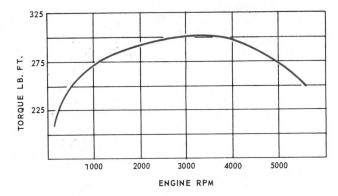

Fig. 9-12. *Typical torque curve of automotive engine.*

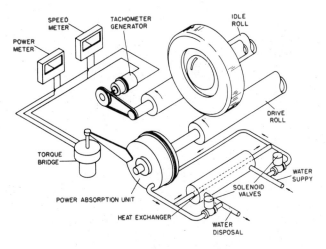

Fig. 9-9. *Essential parts of a chassis dynamometer are shown in diagrammatic form.*

Fig. 9-10. *Type of chassis dynamometer as used in service station and diagnostic centers.*

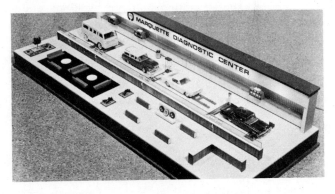

Fig. 9-11. *Detailed layout of diagnostic center.*

due to inertia of the mixture, resistance to its movement offered by the induction system and the valve timing. As a result, volumetric efficiency is reduced and the torque is similarly reduced. Compare the gen-

eral form of the curve, shown in Fig. 9-12, with the curve shown in Fig. 9-12a, which is that of a Ford turbine developed especially for long distance truck work. Note the turbine starts with maximum torque, whereas the gasoline engine does not attain maximum torque until it reaches higher rpm.

Rated Horsepower

The rated horsepower of an engine is based on a formula developed in the early days of the industry and is based on the assumption of a brake mean effective pressure of 67.2 psi and a piston speed of a 1000 fpm. Today's engines operate at much higher speeds and pressures and consequently the formula no longer gives any indication of the power output of an engine.

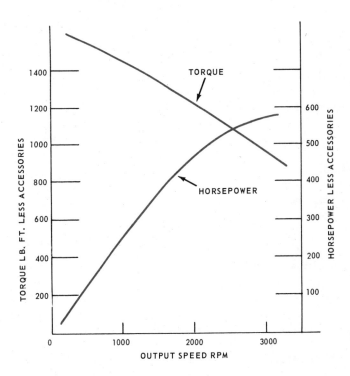

Fig. 9-12a. *Horsepower and torque curves of experimental Ford turbine developed especially for long distance truck service.*

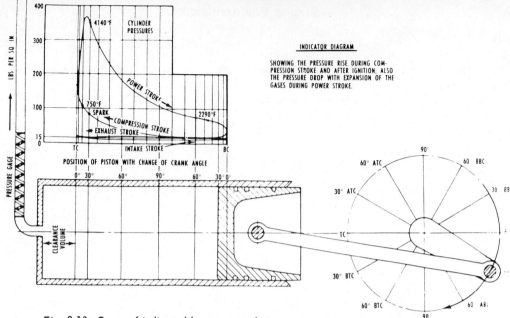

Fig. 9-13. Curve of indicated horsepower of an automotive engine.

It is often incorrectly referred to as the SAE horsepower, but the correct name is rated or AMA horsepower after an automotive association which is no longer in existance. However, the formula is still used for purposes of licensing automotive vehicles. The formula is as follows:

$$\text{Rated Horsepower} = \frac{N B^2}{2.5}$$

where N is the number of cylinders and B is the diameter of the engine bore in inches. For example; consider a six-cylinder engine with a bore of 4 in. Then:

$$\text{Rated Horsepower} = \frac{6 \times 4 \times 4}{2.5} = 38.4$$

Indicated Horsepower

Another method of rating an engine is by the indicated horsepower. This is based on the actual power developed in the engine from an indicator diagram, Fig. 9-13. As the indicated horsepower is the power produced within the engine, it includes the power required to overcome the friction within the engine. Subtracting the friction horsepower from the indicated horsepower gives the brake horsepower:

$$BHP = IHP - FHP$$

The indicator diagram is obtained by means of an oscilloscope or a special instrument which makes an actual drawing of the events that are occurring in the cylinder. It records in diagram form, the pressure existing at each instant of a complete cycle of the engine from the time that the combustible mixture is first drawn into the cylinder until the end of the exhaust stroke. The area of the diagram is then proportional to the power developed, i.e., it is the indicated horsepower.

When calculating the indicated horsepower, it is first necessary to determine the mean effective pressure which is the average pressure during the power stroke, minus the average pressure during the other three strokes of the cycle. The indicated horsepower is then found by the formula:

$$IHP = \frac{PLANK}{33,000}$$

Where P = Mean effective pressure in psi.
  L = Stroke in inches.
  A = Area of cylinder in sq. in.
  N = Number of power strokes per minute.
  K = Number of cylinders.

Friction Horsepower

Friction horsepower is the power required to overcome the friction within the engine. The friction results from the pressure of the piston and rings against the cylinder walls, the friction of the crankshaft and camshaft rotating in their bearings and the friction of other moving parts such as the oil pump, fuel pump, the engine valves, timing gear or chain, etc.

Friction horsepower increases with the speed of the engine and also the size of the engine. A typical friction horsepower curve is shown in Fig. 9-8.

Engine Efficiency

The efficiency of an engine may be defined as the ratio of the power obtained to the power that was supplied. In gasoline engines there are many losses, so that in relation to the inherent power in the fuel, only about 15 percent appears as useful power, Fig. 9-14. The rest is lost in the cooling system, exhaust system, engine friction and friction in the drive line.

In a turbojet engine, the losses are only 1 to 2 percent.

The mechanical efficiency of an engine is equal to the relationship of the brake horsepower and the indicated horsepower:

$$\text{Mechanical efficiency} = \frac{BHP}{IHP}$$

This in most cases is approximately 85 percent.

Detonation - Preignition - Rumble

Detonation, preignition and rumble are three conditions that plague both engine designer and serviceman alike. Preignition and detonation are often confused as they sound alike, but are two entirely different conditions.

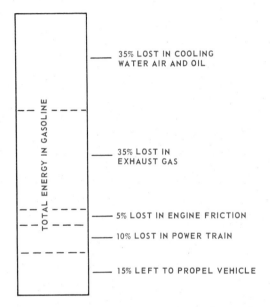

Fig. 9-14. Showing where the power goes in a four-cycle automotive type engine.

35% LOST IN COOLING WATER AIR AND OIL

35% LOST IN EXHAUST GAS

5% LOST IN ENGINE FRICTION

10% LOST IN POWER TRAIN

15% LEFT TO PROPEL VEHICLE

TOTAL ENERGY IN GASOLINE

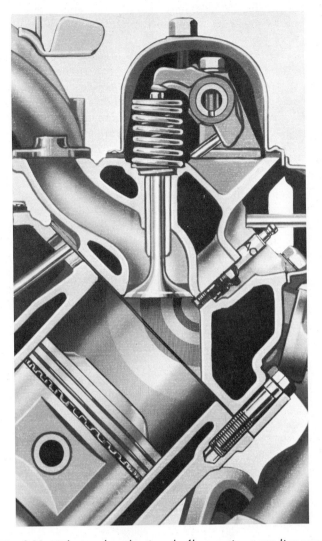

Fig. 9-15. With normal combustion, the flame action expanding away from the point of ignition.

Preignition as the name implies, is ignition that occurs earlier than planned. It results from any heated area or projection in the combustion chamber that has reached a temperature sufficient to ignite the fuel mixture. The result is preignition which has a "pinging" sound.

Detonation has a similar metallic - ringing sound and results from the use of low octane fuel, the shape of the combustion chamber and excessive compression ratio. The sound of detonation is due to vibration of some portion of the combustion chamber wall caused by almost instantaneous rise of gas pressure.

This rapid rise in gas pressure may start as follows: When the spark ignites the fuel, heat is generated and the pressure within the combustion chamber increases. That portion of the fuel mixture which is still unburned is still further compressed and as a further result the temperature soars. In addition, the charge is further heated by radiation from the burning portion of the charge. As a result, the temperature of the unburned charge is suddenly raised to the ignition point and combustion is then virtually instantaneous.

When detonation does not take place, the combustion proceeds in a controlled and orderly manner across the combustion chamber, Fig. 9-15.

In the recent years great progress has been made in the control of detonation by improved fuels which burn more slowly and by advanced design of the combustion chamber.

Rumble is a noise found particularly in high compression engines and is a noise associated with bending vibration of the crankshaft and is caused by abnormally high rates of pressure rise near top dead center.

Surface ignition is a condition which is giving considerable trouble and research reports indicate that this results largely from the quantity and type of lubricant ash that forms in the combustion chamber.

Results of research indicate that for a given metal type of lubricant additive, high ash lubricants have a greater tendency to produce surface ignition than low ash blends. Magnesium based lubricants are less prone to cause surface ignition than barium or calcium lubricants.

After run, or dieseling as it is also called, is a condition that occurs frequently, particularly on engines fitted with modern exhaust emission control devices. Precision timing and a reduction in idling speed will reduce such tendencies. Some fuels are more prone to cause this condition than others.

Quiz - Engine Performance

1. Brake horsepower is a reliable measure of the power developed by an engine. True or False?
2. How is the displacement of an engine determined?
3. Torque is the same as power. True or False?
4. Friction is dependent on the area in contact. True or False?
5. Indicated horsepower does not take into consideration the friction losses within the engine. True or False?
6. Mean effective pressure is another name for: explosion pressure____, compression pressure____, average pressure____.
7. Define the difference between power and torque.
8. Why does torque decrease above a certain speed?
9. A gas is best measured by: volume____, weight____.
10. Given the bore of the cylinder and the volume of the combustion chamber, it is possible to determine the compression ratio. True or False?
11. Rated horsepower is the same as brake horsepower. True or False?
12. The volume within the cylinder of a certain engine is 50 cu. in. and the volume of the combustion chamber is 5 cu. in.; what is the compression ratio?
    a. 10 to 1.
    b. 6 to 1.
    c. One tenth.
14. The use of a supercharger will increase volumeteric efficiency. True or False?
15. Which is correct? Mechanical efficiency of an engine equals:
$$\frac{BHP}{IHP} \text{ or } \frac{Rated\ HP}{IHP}$$

ENGINE LUBRICATION

Without the aid of friction, an automobile could not move itself. Excessive friction in the automobile however, would mean rapid destruction. We cannot eliminate internal friction, but we can reduce it to a controllable degree by the use of friction reducing lubricants.

These lubricants are usually made from the same crude oil from which we obtain gasoline. The petroleum oils are compounded with animal fats, vegetable oils and other ingredients to produce satisfactory oils and greases for automotive use. Lubricating oils and greases are also manufactured from silicones and other materials and have no petroleum products in them.

Lubricating oil in an automobile engine has several tasks to perform:

1. By lubrication, reduce the friction between the moving parts of the engine, thus:
   A. Reduce the amount of destructive heat generated by excessive friction.
   B. Conserve power that would otherwise be wasted in overcoming excessive friction.
2. By acting as a seal to prevent leakage between parts such as pistons, rings and cylinders.
3. By flowing between friction generating parts and thus carrying away much of the heat.
4. By washing away the abrasive metal worn from friction surfaces.

Furthermore; the engine oil must function whether the temperature is below zero or above 200 deg. F. This is contrary to the nature of petroleum products as they tend to thicken at low temperatures and thin out at high temperatures. The oil therefore goes through many processes during manufacture to reduce this tendency to change viscosity with changes in temperature.

Properties of Engine Oil

Engine oil is available in different viscosities and viscosity may be considered to be the internal friction of a fluid. An oil of low viscosity will flow more easily than an oil of high viscosity. Sometimes a low viscosity oil is referred to as a light oil and a high viscosity oil as a heavy oil.

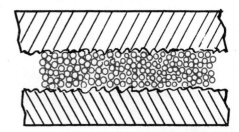

Fig. 10-1. The oil molecules roll one over the other to reduce friction in a manner somewhat similar to ball bearings.

Oils of different viscosities have been assigned numbers by the Society of Automotive Engineers. The lower the viscosity, the lower the assigned number. Thus, SAE 10 engine oil may be recommended for cold weather operation and SAE 30 for warm weather. The SAE number of an oil has nothing to do with its quality.

The added designation of "W" such as 10-W indicates that the W oil has the added ability to remain fluid or flow at a wider range of temperatures. Thus a 10-W oil can be used under more severe conditions than an SAE 10 oil.

The American Petroleum Institute rates engine oils according to nine different classes of service:

SE oils are suitable for most severe service of 1972 and certain 1971 gasoline and other spark ignition engines having emission control devices and operating under manufacturers' warranty. SD oils are for service typical of gasoline engines in 1968 through 1970 cars, certain trucks and some 1971 and/or later models.

SC oils are identified for service in gasoline engines in 1964 through 1967 passenger cars and trucks operating under manufacturers' warranty. SB oils are recommended for older cars operating under moderate conditions. Oils marked ONLY for service SB are NOT recommended for engines under manufacturers' warranty. SA oils are for utility and diesel engines operating under such mild conditions that protection afforded by compounded oils is not required.

CD oils are for severe duty diesel engine service. CC oils are for moderate-to-severe duty in diesels and certain heavy-duty gasoline engines. CB oils are for mild-to-moderate diesel service. CA oils are for light, normal conditions such as are typical of most farm tractor and trucking conditions.

Temperature influences the viscosity of oil. The higher the temperature the more fluid the oil becomes. An oil with a 10W-30 designation will retain its viscosity over a wider span of temperatures than an SAE 10 oil, for example.

The viscosity of an oil is determined in the laboratory by means of a viscosimeter under carefully controlled conditions of temperature.

Engine oils are also designed to form a minimum of carbon, resist oxidation and the formation of sludge. Quality oils are also designed to resist foaming.

In that 60 day period, the average city motorist will have driven approximately 1,500 miles of the hardest type of driving where the engine does not reach full operating temperature and consequently engine wear and oil deterioration are both at a maximum.

Oil in the crankcase, while performing its many functions of protecting the engine from wear and corrosion, becomes more and more loaded with acids, dirt and abrasives, not all of which can be trapped by filters. So there is only one way of removing this wear producing contaminant and that is by changing oil.

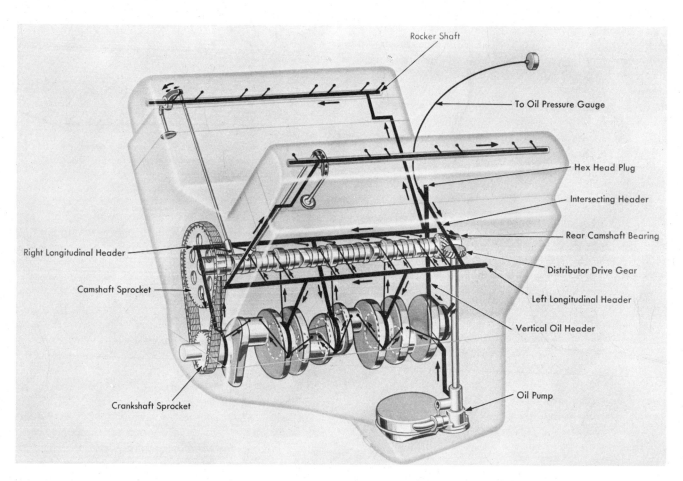

Fig. 10-2. With the full pressure engine lubrication system the oil is fed to practically all of the engine moving parts under pump pressure.

Oil Changes

When should oil be changed is a difficult question to answer as so much depends on the driving conditions, the condition and type of engine and the quality and type of oil being used.

Many car manufacturers are now recommending oil be changed every 6,000 miles or every 60 days whichever comes first. Unfortunately, too many car owners see only the 6,000 mile recommendation and overlook the 60 day recommendation.

Furthermore, many of the additives in the oil become depleted and are no longer effective. Consequently wear is accelerated.

It should be noted that 60 percent of all common carriers and 78 percent of all private fleets change oil in their vehicles between 1,000 and 3,000 miles, and fleet operators are in business to make money. Under extreme driving conditions which produce oil contamination by dust, water and other foreign materials, oil should be changed even more frequently than every 60 days.

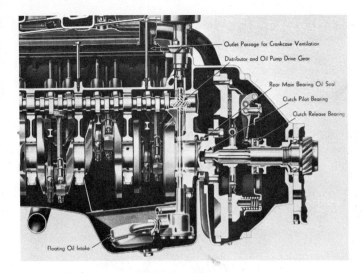

Fig. 10-3. *This Cadillac sump located pump is also fitted with a floating oil intake screen.*

Lubrication Methods

The oil may be supplied to the moving parts of the engine by splashing or by pump pressure, or by a combination of both. Many automobile engines utilize splashed oil--which usually becomes an oil mist--for the lubrication of some parts. The majority of the engine parts are pressure fed, at least to practically all of the bearings. The leakage or "throw-off" from these bearings splashes on the other moving parts inside the engine. A typical system is shown in Fig. 10-2.

Pressure Systems

As may be seen in Fig. 10-3, the oil pump is located in the sump of the oil pan, and the oil enters the pump through a screen. Sometimes the pump is not located in the sump, and the oil is piped from the screen to the pump as shown in Fig. 10-4. Quite often

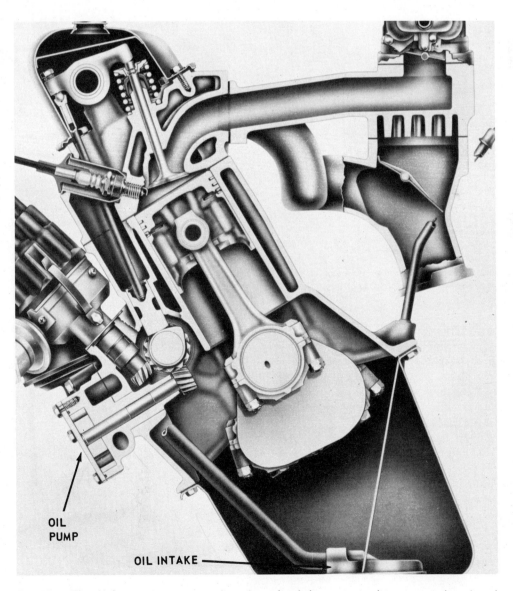

Fig. 10-4. *This Valiant pump is mounted on the side of the engine and is connected to the oil screen by a pipe.*

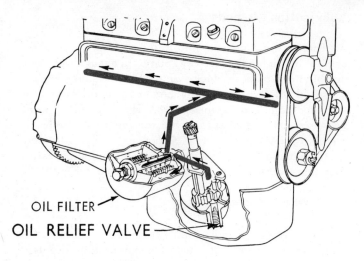

OIL FILTER

OIL RELIEF VALVE

Fig. 10-5. In this case, the oil goes through a filter placed between the oil pump and oil gallery.

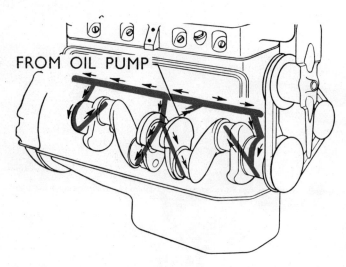

FROM OIL PUMP

Fig. 10-6. Oil passages drilled in the crankshaft conduct the oil from the main bearings to the connecting rods.

the intake screen is mounted on a hinged float that stays on top of the oil in the sump as shown in Fig. 10-3. The idea is to keep the pump intake away from any dirt that might settle in the bottom of the sump.

Fig. 10-5 shows the path of the oil from the pump to the oil gallery or distributing tube in the crankcase. The oil is conducted to the main bearings through drilled passages in the crankcase. Passages are also drilled in the crankshaft to carry the oil from the main bearings to the connecting rod journals. See Fig. 10-6. The path of the oil to the overhead valve rocker shaft is shown in Fig. 10-7. Thus oil is carried under pressure to all parts except the cylinder walls and piston pins.

In some engines the oil is pumped into a groove in the cylinder wall for ring and wall lubrication. Also some connecting rods have oil passages drilled lengthwise to carry oil to the piston pins. See Fig. 10-8. Ordinarily there is enough oil thrown off the main

bearings and rod bearings to supply lubrication for the cylinder walls and piston pins. See Fig. 10-9. As an aid to splash, the top of the connecting rod in some engines has a spurt hole drilled in it on one side so that a squirt of oil is shot out on the cylinder wall as the hole registers with the oil passage in the crankshaft. See Fig. 10-10.

One popular engine used a combination of pressure and splash lubrication for engine bearings. The oil in this case is pumped through pipes into troughs under

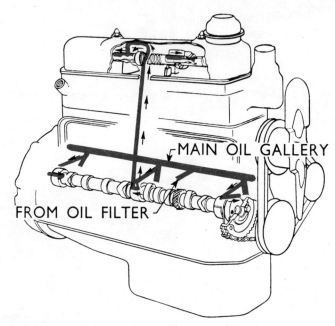

MAIN OIL GALLERY

FROM OIL FILTER

Fig. 10-7. Oil from the gallery goes to the camshaft bearings and then on to the rocker arm shaft.

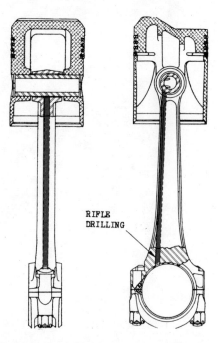

RIFLE DRILLING

Fig. 10-8. Oil passage drilled lengthwise in connecting rod to conduct oil to the piston pin.

Fig. 10-9. A limited amount of oil leaks out at the ends of the crankshaft bearings. The connecting rods throw it on the cylinder walls.

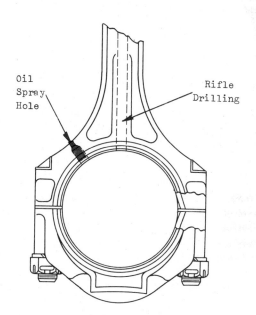

Oil Spray Hole

Rifle Drilling

Fig. 10-10. An oil spray hole in the rod provides lubrication for the cylinder walls.

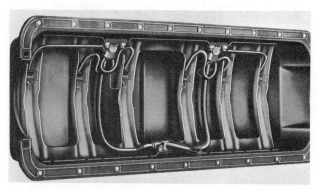

Fig. 10-11. In this case the oil is pumped into troughs under each connecting rod bearing and is also squirted at a scoop on each rod. See Fig. 10-12.

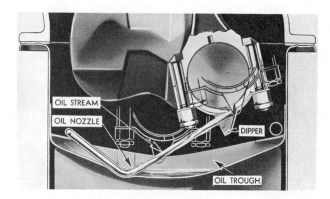

OIL STREAM

OIL NOZZLE

DIPPER

OIL TROUGH

Fig. 10-12. The oil jets are "aimed," or adjusted so that the oil is squirted directly into the dipper on each connecting rod bearing.

each connecting rod as shown in Fig. 10-11. These pipes are located and aimed so that a jet of oil is directed into a scoop on the rod bearing as the rod comes around. See Fig. 10-12. The rod also splashes into the oil in the trough and throws it around the interior of the crankcase. The aiming of the jets is important and special gauges are available for locating them correctly.

Oil Pumps

The pumps used to circulate the oil are of the positive displacement type in several designs. Vanes, plungers, rotors and gears are all used to build up the necessary pressure. A representative type of gear pump is illustrated in Fig. 10-13. A comparison between the gear and rotor types is shown in Fig. 10-14. These pumps are always positively driven, usually from the camshaft either by means of gears or cams.

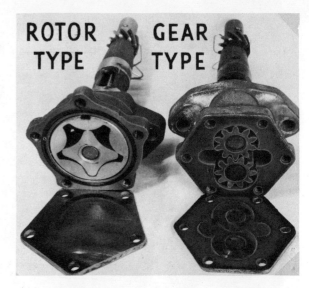

Fig. 10-14. Most automobile engine oil pumps are of either the gear type or the rotor type.

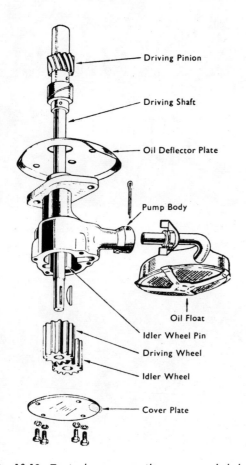

Driving Pinion

Driving Shaft

Oil Deflector Plate

Pump Body

Oil Float

Idler Wheel Pin

Driving Wheel

Idler Wheel

Cover Plate

Fig. 10-13. Typical gear type oil pump as exploded.

As these pumps handle oil, they are well lubricated at all times and do not suffer from excessive wear. They do, in time develop an excess of clearance and require replacement of parts. The gear teeth or vane contours may wear, and the gear ends and housings may wear. When excessive wear does occur, the oil pressure will drop.

Oil Pressure

Most cases of lost oil pressure are due to excessive clearance in the bearings of the engine rather than worn oil pumps. Methods of checking oil pumps for wear are explained later in this text.

Attempts are often made to restore lost oil pressure by adjustment of the oil pressure regulating valve. If the oil pump is in good condition, the pressure regulation valve will REGULATE the pressure of the oil within limits, but it will not increase the capacity of the oil pump. The regulator is a simple spring loaded valve which RELIEVES EXCESS PRESSURE in the circulating system by bypassing the excess oil back to the sump. See Fig. 10-15.

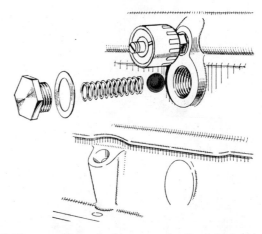

Fig. 10-15. As pressure builds up in the line, the ball is forced back against the spring to uncover a port so that the oil can be returned to the sump.

Another reason for lack of oil pressure is stoppage in the oil pump supply line or screen. This prevents oil reaching the pump in sufficient volume to maintain pressure. A typical case of a stopped screen is shown in Fig. 10-16. This is a case of "sludge" accumulation. This same sludge gets into the oil passages and stops them up with the result that a bearing may "starve" for oil and friction will then melt the metal. It is important to prevent the formation of excessive sludge in an engine.

Oil Sludge

Sludge is a mayonnaise-like mixture of water, oil, dirt and other products of combustion. It is most likely to form in an engine that seldom reaches a satisfactory operating temperature. For example: a light truck used for laundry or milk delivery service in cold weather. Such a vehicle ordinarily runs a short distance at slow speed, stops and then runs another short distance at slow speed.

Fig. 10-16. An accumulation of sludge on the screen as shown at the left will stop the flow of oil and result in burned out bearings.

Such operation means that the engine seldom gets hot enough to drive the water and vapor out of the crankcase. The water condenses on the cold walls of the crankcase, or in some cases gets into the crankcase through leaking cylinder head gaskets. This water emulsifies with the oil, carbon, dirt, etc., to form sludge. See Fig. 10-17.

Sludge formation can be held to a minimum by using the correct cooling system thermostat so as to maintain a high engine operating temperature, using engine oils of high detergency and making sure oil and filter are changed frequently. Adequate crankcase ventilation is also important.

Researchers have found that when the cooling system thermostat was removed from the engine water

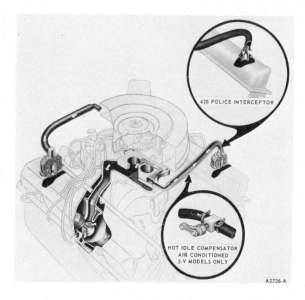

Fig. 10-18. Details of positive closed crankcase ventilating system as installed on 390 cu. in. Ford engines.

jacket outlet, temperatures barely exceeded 100 deg. F. when the ambient temperature was 60 to 70 deg. F. In general, the engine operated at approximately 20 deg. above the ambient temperature.

Water jacket outlet temperature usually corresponds to the setting of the cooling system thermostat. It must be emphasized that oil dilution and sludge formation decrease with 195 deg. thermostats as compared to thermostats having a lower setting. Not only is sludge reduced but production of hydrocarbons and carbon monixide in the exhaust are also reduced.

Equally important to keeping sludge formation to a minimum is proper crankcase ventilation. Adequate crankcase oil temperature must be maintained to assist in evaporation and purging of volatile blow-by con-

Fig. 10-17. Typical accumulation of sludge on cylinder head and on valve cover plates.

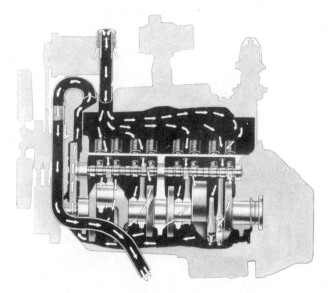

Fig. 10-19. In this case air is drawn in through the filter on the oil filler cap and drawn out through a special outlet pipe.

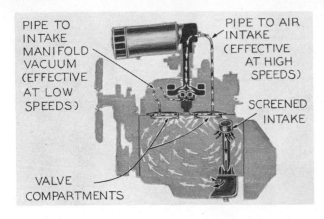

Fig. 10-20. On this system the engine vacuum in the inlet manifold is used to draw ventilating air in through a screen on the oil filler pipe.

taminants. Oil temperatures are usually only a problem under conditions involving excessive idling or operation in severely cold weather.

While fuel is a major factor in the formation of sludge, modern oils with their additives have helped to control the condition by keeping sludge and other foreign materials in suspension.

Crankcase Ventilation

In order to maintain a better climate in the crankcase and reduce sludge forming tendencies, the crankcase is ventilated. As shown in Fig. 10-19, air is drawn through the filter in the oil filler cap and after passing through the valve chamber and crankcase it leaves the engine through the outlet pipe with its opening below the engine where the movement of the passing air helps exhaust the crankcase fumes. In Figs. 10-20 and 10-21, the fumes are drawn into the intake manifold and then through the engine again.

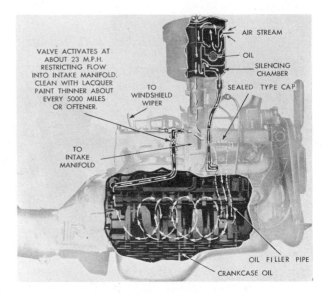

Fig. 10-21. Another method of using intake vacuum to draw in ventilating air through the air cleaner.

Plymouth's redesigned 383 cu. in. V-8 engine has Cleaner Air System (CAS) to comply with exhaust emission control standards, yet it will produce up to 330 hp when equipped with 4-barrel carburetor, high-performance camshaft and high-compression cylinder heads.

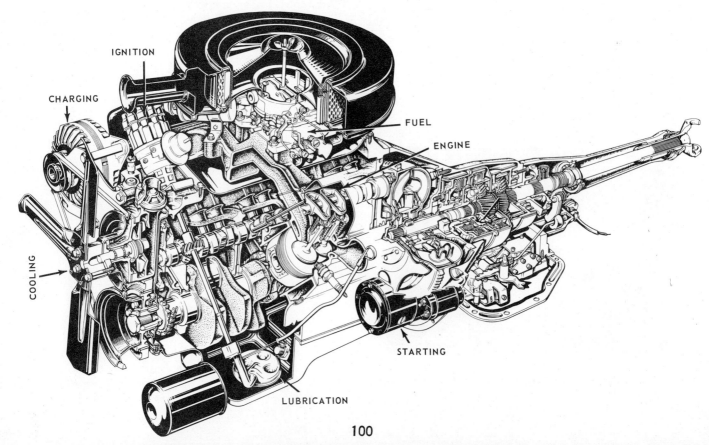

100

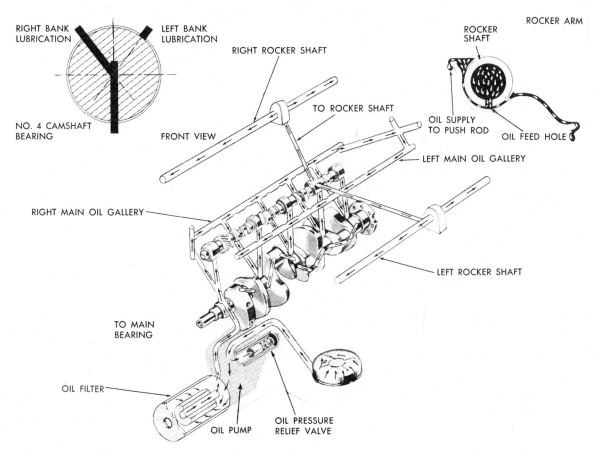

RIGHT BANK LUBRICATION

LEFT BANK LUBRICATION

NO. 4 CAMSHAFT BEARING

FRONT VIEW

RIGHT ROCKER SHAFT

TO ROCKER SHAFT

ROCKER SHAFT

ROCKER ARM

OIL SUPPLY TO PUSH ROD

OIL FEED HOLE

LEFT MAIN OIL GALLERY

RIGHT MAIN OIL GALLERY

LEFT ROCKER SHAFT

TO MAIN BEARING

OIL FILTER

OIL PUMP

OIL PRESSURE RELIEF VALVE

Fig. 10-22. Filters are often connected directly to the pressure side of the pump to catch any contaminants before they reach the small passages in the camshaft bearings or the rocker arm shaft.

The effects of passing the fumes into the atmosphere and the methods used to overcome the condition, are discussed in Chapter 29 on Exhaust Emission Control.

Engine Varnish

Another type of engine deposit is known as "varnish" or "lacquer." It is often also called sludge, but it is an entirely different material and forms in a different manner. Varnish or lacquer is formed when an engine is worked hard enough to get good and hot for extended periods of time. The heat causes the oil to break down and some of the elements to separate out and deposit as a varnish-like substance on the metal parts of the engine.

To avoid such deposits, it is necessary to use the best oil obtainable and change oil regularly. It is also essential to make sure that the cooling system is functioning efficiently.

In the preceding text we have emphasized the importance of regular and frequent oil changes. This for the reason that oil costs less than machinery. Changing oil frequently is merely a form of insurance. It is more economical to throw away a quart of oil costing a few cents than to take a chance on damaging an engine worth several hundred dollars.

Oil Filters

Oil filters are placed in the engine oil system to remove dirt and abrasives from the oil. Diluents, such as gasoline and acids are not removed. However, by removing the solid materials, the possibility of acids forming is reduced, and the rate of wear of engine parts is greatly reduced.

The oil filters installed on passenger car engines at present are of the full-flow type so that all the oil passes through the filter each time before it reaches the bearings. However, in the event the filter becomes clogged or obstructed, a bypass valve is provided so that oil will continue to reach the bearings. The filters in use today are of the "throw-away" type. See Figs. 10-22, 10-23 and 10-24.

Additives

The requirements of today's automobile engines are far beyond the range of straight mineral oils. All automobile manufacturers are now recommending oils which have been improved by additives. The need for improved oil results from higher engine compression, increased bearing loads, stepped-up speeds, greater sensitivity to deposit formation, corrosion and rusting.

There are many different additives in use today.

Probably the first one to be used was a pour point depressant which is designed to overcome the difficulty of pouring oil in cold weather, and more important, would not flow to the engine oil pump. At low temperatures the wax in the oil would form crystals and then form a sort of "honey comb" which in turn would block the flow of oil.

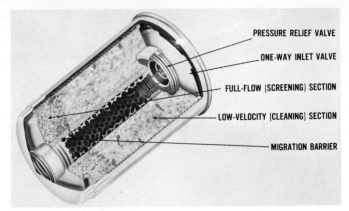

PRESSURE RELIEF VALVE
ONE-WAY INLET VALVE
FULL-FLOW (SCREENING) SECTION
LOW-VELOCITY (CLEANING) SECTION
MIGRATION BARRIER

Fig. 10-24. Autolite depth type full-flow filter.

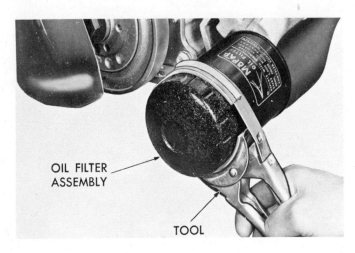

OIL FILTER ASSEMBLY

TOOL

Fig. 10-23. Removing an oil filter.

To prevent sludge and varnish deposits which otherwise would prevent the free flow of oil and cause valves and lifters to stick, detergent-dispersant additives are used.

Foam inhibitors are designed to prevent the formation of foam, which would result from the egg beater action of the rotating engine parts. Unless the foaming is stopped, bearings and other parts would receive only foam instead of oil and would soon fail.

Oxidation inhibitors are used to reduce the possibility of oil being oxidized. This oxidation usually occurs at higher operating temperatures such as are attained during sustained high speed, full throttle operation. Serious oxidation of the oil and resultant deposit formation will occur unless the oxidation is prevented.

Viscosity index improvers, as the words imply, improve the viscosity index. The viscosity index is a measure of the rate of change or variation in the viscosity of a liquid with changing temperature. A high viscosity index indicates a relatively low rate of viscosity change between two temperatures and a low index indicates a high rate. Oils designed for automotive engine use have a relatively high viscosity index and are suitable for use in both high and low atmospheric temperatures.

Corrosion and rust inhibitors are designed to help the detergent-dispersant additives in the prevention of rust and corrosion.

Antiwear additives, one of the most important

used, have the ability to coat metal surfaces with a strong and slippery film that prevents direct metal to metal contact. All modern top-quality oils contain this type of additive.

All these additives combine to produce an oil which not only will withstand heavier loads, reduce corrosion, stop foaming, maintain viscosity, stop sludge and varnish formation, but will also keep the interior of the engine cleaner and increase its useful life.

Quiz - Lubrication

1. Name four tasks that the lubricating oil in an engine is expected to perform.
2. An SAE 10 oil can be used anywhere that SAE 10-W can be used. True or False?
3. Is a light oil always better than a heavier oil? Yes or No?
4. What is meant by "OIL THROW-OFF?"
5. Name two ways of oiling piston rings.
6. Oil pumps are sometimes belt driven. True or False?
7. What is the most frequent cause of low oil pressure?
8. Name three things found in oil sludge.
9. Sludge and lacquer are not the same thing. True or False?
10. Name three engine oil additives.
11. Slow speed driving is always desirable in order to maintain the best engine lubrication. True or False?
12. How does an oil become diluted?
13. Is dilution better or worse when LPG is used as fuel? Better_____, Worse_____.
14. Is it a good idea to run an engine fast as soon as it starts in order to warm the oil up quickly? Yes or No?
15. How thick may an oil film be? Less than one thousandth of an inch_____, one thousandth _____, more than one thousandth_____.

ENGINE
COOLING SYSTEMS

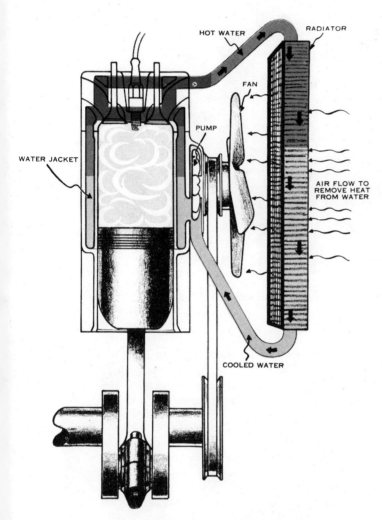

Fig. 11-1. Engine temperatures are regulated by transferring the excess heat to the surrounding air.

Some parts of an internal combustion engine would melt from the heat of the burning fuel and pistons would expand so much they could not move in the cylinders if no cooling system were provided. The cooling system of a water-cooled engine, Figs. 11-1 and 11-2, consists of the engine water jacket, thermostat, water pump, fan, fan drive belt and the necessary hoses. It must be designed to operate at temperatures ranging up to the boiling point of the coolant under pressure, which in the case of ethylene glycol antifreeze may exceed 240 deg. F.

The cylinder walls of air-cooled engines usually operate at temperatures considerably above 200 deg. F. This is hot to the touch, but cool in comparison with the heat generated in the combustion chamber of the engine.

As the fuel is burned in the engine, about one-third of the heat energy in the fuel is converted into power. Another third goes out the exhaust pipe unused, and the remaining third must be handled by the cooling system. This third is often underestimated and even less understood.

Perhaps it will be helpful to describe it in readily understood terms rather than by reference to so many Btu's (British thermal units). The heat removed by the cooling system of an average automobile at normal speed is sufficient to keep a six-room house warm in zero weather.

This means that several thousand gallons of water must be circulated in the cooling system every hour to absorb the heat and carry it to the radiator for disposal. It also means that many thousand cubic feet of air must flow through the radiator every hour in order to dissipate the heat to the air. It is important at this time to distinguish between heat TRANSFER and heat DISSIPATION.

The heat generated by the mixture burned in the engine must be TRANSFERRED from the iron or aluminum cylinder to the water in the water jacket. The outside of the water jacket DISSIPATES some of the heat to the air surrounding it, but most of the heat is carried by the cooling water on to the radiator from whence it is dissipated to the air. See Fig. 11-1.

Heat Transfer

In an automotive engine, heat flows or transfers from the iron or aluminum cylinder to the cooling water, and from the coolant to the copper or aluminum radiator. Iron, aluminum, copper and water are all good conductors of heat, so if they are in good contact with one another, the heat will flow readily from one to another. If, however, there is a coating of lime or rust between the water and the bare metal, the flow will be retarded because lime and rust are poor heat conductors. There is a great amount of surface within the water circulation system on which this lime and rust can accumulate as may be seen from Fig. 11-2.

We are always liable to have some rust in the cooling system. Rust is a combination of iron, water and oxygen. We have iron in the engine, water in the engine and some oxygen in the water. Additional oxygen enters the cooling system in the air that finds its way into the cooling system.

the valve seats may overheat and crack. This type of overheating can and does occur without any indication of overheating on the temperature gauge. The gauge is located at one spot in the water jacket, and the overheating condition is localized in another spot.

The scale that collects in corners and narrow

Fig. 11-2. Illustrating passage of coolant through cooling system of modern V-8. (Buick)

In addition to rust, we usually have some lime in the cooling system. In most parts of the country there is some lime in the water supply; more in some localities than in others along with other minerals. Alternate heating and cooling of the engine causes the lime to collect on the inside walls of the water jacket in the same manner that lime collects in a tea kettle.

This rust and lime in the cooling system combines with a small amount of grease or oil, which often acts as a binder to hold the lime and rust to the iron, and soon we have a coat of insulation on the inside of the water jacket. Grease or oil gets into the cooling system from water pump lubricant, leaking cylinder head gaskets, etc.

In addition to coating the inside of the water jacket, this scale will collect in corners or pockets of the water jacket where the water circulation is sluggish. This often causes "hot spots" which in turn cause distortion of cylinders and valve seats. Another cause of hot spots, particularly around the exhaust valves, is the stoppage or corrosion of water distributing tubes which are added to improve cooling of the exhaust valves. See Figs. 11-3 and 11-4.

These tubes are intended to accelerate the circulation of the cooling water around the exhaust valve seats. See Fig. 11-4. If they rot out or get stopped up,

passages is also a deposit point for bits of rubber from the inside of the hoses, and other trash that finds its way into the cooling system. The result is a mass of insulating sludge and scale which does con-

Fig. 11-3. Water distributing tubes may be inserted in the cylinder block behind the water pump and along side the valves.

siderable harm to the engine. Such accumulations can be avoided by proper maintenance of the cooling system, the use of inhibitor solutions, electrolytic devices and periodic flushing of the cooling system.

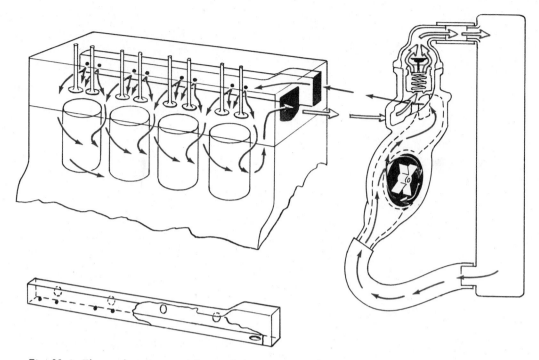

Fig. 11-4. The coolant is sprayed around the valve seats by jets from the water distributing tube.

Cooling System Pumps

Automobile engine water pumps are of many designs, but most of them are of the centrifugal type. That is, they consist of a rotating fan or impeller, and seldom are of the positive displacement type using gears or plungers. Many of them are quite efficient, but some of them are more on the order of agitators or circulators. Sometimes the fan is combined on the same shaft with the water pump. A water pump and fan combined on one shaft is shown in Fig. 11-5.

An exploded view of a typical water pump assembly with all the parts in proper relation to each other, is shown in Fig. 11-6. Sometimes the vanes on the impeller are straight, but in this case they are curved to accelerate the centrifugal flow of the water. These

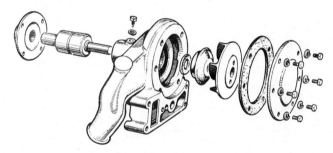

Fig. 11-6. Construction of a typical separate water pump. Note curved vanes.

vanes should not touch the housing, but at the same time should not have excessive clearance. See Fig. 11-7. For this reason, excessive endwise motion of the shaft to which the vane is attached is not permissible.

Obviously, such pumps must turn rapidly in order to be efficient. Worn or loose belts will permit slippage which is not readily detected. It is particularly difficult to detect a worn V-belt fan pulley. In case the pulley is suspected, the groove can be compared with a new pulley for wear.

Most pumps have a spring-loaded seal to avoid leakage of water around the pump shaft. One such type is shown in Fig. 11-7. This particular pump is fitted with prepacked ball bearings which are well sealed at

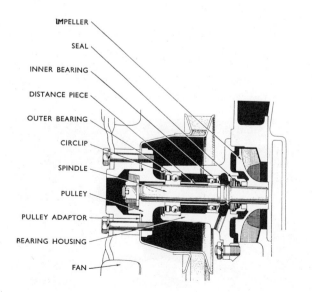

IMPELLER
SEAL
INNER BEARING
DISTANCE PIECE
OUTER BEARING
CIRCLIP
SPINDLE
PULLEY
PULLEY ADAPTOR
BEARING HOUSING
FAN

Fig. 11-5. A single belt is often used to drive both fan and water pump by placing both on the same shaft.

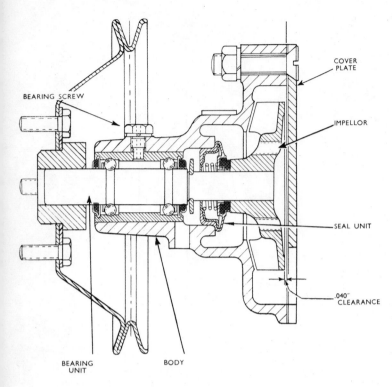

BEARING SCREW

COVER PLATE

IMPELLOR

SEAL UNIT

.040" CLEARANCE

BEARING UNIT

BODY

Fig. 11-7. The shaft ball bearings are sealed at each end to keep lubricant in and water out of the bearings. A spring loaded seal is used to avoid water leakage around the pump shaft. Note clearance between impeller and cover plate.

each end and therefore periodic lubrication is not required. A somewhat similar pump is shown in Fig. 11-8, but this pump has provision for grease insertion through a plug hole if it should become desirable.

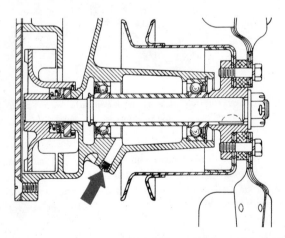

Fig. 11-8. Provision is made in this design for the addition of lubricant if desired by removal of a screw plug.

V-type engines often have a water pump on each cylinder block. In other cases a single pump serves both blocks as shown in Fig. 11-9. While most pumps run on sealed ball bearings and the shaft is sealed from the housing, they do occasionally require attention. There is some sand and grit in the water that

wears the impeller blades and pump housings and also may score the sealing surfaces. The sealing surfaces may be scored enough to leak air if not water. Special reamers are available for resurfacing the seat in the pump housing when the seal is replaced.

If the pump is designed for lubrication, it should not be overlubricated. Excess lubricant may get into the cooling system, and coat the water jacket passages and radiator passages with oil. This causes lime and rust to adhere. The manufacturers' instructions as to the type of lubricant and frequency of lubrication should be followed.

Radiators

The radiator is a device designed to dissipate the heat which the coolant has absorbed from the engine. It is therefore constructed to hold a large amount of water in tubes or other passages which provide a large area in contact with the atmosphere.

The usual radiator construction consists of the radiator core with its water carrying tubes and large cooling area which are connected at top to a receiving tank and at the bottom to a dispensing tank, Fig. 11-10.

Radiator cores are of two basic types, the fin and tube type, Fig. 11-10, and the ribbon cellular or honeycomb type, Fig. 11-11.

The fin and tube type of radiator core has the advantage of fewer soldered joints and is therefore a stronger construction. It consists of a series of parallel tubes extending from the upper to the lower tank and fins are placed around the tubes to increase the area for radiating the heat.

The honeycomb type core consists of a large number of narrow water passages made by soldering pairs of thin metal ribbons together along their edges. These tubes are crimped and the soldered edges form the front and rear of the vertical tubes. These tubes are separated by fins of metal ribbon which help dissipate the heat.

In operation, water is pumped from the engine to the top or receiving tank and then spreads over the tops of the tubes. After passing through the tubes, it enters the lower tank and from there it circulates through the engine again. As the water passes down

Fig. 11-9. A single water pump serves both blocks of this V-type engine.

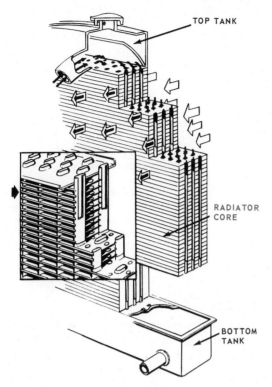

Fig. 11-10. *Construction of a typical tube type radiator core.*

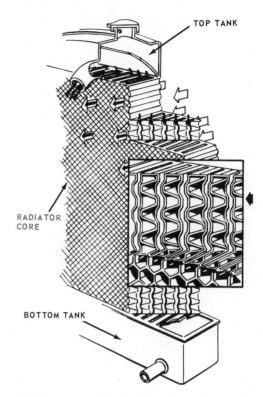

Fig. 11-11. *Details of cellular type radiator core.*

through the tubes it loses its heat to the airstream which passes around the outside of the tubes.

To help spread the heated water over the top of all the tubes a baffle plate is often placed in the upper tank, directly under the inlet hose from the engine.

Special Systems

Some cooling systems are supplied with an auxiliary or supply tank, Fig. 11-12. Its purpose is to provide additional capacity and also act as an expansion chamber. The inlet port of the supply tank is connected to the intake manifold coolant passage at the thermostat, thereby permitting coolant circulation through the supply tank and radiator when the thermostat is open.

While the usual construction of a radiator is to have the water circulate from the top to the bottom, occasionally they are designed to have the coolant flow from one side to the other, Fig. 11-13. It is claimed there is more efficient fan coverage of the radiator core with this design.

Radiator core capacity is much smaller for the same size engine today than it was formerly. This is

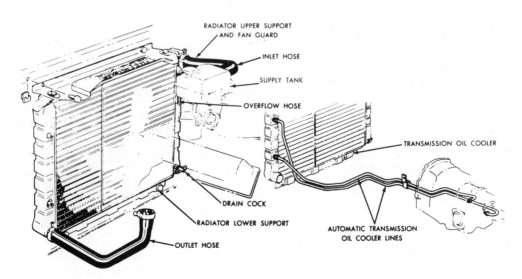

Fig. 11-12. *An auxiliary or supply tank is used in some cooling systems to provide additional capacity.*

due to operating the system at pressures ranging up to 15 lbs., making the engine more efficient in terms of heat rejection to the coolant per horsepower developed and by improving the heat transfer efficiency of the radiator core. For example: the 1954 Chevrolet 235 cu. in. six cylinder engine developed 115 hp, and had a radiator core capacity of 816 cu. in. Ten years later the Chevrolet 230 cu. in. six delivered 150 hp, and had a radiator core capacity of 406 cu. in.

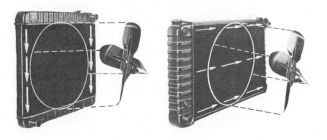

Fig. 11-13. Normal flow of coolant in radiator is from top to bottom. However, in some installations it is from side to side. Better coverage of the fan is claimed.

Radiator Caps

Originally the radiator cap served only to prevent the coolant from splashing out the filler opening. Today's radiator cap, Fig. 11-14 is designed to seal the system so that it operates under pressure. This improves cooling efficiency and prevents evaporation of the coolant. Losses due to surging are also eliminated. As evaporation is reduced or eliminated, it is not necessary to supply additional coolant so frequently and consequently the introduction of rust forming materials is greatly reduced. Also by operating at higher temperatures, it improves the heating characteristics of the car heater, and the engine operates more efficiently.

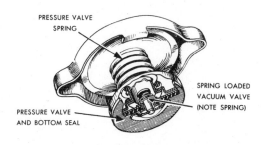

Fig. 11-14. Modern radiator caps are designed to maintain a specified pressure in the cooling system.

The higher temperatures result from the higher pressure as each pound per square inch of pressure increases the boiling point about 3.25 deg. F. As current radiator caps are designed to maintain a pressure of about 15 psi the boiling point would be raised to about 260 deg. F., Fig. 11-15.

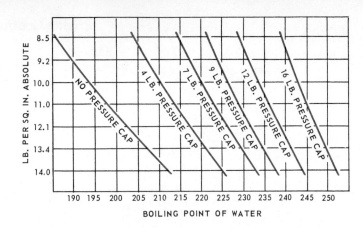

Fig. 11-15. Note how boiling point increases with each increase in pressure. Also how the boiling point drops as the absolute pressure drops, which corresponds to an increase in altitude. 8.5 lb. corresponds to an altitude of about 15,000 ft.

The pressure type radiator cap fits over the radiator filler opening and seals it tightly as the opening for the overflow is on the atmospheric side of the seal. Two spring-loaded valves are provided. The larger, or pressure valve, is designed to relieve pressure when it reaches a predetermined value, currently 12 to 15 psi. The smaller, or vacuum valve, is designed to open to relieve the vacuum which forms when the steam in the system condenses after the engine is stopped. If that were not done, the atmospheric pressure of 14.7 psi on the large flat surface of the upper tank would cause it to buckle and the seams would be opened.

Care must be exercised when removing a pressure cap when the engine is running or soon after it stops. The cap should be turned part way to first let the steam escape. The temperature rises rapidly for the first few minutes after the engine is stopped, causing the water to boil.

Fig. 11-16. To reduce noise of operation, fan blades are often arranged asymmetrically and in addition the ends of the blades may be bent and rounded.

Cooling Fans

The fan is designed to draw cooling air through the radiator core, Fig. 11-1. This is necessary at slow speeds or when the engine is idling as there is not sufficient air motion under those conditions to provide sufficient cooling.

So that none of the force of the fan is dissipated, shrouding is often provided. In that way the full force of the fan is used to draw air through the radiator core.

The fan is usually mounted on an extension of the water pump shaft and is driven by a V-belt from a pulley mounted on the front end of the crankshaft, Fig. 11-5. As the same belt is used to drive the alternator, the belt tension is adjusted by swinging the alternator on its mounting.

In order to reduce the noise made by the rotating fan, the fan blades are often placed asymmetrically, and with the tips bent and rounded, Fig. 11-16.

At 3,000 rpm, an 18 in. fan will consume over 2 hp and the power requirements increase very rapid-

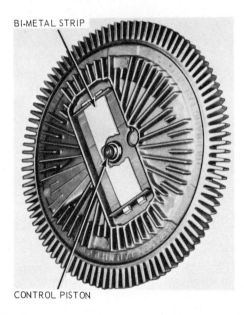

Fig. 11-17. To control fan speed a bimetallic strip and a control piston on the front of the fluid coupling regulates the amount of silicone oil entering the coupling.

ly with the speed. As the fan is required primarily at idling and low vehicle speeds, couplings have been devised to disconnect the fan above certain speeds.

The fan drive clutch used on the Mercury is a fluid coupling containing silicone oil. The more silicone oil in the coupling the greater the speed. In one construction, Fig. 11-17, a bimetallic strip and control piston on the front of the fluid coupling regulate the amount of silicone oil entering the coupling. The bimetallic strip bows outward with an increase in surrounding temperature and allows the piston controlled valve to regulate the flow of oil to and from the reservoir. The

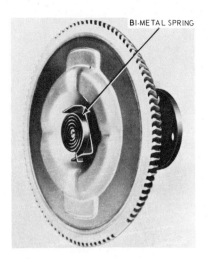

Fig. 11-18. Here a heat sensitive spring connected to an opening plate controls the flow of silicone oil to the fluid coupling in order to control fan speed.

other design uses a heat sensitive bimetallic spring connected plate which brings about a similar result, Fig. 11-18.

In another design, flexible fan blades vary the air drawn through the radiator, automatically increasing the pitch of the fan blades at low engine speeds.

Thermostats

Automotive internal combustion engines operate more efficiently when their temperature is maintained within narrow limits. To attain this objective a thermostat is inserted in the cooling system which is designed to close off the flow of water from the engine to the radiator, until the engine has reached the desired operating temperature.

Formerly a bellows type thermostat was used. Currently the thermostat is operated by a bimetallic coil, Fig. 11-19, which expands and contracts with changes in temperature to open and close the valve.

Fig. 11-19. Two different types of cooling system thermostats in current use.

When the water is cold, the thermostat closes the valve and stops the flow of water to the radiator, Fig. 11-20. Then as the water becomes hotter, the coil expands to open the valve and permitting the water to reach the radiator, Fig. 11-21.

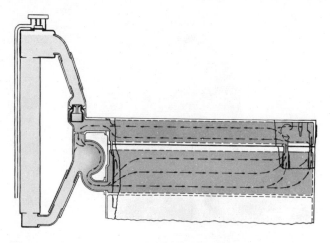

Fig. 11-20. With the thermostat closed, water circulates entirely within the engine water jacket.

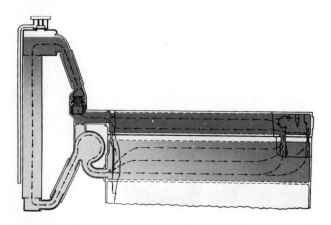

Fig. 11-21. When the thermostat opens, water will circulate through the radiator and then back to the water jacket.

This opening and closing of the thermostatically controlled valve continues as more or less heat is developed by the engine so that its operating temperature is maintained within narrow limits.

Thermostats are calibrated at the time of manufacture and are stamped with the number at which they are designed to open. A thermostat designed for use with an alcohol type antifreeze is usually designed to open at 155 to 160 degs. F. and be fully open at 180 deg. F. Thermostats designed for use with permanent type antifreeze will open between 188 to 195 degs. F. and be fully open between 210 to 212 degs. F.

Special testers are available for checking the opening and closing points of thermostats, Fig. 11-22.

Car Heater

The hot water car heater as used in an automobile is constructed in the same manner as the radiator and hot water from the cooling system is circulated through it. A fan is provided to drive the air from the heater through ducts to different parts of the vehicle, Fig. 11-23.

As the heater is connected to the car cooling system, it is important to keep the water passages clean and free from rust accumulations. Therefore, when flushing the cooling system, make sure any valves in the line going to the heater are also open.

The air which passes through the heater is usually supplied from outside the vehicle through openings provided in the top or sides of the cowl. The motion of the car aided by the action of the fan serves to force the fresh air through the heater. Vent air valves operated by Bowden wire controls serve to control the amount of air passing through the heater and into the passenger compartment. Warm air from the heater can also be directed to the inside of the windshield and melt any frost which might collect there.

Antifreeze Solutions

When water freezes, it expands approximately nine percent in volume. It will therefore break or seriously distort the shape of the vessel in which it is contained.

Fig. 11-22. Type of tester used in checking the opening and closing temperatures of cooling system thermostats.

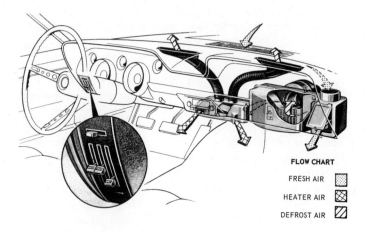

FLOW CHART

FRESH AIR

HEATER AIR

DEFROST AIR

Fig. 11-23. One type of car heater.

For that reason it is necessary to use a nonfreezing solution in the cooling system of water-cooled engines operated in climates where the temperature is below the freezing point of water.

As copper, iron, aluminum, brass, solder, etc. are all used in parts of the engine in contact with the coolant, it is important that the material used for antifreeze does not corrode--singly or in combination-- any of these metals. Also, the material should not be harmful to the various types of rubber used in the connecting hoses. Many different materials have been used as antifreeze solutions. Among the more suitable are: methanol (methyl alcohol), ethanol (ethyl alcohol), and ethylene glycol.

Freezing Protection

The mixing of an antifreeze with water forms a solution which has a lower freezing point than water. Many different solutions have been used in the past, but those in use today include ethyl alcohol, methyl alcohol and ethylene glycol, all of which are available under various trade names.

The temperature at which an antifreeze will freeze depends on the strength of the solution and this varies with each of the antifreezes, Fig. 11-24. Pure ethyl alcohol freezes at -174.6 deg. F. and methyl alcohol at -144.2 deg. F., while a 68 percent solution of ethylene glycol freezes at -92 deg. F. Further concentrations would not further reduce the freezing point of the solution.

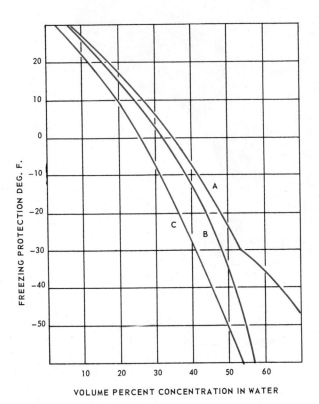

Fig. 11-24. Freezing protection afforded by different concentrations of (A) ethyl alcohol, (B) ethylene glycol, (C) methyl alcohol.

Expansion of Antifreeze

Antifreeze solutions will expand slightly more than water when heated as shown in Fig. 11-25. When water is heated from 40 deg. F. to 180 deg. F. it will expand approximately 1/4 pint per gallon. For the same range of temperature, ethylene glycol will ex-

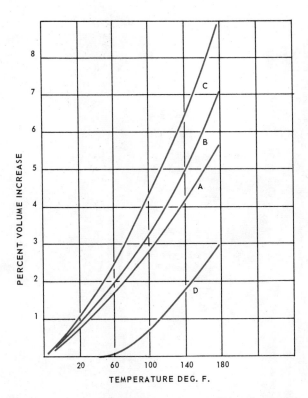

Fig. 11-25. Expansion due to heat of water (D), ethylene glycol (A), methyl alcohol (B), and ethyl alcohol (C). The antifreeze solutions giving protection to -20 deg. F.

pand 1/3 pint per gallon, methyl alcohol 2/5 pint per gallon, and ethyl alcohol 1/2 pint per gallon. This data is for antifreeze solutions affording protection to -20 deg. F.

To avoid loss of antifreeze due to expansion, the cooling system must not be completely filled. In the case of a 20-quart capacity cooling system completely filled at -20 deg. F., there would be a loss of 2 1/3 pints of ethylene glycol; 2 7/8 pints of methyl alcohol; or 3 2/3 pints of ethyl alcohol when the temperature goes up to 180 deg. F.

Boiling Point

When ethylene glycol is added to water, the boiling point of the solution is raised. When either methyl alcohol or ethyl alcohol is added to water, the boiling point of the solution is lowered. For example, methyl and ethyl alcohol solutions affording protection to -20 deg. F. will have boiling points of about 180 deg. F. A similar solution of ethylene glycol will have a boiling

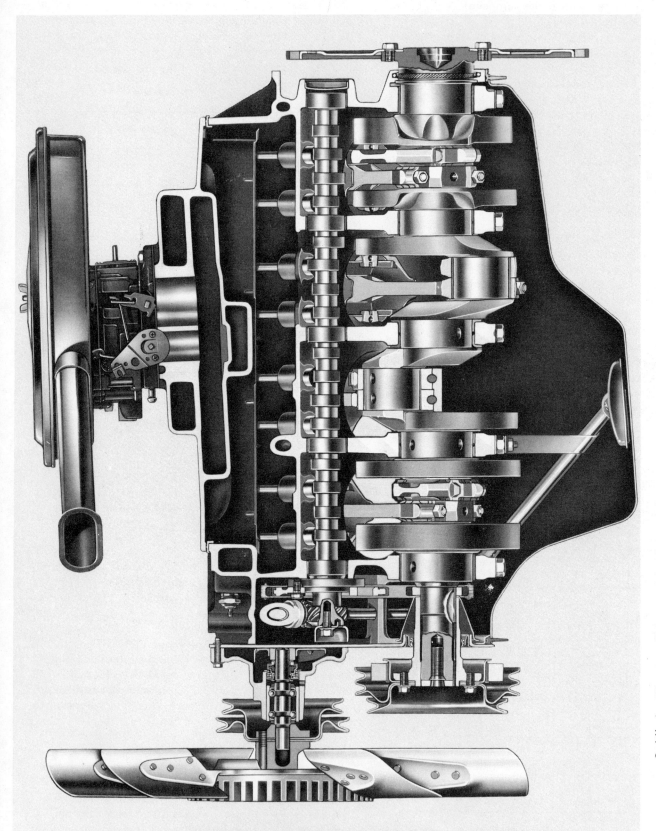

Cadillac's 472 cu. in. V-8 engine develops 375 hp and 525 ft. lbs. of torque. Engine design provides internal-distribution air injection system for exhaust emission control. A metal temperature sensing device buzzes and lamp lights if engine overheats.

point of 223 deg. as compared to 212 deg. for clear water. As the pressure is increased, the temperature at which the solution boils is increased as explained previously. Also see Fig. 11-26.

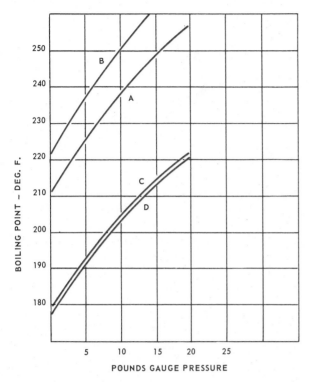

Fig. 11-26. Effect of pressure on boiling point of various antifreeze solutions, (A) water, (B) ethylene glycol, (C) ethyl alcohol and (D) methyl alcohol.

Evaporation

There is virtually no loss of ethylene glycol solution due to evaporation. Any such loss that does occur is practically all water. In the case of the alcohol types of antifreeze solution some of the alcohol is lost thus weakening the solution and lowering the protection. This evaporation loss is greatest under prolonged high speed driving conditions or extended idling periods in heavy traffic.

Removing Glycol from Crankcase

Should ethylene glycol, as the result of leakage, get into the engine oil, it will clog the oil lines and cause the pistons to seize. As the result, severe damage to the engine will result. When it has been determined that ethylene glycol has gotten into the lubricating system, the first step is to locate the cause for the coolant leak (such as a blown gasket or cracked block) and then make the necessary repairs.

The engine oil filter should then be removed and the engine oil drained completely. The crankcase should then be filled to the full mark on the dipstick,

Fig. 11-27. Tecumseh single cylinder air cooled engine. Note fan blades built into the flywheel.

with a mixture of 3 qt. SAE 10W engine oil and 2 qt. of Butyl Cellusolve (note, material can be obtained from a chemical supply house). The engine should then be run at idling speed for about 30 minutes. Pay particular attention to the oil pressure. Then drain and flush with 3 qt. SAE 10W oil and 2 qt. kerosene. Idle the engine with this flushing oil for about 10 minutes. Then drain. Install filter and refill crankcase with normal oil.

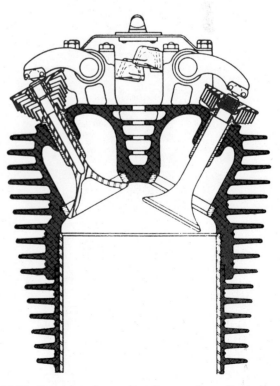

Fig. 11-28. Note that the cooling fins on the cylinder head are larger in diameter as well as heavier than those around the cylinder.

113

Fig. 11-29. In this V-type, air cooled Diesel (Deutz) the cooling fins are larger in diameter on the head and have a much greater mass of metal under the fins.

Rust Inhibitors

In order to reduce the formation of rust, commercial antifreeze contains an inhibitor designed to prevent such corrosion. Some products also contain antifoaming agents. The prevention of rust is of course essential if the cooling system is to be maintained at maximum efficiency. After the cooling system is drained at the end of cold weather, a rust inhibitor should be added to the clear water to prevent the formation of rust.

Air Cooled Engines

Air cooled engines for automobiles are not new as they were used successfully in the early days of the automobile, but have not been used widely in this country until recently.

Air cooling of a reciprocating piston engine as used in an automobile requires CONSTANT circulation of COPIOUS QUANTITIES of air. This air must be directed where wanted and the volume of air controlled. Forced air circulation is provided by a fan of generous capacity which is usually driven from the engine crankshaft by a belt or by fan blades forming the spokes of the flywheel, Fig. 11-27.

If difficulty is encountered in cranking the engine, or if there is no oil pressure when the engine starts, run some hot water from steam cleaner through the cooling system. The heat will soften the glycol on the cylinder walls and in the oil lines, making it easier to crank the engine and also help clear out the oil lines so the cleaning solution can flush the lines.

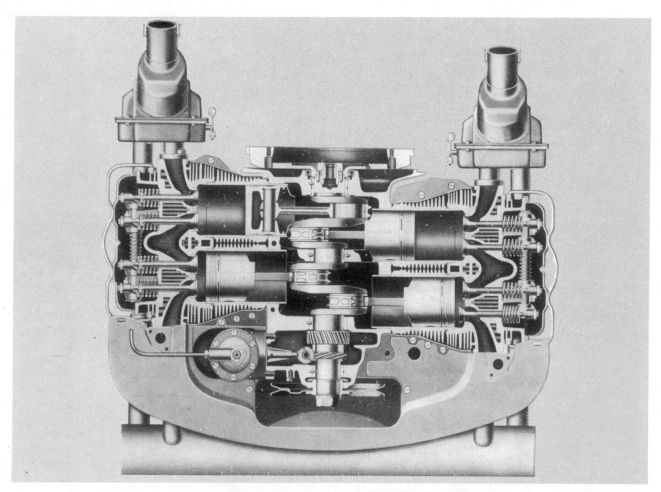

Fig. 11-30. Instead of solid masses of metal around the valves in this engine (Volkswagen), the metal is finned to increase the radiation surface. Note how closely the sheet metal baffle plates fit the contour of the cooling fins.

Fig. 11-31. *The entire Volkswagen cooling system is enclosed by a sheet metal housing. Thermostat at 17, fan at 18.*

This air must be directed over and through the radiation fins which are a part of, or attached to the cylinder head and walls. See Fig. 11-28. These fins have more radiation surface on the head where the heat is

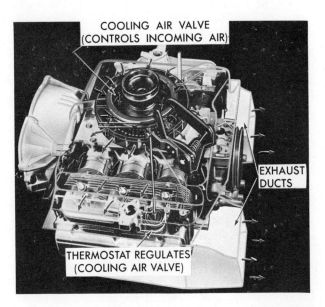

Fig. 11-33. *The thermostat is connected directly to the air valve or damper ring which controls the volume of cooling air entering the system. In this case (Corvair), the fan has a capacity of 1,800 cubic feet per minute at 4,000 rpm and about 60 percent of the cooling air flows over the cylinder heads. The other 40 percent is directed over the cylinders.*

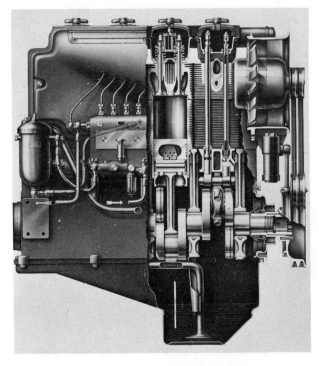

Fig. 11-32. *This air cooled, in-line Diesel (Deutz) has fan mounted in one end of the engine enclosure. Note fins between valves.*

more intense than on the lower cylinder walls which run cooler. See Figs. 11-29 and 11-30.

Air cooled engines are, therefore, usually surrounded by a metal housing and suitable baffle plates to direct the cooling air where desired. Examples of this are shown in Figs. 11-31 and 11-32. In order to

Fig. 11-34. Three cylinder, air cooled *Teledyne Wisconsin* engine. This two cycle engine develops 80 hp. Note cooling fins on cylinder head, cylinders and crankcase.

regulate the engine temperature by controlling the volume of cooling air, it is customary to install a thermostat inside the metal housing which encloses the engine. See Figs. 11-33 and 11-34.

The thermostat is connected directly to a damper, or air control ring. As the engine becomes hotter the control ring opens wider to admit more air, and closes when the engine is cold. See Figs. 11-33, 11-34, 11-35 and 11-36.

With the ring closed, air circulation is restricted, and a cold engine warms up more rapidly. Rapid warm-up is characteristic of air cooled engines, as they do not have to heat water in cylinder jackets and radiator. This rapid warm-up is helpful in avoiding sludge and crankcase dilution.

Air cooled engines normally operate at somewhat higher temperatures than water cooled engines, but do not overheat under almost any operating conditions if the cooling system is maintained in reasonably good order. If they should overheat, it might be due to improper operation. Air cooled engines should never be "lugged." If the engine is pulling hard at slow speed, more than usual heat is generated in the cylinders at the same time that less cooling air is supplied because of the slower fan speed. In this case there is no reservoir of water to absorb the excess heat, as on a water cooled engine. Therefore the engine speed should be maintained by shifting to a lower gear.

This higher engine operating temperature is claimed to mean higher engine efficiency, but is also accused of causing noise. One reason given for air cooled engines being noisier than water cooled engines is that there is no silencing provided by water jackets. Another reason given is the somewhat greater clear-

ance sometimes provided between some operating parts. This for the reason that higher temperatures require more room for expansion of the metals.

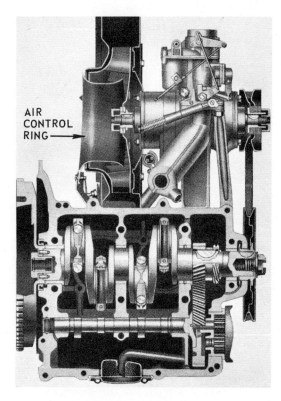

Fig. 11-35. The air control ring or valve on the Volkswagen is mounted within the fan and moves in and out as required to control the volume of cooling air supplied to the fan.

Regardless of the advantages and disadvantages of air cooling, it has proved to be entirely successful for automobiles, trucks, tractors, airplanes, boats and all kinds of small engines.

Fig. 11-36. Method of controlling Volkswagen air control ring by swinging it in or out on cross shaft.

Draining Cooling System

Draining the cooling system in the past has been mostly a matter of opening the pet cock at the bottom of the radiator and also the drain cocks in the engine water jacket.

That is still true of most models. However, on the 1972 Vega drain plugs have been eliminated from both the radiator lower tank and the engine block.

To drain the cooling system on this engine it is necessary to use a syphoning procedure. The procedure is as follows: First fill the system until the water level is even with the top of the filler neck. Insert a length of tubing into the filler neck until the inserted end touches the bottom of the tank. Attach the free end of the tubing to a syphoning device and start the syphoning process by squeezing and releasing the bulb. When the flow begins, pinch the tube and remove the syphoning device. The flow should continue when the pinch is released.

Quiz - Cooling Systems

1. How much of the heat energy in the fuel must be handled by the cooling system: one fourth _____, one third _____, one half _____?
2. What happens to the balance of the heat energy?
3. Several thousand gallons of water are circulated through the cooling system every hour of operation. True or False?
4. The water jackets dissipate most of the heat from the cylinders to the air. True or False?
5. What is rust?
6. Name two causes of engine hot spots.
7. Automobile engine water pumps are usually of the positive displacement type. True or False?
8. Why are water pump vanes often curved?
9. A water pump seal may leak: air _____, water _____, both _____.
10. Thermostats are installed: between the pump inlet and the radiator _____, between the pump outlet and the water jacket _____, between the water jacket outlet and the radiator _____.
11. Where does the water from the engine usually enter the radiator?
    a. Top.
    b. Bottom.
12. In addition to providing greater capacity what is the purpose of an auxiliary tank.
    a. Provides additional capacity.
    b. Acts as an expansion chamber.
    c. Connects engine to radiator.
13. Under pressure does water boil at a higher or lower temperature?
    a. Higher.
    b. Lower.
14. Why is a vacuum valve needed in a radiator pressure cap?
15. When water freezes, it expands approximately: 4 percent _____, 6 percent _____, 9 percent _____.
16. Which protects against freezing to the lowest temperature: ethylene glycol _____, methyl alcohol _____, ethyl alcohol _____?
17. An ethylene glycol solution will boil at a lower temperature than water. True or False?
18. In an air cooled engine, how much of the total volume of cooling air is usually directed to the cylinder heads: 40 percent _____, 60 percent _____, 80 percent _____.
19. How can an air cooled engine with the cooling system in good working order become overheated?
20. What can be done to avoid such overheating?
21. Name two possible reasons why an air cooled engine might make more noise than a comparable water cooled engine.
22. What is one distinct advantage of an air cooled engine?

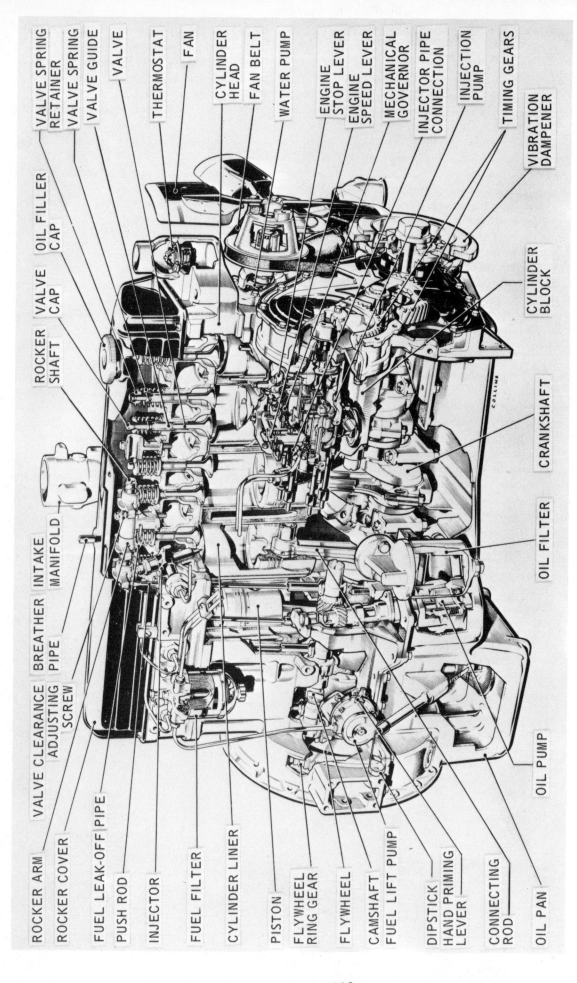

ROCKER ARM VALVE CLEARANCE BREATHER INTAKE
ROCKER COVER ADJUSTING PIPE MANIFOLD
SCREW

VALVE SPRING RETAINER
VALVE SPRING
VALVE GUIDE
VALVE
THERMOSTAT
FAN
CYLINDER HEAD
FAN BELT
WATER PUMP
ENGINE STOP LEVER
ENGINE SPEED LEVER
MECHANICAL GOVERNOR
INJECTOR PIPE CONNECTION
INJECTION PUMP
TIMING GEARS
VIBRATION DAMPENER

ROCKER VALVE OIL FILLER
SHAFT CAP CAP

CYLINDER BLOCK

FUEL LEAK-OFF PIPE
PUSH ROD
INJECTOR
FUEL FILTER
CYLINDER LINER
PISTON
FLYWHEEL RING GEAR
FLYWHEEL
CAMSHAFT
FUEL LIFT PUMP
DIPSTICK
HAND PRIMING LEVER
CONNECTING ROD
OIL PAN

OIL PUMP

OIL FILTER CRANKSHAFT

Fig. 12-1. Details of Ford diesel engine.

118

OTHER ENGINES

Diesel Engines

Diesel engines are similar to gasoline engines and are built in both two and four-cycle designs. They may be water cooled or air cooled. In general, they

Diesel" engine usually employs a somewhat lower compression ratio and may use spark plugs for ignition.

Previously we have considered the fact that compressing a gas—such as air—generates heat. In the

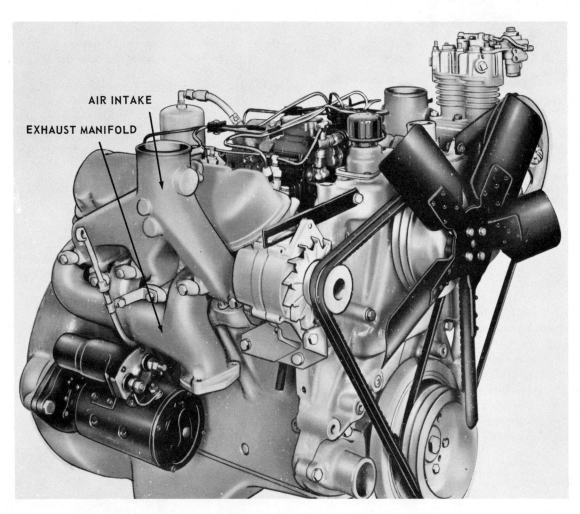

AIR INTAKE

EXHAUST MANIFOLD

Fig. 12-1a. Typical GMC Toro-flow V-Six Diesel engine.

are heavier in structure to withstand the higher pressures resulting from the high compression ratios used. In a full Diesel engine the compression ratio may be as high as 18 to 1. What is known as a "semi-

Diesel engine, air is compressed so much that it becomes hot enough (1,000–1,200 deg. F.) to ignite the fuel. The fuel in this case is a petroleum product which is lighter than crude oil, but heavier than gasoline. A gasoline-air mixture cannot be used in a Diesel because it would start to burn from the heat generated by the high compression long before the piston reached the top of the stroke.

The Diesel has no carburetor. The air is compressed in the cylinder and at the proper time the fuel is sprayed into the heated air under pressure. The fuel-air mixture then ignites and burns the same

Fig. 12-2. A two-cycle Diesel engine as built by General Motors.

as in a gasoline engine to produce power. Obviously, the entry of the fuel must be "timed" the same as a spark to the spark plug in a gasoline engine. The fuel pumping device is driven from the crankshaft and mounted on the side of the engine, Fig. 12-1. A typical GMC Toro-flow V-Six Diesel engine is shown in Fig. 12-1a. Details of Diesel fuel injection are given in a later chapter.

Fuel Vaporization

As Diesel fuel is more on the order of oil than gasoline, it does not vaporize as readily. This means that it must be broken up into fine particles and sprayed into the cylinder in the form of mist. This is accomplished by forcing the fuel through a nozzle or a series of very fine holes. Thus as it enters the cylinder, the fuel combines more thoroughly with the air in the cylinder to form a combustible mixture. This is dealt with more fully in the fuel system section of this text.

Two-Cycle Diesels

As two-cycle engines are not efficient as air pumps, it is necessary to force air into the cylinder and to force out the burned gas. One means of doing this is to use a supercharger or "blower." The GM two-cycle Diesel, Fig. 12-2, uses a positive displacement type supercharger as shown in Fig. 12-3. There are two exhaust valves, but no inlet valve in each

cylinder. The fuel injection nozzle complete with individual pump is located between the two exhaust valves and is operated by a camshaft, push rod and rocker arm.

Air enters the cylinder through holes in the cylinder liner as shown in Fig. 12-3. The blower forces fresh air into the cylinder through these holes during the time the holes are uncovered by the piston at the bottom of the stroke, and at the same time forces the exhaust out through the exhaust valves.

Diesel Operation

As the Diesel engine depends upon the heat of the compressed air to ignite the fuel, the compression pressure must be maintained. Leaking valves or piston rings cannot be tolerated, and must be kept in good condition.

Of equal importance is the proper fuel. While it is possible to build a Diesel engine to run on almost anything that will burn, the automotive type Diesel is designed to operate on a specific type and grade of fuel. Trouble will surely be experienced if an attempt is made to operate on other than the proper type.

Diesel Combustion Chambers

A major difference in the design of the various Diesel engines is the form or type of combustion chamber. There are four general types:
1. Open combustion chamber.
2. Precombustion chamber.
3. Turbulence chamber.
4. Energy cell.
Each design has certain advantages.

The open combustion chamber, Fig. 12-3a, is probably the most common and is also known as the direct injection type. In addition to the form illustrated and

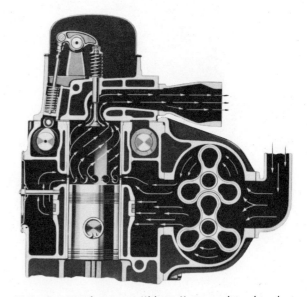

Fig. 12-3. A supercharger or "blower" is used in this design to force air into the cylinders.

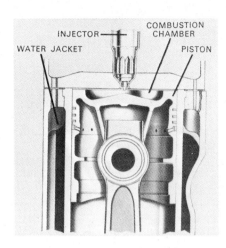

Fig. 12-3a. Open combustion chamber of the Mexican Hat type.
Also known as direct injection.

The fuel is directed to the upper portion of the spherical chamber. High turbulence is created by means of the directional intake port, plus the shape of the chamber, and the direction of the injected fuel.

Advantages claimed for the open combustion chamber include a high degree of efficiency, low manufacturing costs and high turbulence. A special advantage of the M-system is the ability to operate on a wide variety of fuels from gasoline to Diesel fuel.

Precombustion chamber: When a portion of the combustion chamber is contained in the cylinder head or cylinder wall and is connected to the space above the piston with a small passage, the design is known as a precombustion type, Fig. 12-3c.

which is known as the Mexican Hat type, there are many variations in the shape of the piston crown and cylinder head. Such variations range from the flat topped piston head through cylindrical forms made by a ridge around the edge of the piston. However, the basic characteristic of the open combustion chamber is that the fuel is sprayed directly into the combustion chamber. The form of the combustion chamber, together with the manner in which the air enters and the direction of the fuel spray are designed to give maximum turbulence and improved combustion. The turbulence is of maximum importance if complete combustion of fuel is to be obtained.

An important variation of the open combustion chamber is the M-system which has a special combustion chamber formed in the piston head, Fig. 12-3b.

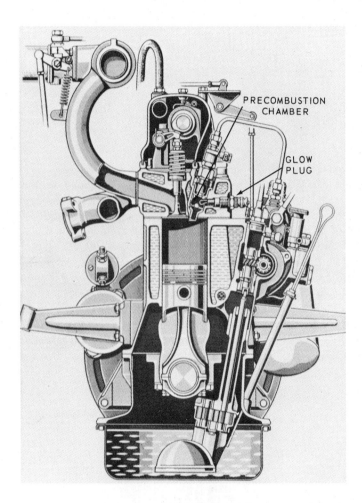

Fig. 12-3c. Precombustion chamber as used in some models of
Mercedes-Benz.

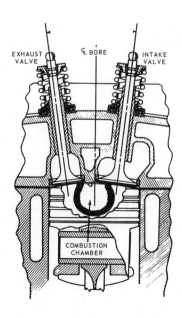

Fig. 12-3b. M-type combustion chamber is spherical and located
in piston head.

Thermal efficiency of the precombustion chamber engine is slightly lower than the open chamber type due to the greater heat loss from the larger combustion chamber area. The precombustion chamber contains approximately 30 percent of the total volume. However, cylinder pressure is lower and combustion smoother which is important particularly when the engine is used in an automotive vehicle. Another important advantage is that the precombustion chamber engine is not as sensitive to the type of fuel used and it is not necessary to provide such fine atomization.

Turbulence Chamber: In the turbulence chamber type of construction, up to 80 percent of the clearance volume is contained in the chamber, Fig. 13-3d. The

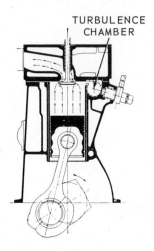

Fig. 12-3d. Turbulence type of combustion chamber. (Hercules Motors)

passage to the space over the piston is relatively large and a high degree of turbulence is developed to provide a good mixture of air and fuel. Like the pre-combustion chamber engine it is sensitive to the type of fuel provided. Cold weather starting without a glow plug is difficult.

Energy Cell: The energy cell (also known as the air cell) type of combustion chamber has the main combustion chamber located in the cylinder head and an anti-chamber placed on the opposite side of the combustion chamber from the injection nozzle, Fig. 12-3e. In general, this design is used primarily in high speed Diesel engines with a cylinder bore less than 5 in.

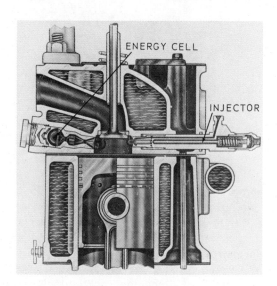

Fig. 12-3e. Energy cell type of combustion chamber.

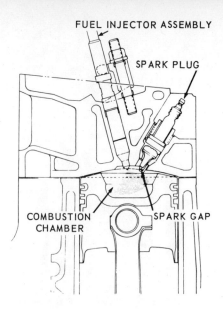

Fig. 12-3f. Ford experimental Proco Diesel engine with open combustion chamber and spark ignition.

High performance approaching that of the open chamber Diesel is claimed for the energy cell. High peak pressure and rough operation are controlled as the result of the controlled combustion.

Ford Engine: In an effort to develop an engine with a marked reduction in exhaust emission gases, Ford has been doing research on a Diesel with spark ignition, Fig. 12-3f. This engine combines Diesel fuel injection and a compression ratio of 11 to 1. The reduction in exhaust emissions has been achieved basically by using air throttling and exhaust gas recirculating. Nitric oxide formation is controlled within the engine as well as in the exhaust system. The nitric oxide formation is accomplished by controlling peak cycle temperatures, exposure time at high temperatures and availability of oxygen. Recirculation of exhaust gas also plays an important part in reducing nitric oxide.

Hydrogen oxide emission control is effected primarily by injecting fuel late in the compression stroke with an overall air fuel ratio of 15.5 to 1. The significance of the air fuel ratio is the fact that it provides sufficient oxygen for secondary oxidation without additional oxygen for the formation of nitric oxide formation.

Motor Truck Engines

Engines used in light duty trucks are very similar to automobile engines. There are some differences in design and operating conditions, but they are rather minor in nature. Actually, many light trucks use passenger car engines without any change whatever. Heavy duty trucks usually have special engines.

Any changes that are made in a passenger car engine to adapt it to truck use are intended to compensate for the difference in operating conditions. For example, the engine in a truck will be required to move a heavier load, so the axle gearing will be such

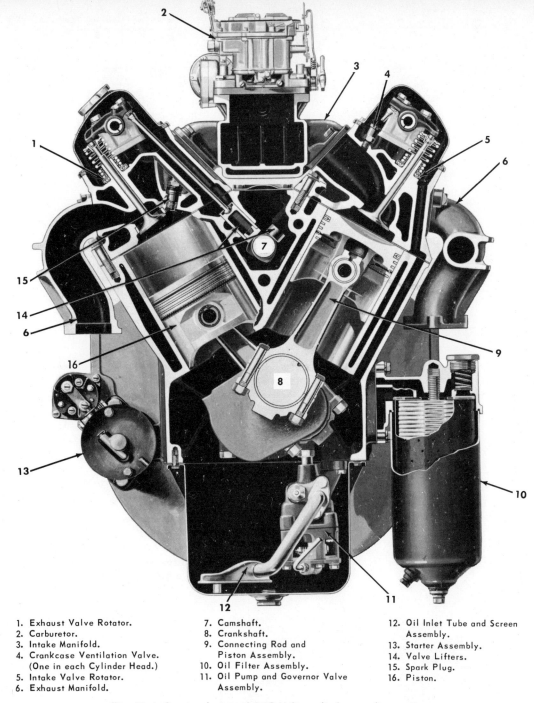

1. Exhaust Valve Rotator.	7. Camshaft.	12. Oil Inlet Tube and Screen
2. Carburetor.	8. Crankshaft.	Assembly.
3. Intake Manifold.	9. Connecting Rod and	13. Starter Assembly.
4. Crankcase Ventilation Valve.	Piston Assembly.	14. Valve Lifters.
(One in each Cylinder Head.)	10. Oil Filter Assembly.	15. Spark Plug.
5. Intake Valve Rotator.	11. Oil Pump and Governor Valve	16. Piston.
6. Exhaust Manifold.	Assembly.	

Fig. 12-4. Sectional view of GMC V-Six cylinder gasoline engine.

that the engine can run at higher speed for the same vehicle speed. The result may be that the truck at 60 mph will have a wide-open throttle. Therefore the truck engine will be operating more of the time at full power.

Under these conditions the exhaust valves will run hotter, and may need to be made of heat-resisting steel, and also require special valve seat inserts. The pistons and rings may need slightly greater clearance for heat expansion, etc. The cooling system may require a larger water pump, or a larger radiator or some increase in capacity. A different bearing material may be used on the crankshaft to withstand the higher bearing loads, and an oil pan of larger capacity might be used.

As accelerating ability in a truck is of less importance than in a passenger car, a heavier flywheel may be used in the truck engine. Such changes often serve to adapt the passenger car engine to use in a truck without making any major design changes.

Heavy-duty trucks usually have engines that are designed and built for truck use. They may be of either the two or four-cycle type, and may operate on gasoline or Diesel oil. Such engines are customarily much heavier in construction than passenger car engines. See Fig. 12-4. Crankshafts are larger in diameter and the bearings are longer. Crankcases are heavier and braced with webs at points of strain. In general, the piston displacement is increased and the engine speed decreased for a given amount of power.

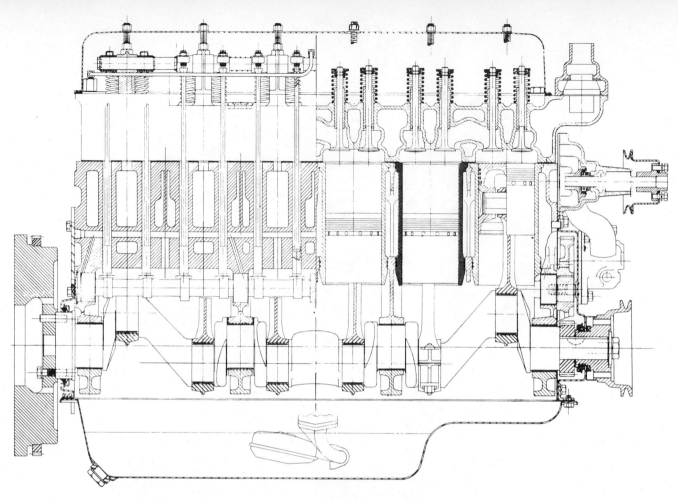

Fig. 12-5. *This typical tractor engine (Oliver) has individual cylinder sleeves and full length water jackets around each cylinder. Note that crankcase extends below crankshaft bearings.*

Fig. 12-6. *This two cylinder, horizontal engine (Deere) is an example of a special tractor engine which is different from the conventional type of automobile engine.*

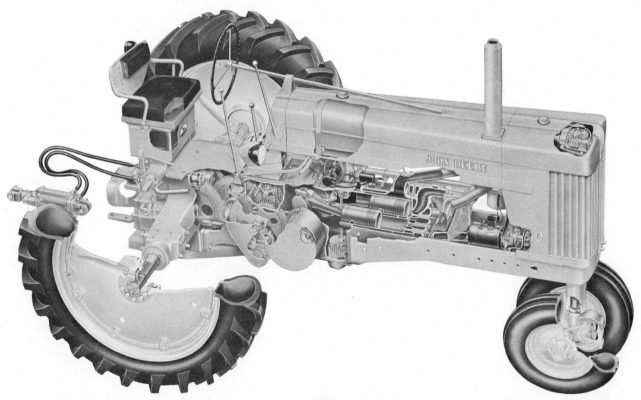

Tractor Engines

Engines used in farm tractors are usually designed for tractor use, but may be converted from a basic automobile engine design with design changes as needed to better suit tractor operating conditions. See Fig. 12-5. A passenger car engine is constantly changing speed and seldom operates for any length of time at a steady pace. A tractor engine may operate for hours at a time at a governed speed.

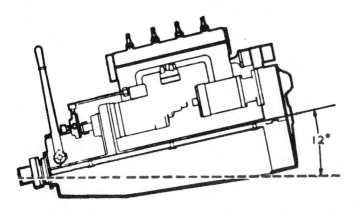

Fig. 12-7. In order to reduce the angularity of the propeller shaft, inboard marine engines are often mounted at a considerable angle in the boat.

Some of the larger wheel tractors and most of the larger industrial tractors, particularly of the crawler type, have engines of special design which are as heavy or heavier than truck engines. Huge industrial crawlers often have Diesel engines so large that it is impractical for an electrical motor of reasonable size to crank them. In such cases an auxiliary gasoline engine of smaller size is attached, which serves as a starting engine.

Marine Engines

Automobile engines can be adapted for use in boats but the operating conditions are more like a truck or tractor as boat engines usually run at more constant speed. Changes must be made in the cooling system to avoid overcooling of the engine. Unless closely regulated by suitable thermostats in the cooling system, the engine would be operated too cold. The fan and radiator are usually discarded.

It is also necessary in many cases, to use an oil pan of different shape because the engine is often installed with the rear end much lower than the front to reduce the angularity of the propeller shaft. See Fig. 12-7. It is desirable to equip the engine with a governor to prevent the engine from racing itself to destruction if the propeller shears a pin, or comes out of the water temporarily in rough water.

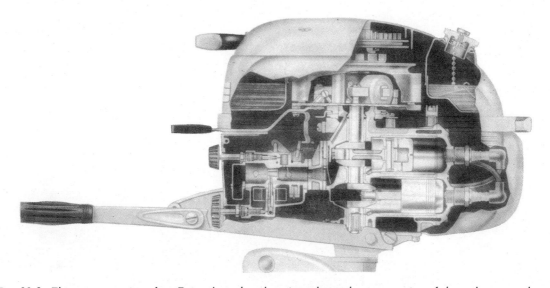

Fig. 12-8. This cross section of an Evinrude outboard engine, shows the construction of the carburetor and magneto as well as the engine.

The farm tractor engine is usually equipped with a governor which holds it at or near the peak of the torque curve. It can accelerate or decelerate freely up to the governed speed. Some farm tractors have special design engines of low speed and large displacement characteristics. See Fig. 12-6. However, most tractor engines follow automobile engines very closely in design and construction, and service procedures are substantially the same.

Special marine engines of the inboard type are built quite sturdily to withstand the rigors of constant speed operation. At the other extreme, outboard engines are built as light as possible as they must be portable. They are usually of the two-cycle type. Oil for lubricating the engine parts is mixed with the fuel. See Fig. 12-8.

The bearings in these two-cycle engines are often of the antifriction type, using steel balls or rollers

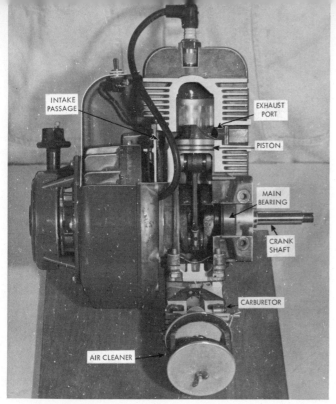

Fig. 12-9. Partial cut-away showing construction of two-cycle air cooled engine as made by West Bend Aluminum Co.

Fig. 12-10. Ford Indianapolis race engine. Note idler gears to drive camshaft gear. There are two camshafts for each bank of cylinders. Covers over camshaft have been removed.

in hardened races. These engines are available in single and multiple cylinder designs to develop almost any amount of power desired. They are available in air or water cooled types.

Small Engines

Air cooled engines are used almost exclusively for small machinery such as lawn mowers, chain saws, gardening equipment, etc. Single or multiple-cylinder engines of both two and four-cycle types are entirely satisfactory, and operate for long periods of time with little attention and few repairs. See Fig. 12-9.

Such small industrial engines are usually self-contained power units having built-in fuel and ignition arrangements similar to an outboard engine. The ig-

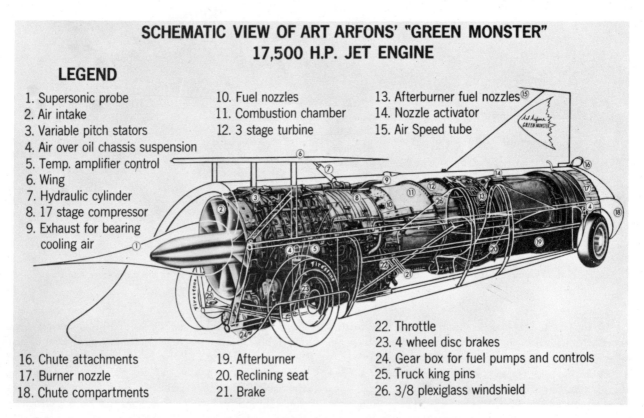

SCHEMATIC VIEW OF ART ARFONS' "GREEN MONSTER" 17,500 H.P. JET ENGINE

LEGEND

1. Supersonic probe
2. Air intake
3. Variable pitch stators
4. Air over oil chassis suspension
5. Temp. amplifier control
6. Wing
7. Hydraulic cylinder
8. 17 stage compressor
9. Exhaust for bearing cooling air

10. Fuel nozzles
11. Combustion chamber
12. 3 stage turbine

13. Afterburner fuel nozzles
14. Nozzle activator
15. Air Speed tube

16. Chute attachments
17. Burner nozzle
18. Chute compartments

19. Afterburner
20. Reclining seat
21. Brake

22. Throttle
23. 4 wheel disc brakes
24. Gear box for fuel pumps and controls
25. Truck king pins
26. 3/8 plexiglass windshield

Schematic view of turbine powered Green Monster, holder of land speed record of 434.02 mph, 536.71 mph, and 576.553 mph. Illustration shows major changes made since record runs. Changes include air-over-oil chassis suspension designed to eliminate a massive overloading problem at right rear wheel.

nition is often supplied by an in-built high tension magneto which is a part of, or attached to the engine flywheel. Thus rotation of the engine generates electricity for ignition. These magnetos are described in the electrical section of this text.

Racing Engines

The most successful racing engines are designed for the purpose, are made of special materials, and differ from passenger car engines. Passenger car engines can be adapted for racing purposes, but considerable alteration is usually required. When used in a racing car, the engine is designed or altered to get the utmost in power and rotational speed regardless of anything else.

As noise is a minor consideration, the average race car engine sounds like a bucket full of bolts. Actually, however, the clearances are very carefully measured on each working part. Some of this clatter comes from the valve mechanism which is designed to smack the valves open quickly, raise them high off the seat and close them quickly. Large valves with a high lift, will expedite the flow of the gases into and out of the cylinders.

The opening and closing time of the valves, as well as the duration of the valve opening, is designed solely for efficiency at high speed. As a result, racing engines seldom idle smoothly. Other reasons for rough idling are light weight flywheels for rapid acceleration, and the extremely high compression ratios, which approach Diesel practice.

In addition to the greater clearances between all moving parts, each rotating part in the engine is balanced to extremely close tolerance. This is done not only to increase the speed of the engine, but to reduce destructive vibration. Every part of the engine is made of the finest material available for the purpose to insure reliability and freedom from mechanical failure.

Airplane Engines

Liquid cooled engines have been used in airplanes, but the air cooled engine dominates the field. Cylinders are arranged in several ways: in-line, pancake, V and radial style. If radial, they may have more than one circle of cylinders around the crankcase. Turbines and jet engines are also used, particularly in military and commercial aircraft.

Aircraft engines of the reciprocating type are made with great precision, but the clearance of most working parts is greater than is usually provided for water cooled engines. This excessive clearance is necessary to provide for the great expansion which occurs in operation. Airplane engines operate at or near full power almost all of the time. The engine is wide open at take-off, and not too far from wide open at so-called cruising speed. Such operation for hours at a time is indeed severe.

Free Piston Engines

Free piston engines are closely related to both the Diesel and turbine types of power plants, as they use the Diesel cycle along with a turbine which is an essential part of the power plant. See Fig. 12-11.

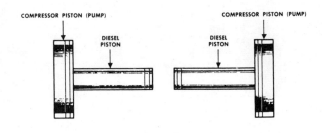

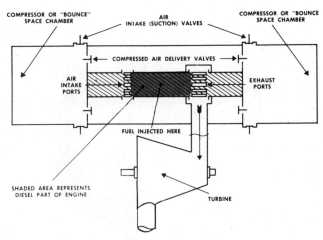

Fig. 12-11. Diagram of free piston type of cylinder and dual pistons with the combustion chamber area in color.

The engine consists of large and small cylinders, each containing a set of two (one large and one small) horizontally opposed pistons. Several of these pairs of cylinders may be assembled into one power plant and coupled to one turbine. An air-fuel mixture is fired between the opposed small pistons--with injectors as in a Diesel--which drives the pistons apart, compressing air in the closed chambers at ends of the large pistons.

Air thus compressed in the large cylinders then bounces the pistons back toward inner center compressing the mixture in the small cylinders for the next firing stroke. It will be apparent that the compression ratio and piston stroke will vary with the speed of the engine. As the pistons travel inward, the large pistons also compress air and pump it into the Diesel cylinder through the ports uncovered by the small pistons. The cycle of operation is shown in Fig. 12-12.

The expanding hot gas thus generated, goes to the turbine part of the engine to make the power usable. As there are no connecting rods or crankshaft, the pistons are kept in phase with the aid of connecting linkage.

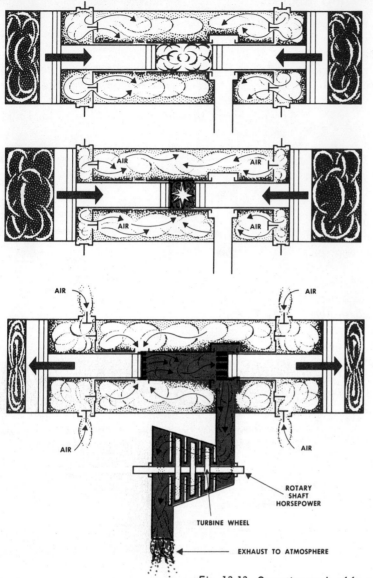

Pistons travel inward pumping air from the compressor cylinder into the air box, trapping air in Diesel combustion space. Intake and exhaust ports are closed-air delivery valves are open.

Pistons are completing inward travel. Fuel is injected into cylinder. This is combustion or the beginning of the power stroke. Intake and exhaust ports are still closed—air delivery valves are open.

End of power stroke compressing air in bounce space to return pistons for next cycle. Exhaust and intake ports are just opening to scavenge Diesel cylinder. Exhaust gases escape to turbine, spinning turbine wheels for usable power. Air is being drawn into compressor cylinder.

AIR

AIR

AIR

AIR

ROTARY SHAFT HORSEPOWER

TURBINE WHEEL

EXHAUST TO ATMOSPHERE

Fig. 12-12. Operating cycle of free piston engine.

Turbines and Jets

Gas turbines are used to propel automobiles, trucks, boats, airplanes and as stationary power plants. See Fig. 12-13. The fundamental principle of a turbine consists of an inclined plane mounted on a rotating shaft, and located in the path of fluid force.

An actual turbine operating with oil as a fluid is found in automatic transmissions of the torque converter type. Several of these are described and illustrated in the transmission section of this text.

A gas turbine is a heat engine which utilizes the expansion from the combustion of fuel and air in a combustion chamber, by transforming that energy directly into either thrust or shaft power. This thrust power can be utilized directly to push an airplane or vehicle, or it can be turned into shaft power to turn an airplane propeller, or an automobile wheel.

This thrust force may be understood by using a toy balloon for demonstration. A toy balloon is inflated with air, and then the balloon is released. As the air rushes out through the neck of the balloon, the balloon will shoot away in the direction opposite the air flow. It must be understood that the force for propulsion is applied against the inside of the balloon rather than being supplied by a jet of compressed air pushing against free air. This is the same principle of operation employed in a rocket or jet engine. See Fig. 12-14.

The same force can be exerted against a turbine wheel to produce rotary motion. Fig. 12-15 illustrates this feature. The first stage, or gasifier section produces the thrust. If shaft power is wanted, the section to the right (power section) is added as a second stage. In this particular turbine, the first turbine wheel drives only the compressor. Fuel is sprayed into the two burners receiving compressed air from the compressor. Only a portion of the air is burned in the burners, and the compressor requires only a portion of the energy in the hot gas. The remainder of the air and hot gas is utilized as a thrust force.

If shaft power is wanted instead of thrust, the air

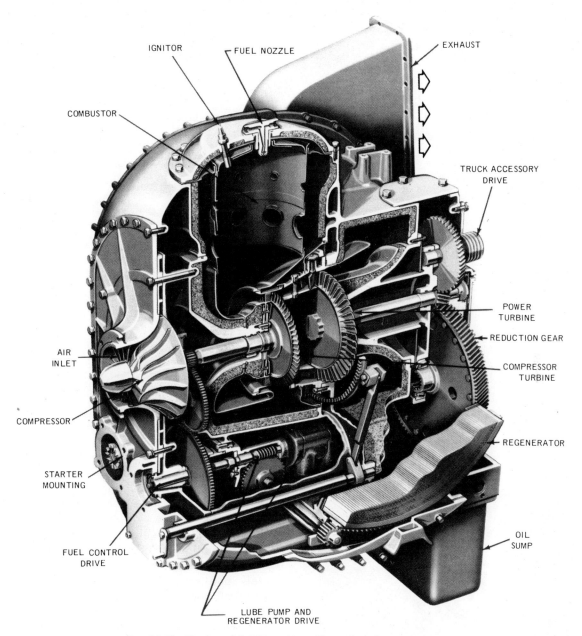

Fig. 12-13. Ford model 707 turbine. Note air inlet, compressor, fuel nozzle, ignitor and combustor.

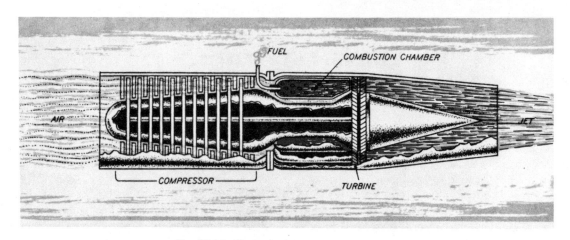

Fig. 12-14. Diagram of jet engine construction.

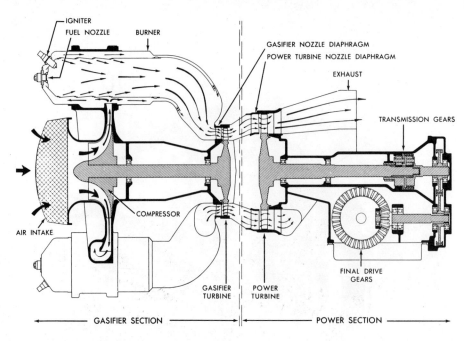

Fig. 12-15. GM turbine arrangement as used to propel a vehicle.

and hot gas are directed to the second turbine. Thus a gas turbine provides rotary power from the expansion of burning gas without the use of reciprocating pistons and connecting rods along with a crankshaft.

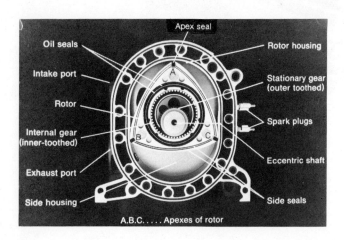

Fig. 12-16. Major parts of Wankel engine.   (Mazda)

Wankel Rotary Engine

The Wankel rotary engine does not have reciprocating parts as found in the piston engine. Instead it has a triangular shaped rotor with slightly curved sides that orbits eccentrically around a fixed gear in a housing shaped slightly like a figure eight, Fig. 12-16.

Currently, in the United States, the Japanese Mazda equipped with a Wankel type rotary engine is receiving considerable attention.

The rotary engine of the Wankel type is being used in virtually all fields including automotive, aircraft, farm equipment, marine, outboard engines, motorcycles and small electric generators. Air cushion vehicles have also been produced.

The Wankel type rotary engine, Fig. 12-17, is a compact power plant requiring less space than a piston type engine of the same horsepower. It is an exceptionally quiet engine with very little vibration. The reduced vibration results mostly from the fact there are only rotating parts and no reciprocating parts as is the case with a piston type engine. There are approximately 630 parts for a Wankel engine compared to about 1050 parts for a piston type engine. Ports are used instead of valves, eliminating the need for the complicated valve train of the piston engine.

A Wankel engine weighing 237 lbs. produced approximately the same power as a V-8 weighing over 600 lbs. The same comparison showed the Wankel occupied 5.1 cu. ft., while the V-8 required 23.2 cu. ft. Production costs are also said to be less for the rotary than for the piston engine. Fuel distribution to the rotor chambers is better than the distribution to the piston engine, consequently volumetric efficiency is higher.

Most of the Wankel type rotary engines in production have two rotors. Fig. 12-17 shows the engine which powers the Japanese Mazda. However, some rotary engines have three rotors. The Daimler-Benz CIII which develops 330 hp is an example. Four rotor (or chamber) engines have also been built. Wankel type engines can be built as small as 18.5 cu. in. per working chamber up to 1920 cu. in. per working chamber.

Fig. 12-18 shows the heat balance chart of a typical Wankel rotary engine. This compares favorably with the average piston type engine.

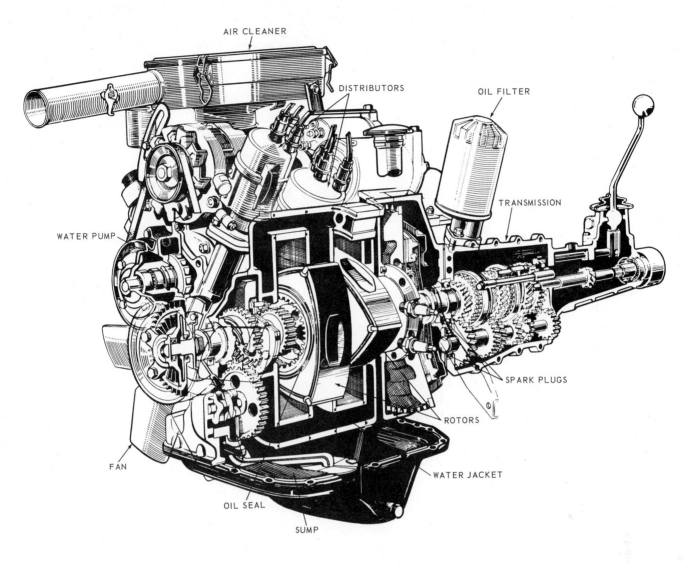

AIR CLEANER

DISTRIBUTORS

OIL FILTER

TRANSMISSION

WATER PUMP

SPARK PLUGS

ROTORS

FAN

OIL SEAL

SUMP

WATER JACKET

Fig. 12-17. Sectional view of Mazda rotary engine of the Wankel type.

Wankel Fundamentals

The Wankel rotor is triangular in shape with slightly curved sides and orbits eccentrically on a fixed gear in a housing shaped slightly like a figure eight, Fig. 12-16. In other words, the rotor rotates around its own axis while orbiting around the main-shaft. However, the output shaft makes three turns per rotor revolution and as a result one operation cycle takes place per output shaft revolution.

As the rotor swings around the fixed gear, the internal gear (also known as the rotor gear) trans-mits the rotary motion to the output shaft. The output shaft is an eccentric shaft and the rotation is such that the tips of the apexes of the rotor, Fig. 12-16, are always in contact with the side surface of the rotor housing. These tips are provided with seals shown at A, B, and C, Fig. 12-16.

All four cycles; intake, compression, power and ex-

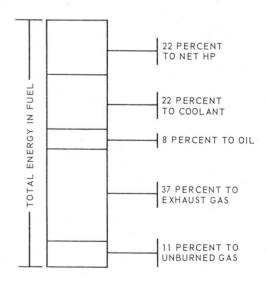

TOTAL ENERGY IN FUEL

22 PERCENT TO NET HP

22 PERCENT TO COOLANT

8 PERCENT TO OIL

37 PERCENT TO EXHAUST GAS

11 PERCENT TO UNBURNED GAS

Fig. 12-18. Showing where the power goes in a Wankel engine. Typical.

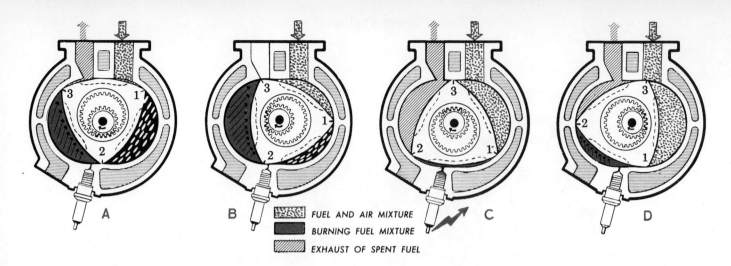

FUEL AND AIR MIXTURE
BURNING FUEL MIXTURE
EXHAUST OF SPENT FUEL

Fig. 12-19. Sequence of events in a Wankel type rotary engine.

haust, take place in one revolution of the rotor. As there are three lobes to the rotor, there is a continuous performance of these cycles on every lobe, Fig. 12-19. The crankshaft turns three times for every revolution of the rotor. With one power impulse for each of the rotor sides, there will be three power impulses per rotor revolution, or one power impulse per revolution of the eccentric shaft.

The sequence of the cycles is shown in Fig. 12-19. Position A, intake is starting between 1 and 3; compression is occuring between 1 and 2, and power is being produced between 2 and 3; exhaust is finishing between 3 and 1. When the rotor has moved to position B, intake continues between 1 and 3; compression continues between 1 and 2, power is finishing between 2 and 3. In position C, intake is finishing between 1 and 3; spark has ignited the compressed charge between 1 and 2; exhaust is occuring between 2 and 3. In position D, intake of the charge is completed between 1 and 3, power is produced between 1 and 2, and exhaust is continuing between 2 and 3.

From the foregoing it can be seen gas pressure on one face turns the rotor, which brings another face into position to produce power.

Displacement of Wankel Engine

There has been considerable discussion as to the method of calculating the displacement of the Wankel engine. The currently accepted method is use twice the combustion volume multiplied by the number of rotors.

Power Developed

Just as in the case of the conventional piston engine, the horsepower developed by the different makes of Wankel engine varies considerably. For example: The Audi-NSU model R080 is a 60.7 cu. in. rotary engine and develops 130 hp @ 5500 rpm. Compression ratio is 9 to 1. The Mazda R100 engine with a dis-

placement of 60 cu. in. develops 100 hp @ 7000 rpm with a compression ratio of 9.40 to 1.

In the rotary engine, the compression ratio is limited by the rotor radius and the eccentricity. When those two dimensions have been selected, the maximum compression ratio is determined. The compression ratio is then equal to the radius to eccentricity ratio or R/e, Fig. 12-20.

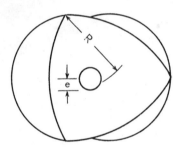

Fig. 12-20. Compression ratio of a Wankel engine equals R/e.

Performance

Reports indicate that fuel consumption of about 20 to 25 mpg is not unusual for the two rotor engine of approximately 60 cu. in. displacement.

Carburetors are used on most engines. However, Mercedes-Benz after preliminary work with carburetors changed to fuel injection.

Usually carburetors are of the 2-V type. Webber, Solex, and Hitachi-Stromberg are among the carburetors used on the various engines.

The location of intake and exhaust ports are factors in performance and fuel economy. NSU and Daimler-Benz are advocates of peripheral ports, while Togo Kogyo manufacturer of the Mazda prefers side location of ports claiming better low speed performance and better idling and light load scavenging. In general the peripheral ports, Fig. 12-21, provide high speed and power while the side ports, Fig. 12-17, provide performance over a wide range.

The fuel used in the Wankel rotary engine is the same as that used in conventional piston engine. Normal fuel ranges from 87 to 91 octane. Leaded fuel is not required. Tests made on the Mazda showed satisfactory operation with 67 octane fuel. Satisfactory operation has also been obtained on some Wankel type engines with diesel fuels.

Fuel flow from the carburetor to the Wankel engine is described as being constant, hence there is not the difficulty of uneven distribution that is encounted in piston engines where some cylinders receive a greater quantity of the air/fuel mixture than others.

Ignition

Ignition system used on the Wankel rotary engine is of the battery-coil-distributor type. In many cases two distributors are used and two spark plugs per chamber. A transistor system is used on the Mercedes-Benz CIII MK II together with a direct fuel injection system with a mechanical pump. Note the location of the spark plugs in Fig. 12-17.

Spark plugs differ greatly from those used in the piston type engine. Note the side electrodes shown in Fig. 12-22. Location of the spark plugs is sensitive in the rotary engine just as it is in piston engines.

Fig. 12-22. *Type of spark plug used in Wankel Rotary engine.*

Research has shown that by using two spark plugs in each chamber exhaust emissions are reduced, power is increased, combustion is more complete and duration of combustion is minimized.

Two distributors, Fig. 12-17, are usually provided with both centrifugal and vacuum advance. Researchers have found that a spark advance of approximately five degrees is usually required. This corresponds to an advance of approximately 28 degrees on a piston engine.

In piston type engines the spark plugs receive the benefit of the cooling effects of the incoming fuel charge. In the case of the Wankel this is not true, consequently spark plug temperatures are materially higher. The spark plugs used in the Wankel engine are therefore an extremely cold type.

Timing the ignition on these rotary engines is in relation to the angle of the shaft. Top center is the same as the top center on a piston engine, but the angle of the shaft is greater than the corresponding angle of the piston engine crankshaft.

Emissions

Currently the Mazda and the NSU rotary engines have met the Federal requirements of exhaust emissions. Intense combustion chamber turbulence claimed for the Wankel type engine contributes largely to improved exhaust emissions. In additon, the Wankel engine can give satisfactory operation on relatively

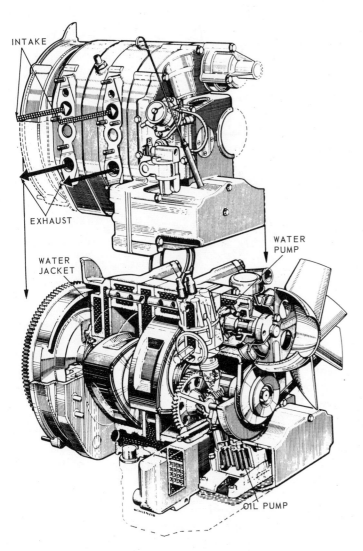

Fig. 12-21. *NSU Wankel engine showing peripheral intake and exhaust ports.*

INTAKE

EXHAUST

WATER JACKET

WATER PUMP

OIL PUMP

lean mixtures which also contributes to improved exhaust emissions.

In general, the hydrocarbon emission level of the Wankel rotary engine is higher than a piston type engine of the same general size. However, the carbon monoxide and nitrous oxide levels are lower than that of a reciprocating piston engine. As in the case of the piston engine, the exact emission quantity and composition of the Wankel exhaust depends on throttle opening and engine speed. With a rich or lean mixture there is the possibility of incomplete combustion. The problem is worse under light load conditions. However, the Wankel engine operates well under a lean mixture and therefore has an advantage over the piston engine in that respect.

Thermal reactors have been shown to produce a material reduction in the hydrocarbon emmission from the Wankel engine. Tests have shown reductions up to 90% in hydrocarbon emissions when a thermal reactor has been used on a Wankel engine, Fig. 12-23.

Cooling

While air cooled Wankel type rotary engines have been produced, the water cooled type is used most extensively. While called water cooled, the water is used primarily for cooling the housing and oil is used to cool the rotor. Typical water cooled engines are shown in Figs. 12-17 and 12-21.

Cooling of the Wankel engine is required primarily in the area where combustion and expansion take place, that is, the area around the spark plugs. The concentration of heat in such a small area tends to cause distortion which in turn makes sealing of oil and fuel mixture difficult. Unless adequate cooling is provided, thermal fatigue or shock cracks may form in the spark plug hole area.

To aid in the dissipation of heat and reduce tendency toward distortion, special alloys have been developed for the rotor housing. In the Curtiss-Wright engine, the coolant passages are designed so the coolant passes back and forth through the housing from one end cover to the other. In the area around the spark plug passages, the velocity of the coolant is increased to provide additional cooling needed in that area.

The cooling of the rotor presents a special problem. It is completely enclosed within the housing and does not have the benefit of the cooling provided by the crankcase in a reciprocating engine. In addition, the rotor turns at one third of the mainshaft speed.

While aluminum is lighter than cast iron and also has excellent heat conductivity, most manufacturers prefer cast iron for rotors. For actual cooling, lubricating oil is used. Basically the oil is circulated from the sump, Figs. 12-17 and 12-24, then through the rotor. After cooling the rotor it passes through a filter and heat exchanger, through the hub of the rotor and returns to the sump. The inside is care-

fully designed as it affects not only the cooling of the rotor but also engine balance. Excessive rotor temperatures will result in carbon formation on the interior of the rotor which will cause an unbalanced condition as well as further increasing engine temperature.

The oil seals on the rotor bearings permit a measured amount of oil leakage to provide lubrication for the sides of the rotor.

Cooling of the engine housing is by water which passes through passages in the housing. Water pumps are of the vane type, similar to those used on the piston type engine.

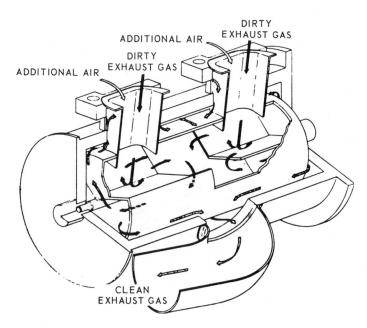

Fig. 12-23. One type of exhaust gas reactor. (Curtiss-Wright.)

Seals

To provide adequate seals for the various areas in the Wankel engine proved to be one of the most difficult problems in the early stages of its development. Seals, Fig. 12-16, must be provided to prevent leakage from the working chambers. Such seals include the apex seal and the side seals. The problem of designing effective seals for the apex of the rotor is complicated by the different forces which act on the seal. These forces include positive and negative centrifugal force, gas pressure both positive and negative and friction against the working surfaces. In addition, the position of the apex seal varies. When at the major and minor axis it is perpendicular to the working surface. At other positions of the rotor the seal is at an angle other than 90 deg. to the surface.

The apex seals are straight and are inserted in radius slots at each rotor apex. Side seals are curved to conform to the curvature of the rotor and are placed in grooves in the rotor sides. These seals are provided with interlocking ends to reduce leakage.

Various materials have been used for seals. For example Mazda originally used carbon for their apex seals because of its lubricating qualities. Later a sintered material impregnated with aluminum was adapted. Ceramic seals have also been used in some instances.

Lubrication

As the lubricating oil in the Wankel type rotary engine is not subject to blow-by and consequent contamination, periodic oil changes have been eliminated at least in the NSU engine. However, additional oil is needed occasionally to replace that metered for lubricating the rotor seals and housing. With fast driving a quart of oil every 1000 miles has been experienced.

Bearings of the output shaft are lubricated with oil from the sump in the normal manner, the oil being supplied under pressure from a gear type pump, Fig. 12-21. The oil supplied to the rotor

seals is needed to keep them from sticking. Originally oil was mixed with the fuel, much in the same manner as oil and fuel are mixed with the two cycle outboard engines. Subsequently an automatic metering of the lubricating oil from the rotor side was used. A third method consisted of introducing oil into the intake ports in accordance with engine operating conditions.

Servicing the Wankel

While the Wankel type rotary engine is new to the service field, servicing should not present any major problem. First of all, there are no valves to stick or burn. While there are no piston rings as is the case with the familiar piston engine there are seals on the rotor which should present no problem when replacement is necessary. It can be expected that the life of the seals should approximate that of piston rings.

The carburetor and ignition systems are readily accessible which greatly simplifies tune-up work. The Webber and Solex carburetors are similar to those used on other imports. Ignition units also follow conventional design.

Quiz - Other Engines

1. Carburetors are not used on Diesel engines. True or False?
2. Diesel fuel pumps are usually driven by double or triple V belts. True or False?
3. Name two purposes of a supercharger on a two-cycle Diesel engine.
4. Name five alterations that are often made to passenger car engines to adapt them for use in light trucks.
5. All farm tractor engines are quite similar to automobile engines. True or False?
6. Inboard marine engines are made as light as possible. True or False?
7. Outboard engines are cooled by: Air_____, Water _____, Either_____.
8. Small industrial engines are usually air cooled. True or False?
9. Give three reasons for poor idling of racing engines.
10. Free piston engines are related to: Diesel engines _____, Gasoline engines _____, Neither_____.
11. Do free piston engines have a variable compression ratio? Yes_____, No_____; a variable stroke? Yes_____, No_____.
12. Will a free piston engine produce useful power without the aid of a turbine? Yes or No?
13. Can a turbine engine without gearing be used to

propel a vehicle? Yes or No?
14. Describe the operating principle of a jet engine.
15. Name four problems to be overcome in the design of a successful rotary engine.
16. How many general types of combustion chambers are used in diesel engines?
   Four
   Five
   Two
   Six
17. In the M-system the combustion chamber is formed in what part of the engine?
   Cylinder head
   Piston
   Cylinder bore
18. Special fuel is required for the Wankel engine used in the Mazda car.
   True or False?
19. The Wankel type engine requires more space than a piston type engine of the same power.
   True or False?
20. The Wankel type engine is limited to two rotors.
   True or False?
21. What is the shape of the rotor used in the Wankel engine?
   Round   Square
   Triangular   Elliptical

22. There are _____ power impulses in a Wankel engine for each revolution of the rotor.

23. Fuel injection can not be used in a Wankel rotary engine. True or False?

24. In general the hydrocarbon emission level of the Wankel engine is higher than a piston type engine of the same general size.
True or False?

ENGINE RECONDITIONING

The starting point for engine reconditioning is the cylinder block because practically all other parts are fitted to it. If the block is damaged in any way, it must be repairable or else it must be replaced. There are many things to be inspected and checked.

The first step is dismantling and THOROUGH cleaning. If it is not cleaned down to the bare metal, inspection and accurate measurement will not be possible as measurements must be made in thousandths and fractions of thousandths of an inch. Obviously, the inspector must know how to use precision measuring tools and use them with care.

The engine block or head may be cracked, warped, worn or otherwise damaged. The damage may affect the operation of the crankshaft, pistons, rings, bearings, camshaft, cooling, lubrication, etc. The extent of the damage will determine whether or not the block is repairable. There are many methods of changing the condition or dimensions of metal parts. Several different methods may be used to restore an engine to good condition.

Metal Parts Restoration

If we wish to reduce the size of a part, we can cut or grind or etch the metal away or in some cases we can shrink it with freezing, or pressure.

If we wish to increase the size of a part, we can add metal by soldering, brazing, welding, plating or spraying. In some cases we can expand it by heat and pressure.

Thus in many cases we can compensate for wear by expanding or shrinking the metal. Or we can add metal to the worn surface to restore it to usefulness. In adding metal we have a wide choice of materials each of which possesses certain characteristics which may be desired for the particular purpose.

If we want a soft surface, we can use tin or bronze. If we want a hard surface we can add steel of any desired degree of hardness by welding. Another method of adding a hard surface is by the electroplating process. An example of this is a chrome surface on a piston ring.

In engine repair work, we often add material to, or increase the size of, one part without disturbing the mating part. An example of this is to spray molten metal on a worn crankshaft journal to avoid installation of undersize bearings. Or, we may expand a piston with heat or pressure or both, and reinstall it in the mating cylinder.

In other cases we remove metal from one part, and install an oversize or undersize mating part, in order to obtain the proper clearance. Examples of this are rebored cylinders and oversize pistons or a reground crankshaft and an undersize bearing.

In still other cases we may remove metal for the sole purpose of obtaining a better surface fit of two mating parts. An example of this is the correction of a warped cylinder head, by surface grinding to restore a flat and true surface.

For practically all of these operations special tools and equipment are available. These tools will do a satisfactory job if they are properly handled. Obviously, it will be essential to measure accurately, adjust carefully and operate in accordance with the manufacturers' instructions.

Cracked Cylinder Blocks

After the cylinder block and head are completely cleaned, a visual inspection is made for cracks or serious damage. Included in this inspection is the condition of the core hole or water freeze plugs. See Fig. 13-1. If signs of leakage or corrosion are found, the plugs should be replaced. Threads on studs and in

Fig. 13-1. Leaking plugs are punched or cut out, and new expanding plugs installed.

stud holes are checked, and new studs installed if needed. If a stud hole in the casting has worn or damaged threads, they can be repaired by means of special inserts as shown in Fig. 13-2. This thread check is particularly important in the case of aluminum blocks, or heads, as careless tightening often overstresses the metal and the threads are deformed or stripped.

Fig. 13-2. Special Helicoil thread insert restores damaged threads in holes.

If the block was cracked by water freezing in the water jacket, the crack can usually be closed satisfactorily by a process known as copper-welding or by brazing. It can also be welded shut with iron. See Fig. 13-3. In the case of welding with iron, it is difficult to prevent warping of the block unless the block is preheated and the welding expertly done.

Fig. 13-3. Typical repair to bursted water jacket.

In cases where a panel or section of the water jacket is broken out, it is sometimes possible to shape a metal plate into a patch corresponding to and slightly larger than the opening. The patch is then attached to the block by means of multiple screws around the edge of the patch. Holes are drilled and tapped in the block for the screws.

In the case of small cracks--depending upon the location--iron cement can be used for a quick repair. If the crack is in a thin, large section which is readily accessible, it may be possible to tin the cast iron and solder the crack. It is very difficult to solder aluminum.

Fig. 13-4. A cracked valve seat may extend into the cylinder bore or water jacket of block or head.

The choice of the repair method will depend upon the size of the damaged area, the location of the crack, the cost of a new block as well as the value of the automobile.

Internal Cracks

At times, the cylinder wall will crack through to the valve port as shown in Fig. 13-4. Or the crack may be in the cylinder head of overhead valve engines. Such cylinder heads are often replaced rather than repaired. If the crack is between the cylinder wall and the valve seat, the repair will need to be made with extra care. One method is welding. If the crack is small it may be possible to peen it shut with a power peening hammer. See Fig. 13-5.

Still another method consists of drilling holes at the ends of the crack, threading the holes and inserting threaded plugs or screws. Another hole is then drilled partly in the block and partly in the plug or screw. A second plug or screw is then inserted and this process continued to the other end of the crack.

After the screws are all installed and the crack thus sealed, the surface is then machined smooth and the cylinder bore and valve seat are resurfaced. If the valve seat is badly damaged, the block can be counterbored and a new valve seat inserted. Some-

Fig. 13-5. Cylinder blocks may crack between the valve port and the cylinder wall. If not too serious, these cracks may be closed with a peening hammer as shown here. In more serious cases, welding or plugging may need to be employed.

times these seats are screwed into place and in other cases, they are pressed in place and the edge of the metal block peened over slightly to hold them in place.

In either case, they must fit tightly so that metal-to-metal contact will be intimate enough to offer a full and free flow of heat from the insert to the block and cooling water. The same is true in the case of serious cylinder damage where the repair consists of reboring the cylinder and inserting a sleeve. The contact between sleeve and cylinder must be full and complete.

In repairs of this nature, it must be kept in mind that the heat and pressure in the cylinder will cause expansion, contraction and possibly warpage of the cylinder wall, valve seat and cylinder block surface as soon as the engine is operated. Therefore the work must be done as carefully and accurately as possible, and no great amount of excess metal added at any point to aggravate distortion.

Locating Cracks

The cracks that form in cylinder heads and blocks are often so fine that they are difficult to see with the naked eye. Consequently many shops use a strong magnifying glass to aid in locating such cracks. A better procedure is to make use of one of the special methods that have been developed for that purpose.

One method is to use special dyes or chemicals which when painted on the surface of the metal will quickly make the cracks visible. There are also several magnetic or electrical methods which will quickly reveal the locations of cracks. One such method is shown in Fig. 13-5a.

Fig. 13-5a. Checking for cracks in a cylinder head with special equipment.

Corrosion

In the case of aluminum engine blocks or heads, the visual inspection should be particularly thorough to detect any possible corrosion of the metal. Sometimes corrosion of the metal around the water cir-

① ③ CHECK DIAGONALLY
② CHECK ACROSS CENTER

Fig. 13-6. The cylinder block head surface may be checked for distortion in the same manner.

culation openings will occur from chemicals in the cooling water--particularly in localities where the water supply contains more than the usual amount of chloride. Corrosion from electrolytic action may also occur, because of the dissimilar metals found in the engine cooling system. If corrosion is serious enough, it may interfere with the seal of the gasket between head and block, and permit coolant to enter the combustion chamber, or compression pressure to escape to the water jacket.

Cylinder Head Warpage

Cylinder heads often become warped and sometimes the cylinder block mating surface also. These surfaces should be true within .003 in. in any 6 in. or .006 in. overall. Measurement is made by means of a steel straightedge and thickness gauge strips as shown in Fig. 13-6. If the surfaces are warped or otherwise damaged, they can be reconditioned on special equipment as shown in Fig. 13-7.

Cylinder Reconditioning

Cylinder wall wear and the reasons for it were described previously in this text. They wear in tapered form, and also out-of-round and after such wear ex-

Fig. 13-7. One type of equipment used to resurface cylinder heads and blocks.

Fig. 13-8. *Cylinder bore reconditioning equipment mounted on V-8 block.*

Before any cylinder is refinished, all main bearing caps must be in place and tightened to the specified torque. Otherwise the crankshaft bearing bores may become distorted from the refinishing operation.

Special precautions must be taken to insure that the cylinders be refinished parallel to each other and at right angles to the crankshaft. Special precautions must therefore be taken when setting up the reconditioning equipment, particularly when the top of the cylinder block is not at right angles to the cylinder bore as shown in Fig. 13-9.

When the cylinder block is formed in that manner, special adapters must be used with the cylinder boring bar so that the cylinder will be reconditioned parallel to its original center line.

When dry honing, a vacuum cleaning device is provided. However, regardless of the method used in reconditioning the cylinders, it is essential that the block be thoroughly cleaned to remove all cutting and abrasives. Some machinists advise scrubbing with soap and water. Some advise first wiping down the walls with fine crocus cloth. The job of cleaning a cylinder block after reconditioning is not easy and many jobs which

Fig. 13-8a. *Hone type cylinder reconditioning equipment as used in engine rebuilding shop.*

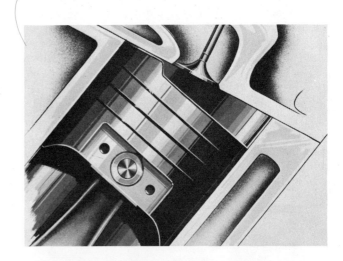

Fig. 13-9. *Here a flat head is used with an angle block and the combustion chamber is mostly in the piston head.*

ceeds specifications, the cylinders require machining to restore the wall surface.

Usual wear limitations are .005 in. out-of-round and .010 in. taper.

Either boring bars, Fig. 13-8, or hones, Fig. 13-8a, may be used to recondition the cylinder walls. In many shops the preferred method is to first use a boring bar, Fig. 13-8, and then finish with a hone, Fig. 13-12. Another method is to first use a hone with coarse stones and then finish with stones of about No. 180-220 grit, making sure the stones are clean and sharp.

It should be pointed out that many manufacturers of piston rings claim their rings give satisfactory service in cylinders up to .005 in. out-of-round and .010 in. taper.

Fig. 13-10. *One type of engine cleaning equipment.*

were mechanically correct have been ruined because some abrasives and dirt remained in the cylinders. All the oil holes in the block must also be cleaned. In addition the core plugs should be removed so the water jacket can be cleaned. The final cleaning is usually done on specialized cleaning equipment, Fig. 13-10.

In connection with reconditioning cylinders, it is best to find out what sizes are available in oversize pistons before starting the operation. Otherwise the cylinders may be bored to a size for which stock pistons are not available. This would then involve having the pistons reground to the desired size.

Cylinder Wall Repairs

Occasionally a cylinder wall will be so damaged that so much metal would be removed in the reconditioning process that the cylinder walls would be severely weakened. Because of variations in engine construction it is impossible to give any figure on the amount of metal that could be removed without weakening the cylinder wall. However, the mechanic can be governed by the size of the replacement pistons that are available.

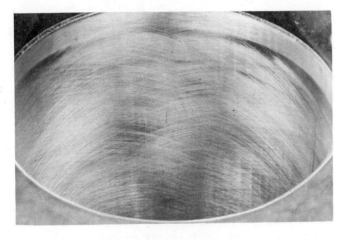

Fig. 13-11. Note pattern of cutting marks left by refinishing hone.

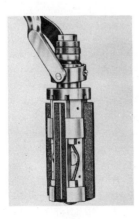

Fig. 13-12. Typical cylinder hone.

If damage is so deep that reboring to the largest oversize piston is not sufficient to remove the score marks, it is still possible to recondition the cylinder by installation of a cylinder sleeve.

The procedure is to rebore the cylinder until the score marks are removed. A sleeve is then prepared with an outside diameter .0001 in. larger than the diameter of the rebored cylinder and an inside diameter slightly smaller than the required for the available piston. The sleeve is then shrunk in dry ice to reduce its diameter and then pressed into the cylinder with an hydraulic press. The cylinder is then finish honed. This honing is required to remove any wrinkles that may have formed when the sleeve was pressed in position.

Another method of reconditioning a cylinder which has been badly scored and which is used occasionally on industrial engines or when it is impossible to obtain a replacement cylinder block, is to cut a deep groove in the cylinder wall so as to remove the score. This can be done on a milling machine. A strip of metal (the same as the cylinder) is then machined to fit the prepared groove and after being packed in dry ice, it is pressed in place in the groove.

Cylinder Wall Surface

After reconditioning, check cylinder walls with a dial type cylinder gauge to make sure of roundness and straightness. It is desirable to hone cylinder sleeves after installation to remove any wrinkles that may have been formed during installation process.

When new rings are installed in cylinders which have not been reconditioned, the hone should be run through the cylinder a few times to break the glaze formed on the cylinder wall through normal operation.

The desired cylinder wall finish is not a mirror surface as this type surface does not produce the best lubricating conditions for the piston rings. The proper finish should have a pattern of diagonal crosshatch scratches, but no longitudinal scratches, Fig. 13-11. Such a pattern is obtained with a few strokes of the hone, the hone being pulled up and down in the bore while the hone is rotating. If a hone is not available, the pattern can be made by using abrasive cloth or paper of the proper grit.

Fine scratches in surface of cylinder wall permit more rapid seating of rings which is highly desirable and also the fine scratches retain a film of oil to provide lubrication for ring surface and prevent scoring.

Wet Type Cylinder Sleeves

Passenger car engines built in the U.S.A. usually have the cylinders bored directly in the engine block; while some truck, tractor, and industrial engines use the wet type of cylinder sleeve. A wet sleeve is in the form of a barrel or sleeve which is inserted in the block in contact with the cooling water. Several

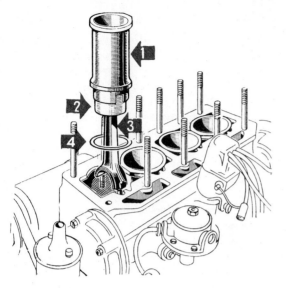

Fig. 13-13. Wet type sleeve as used by Renault. 1-Sleeve; 2-Piston; 3-Connecting rod; 4-Copper sealing ring.

European passenger car engines have liners or inserted sleeves. An example of this is the 4CV Renault built in France. See Fig. 13-13.

In the wet-sleeve type of construction, each cylinder barrel is a separate sleeve inserted in the block, and sealed at the bottom of the water compartment by means of a copper or rubber gasket. See Fig. 13-14. The cylinder head gasket, of course, provides a seal at the top end of the sleeve. In this construction, the engine coolant circulates directly around and in contact with the sleeve. As the thickness of the sleeve or cylinder wall is uniform, it is felt that cylinder wall distortion is thus minimized.

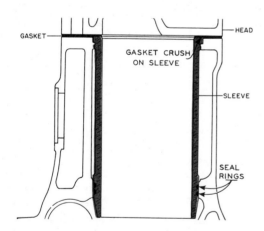

Fig. 13-14. Rubber seals are used at the bottom of the sleeves in this Oliver tractor engine.

Another advantage of cylinder sleeves is of course the ease and comparative low cost of replacing a damaged cylinder bore. These sleeves are easily pulled out, Fig. 13-15, and a new sleeve slipped in place.

The foregoing advantages apply to most air cooled automobile engines, as the cylinders are usually in the form of sleeves or barrels. The Corvair and the Volkswagen are both good examples of this type of construction. Each cylinder is simply a tube with cooling fins on the outside. One end of this tube fits into a recess in the crankcase, and the other end fits into a recess in the cylinder head.

Piston Clearance

There is no set rule on the amount of clearance to be provided between the piston and cylinder. Much depends upon the design of the engine cylinders and the cooling system, the piston design and material, and to a certain extent the service conditions under which the engine operates.

For example, if it is a passenger car engine that will be driven mostly at slow speeds in city traffic, the pistons can be fitted with a minimum of clearance. If the engine is in a fire department pumper, it may

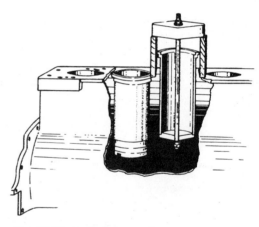

Fig. 13-15. Method of removing wet type sleeves.

be required to stand in one spot and run at full power for hours at a time. Such service would generate a great amount of heat in the cylinders, cause the pistons to expand considerably and thus require the maximum clearance.

In general, it is customary to fit solid skirt cast iron pistons to about .00075 to .001 in. per inch of piston diameter. A four inch piston would thus be .003 to .004 in. smaller than the cylinder. Some aluminum pistons can be fitted more closely but much depends upon the design of the piston. The instructions of the manufacturer should be obtained and followed.

Surface treatment will also have a bearing on the piston clearance. Some pistons are tin plated, others have an oxide coating or some other surface treatment. Sometimes the surface is serrated or interrupted to provide minute pockets for the retention of oil. These treatments are intended to lessen the tendency of the piston to stick or score, most particularly during the time it is seating to the wall.

Clearance Measurement

The clearance between cylinder and piston is measured in most cases by means of a feeler gauge inserted between piston and cylinder. See Fig. 13-16. The strip of feeler gauge should be about 1/2 in. wide and long enough to extend the full length of the cylinder. This strip of a thickness equal to the desired clearance should be placed on the thrust side of the skirt. Four to five pounds pull as measured on a spring scale should be required to remove the feeler.

The clearance can also be measured by subtracting the maximum diameter of the piston from the minimum diameter of the cylinder as measured by inside and outside micrometers. In this case, measurement must be made at several points in the cylinder and on the piston. All piston clearance recommendations are made for use with the temperature approximately 70 deg. F.

As pistons wear, or if they become overheated, the skirt is liable to collapse or become smaller in diameter. When this happens the piston will "slap" in the cylinder, and will also allow an excessive amount of oil to pass up to the rings. This of course places an undue load on the oil control rings, and may result in oil pumping.

Cylinder Wear

The greatest amount of wear in a cylinder occurs at the top of the travel of the piston rings. The difference between the diameter at that point and the diameter of the cylinder at the lower end is known as the taper. Cylinders also wear most on the area where the greatest thrust of the piston occurs. The difference between that diameter and the fore-and-aft diameter is known as the out-of-round.

In passenger car engines the maximum taper, or wear limit is usually specified as 0.010 in. and the out-of-round as 0.005 in.

Both of these measurements can be made with the aid of inside and outside micrometers. Or if preferred a dial gauge can be used. Using a dial gauge requires less skill than using a micrometer.

Piston Resizing

There are several ways to expand or resize the pistons. One method consists of heating the piston, and expanding it with special equipment made for the purpose. Another method requires special equipment for "peening" the inside of the piston with steel shot. This procedure compacts the metal on the inside and causes it to expand on the outside. Electric and pneumatic peening hammers are made for the same purpose.

Various types of equipment or tools are available for "knurling" the piston skirt. This method raises the surface of the metal in ridges or patterns along

the path of the knurling and thus increases the diameter of the piston. An additional claim made for this method is that it creates "pockets" on the piston surface, which gather and retain a film of oil to assist in sealing and lubricating.

Another procedure is to install piston expanders inside the pistons. There are a great number of these devices on the market. They vary in design, but usually consist of a steel spring strut that is compressed and installed in such a way it exerts internal pressure on the split piston skirt. See Fig. 13-17.

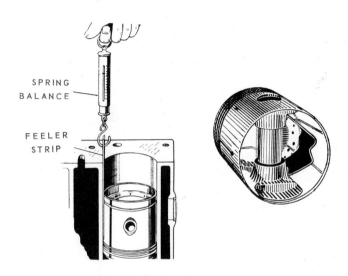

SPRING BALANCE

FEELER STRIP

Fig. 13-16. Left. Method of using spring scale with feeler strip to check piston clearance in cylinder. Fig. 13-17. Right. This type of piston expander pushes outward on each of the piston bosses.

Such expanders are often effective for collapsed pistons, but they should not be installed in only one of the cylinders. If used, they should be installed in all pistons of any one engine because of balance requirements. The expanders are made as light in weight as possible, but most automobile engines have pistons matched in weight at the factory to a few hundredths of an ounce. Any replacement pistons should also be carefully matched for weight with the other pistons as otherwise engine vibration may occur.

Gasket Installation

Gaskets should never be used the second time. This applies not only to cylinder head gaskets, but other gaskets as well. The reason is that the gasket having been compressed between the two surfaces now conforms to all the microscopic irregularities and when reinstalled would invariably leak.

Before installing a gasket, the mating surfaces of the parts, such as the cylinder head and cylinder block must be carefully cleaned and checked for warpage. (See additional information in this chapter under the heading Cylinder Head Warpage.)

Bolts holes should be chamfered and the area around stud and bolt holes should be smoothed with a file as the metal has often been pulled up by the force of tightening the bolts or nuts. Always be sure the correct gasket is being used for the particular installation.

All threads must be clean and not damaged in any way so that the nuts will spin on easily. A thread compound should be used, particularly on aluminum heads and cylinder blocks. This will prevent leakage in those cases where the bolt holes enter the water jacket.

Be sure to install the specified bolt in the correct hole as bolt holes frequently vary in depth. A torque wrench should always be used to tighten bolts and nuts to the specified torque, Fig. 13-18. They

Fig. 13-18. Typical torque wrench. All bolts and nuts must be tightened to the specified torque.

should also be tightened in the correct sequence. This is necessary to prevent distortion of parts. If the manufacturer's diagram of tightening sequence is not available, start tightening at the center of the head and work progressively from side to side and toward the ends of the head, Fig. 13-19.

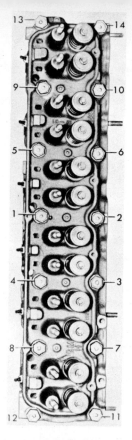

Fig. 13-19. The numbers indicate the sequence in which the cylinder head bolts should be tightened. (Typical.)

The usual procedure is to tighten the bolts in three successive steps until the final tightening is at the specified torque.

Gaskets should always be stored flat and in their original carton. They should never be hung on hooks.

Quiz - Engine Reconditioning

1. Name five ways of increasing the size of a metal part.
2. An oversize bearing is required on a reground crankshaft journal. True or False?
3. Name five ways of repairing a water jacket cracked by freezing.
4. How much warpage can usually be tolerated in a cylinder head? .001 in., .003 in. or .006 in. overall?
5. When installing a new dry sleeve in a cylinder, should the sleeve be smaller or larger in diameter than the cylinder? Larger_____. Smaller_____.
6. Why do pistons sometimes seize in cylinders?
7. Name two ways of repairing badly scored cylinders.
8. Why must dry cylinder sleeves fit tightly in the block?
9. If a newly installed dry sleeve is round, straight, smooth and free from wrinkles, is it ready for service? Yes or No?
10. Should a cylinder sleeve be honed after installation? Yes or No?
11. The wear limitations for cylinder wear is .010 in. out-of-round and .005 in. taper. True or False?
12. How can a proper cylinder wall finish be described?
13. A wet type cylinder sleeve should be frozen before installation. True or False?
14. In general, cast iron pistons should have about .0075 to .01_____, .00075 to .001_____, .00005 to .00015_____in. per inch diameter clearance in the cylinders.
15. Name three ways of expanding pistons.
16. Piston expanders should always be used in sets. True or False?
17. The greatest amount of wear in the cylinder takes place at the top of the travel of the piston rings. True or False?
18. What is the maximum amount of taper usually specified for cylinder wear in passenger car engines?
    0.010 in.
    0.005 in.
    0.075 in.

PISTON RING
AND PIN FITTING

Previously in this text, we have studied piston ring design and purpose. We have also noted that a ridge is formed at the top of the cylinder wall as the cylinder wears. To avoid damage to pistons and rings, this ridge should be cut away before an attempt is made to remove the pistons from the cylinders. Special tools are made for this purpose as shown in Fig. 14-1.

Fig. 14-2. *Piston ring gap should be measured with the rings seated squarely in the smallest diameter of the cylinder.*

Piston ring gap clearance is measured as shown in Fig. 14-2. The ring is pushed into the smallest diameter of the cylinder bore, which is usually below the travel of the bottom ring. A piston without rings is used to push the ring in place as this method locates the ring squarely in the bore. The rings should be purchased for the correct size to avoid fitting. Minor increases in gap clearance can be made by filing the ends of the ring. This should be done carefully with the aid of special tools made for the purpose.

In case specific clearance dimensions are not available, it is customary to allow .004 in. gap clearance per inch of piston diameter for the top ring, and .003 in. per inch diameter on the other rings. For example, a three inch diameter cylinder would require .012 in. gap on the top ring, and .009 in. on the other rings. The exception to the foregoing is the "U" type oil ring that is extremely flexible. These rings are flexible endwise and require no gap clearance.

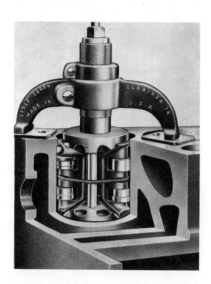

Fig. 14-1. *One type of special tool as used for removing ridge at top of cylinder.*

We have also considered cylinder wall reconditioning and piston fitting. We must now devote some consideration to proper fitting of the rings to the piston and cylinder, and also to fitting of the piston pins in the pistons.

Piston Ring Gap

It is obvious that the top piston ring runs hotter than the lower rings, and therefore the top ring will expand the most. This means that the top ring will need more gap clearance at the ends, and more sidewise clearance in the piston grooves than the other rings. The piston ring manufacturer specifies the clearance needed, and his instructions should be followed.

Ring Groove Clearance

The sidewise clearance of the ring in the groove is measured as shown in Fig. 14-3, using a feeler or thickness gauge. In the absence of specific instructions, it is customary to allow at least .003 in. side clearance on the top ring and at least .002 in. on the other rings. More than .005 in. side clearance on any ring calls for new rings.

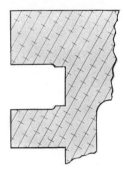

Fig. 14-3. Method of measuring side-wise clearance of ring in grooves.

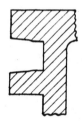

Fig. 14-4. The shoulders in the bottom of the groove might not leave clearance for new rings.

New rings can be purchased in almost any size as well as oversize and overwidth as desired. Overwidth rings may be used if the sides of the ring grooves are flat, smooth and square. If the grooves are worn excessively as shown in Fig. 14-4, or in tapered fashion as shown in Fig. 14-5, they can be repaired in two ways. One way is to machine the grooves out wider and install overwidth rings. The other way is to install spacers with standard width rings as shown in Fig. 14-6. In either case the ring grooves in the piston will need to be trued up. Special equipment is available for this purpose. See Fig. 14-7.

The depth of the ring groove must be checked also when replacing rings. Sometimes shallow grooves are used with thin rings, and a replacement with normal thickness rings will cause them to "bottom." The groove must be deep enough to allow the ring to enter the groove below the surface of the ring land. See Fig. 14-8. If the grooves are too shallow, they can be machined out deeper.

Sometimes rings turn slightly in the groove, and sometimes they do not. When installing rings, the gaps are usually spaced around the pistons, to avoid any possibility of the gaps getting one above the other and encouraging blow-by.

The manufacturers' instructions should always be followed when installing new rings. They know how their own products should be fitted, and they have studied the peculiarities of the different engines.

It is important that the piston ring grooves be thoroughly cleaned before installing new rings. Special tools are available for scraping the carbon from the grooves, Fig. 14-7. In an emergency, a broken segment of a piston ring can be used for that purpose.

Piston rings are fragile and must be handled carefully. They should be placed in the piston ring grooves with the aid of a ring tool and not by stretching them over the piston. Even if they do not break, they may become so distorted by careless handling as to be useless. It is also important to use a ring compressor when inserting the piston with rings into the cylinder. Otherwise the sharp edge of the ring may be deformed and the ring rendered useless. See Fig. 14-9.

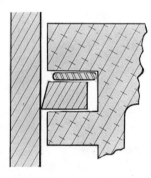

Fig. 14-5. The usual wear pattern is tapered in form.

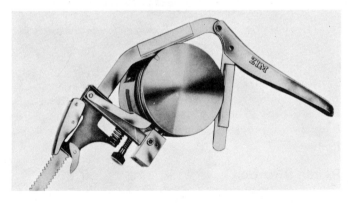

Fig. 14-6. Standard width rings may be used with a spacer in re-machined grooves.

Fig. 14-7. One type of special ring groove tool.

In any case of doubt as to the proper clearance for rings and pistons, it is safer to err on the side of too much clearance rather than too little. In this connection, it is all too often assumed that an engine pumps

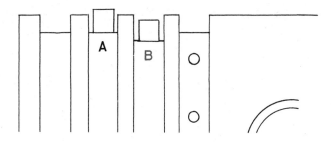

Fig. 14-8. The ring should fit freely in the ring groove below the surface of the lands as shown at B.

Fig. 14-9. One type of piston ring compressor used to hold rings in place while installing pistons.

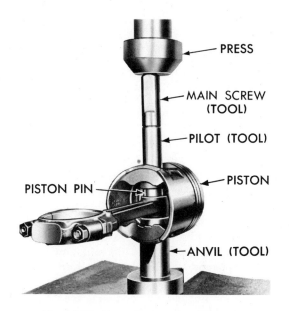

Fig. 14-10. Piston bosses should be supported when pins are pressed in or out.

oil because of worn piston rings. In a great number of times, new rings have been installed only to have the engine pump oil worse than ever.

If the bearings are worn in a pressure lubricated engine so that an excess of oil is thrown up in the cylinders, the engine will pump oil regardless of how good the rings are or how well they are fitted. The oil simply gets on the cylinder walls and pistons in such quantities, that it is beyond the ability of any ring to control it. This will be further explained in the section on bearings.

Piston Pin Replacement

It is the usual thing to find wear in both pin and bearings when piston pins become loose. Where the bushing is in the connecting rod only, it can be pressed out and a new standard size bushing pressed in and reamed or honed to fit a new standard size pin. The old bushing should not be removed with a hammer and drift, as there is danger of bending the connecting rod.

Where the pin is clamped in the rod and the bushings are in the piston bosses, the same method can be used. When replacing bushings in the piston, it is extremely important to avoid hammering, as the piston can be easily distorted by rough handling. The piston boss should be supported firmly in the press while the old bushings are pressed out and the new bushings pressed in. See Fig. 14-10.

Many piston pins are an interference fit in the upper end of the rod, that is the diameter of the piston pin is slightly larger than the diameter of bearing in the upper end of the connecting rod. Special equipment, Fig. 14-10, is therefore needed for removing and installing the pins in the piston and rod assembly. In addition to an hydraulic press, the equipment includes special anvils on which the piston assembly is mounted, pilots, and in some cases a spring for the anvil. These differ for each piston design. The procedure is to mount the piston assembly on the anvil. Then by means of a pilot, the pin is pressed from the assembly by means of the hydraulic press. A similar procedure is followed when assembling the piston pin to the rod and piston.

Oversize Piston Pins

If it is decided to install oversize new pins, and ream or hone the old bushings in the piston to fit the oversize pin, the connecting rod clamp hole will need to be enlarged accordingly. This condition also arises where the pistons are not bushed, and the pin bearing is directly in the piston bosses. If difficulty is experienced in reaming the rod end due to the split for clamping, a shim may be placed in the slot, and the clamp bolt drawn down tight. The shim will have to be the same thickness as the opening in the slot when the rod is clamped on the standard size pin. The inner edge of the shim should be flush with the hole so that the reamer will cut both shim and rod.

In the full floating type, the installation of new oversize pins will require reaming or honing of the piston bushings or bosses, and the bushing or rod (in the case of aluminum rods without bushings). In every case where reaming or honing is done on either piston or connecting rod, it is of utmost importance to have the finished hole at precisely a right angle to the connecting rod. Also both piston boss bearings must be in precise alignment. In other words, the hole must be straight through both bosses. Equipment used for reconditioning piston pin holes is shown in Figs. 14-11 and 14-15.

Piston Pin Fitting

Fitting piston pins is one of the most delicate operations to be found in automobile repair work. Millions of pins have been improperly fitted -- and are still being improperly fitted. The reason for this is that suitable equipment for fitting piston pins properly is a comparatively recent development.

Accuracy measurements in thousandths and tenths of thousandths is fairly common in automobile repair work. However in dealing with piston pins we are splitting up the tenths. We are dealing with microinches or millionths. In fact it is useless to use the term microinch in most cases without specifying the temperature at which the measurement is made. This is because a few degrees rise or fall in the temperature will expand or contract the metal enough to change the measurement given in microinches.

Furthermore, as previously mentioned, we are dealing with steel, bronze and aluminum, each of which has a different rate of heat expansion. We fit the piston pins at room temperature (assumed to be 70 deg. F.) and then put them in an engine which quickly attains a temperature of at least 140 deg. F. This temperature expands the pin, the bushings, if used, and the piston. If it is a cam ground piston it also changes shape from oval when cold to round when hot.

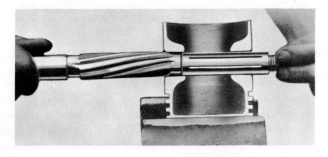

Fig. 14-11. Aligning type of reamer used to insure straight holes in both piston bosses.

This change in shape of the piston may also disturb the alignment of the two holes in the piston bosses. If we had a round, straight hole through the two bosses --which would stay round and straight when hot--and a round and straight pin to fit, it would then be only a matter of suitable clearance for the oil film. There must be room for a film of oil around the piston pin. Otherwise metal-to-metal contact will occur and the friction thus generated will score the pin or bushing or both.

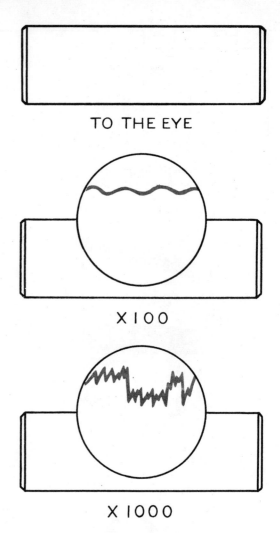

TO THE EYE

X100

X1000

Fig. 14-12. An apparently smooth pin may be rough indeed when magnified on the surface.

Standards of manufacture have improved and most piston pins are round and straight within one tenth of a thousandth of an inch. A pin so finished looks perfect and appears to be glass-smooth. When the surface is magnified 100 times it does not look so smooth and when magnified 1,000 times it looks rough indeed. See Fig. 14-12.

Reaming, grinding and honing equipment is now available which will produce a hole which appears to be dead smooth. It is, like the pins, accurate to one tenth of a thousandth, but when magnified it looks much like the bearing surface on the pins. It is possible, however, with the use of good equipment to produce a hole that enables a good working fit to be made. It should be obvious that in working with such close dimensions, the clearance will be determined by the surface finish.

If the hole finish is not practically perfect, it will be seen that when the pin is forced into the hole the "peaks" will be sheared off as shown in Fig. 14-13. The result of such a condition is rapid wear of the peak base, and the pin and bushing are worn OUT before they wear IN to a working fit.

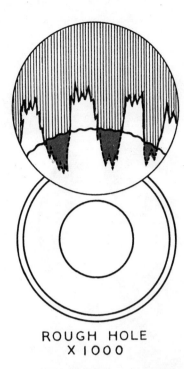

ROUGH HOLE
X 1000

Fig. 14-13. Forcing a smooth pin into a rough hole will cause the high points of the peaks to be sheared off and we will actually have metal-to-metal contact between the pin and parts of the bushing.

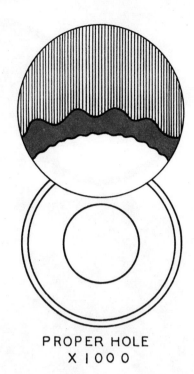

PROPER HOLE
X 1000

Fig. 14-14. A proper surface on the pin and in the bushing should result in space for an oil film between the two.

In this connection, it has been found that many experienced mechanics fit piston pins entirely too tight. These same mechanics often wonder why many of the jobs they do develop knocks and rattles and pump oil in a short time. The reason is, of course, that the tight fit they insist on having results in the condition shown in Fig. 14-13 with consequent rapid wear.

If the hole is properly finished to the proper size, there will be room for a film of oil to prevent metal-to-metal contact and thus reduce wear. See Fig. 14-14. When such a fit is obtained, the pin will enter the hole readily without force being applied, and will have a sufficient bearing surface to wear satisfactorily. Such a fit can be obtained by a skillful operator using modern equipment in accordance with the manufacturers' instructions.

Fig. 14-15. Hone type equipment for honing piston pin bosses for installation of new piston pins.

Quiz - Piston Ring Fitting

1. How much end gap should the top ring have in a four inch diameter cylinder? .009____, .012____, .016____ in.

2. How much gap should the oil ring have in a cylinder three and one half inches in diameter? .009____, .012____, .015____ in.

3. The top ring should have at least .005 in. side clearance in the ring groove. True or False?

4. How deep should the ring groove be?

5. Piston pins are casehardened, so do not wear. True or False?

6. Can oversize pins be installed when the pin floats in both piston and connecting rod? Yes____, No____.

7. What is meant by "room temperature?"

8. New piston pins can be expected to be round within: .002____, .0001____, .00005____ in.

9. New piston pins are often fitted: too tight____, too loose____.

Chevrolet 307 cu. in. V-8 engine with 2-barrel carburetor. Develops 200 hp. Fitted with Controlled Combustion System.

CRANKSHAFT
WEAR

We have seen that the forces applied to the journal are much heavier at some points of rotation than at others. For example, the force of the explosion is several times as strong as the force of the compression stroke. Also the explosion stroke applies the force always at the same spot on the journal. There is also the action of centrifugal force resulting from the rotation of the crankshaft with its connecting rods and pistons. The result is an out-of-round condition forms on the crankshaft journals and crankpins.

Fig. 15-1. With the ''Magnaflux'' method the part is sprayed with a material that will show any fracture by glowing under the hood which shuts out some of the light.

If a connecting rod is bent, or is out of alignment, it will tend to wear the crankpin journal in a tapered fashion--that is, more at one end of the bearing surface than the other end. Also any twisting of the engine crankcase or any excessive vibration of the crankshaft will tend to cause the main crankshaft journals to wear in tapered form.

Furthermore, if abrasive material gets into the oil the wear may be unequal, more at one bearing or more on one spot of the bearing depending on which bearing, and where on the bearing the abrasive enters in greatest quantity.

Bearings seldom wear equally for these and other reasons. One bearing may operate with a smaller volume of oil than another. Likewise, one bearing, due to its location in the engine, may operate at a higher tem-

perature than the others. All of these things cause or contribute to unequal wear on the crankshaft journals.

If a connecting rod journal has the least taper, or has a flat spot on it, it simply cannot be used. Such a condition would ordinarily cause such an increase in oil consumption that it would be essential to recondition the crank throw.

Due to close clearances in the bearings, a sprung crankshaft cannot be tolerated. The main bearings must fit the crankshaft journals all around the circumference with only enough clearance for a film of lubricating oil. If the bearing journal is scored or other than absolutely round, it cannot be used until it is reconditioned or replaced.

Damaged Crankshafts

As engine crankshafts are usually large and expensive parts, it is often desirable to repair damage rather than replace them. Before any extensive work is started however, it is well to have the shaft checked by a specialist with proper special magnetic or chemical equipment to make sure there are no invisible cracks in it. See Fig. 15-1.

In case damage has occurred to one or more crankpin journals and the crankshaft is not removed from the engine, it is possible to recondition the crankpin with the aid of special equipment made for this specific purpose. See Fig. 15-2.

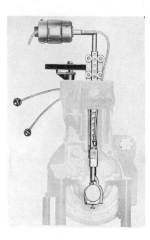

Fig. 15-2. One type of special equipment for machining connecting rod journals with the engine in the car.

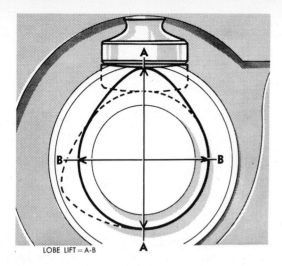

LOBE LIFT=A-B

Fig. 15-2a. The difference between measurements, A and B, equals the cam lift. Comparison should then be made with the specified lift to determine the extent of wear.

An engine crankshaft is subjected to terrific vibration and stress and may develop tiny cracks, particularly at or near the ends of the connecting rod throws or at the ends of the main bearing journals. Occasionally an invisible crack may develop near the oil feed holes in the shaft.

If the crankshaft is sound and the journals are worn slightly tapered or out-of-round, the shaft journals can be reground and undersize bearings fitted. See Fig. 15-3. Here again, as in the case of reboring cylinders, it is desirable to find out the available sizes of bearings that are carried in stock so that the extra work of boring the bearings to fit the shaft will be avoided.

Fig. 15-3. Special equipment used for reconditioning crankshafts.

If the shaft is badly damaged, it is possible to restore the journal by spraying metal on it. The shaft is built up oversize and then reground to the desired size. This type of work is usually done by specialists. See Fig. 15-4.

Worn Camshafts

Some wear does occur on camshafts, as on any other engine part, but as they operate at slower speed than the crankshaft the wear is usually slower. As the entire shaft is hardened, the bearing wear ordinarily occurs in the bushings rather than on the shaft journals. However, because of the weight of push rods and rocker arms, plus the stronger valve springs and higher engine speeds of today's engines, the load on the cams is greater and consequently there is a tendency toward increased wear.

The lift of the cam is the difference in the measurements of A and B, Fig. 15-2a, and the amount of wear is then obtained by comparison with the specified lift. The lift can also be measured by mounting a dial gauge on the cylinder head with its button contacting the upper end of the valve push rod. Then as the engine is slowly cranked, the distance from the lowest point to the highest will be the lift of the cam.

It is important that the lift of all the cams of the engine should be measured in order to determine if any are worn as the cams do not all wear at the same rate.

Worn cams are occasionally the cause of lost power or misfiring which is often overlooked when trouble shooting. If a check on the valve lift shows that it is less than it should be, the cams can be reground on special machinery. In most cases however, the camshaft is replaced.

Bearing Clearances

In our previous study of lubrication, we found that oil is pumped under pressure to the various bearings in the engine. In order for this oil to get into the bearing and lubricate it, clearance for an oil film must exist.

The one most important thing to keep in mind in this connection is that the steel crankshaft journal MUST be separated from the bearing metal when the engine is running or the bearing will melt. The heat generated by friction when steel moves rapidly on soft dry metal WILL melt the soft metal--almost at once. Therefore in an automobile engine we use a film of oil

Fig. 15-4. Metal worn away can sometimes be replaced by spraying new metal on with special equipment. The part is then refinished to size.

between the journal and the bearing. THERE MUST BE SPACE PROVIDED FOR THAT FILM. The film serves to hold the two metals apart and also circulates to carry away the heat generated by friction. The space is not great--it is measured in thousandths--but those thousandths are all important.

This film thickness will vary with the design of the engine and the type of lubrication system used. In general, a splash lubrication system is less critical of

In the pressure lubricated engine, the oil is pumped under pressure to the bearings. See Fig. 15-5. In this case, we must control the flow of oil by maintaining limited clearance all around a ROUND bearing and a ROUND shaft. If we have unequal clearances in the circulation system, we will have too much oil in one place, and not enough in other places. This is because the oil being under pressure will go through the largest clearance space in the greatest quantity.

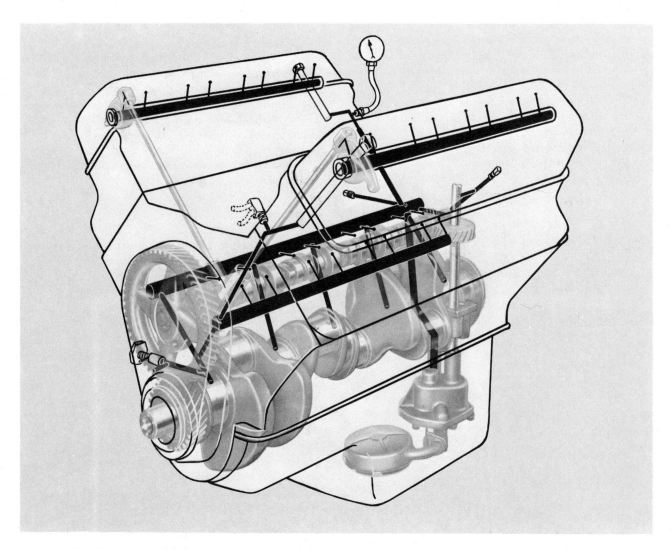

Fig. 15-5. A typical full pressure oil circulation system carries the oil to practically all of the working parts.

oil clearances than a pressure lubrication system. In the splash system, the oil in the pan is churned up by the internal parts of the engine into a combination of liquid and mist which is sprayed over the entire interior of the engine.

Some of this oil, in a splash lubricated engine, is collected in pockets above the main bearings, and flows through the bearing by means of grooves in the bearing surfaces. The connecting rods dip into the oil and obtain lubrication. These bearings can be operated when slightly out-of-round, and are usually made adjustable for wear.

Clearance Measurement

One method of measuring oil clearance is to measure the diameter of the journal with a micrometer caliper, the use of which is described elsewhere in this text. The diameter of the shaft is measured at several points around the circumference to determine the size and to check for roundness. See Fig. 15-6. It is also measured at each end of the bearing surface to determine the amount of taper, if any.

The inside of the bearing is then measured with the cap bolted in place, using a telescoping gauge or an inside micrometer. See Fig. 15-7. The difference in these two measurements represents the clearance between the journal and the bearing.

An alternate method is the use of a plastic material which deforms or flattens between the journal and the bearing when the cap is drawn down to the proper tightness. The amount of increase in the width of the plastic material as it flattens out, is then measured with a gauge provided to determine the clearance between journal and bearing. See Fig. 15-8.

With the integral type of bearing, it is not possible, or necessary, to measure the bearing bores with the bearing in place. With the precision type of bearing, it is desirable when possible (when the crankshaft is out) to measure the bearing bores for roundness when replacing bearings. If the bearing bores are out-of-round the bearing shells will be distorted when the caps are bolted on tightly.

The oil pressure test, page 175 will also disclose if there is excessive clearance and is used extensively for that purpose.

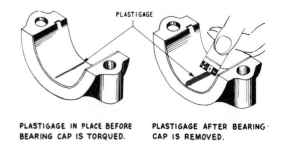

PLASTIGAGE IN PLACE BEFORE BEARING CAP IS TORQUED.　PLASTIGAGE AFTER BEARING CAP IS REMOVED.

Fig. 15-8. Using plastic material to check bearing clearance.

The amount of diametral clearance on automobile crankshaft bearings is specified by the manufacturer. These dimensions should be followed. In the absence of specific instructions, it is customary to use a minimum of .0005 to .001 in. for small shafts and up to .0015 to .002 in. for a large shaft. Any clearance in excess of .005 in. on either main or rod bearing is usually regarded as reason for adjustment or the installation of a new bearing.

Endwise Clearance

Obviously the crankshaft must not move endwise to any great extent; so one of the main bearings is usually provided with cheeks or flanges that bear against a machined flange on the crankshaft. See Fig. 15-9. In other cases bronze washers are installed to absorb the end thrust. See Fig. 15-10. There is always some end thrust on the crankshaft. This may originate in the clutch pushing against the end of the shaft, or the thrust of the helical teeth on the timing gears, or both.

Just as in the case of diametral clearance, there must be some clearance on the thrust faces. Otherwise expansion of the shaft and bearings from the normal heat of operation would cause metal-to-metal contact and burning of the thrust bearing. Here again the car manufacturers' instructions should be followed. In general, it is customary to provide a minimum of .004, and a maximum of .008 in. clearance. End thrust can be measured with a feeler gauge, as shown in Fig. 15-11.

Integral Bearing Replacement

In the case of poured or integral bearings, it is possible to ream or bore them straight and true to whatever dimension is wanted. This is made possible by tools of great accuracy which are now available. At one time it was necessary to fit the bearing to the journal surface by a laborious method known as scraping which required considerable skill. Modern boring equipment has sufficient accuracy to produce almost a 100% surface contact with each bearing in precise alignment. The boring is done with the bearing caps and shims, if used, all in place and the bolts drawn down to the specified torque.

One advantage of the integral main bearing design is that new bearings will compensate for any warpage

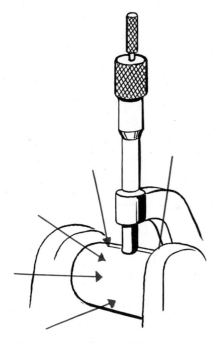

Fig. 15-6. Bearing journals should be measured at several points around the diameter and also along the length of the bearing surface.

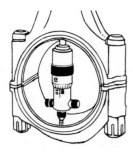

Fig. 15-7. The inside bore of the bearing is measured for size and roundness with an inside micrometer or a special dial gauge.

that may have occurred in the crankcase as the boring bar will cut a straight hole through all the bearings. One disadvantage is the great amount of work required to replace the bearings as compared to the shell type of bearing.

Poured bearings are still in use to some extent for connecting rod bearings. One reason for this is perhaps the feeling that the heat flows from the bearing surface to the rod more readily because of the close bond between the bearing metal and the rod. One disadvantage is that replacement of the bearing and rod assembly usually requires removal of the cylinder head, piston, rings and rod assembly. Few engines permit removal of the pistons and rings from below.

Fig. 15-11. Usual method of checking endwise clearance of crankshaft. A suitably mounted dial gauge can also be used.

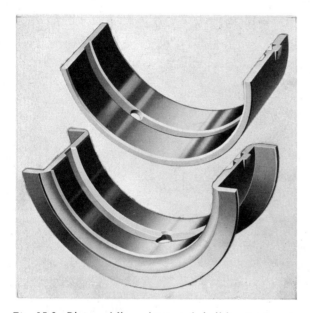

Fig. 15-9. Plain and flanged types of shell bearing inserts.

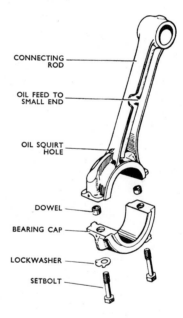

Fig. 15-12. Some connecting rod big ends are split at an angle, thereby making it easier to remove them from the cylinder.

Connecting Rod Removal

In this connection, it is quite a chore to get the rods out of some engines. On many small bore European engines, the big end of the connecting rod is too large to go through the cylinder bore. In some cases the engine has removable cylinder sleeves which when removed will allow the rod to come through the block opening. In many cases the rod is split at an angle as shown in Fig. 15-12 to facilitate removal. It will be noted that cap screws with locking plates, rather than studs or bolts, are used to hold the rod bearing cap in place with this type of construction.

One English engine--used in the Armstrong Siddeley --is so designed that the crankshaft must be removed

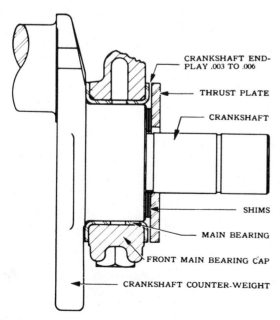

Fig. 15-10. Bronze washers are also sometimes used in connection with shims to regulate endwise motion of the crankshaft.

in order to get the pistons out of the engine. In this case, the pistons will not clear the crankshaft in the crankcase, and the connecting rods will not clear the cylinder bores. Later models have removable cylinder sleeves which when removed allow the piston and rod assembly to come out from above.

A somewhat similar situation is found on the English Riley; the connecting rod will not come out through

If the crankshaft journal is round and smooth, and not worn to any extent, a new standard-size bearing shell is simply inserted in place. If the crankshaft is round and smooth, but worn slightly undersize, a shell of the proper undersize bore is used. If the crankshaft has been damaged, and then reconditioned to a standard undersize dimension, a still smaller undersize bearing is used.

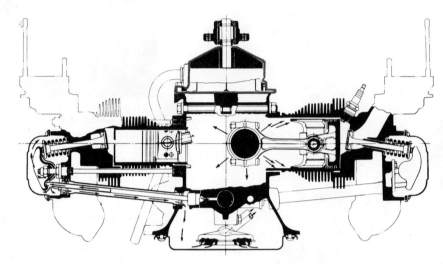

Fig. 15-13. The Corvair engine has a removable plate on top of the crankcase for access to the connecting rods.

the cylinder bore, and the piston will not clear the crankshaft. The solution in this case however, is to remove the connecting rod cap and push the piston up out of the bore on top. The floating piston pin is then easily removed to free the piston, and the rod is removed from below.

The opposed, or pancake, type of engine usually has a barrel crankcase which is split longitudinally, and it is necessary to dismantle the engine to get the rods out. Sometimes it may be possible--with the engine out of the car--to get one rod out by removal of the cylinder barrel on the opposite side. The Corvair is an exception to the foregoing. This engine has a cover plate on top the crankcase, which when removed, allows replacement of the connecting rod bearings. See Fig. 15-13.

Replacement of Inserts

With the insert or shell type of bearing, it is usually possible to replace all main and all connecting rod bearings without removing the crankshaft or cylinder head. See Fig. 15-14. These bearing shells require no fitting by hand, as they are made to extremely close limits of accuracy. It is only necessary to obtain and install the proper size.

Even in the case of bushing or sleeve type bearings such as used in the Volkswagen engine, Fig. 15-15, replacement bearings are available in an assortment of sizes to meet almost any requirement.

If the crankshaft journal has been reduced in diameter so much that a standard undersize shell will not fit, shells are available with excess bearing metal that can be bored out to the size desired.

If the bearing bore and journal are round, these new inserts require no fitting or adjustment. If the journal is out-of-round more than .0015 in., it should be trued up or machined until it is round. The same applies to the bearing bore in which the insert seats. Any errors in the bore will distort the bearing shell when the bolts are drawn down to the proper specification.

It is, of course, impractical to measure the bore of the main bearing seats with the crankshaft in place to

Fig. 15-14. Proper size of the insert needed can be determined with the crankshaft in place by means of this special tool.

make sure they are round. However, the main bearing caps are heavier and less liable to distort than the connecting rod caps. The connecting rod cap can be installed and bolted down without the bearing shell in it, and measured for roundness or taper with inside micrometers or gauges made for the purpose. If slightly distorted they can be machined true. If seriously distorted, the rod and cap should be discarded, as it is not advisable to remove any appreciable amount of metal which might weaken the connecting rod.

Bearing Shell Seating

The bearing seat and bearing shell MUST be round and true, as there MUST be intimate contact between the inside of the bearing seat bore, and the outside of the bearing shell. This is not generally understood as well as it should be. If true and intimate contact does not exist, the heat will not flow from the shell to the crankcase or connecting rod, and the bearing may melt. It may thus be seen that no shims of any sort

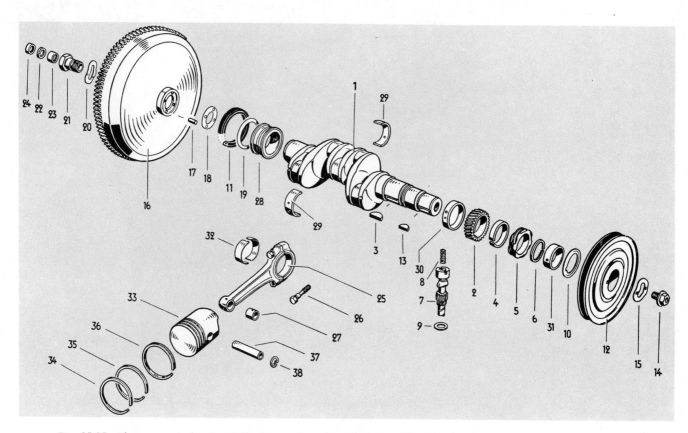

Fig. 15-15. The rear main bearing (28), the two front main bearings (30 and 31) on the Volkswagen engine are of the sleeve type. The center main (29) is split.

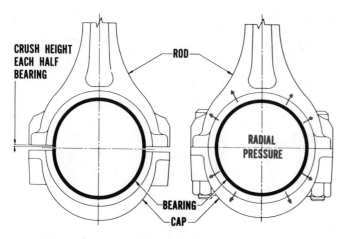

Fig. 15-16. The edge of the bearing shells should extend slightly beyond the bearing seat in order that they will be forced into intimate contact with the seat when the cap is drawn up tight.

should be used between the shell and seat in an effort to correct for wear or distortion.

This matter of heat dissipation is one reason for bearing "crush." Crush means that the two halves of the bearing shell extend a few thousandths beyond the bearing seat bore as shown in exaggerated form in Fig. 15-16. When the bearing cap nuts are drawn down to the specified degree of tightness, the shell is thus forced to seat solidly and intimately in the bearing seats.

Another reason for crush is to make sure the bearing remains round. If it were not tightly held on the edge it might distort as shown in exaggerated form in Fig. 15-17, enough to allow the edges to touch the journal.

Still another reason for crush is to avoid any possible movement of the shell in the seats. If the shell should become slightly loose, it might oscillate in the

Ford double overhead camshaft engine which develops 495 hp. Similar engine used in Indianapolis race to set new record.

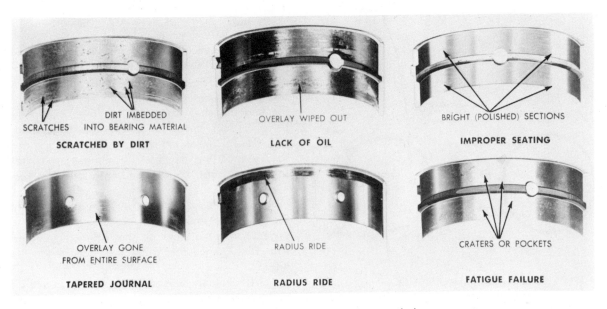

Illustrating major causes of engine bearing failures.

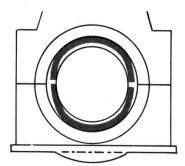

Fig. 15-17. Lack of proper crush in bearing installation may permit the edges of the bearing to curl in toward the shaft.

seat and wear on the outside. This would interfere with both oil control and heat transfer. Any dirt between the shell and the bore will have the same effect. See Fig. 15-18.

This bearing crush must always be there and therefore the edges of the shell should not be dressed down flush with the bearing seats. Of course, the amount of

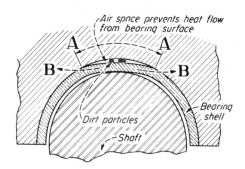

Fig. 15-18. Dirt between bearing shell and bore creates a dry spot on the bearing surface as well as hindering heat flow.

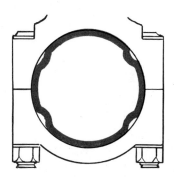

Fig. 15-19. An excessive crush will cause the bearing to buckle when the cap is drawn down tight.

crush must not be excessive. If it were, the shell would be distorted when the cap is drawn down and the bearing would be deformed as shown in Fig. 15-19.

The amount of crush is only .001 or .002 in., and is finished to dimension the same as the bore and outside diameter. These shells are extremely accurate as they come from the manufacturer, and must be handled with care. They should be purchased to the precise size required, and inserted with no alteration or fitting.

Integral Bearing Adjustment

When bearings of the integral type require adjustment it can be done at the bearing cap. The result will probably be a bearing that is out-of-round, but an engine lubricated by the splash method can operate satisfactorily with a slightly oval bearing on a round shaft. A pressure fed bearing uses a controlled volume of oil and must be round.

An adjustable bearing is usually provided with thin shims on each side. See Fig. 15-20. These shims are placed between the crankcase or rod when the bearing is poured, so we start out with a round bearing. Each time the bearing is adjusted for wear by the removal of these shims, it becomes more oval.

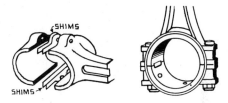

Fig. 15-20. An adjustable connecting rod bearing provided with shims for adjusting clearance.

These shims are usually installed in several thicknesses; that is, .0005, .001, .002 in. etc., and the same quantity of each on both sides. Also the shims may be in laminated form; that is, a stack of shims each .0005 in. thick are soldered together at the edge to form a block. By peeling off as many layers as desired, the shim block is thus reduced in thickness. See Fig. 15-21.

The usual adjustment procedure for main bearings, is to loosen all of the bearing caps and adjust one bearing at a time. Shims are removed in equal numbers of the same thickness from each side until a slight resistance to rotation of the shaft is felt. Shims of proper thickness to provide the clearance desired are then reinserted, and shaft rotation again checked.

If the bearing cap is warped so that the faces are not flat and level; or if the bearing is not provided with shims, the cap is dressed down. This is usually done by placing a sheet of emery paper on a face plate, or piece of plate glass and rubbing the cap face on the abrasive. Care must be exercised to avoid lap-

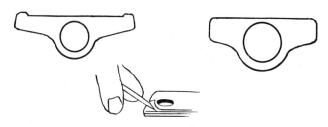

Fig. 15-21. Laminated shims may be of any shape desired and if equipped with a babbitt edge, this babbitt will need to be dressed down as the laminations are peeled off.

ping the cap crooked when this method is used. A skilled machinist can dress the cap down by draw-filing, but an amateur will ruin the cap by filing it crooked.

When all main bearings are adjusted properly and the caps drawn up tight, there should be little resistance toward rotation of the shaft. If there is resistance, one or more bearings are fitted too tightly, there is insufficient end clearance on the thrust bearing, the crankshaft is sprung or the bearings are not in correct alignment. If the engine is stiff after a bearing job, it should not be started until the cause of the stiffness is located and eliminated.

Side Clearance

The connecting rod bearing must have some side clearance. If it has too much, the bearing may move sidewise and cause a knock. The clearance is measured by inserting a feeler gauge between the end of the bearing and the cheek of the crankshaft throw as shown in Fig. 15-22. While manufacturers' specifications vary somewhat, the usual clearance is .005 to .010 in. As there is no adjustment of the side clearance, excessive clearance requires replacement of the bearing.

Fig. 15-22. A feeler gauge can be used to check end clearance of connecting rod bearing.

Connecting Rod Alignment

In addition to the proper fit of the connecting rod bearing on the crankshaft, and the proper condition of the piston pin at the other end of the rod, we must consider the alignment of the rod itself.

Most V-type and also opposed cylinder type engines have the cylinder blocks slightly offset from each other endwise to facilitate placement of the rod bearings on the crankshaft. It is also customary to offset the connecting rods, as shown in Fig. 15-23. This is done to place the power load as near to the main bearings as possible, which tends to reduce vibration of the crank-

shaft. While most connecting rods are all marked on the same side, it is something that should be watched during engine assembly.

Obviously, the piston pin and crankshaft journal must be parallel--not just approximately parallel, but precisely parallel. If the piston pin is not parallel with the crankshaft, every force on the piston will cause it

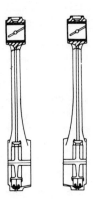

Fig. 15-23. Connecting rods are often off-set with regard to the bearing surface, the short side of the off-set usually being nearest the main bearing.

to try to slide endwise on the piston pin. This will cause the piston to "slap" in the cylinder and create a knock or noise. The connecting rod and bearing will also have a tendency to knock.

Special equipment of suitable accuracy is available for checking the connecting rods as shown in Fig. 15-24. This type of equipment checks the rods for twist as well as bends. EVERY connecting rod should be checked for proper alignment just before it is installed in the engine. Many hard-to-locate noises in an engine originate in misalignment of the connecting rods.

Each rod should be checked again for location after it is installed in the engine. This for the reason that the rod might have a double bend in it, which would not

Fig. 15-24. Typical connecting rod alignment fixture.

be noticed on the alignment tester. Such a double bend might leave the piston pin parallel with the crankshaft, yet the upper end of the rod might be close enough to one of the piston bosses to cause a knock. See Fig. 15-25.

Fig. 15-25. Exaggerated illustration of a connecting rod with a double kink causing the upper end of the rod to ride against the piston boss.

Camshaft Bearings

Camshafts sometimes bear directly in the metal of the crankcase as previously explained, but in most cases bearings are in the form of bronze bushings pressed into the crankcase. These bushings are not adjustable for wear, and are replaced when worn. The degree of wear dictating replacement is more a matter of their oil clearance than any tendency toward noise. If seriously worn, they may create noise and vibration in the timing gears and valve operation train.

In order to replace the camshaft bearings, the camshaft must be removed. This involves removal of the valves and operating mechanism, or else raising and holding the valve lifters up off the camshaft against the tension of the valve springs. Actually it is seldom necessary to replace a camshaft bearing or bearings until the engine is dismantled for other work.

After the camshaft is removed, the bearings are pressed out of their bores with a special tool made for the purpose. Of course, the bushings can be driven

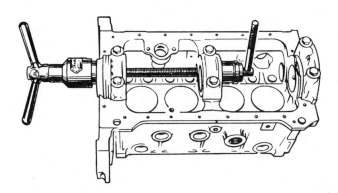

Fig. 15-26. One type of special tool for removing and inserting camshaft bushings.

out with a hammer and drift, but the special tool will be needed for inserting the new bushings, and might as well be used for removal of the old ones. See Fig. 15-26.

New bushings are available in the proper outside diameter and standard, as well as undersize inside diameter. If the camshaft has been undersized by regrinding worn journals, the bearings can be align reamed to any size desired by use of the proper equipment. See Fig. 15-27.

Before the new bushings are pressed into place, they are coated lightly on the outside with white lead. The white lead facilitates insertion by acting as a lubricant, and helps avoid distortion of the bushing. The oil holes in the bushings are lined up with the oil holes in the crankcase before pressure is applied, as the bushing cannot be turned after it starts in the bore.

It is essential to start the bushing squarely in the bore and apply pressure steadily and evenly. If the bushing cocks in the bore, it will be distorted and the inside diameter decreased.

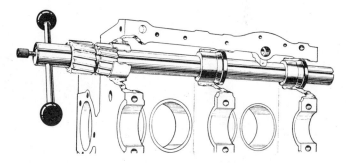

Fig. 15-27. Special boring bar for align reaming camshaft bearings.

The bushings should be pushed fully into the bore as if one end extends, the valve lifter may strike it. It is good policy to check the installation after the valve operating parts are installed to make sure there is sufficient clearance for the lifters. Also the end-play of the camshaft should be checked and corrected if it exceeds the manufacturers' specifications which are usually about the same as for crankshafts.

Usually the camshaft is provided with a thrust plate under which shims are placed for adjustment of clearance. In other cases there is a spring and button at the end of the shaft, that holds the camshaft against a flange on one of the bearings to eliminate excessive end-wise movement. See Fig. 15-28.

Main Bearing Installation

The replacement of main bearings of the slip-in type present a problem only when the cylinder block has become warped, Fig. 15-29, and/or when the crankshaft is scored or badly worn. If the cylinder block is not warped and the shaft is in good condition, all that is necessary is to remove the old bearing

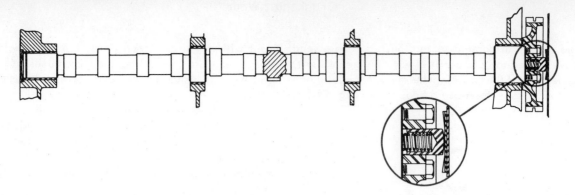

Fig. 15-28. *A spring loaded plunger prevents excessive endwise motion of this camshaft.*

shells and slip in new ones of the correct size.

In such cases the bearing shells are replaced on one bearing at a time. The procedure is to remove the bearing cap, from which the bearing shell is easily slipped. To remove the upper half of the bearing shell a "roll-out-pin" is inserted into the oil hole of the crankshaft. The end of this pin protrudes from the surface of the crankpin sufficiently so that when the crankshaft is rotated it will force out the upper half of the bearing.

is then reground to the correct size to fit the new bearings in the crankshaft.

Before align boring the semifinished bearings, make sure caps are properly assembled and bolts tightened to the specified torque. Also all oil ways should be plugged with substantial pieces of clean cloth to prevent chips and bearings from getting into the lubrication system.

When locating the boring bar, great care must be exercised to insure that the center line of the finished

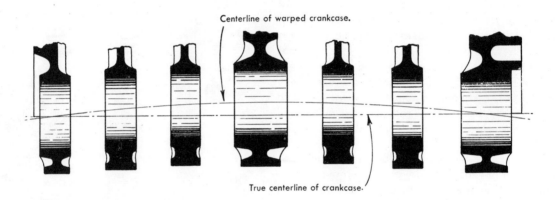

Centerline of warped crankcase.

True centerline of crankcase.

Fig. 15-29. *When a crankcase becomes warped, the center line of the bearing bores will form an arc. The condition is remedied by align boring.*

The new bearing shell is then slipped into position by hand. In some cases it may be necessary to use "roll-out-pin" to complete the installation. After installing the bearing cap with its bearing insert, the same procedure is followed with the other bearings.

Bearing cap bolts are not tightened completely until all the bearing inserts are in position. Then the bolts are tightened to the specified torque.

If the crankshaft is scored and the crankcase warped, it becomes necessary to remove the engine and do a complete reconditioning job, including regrinding the crankshaft Fig. 15-3, and align boring the bearings.

If the crankcase is not warped, then the crankshaft will be reground to a standard size for which standard size bearings are readily available.

However, if the crankcase is warped, then semifinished bearings will be installed in the crankcase and the bearings are then align bored. The crankshaft

bearings will be the correct distance from the top of the cylinder block, parallel with it and at right angles to the cylinder bores. In an engine built with a gear to drive the camshaft, the distance between the center line of the camshaft and the bore of the main bearings must be very accurately maintained so that the crankshaft and the camshaft gears will mesh properly. A little more tolerance is permitted if the camshaft is driven by chain or cog belt.

After all boring and thrust bearing facing operations are completed, be sure to remove all plugs from the oilways and all chips from the interior of the crankcase. Hand chamfer all inside edges of each bored surface with a scraper about 1/64th in.

In all bearing work, extreme accuracy and cleanliness are required. Particular attention must be paid to the areas contacting the backs of the bearing shells, the bearing surfaces and also the interior of all oil lines and oil passages.

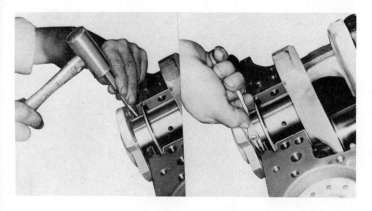

Fig. 15-30. Removing seal from rear main bearing.

In case of a leaking rear main bearing it is often possible to replace the bearing seal and bearing without removing the crankshaft.

To do this, loosen all the main bearing caps slightly to lower the crankshaft. Then remove the rear main bearing cap. With a small pin punch drive out the seal, Fig. 15-30. The seal is driven far enough until it can be grasped with a pair of pliers and pulled out the rest of the way. To replace the upper part of the seal, first lubricate it with engine oil. Start it into the groove by hand and have the crankshaft turned at the same time until the seal is in place.

The upper half of the bearing can be removed by first inserting a small tool or a bent cotter pin, Fig. 15-31, into the oil hole of the crankshaft. Then as the crankshaft is turned the pin will push out the bearing half.

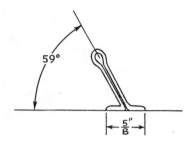

Fig. 15-31. Method of bending cotter pin which is then placed in oil hole to remove upper main bearing shell.

Quiz - Crankshaft Wear

1. Give three reasons for crankshaft wear.
2. Invisible cracks in steel parts may be found by means of: chemical equipment__, magnetic equipment__, either__.
3. An undersize crankshaft journal can be altered to become oversize. True or False?
4. Camshafts are hardened all over. True or false?
5. Clearance between crankshaft and bearing in a splash lubricated engine may be: more__, the same__, less__, than in a pressure lubricated engine.
6. What happens if oil clearances are unequal in a pressure oiling system?
7. Name two ways of measuring bearing clearance.
8. In general, the diametral clearance in a small engine main bearing should be: .0005 to .001__, .001 to .0015__, .0015 to .002__in.
9. In general, endwise clearance for crankshafts should not exceed: .004__, .006__, .008__in.
10. What provision is made for removing connecting rods from top of engine where rod end is too large to pass through cylinder bore?
11. A bearing bore should be trued up if it is out-of-round more than: .0015__, .0025__, 005__in.
12. Name two reasons for bearing crush.
13. In adjusting integral bearings, the same quantity of shims should be removed from each side. True or False?
14. Should the short side of the offset on the No. 1 connecting rod be toward the front__, or rear__of the engine?
15. A piston pin can be properly fitted and parallel with the crankshaft and still cause a knock. True or False?
16. If a camshaft bushing is pressed in crooked, the inside diameter will be: increased__, decreased __.

Ford's Ranger 2 is an ultramodern pickup truck that converts from 2-passenger vehicle to 4-passenger. Rear portion of cab moves 18 in. into bed of truck, roof section moves up and two additional seats fall into place.

VALVE SERVICE

This text has previously emphasized that the condition of the valves has much to do with engine efficiency. We have also seen that poppet valves lead a hard life. It is not surprising that valve service is therefore a frequently performed operation in the service station.

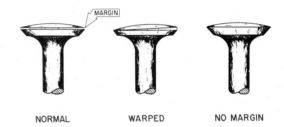

NORMAL   WARPED   NO MARGIN

Fig. 16-2. *Visual inspection may disclose serious defects.*

Visual inspection may also disclose a seriously warped valve head, a split valve face, or a lack of margin. See Fig. 16-2. If the face is burned, badly warped or worn to a thin margin the valve is discarded. See Fig. 16-3. If the valve appears to be in good condition, it is placed in a special grinding machine known as a valve refacer, and a new surface is ground on the face at the proper angle with and concentric with the stem. See Fig. 16-4.

Most valve faces are cut at an angle of 45 deg. with the stem. An angle of 30 deg. is also used. In

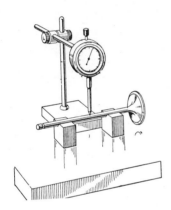

Fig. 16-1. *Method of mounting dial gauge to check valve stem for straightness.*

Valve service was once a hand lapping procedure using an abrasive paste between the valve face and valve seat. This procedure was assumed to provide a gas-tight valve, and little attention or thought was given to valve seat width, heat dissipation, concentricity of valve with seat, strength of valve springs, wear in valve guides and all the other things that require attention on the modern high speed, high compression engine.

Modern "valve grinding" is a true grinding process rather than a lapping procedure. Every part of the operation is governed by careful measurement with accurate equipment. The first step after the valves are removed and cleaned, is to determine whether the valve can be reconditioned or whether it must be replaced. If the stem is scored, pitted, bent or worn more than .002 in. it is usually discarded.

Visual inspection will disclose obvious damage. The stem diameter can be checked for wear with a micrometer. A dial gauge and V-blocks can be used to check the stem for straightness. See Fig. 16-1.

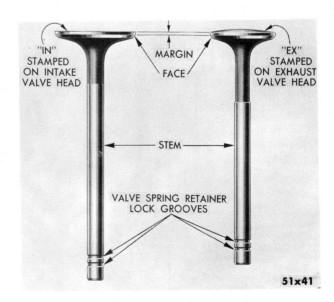

Fig. 16-3. *1/32 in. is usually regarded as the minimum suitable width for the valve margin.*

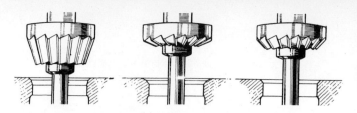

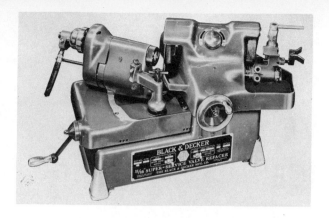

Fig. 16-4. A typical special machine designed for grinding valves accurately.

Fig. 16-7. A set of special reamers for narrowing valve seats.

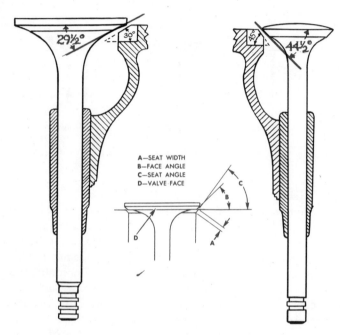

A—SEAT WIDTH
B—FACE ANGLE
C—SEAT ANGLE
D—VALVE FACE

Fig. 16-5. In some cases a slight interference angle is cut on the UNDER side of the valve seat or face as shown here.

Fig. 16-8. A specially mounted dial gauge is used to check the concentricity of the valve seat with the valve guide.

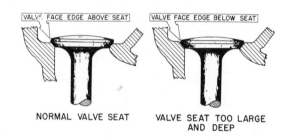

NORMAL VALVE SEAT

VALVE SEAT TOO LARGE AND DEEP

Fig. 16-9. Oversize valves can be used in cases where the block or head cannot be bored out for inserted valve seats.

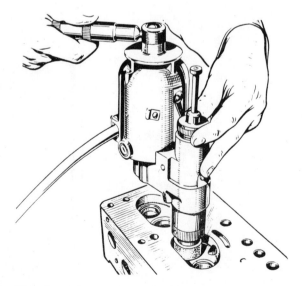

Fig. 16-6. Special equipment as used for grinding valve seats. Such equipment is essential where hardened seats are used.

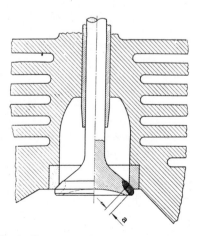

Fig. 16-10. The Volkswagen engine has a special heat resistant alloy valve face.

either case a slight interference angle—about 1/2 to 1 deg.—may be cut on either the valve face or valve seat, to improve the seating ability, Fig. 16-5. However it is invariably cut on the valve face as valve refacers can be adjusted to any desired angle.

Valve Seat Reconditioning

The seat in the block or head is also resurfaced with the aid of special reamers or grinders. See Fig. 16-6. First of all, it is necessary to position the tool so it will be located to cut the seat concentric with the valve stem guide and at the proper angle. This is difficult to do if the guide is worn. Guides should be replaced if worn out-of-round, bell-mouthed, or to an excessive degree at any point.

As previously mentioned, valve seats that are too narrow will not dissipate the heat properly, and if too wide will encourage carbon to adhere to them. In the absence of factory specifications, a seat 1/16 in wide is usually satisfactory. If the seat is wider than this, the first operation will be to narrow the seat by cutting an acute angle under the seat, and an obtuse angle above the seat. This is done with special reamers or grinders made for the purpose. See Fig. 16-7.

After the seat is sufficiently narrowed, the seat surface is then cut or ground to the proper angle. This cutting or grinding must result in a smooth true surface if the valve is to be gas-tight. It cannot be true, if the seat is not concentric with the valve stem. A method of testing with a dial gauge is shown in Fig. 16-8. The seat should be concentric with the guide within .001 in.

Sometimes the valve seat becomes so enlarged that the valve head sinks into the seat. See Fig. 16-9. In this case, the remedy is to install oversize valves or install valve seat inserts.

Valve Seat Inserts

Hardened valve seat inserts are ordinarily used in air cooled automobile engines having aluminum cylinder heads. In some cases the exhaust valves will also have a heat resistant face attached. See Fig. 16-10. Valve seat inserts are also used in many engines having cast iron blocks or heads.

If the insert is badly worn or burned, it may be easier to replace the insert than to try to recondition it. These seats are made of hard, heat-resisting metal, and cannot be reamed like an integral seat in a cast iron head or block. The inserts are refaced by grinding with special grinders.

If the seat is of the screw-in type, it is a simple matter to unscrew the old seat and screw in the new one. The seating surface is of course ground after the insert is in place. The pressed-in, or shrunk-in inserts are usually held tightly in place by rolling or peening the metal around the edge of the insert, after it is in place.

As it is sometimes difficult to clean up the peening enough to allow the insert to be pulled, the inserts are usually broken for removal. Whether the old insert is pulled or broken out, it is essential that the hole for the insert be round and true. If the insert does not bottom fully in the hole, or if it does not fit tightly all around the hole, there will be poor heat transfer from the insert to the head or block, and the insert will run hotter than it should.

For this reason, the inserts are usually of such size as to provide an "interference fit;" that is, the insert is one or two thousandths larger in diameter than the hole into which it is to be installed. In this case, to avoid the stresses imposed in pressing them in place, the inserts are often shrunk for insertion. This is often done at the factory by immersing the insert in liquid air for a short period.

For service installation, the inserts may be placed in a deep freeze for a few hours, or packed in dry ice for a few minutes. Either of these procedures will shrink them sufficiently for easy insertion. When so frozen, the inserts must be handled carefully and quickly, as they are quite brittle and will crack or split easily.

After insertion, the metal around the insert may be lightly rolled or peened over the top outside edge of the insert, to help hold it firmly in place. The final step is to grind the seat for the valve on the insert true with the valve guide.

Valve Stem Guides

Some engines have separate valve guides of the pressed-in type, but most are now built with the valve stem in direct contact with a hole bored in the cylinder block or head. Heat dissipation is better where guides are not used, but wear in the guides means boring the holes out larger, and fitting new valves with oversize stems. In most cases the separate guides are made of cast iron, but bronze is used in some cases, because of the superior wearing characteristics, and more rapid heat dissipating ability.

Press-in guides are often identical for the exhaust and inlet valves, but are sometimes installed differently. In other cases the exhaust and inlet guides are not interchangeable. See Fig. 16-11. In still another case the guides are identical, but the inlet guides are installed upside down from the exhaust guides. Some exhaust guides are cut off shorter in the port opening, and others are counterbored in the port end, to reduce the tendency for carbon to accumulate in the guide.

Carbon does accumulate in the guide bore and on the stem of exhaust valves, and causes them to stick partly open or to slow down in action. The tendency for carbon to accumulate increases as the valve stem and guide wear, because more hot gas blows by between valve stem and guide. Wear on the intake stem and guide is equally undesirable because such wear per-

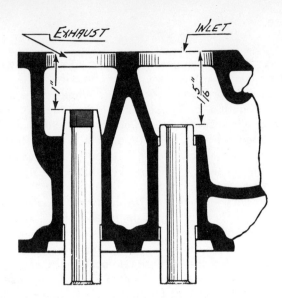

Fig. 16-11. *These valve guides are not identical and the exhaust extends farther into the port than the inlet. Note the counterbore in the exhaust guide.*

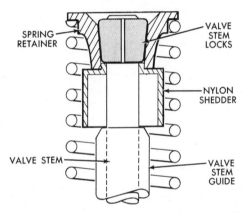

Fig. 16-12. *Special oil shedder of nylon used on Cadillac engine valves. While not an oil seal, it greatly reduces the amount of oil reaching the valve stems.*

SPRING RETAINER
VALVE STEM LOCKS
NYLON SHEDDER
VALVE STEM
VALVE STEM GUIDE

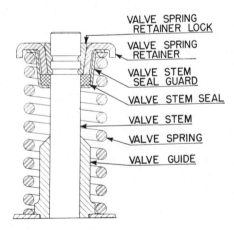

VALVE SPRING RETAINER LOCK
VALVE SPRING RETAINER
VALVE STEM SEAL GUARD
VALVE STEM SEAL
VALVE STEM
VALVE SPRING
VALVE GUIDE

Fig. 16-13. *Here a retainer or guard is used to hold a seal near the end of the overhead valve stem.*

mits air to be drawn in through the clearance, and dilute the air and gasoline mixture. Under such conditions it is impossible to obtain a satisfactory carburetor adjustment.

Furthermore, oil from the valve chamber may be sucked in between valve and guide, to increase oil consumption and carbon up the engine. This oil leakage is sometimes pronounced on overhead valve engines, as oil is pumped up on the valve operating rocker arms. To discourage this tendency, a special cutter is available to cut a bevel on the end of untapered valve guides.

It is customary to place seals either on the valve stem or in the guide on overhead valve engines, to exclude excess oil. Several types are shown in Figs. 16-12, 16-13, 16-14 and 16-15. One manufacturer vents the valve guide to the atmosphere to break up this suction as shown in Fig. 16-16.

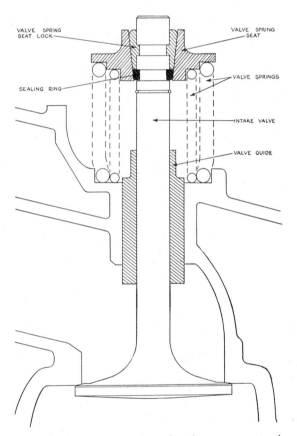

VALVE SPRING SEAT LOCK
VALVE SPRING SEAT
SEALING RING
VALVE SPRINGS
INTAKE VALVE
VALVE GUIDE

Fig. 16-14. *In this case a seal is placed in a groove in the overhead valve stem.*

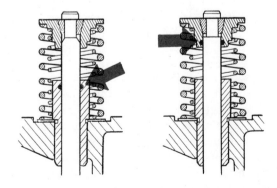

Fig. 16-15. *Two methods using "O-ring" seals on overhead valves.*

Another undesirable result of excessive valve guide wear is to permit the valve to wobble enough to cause it to ride to one side of the valve seat as shown in Fig. 16-17. Quite naturally, this interferes with proper seating and sealing of the valve and also promotes wear. It is customary to replace the valve guides or valves, or both, whenever more than .005 in. clearance for small valves or .006 in. for large valves exists between valve stem and guide. One method of measuring clearance is shown in Fig. 16-18.

Before any measurement is made, the valve stem must be cleaned and polished, and the valve stem guide thoroughly cleaned of carbon deposits. Special tools are made for cleaning carbon out of valve guides as shown in Fig. 16-19. The measurement for clearance

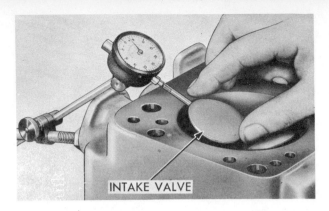

Fig. 16-18. *When measuring the clearance between valve and guide, the valve must be off the seat as shown here.*

Fig. 16-19. *Method of cleaning carbon out of valve guides with special tool made for the purpose.*

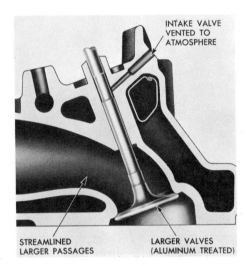

Fig. 16-16. *Note reduction in part of valve stem diameter at vent opening on this Pontiac inlet valve design.*

Fig. 16-20. *Valve guide partially cut away to show spiral groove made by special tool.*

should be made with the valve slightly off the seat as shown in Fig. 16-18. The valve spring must also be removed while making the measurement.

One repair method for valve guide troubles that does not involve replacement of the guides, is to upset the metal inside the valve guide bore by rolling a spiral groove through it. See Fig. 16-20. The idea here is to decrease the inside diameter slightly, and at the same time to form a continuous pocket for oil to gather and act as a seal. A special tool is made for this purpose.

When valve guides of the press-in type are replaced, it is important to have them positioned properly in the block or head. See Fig. 16-21. The car manufacturer specifies the proper position with regard to some accessible surface, from which measure-

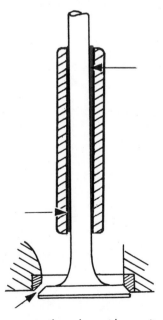

Fig. 16-17. *Looseness in the valve guide permits the valve to wobble and cause undue wear of valve and seat.*

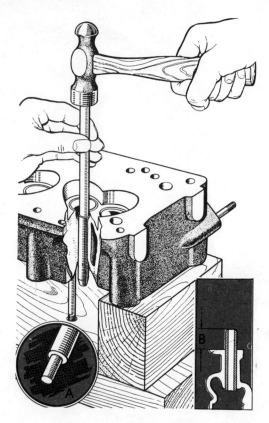

Fig. 16-21. A is the end of the pilot driver used in removing and replacing the valve guide. B is the dimension specified by the manufacturer.

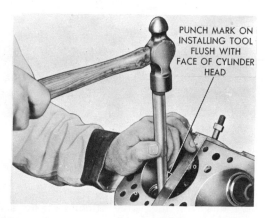

Fig. 16-22. Valve guides must be accurately positioned in the head or block in accordance with the manufacturers' specifications.

ment can be made. An example of this is shown in Fig. 16-22.

In some cases where an unusual amount of trouble is experienced with exhaust valves sticking due to rapid accumulation of carbon, it has been found helpful to cut off the end of the exhaust guide. This is often done with a drill ground to a flat angle on the end. The guide is cut down even with the opening in the port in which the guide is located.

After the guides are pressed in place, it is usually necessary to ream them to proper size, and provide clearance for heat expansion of the valve stem. Special

reamers are made for this purpose as shown in Fig. 16-23. This operation must be performed carefully so that the hole will be straight and true with a good surface.

Exhaust valve stems will require more clearance in the guides than inlet valves. In the absence of specific instructions, it is customary to fit intake valves with .001 – .003 in. clearance, and exhaust valves with .002 – .004 in. clearance, depending upon the size of the valve stem.

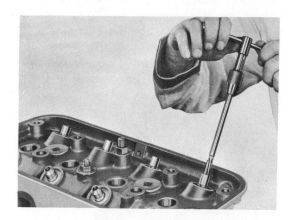

Fig. 16-23. Special reamers make it possible to ream valve guides to the accurate dimensions required.

Valve Springs

Valve springs seldom receive the attention they deserve. They are an exceedingly important part of the engine, and have much to do with the engine perfor-

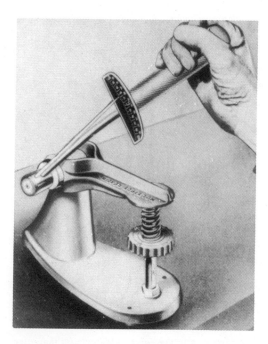

Fig. 16-24. Typical tool for measuring valve spring length and strength.

Fig. 16-25. Valve springs should be square on each end and of the proper length.

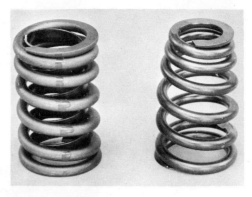

Fig. 16-27. Dual coil spring at left, tapered spring at right.

mance. They are seldom replaced unless broken, yet should be replaced when they are not up to specifications. They work hard, being subjected to millions of cycles of high speed operation, and all of it under shock conditions.

The valves are opened with lightning-like speed by the action of the cam and the spring is expected to close the valve just as fast as it is opened. The valve lifter is thus kept in contact with the cam. If the spring is weak and does not hold the lifter in contact with the cam, noise will be created and the valve, spring, lifter and cam will be subjected to hammer-like blows that cause metal fatigue. Many broken valves result from shock caused by sticking stems, weak valve springs or excessive tappet clearance.

The car manufacturer provides specifications on the free length of the spring, and the pressure in pounds that the spring should exert when it is compressed to a measured length. Special tools are available for measuring the length and strength of the spring. See Fig. 16-24. Valve springs are simple, inexpensive coil wire springs, and should not be expected to last forever.

They should be square on each end, as otherwise they will have a tendency to pull the valve stem to one side, and cause undue wear on the valve stem and guide. They can be checked for squareness and free length as shown in Fig. 16-25. When the coils of the spring are wound closer together at one end than at the

other, the close coils are to be placed next to the engine block or head. See Fig. 16-26. This uneven coiling is done to lessen the tendency of the spring to vibrate or "flutter" at high speeds.

Another method of reducing flutter is to install dampers as shown in Fig. 16-26. Still another method is to taper the spring or to use two lighter springs, one within the other, instead of one heavy spring. See Fig. 16-27. The two springs are usually wound in opposite directions. Whatever the construction used, it is important to check the springs whenever they are out, and replace them whenever they are not up to specifications.

Periodic replacement is also good to avoid unexpected failure. Valve springs often become "etched" when the valve chamber is subject to corrosive vapors. Some valve chambers are not well ventilated and steam or moisture containing acids formed from combustion will collect and cause flecks of rust to form on the valve springs. This etching is likely to cause the spring to break. See Fig. 16-28.

Fig. 16-28. Although not heavily etched, spring broke in service.

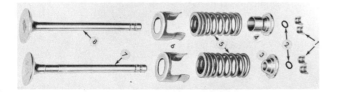

Fig. 16-26. Typical valve with accessory parts. 1-Split cone type valve spring keepers. 2-"O" type oil seals. 3-Valve spring retainer. 4-Valve spring retainer and oil shedder. 5-Valve springs. 6-Surge dampers. 7-Exhaust valve. 8-Intake valve.

This corrosive action is similar to the corrosion that causes pits and rust to eat into valve stems. On the valve stems it means wear, but a broken valve spring on an overhead valve engine may permit the valve to drop into the cylinder and damage or ruin a piston, or cylinder head.

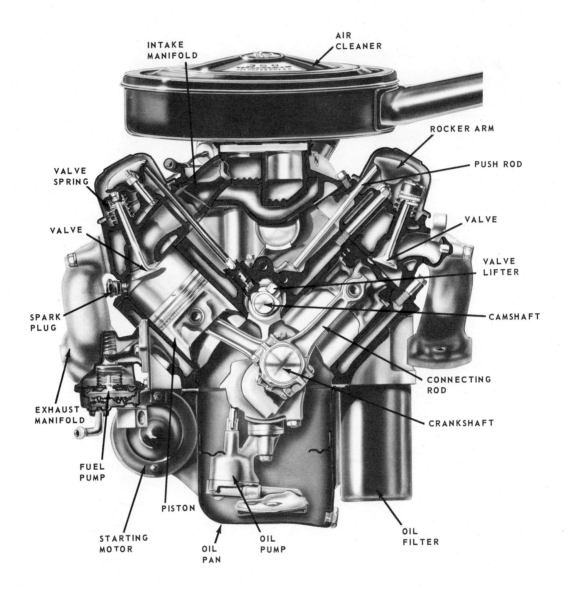

Camaro 350 cu. in. V-8 engine, section view.

Valve Spring Retainers

Valve spring locks or keepers are usually of the split cone, horseshoe or flat rectangular key type. They fit into an appropriate slot in the end of the valve stem. Fig. 16-29 shows the split cone type in position. A cupped washer called the spring retainer fits over these keepers, Fig. 16-26, and the tension of the spring bearing on the retainers holds the locks in place. Other methods are also used. Slots cut near the end of the stem and a key or pin pushed through the slot, threads cut on the end of the stem for a·nut and locknut, etc.

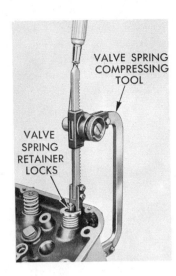

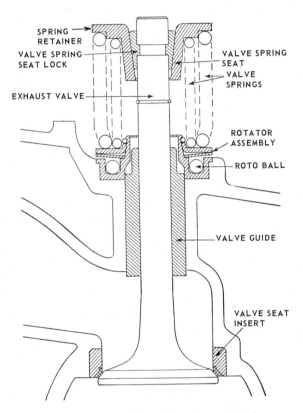

Fig. 16-29. Typical tapered C valve spring seat lock as installed on valve assembly.

Removal is accomplished by holding the valve stationary while the spring is compressed enough to allow the retainer to be raised from the locks. See Fig. 16-30. The locks are then removed and the valve spring released. This allows the valve to be removed, and then the spring and retainer can be removed. Valves should never be mixed up when removed, unless it is known that new valves or guides are to be installed. The valves should always be replaced in the same guide from which they were removed.

Valve Rotators

Some retainers are more complicated and are intended to permit or encourage the valve to rotate slightly with regard to the seat. Some of these are

Fig. 16-30. Compressing the valve spring allows the retainer locks to be removed which frees the valve and the spring for removal.

called "free valves" and the purpose is to provide a longer lasting seal between valve and valve seat. Rotation of the valve will discourage the formation of carbon deposits, and help prevent valve warpage.

Some of these free valve devices release the valve from the valve spring tension at one point in the cycle of operation, so that it is free to rotate slightly. One type is illustrated in Fig. 16-31. With this type it is

Fig. 16-31. Construction of free valve device.

important to maintain the clearances between stem and cup and between cup and retainer within specified limits. See Fig. 16-32. If the clearance between stem end and cap is too little, the end of the valve stem is ground off as needed. If the clearance is too great, the skirt of the cap is ground off as required. A special tool is available for measuring the clearance accurately. See Fig. 16-33.

Other devices are known as valve rotators, and impart a positive rotational effort to the valve once during each cycle of operation. One such device is illustrated in Fig. 16-34. Also see Fig. 16-29.

Regardless of the type device used to provide or permit rotation of the valves, there appears to be no question about their ability to assist in maintaining a satisfactory seal between valve and seat. They are

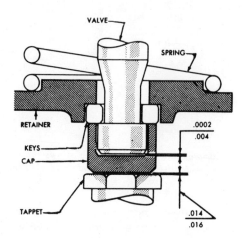

Fig. 16-32. With this free valve device, it is important to maintain the clearance between the end of the valve and the cap.

also claimed to minimize sticking and wear between guide and stem. Other than cost and complication, the only apparent objection to them is the slightly increased weight of the reciprocating assembly, which might encourage a tendency toward flutter in an extremely high speed engine.

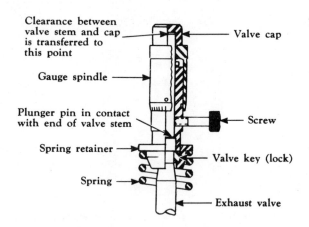

Fig. 16-33. Special gauge for measuring free valve clearance.

The German Volkswagen engine design contemplates slight rotation of the valves without adding any extra parts. This is done by adjusting the valve rocker arms to contact the valve stems slightly off center. The correct amount of offset is indicated in Fig. 16-35. This adjustment is accomplished by adding or removing spacers on either side of the rocker arms, as required to move the rocker arm lengthwise as needed. See Fig. 16-36.

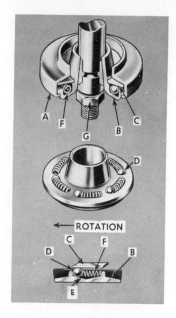

Fig. 16-34. In this case, positive rotation of the valve is caused by the inclines down which the balls roll when pressure is applied. A-Housing. B-Retainer. C-Cupped washer. D-Balls. E-Ramp. F-Spring. G-Valve lifter.

Valve Actuating Mechanisms

It is customary in U.S.A. built engines to mesh the camshaft drive gear directly with the crankshaft gear, or in the case of chain drive to locate the sprockets near each other. See Figs. 16-37 and 16-38. In the case of the overhead cam engine such as the Chevro-

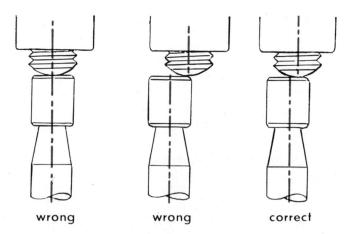

Fig. 16-35. Method of obtaining valve rotation on a Volkswagen engine.

let Vega, Fig. 8-14a, a cog belt is used and on the Willys Jeep 230, Fig. 16-39, and Opel, Fig. 16-39a, the camshaft is chain driven.

The cog belt used on the overhead camshaft Chevrolet is made of reinforced fiber glass. While this is a relatively long drive, no difficulties have resulted from stretching. Adjustment of the cog belt tension is made by positioning the water pump housing. The material of which the belt is made is described as being heat resistant as well as oil resistant. It is inherently silent in operation, requires no lubrication and absorbs the shock of opening and closing the valves.

Where long chains are used to operate camshafts, the problem of slack or lost motion presents itself. Valve timing must be precise. Sloppy motion cannot

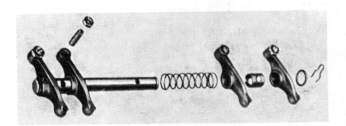

Fig. 16-36. Spacers are placed on the valve rocker shaft on either side of the rocker arms to obtain proper offset.

be tolerated. Several devices have been tried to control this, and one of the most interesting is an automatic hydraulic chain tightener, as used on the English Rover. This design is shown in Fig. 16-40. Engine oil pressure is used in the hydraulic cylinder.

Worn Valve Mechanism

Of course the camshaft and camshaft drive are only part of the mechanism used to operate the valves. To continue the study of valve action and timing, we must consider parts such as lifters, push rods, rocker arms, etc. Each of thse parts has something to do with valve timing. It is well to consider at this time that many minor faults may equal a major fault. In other words, a little wear at many points in the valve train may be equal in effect to considerable wear at one point.

For example, suppose there is .005 in. excess wear between the gear teeth. This will allow the valves to

Fig. 16-37. Typical timing gear installation.

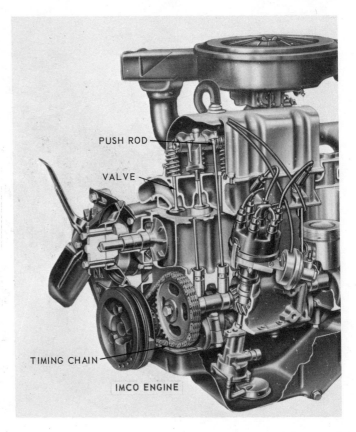

Fig. 16-38. Location of timing chain on six cylinder overhead valve, push rod operated engine. V-8 is similar.

open late and close early. Add to this another .005 in. excess wear in the camshaft bearings, which will reduce the valve lift as well as increase the late opening and early closing of the valves. Add another .005 in. worn from the cam contour which also changes the valve lift or timing or both. Now on top of all this, add another .005 in. excess wear between the lifter and guide. This results in the lifter moving sidewise in the guide, before it starts to lift the valve.

Obviously all this cumulative wear will interfere with efficient operation of the engine. Such conditions are often further aggravated by careless adjustment of the valve tappets. Many mechanics who do not understand valve action, adjust the tappets with too much clearance to make sure there is no possibility of the valve holding open. They do not realize that they are restricting the ability of the engine to draw in a full charge of mixture, and dispose of the exhaust gas properly.

The foregoing example does not embrace the condition in an overhead valve engine which can become much worse. Here we have additional wearing parts such as both ends of the rocker arm operating rod, the rocker arm, rocker arm bushing and shaft. See Fig. 16-41. If excess wear exists at these points, and it is added to the other points listed, it becomes a serious matter indeed. For these reasons, the valve

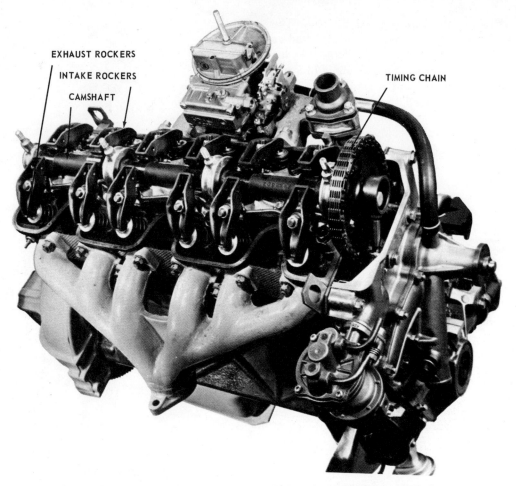

EXHAUST ROCKERS
INTAKE ROCKERS
CAMSHAFT
TIMING CHAIN

Fig. 16-39. Details of Willys Jeep six cylinder single overhead camshaft engine.

tappet clearance on overhead valve engines must be more carefully adjusted.

The engine manufacturer furnishes precise valve tappet clearance specifications in all cases, and these should be followed explicitly. Otherwise, the efforts of the design engineer to build efficiency into the en—

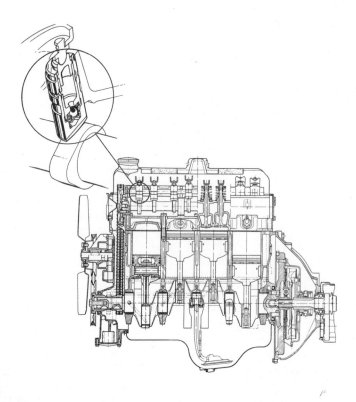

Fig. 16-39a. Note timing chain driving overhead camshaft on Opel four cylinder engine. Hydraulic lifters are also a feature.

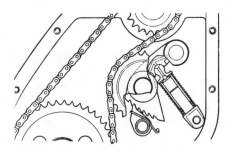

Fig. 16-40. Automatic hydraulic timing chain tensioner, or adjuster used on Rover engine.

gine are partially wasted. These specifications are so precise that they state whether the engine should be hot or cold when the adjustment is made. Furthermore, some manufacturers provide a different specification for checking the valve timing.

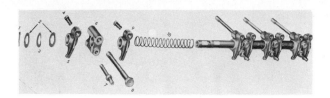

Fig. 16-41. The rocker shaft assembly consists of multiple parts.

It should be evident that accurate adjustment is impossible if the various contacting surfaces are worn to untrue dimensions. See Figs. 16-42 and 16-43. If such parts are not too seriously worn, they can be restored by grinding with equipment made for the purpose. If they are worn enough to be through the case-hardened shell, they should be discarded and replaced with new parts.

Valve Spring Installed Height

As the result of valve and seat reconditioning, the valve will be recessed further into the cylinder head (or block) with the result the valve spring will not be

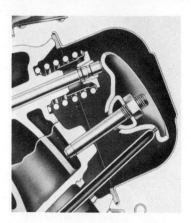

Fig. 16-43. Instead of a rocker arm shaft, many cars now have rocker arms mounted on individual studs.

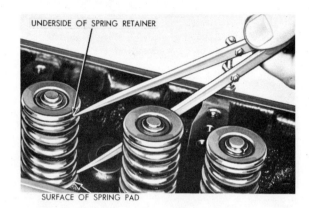

UNDERSIDE OF SPRING RETAINER

SURFACE OF SPRING PAD

Fig. 16-43a. Measuring the installed valve spring height.

compressed as much as it normally would be. In other words, the installed height of the spring would be increased. The effect is just the same as weak valve springs.

The installed height is measured from the surface of the spring pad to the underside of the spring retainer, Fig. 16-43a.

This condition can be remedied by the installation of new valves and seats. Another method is to install spacing washers between the spring and the cylinder head. These spacers should be of such thickness that the installed height of the spring is in accordance with the specified height.

Valve Tappet Adjustment

Adjustment of the tappet clearance is made by means of a feeler gauge as shown in Fig. 16-44, or with the aid of a special dial gauge as shown in Fig. 16-45. In these cases, the adjustment is accessible being on top an overhead valve engine. In some cases where an L-head engine is mounted low in the frame with high fenders, it is extremely difficult to get at the valves. In some cases it is necessary to remove the front wheel to get at a detachable panel in the fender, which permits access to the valves. See Fig. 16-46.

Several European engines are of the flat or pancake type with opposed cylinders. In these cases the overhead valves are on the outside of the engine. On

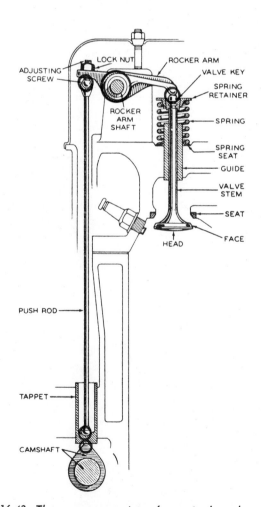

Fig. 16-42. There are many points of wear in the valve operating train: the valve cam contour, the lower face of the valve lifter, the sides of the lifter and guide, both ends of the push rod and the sockets in which they fit, the rocker arm shaft and bushings, the rocker arm and contacting the valve stem. A little wear at each of these points adds up to a lot of wear in the train.

Fig. 16-44. *Method of using a feeler gauge to adjust valve clearance on an overhead valve engine.*

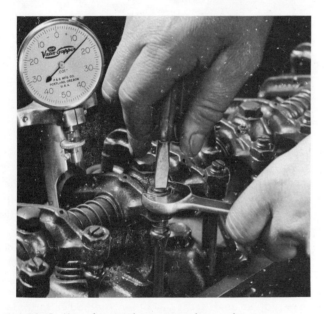

Fig. 16-45. *Use of special gauge to adjust valve tappets on overhead valve engine.*

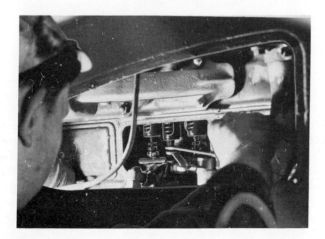

Fig. 16-46. *Removable access panels are provided in some cases where it is difficult to get to valves to adjust them.*

the German Volkswagen for example, the engine is a flat four in the rear of the car. Adjustment of the valve clearance is made from under the rear fender on each side. See Fig. 16-47.

In the case of the English Jowett, which also has a flat four, the engine is mounted in front of the front axle. In this construction, the cylinder heads and valve rockers can be removed from either side from under the front fender, after the wheel is removed.

Early English Jaguar engines had overhead valves operated by means of push rods and rocker arms. Later models had a chain driven overhead camshaft, and still later a double overhead camshaft was adopted. The clearance between valve stem end and camshaft is difficult to adjust, as it consists of inserting different thickness pads on the end of the valve stem.

The English Morris and the Wolseley engines have overhead camshafts driven by a shaft and gears. In this case, the valve clearance is adjustable by means of a threaded collar between the cam and the valve stem. See Fig. 16-48. Special wrenches are required to make the adjustment on these engines.

Hydraulic Valve Lifters

Many engines have self-adjusting valve lifters of the hydraulic type which operate at zero clearance at all times. See Fig. 16-49. In this case, the engine oil circulation system supplies a constant flow of oil under pressure to the lifters. See Fig. 16-50. Operating at zero clearance, these lifters compensate for changes in engine temperature, adapt automatically for minor wear at various points, and thus provide ideal valve timing as well as freedom from noise.

One type of hydraulic lifter is shown in Fig. 16-51. In this illustration, 1 is the tube that carries the oil coming in at 2 from the engine supply to the ball check 3, which rests on seat 8. The supply chamber inside the body 9 is kept full of oil at all times, when the engine is running, as port 2 is connected into the engine oil pressure system. Similarly, the oil—being under

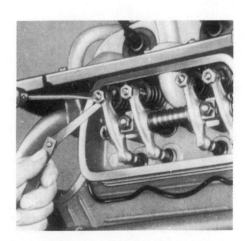

Fig. 16-47. *Volkswagen valves can be adjusted from under the rear fenders on each side.*

pressure--can raise the ball 3 and keep the pressure chamber below 6 full at all times, by going through port 4.

When the lifter body 9 rests on the heel of the cam, spring 5 pushes the plunger 6 into contact with the end of the valve stem. This spring is not strong enough to lift the engine valve off its seat. This gives zero tappet clearance. As the plunger lifts, it creates a slight vacuum in the pressure chamber, and oil is drawn through port 4, through tube 1 and seat 8, past the ball check 3.

As the cam rotates and lifts body 9, it carries cylinder 7 with it. This tends to push plunger 6 down into cylinder 7. The pressure thus generated causes the ball check valve to seat and hold the oil in the pressure

Fig. 16-50. On this overhead valve installation, the oil supply holes are drilled directly into the oil galleries on each side.

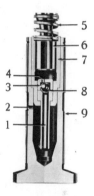

Fig. 16-51. Cut-away section of hydraulic valve lifter shows how oil from the engine oiling system enters the lifter assembly through port hole 2 located in an external groove.

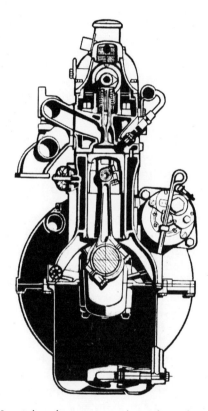

Fig. 16-48. Special tools are required to adjust the clearance between cam and valve end on the Morris engine.

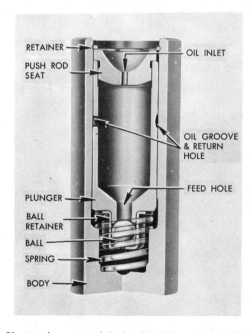

Fig. 16-52. Another typical hydraulic lifter which differs in design, but operates on the same principle as the example described in the text.

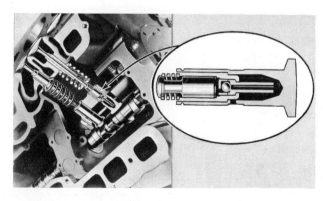

Fig. 16-49. Hydraulic valve lifters as installed on L-head engine.

chamber under plunger 6. As oil, for all practical purposes is incompressible, the valve is lifted on a column of oil and supported thus while the valve is open. When the valve seats, the foregoing cycle is repeated.

There are several types of hydraulic valve lifters in use and they vary somewhat in design. Another type is shown in Fig. 16-52. However, they all work on the same general principle.

There is a small amount of oil leakage between the lifter plunger and the cylinder while the engine valve is off its seat. This is desirable in order that the valve clearance be adjusted to zero each time it is opened. This clearance must be controlled closely as excess leakage at this point would reduce the valve lift. The leakage rate is specified by the manufacturer who also supplies tools for checking the leakage rate. See Figs. 16-53 and 16-53a.

Fig. 16-53a. Measuring leak-down rate of hydraulic valve lifter.

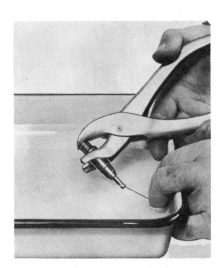

Fig. 16-53. Special tools are available for checking the leak-down rate of hydraulic valve lifters.

Hydraulic Lifter Problems

While hydraulic valve lifters do provide ideal valve operation, like any other mechanical device, they are subject to certain difficulties and require some attention. It should be obvious from the foregoing that clearances between the moving parts must be controlled closely.

This necessity for controlled clearance has caused some difficulty in operation due to dirt or varnish, causing the lifters to stick. The plunger and cylinder are often held to dimensional tolerances of one-tenth of a thousandth of an inch or less in manufacture, and then selectively assembled. That is, different plungers are tried in different cylinders until a pair is found that fits closely enough without being too tight.

For this reason they should not be mixed up when they are removed for service. Each plunger should be kept with the cylinder in which it operates.

With clearances of this nature, it will be understood

that the tiniest fleck of carbon, a fine thread of lint from a wiping cloth, a speck of dust, or any foreign matter whatever will wedge between the plunger and cylinder, and cause them to stick. Anything as large as an eyelash or hair will put it completely out of order.

For this reason, it is necessary to keep the engine oil CLEAN when hydraulic lifters are used. The very best grade of oil must be used in the engine and the oil MUST be changed frequently. Oil filter cartridges must also be replaced regularly.

Another reason for using the best possible oil in the engine and changing it frequently comes about from a general increase in driving speeds for long continued periods. Highways and cars are such that car owners do not hesitate to drive at high speeds for hours at a time. Such operation is certain to generate heat, and the inside of the engine and oil, reach temperatures that are destructive to the oil.

The oil often becomes hot enough to "crack" some of the petroleum fractions (just as in an oil refinery) and in decomposing, these elements form a "varnish" or "lacquer." This varnish-like material collects on the plunger and in the cylinder, and causes sticking. In many cases this varnish is so thin and clear as to be invisible to the naked eye.

Such deposits can be removed mechanically by brushing or friction, but there is a danger of harming the surface of the plunger or cylinder. The safest method of removal appears to be the use of chemical solvents. After cleaning, the units should be dried by air and kept covered to avoid dust until they are installed in the engine. They should not be wiped with a cloth for fear that a thread of lint will adhere to them.

It is clear that such parts must be handled with extreme care when out of the engine. If dropped on the floor, or dropped one on another, a nick or scratch may result that would cause them to stick. When clean and dry, the plunger should fall into or drop out of the cylinder of its own weight.

Valve Service

When reinstalled, the clearance should be checked to make sure there is enough. The tappet clearance dimension is much greater than with mechanical linkage, and varies considerably among the different makes. The manufacturers' recommendations should be obtained and followed. As in the case of any other valve tappet adjustment, the lifter must be on the heel of the cam when measured. The usual procedure is to turn the engine until the ignition distributor rotor is in the firing position for the cylinder to be checked. This assures that the piston is on top center and both valves completely closed.

Quiz - Valve Service

1. A valve should be discarded if the stem is bent more than: .002____, .004____, .006____ in.
2. A valve interference angle should be cut on: the the combustion chamber side____, the port side ____, both sides____.
3. A narrow valve seat will dissipate the heat better than a wide one. True or False?
4. The valve seat should be concentric with the guide within: .001____, .002____, .003____ in.
5. Valve seat inserts are not used in cast iron cylinder blocks or heads. True or False?
6. Describe an interference fit for a valve seat insert.
7. Name three ways of shrinking inserts.
8. Heat dissipation is better when valve guides are not used. True or False?
9. Leaking intake valve guides: cause excess oil consumption____, upset carburetor adjustment____, both____.
10. Valve stem seals are placed: on the valve stem ____, in the valve guide____, either____.
11. Valve stem to guide clearance should not exceed: .003 - .004____, .004 - .005____, .005 - .006____ in.
12. Why must valve springs be square on each end?
13. What causes valve stem and valve spring etching?
14. What is the difference between a free valve device and a valve rotator?
15. Worn camshaft bearings will cause a valve to open early. True or False?
16. Valve tappet adjustment is more critical on: L-head engines____, I-head engines____.
17. It is sometimes necessary to remove a wheel from the car in order to adjust the valves. True or False?
18. No leakage is permissible between the plunger and cylinder of hydraulic valve lifters. True or False?
19. What is meant by a selective fit?
20. Clean cloths must be used to wipe parts of hydraulic valve lifters. True or False?

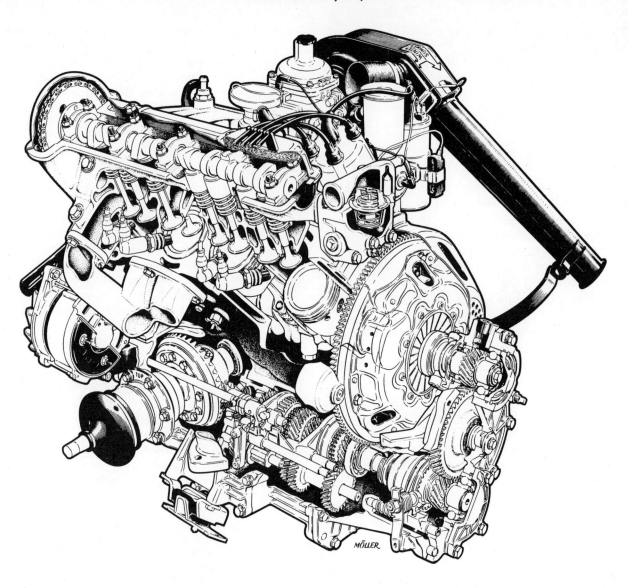

Sweden's Saab 99 is powered by a 105 cu. in., 87 hp, 4-cylinder engine which mounts over transaxle of front wheel drive car. Engine and transaxle have separate lubricating systems. Engine block is set at 45 deg. angle to right; overhead camshaft is driven by a single track chain.

ENGINE
TROUBLE-SHOOTING

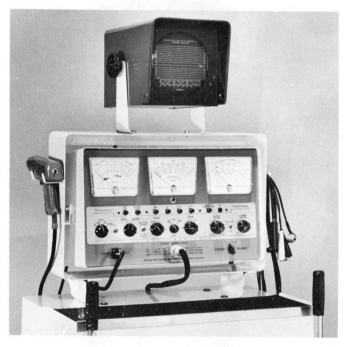

Fig. 17-1. Specialized engine testing equipment with oscilloscope, voltmeter, tachometer, ammeter and timing light.

Trouble-shooting is a process of reasoning supported by deduction and elimination. As a defect in one part may have a definite relation to trouble in another--perhaps remote spot--the trouble-shooter must of necessity have the ability to keep the entire automobile in mind at all times. This requires mental alertness as well as specific knowledge.

Trouble-shooting in its most elementary form consists of "shorting out" a spark plug with a screwdriver to locate a misfiring cylinder. In its most advanced form it involves the use of elaborate testing equipment. A good example of this is the equipment widely used to determine the condition of the electrical system in an automobile.

Testing Equipment

Typical test stands are shown in Figs. 17-1 and 17-2. These instruments are provided with accurate voltmeters, ammeters, gauges and other testing devices. When used properly, it is possible to locate leaks or breaks in the wiring of the automobile, determine the amount of current developed or consumed by any part of the electrical system. Some of these instruments indicate what is going on inside the engine combustion chamber. See Figs. 17-1, 17-3 and 17-4.

Such equipment also facilitates precise adjustment of the carburetor, ignition and engine in general as well as the generator, voltage regulator, etc. This equipment is covered in detail in the electrical and carburetor sections of this text.

Equipment is also available and coming into extended use for testing the entire automobile under road operation conditions. These instruments are known as dynamometers, and are operated by the driving wheels of the automobile. See Fig. 17-5.

Dynamometers are also widely used in the testing and adjustment of automatic transmissions. See Fig. 17-6.

Other small individual instruments are used to test engine compression, test engine lubrication systems, carburetor adjustment, etc. These instruments are all essential and MODERN AUTOMOBILES CANNOT BE SATISFACTORILY REPAIRED AND ADJUSTED WITHOUT THEM. For example, many engines are rebuilt because they use an excessive

Fig. 17-2. This test stand has a power-driven ignition distributor tester in addition to other gauges used in engine analysis.

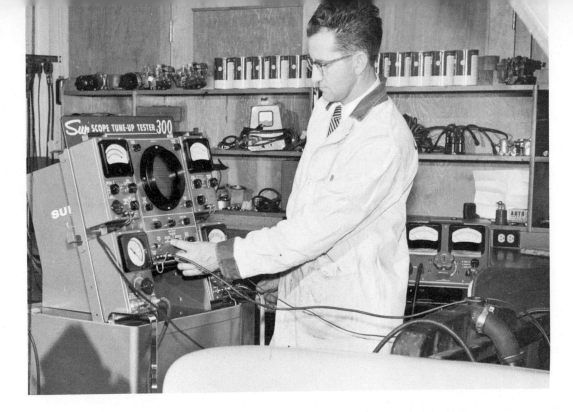

Fig. 17-3. An oscilloscope in use with the operator studying the pattern.

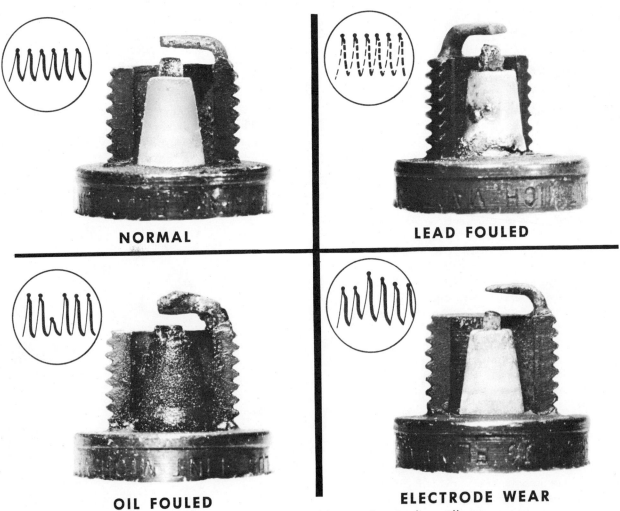

NORMAL

LEAD FOULED

OIL FOULED

ELECTRODE WEAR

Fig. 17-4. Spark plug conditions as portrayed by wavy lines on the oscilloscope screen.

amount of oil only to find that the rebuilding did not stop the use of excessive oil. Equipment for testing the oil system would have located the source of the trouble.

High Oil Consumption

Quite often high oil consumption is blamed on the piston rings. The engine is disassembled, the cylinders reconditioned, and the new piston rings carefully fitted. Upon reassembly, the engine may use

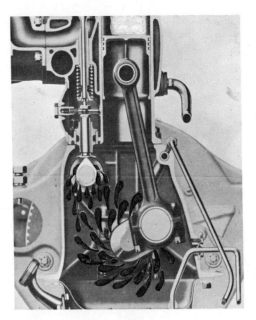

Fig. 17-7. *Loose bearings can cause a flood of oil to be thrown up on cylinder walls so no piston ring can control oil consumption.*

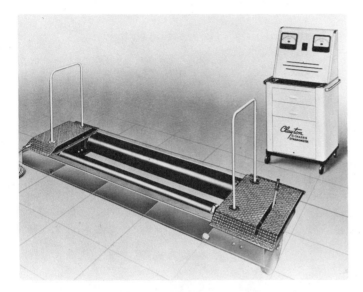

Fig. 17-5. *This is a floor type dynamometer. The car is driven into position with the drive wheels on the rollers. The recording instruments are shown in the stand.*

more oil than before. The mechanic often hopes the new rings will "wear in" to a better fit in the cylinders, and advises the car owner to drive the car a few hundred miles.

Fig. 17-6. *Typical automatic transmission test stand.*

The driving seldom does any good, and the engine is again disassembled to find the trouble. While worn piston rings and cylinder walls may cause increased oil consumption, there are a great number of other things that are at fault either singly or in combination. In most cases the oil is leaking out of one or more of

the pressure lubricated bearings, and is being splashed or thrown up into the cylinders under the pistons in such large quantities, that no piston ring can control the excess. See Fig. 17-7. This is covered under piston rings elsewhere in this text.

Oil Pressure Test

An oil pressure test is made before the engine is disassembled with the aid of special equipment made for the purpose. See Fig. 17-8. Such a test will ordinarily disclose the following defects:

1. Worn connecting rod bearings.
2. Loose connecting rod bearings.
3. Excess side clearance in connecting rod bearings.
4. Worn main bearings.
5. Loose main bearings. See Fig. 17-9.
6. Excess crankshaft end play.
7. Worn camshaft bearings.
8. Worn camshaft journals.
9. Worn crankshaft journals.
10. Oil leaking past front and rear main bearings.
11. Defective crankshaft seals.
12. Leaking seal plug at rear camshaft bearing.
13. Broken oil line.

The testing equipment can be used with the engine in or out of the car, as it is a special pressure tank connected into the oil line. The oil pan is removed so that each of the bearings can be observed. The pipe from the test tank is connected to the engine oil line. It is customary to use SAE 20 oil in the pressure tank. The oil and the engine should be at a comfortable temperature when the test is made. If in an uncomfortably cold shop, allowance will have to be made for the lessened flow.

The engine crankshaft is rotated slowly by hand after the air pressure is applied to the oil in order that the various passages may register. The amount of oil coming from each bearing is an indication of the amount of clearance between the shaft and the bearing. Fig. 17-8 provides an idea as to how this clearance is judged.

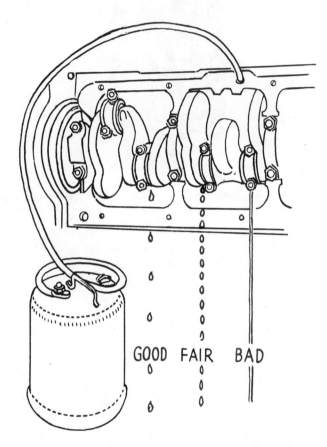

GOOD FAIR BAD

Fig. 17-8. An indication of how clearance in the engine bearings is judged by the amount of oil under pressure flowing from the sides of the bearings.

Fig. 17-9. This bearing insert might not cause a knock, but certainly would leak oil.

Such oil pressure tests are of no value on a splash lubricated bearing, or in a few cases where the bearings of a pressure system are beveled at the parting halves. It is, on all other pressure feed engines, the one best method of checking for the cause of oil pumping.

Many first class shops make this test on an engine before it is dismantled for repair. By so doing, they know where to look for trouble when the engine is apart. Shops use this test after the repair work is completed in order to make sure the job is correct.

In the following list of additional causes of high oil consumption, it must be kept in mind that the fault is usually a COMBINATION OF SEVERAL DEFECTS rather than one single defect. Also oil may be leaking out as well as being burned in the cylinders. Most of the following defects are discoverable by measurement, or, are susceptible of adjustment as outlined previously in this text.

The following can be detected by observation:
1. Bent or twisted connecting rods.
2. Bent crankshaft.
3. Out-of-round crankshaft journals.
4. Scored crankshaft journal. See Fig. 17-10.

Fig. 17-10. Note scored condition of the crankshaft journal.

5. Damaged crankshaft oil slingers and seals.
6. Worn cylinder bores. See Fig. 17-11.
7. Tapered cylinder bores.
8. Distorted cylinder bores. See Fig. 17-12.
9. Worn pistons.
10. Collapsed pistons.
11. Improperly fitted pistons.
12. Stopped up piston drain holes.
13. Worn piston ring grooves.
14. Worn piston rings.
15. Wrong size piston rings.
16. Distorted piston rings.
17. Incorrectly installed piston rings.
18. Rings too tight in ring grooves.
19. Improperly fitted rings.
20. Clogged piston ring slots.
21. Worn piston pins.
22. Worn piston pin bushings.
23. Worn intake valves.

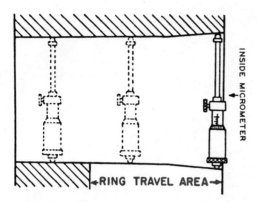

Fig. 17-11. *Here we have wear over all the ring travel area, with the customary taper at the top of the cylinder.*

24. Worn intake valve guides.
25. Worn or damaged intake valve or guide seals.
26. Oil level too high.
27. Excessive oil pressure.
28. Clogged oil return from valve chamber.
29. Clogged oil return from timing gear case.
30. Clogged oil filter.
31. Clogged crankcase breather pipe.
32. No baffle in breather pipe.
33. Clogged vents in clutch housing.
34. Defective vacuum booster diaphragm.
35. Ruptured diaphragm in transmission modulator.
36. Engine overheating.
37. Clogged water jackets.
38. Cracked crankcase.
39. Crankcase gasket leaks.
40. Leaking timing gear case gasket.
41. Leaking oil filter gasket.
42. Leaking oil filter connections.
43. Leaking valve cover gasket.
44. Defective gasket on external oil pump.
45. Defective gasket on oil pressure regulator.
46. Leaking oil pan drain plug.
47. Miscellaneous other oil leaks.

Among the reasons listed in the foregoing are "overheating" and "clogged water jackets." These items cause oil to be consumed in two ways. Due to the increased engine temperature, more oil is vaporized and burned up when the engine overheats. Also

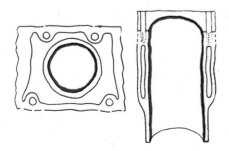

Fig. 17-12. *Exaggerated illustration of cylinder distortion caused by unequal or excessive tightening of cylinder head bolts.*

overheating due to a clogged water jacket will result in cylinder wall distortion as previously explained. When the cylinder distorts, the rings cannot seal and the oil passes between them and the cylinder walls.

Engine Overheating

There are many conditions of the automobile that result in overheating and the degree of overheating is indicated by the temperature gauge on the instrument panel. Some conditions will cause only a slight change in the recorded temperature, other causes will result in a rapid rise in temperature and violent boiling of the coolant. Still others, while causing only a slight increase in recorded temperature, will be more noticeable in engine performance.

Before discussing the many causes of overheating it is important to emphasize that when the coolant level is low in a radiator, water should not be added unless the engine is running. When the system is hot and the water level low, cold water will go directly to the cylinder head and the rapid chilling could cause the cast iron to crack.

Water has the physical characteristic of changing its boiling point with every change in pressure. For example; under a vacuum of 22 in., water will boil at 150 deg. F. At atmospheric pressure 14.7 psi, it boils at 212 deg. F. At 15 psi above atmospheric pressure it will boil at 250 deg. F. and most cooling systems on recent model automobiles operate at 15 psi.

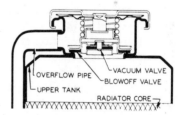

Fig. 17-13. *Details of typical pressure type radiator cap. Note vacuum valve and blow-off valves.*

The higher the temperature, the more effective the cooling system will be in dissipating heat. Heat dissipation from the radiator results from the difference in temperature between that in the cooling system and the air flowing through the radiator. Increased operating temperature also improves economy, Fig. 17-18, and reduces wear, Fig. 17-18a.

Modern automobiles because of cost and styling limitations have had radiator sizes reduced, while horsepower was increased. As a result, more heat is being dissipated from smaller radiators. This is made possible by pressurizing the cooling system.

To produce the desired pressure in the cooling system, the radiator is provided with a pressure type cap, Fig. 17-13. This is basically a safety valve, designed to release the pressure at some specified amount, usually 12 to 15 psi, Fig. 17-13a. This pressure relief valve seals the cooling system off from the overflow tube and the atmosphere so the system is automatically pressurized as the coolant is heated. The pressure cap is also provided with a vacuum valve which opens as the temperature drops and the steam condenses. The condensation of the steam produces a vacuum and the atmospheric pressure of 14.7 psi acting on the broad surfaces of the radiator tank would cause them to collapse.

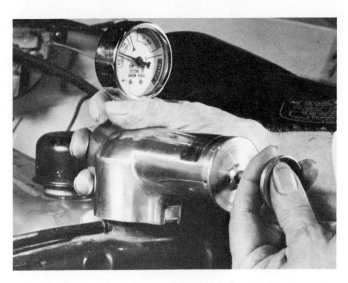

Fig. 17-14. Testing a cooling system for leaks by placing it under pressure. The same equipment can be used for checking radiator caps.

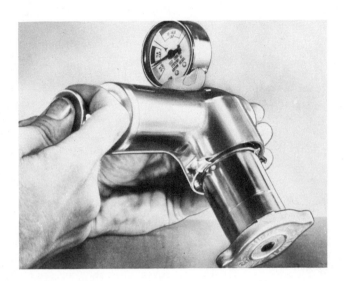

Fig. 17-13a. Pressure type radiator cap being tested on specialized equipment.

When trouble-shooting the cause of overheating and consequent loss of coolant, Fig. 17-18b, the first step is to make a careful visual inspection to see if there is any evidence of external leakage. All surfaces of the radiator and its hose connections should be carefully inspected. Leaks will have generally caused corrosion which is easily seen. The engine must also be carefully inspected, paying particular attention to the core plugs and edges of the cylinder gasket. Do not overlook the rear face of the engine. As there is little clearance between the rear face of the engine and the fire wall, a mirror will sometimes be of assistance. The water pump must also be carefully checked for evidence of leakage, and the car heater and its hose connections.

The visual inspection must also include the fan and its drive belt. The blades should not be bent and the belt must be adjusted to the proper tension and in good condition. It should not have any ridges, nor should it be frayed.

But not all coolant leakage is external. Severe cases of overheating and coolant loss result from leaks into the combustion chamber. When the cylinder head is cracked or there is a blown cylinder head gasket, the hot gases of combustion can enter the cooling system. As the temperature of combustion is in excess of 5,000 deg. F.. The coolant temperature rises rapidly and boiling takes place.

If the crack in the head or the opening in the gasket is large, water will flow into the combustion chamber in such quantities, that on the compression stroke, the water, being incompressible will either break the cylinder head or the top of the piston.

Applying pressure to the system will help disclose any leaks, but not their location. To make the test, pressure is applied to the system and a system free from leaks should maintain pressure for an appreciable time, Fig. 17-14.

Another test, known as the combustion pressure test should also be made. Such a test involves operating the engine under load to detect high-pressure leaks into the combustion chamber.

To perform this test, remove the fan belt, drain coolant and remove thermostat. Add coolant until the level is just below the water outlet opening of the cylinder head and all trapped air removed. To load the engine, raise the rear wheels and run the engine in high gear while simultaneously opening the throttle and applying the brakes. While applying engine load, watch coolant for the appearance of bubbles or sudden rise of level which would indicate leakage from the combustion chamber into the cooling system.

The preceding test should be made before boiling starts to avoid confusion with any steam bubbles that might be formed.

A faster method is to use a combustion leakage tester. This is a chemical test and the tester is applied to the filler neck of the radiator, Fig. 17-15. Then with the engine running, any gas from the combustion chamber which enters the coolant will be drawn into the tester and cause the chemical to change its color.

Making a compression test, Fig. 18-1, of the system will also be helpful in checking for internal leaks, particularly in the case of a blown head gasket. Similarly the spark plugs should be examined for evidence of moisture.

Fig. 17-15. *Using a special tester to check for combustion leakage. Leakage of combustion gases will cause the color of the chemical in the tester to change.*

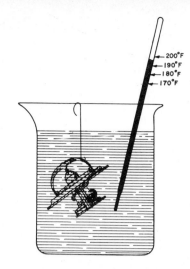

Fig. 17-16. *Using a thermometer to check the opening and closing points of a cooling system thermostat as the water is being heated.*

A thermostat "frozen" in the closed position will also cause extreme overheating and it is important to check each thermostat in a tester, Fig. 17-16, to be sure they are opening and closing at the correct temperatures.

Flushing the Cooling System

It is important to flush the cooling system, preferably twice each year. This is usually done before filling the system with antifreeze and again when the system is drained of antifreeze. In climates where antifreeze is not needed, the system is flushed in the fall and again in the spring.

Most authorities are in agreement that permanent

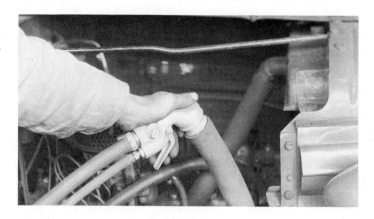

Fig. 17-17. *Using a power flushing gun to reverse flush the cooling system.*

This view from the left rear of the Oldsmobile front drive Toronado shows the 425 cu. in. V-eight engine with the Turbo Hydra-Matic transmission and differential attached. The oval shaped housing at the right conceals the power transfer chain.

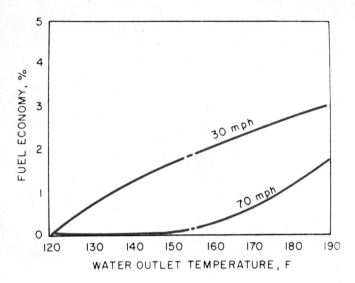

Fig. 17-18. Note how fuel economy improves as water outlet temperature is raised.

type antifreeze should not be left in the system throughout the year. It is important to remember that water should not be added to certain types of permanent antifreeze, as that would form a heavy mud-like substance which effectively clogs the system.

When flushing the system, it is important that the car heater be in the "ON" position so that it too will be drained and flushed. Also that the engine drain plugs be opened as well as the drain plug at the bottom of the radiator.

The thermostat should also be removed and the water outlet housing should then be installed. Disconnect the radiator upper hose at the engine and direct it away from the engine and toward the floor. Also disconnect the radiator lower hose. With a "reverse flush" gun, Fig. 17-17, air and water are then applied to the lower hose forcing water in a

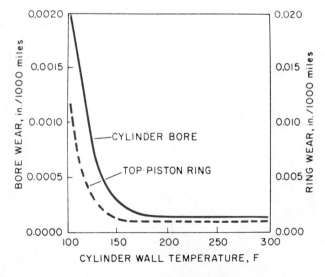

Fig. 17-18a. Both cylinder wall and top piston ring wear decrease as cylinder wall temperature is raised.

reverse flush through the radiator.

With the radiator disconnected, the engine is reversed flushed in the same manner by applying the air and water to the upper outlet.

The reverse flush gun is so designed that water and compressed air are delivered to the nozzle and the quantity of water and the amount of air pressure can both be controlled with suitable valves.

This method is effective in flushing out all soft mud and sludge that may have collected in the system.

To determine whether a radiator is clean, first plug the lower outlet and fill the radiator to the top with water. Then remove the plug from the lower outlet and the water should spurt out with a vigorous stream to a height of approximately 5 in., Fig. 17-18c.

Cooling System Checks

To test for restrictions in the radiator, first bring the system up to operating temperature. Then shut off the engine and feel the front surface of the radiator. On cross flow radiators, the radiator should feel hot along the left side and warm along the right side with an even temperature rise from right to left bottom to top. On vertical flow radiators, the radiator should feel warmer at the top than at the bottom. Any cold spots would indicate clogged sections.

Water pump operation can be checked by running the engine while squeezing the radiator upper hose. A pressure surge should be felt. Check for plugged vent hole in pump.

Note: A defective head gasket may allow exhaust gases to leak into the cooling system. This is particularly damaging to the system as the gases combine with the water to form acids which will tend to corrode radiator and engine parts. This is also a cause of excessive temperature.

Cleaning the Cooling System

Unless very severely clogged with rust and hard scale, cooling systems can be cleaned with special chemicals designed for the purpose. The procedure is to put the chemical into the system which is first filled with water. The engine is then operated for a designated length of time. The chemical, after dissolving the rust and scale is flushed from the system.

Care must be taken not to leave the chemical in the system longer than the designated length of time as it may attack the metal core of the radiator and cause leaks.

In severe cases of clogged radiators it is necessary to remove them and have them cleaned by specialized equipment, Fig. 17-18d. In some cases the entire radiator is immersed in a cleaning solution. In other cases the upper and lower tanks are removed, and after softening the rust by placing in a chemical bath, thin rods are forced through the radiator tubes to clean out the softened rust.

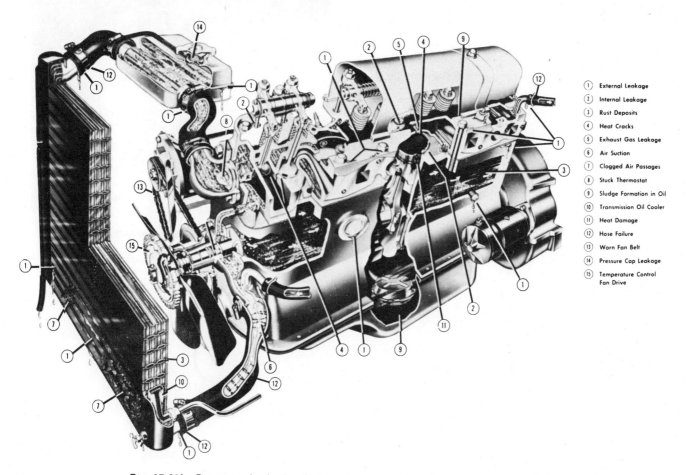

1. External Leakage
2. Internal Leakage
3. Rust Deposits
4. Heat Cracks
5. Exhaust Gas Leakage
6. Air Suction
7. Clogged Air Passages
8. Stuck Thermostat
9. Sludge Formation in Oil
10. Transmission Oil Cooler
11. Heat Damage
12. Hose Failure
13. Worn Fan Belt
14. Pressure Cap Leakage
15. Temperature Control Fan Drive

Fig. 17-18b. Points to check when looking for causes of overheating and loss of coolant.

Fig. 17-18c. One method of checking a radiator for free flow.

Rust Inhibitors

Whenever a cooling system has been cleaned and flushed it is necessary to use a rust inhibitor when refilling the system with water. This is necessary to prevent the formation of rust. Antifreeze solutions include an inhibitor so it is not necessary to use an additional inhibitor.

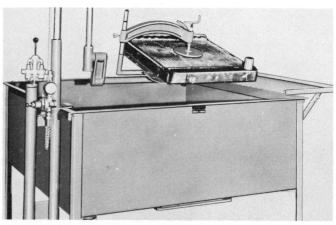

Fig. 17-18d. Specialized equipment used in cleaning, testing and repair of radiators.

Causes of Overheating

A slight amount of overheating may result in little or no coolant loss. However, when the condition causing the overheating becomes more extreme coolant loss will result. The list of causes follows:

Manifold heat control valve sticking.
Fan belt slipping.
Thermostat stuck.
Radiator fins obstructed.
External leak from cylinder head gasket.
Internal leak from cylinder head gasket.
Internal leak from combustion chamber.
Radiator cap leaks.
Radiator cap stuck.
Faulty fan drive clutch.
Worn fan pulleys.
Defective water pump.
Radiator hose collapsing.
Blocked or restricted water manifold.
Cooling system clogged with rust and scale.
Radiator frontal area obstructed.
Air pocket in cooling system.
Leaking radiator.
Leaking cooling system hoses.
Leaking engine water jacket.
Leaking car heater.
Leaking radiator supply tank.
Cylinder core plugs leaking.
Excessive engine friction.
Thermostat defective.
Ignition timing retarded.
Brakes dragging.

Air Cooling Problems

It is important to remember in the operation of air cooled engines that they never be overloaded or "lugged," because the cooling system is dependent on fan speed, which in turn is dependent on engine speed. Transmission gears should be shifted as needed to maintain engine speed at a good level.

Air cooled automobile engines are usually enclosed entirely in a sheet metal housing or shroud. See Fig. 17-19. The cooling air volume entering this shroud is controlled by an automatic thermostatically operated valve. Obviously the air flow cannot be controlled and directed where it is wanted, if there are any air leaks in the shroud. Even the spark plugs are sealed to the shroud as shown in Fig. 17-20. These seals must be in good condition and properly installed.

The Volkswagen has an unusual method of adjusting the fan belt tension by fitting more or less spacer washers between the two pulley halves. See Fig. 17-21. Removal of washers increases the effective diameter of the driven pulley. When all washers have been removed, a new belt is installed. The correct relation is shown in Fig. 17-22. When washers are removed from between the pulley halves, they are placed be-

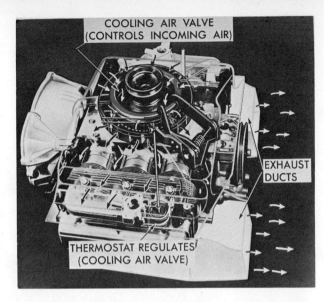

Fig. 17-19. The entire Corvair cooling system is enclosed by a sheet metal housing.

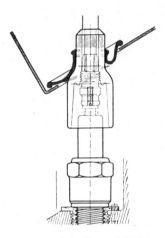

Fig. 17-20. Location of seals on Volkswagen spark plugs.

tween outer pulley half and pulley nut, and left there until needed. DO NOT attempt to remove or replace this belt by stretching it over either of the pulley flanges. Basic causes for overheating of air cooled engines are:

A. Dirt on cooling fins.
B. Oil cooler dirty.
C. Air leaks in shroud or seals.
D. Loose spark plug boots.
E. Thermostat stuck in closed position.
F. Improper adjustment of air control ring.
G. Worn fan belt.
H. Slipping fan belt.

Related Troubles

It will be seen from the foregoing that many engine defects are common to both high oil consumption and overheating. There is a definite relation between the two, and searching for the cause of either trouble will often disclose the need for correction in either or both the oil and water circulation systems.

192

Fig. 17-21. *Method of transferring spacing washers to tighten Volkswagen fan belt.*

Low Oil Pressure

In most cases of low oil pressure, it will be found that the oil pressure is satisfactory when the engine is first started up, and then drops as the engine warms up. Such a condition is almost positive proof that excessive clearance exists at some point, or points, such as connecting rod bearings, main bearings, camshaft bearings, etc. The reason is that the cold oil has thickened, and does not flow as readily through the clearance. When the oil heats up and thins out, it flows through the worn bearings so fast that the pump cannot maintain sufficient pressure. See also Oil Pressure Test, page 175.

Exhaust Back Pressure

If the exhaust pipe, muffler or tail pipe should be partially restricted, the heat is unable to escape readily with the result the combustible charge will be severely diluted and full power will not be developed. In addition, temperature of the exhaust valves will rise to such an extent that the valves will burn and have to be replaced. In extreme cases the engine will start readily, but quickly lose speed and power and then stop.

Excessive Vibration

A process of elimination is often the only way to discover where the trouble lies. Consider the case where there is a pronounced vibration in the car at a

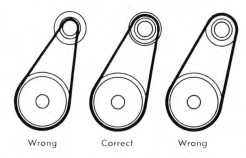

Wrong   Correct   Wrong

Fig. 17-22. *Proper and improper pulley relations on Volkswagen engine.*

certain speed range. First of all it is necessary to determine whether the unbalance is in the engine or the chassis, or both.

If it is in the engine or the parts that rotate with the engine, the vibration should occur at the critical engine speed when the car is not in motion. If it is in the chassis, it will occur only when the car is operated at the critical speed. It is most likely to be found in the chassis, because the engine assembly is carefully balanced at the factory. Out-of-balance tires and propeller shafts are a common cause of chassis vibration.

Unbalance Correction

Wheel unbalance may be in the wheel itself, but is more often found in the tire or brake drum assembly. Each wheel can be checked easily with a wheel spinning device, and the correction made by the addition of weights as described in the wheel alignment section of this text.

Another frequent cause of chassis vibration is unbalance in the driveshaft or universal joints. Methods of location and correction are described under that subject elsewhere in this text.

If the chassis is eliminated as a source of the trouble, and the vibration is in the engine or related parts, we can carry the process of elimination further. If the vibration can be altered or eliminated by holding the clutch out of engagement, the trouble could be in the clutch or transmission shaft. This of course does not apply to cars equipped with automatic transmissions.

If the trouble is suspected to be in the fan, water pump or generator, the drive belts can be removed temporarily and the engine checked with these units not in operation.

If the vibration continues with all the foregoing possibilities eliminated, it is possible that repair work on the engine or clutch has destroyed the original balance of the engine; for example, the installation of one or more new pistons or connecting rods of unmatched weight, reinstallation of the clutch cover plate in incorrect position, etc. Even the accumulation of dust from the wear of the clutch facing lodging in one place in the clutch housing can cause trouble. With automatic transmission equipped cars, a low fluid level in the transmission may even cause unbalance.

It is often possible to compensate for minor unbalance in the engine and clutch assembly, by installing flat washers under the heads of the cap screws holding the clutch to the flywheel. This is a tedious procedure of trying the washers at different spots around the bolt circle, and checking each time for any improvement or worsening of the vibration. The same procedure is possible where an automatic transmission torque converter or fluid flywheel needs correction for unbalance.

Engine Noise

One of the most difficult of all trouble-shooting jobs--and one which occurs frequently--is to locate the source of noise or "knocks" in an engine. Actually, every rotating or reciprocating part in the engine is a potential source of noise. In many cases however, certain noises possess characteristics which help identify their origin.

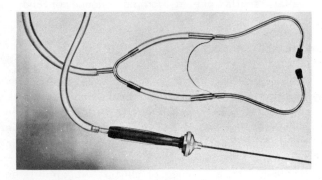

Fig. 17-23. Stethoscope type of instrument for locating noise in engine parts.

These characteristics vary somewhat between different engines. In most cases it will be helpful to utilize an instrument of the stethoscope type to localize the noise at some definite section of the engine. See Fig. 17-23. These instruments magnify the intensity of the noise and the sound becomes louder as the instrument nears the origin of the noise. See Fig. 17-24.

Fig. 17-24. Method of using a stethoscope instrument to locate engine noises.

Loose Connecting Rods

The conditions of operation under which the noise is heard and the "timing" of the noise are also useful in determining the source. Some noises are louder as the engine speed is increased, or the engine is put under load. For example, a connecting rod bearing that is slightly loose will usually knock loudest around an engine speed of about 40 mph, and of greatest intensity just as the engine goes from a pull to a coast. In other words, just as the driver takes his foot off the accelerator.

A rod in very bad condition will be heard at all speeds and under both idle and load conditions. One rod will make a distinct noise, and if all rods are loose, the noise becomes a rattle or clatter. A pressure lubricated engine seldom becomes this bad, as ordinarily the oil consumption would become so high that the rods would need to be replaced long before they became noisy.

In many cases, slightly loose rods are confused with piston slap or loose piston pins. This is particularly true when all rods are loose, and experience will be helpful in deciding which part is at fault. It is not of too much importance to decide definitely, because the remedy for either fault involves removal of the rod or rods in practically all cases. Measurement and inspection of the parts will then disclose where the trouble lies.

Loose Piston Pins

Using a stethoscope is sometimes helpful, as a piston or pin may sound loudest when instrument prod is placed on the cylinder head or block. The rod knock is often loudest with the prod on the crankcase. Shorting out the spark plug on one cylinder may change the intensity of the knock but will not always eliminate it entirely.

Shorting out one or more spark plugs will thus help to locate which cylinder or rod is at fault in cases where the noise is not due to looseness in all cylinders or rods.

Piston Slap

There is much confusion between the noise caused by a piston with excessive clearance in the cylinder and a loose piston pin. Either defect produces a click which is quite distinct. If in all cylinders, it becomes a rattle. One indication of piston slap, is a decrease in the noise as the engine warms up. A piston slap is always louder when the engine is cold.

A piston slap may occur in an engine when new piston pins are installed in old pistons. This is particularly true, if the pins are fitted somewhat too tight. Such noise may disappear entirely after the engine is operated a few hundred miles, and the pins have loosened up a bit.

Loose piston pins usually, but not always, produce a double rap each revolution of the crankshaft--once at the top of the stroke, and again at the bottom. On most engines, the knock is loudest at idling speed, and will become even louder if the spark is advanced. Quite often the knock will be louder, if the plug is shorted out in cases where all pins are not loose.

Piston Ring Noise

The installation of new piston rings will almost surely cause a knock, if the ridge at the top of the cylinder bore is not removed completely before the new rings are installed. Somewhat similar is the condition where the cylinders have been rebored oversize, and the cylinder head gasket extends into the combustion chamber. The piston strikes the gasket, and makes a distinct knock. See Fig. 17-25.

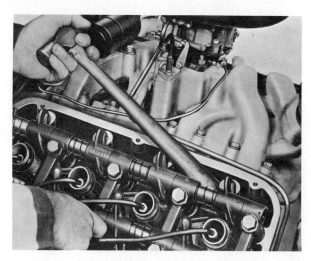

Fig. 17-26. A noisy valve may sometimes be located by sidewise pressure.

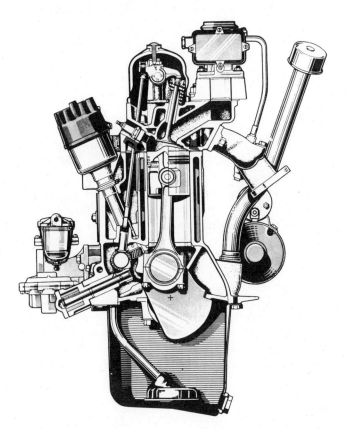

Fig. 17-25. In a rebuilt engine the piston may strike the edge of the head gasket when the engine is first started.

Piston rings that are loose in the grooves will not ordinarily make any noise, as the oil tends to cushion them. If they are excessively loose however--particularly the top ring--they may cause a clicking noise similar to a loose valve tappet. There is a difference in the timing of the click. The rings will click twice each revolution of the crankshaft, while the valve click will be heard once every other revolution.

Valve Noises

Valves are a prolific source of noise for two reasons: there are two valves for each cylinder, and there are several points in each unit of the valve train that can create noise. These several points were described and illustrated earlier in this text. It is usually easy to determine which valve or valves are causing

the noise by inserting a feeler gauge of suitable thickness between the end of the valve and the tappet, or rocker arm with the engine running. Another method as illustrated in Fig. 17-26, may be helpful on overhead valve engines.

If the clicking is caused by wear between the valve lifter and lifter guide, pressing against the side of the lifter with a hammer handle will often stop the noise. A damaged roller or mushroom on the end of the lifter next to the camshaft is not so readily located. Here the timing of the click is helpful as well as the use of a stethoscope.

In the case of hydraulic valve lifters, these will often be noisy when the engine is first started because all the oil has leaked from the unit. The noise should disappear after a few minutes operation during which the lifter will be filled with oil. If the noise does not disappear, the defective lifter can be located by means of a stethoscope.

Worn Timing Gears

Another knock that is difficult to diagnose is caused by worn timing gears. Shorting out the plugs has no effect on the noise and it is about the same intensity whether the engine is idling or pulling. A stethoscope is useful in this case to determine where the noise originates. On engines having an exposed accessory shaft, driven from the timing gears, the knock can be made better or worse by pressing firmly on the accessory shaft with a hammer handle.

Loose Main Bearings

A main bearing knock is more of a bump than a knock and can be located by shorting out the plugs near it. The noise is loudest when the engine is "lugging," that is, pulling hard at slow speed. The sound is heavier and duller than a connecting rod knock.

Crankshaft End Play

Excessive end play in the crankshaft will produce an intermittent rap or knock that is sharper than a loose main bearing. The noise will usually be affected by applying or releasing the clutch. If the car is equipped with an automatic transmission and has no clutch, the noise is more difficult to diagnose.

Loose Flywheel

If the flywheel should be loose on the crankshaft flange, the noise will be similar to a main bearing knock, but ordinarily will not change when the plugs are shorted out. Furthermore, the noise may come and go rather than being constant. One sure test is to turn off the ignition and then turn it on again just as the engine is about to stop. The sudden twist thus applied to the crankshaft will produce the knock in noticeable form.

Noisy Engine Mountings

If the rubber engine mountings are drawn down too tightly, or if the rubber has deteriorated enough to allow the metal parts of the mounting to contact each other a knock may occur. See Fig. 17-27. Such a knock occurs under rapid acceleration.

Miscellaneous Noises

At times a knock will occur in an engine when all parts have been checked for wear, or even in a rebuilt engine. Such knocks are usually due to misalign-

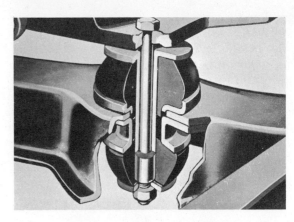

Fig. 17-27. A typical rubber "biscuit" or insulator type of engine mounting pad.

ment or excessive endwise motion. Too much side clearance in a connecting rod bearing, excessive endwise motion of the crankshaft or camshaft are examples. A loose manifold heat control valve or endwise movement of an oil pump or distributor shaft are other examples.

Improper alignment of connecting rods is a common source of hard-to-find engine knocks. Checking and cure of this defect has been covered previously in this text.

Fan and accessory drive belts often cause noise, but the defect is readily detected. Squeaking belts can often be made quiet by the application of available special materials. In the absence of such materials a small amount of soap or talcum powder may serve.

Noise in belt driven units such as water pumps, fans and generators can be quickly isolated by removing the drive belts and then operating the engine.

Quiz - Engine Trouble-Shooting

1. What is the principal cause of high oil consumption?
2. Name two defects, other than worn journals and bearings, that can be found by an oil pressure test.
3. Why must the crankshaft be rotated while an oil pressure test is being made?
4. An oil pressure test should be made: before an engine is disassembled_____, after it has been rebuilt_____.
5. List five causes of engine overheating.
6. Water under 25 psi pressure has a higher or lower boiling point than water under atmospheric pressure? Higher or Lower?
7. What is the pressure in a modern automotive cooling system? 2 psi_____, 5 psi_____, 15 psi _____, 25 psi_____.
8. When flushing a cooling system, should the thermostat be removed? Yes or No?
9. What procedure should be followed when most of the coolant has boiled from the cooling system?
   a. Add water immediately.
   b. Stop the engine and add water.
   c. Keep the engine running and add water.
10. Water coming from the exhaust tail pipe is a sure indication that a cylinder head gasket is blown. True or False?
11. Spark plugs on an air cooled engine are sealed in the shroud. True or False?
12. When flushing the cooling system should the hot water car heater be in the "on" or "off" position? On_____, Off_____.
13. What is the function of a pressure type radiator cap?
    a. Control pressure in a cooling system.
    b. Control vacuum in a cooling system.
    c. Control vacuum and pressure in a cooling system.
14. What is the principal cause of low oil pressure?
15. A kink in the muffler tail pipe may cause engine overheating. True or False?

16. Name two common causes of chassis vibration.

17. How can vibration in a generator be detected?

18. Insufficient fluid in an automatic transmission may cause engine vibration. True or False?

19. A slightly loose connecting rod bearing will usually knock loudest at: high speed_____, medium speed_____, low speed_____.

20. Shorting out a spark plug will help locate a loose piston pin. True or False?

21. Shorting out a spark plug will help locate a loose flywheel. True or False?

22. A loose main bearing and end play in a crankshaft sound about the same. True or False?

23. What is a common source of knocks in a rebuilt engine?

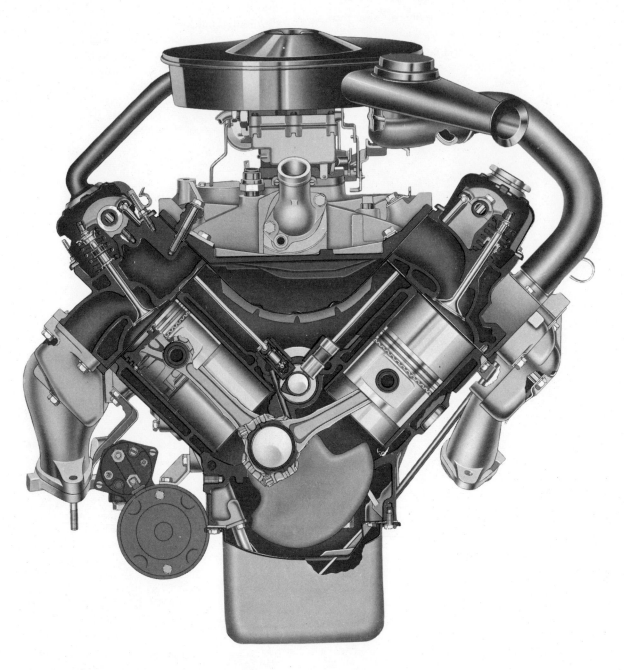

Buick's 430 cu. in. V-8 with 4-barrel carburetor produces 360 hp and 475 ft. lbs. of torque. Its Controlled Combustion System features cylinder head modifications, closed crankcase ventilation and heated carburetor intake air.

ENGINE
TUNE-UP

The term "tune engine" is used and abused to such an extent that its meaning has become unclear. Some so-called "tune-ups" entail nothing more than replacement of plugs, points and condenser. Others are performed with the aid of diagnostic instrumentation that enables the mechanic to solve a particular problem in a particular system rather than make the overall checks and corrections according to a prescribed tune-up test procedure. So confusion does exist about one of the most important of all service operations.

The dictionary definition of "tune-up" as applied to machinery is:

"To make the necessary adjustments, especially the FINER adjustments, which are necessary to bring an engine, as an automobile or airplane engine, into FIRST-CLASS running condition."

The emphasis on "finer" and "first-class" is ours because for our purposes it seems necessary. Obviously, the "finer" adjustments will have to be made before the engine can attain "first-class running condition." Equally obvious is the fact that these finer adjustments cannot be made if the engine has major defects.

Modern Engines Need Modern Service

Engine tuning has become increasingly important as modern engines decrease in size, yet increase in power output. This amazing improvement in efficiency is due to improved design, better materials, more sophisticated manufacturing methods and more exacting quality control. This continuing refinement of engine design and manufacture, with comparable advances in fuels and carburetion, demands a similar refinement of servicing techniques. It means that closer clearances, finer fits, and more accurate adjustments are essential to the maintenance of satisfactory engine performance.

Proper tune-up of a modern engine means splitting degrees, inches and seconds into thousandths. And, obviously, such precise readings can only be obtained by using test instruments that are capable of indicating the measurement of time and space to the fine degree of accuracy that is specified.

It becomes clear then that such close control cannot be maintained if cooling, lubrication or other defects exist in the engine. A tune-up should not be attempted on an engine having leaking pistion rings, faulty valves or valve timing, leaking or loose bearings or worn camshaft lobes. Likewise, if the radiator, water pump or other components of the cooling system are malfunctioning, satisfactory tune-up results cannot be obtained.

Checking Compression Pressure

One of the first steps of an engine tune-up is to make sure that every one of the cylinders has good compression pressure. It is also important that no wide variation in pressure exists between the various cylinders. Engine manufacturers generally prescribe a specific pressure range such as 130-170 psi and a maximum variation between cylinders, such as 20 psi. A special compression gauge is used to make the test, Fig. 18-1. The engine should be at normal operating temperature. The engine oil should be of proper grade and not seriously diluted.

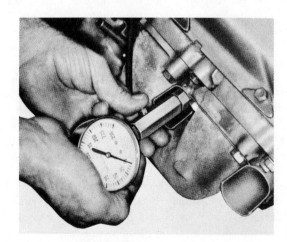

Fig. 18-1. A compression test will give good indication of internal engine condition. Manufacturers specify minimum psi requirement and maximum variation between cylinders.

Make the test with all spark plugs removed and with choke and throttle valves of the carburetor wide open. Use a remote starter switch to crank over the engine while holding the tip of the compression gauge

Maximum Pressure Pounds/ Sq. Inch	Minimum Pressure Pounds/ Sq. Inch	Maximum Pressure Pounds/ Sq. Inch	Minimum Pressure Pounds/ Sq. Inch
134	101	186	140
136	102	188	141
138	104	190	142
140	105	192	144
142	107	194	145
144	108	196	147
146	110	198	148
148	111	200	150
150	113	202	151
152	114	204	153
154	115	206	154
156	117	208	156
158	118	210	157
160	120	212	158
162	121	214	160
164	123	216	162
166	124	218	163
168	126	220	165
170	127	222	166
172	129	224	168
174	131	226	169
176	132	228	171
178	133	230	172
180	135	232	174
182	136	234	175
184	138	236	177
		238	178

Fig. 18-2. *This Buick compression pressure limit chart is typical of psi range calculated to provide 25 percent variation between highest and lowest pressure reading.*

in each spark plug port in turn. Crank the engine for at least four revolutions, recording the highest reading on the gauge for each cylinder. Compare the complete compression score with the manufacturer's specifications, Fig. 18-2. If one or more cylinders is "out-of-specification," there is no use tuning up the engine until the cause has been determined and corrected.

If the compression pressure varies more than the prescribed range between cylinders, it can be assumed that the cylinders, rings or valves—or all three—are defective. To check, introduce a tablespoonful of engine oil into the low-reading cylinder. Then recheck compression. If there is a definite improvement, the piston rings are probably at fault. If there is no improvement, one or both valves may be burnt or not seating.

If two weak cylinders are adjacent, it might indicate a "blown" cylinder head gasket. In any case, the cylinder head will probably have to be removed to remedy the defect. It is good practice, however, to check further with a vacuum gauge before removing the head.

Using a Vacuum Gauge

In the hands of an experienced operator, a vacuum gauge can provide considerable useful information about the condition of the internal parts of an engine. However, it is easy to misinterpret the readings of the

instrument and reach false conclusions. In using the gauge on an engine, it is much more important to note the action of the needle (floating or vibrating, for example) rather than the numbers on the dial.

When properly used and understood, a vacuum gauge will indicate these kinds of defects:

Incorrect carburetor adjustment.
Ignition timing errors.
Ignition defects.
Improper valve action.
Restricted exhaust system.
Cylinder leakage.
Intake system leakage.

Experienced mechanics can break these troubles down to pinpoint just where the trouble lies.

If an engine is in good internal condition and running in good adjustment, the vacuum gauge needle will hold steady at a reading between 17 and 21 at idling speed. There will be some variation with changes in altitude and atmospheric conditions. For example, each 1,000 ft. above sea level will lower the reading about one point (or one inch of mercury). See Fig. 18-3. An eight-cylinder engine will ordinarily read somewhat higher than a four or six.

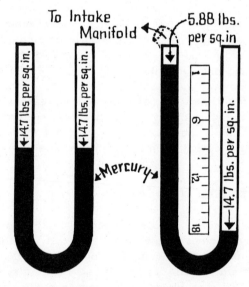

Fig. 18-3. *Vacuum gauge dials are marked in inches of mercury to to correspond with "U" tube laboratory instrument.*

Interpreting the Readings

With the engine warmed up to operating temperature and running slightly higher than at low idling speed, attach a vacuum gauge to the intake manifold. Attach it directly to the vacuum pipe on the inlet manifold, in order to avoid any leaks that might exist in the windshield wiper or connections. Then make the following tests:

NORMAL: Needle will be steady between 17 and 21 while idling. When the throttle is suddenly opened

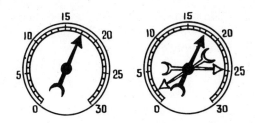

Fig. 18-4. If engine vacuum is good, gauge needle will remain steady between 17 and 21 psi at sea level and bounce violently when throttle is opened and closed.

and closed, the needle will drop to below 5, then bounce up to around 25. See Fig. 18-4.

LEAKING RINGS: Needle may be fairly steady, but will read 3 to 4 points lower than normal. When throttle is suddenly opened and closed, needle may sink to zero, then bounce back to around 22. A compression pressure test, following introduction of oil in the cylinder, may be necessary as a final check.

SLOW TIMING: If compression is good and needle reads lower than it should, ignition timing may be slow, Fig. 18-5. If reading is considerably lower than it should be, valve timing may be slow. If adjusting carburetor will not increase vacuum to normal, make a check to see if either or both, ignition or valve timing, should be advanced.

LEAKING INTAKE: If needle is steady but from 3 to 9 points low, throttle valve is not closing, or an air leak probably exists in carburetor, intake manifold or gaskets.

LEAKING CYLINDER HEAD GASKET: If needle floats regularly between a low and a high reading, the cylinder head gasket probably is "blown" between two adjacent cylinders.

CARBURETOR OUT OF ADJUSTMENT: Needle floats slowly over a range of 4 to 5 points.

SPARK PLUG GAPS: If needle floats slowly over a narrower range--perhaps 2 points--the spark plug gaps may be spaced too close or else the ignition points are not operating properly.

RESTRICTED EXHAUST: If needle reads in normal range when engine is first started, sinks to zero, then rises slowly to below normal, the muffler may be clogged or the tail pipe kinked or plugged.

DEFECTIVE VALVE ACTION: Experience will help you to distinguish between valve troubles such as leaking, burned, sticking valves, weak valve springs or worn valve guides. Action of the needle and range of motion are indications of which is at fault. A study of diagram, Fig. 18-5, will be helpful. Since the valve must be removed in most cases to remedy the defect, correctness of the diagnosis can be determined.

ENGINE MECHANICAL CONDITION: If vacuum gauge indicates loss of compression or improper valve action, do not try to proceed with tune-up until the faults are corrected. If, however, tests indicate timing errors, intake leaks, carburetor out of adjustment or a restricted exhaust system, correct these defects as the next step.

Tune-Up Procedure

Much of tune-up work is concerned with components of the fuel and ignition systems, particularly the carburetor, battery, spark plugs, ignition points and condenser. Each is a complete subject in itself and is covered in another chapter of this text.

However, to illustrate the broad scope of tune-up, the following test procedure gives the latest techniques and most efficient sequence of operations for doing an effective tune-up job:

1. Preliminary Tests and Inspection.
    A. Remove air cleaner and make a general visual inspection of engine and accessories, including battery condition and possible need for carburetor cleaning.
    B. Use an oscilloscope, if available, to make area checks of ignition system operation. Or, use an ignition tester to test ignition efficiency.

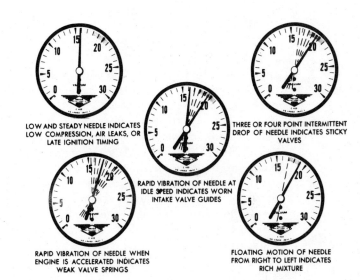

LOW AND STEADY NEEDLE INDICATES LOW COMPRESSION, AIR LEAKS, OR LATE IGNITION TIMING

THREE OR FOUR POINT INTERMITTENT DROP OF NEEDLE INDICATES STICKY VALVES

RAPID VIBRATION OF NEEDLE AT IDLE SPEED INDICATES WORN INTAKE VALVE GUIDES

RAPID VIBRATION OF NEEDLE WHEN ENGINE IS ACCELERATED INDICATES WEAK VALVE SPRINGS

FLOATING MOTION OF NEEDLE FROM RIGHT TO LEFT INDICATES RICH MIXTURE

Fig. 18-5. Diagrams show typical action of vacuum gauge needle when various abnormal conditions exist in engine under test.

2. Internal Engine Condition.
    A. Remove spark plugs and use a compression gauge and remote starter switch to test compression pressure of individual cylinders.
    B. Or, use a cylinder leakage tester to test for leakage of air under pressure into intake or exhaust manifold, crankcase or cooling system.
    C. Use a vacuum gauge to check for vacuum leaks.
3. Inspect and Test Spark Plugs.
    A. Examine spark plug insulators and electrodes for wear or breakage, Fig. 18-6.
    B. Analyze deposits to pinpoint problem in individual cylinders or need for plugs of a different heat range.

C. Use spark plug cleaner and tester to test efficiency of plugs under pressure.

D. Clean electrodes, then file and regap good used plugs, or replace defective ones with a new set of specified type and proper heat range (use new gaskets).

E. Install plugs to correct torque tightness.

F. Connect cable terminals securely to plugs in correct firing order.

4. Test and Service Battery.

A. Clean posts, cable clamps and top of battery.

B. Check level of electrolyte in cells, and use a hydrometer to check specific gravity of each cell. (Should be at least 1.250 with no more than 25 points of gravity difference between high and low cells.)

C. Load test battery at three times its ampere hour rating, noting voltmeter after 15 sec. discharge. (Should be 9.5 volts or more.)

D. Recharge or replace a defective battery.

5. Check Starting System.

A. Inspect condition of cables and wires, mounting of components.

B. Use a voltmeter to test for voltage drop in cables, connections, switch, solenoid and starting motor.

C. Use a battery-starter tester to test amperage draw of starter. Ground distributor terminal of ignition coil and connect test leads to battery terminals. Crank engine for 15 seconds and note voltmeter reading. Stop cranking and adjust resistance unit on tester to obtain voltage previously noted, then read amperage draw on ammeter. (Check reading against manufacturer's specifications.)

6. Test Ignition Coil.

A. Use a voltmeter to check primary ignition voltage at battery side of ignition coil. (Voltage should be equal to battery voltage while starting motor is operating since ballast resistor is bypassed.)

B. Perform same test with engine running. (Voltage should be between 8 and 10 volts.)

C. If an oscilloscope is available, check required and available high tension voltage and high tension polarity. (Should be negative.)

D. Test high tension cables with ohmmeter. (Readings should not exceed 4,000 ohms per foot, not more than 16,000 ohms maximum per cable.)

7. Service Ignition Distributor.

A. Check condition of distributor cap (inside and out) and rotor.

B. Note position of rotor and remove distributor from engine.

C. Clean distributor and check condition of lead wires, plate, cam, bushings and advance mechanism.

D. Replace breaker points and condenser. Align points, if necessary, and adjust gap to manufacturer's recommended setting.

E. Test breaker arm spring tension.

F. Lubricate oil cup, if so equipped. Also lubricate wick and cam lobes (use high melting point grease).

G. Check operation of mechanical and vacuum advance units.

H. Test point dwell and readjust point gap, if necessary. (Generally, dwell variation at 250 and 2,000 rpm should not exceed 3 deg.)

I. Install distributor in engine with rotor in original position.

J. Leave spark advance vacuum line disconnected, but cover open end with tape.

8. Check Cooling System.

A. Inspect condition of radiator, hoses and clamps, including transmission oil cooler lines and connections.

B. Test radiator cap for pressure release point and pressure-holding ability.

C. Check level of coolant in radiator and degree of antifreeze protection.

D. Use pressure tester to test cooling system for leaks. (Pressurize to pressure release point of cap and observe for at least two minutes.)

E. Check condition and tension of V-belts.

9. Inspect Fuel System.

A. Torque tighten intake manifold attaching bolts.

B. Check freedom of operation of manifold heat control valve, if so equipped.

C. Check carburetor base heating units on engines so equipped.

D. Service all air filters and fuel filters; clean or replace elements as required.

E. Tighten carburetor attaching nuts or bolts and cover screws.

F. Clean automatic choke mechanism and test vacuum piston for freedom of operation.

G. Check adjustment of choke, unloader, dashpot and kickdown; tighten heat tube fittings.

H. Inspect fuel lines, hoses and connections for fuel leaks, kinks, restriction or deterioration.

I. Check operation of accelerator linkage; clean and adjust as required.

J. Check for proper fuel tank venting.

K. Test fuel pump for pressure, capacity and vacuum.

L. Service positive crankcase ventilation system, as required.

M. Service exhaust emission control system on engines so equipped.

10. Start Engine and Make Preliminary Adjustments.
    A. Run engine, check choking action and fast idle operation.
    B. Connect timing light to ignition system and check initial timing. Reconnect vacuum line and recheck advance with timing light.
    C. Examine exhaust system for leaks.
    D. Warm engine to operating temperature and check thermostat operation.
    E. Install tachometer and vacuum gauge; adjust air-fuel mixture and engine idle speed.
    F. Connect an exhaust gas analyzer to car and test combustion efficiency of engine at speeds ranging from 500 to 1750 rpm.
    G. Adjust valve lash, if engine has solid lifters.

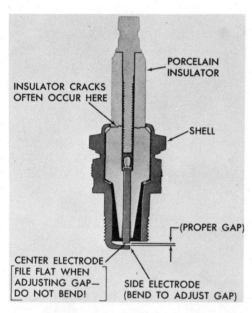

Fig. 18-6. Details of spark plug construction are indicated in this phantom cross-sectional view. Use round feeler gauge to adjust gap.

11. Test Charging System.
    A. Use a volt-amp tester to test DC generator output and settings of voltage regulator, current regulator and cutout relay.
    B. Or, use an alternator tester to test voltage and current output of alternator and operation of voltage regulator.
12. Road Test Car.
    A. Check starting and idle; test engine performance at all speeds.
    B. Check automatic transmission shift points and kickdown operation.
    C. Make final adjustments to carburetor, ignition timing, throttle linkage, etc., as required, for best overall performance of engine.

High Speed Tuning

Engine tuning is carried to extremes when it is desired to obtain the maximum speed and power out of an engine. This procedure often involves extensive mechanical alteration of the engine, such as porting and relieving the cylinder block, increasing the compression ratio, enlarging the valves, altering the bore and stroke of the engine, installing special, custom-made camshafts, etc.

Intake and exhaust manifolds are increased in size and streamlined, multiple carburetors or fuel injectors are installed, valve timing and ignition timing are altered, etc. This is a complete and complicated subject in itself and is not within the scope of this text.

Exhaust Emission Tuning

Great care and precision are required when tuning late model cars which have equipment designed to reduce exhaust and crankcase emissions. Failure to follow factory instructions and specifications may result in rough idle, surging, loss of power, increase in emissions and dieseling.

Equipment installed to reduce these emissions includes:
1. Closed crankcase ventilating system.
2. Limiter on idle fuel adjustment.
3. Transmission controlled spark advance.
4. Injection of air into exhaust ports.
5. Heated carburetor air intake.
6. Distributor advance control.
7. Dual diaphragm distributor.
8. Evaporative control system.

These devices must be in good working order and properly adjusted. Government regulations state that none should be disconnected or made inoperative. Emission control units and their functioning are described in appropriate sections of this text.

Quiz - Engine Tune-Up

1. What is one of the first and most important steps of an engine tune-up?
2. Name five engine defects that can be discovered by use of a vacuum gauge.
3. At an elevation of 5,000 ft. above sea level, an engine in good condition will give a vacuum gauge reading of:
   a. 12-17.
   b. 17-21.
   c. 21-26.
4. If the vacuum gauge needle is steady, but the reading is extremely low, the trouble is likely to be:
   a. Narrow spark plug gaps.

b. Leaking piston rings.

c. Air leak in intake system.

5. When the needle floats slowly over a range of 4 or 5 points, the trouble may be:

   a. Ignition timing is slow.

   b. Carburetor is out of adjustment.

   c. Exhaust system is restricted.

6. What is the maximum time of high rate discharge during a battery load test?

   a. 5 seconds.

   b. 15 seconds.

   c. 25 seconds.

7. What should the manifold heat control valve be tested for?

   a. Valve lash.

   b. Torque tightness.

   c. Freedom of operation.

8. What instruments are used to help set the carburetor air-fuel mixture adjustment and engine idle speed?

9. What three tests should be made on the fuel pump?

10. What test instrument is used to test DC generator output and settings of voltage regulator, current regulator and cutout relay?

Using a voltmeter to check voltage at ignition coil.

AUTO
SHOP SAFETY

Safety is everyone's responsibility. It cannot be left to a committee or a few individuals, but everyone must always be on the alert so that he is not the cause of an accident to himself or any of his fellow workers.

One of the basic rules of safety in any shop is proper and correct conduct of every individual. There can be no running, no practical jokes, no horseplay. Such conduct invariably results in accidents as well as distracting the others in the shop from the work they are supposed to do.

Because of the many combustibles, such as gasoline, lacquer thinner and certain cleaning fluids used in automobile repair shops, special precautions are needed to prevent fire. Fuel, thinner and other combustibles should always be kept in closed containers designed for the purpose. This will not only help prevent fire but also the evaporation of the chemicals with attendant loss of profits. Painting should be done in paint spray booths provided with exhaust fans and conforming to underwriters requirements. Smoking and unshielded flames should never be permitted. No smoking signs, Fig. 19-1, should be prominently displayed.

Fig. 19-1. "No Smoking" signs are displayed in the interest of safety. They should be obeyed.

All shops should be provided with an ample number of fire extinguishers. Everyone should be familiar with their location. Remember that water cannot be used to extinguish a gasoline or grease fire. For such fires, carbon tetrachloride, foam or if nothing else is available, sand can be used.

As a further protection against fire, oil and paint rags should be kept in suitable containers. Care must always be exercised so that spontaneous combustion does not occur.

Fig. 19-2. Protective goggles or eye shield should be worn during grinding operations or other jobs when there is a possibility of injury to the eyes.

Painters should always use masks when spraying paint as a guard against respiratory illnesses resulting from the inhalation of paint fumes. Mechanics when using grinding wheels, sanders or when chipping metal should wear goggles as a protection for the eyes, Fig. 19-2. These should also be used when using compressed air to blow dirt from parts.

Special safety precautions are also necessary when working on automotive electrical circuits. Unless the starting battery is needed for making tests of the circuit, it should be disconnected to eliminate the possibility of any short circuits and attendant possibility of fire or damage to the circuit and tools. Most important, a naked flame should not be used to observe the level of the electrolyte in the starting battery. Acid fumes are highly explosive and acid would be splashed into the mechanics eyes. When it becomes necessary to note the electrolyte level a flashlight should be used, Fig. 19-3.

Special care must be observed when removing the cap from an automotive radiator. The cooling system on the modern automobile is under pressure and the sudden removal of the radiator cap will cause the superheated steam and water to be forced out. This will cause severe burns. When removing a radiator cap, it should be covered with a cloth and given a half turn. Then after the steam has escaped and the pressure reduced, the cap can be removed completely without any danger to the mechanic.

Fig. 19-3. The fumes from starting batteries are highly explosive. Use a flashlight when checking the level of the electrolyte.

Ventilation Is Important

One of the most important safety precautions to be followed in any automotive shop is that of proper ventilation. If it is necessary to operate an engine for more than a few moments, the car should be driven outside. A large portion of exhaust fumes consist of carbon monoxide which is a deadly poison. In small quantities it produces drowsiness and headaches. In larger quantities, death results. Many of larger shops are provided with special conduits which are connected to the exhaust of the automobile. These conduits conduct the exhaust gases out-of-doors and in that way danger from carbon monoxide poisoning is eliminated.

Care must be exercised to keep the shop floor clean and free from grease and oil. Such spots are slippery and frequently result in accidents to mechanics and other persons walking through the shop. Whenever any oil or grease is spilled or drips on the floor, it should be immediately wiped up. Special preparations are available for absorbing oil, and cleaning the spots.

Equally important, is the necessity of keeping the floor clear of tools and parts. When laid in the aisle, there is always the possibility of someone tripping on them. A similar condition results from a jack handle sticking out into the aisles where it may cause someone to fall. If lifts are not available, and it is necessary to keep the car raised for a protracted period, the car should be placed on horses or stands. In that way there will be no chance of the car falling as the result of a faulty jack. In addition such practice frees the jack for work on other vehicles.

There are also many safety precautions to be followed in the use of tools.

Using Tools Safely

Files should never be used without a handle as there is always the danger of running the pointed tang into the palm of the hand. Neither should files be used as prybars, nor should they be hammered. Files are made with hard temper and consequently are quite brittle and when hammered, small pieces may fly off and cause severe wounds or loss of eyesight. Hardened surfaces such as the face of an anvil should not be struck with a hammer as bits of steel may fly off and cause damage. Further, in connection with hammers and sledges, care must always be exercised that the head is always securely attached to the handle. Loose hammer and sledge heads may fly off when the tool is used and anyone standing in the way will be struck and severely injured.

When the head of a chisel becomes swagged over, it should be discarded or reground to remove the swagged edges. This will prevent bits of steel from flying off and causing damage.

Whenever grinding is done, the mechanic should wear goggles to protect his eyes. The grinding wheel should always be provided with a protecting guard. The reason for the guard is that in the event of the grinding wheel bursting due to centrifugal force, the danger to the operator will be minimized. Unless the grinding wheel is designed to take such strains, its side surfaces should not be used for grinding.

As there is always a possibility of a driving belt breaking or a rotating wheel bursting, it is always advisable to stand away from the plane of rotating parts. In the event of any such breakage, parts will be hurled with terrific force and anyone standing in line with the rotating part may be severely injured.

When using a wrench, there is less danger to the mechanic if he pulls on the handle, rather than pushes on it. In that way, should the wrench slip, there will be less danger of skinning the knuckles. Further in that connection, when the jaws of a wrench become worn or sprung, the wrench should be discarded, as it will no longer fit the nut securely and will tend to slip.

Compressed air is an important "tool" in every shop. The air gun should not be pointed at anyone. The high pressure of the air can blow dirt and dust particles at such high speed that they will puncture the skin, and get into the eyes.

When changing large size truck tires, which have a detachable ring to secure the tire to the rim, do not lean over the tire while it is being inflated. These rings have been blown off the rim by the force of the compressed air and the mechanic severely injured.

Never stand in the same plane as a rotating part, such as the fan belt on an automobile, drive belts of lathes and other machinery, and flywheels. Should a belt break, or part of the rotating unit be thrown off by centrifugal force, severe injuries could result.

Care must always be exercised, when working around any machinery, engine or motor that there is no chance of loose clothing being caught and entangled in rotating parts. For that reason, it is advisable to tuck neckties within the shirt. If long sleeves are being worn, these should be buttoned at the cuff. Caps without brims are considered safer than those with brims, because of the possibility of the protruding brim being caught in some rotating part.

In regard to safety precautions when using oxygen and acetylene for welding there are many points to observe. Never allow oil or grease to contact oxygen under pressure. Do not lubricate welding and cutting apparatus. Never use oxygen as a substitute for compressed air, as a source of pressure, or for ventilation. Before starting to weld or cut, make sure that flame, sparks, hot slag, or hot metal will not be likely to start a fire. Always wear goggles when working with a lighted blowpipe.

Be sure to keep a clear space between the cylinders and the work as you may find it necessary to reach and adjust the regulators quickly. Do not risk hand burns by lighting the torch with a match. Use a friction type lighter as it is safer and also easier. Never use acetylene pressure higher than 15 psi. Never release acetylene where it might cause a fire or an explosion. Always check equipment before starting to work. Never braze, weld or use acetylene flame on gasoline or other fuel tanks.

Oxygen and acetylene tanks should always be in a special carrier or chained to a post to prevent falling.

Quiz - Auto Shop Safety

1. Why are running and practical jokes prohibited in shops?
2. Why should a mask be worn while spraying paint?
3. Starting batteries should always remain connected in the circuit while working on the electrical system. True or False?
4. What happens when a file is used as a pry bar?
   a. It bends
   b. It breaks
   c. It will mar the surfaces
5. Which of the following is correct?
   a. Carbon monoxide is used in welding
   b. Carbon monoxide is a deadly poison
   c. Carbon monoxide is used to inflate tires on race cars
6. Why is it dangerous to stand in the plane of a rotating part?
7. Oxygen fittings on welding equipment should be well lubricated with mineral oil. True or False?

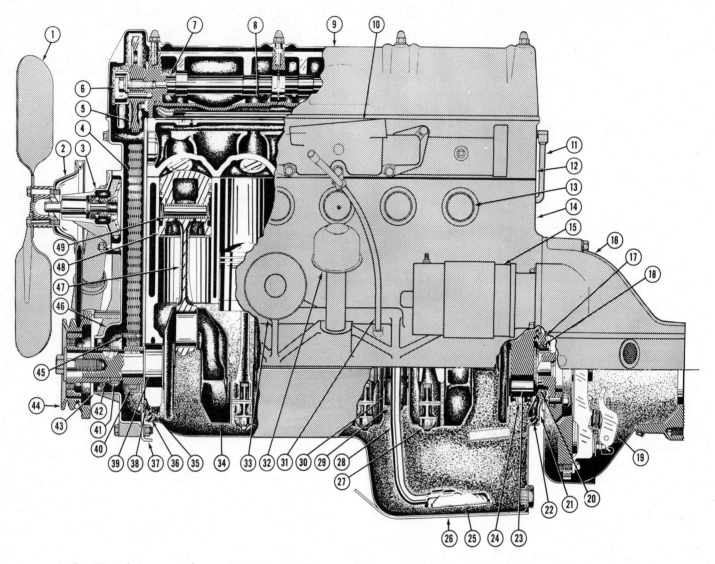

Fig. 19-4. Side sectional view, Jeep Tornado-OHC engine with parts identified. 1—Cooling fan, 2—Fan drive pulley, 3—Water pump, 4—Timing chain, 5—Camshaft sprocket, 6—Fuel pump eccentric, 7—Camshaft, 8—Cam bearing support deck, 9—Rocker arm cover, 10—Intake manifold, 11—Lubrication tube, 12—Cylinder head, 13—Core plug, 14—Cylinder block, 15—Starting motor, 16—Clutch housing, 17—Filler block guard, 18—Upper rear oil seal, 19—Clutch, 20—Lower rear oil seal, 21—Rear filler block, 22—Oil pan seal, 23—Rear main bearing, 24—Rear main bearing cap, 25—Oil intake screen, 26—Oil pan, 27—Connecting rod bearing cap, 28—Oil intake pipe, 29—Intermediate main bearing cap screw, 30—Intermediate main bearing cap, 31—Dipstick guide, 32—Breather cap, 33—Oil filter, 34—Crankshaft, 35—Front filler block, 36—Oil pan seal, 37—Front engine plate, 38—Front main bearing cap, 39—Front main bearing, 40—Timing chain sprocket, 41—Oil pump drive gear, 42—Oil slinger, 43—Timing chain cover oil seal, 44—Vibration damper, 45—Oil fitting, 46—Timing chain cover, 47—Connecting rod, 48—Piston, 49—Piston pin.

AUTOMOTIVE
FUELS

The fuel used in most automobiles and internal combustion engines is gasoline. Other fuels include methanol, benzol, alcohol, alcohol-gasoline blends, and liquid petroleum gas.

Gasoline is a colorless liquid obtained from crude petroleum, as a result of a complicated distillation and cracking process. Two important characteristics of gasoline as used for fuel in automotive engines are volatility, and antiknock characteristics.

The volatility of any liquid is its vaporizing ability. In the case of a simple substance, it is usually determined by its boiling point. For example, the boiling point of water is 212 deg. F. Gasoline is a mixture of hydrocarbon compounds each having its own boiling point. Gasoline as used for motor fuel therefore has a range of boiling points extending from approximately 100 deg. F. up to 400 deg. F., Fig. 20-1.

The fuel must remain a liquid until it enters the air stream in the carburetor throat. At this time, it must quickly vaporize and mix uniformly in the correct proportions with the intake air.

The volatility of gasoline affects ease of starting, length of warming up period, and engine performance during normal operation. For easy starting with a cold engine, the fuel must be highly volatile. In other words, it must vaporize easily. Therefore when cold weather approaches, fuel refiners increase the percentage of highly volatile fuel contained in gasoline, to insure easier starting under the cold weather operating conditions.

If the percentage of volatile fuel is too high, a condition known as vapor lock occurs. Vapor lock results from fuel vaporizing in the fuel line, fuel pump, or in the carburetor before the fuel is actually discharged from the jet. As a result of vapor lock, the engine is starved for fuel, and will stop running. This is not an unusual occurrence, particularly in the springtime before the refiners have reduced the percentage of highly volatile fuel in the gasoline.

In addition to the highly volatile fuel needed for easy starting, fuel not quite so volatile is required for quick warm-up.

A portion of the fuel must also be sufficiently volatile to insure proper vaporization during periods of acceleration. If fuel as sprayed from the acceler-

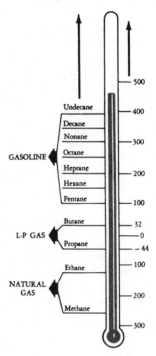

Fig. 20-1. Range of boiling points of hydrocarbons such as gasoline, LPG and natural gas.

ating pump jet does not vaporize readily, it will result in a lean mixture which would exist only for a moment, but which is known as a "flat-spot."

For maximum power and economy of operation, fuel with a lower volatility but high heat content is required.

When weather conditions or overchoking, or a over-rich mixture caused by any condition leaves an excessive amount of fuel unvaporized, the unvaporized fuel seeps by the piston and piston rings into the crankcase. This dilutes the lubricating oil, reduces its lubricating qualities, and tends to form sludge and deposit varnish on the pistons and rings.

Petroleum contains many impurities that must be removed during the refining process before gasoline suitable for automotive use is produced. At one time, considerable corrosion was caused by the sulfur contained in petroleum products. However, modern refining procedure has greatly eliminated that problem.

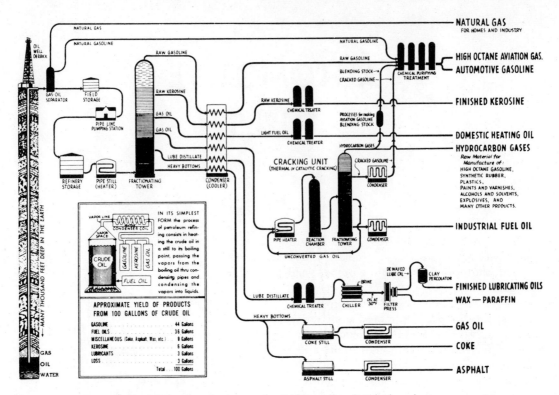

Typical flow chart tracing crude oil from well to finished products.

Another difficulty was the tendency for the hydrocarbons in gasoline to oxidize into a sticky gum when exposed to air. This resulted in clogged carburetor passages, stuck engine valves and excessive deposits in the combustion chamber. Chemicals that control the gumming tendency are now added to gasoline.

Antiknock Qualities

One of the most important qualities of modern fuel is the ability to burn without causing detonation or knocking. The tendency toward detonation is overcome by the addition to the fuel of such compounds as tetra-ethyl lead. In addition, refining processes also aid materially in producing knock-free gasoline.

To understand what is meant by antiknock quality, it is necessary to understand the process of combustion.

When substance burns, it is actually uniting in rapid chemical reaction with oxygen, which is one of the constituents of air. During the burning process, the molecules of the substance and oxygen are set into very rapid motion and heat is produced. In the combustion chamber of an engine cylinder, the gasoline vapor and oxygen in the air are united and burned. They combine, and the molecules begin to move about very rapidly as the high temperatures of combustion are reached. The molecules bombard the combustion chamber walls, and the head of the piston with a rain of fast-moving molecules. It is this bombardment that causes the heavy push on the piston, and forces it downward on the power stroke.

Normal Combustion

The normal combustion process in the combustion chamber, Fig. 20-1a, goes through three stages that are sometimes termed formation or nucleus of flame, hatching out, and propagation.

As soon as the ignition spark jumps the gap of the spark plug, a small ball of blue flame develops in the gap. This ball is the first stage or nucleus of the flame. It enlarges with relative slowness, and during its growth there is no measureable pressure created by the heat.

As the nucleus enlarges, it develops into the hatching-out stage. The nucleus is torn apart so that it sends fingers of flame into the mixture in the combustion chamber. This causes enough heat to give a slight rise in temperature and pressure in the entire fuel-air mixture. Consequently a lag still exists in the attempt to raise pressure in the entire cylinder.

It is during the third stage or propagation, that the effective burning of the fuel takes place. The flame burns in a front which sweeps across the combustion chamber, burning rapidly and causing great heat with its accompanying rise in pressure. It is this pressure which causes the piston to move downward. During normal combustion, the burning is progressive. It increases gradually during the first two stages, but during the third stage the flame is extremely strong as it sweeps through the combustion chamber. However, there is no violent or explosive action such as when detonation, ordinarily responsible for pinging or knocking, occurs.

Detonation

If detonation takes place it occurs during the third stage of combustion, Fig. 20-2. As was pointed out, in the propagation stage, flame sweeps from the area around the spark plug toward the walls of the combustion chamber. Parts of the chamber the flame has passed may contain inert nonburnable gases, but the section not yet touched by flame contains highly compressed heated combustible gases. As the flame races through the combustion chamber, the unburned gases, ahead of it are still further compressed and are heated to higher temperatures. Under certain conditions, the extreme heating of the unburned part of the mixture may cause it to ignite spontaneously and explode. It is this rapid uncontrolled burning in the final stage of combustion which is called detonation. It is caused by the rapidly burning flame front compressing the unburned part of the mixture to the point of self-ignition. This secondary wave front collides with the normal flame front and makes an audible knock or pinging sound.

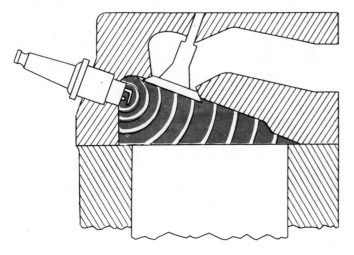

Fig. 20-1a. Normal process of combustion. Compare with Figs. 20-2 and 20-3.

Detonation may harm an engine or hinder its performance in several ways. In extreme cases pistons have been shattered, cylinders burst, or cylinder heads cracked. At times these temperatures resulting from detonation may reach the point where the piston is actually melted. Other effects of detonation may be overheating of the engine, broken spark plugs, overloaded bearings, high fuel consumption, loss of power, etc.

Octane Rating

The ability of a fuel to resist detonation is measured by its octane rating. The octane rating of a fuel is determined by matching it against mixtures of normal heptane and iso-octane in a test engine under specified test conditions, until a mixture of these pure hydrocarbons is found which gives the same degree of knocking in the engine as the gasoline being tested. The octane number of the fuel is then the percent of the iso-octane in the matching iso-octane normal-

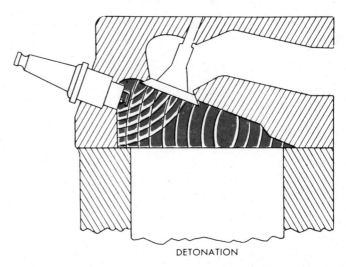

Fig. 20-2. When detonation occurs, unburned gases are compressed ahead of the flame front, raising their pressure and temperature so that it is ignited.

heptane mixture. For example, a gasoline rating of 90 octane is equivalent in its knocking characteristics, to a mixture of 90 percent iso-octane and 10 percent normal heptane.

The tendency of a fuel to detonate varies in different engines, and also in the same engine under different operating conditions. The shape of the combustion chamber is an important factor, but most important of all is the compression ratio. It is important to emphasize that octane number of a fuel has nothing to do with its starting qualities, power, volatility or other major characteristics. If an engine operates satisfactorily with a fuel of a certain octane rating, its performance will not be improved by using fuel of a still higher octane rating.

Fuel Additives

Tetraethyl lead is the most popular compound added to fuel to suppress knocking. In addition to additives used to supress the detonation, some fuels also contain additives designed to reduce the accumulation of deposits in the combustion chamber, and to absorb any moisture which may condense in the fuel. Still another additive is provided to lubricate the valve stems, and the upper area of the cylinder wall. Detonation is not to be confused with preignition. Detonation takes place late in the burning process after the spark has occurred. Preignition, Fig. 20-3, however, is an igniting of the fuel-air mixture during compression, before the spark has occurred as caused by some form of hot spots within the cylinder.

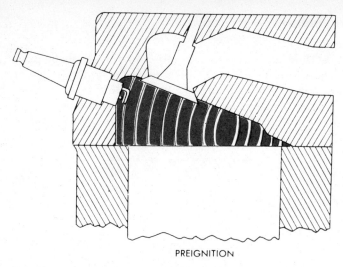

PREIGNITION

Fig. 20-3. Preignition is the igniting of the fuel mixture, before the spark occurs.

Diesel Fuels

The type of fuel available for use in Diesels varies from highly volatile jet fuels and kerosene, to the heavier furnace oil. Automotive Diesel engines are capable of burning a wide range of fuel between these two extremes. How well a Diesel engine can operate with different types of fuel, is dependent upon engine operating conditions, as well as fuel characteristics.

A large variety of fuel oils are marketed for Diesel engine use, by the petroleum industry. Their properties depend on the refining practices employed, and the nature of the crude oil from which they are produced. Fuel oils, for example, may be produced within the boiling range of 300 to 750 deg. F. having many possible combinations of other properties. The classification of commercially available fuel oils that has been set up by the American Society for Testing Materials is shown in Fig. 20-4. Grade 1D fuels range from kerosene to what is called intermediate distillates. Grades 2D, and 4D, each have progressively higher boiling points, and contain more impurities.

The fuels commonly known as high-grade fuels, kerosene and 1D fuels, contribute a minimum amount to the formation of harmful engine deposits and corrosion. There are less impurities present in those fuels, and therefore the tendency for such action to take place is kept to a minimum.

While refining removes the impurities it also lowers the heat value of the fuel. As a result, the higher grade fuels develop slightly less power than the same quantity of low-grade fuel. However this is usually more than offset by other maintenance advantages. Some Diesel fuel systems undergo modification to form what are classified as jet fuels.

Cetane Rating

The delay between the time the fuel is injected into the cylinder and ignition by the hot air is expressed as a cetane number. This is usually between 30 and 60. Rapidly ignited fuels have high cetane ratings, while slow ignited fuels have low cetane ratings.

A fuel with better ignition quality would assist combustion more than a lower cetane fuel during starting and idling conditions when compression temperatures are cooler. For that reason, either with a very high cetane rating of 85-96, is often used for starting Diesel engines in cold weather. The lower the temperature of the surrounding air, the greater the need for fuel that will ignite rapidly.

When the cetane number of the fuel is too low, it may result in difficult starting, engine knock and puffs of white exhaust smoke, particularly during engine warm-up and light load operation. If such conditions continue, harmful engine deposits will accumulate in the combustion chamber.

Boiling Range

The boiling temperature of fuel is also the temperature at which it is completely vaporized. Furthermore, fuel can be completely burned in an engine only in vaporized form. Because of this, the boiling range of fuel oil should be low enough to permit complete vaporization at the existing engine temperature.

For engines operating at reduced speed and load, or in cold weather, lower boiling point fuels will give more satisfactory performance. Fuels that cannot be completely vaporized and burned will accumulate and form sludge and other harmful deposits in the engine.

Sulfur Content

Sulfur content in fuel oil should be as low as possible in order to keep the amount of corrosion and deposit formation at a minimum. Tests have shown that increasing sulfur content from .25 to 1.25 percent increases deposits and wear 135 percent.

Liquefied Petroleum Gas

A mixture of gaseous petroleum compounds, principally butane and propane, together with smaller quantities of similar gases, is known as liquefied petroleum gas. This is frequently abbreviated as LPG or LP gas.

Liquefied petroleum gas is used as fuel for internal combustion engines, principally in the truck and farm tractor fields.

Chemically, LPG is similar to gasoline as it consists of a mixture of compounds of hydrogen and carbon. However, it is a great deal more volatile, and at usual atmospheric temperatures it is a vapor. For that reason, when used as a fuel for internal combustion engines, a special type of carburetor is required.

For storing and transporting LPG, it is compressed and cooled so that it is a liquid, and depending upon conditions; approximately 250 gallons of

LPG are compressed into one gallon of liquid. Because of the pressure it must be stored in strong tanks. The boiling point of propane is approximately 44 deg. F. below zero.

At temperatures below their boiling points, butane and propane exert no pressure, but as the temperature increases, the pressure increases rapidly. For example, at 40 deg. F., liquid propane will have a pressure of 65 lb., while butane will have a pressure of about 3 lb. At 65 deg. F., the pressure of propane will have increased to 100 lb. and butane to 15 lb.

LPG gas is made of surplus material in the oil fields, and is becoming more widely distributed as an increasing number of trucks and tractors are being fitted with the equipment necessary to use it.

In addition to its low cost, LPG has the advantage of having a high octane value. Pure butane has a rating of 93 octane while propane is approximately 100. The octane rating of LPG will range between these two values, depending upon the proportion of each gas used.

As it is a dry gas, LPG does not create carbon in an engine, and does not cause dilution of the engine oil. As a result, maintenance and parts replacement on engines is reduced. In addition, oil changes for the engine can be made at less frequent intervals, because it is such a clean-burning fuel.

Other advantages claimed for LPG are easy cold weather starting, lack of objectionable exhaust odor and elimination of evaporation.

Alcohol

Alcohol is sometimes used as fuel for automotive internal combustion engines. It is a distillate of wood or grain, and has a relatively high octane rating.

Alcohol is frequently used as an additive to commercial gasoline, and in that way will absorb any condensed moisture which may collect in the fuel system.

Water will not pass through the filters which are placed in the fuel line, and consequently when any water collects it will prevent the free passage of fuel. In addition, water will tend to attack or corrode the zinc die castings of which many carburetors and fuel pumps are made. This corrosion will not only destroy the parts but also will clog the system, preventing the the flow of fuel. By using alcohol in gasoline, any water present will be absorbed and will then pass through the fuel filters and carburetor jets, and into the combustion chamber.

Alcohol is frequently used in combination with benzol as a fuel for race engines.

Benzol

Benzol is a volatile liquid hydrocarbon obtained in the refinement of coal tar. It has a high octane value, and is used occasionally to blend with gasoline to increase its octane value, and is also used in combination with alcohol for race car engines.

Heat Value

The power obtained from any fuel is determined by its heat value. This is measured by burning a unit amount of fuel in an excess of air or oxygen, and is measured in British thermal units per pound of fuel. One British thermal unit (Btu) is the amount of heat required to raise one pound of water from 39 deg. to 40 deg. F. One Btu is equal to 778.6 foot-pounds.

Higher Heat Values of Hydrocarbon Found in Gasoline:

Hexane	20700
Octane	20500
Monane	20450
Heptane	20600
Dodecane	20350
Undecane	20375
Dicane	20420

Combustion of Gasoline

The rapid combination of fuel with oxygen producing heat, is known as combustion. In the case of gasoline, it is the rapid oxidation of the carbon and the hydrogen constituting the fuel. The heat produced is the result of the chemical change. The chemical equation of combustion for octane is:

$$C_8H_{18} + 12.5\ O_2 = 8\ CO_2 + 9\ H_2O$$

In this equation, C_8H_{18} represents the chemical formula for gasoline, and the 12.5 O_2 is the oxygen which is required to burn one part of gasoline. This produces eight parts of carbon dioxide (CO_2) and nine parts of water (H_2O).

However, in actual operation of an engine instead of pure oxygen, air is used, which consists of a mixture of 1/5 oxygen and 4/5 nitrogen, by volume. From the standpoint of weight, it consists of one part oxygen, and 3 1/2 parts of nitrogen, or more exactly 23 parts of oxygen, and 77 parts of nitrogen.

The atomic weights for the different elements entering into the combustion of octane and air are as follows:

Carbon	12
Nitrogen	14
Oxygen	16
Hydrogen	1

On a weight basis, the chemical formula of combustion is:

$$114\ C_8H_{18} + 400\ O_2 = 352\ CO_2 + 162\ H_2O$$

As air is a mixture of oxygen and nitrogen in a ratio of 23 to 77, the nitrogen must also be considered in writing the combustion equation for octane and air. The amount of nitrogen present with 400 weight units of oxygen is:

$$400 \times \frac{77}{23} = 1339$$

This nitrogen is present in the combustible mixture and also in the products of combustion. It must therefore be added to both sides of the equation:

$$114\ C_8H_{18} + 400\ O_2 + 1339\ N_2 = 352\ CO_2 + 162\ H_2O + 1339\ N_2.$$

For one pound of octane the formula becomes:

$$3.09\ lb.\ CO_2 + 1.42\ lb.\ H_2O + 11.76\ lb.\ N_2$$

or 1 lb. of fuel + 15.27 lb. air = 16.27 of exhaust gas.

The amount of power developed in an internal combustion engine is dependent on the heat that can be obtained from burning the fuel. This in the case of gasoline or any of the hydrocarbons, is equal to the total of the heats due to the combustion of the carbon and hydrogen. From that must be subtracted the heat required to break up the hydrocarbon molecules.

When carbon becomes carbon dioxide, due to combustion, 14,542 Btu are liberated for each pound of carbon burned. In the combustion of hydrogen to steam, 62,032 Btu are liberated for each pound of hydrogen. To break up the octane into carbon and hydrogen, 1,523 Btu are required for each pound of octane.

ASTM DIESEL FUEL CLASSIFICATION D075-49T

Grade of Diesel Fuel Oil	Cetane Number (Min.)	Sulfur % by Wt. (Max.)	Distillation Temperatures, °F		Viscosity at 100°F Kinematic Centistokes (or SUS)	
			90% Boiling Point (Max.)	100% Boiling Point (Max.)	(Min.)	(Max.)
No.1-D	40	0.50		625	1.4	
No.2-D	40	1.0	675		1.8 (32.0)	5.8 (45)
No.4-D	30	2.0			5.8 (45)	26.4 (125)

Fig. 20-4. Excerpt from American Society of Testing Materials specifications for Diesel fuels.

In octane (C_8H_{18}) the carbon is 84.2 percent while the hydrogen is 15.8 percent. The heat produced by the combustion is:

84.2 percent of 14,542 Btu = 12,244
15.8 percent of 62,032 Btu = 9,801

making a total of 22,045 Btu. From this must be subtracted 1,523 Btu required to break up the fuel into carbon and hydrogen. The total heat from burning one pound of octane is therefore 20,522 Btu.

Combustion Chamber Temperature

Temperatures in the combustion chamber reached through the combustion of fuel vary through a relatively wide range. These temperatures are affected by compression ratio, combustion chamber contours, the effectiveness of the cooling system, the richness of the combustible mixture, and also the amount of burned gases that have remained in the cylinder from the previous cycle.

At the end of the compression stroke, but before ignition, temperatures of approximately 1500 deg. F. may be considered as average for an engine with a compression ratio of 9 to 1.

Immediately after ignition, the temperature increases very rapidly and will reach a value of approximately 5500 deg. F.

Lead Free Fuel

Rsearchers of the Ethyl Corp. point out that two of the problems that arise when lead free gasoline is used in passenger cars are:

1. Larger quantities of undesirable exhaust pollutants are produced.
2. Octane requirement of the engine is increased.

The deposits left in the combustion chamber by lead free fuel have a higher heat capacity than the lead deposits and after extended mileage result in higher octane requirements to operate the engine.

It was found, according to the Ethyl Corp. engineers, that a 96.4 research octane-number will satisfy the average car using leaded fuel, but a non-leaded fuel of about 101 octane is needed to satisfy the average engine operating on non-leaded fuel.

An SAE committee has pointed out that combustion chamber deposits were responsible for up to 100 percent of the observed increase in hydrocarbon emission levels with mileage accumulations in a correctly maintained engine. This committee also found that the stabilized hydrocarbon emissions of the cars using non-leaded fuel were generally lower than those using leaded fuel. Lead in fuel is reported as not having any effect on carbon monoxide emissions.

Experiments have also been made on the use of natural gas for operation of automobiles. These experiments, as reported in the SAE Journal, show that exhaust emissions from dual-fuel cars burning natural gas are below the levels set by California and are substantially below those from the same engine using gasoline. Both carbon monoxide and reactive hydrocarbons are well within the prescribed limits which equal or surpass the proposed standard set for 1975 by California.

Natural gas is rated as 130 octane without any lead additive and consequently there is no lead in the exhaust. Also there are virtually no combustion chamber deposits. However, power is reduced approximately 10 percent.

Quiz - Automotive Fuels

1. Name three different fuels used in internal combustion engines.
2. The volatility of gasoline is equivalent to its:
   a. Octane rating.
   b. Boiling point.

c. Cetane rating.
d. Distillation.
3. What characteristic of fuel affects easy starting?
4. Name the three stages of normal fuel combustion in an internal combustion engine.
5. Describe detonation.
6. Describe preignition.
7. Iso-octane and what other material are used to determine the octane rating of a fuel?
a. Cetane.
b. Propane.
c. Heptane.
d. Benzol.
8. Alcohol is added to gasoline primarily to:
a. Provide easier starting.
b. Absorb any moisture that may be present.
c. Increase the volatility of the fuel.
9. Automotive Diesel engines are capable of burning a wide range of fuels. True or False?
10. Cetane number of a Diesel fuel is a measure of:
a. Volatility.
b. Viscosity.
c. Time between fuel injection and ignition.

11. Sulfur content of a fuel should be:
a. High as possible.
b. Low as possible.
c. Does not matter.
12. Liquid petroleum gas is a mixture of:
a. Benzol and heptane.
b. Butane and propane.
c. Butane and heptane.
d. Heptane and cetane.
13. The power of any fuel is determined by its:
a. Molecular weight.
b. Heta value.
c. The amount of carbon it contains.
14. Immediately after ignition, combustion chamber temperatures may reach a value of:
a. 1500 deg.
b. 2500 deg.
c. 5500 deg.
d. 7500 deg.
15. Carbon deposits in the combustion chamber are responsible for increased levels of hydrocarbon emissions.
True or False?

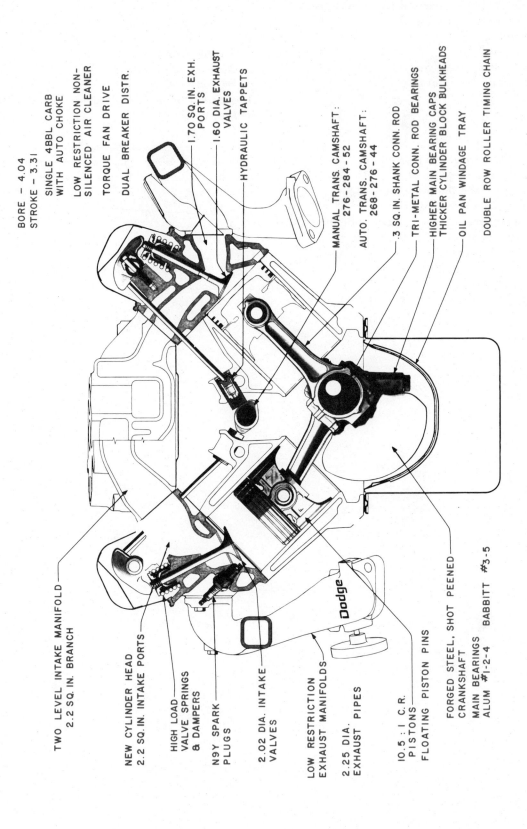

BORE – 4.04
STROKE – 3.31

SINGLE 4BBL CARB
WITH AUTO CHOKE

LOW RESTRICTION NON-
SILENCED AIR CLEANER

TORQUE FAN DRIVE

DUAL BREAKER DISTR.

1.70 SQ. IN. EXH.
PORTS

1.60 DIA. EXHAUST
VALVES

HYDRAULIC TAPPETS

MANUAL TRANS. CAMSHAFT:
276-284-52

AUTO. TRANS. CAMSHAFT:
268-276-44

.3 SQ. IN. SHANK CONN. ROD

TRI-METAL CONN. ROD BEARINGS

HIGHER MAIN BEARING CAPS
THICKER CYLINDER BLOCK BULKHEADS

OIL PAN WINDAGE TRAY

DOUBLE ROW ROLLER TIMING CHAIN

TWO LEVEL INTAKE MANIFOLD
2.2 SQ. IN. BRANCH

NEW CYLINDER HEAD
2.2 SQ. IN. INTAKE PORTS

HIGH LOAD
VALVE SPRINGS
& DAMPERS

N9Y SPARK
PLUGS

2.02 DIA. INTAKE
VALVES

LOW RESTRICTION
EXHAUST MANIFOLDS

2.25 DIA.
EXHAUST PIPES

10.5 : 1 C. R.

PISTONS
FLOATING PISTON PINS

FORGED STEEL, SHOT PEENED
CRANKSHAFT

MAIN BEARINGS
ALUM #1-2-4   BABBITT #3-5

Dodge 340 cu. in. V-8 engine, is designed to provide free breathing and near-complete combustion to conform with government standards set up to control exhaust emissions. This illustration of 340 calls out design features, dimensions and performance figures.

PRINCIPLES OF CARBURETION

The purpose of the complete fuel supply system is to provide a combustible mixture of fuel and air to the engine cylinders. The ratio of fuel to air must always be in the correct proportion regardless of the speed and load of the engine.

The complete fuel supply system consists of: fuel supply tank, fuel pump, carburetor, and manifold, Fig. 21-1. In addition, there are the fuel lines connecting the various units together, the fuel gauge for indicating the amount of fuel in the tank, the fuel filter, and the air cleaner.

larger proportion of fuel is required. When the engine reaches operating temperatures, better vaporization of the fuel is attained, and as a result the initial mixture of fuel and air is too "rich." Such a mixture, which contains more fuel than is normally required, is not efficient, and the engine will not operate satisfactorily, particularly at idling speed.

Another difficulty that must be overcome by a carburetor is that when the engine is idling or operating at low speed, a richer mixture is required than when operating at medium speed and power. When

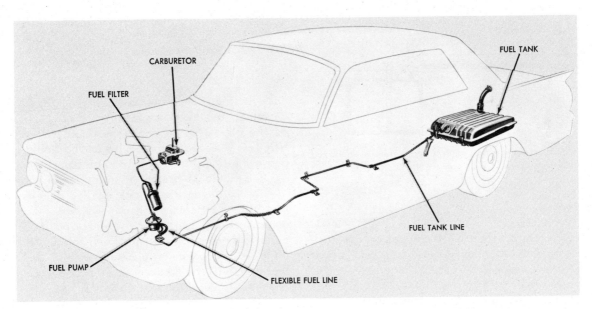

Fig. 21-1. Details of fuel system on late model car.

Purpose of Carburetor

The purpose of the carburetor is to prepare and supply a mixture of fuel vapor and air, in proper proportion for efficient combustion to the engine cylinders.

Because of the varying conditions such as temperature, engine speed and load on the engine, perfect carburetion is very difficult to attain.

First of all, when an internal combustion engine is started it is cold, and a fuel mixture containing a

maximum power is required, the amount of fuel in relation to air is again increased. Similarly, during periods of acceleration, a richer mixture is needed.

A difficulty encountered in designing carburetors results from the fact that the rate of air flow through the carburetor changes in a ratio of more than 100 to 1. This is a direct result of the changes of engine speed. At low speed, the flow of air through the carburetor is at a minimum, while at maximum engine speed, it will be 100 or more times as great.

Variations in types and characteristics of fuels

also are complications to be overcome in efficient operation. Gasoline is a blend of various parts or fractions of crude petroleum. As a result, some of the fractions contained in present day commercial gasoline will boil or vaporize at 100 deg. F., others at temperatures ranging up to 400 deg. F. Depending on the temperature of various parts of the intake manifold, some cylinders may receive a mixture with some portions of the fuel completely vaporized while other portions of the fuel may be in liquid form. In addition, some cylinders will receive fuel having greater antiknock qualities than others. Obviously when the engine and manifold are cold, the problem is still more difficult.

Air-Fuel Ratio

For normal operating conditions, the best economy is obtained by a mixture of 1 part by weight of gasoline to between 16 to 17 parts of air. For quick acceleration and maximum power, a somewhat richer mixture is needed--one having about 1 part of gasoline to 12 to 13 parts of air. Also for idling, a somewhat richer mixture is required than for normal operation. Similarly, when starting a cold engine an extremely rich mixture is needed.

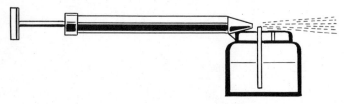

Fig. 21-2. Fuel, as it leaves the jet in a carburetor, is vaporized in the same way as spray from a conventional spray gun.

Evaporation

All substances, whether solid, liquid or gas, are made of molecules. In solids such as steel and copper the particles are held very closely together so that they seem to have no motion. In liquids, the molecules are not held together so tightly, so they can move with respect to each other. As a result, liquids can flow. In gases, such as air, there is still less tendency for the molecules to hold together, and they can therefore move quite freely.

When molecules of a liquid move from the liquid into the air, the liquid is said to evaporate. As this continues, the liquid disappears from its container and forms vapor in the air.

Rapidity of evaporation varies with a number of factors. These factors include temperature, the pressure above the liquid, the amount of liquid that has already evaporated into the air and the volatility. The term volatility refers to the ease with which a liquid vaporizes. For example, alcohol and benzine evaporate

more easily than water. A highly volatile liquid evaporates rapidly, and a liquid of low volatility evaporates slowly.

At higher temperatures, molecules move faster, and as a result the rate of vaporization is increased. Furthermore, when there is little pressure above the liquid, the molecules can escape from the liquid more

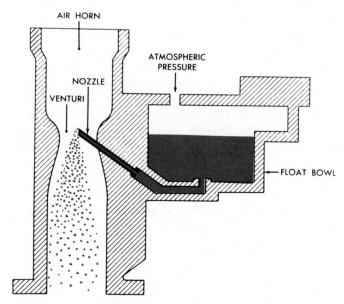

Fig. 21-3. Simplified carburetor consisting only of air horn, venturi, float bowl and nozzle or jet.

easily. If the evaporation is taking place in a closed chamber, the evaporation of the liquid will soon stop as the closed space above the liquid will soon become filled with escaped molecules of the liquid. The space above the liquid is then said to be saturated.

If a liquid is broken up into tiny particles or globules it will vaporize more easily. Breaking a liquid into tiny particles is known as vaporization. Spray guns such as are used for spraying insecticides or paint will vaporize a liquid. For example, if some gasoline is placed in an ordinary spray gun, Fig. 21-2, the fuel will be broken into a fine mist which will change into vapor almost instantly.

Principles of Carburetor Operation

Both air and gasoline are drawn through a carburetor and into an engine cylinder by suction created by the piston moving downward in the engine cylinder. In other words, as the piston moves down in the cylinder, a partial vacuum is created in the cylinder and combustion chamber. It is the difference between the pressure within the cylinder and the atmospheric pressure outside of the carburetor which causes air and fuel to flow into the cylinder from the carburetor.

The principle or method whereby the moving air draws fuel from the carburetor jet and fuel supply, is important and of interest.

In order to increase the difference in pressure, i.e. increase the suction within the carburetor, a device known as a venturi is used. A venturi is an hour-glass shaped constriction placed in a carburetor, Fig. 21-3, so the incoming air must pass through it on its way to the intake manifold and the engine cylinders. A venturi is simply a specially designed section of a pipe line or tube, where the area of the tube is reduced. This reduction in area increases the speed of the air that is passing through the tube. Since the same volume of air or other fluid flows through all sections of the tube, it is obvious that if the area of the tube is decreased, the velocity of the air or fluid must increase as it passes through the restricted area.

The venturi not only increases the velocity of the flow of air which passes through it, but it also produces a vacuum at its point of maximum restriction,

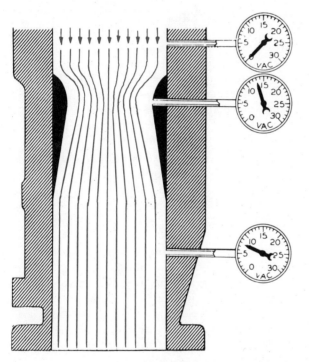

Fig. 21-4. Note how vacuum varies through different sections of the carburetor.

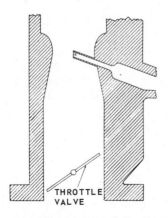

THROTTLE VALVE

Fig. 21-5. Illustrating the position of the throttle valve or plate.

Fig. 21-4. The outlet of a fuel jet is placed at that point, with the result the fuel is drawn from the jet and mixes with the passing air.

This mixing of the fuel with air is known as vaporization, and closely resembles the action of the familiar spray gun used for spraying insecticides, Fig. 21-2.

It must be remembered that it is the difference between the pressure at the open carburetor jet at the venturi, and the pressure on the surface of the fuel in the float bowl, Fig. 21-3, that causes the flow of fuel.

Carburetor Circuits

A carburetor to supply a fuel mixture suitable for all the different operating conditions of low to high speeds, and light loads to full loads, must be provided with additional circuits and controls. These circuits include: the float system, the idle system, main metering system, accelerating system and high speed system. Under the heading of controls, there is included: the throttle, antipercolator, fast idle, unloader, anti-icing, hot idle compensator, and anti-stall dashpot.

Throttle

One of the important controls on a carburetor, is a device for varying the amount of air-fuel mixture that enters the intake manifold. This is necessary so the speed of the vehicle can be changed. The throttle, Fig. 21-5, is simply a round disk mounted on a shaft so that it can be tilted at various angles in the carburetor throttle valve body. It is connected by means of suitable linkage to the accelerator pedal in the driving compartment of the vehicle. Depressing the pedal opens the throttle valve, permitting an increased amount of air-fuel mixture to reach the manifold.

Float Circuit

In order to keep the operating characteristics of the carburetor and its atomization of fuel as nearly constant as possible, it is essential that the level of the fuel in the jet is always maintained at the same level. This is accomplished by means of a float system, Fig. 21-6, which automatically permits fuel to flow into the float bowl when the fuel level drops below a predetermined value, and shuts off the supply of fuel when the level exceeds the specified height.

Up-and-down movement of the float on the fuel, controls the fuel supply by means of a needle valve and seat.

The float level must be set with a high degree of accuracy, for if the fuel level is too low, insufficient fuel will be supplied to the jets, and engine performance will be sacrificed. On the other hand, if the fuel level is too high, excessive fuel will reach the jets. In fact, fuel will continue to flow from the jet, even

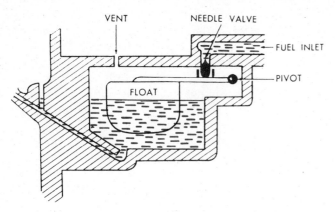

Fig. 21-6. Typical carburetor float system.

when the engine is not operating. Not only will economy decrease but excessive carbon formations will form in the combustion chamber of the engine. In actual operation, the float and needle valve maintain a position that permits the fuel coming in to just balance the fuel that is flowing to the jets.

Low-Speed Circuit

The idle system or low-speed circuit, Fig. 21-7, is designed to supply the proper amount of mixture for the engine at idle and extremely low speeds. It operates from idle to approximately 15 mph. Above that speed the idle system gradually passes out of operation, and fuel is then supplied by the main metering system.

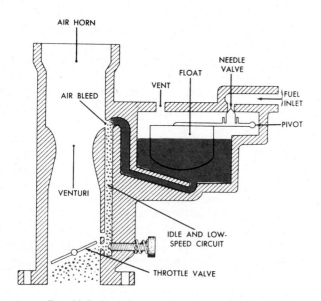

Fig. 21-7. Details of carburetor idle system.

When the throttle valve is almost closed, there will be very little air passing through the venturi. Consequently there will be very little vacuum at that point to draw fuel from the fuel nozzle. However, on the manifold side of the throttle valve, the vacuum

will be at a maximum as long as the throttle is in the closed position. A fuel discharge port is located immediately below the closed position of the throttle, Fig. 21-7, and is supplied by fuel from the float bowl. Atmospheric pressure in the float bowl will force fuel from the idle discharge hole as long as there is some degree of vacuum at the discharge hole. As the throttle moves toward the wide open position, the vacuum at the idle discharge hole continues to decrease until there is no flow of fuel from that port. An adjustable needle valve is provided so that adjustment can be made to govern the amount of fuel discharged from the idle port.

Immediately above the venturi is another port, Fig. 21-7, which is designed to permit air to bleed into the idle circuit as long as the idle circuit is operating. This air mixes with the fuel, and aids in its atomization before it leaves the idle discharge port.

Airflow is Restricted

When the throttle is opened a little, the flow of air is still too restricted for the venturi to discharge fuel from the main jet or nozzle, Fig. 21-3. However, with the increased movement of air through the carburetor, more fuel must be supplied in order to maintain the correct proportions of air and fuel. To supply this additional fuel, another port is included in the idle circuit. This hole is positioned slightly above the closed position of the throttle valve, Fig. 21-7. As soon as the throttle is opened a small amount, the port will be uncovered. Intake manifold vacuum will act on this low speed port, and the additional fuel needed will be obtained.

Another type of idling system is used on Zenith carburetors on many industrial engines. In this system, air mixes with the fuel in proportions determined by the position of the idle adjusting needle valve. And the tube of the idling jet projects down into the well which is filled with fuel when the engine is at rest. As more air is admitted by means of the needle valve adjustment, less fuel will flow.

Main Circuit

As the throttle is opened and the flow of fuel from the idle ports gradually decreases in volume, vacuum at the venturi gradually increases, so that fuel will start to flow from the main or high-speed system. The main system consists essentially of the main nozzle or jet which is centered in the venturi, Fig. 21-8, and supplies fuel from partly open to fully open throttle positions.

It must be remembered, that as the rate of flow of the air through the carburetor increases, the rate of flow of the fuel also increases, but at a much faster rate. This results from the fact that the density of the fuel does not change, while that of the air does. So in a simple carburetor, the mixture will be much too rich under wide-open throttle conditions. In fact with a simple carburetor, the correct mixture of air and fuel would be provided at only one position of the throttle. Provision must therefore be made to supply the correct ratio of air to fuel for all positions of the throttle.

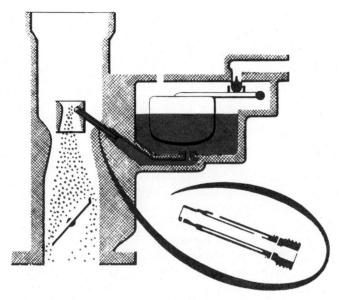

Fig. 21-8. Main or high-speed system.

Compensation Or Double Nozzle Principle

One method of controlling the mixture of fuel and air is to provide, in addition to the main nozzle, another nozzle with a constant rate of discharge. In combination, the two nozzles give substantially a constant mixture. In Fig. 21-9, the main nozzle is supplied

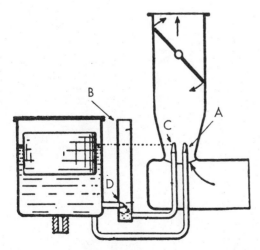

Fig. 21-9. The main nozzle (A) secures its fuel directly from the float chamber, and the compensating nozzle (C) receives its fuel from the standpipe (B). The fuel supplied by nozzle (C) depends on the size of the metering orifice (D) which delivers fuel to the standpipe (B).

with fuel directly from the float chamber. The compensating nozzle, which has a constant rate of discharge, is supplied from what is known as a standpipe, which receives its fuel from the float chamber. The upper end of the standpipe is open to the atmosphere. The supply of fuel in the standpipe is through a metered opening. As the fuel in the float chamber is at a constant level, the flow to the standpipe will be constant. In addition, the rate at which fuel can be drawn from the compensating nozzle will also be constant. At high engine speed, the compensating nozzle delivers less fuel than at low engine speed. In that way it compensates for the natural tendency of the main nozzle to deliver a mixture that is too rich at high speed.

Also at high engine speed and when the compensating nozzle is delivering smaller amounts of fuel (due to reduced vacuum), the level of the fuel in the standpipe will rise until its level is equal to that in the float chamber. Then, as the suction on the compensating nozzle is such that fuel will be drawn from it, the fuel level in the standpipe will be lowered. If the throttle is maintained at the same opening for a sufficient length of time, all the fuel will be drawn from the standpipe, and the compensating nozzle will be supplied only from the compensating jet or submerged metering orifice.

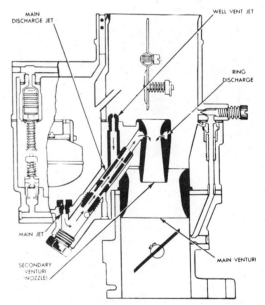

Fig. 21-10. Illustrating the air bleed principle as used on the Model 228 Zenith carburetor.

Air Bleed Principles

Another method of compensating for the increased richness of the mixture due to the effect of the plain nozzle with the increase in air velocity through the carburetor throat, is by means of air bleeds. The illustration, Fig. 21-10, shows the air bleed system as used on a Zenith carburetor. Here the high speed

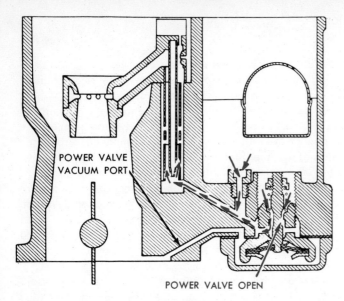

Fig. 21-11. *The power or economizer valve is designed to supply additional fuel needed for maximum power at wide open throttle.*

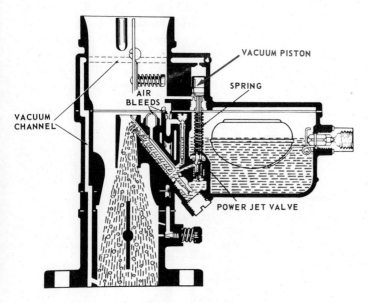

Fig. 21-12. *Power jet valve controlled by vacuum piston supplies additional fuel for maximum power.*

system of the carburetor consists of a primary venturi, a secondary venturi, a main jet, a well jet and a discharge jet. The main jet controls the fuel mixture from about one-fourth to about three-fourths throttle opening. The mixture is controlled by a small amount of air which is admitted through the well vent or high speed bleeder. Air bleed holes are located in the upper section of the discharge jet at a point below the level of the fuel in the jet. Introduction of air at that point reduces the surface tension of the fuel, and helps the fuel flow at low pressures. This bleed also restricts fuel flow through the main jets under high vacuum conditions. These two factors in combination control the air-fuel ratio, and offset the tendency for increasing the richness of the mixture in a plain nozzle with increasing air velocity.

Full Power Circuit

As pointed out, by means of the air bleed principle, the air-fuel ratio is maintained at a constant rate. The system with its air bleed is then designed to provide economical operation for all speeds, from low speed up to but not including wide-open throttle. However, for maximum speed and power, additional fuel must be supplied. There are several ways that this additional fuel is provided for maximum power. These methods include the economizer valve or power jet, and the metering rod.

Economizer Valve

The economizer valve or power valve, Fig. 21-11, as it is also called, depends upon manifold vacuum for its operation, and is connected to a point in the carburetor on the engine side of the throttle valve. The design is such that as full throttle operation is approached, the engine vacuum acting on the diaphragm or plunger of the power valve, will permit the required amount of fuel to pass through the main nozzle.

Another type of power jet is shown in Fig. 21-12. In this design, the power jet valve is controlled by a vacuum-actuated piston assembly, operating in accordance with throttle opening. With the throttle closed, a high manifold vacuum is present and the vacuum-controlled piston assembly is moved by atmospheric pressure in the float chamber to the top of its cylinder against the tension of a spring, closing the valve. When the throttle is opened to a point where additional fuel is required, the manifold vacuum has decreased

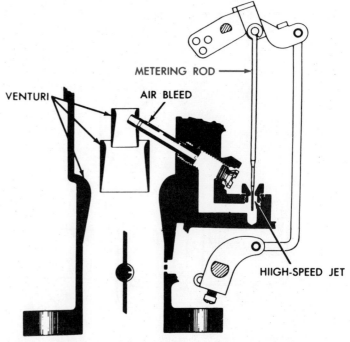

Fig. 21-13. *The metering rod varies the amount of fuel flowing from a jet.*

sufficiently so that the spring on the piston assembly moves the piston down, opening the power jet to feed additional fuel into the high-speed circuit.

Mechanical means are also used for supplying the additional fuel needed for high-speed operation. In such a design, the economizer or power jet is opened by the accelerator pump when the pump is at the bottom or end of its stroke.

Metering Rod

Instead of using a power jet, some carburetors accomplish the same results by employing a metering rod which varies the size of the high-speed jet openings. In this design, such as is used on some Carter carburetors, Fig. 21-13, fuel from the float bowl is metered to the high-speed circuit through the calibrated orifice provided by the high-speed jet, and the metering rod within it. From this point, the fuel is conducted to the nozzle extending into the venturi. As the throttle valve is opened, its linkage raises the metering rod in the jet. The rod has several steps or tapers on the lower end, and as it is raised in the jet, it makes the effective size of the fuel orifice greater, permitting more fuel to flow through the circuit. In this design, the metering rod position must be carefully synchronized with every throttle position, so that the proper air-fuel ratio is maintained throughout all engine speeds.

Metering rods are also operated by means of a vacuum controlled piston as shown in Fig. 21-14.

Vacuum Step-Up

The vacuum step-up, Fig. 21-15, operates much like the power jet. It consists of a step-up piston which is fastened to a step-up rod. When high vacuum develops in the intake manifold, as it does during part throttle operation, atmospheric pressure holds the step-up piston down against its spring pressure so that in turn the step-up rod is held down in the step-up jet, closing the jet. With wide-open throttle, there will be low vacuum in the intake manifold and the difference in pressure above and below the piston is small. Consequently, the piston is moved up by its spring pressure, and the rod is raised out of its jet, and in that way the additional fuel needed for maximum power is supplied.

Accelerating Pump

When a throttle is opened quickly to produce rapid acceleration of the engine, the carburetor fuel mixture tends to become too lean, and what is known as a "flat spot," results. This results from the fact that the fuel is of greater weight than air, and consequently when the accelerator is opened suddenly the flow of fuel will lag behind the flow of the air, resulting in a lean mixture.

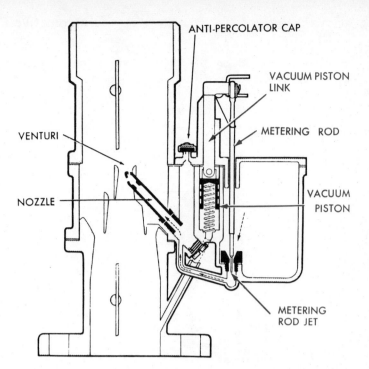

Fig. 21-14. *Metering rod operated by vacuum controlled piston.*

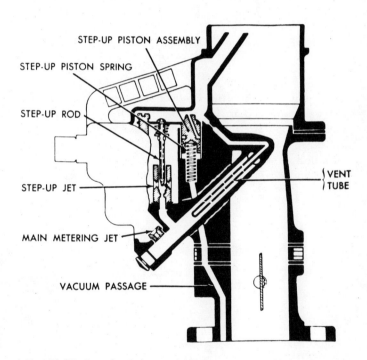

Fig. 21-15. *Details of the vacuum step-up circuit designed to supply the additional fuel needed for full power operation.*

To supply the additional fuel needed to overcome this condition, a small pump is incorporated in the design of the carburetor, Fig. 21-16. This pump is operated by the throttle linkage. In many designs, the strokes of the pump can be adjusted to any one of three positions. The longest stroke provides the maximum amount of fuel and is usually used during cold weather.

The accelerating pump circuit usually consists of a pump cylinder, a plunger mechanically actuated by

223

a lever mounted on the throttle shaft, or vacuum operated by intake manifold vacuum; an intake check valve located in the bottom of the pump cylinder to control the passage of fuel from the bowl into the pump cylinder; a discharge or outlet check valve; and an accelerating jet to meter the amount of fuel used.

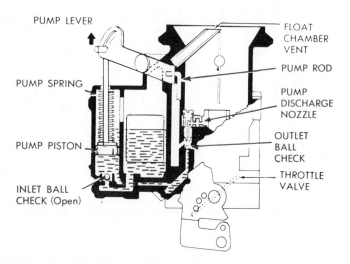

Fig. 21-16. The accelerator pump supplies the additional fuel needed for rapid acceleration.

When the throttle is opened, the pump plunger moves downward in its cylinder. In the mechanically-operated design, the downward movement is obtained by direct linkage with the throttle. In the vacuum-actuated design, a sudden throttle opening will cause the manifold vacuum to drop, allowing the accelerat-

ing pump spring to force the pump plunger down in the cylinder. The downward travel of the plunger forces the fuel past the discharge check valve of the accelerating jet. Fuel is supplied to the pump cylinder through the intake check valve at the bottom. The intake check valve in the bottom of the cylinder permits a supply of fuel to reach the cylinder, but closes on the down stroke of the plunger, thereby preventing the fuel in the cylinder from being pushed backward into the float bowl.

Anti-Percolator

During extremely hot weather, there is a tendency for the fuel to vaporize in the fuel line, the fuel pump or within the carburetor. This condition is known as vapor lock. To overcome this condition when it occurs in the carburetor special provisions are made. One method is to provide a passageway or vent tube between the top of the float bowl chamber, and the upper part of the air horn as shown in Fig. 21-17. By that means, any vapor developing in the float bowl chamber will be drawn into the air stream in the air horn, from there through the carburetor and into the intake manifold.

Venting the float bowl in this manner has the added advantage that it will equalize the effect of a clogged air cleaner. A clogged air cleaner will cause a somewhat greater vacuum at the venturi and consequent increased flow of fuel. Venting the float bowl into the carburetor air horn will equalize this condition.

Another method vents the float bowl chamber directly into the atmosphere as shown in Fig. 21-14.

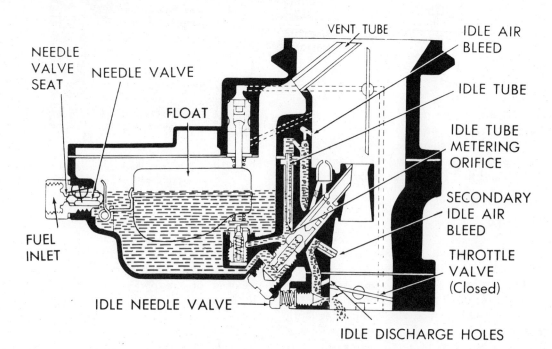

Fig. 21-17. The vent tube from the float bowl to the air horn prevents vapor lock and also equalizes the effect of a clogged muffler. This illustration also shows a typical idling system.

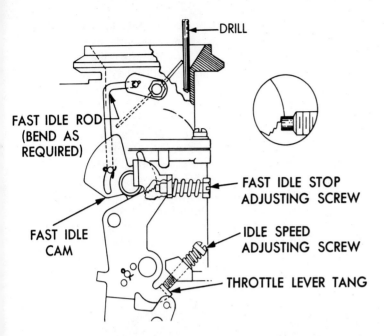

Fig. 21-18. Showing the fast idle and choke linkage, together with fast idle adjustment and idle speed adjustment.

To prevent dust and dirt from entering the float bowl chamber, the vent is provided with a cap.

Another design (Rochester) incorporates a special valve which vents the main discharge nozzle to the atmosphere. The valve is linked to the throttle in such a way that when the throttle is closed, an anti-percolator valve is opened. A similar method designed to accomplish the same thing provides a vent for the passages to the discharge nozzle without the use of a valve.

Fast Idle

To prevent an engine from stalling until it reaches operating temperature, it is necessary that the engine be operated at a faster than normal speed. This is done by preventing the engine speed from dropping below a predetermined amount. To accomplish this, the choke shaft is linked to a cam on the outside of the carburetor, Fig. 21-18, so that as long as the choke is in a partially closed position the high spot on the cam comes under the fast idle speed adjusting screw. In that way the throttle will be held open a sufficient amount to prevent stalling.

After the engines reaches operating temperature, the operation of the choke will move the cam from under the fast idle speed adjusting screw so the engine will idle at a normal speed.

Carburetor Unloader

When an engine does not start immediately, prolonged cranking will result in a flooded condition. In other words, the mixture in the manifold and engine is so rich that it is no longer a vapor, and conse-

quently will not explode. To overcome this condition, linkage is provided on the carburetor which when the accelerator is pushed to the floor, will hold the choke open, Fig. 21-19. Then as the engine is cranked again, air will enter the manifold and cylinders to clear the excessive gasoline from the system. This is accomplished by special linkage between the throttle and choke levers, Fig. 21-19.

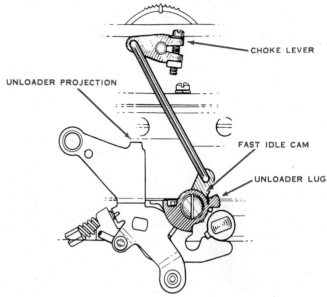

Fig. 21-19. Showing the relation between the unloader lug or cam, the unloader projection, the choke lever and the fast idle cam.

Anti-Icing

When fuel is evaporated it absorbs heat, which it obtains from the surrounding air and metal parts of the carburetor. When the humidity of the air is high and temperatures are at approximately the freezing point, the evaporation of fuel in the carburetor will often cause ice to form. This ice forms around the closed position of the throttle, and the idle port will quickly become closed with ice. This in turn will cause the engine to stall at low speeds.

To overcome this condition, some carburetors are provided with special passages which carry hot exhaust gasses around the carburetor, so that heat is supplied in the area surrounding the throttle plate, Fig. 21-20.

Another method of overcoming this difficulty is to provide a water jacket for the carburetor. This water jacket is then connected to the cooling system of the vehicle.

Hot Idle Compensator

During long periods of idling with an extremely hot engine, the fuel in the carburetor bowl becomes hot enough to form vapors. These vapors enter the carburetor bores by way of the inside bowl vents,

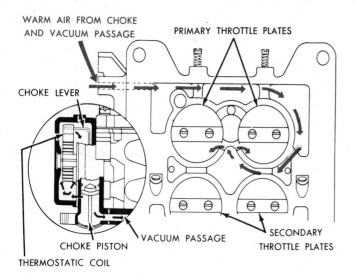

Fig. 21-20. *Showing path of warm air from the choke passing around the throttle valves to prevent the formation of ice.*

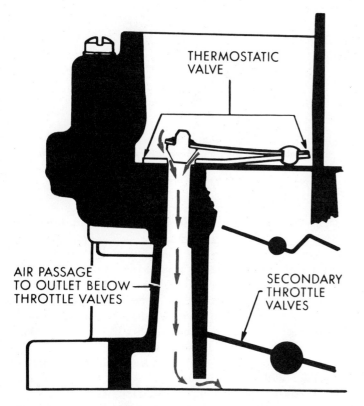

Fig. 21-21. *The hot idle compensator permits additional air to enter the primary bores of the carburetor under extreme hot idle conditions.*

and mixing with the idle air causes an extremely rich mixture. This will result in loss of engine rpm's and eventually in stalling. To overcome this condition, on Carter AFB carburetors, for example, a hot idle compensator valve is placed in the secondary side of the carburetor. This is so calibrated that it will permit additional air to enter the manifold below the secondary throttle valve, and mix with the fuel vapors to provide a more combustible mixture.

On Rochester 4GC carburetors, the hot idle compensator is placed on the secondary side of the float bowl and permits additional air to enter the primary bores under extreme hot idle conditions, Fig. 21-21.

Anti-Stall Dashpot

Most cars with automatic transmissions have an anti-stall dashpot connected to the carburetor linkage, Fig. 21-22. The purpose of this dashpot is to prevent the throttle from closing too fast after the foot is removed from the accelerator pedal. Too rapid closing of the carburetor throttle will often cause the engine to stall. The installation of the dashpot prevents the throttle from being closed too quickly.

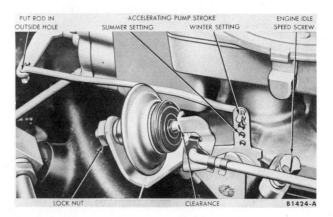

Fig. 21-22. *Showing anti-stall dashpot mounted on side of Ford carburetor. Some carburetors have the anti-stall dashpot built integral with the carburetor. Note provision for adjustment of accelerator pump.*

This would not occur with a conventional transmission, as the momentum of the vehicle would continue to drive the engine through the stall period.

In order to insure easy starting, it is essential that the carburetor throttle be open slightly. On modern cars, this is accomplished automatically by special linkage between the cranking motor and the carburetor throttle linkage. Whenever the starter is operated, the throttle will also be opened a slight amount.

Vacuum Advance

Vacuum from the carburetor is used to control the spark advance on the Ford Loadomatic distributor. In the latest design, vacuum is transmitted to the distributor diaphragm from three interconnected passages in the carburetor, Fig. 21-23. All manifold vacuum to the distributor passes through the spark control valve, Fig. 21-23. Under normal load conditions, the spark valve is held open against spring pressure by a combination of atmospheric pressure and manifold vacuum. When accelerating, manifold vacuum drops and spring pressure closes the spark valve, shutting off the vac-

Electric vehicle research by Ford produced Comuta, a short-range car only 6 ft., 8 in. long, with 53.5 in. wheelbase and an 18 ft. turning circle. Experimental car is powered by four, 12-volt, lead-acid batteries and two, 24-volt, electric motors which drive the rear wheels.

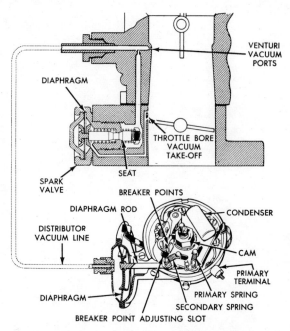

Fig. 21-23. Method of using vacuum at the venturi and at the throttle to control spark advance.

At low engine rpm, the governor control valve weight, of this Holley built unit, is held away from its seat by the tension of the valve weight spring. During this period the valve is wide open, allowing atmospheric air to flow to the governor so that no governing action occurs. As engine speed increases, the differential between atmospheric pressure and engine vacuum decreases, so the governor diaphragm is permitted to exert a pull on the governor lever which turns the throttle shaft and partly closes the throttle.

Another method of limiting the speed of an engine, is by means of a velocity type governor. In this design, the unit is inserted adjacent to the throttle, and the velocity of the gas going through the manifold acts on a spring-loaded floating obstruction in the form of a ball or disk attached to the throttle. As engine speed is increased, the velocity of the gas flowing through the manifold also increases and tends to carry the obstruction along with it. As this disk or ball is attached to the throttle plate of the carburetor, the result is to close the throttle against the tension of a spring. In that way, the speed of the engine is controlled.

uum and preventing excessive spark advance. Venturi vacuum prevents full retard. As manifold vacuum increases, the spark valve again allows a higher vacuum to advance the distributor.

Governors

Governors are used principally on industrial engines and commercial vehicles so that economical and safe speeds are not exceeded. One type of unit, Fig. 21-24, is inserted between the carburetor and the intake manifold, and is actuated by the pressure differential acting against the governor diaphragm. This pressure differential is provided by the vacuum below the governor throttle plates, and the atmospheric pressure above the plates.

Types Of Carburetors

While there are many variations in the design and construction of carburetors, there are three basic types:

1. Updraft
2. Downdraft
3. Sidedraft

The direction of the airflow at the carburetor outlet to the manifold determines the classification.

The updraft carburetor, Fig. 21-25, can be placed low on the side of the engine, and supplied with fuel by gravity feed. However, the fuel mixture must be lifted from the carburetor, through the manifold, and into the engine. Air velocities must therefore be high, and these can be attained only by using carburetors

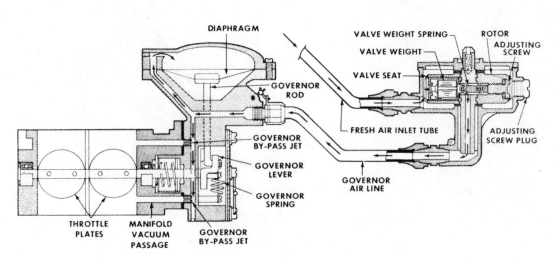

Fig. 21-24. This Holley governor uses the vacuum below the governor throttle plates, and the atmosphere, to control the speed of the vehicle.

Carburetion

and manifold passages of small diameter. As a result, power output is limited.

The downdraft carburetor, Figs. 21-12, and 21-27, is used almost exclusively on American passenger car engines. In this design the fuel mixture will reach the engine, even though the air velocity is low. Carburetor throat and manifold can be made larger, which in turn makes high speeds and high specific output possible.

The side outlet carburetor, (also known as the crossdraft) Fig. 21-26, is used on engines where there is little space over the engine and also where the vaporized mixture is heated by the water in the engine water jacket.

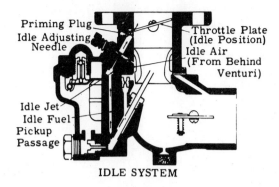

Fig. 21-25. Sectional view of updraft carburetor. Air enters at right and passes upward through venturi and past throttle plate.

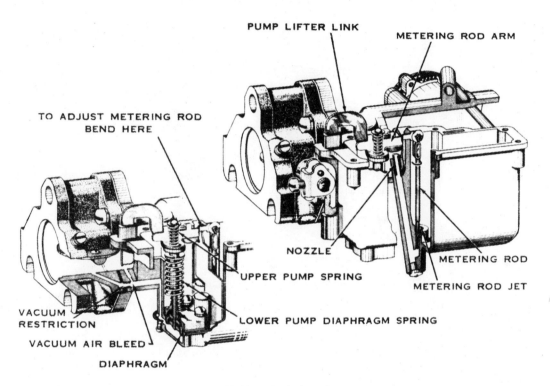

Fig. 21-26. Side draft carburetor.

Single-Barrel Carburetor

While there are three basic types of carburetors, they may also be classed in accordance with the number of throats or barrels. A single-barrel carburetor, Fig. 21-27, has one outlet to the intake manifold. It is designed to take care of all the requirements of the engine for all operating conditions. Such carburetors are used extensively on engines of six cylinders or less.

Dual Carburetors

Carburetors with two outlets to the intake manifold are known as two-barrel or two-throat carburetors, Fig. 21-28. Such a unit is basically two carburetors in one, and usually has two complete idling systems, two high-speed systems, two power systems, two accelerating systems, two throttles, two chokes, but only one float system.

With a dual carburetor, each barrel or mixing tube, supplies alternate cylinders in the firing order. In a conventional six-cylinder engine, one barrel of the dual carburetor would supply cylinder numbers 1, 3 and 2, while the other barrel would supply cylinder numbers 5, 6 and 4.

Four-Barrel Carburetor

In the four-barrel carburetor, Fig. 21-29, generally used on V-8 engines, there are four openings to the intake manifold within the single unit. Some of the systems, such as the float system, may be common to all four barrels. In some designs, half of the carburetor operates as a two-barrel unit during light load and cruising speeds, while the other half of the carburetor is supplemental for top speed, and full-throttle operation. The two barrels supplying fuel for light load operation are usually known as the primary side, while the other two barrels are known as the secondary side.

barrels for satisfactory fuel distribution. Also in this design, the secondary throttles remain closed at lower engine speeds. As engine speed increases, the throttle plates of the secondary barrels are opened. In some designs, the secondary throttle plates are operated mechanically through linkage. On other models, the secondary throttle plates are controlled automatically

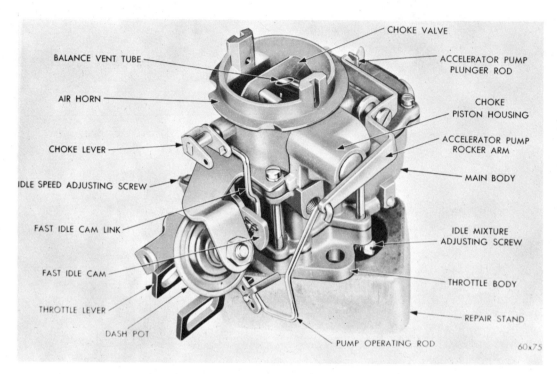

Fig. 21-27. *Single-barrel downdraft carburetor. Note parts identification.*

When a four-barrel carburetor is designed so that two barrels supply fuel to the engine throughout the entire speed range, then some provision is made to route a portion of the idle system fuel to the secondary

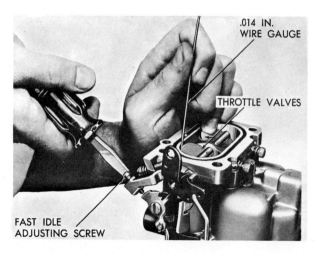

Fig. 21-28. *Adjusting the position of the fast idle cam on this dual, or two-barrel carburetor.*

by a vacuum-operated diaphragm. In general, the secondary throttle plates will start to open when the primary plates are open 50 deg.

In a four-barrel carburetor, as used on V-8 engines, primary and secondary barrels form a pair to supply cylinders 1-7-4-6, while the other primary and secondary barrels will supply fuel to cylinders 3-5-2-8. However, this applies only to an engine having a firing order of 1-8-4-3-6-5-7-2. In general, manifolding for both two and four-barrel carburetors is designed so that one half of the carburetor will supply fuel to the end cylinders on one side of the engine, and the two center cylinders on the other side. The other half of the carburetor will then supply fuel to the remaining cylinders.

Multiple Carburetors

Maximum performance requires perfect distribution of large quantities of the air-fuel mixture. One method of obtaining this is to use several carburetors. One installation on a V-8 engine uses three two-barrel carburetors.

Carburetion

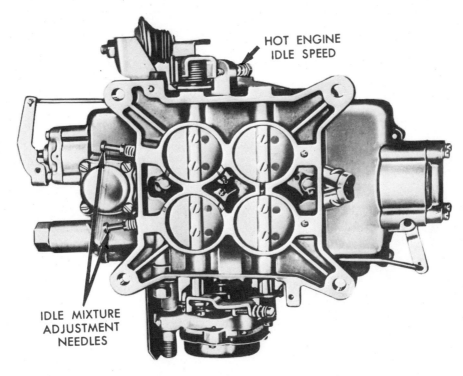

Fig. 21-29. Bottom view of four-barrel carburetor, showing location of idle mixture adjustment, dashpot and hot engine idle speed adjustment.

In this installation (Chevrolet), the center carburetor is known as the primary, Fig. 21-30, and takes care of all engine requirements up to 60 deg. opening of the throttle. Above that, opening the secondary carburetors comes into operation, to supply the additional fuel required for maximum performance.

The primary carburetor is a complete unit and contains all the usual carburetor systems (float, idle, choke, part throttle, power and accelerator pump). The front and rear carburetors do not include idle, part throttle or choke systems.

A combined mechanical and vacuum linkage is used to operate the throttles. The primary carburetor throttle is operated mechanically. When it is opened 60 deg., a vacuum slider valve is operated which causes vacuum to act on a diaphragm, which in turn operates the throttle valves on the secondary carburetors.

Fig. 21-30. Showing the installation of three dual carburetors on a Chevrolet V-8 engine.

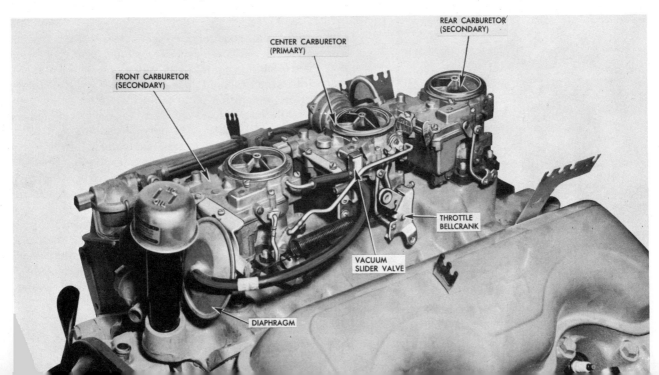

Autolite 4300 Carburetor

The Autolite model 4300 4-V carburetor, Fig. 21-31, is a three-piece, separately cast design consisting of the air horn, main body and throttle body.

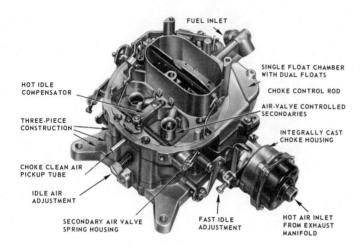

Fig. 21-31. Details of Autolite 4300 4-V carburetor. Note the idle air adjustment.

A cast-in center fuel inlet has provision for a supplementary fuel inlet system. The fuel bowl is vented by an internal balance vent and a mechanical atmospheric vent operates during idle.

The idle bypass system is designed to provide a more consistent idle and a hot idle compensator, Fig. 21-31, is used to help idle stability.

There are adjustments for both idle air and idle fuel. These adjustments must be made at the same time. Opening the idle air screw to increase engine rpm leans the air-fuel mixture. Consequently, the idle

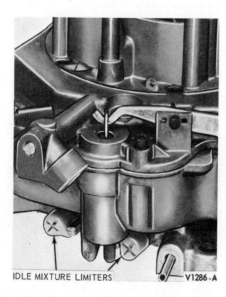

Fig. 21-32. Note idle mixture limiters on Autolite carburetor.

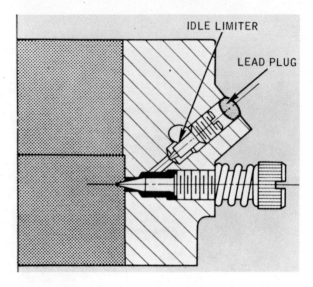

Fig. 21-32a. Details of idle fuel limiter on Carter model YF carburetor.

fuel mixture must also be adjusted to provide proper air-fuel mixture for smooth engine idle.

Exhaust Emission Control Carburetors

Starting with the 1968 models, most carburetors have been modified or recalibrated to provide leaner mixtures in order to conform to the Federal regulations governing exhaust emissions.

These leaner mixtures result primarily from better control of the idle mixture and during periods of deceleration. In some cases the idle mixture screws have a finer pitch, making for more accurate control of the air-fuel ratio. On Autolite carburetors, idle mixture adjustments are provided with an idler limiter device, Fig. 21-32, which sets a limit on enrichment of the idle mixture. Holley and single-venturi Carter carburetors contain a preset fixed mixture restriction in idle fuel passages that accomplish the same thing, Fig. 21-32a.

In the case of the Rochester Monojet carburetor used on six cylinder Chevrolet, Buick, Pontiac and Oldsmobile engines with automatic transmissions, an idle stop solenoid is used to stop engine "Dieseling" after the ignition is turned off.

Idle rpm with exhaust emission control carburetors is slightly higher than normal and in every case must be accurately set to specified value. On the Rochester Monojet, Fig. 21-33, the idle speed is adjusted with the transmission in "drive" position. When the owner is about to turn off the ignition, he places the transmission in "park" or "neutral." Since the load is then off the engine, idle speed will rise to the 700 rpm range. With the engine running at that speed, plus higher operating temperatures and slightly retarded spark, "Dieseling" may occur. The idle stop solenoid eliminates the possibility by closing the throttle valve when the ignition key is turned off.

erating temperatures and slightly retarded spark, "Dieseling" may occur. The idle stop solenoid eliminates that possibility by closing the throttle valve when the ignition key is turned off.

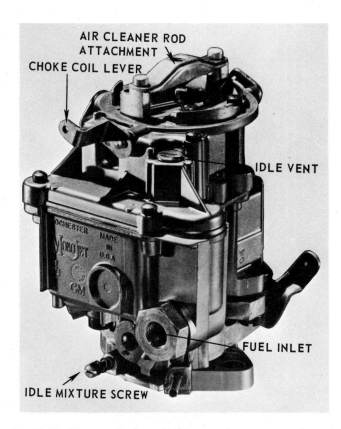

Fig. 21-33. The new Rochester Monojet carburetor as used on six cylinder Buick, Chevrolet, Oldsmobile and Pontiac engines.

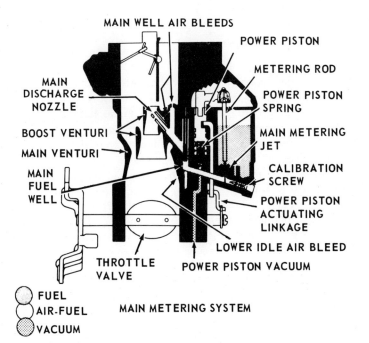

Fig. 21-34. Details of main metering system on Rochester Monojet carburetor.

The main metering system of the Rochester Monojet carburetor, Fig. 21-34, feeds fuel at all times when the airflow through the venturi is great enough to maintain fuel flow through the main discharge nozzle. The triple venturi stack-up is particularly sensitive to airflow which results in finer and more stable metering control from light to heavy loads and which is so important in the control of exhaust emissions. The main metering system consists of the metering jet, a mechanical and vacuum operated metering rod, main fuel well, main well air bleeds, fuel discharge nozzle and the triple venturi.

Power enrichment is obtained by the movement of a spring-loaded vacuum piston which senses changes in manifold vacuum. The amount of enrichment is controlled by the clearance between the groove in the power piston and the diameter of the power piston drive rod.

Fig. 21-35. Thermostatically controlled heated air inlet is provided on some carburetors. The Ford 302 cu. in. V-8 is shown.

Hot Air Intakes

Many of the carburetors designed for exhaust emission control have thermostatically controlled dual air intake systems, which provide advantages ranging from improved cold start-up through warm-up and more particularly in more complete combustion and reduced exhaust by-products. The warm air is obtained from a heat stove on the exhaust manifold. The Ford design is shown in Fig. 21-35, and the General Motor design in Fig. 21-36.

The Ford design is also equipped with a vacuum override control which opens the upper valve for direct air intake of unheated air for maximum air volume at full throttle opening. The override operates only when needed to deliver maximum air volume for rapid acceleration. When high air volume is no longer needed, the override is released and the selector valve returns to the position indicated by the under hood temperatures.

All Ford carburetors have dashpots to control the rate of throttle valve closing. In that way more air is allowed to pass through the carburetor on deceleration and thereby helps to keep the mixture lean, and to conform to Federal regulations on emission control. It also tends to reduce any tendency to backfire.

Float needle valves: Instead of using steel for float needle valves, most carburetors are now using nylon or some similar material for their construction. A better seal is obtained and in addition, the material has better wearing qualities. Also it is not readily affected by small foreign particles.

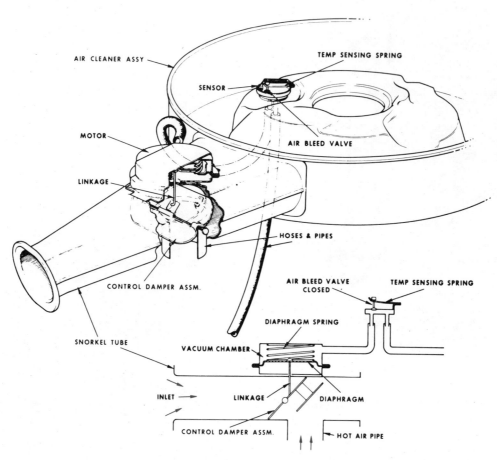

Fig. 21-36. Illustrating the hot air intake as used on some Buick engines.

Ram Air

By placing the carburetor air intake at the front of the vehicle, full advantage is taken of air motion due to the speed of the car. This gives a ramming effect to the air entering the carburetor and in that way a degree of supercharging is obtained. Fig. 21-37 shows the installation on the 4-4-2 Oldsmobile high performance models. The air scoops at the front have 13 by 2 inch openings. The illustration shows a 400 cu. in. V-8 with 10.5 to 1 compression ratio, and has selected low friction fits or clearances.

Special Features

A basic requirement of fuel metering systems is that the fuel level in the float bowl be maintained at as near a constant level as possible. In the Holley 4150C carburetor a float spring is incorporated under the float to keep the float in a stable position Fig. 21-38.

Secondary throttles: Four-barrel carburetors may be considered as two dual carburetors; two primary bores supplying fuel-air mixtures throughout the entire engine operation, while the two secondary bores function only when speed and load require them. At lower speeds the secondary throttle plates remain closed. When engine speed increases to a point where additional breathing capacity is required, vacuum is used to open the secondary throttle plates. Vacuum taken from one of the primary barrels and the secondary barrels, acts on a diaphragm which controls the secondary throttle plates, Fig. 21-39.

Carburetor Degasser

The degasser, Fig. 21-40, is an auxiliary device built into the carburetor and is used to correct the over-rich mixture condition which occurs when the throttle is closed suddenly. Under those conditions, abnormally high vacuum builds up above the throttle

Fig. 21-37. The 4-4-2 Oldsmobile 400 cu. in. engine has a compression ratio of 10:1. Note the air scoops for the carburetor which are designed to produce a supercharging effect.

against a needle valve. The valve is normally held off its seat by the spring. The upper diaphragm chamber is connected by means of a bypass line to an opening into the intake manifold above the throttle.

With the throttle in the idle position and the engine turning over at idle speed, the proper amount of fuel is drawn through the idle jet. During periods of deceleration, the engine rpm will be much higher than normal idle rpm, causing the vacuum in the passages above the throttle plate to rise much higher than at normal idle speeds.

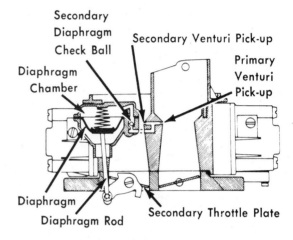

Fig. 21-39. Showing connections for operation of secondary throttle plate in a Holley carburetor.

With the degasser in operation, the abnormally high vacuum during deceleration is transferred to the chamber above the diaphragm, raising the plunger and compressing the diaphragm spring. This movement actuates the walking beam to force the needle valve against its seat to shut off the flow of fuel through the idle hole.

As engine speed approaches idle, and intake manifold vacuum decreases to normal, the needle valve also returns to its normal position and restores the flow of fuel to the idle hole.

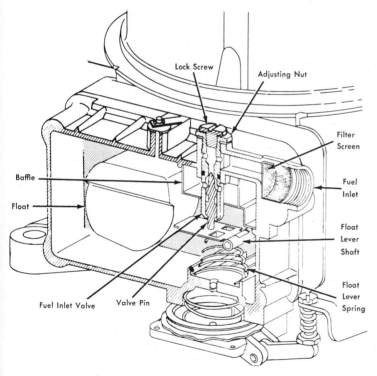

Fig. 21-38. Note float lever spring to help steady the action of the float in maintaining a constant fuel level in the float bowl.

valve resulting in an excessively rich mixture being drawn into the engine through the idle system.

The degasser consists of two die-cast housings clamped together with a diaphragm between the castings. The diaphragm is attached to a plunger which actuates a walking beam, the end of which bears

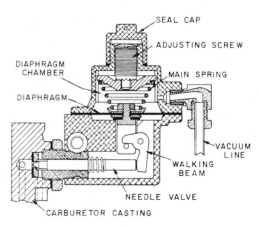

Fig. 21-40. Details of Bendix degasser.

Decel Valve

Some recent model cars, such as the Ford Pinto, are equipped with a decel valve which is designed to meter to the engine an additional amount of fuel and air during engine deceleration. This additional amount of fuel and air together with engine modification, permits more complete combustion with resultant lower levels of exhaust emissions. During periods of engine deceleration, manifold vacuum forces the diaphragm assembly against the spring, Fig. 21-41, which in turn raises the decel valve. With the valve open, existing manifold vacuum pulls a metered amount of fuel and air from the carburetor and travels through the valve body assembly into the intake manifold. The decel valve remains open and continues to feed additional air and fuel for a specified time.

Fig. 21-42. Throttle solenoid adjustment on Autolite-Weber model 5200 carburetor.

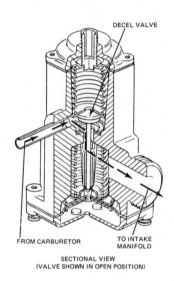

Fig. 21-41. Sectional view of decel valve showing valve in open position.

Throttle Solenoid

The Autolite-Weber model 5200 carburetor as installed on the Ford Pinto 2000 cc engine is equipped with a throttle solenoid adjustment which is designed to control the idling speed on automatic transmission equipped cars. The curb idle is adjusted by turning the throttle solenoid plunger. First disconnect the throttle solenoid wire, and set the lower curb idle using the curb idle screw. Connect the throttle solenoid wire, open the throttle slightly by hand to allow the pluger to extend; then, set the higher curb idle speed by turning the solenoid plunger, Fig. 21-42.

Small Engine Carburetors

Many of the basic principles found in large carburetors are also found in the carburetors used in small engines. This is particularly true in the case of engines used on chain saws and many lawn mowers.

Engines operated at varying angles, as is the case in chain saws, are often equipped with a floatless type of carburetor. On such installations a diaphragm type carburetor is often used. Such carburetors can be operated at a steep angle and even operated in an inverted position for a short time.

A Tillotson diaphragm type carburetor is shown in Fig. 21-43. The upper portion of the illustration shows the carburetor, while the pump is shown below. However, the two portions are bolted together to form a single unit.

The pump utilizes the positive and negative pressure pulsations in the crankcase of a two-cycle engine for its operation. The engine crankcase is connected to the pump connection, (10), Fig. 21-41, and the fuel tank to the connection (14). When pressure occurs in the crankcase, the pump diaphragm (9) is forced upward unseating the check valve (13) and closing the outlet check valve (11) causing fuel to enter channel (12). When the diaphragm is pulled downward, it closes the inlet check valve (13) and opens the outlet check valve (11), forcing the fuel from channel (12) to the inlet supply channel (5) of the carburetor. In some versions of the pump, flapper type valves formed integral with the fabric diaphragm are used instead of the ball type checks. Fuel is delivered to the inlet supply channel either by the integral fuel tank or by gravity.

When the crankshaft is rotated several times with the choke valve (3) closed, cylinder vacuum is transmitted to the carburetor diaphragm chamber (23) through the idle discharge port (32) and main nozzle (30) creating a vacuum of low pressure area on the fuel side of the diaphragm (8). Atmospheric pressure acting on the opposite side of diaphragm (8) will force it upward moving the pivoted lever (21) overcoming

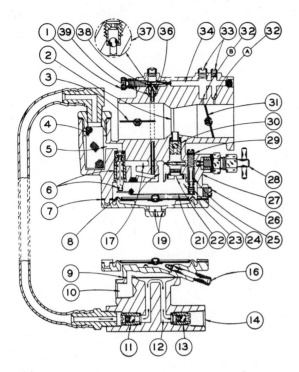

1. Idle mixture adjusting needle.
2. Venturi.
3. Choke.
4. Fuel strainer.
5. Inlet supply channel.
6. Fuel inlet needle and seat.
7. Gasket.
8. Diaphragm for carburetor.
9. Fuel pump diaphragm.
10. Impulse channel.
11. Pump outlet check valve.
12. Passage.
13. Pump inlet check valve.
14. To fuel supply tank.
16. Flushing plunger.
17. Fuel supply channel.
19. Atmospheric vent.
21. Inlet control lever.
22. Main nozzle plug.
23. Diaphragm chamber.
24. Fuel valve spring.
25. Spring screw.
26. Drain screw.
27. Channel.
28. Main mixture adjusting needle.
29. Washer.
30. Main nozzle.
31. Throttle shutter.
32A. Primary idle discharge port.
32B. Secondary idle discharge port.
33. Idle port plugs.
34. Idle passage.
36. Idle tube.
37. Check valve.

Fig. 21-43. Tillotson carburetor designed for use on chain saw and similar small engines.

force to move the fuel. The fuel tank cap is vented to allow pressure in the tank to remain constant. As the piston goes down on the inlet stroke with the throttle open, a low pressure is created in the carburetor throat. A slight restriction is placed between the air horn and the carburetor throat and the choke. This helps maintain the low pressure. The difference in pressure between the tank and the carburetor throat forces the fuel up the fuel pipe, past the needle valve, through the two discharge holes. The throttle is relatively thick on this type of carburetor, so there is in effect a venturi at this point, thus aiding vaporization. A spiral is placed in the throat to help acceleration and also to help keep the engine from dying when the throttle is opened suddenly.

The amount of fuel at operating speed is metered by the middle valve and seat. This type of carburetor is used primarily on lawn mowers.

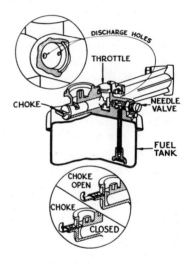

Fig. 21-44. Sectional view of suction feed carburetor, such as is used on lawn mowers and similar small engines.

spring pressure (24) opening fuel inlet valve (6) and admitting fuel into idle and main fuel supply channels (34) and (17).

When the engine is idling at nearly closed throttle, fuel is drawn through the idle tube or the alternate construction for inverted operation, check valve (37), past the idle adjusting screw (35) and into the engine via the primary idle discharge port (32a).

As the throttle is opened progressively, the vacuum at idle position is nearly eliminated, but the increase in air velocity through the venturi (2) puts increased vacuum on the nozzle (3) and unseats the nylon ball. The nozzle then delivers the power mixture metered in relation to the demands of the engine.

Suction Feed Carburetor

In the case of the suction feed carburetor fuel system, the fuel tank is mounted below the carburetor, Fig. 21-44. Atmospheric pressure is utilized as the

Quiz - Principles Of Carburetion

1. What is the purpose of the fuel system in an internal combustion engine?
2. List the main parts of a fuel system.
3. The rate of flow through a carburetor is the same under all operating conditions. True or False?
4. When starting an internal combustion engine, the fuel mixture should be:
   a. Rich
   b. Lean
   c. Average
5. Which speed requires a richer mixture?
   a. Idling
   b. 30 mph
6. Will all cylinders of a multi-cylinder engine receive an air-fuel mixture having the same octane rating?

7. For normal operating conditions, what fuel-air ratio will give the best economy?
   a. 16 to 1
   b. 20 to 1
   c. 25 to 1
8. For quick acceleration, what is the best fuel-air ratio?
   a. 5 to 1
   b. 10 to 1
   c. 12 to 1
   d. 20 to 1
9. Are the molecules forming a gas held more tightly together than those of a metal?
10. Name two factors affecting the rapidity of evaporation.
11. What causes the air-fuel mixture to be drawn into the combustion chamber of an internal combustion engine?
12. The purpose of a venturi in a carburetor is to:
    a. Increase the speed of the air passing through the carburetor
    b. Maintain the correct air-fuel ratio
    c. Provide extra fuel for acceleration
13. There are five main circuits in a modern carburetor. Name four of them.
14. In a carburetor venturi, which point has the highest vacuum?
    a. Entrance to the venturi
    b. Narrowest point of the venturi
    c. Point one inch beyond the venturi
15. The idle system of a carburetor supplies fuel at what speeds?
    a. Idle speed only
    b. Speeds up to 40 mph
    c. Speeds up to 15 mph
16. How many fuel discharge ports does the conventional idle system have?
    a. One
    b. Two
    c. Three
    d. Four
17. When the idle system is no longer supplying fuel to the engine, which system then supplies fuel?
    a. Air bleed system
    b. Main system
    c. Vaporizing system
18. The purpose of an economizer valve is to supply more fuel, or less fuel?
19. The metering rod is designed to vary the size of which jets?
    a. Idle jets
    b. Accelerating jets
    c. High speed jets
    d. Float level jets
20. Under what conditions is ice most likely to form in a carburetor?
    a. 20 deg. below zero and high humidity
    b. 32 deg. above zero and high humidity
    c. Zero deg. and low humidity
21. On what type of car are you most likely to find an anti-stall dashpot?
    a. Cars with automatic transmission
    b. Cars with conventional transmission
    c. Cars fitted with four-barrel carburetors
22. In addition to updraft and downdraft carburetors, what other basic type is there?

MANUAL AND
AUTOMATIC CHOKES

To start an internal combustion engine which is operated with gasoline, it is necessary to supply an extremely rich mixture. This mixture must be gradually leaned until the engine reaches operating temperature, after which operation will be maintained by the air-fuel ratios supplied by the carburetor.

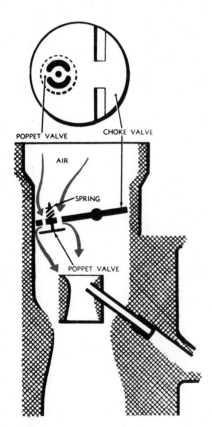

Fig. 22-1. Details of choke valve or choke plate. Note that plate is mounted off-center on its shaft and is provided with a spring loaded poppet valve.

The extremely rich mixture is secured by obstructing the air intake of the carburetor with a choke valve of the disk type, Fig. 22-1. With this choke valve closed, very little air is admitted, with the result that the suction, created by the piston on its downstroke, acts on the fuel nozzles and large quantities of fuel are drawn into the engine cylinder.

As soon as the engine is started, a somewhat leaner mixture is immediately required. Two methods are used to accomplish that condition. One method is to have the choke disk, or plate as it is also known, mounted slightly off-center on its shaft, Fig. 22-1. In that way, the atmospheric pressure will bear on a greater area on one side of the shaft than on the other, with the result that the disk will be forced open against spring pressure. Another method is to provide a small spring loaded poppet valve, which is built into the choke plate, Fig. 22-1. The engine suction, as soon as the engine starts, will pull this poppet valve open permitting air to pass through and dilute the mixture.

Choke Controls

The opening and closing of the choke plate can be controlled manually or automatically. When it is manually controlled, a push-pull rod is provided which extends from the choke on the carburetor to the instrument panel. The driver can close the choke for starting the engine, and open it gradually as the engine reaches operating temperature.

The obvious difficulty with such an arrangement is that the driver is apt to forget to open the choke fully, with the result that the excessively rich mixture will cause carbon to form in the combustion chamber and on the spark plugs, with loss in power.

To overcome this difficulty, the automatic choke was developed. Some automatic chokes depend on exhaust manifold heat only for their operation, while others combine such heat with intake manifold vacuum and the velocity of air acting on the offset choke disk for their operation.

Automatic Choke Operation

The operation of an automatic choke depends primarily on the unwinding of a thermostatic coil spring, Fig. 22-2, as heat is supplied. As the spring unwinds, it causes the choke plate in the carburetor air horn to open, permitting more air to pass through the carburetor. Heat for the operation of the thermostat, in most cases, is obtained from the exhaust manifold. In one design, the thermostat is mounted in a well located in the exhaust manifold, Fig. 22-8. Movement

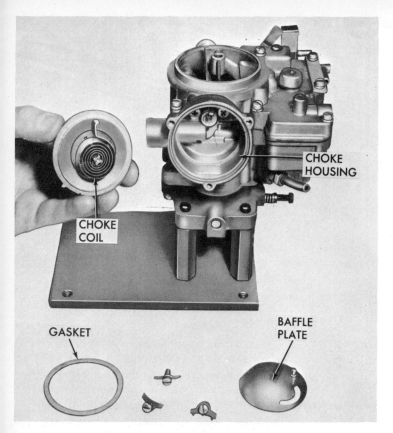

Fig. 22-2. Parts of typical choke mounted on side of carburetor. Note particularly the choke coil.

of the thermostatic coil is then transmitted to the choke valve by means of linkage and levers.

When the thermostat is mounted on the side of the carburetor, Fig. 22-3, it is necessary to conduct the heat from the exhaust manifold to the thermostat. This is accomplished by passing a tube through the exhaust

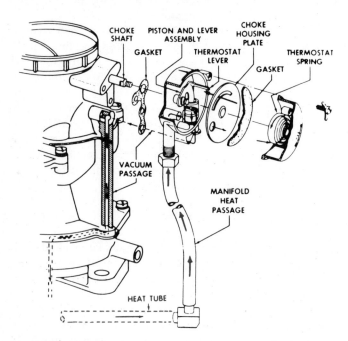

Fig. 22-3. Exploded view of automatic choke mounted on side of carburetor. Note the heat tube which supplies heat from the exhaust manifold.

manifold, so that as air is drawn through the tube it is heated by the exhaust gases passing around the tube. This tube then conducts the heated air to the thermostat.

To aid the circulation of this warm air around the thermostat, vacuum connection is made with the intake manifold, Fig. 22-4.

Another design of automatic choke uses electrical means and heat from the exhaust manifold to operate the choke.

Descriptions of typical chokes are provided in the following paragraphs.

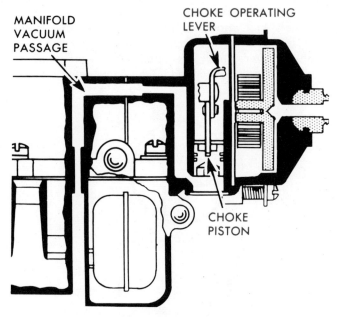

Fig. 22-4. Choke system on Carter carburetor.

Carter Climatic Control Choke

The Carter Climatic Control Choke as used on many Carter carburetors, is shown in Figs. 22-4 and 22-5. In this choke, air velocity, intake manifold vacuum and heat from the exhaust manifold, are used to control the operation of the choke.

When the engine is cold, tension of the thermostatic coil, Fig. 22-5, holds the choke plate closed. When the engine is started, air velocity against the choke plate causes the choke to open slightly against the tension of the thermostatic coil. Intake manifold vacuum applied to the choke piston, Fig. 22-5, pulls the choke piston down, opening the choke valve. The choke valve assumes a position where the tension of the thermostatic coil is balanced by the pull of the vacuum on the piston and air velocity on the offset choke plate.

When the engine starts, slots in the side of the choke piston, Fig. 22-5, are uncovered allowing intake manifold vacuum to draw warm air from the hot air tube located in the exhaust manifold through the center of the choke housing, Fig. 22-4. The hot air passes around a delayer plate on which the choke thermostatic coil is mounted. The incoming air loses some of its heat to the delayer plate, keeping the choke on longer to improve warm-up performance. The flow of warm air in turn heats and expands the thermostatic coil, causing it to gradually lose some of its tension, until finally the choke valve assumes wide-open position.

When the engine is accelerated during the warm-up period the corresponding drop in manifold vacuum applied to the choke piston, allows the thermostatic coil to momentarily close the choke valve, providing the needed richer mixture.

The fast idle linkage as used on this carburetor, is shown in Fig. 21-18.

Should the engine become flooded during the starting period, the choke valve can be opened manually by depressing the accelerator pedal to the floor. The unloader projection, Fig. 21-19, will then rotate the fast idle cam and in turn open the choke valve.

Rochester Automatic Choke

The automatic choke system as used on the four-throat Rochester carburetor, Fig. 22-6, consists of a thermostatic coil (3) vacuum piston (4) offset choke valve and fast idle cam (2). Its operation is dependent on the combined effects of intake manifold vacuum, the offset choke valve, atmospheric and exhaust manifold heat.

When the engine is cold the tension of the coiled thermostatic springs keeps the choke valve in the closed position. Then, as the engine starts, the velocity of the air passing through the carburetor air intake acting against the offset choke valve tends to force it into the open position against the tension of the thermostatic spring. At the same time, intake manifold vacuum acts on the vacuum piston (4) through the

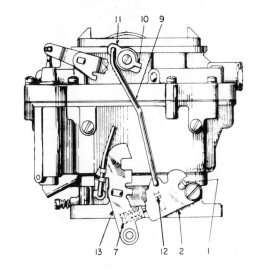

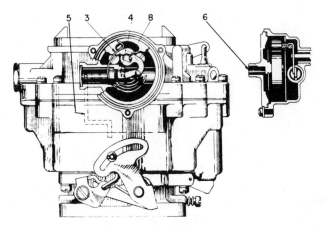

Fig. 22-6. Automatic choke used on Rochester carburetors.

passage (5) which also tends to open the choke valve. In other words, the choke valve assumes a position where the torque of the thermostatic coil is balanced by the vacuum pull on the choke piston and air velocity against the offset choke valve. This causes a regulated air flow into the carburetor providing a richer mixture during the engine warm-up period.

Also during the warm-up period, the vacuum piston (4) serves to modify the choking action to compensate for different engine loads. As any acceleration or increased load decreases, the vacuum exerted on the choke piston, the thermostatic coil torque momentarily increases the closure of the choke valve, thereby providing the needed richer mixture for acceleration.

As the engine temperature increases, hot air from the exhaust manifold is drawn into the thermostatic coil housing through the connection (6). This warm air acting on the thermostatic coil (3) causes it to relax its tension. As a result the choke valve gradually assumes a fully open position.

In order to prevent stalling during the warm-up period, the engine idling speed is made greater than normal. This is accomplished by means of the fast idle screw (7) which contacts the steps of the fast idle cam (2). The fast idle cam is in turn linked to the

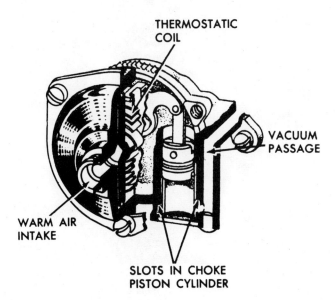

THERMOSTATIC COIL

VACUUM PASSAGE

WARM AIR INTAKE

SLOTS IN CHOKE PISTON CYLINDER

Fig. 22-5. Details of Carter choke shown in Fig. 22-4.

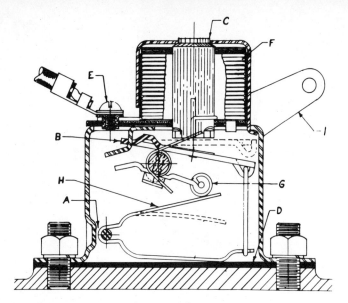

Fig. 22-7. Sisson electric choke. C and F form the electromagnet with armature B, thermostat H, shaft plate G, choke lever I.

shaft (8) of the choke valve by the choke rod (9), choke trip lever (10) and choke lever and collar assembly (11), holding the throttle valves open sufficiently during the warm-up period to maintain the desired faster idling speed. This speed is maintained until the choke valve is in the fully open position.

While the choke valve is only partly open, and the driver wishes to open the throttle to the fully open position, the pull on the vacuum piston (4) would be decreased, thereby closing the choke valve. It is therefore necessary to open the choke valve mechanically. This is accomplished by the tang (12) on the fast idle cam (2) which is made to contact the throttle lever (13) at wide-open throttle position, thereby opening the choke valve.

This mechanism is also called the choke unloader and serves to unchoke a flooded carburetor.

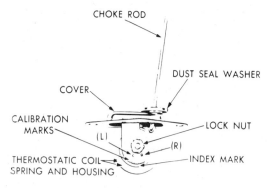

Fig. 22-8. Details of crossover type thermostatic choke control, which is mounted in a well in exhaust crossover in intake manifold.

Sisson Automatic Choke

The Sisson automatic choke, Fig. 22-7, controls the position of the choke valve by means of an electromagnet and a thermostat. The unit is mounted on the

exhaust manifold and is connected to the choke valve by means of a rod and levers. The electrical circuit is controlled through operation of the starter switch. When the starter switch is operated, the choke circuit is closed so that current flows through the electromagnet in the choke. This operates the choke lever, closing the choke valve. As soon as the engine is started, the starter switch is opened and the choke circuit is also opened. This demagnetizes the choke electromagnet and the position of the choke valve is then controlled by the thermostat. Then, as the engine attains operating temperature, the choke valve is fully opened. Should the engine be started when it is hot, the tension of the thermostat will hold the choke open against the action of the electromagnet.

Crossover Type Choke

This automatic choke is thermostatically operated. The thermostatic coil, Fig. 22-8, is mounted in a well in the exhaust crossover in the intake manifold on V-type engines. The operation of the choke valve is controlled by the thermostatic spring, the choke piston, Fig. 21-27, and by the offset position of the choke valve on its shaft. The complete installation is shown in Fig. 22-9.

As the thermostatic coil gains heat, it gradually unwinds and allows the choke plate to open. At the

Fig. 22-9. Remote temperature sensing control used on 230 cu. in. Chevrolet engine.

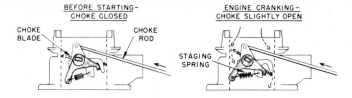

Fig. 22-10. Spring-staged choke permits choke to open slightly as an aid to starting.

same time, the vacuum-operated choke piston, connected by a rod to the valve, keeps a constant pull on the valve against the tension of the spring. This continues as long as the engine is operating. Thus the choke valve opens gradually. In addition the offset position of the choke valve on its shaft also tends to open the valve as the result of the velocity of air passing.

Spring-Staged Choke

To more accurately provide the correct amount of choke for starting, a spring-staged choke device is provided on some carburetors. As shown in Fig. 22-10, the choke plate is closed before starting, but as soon as the engine is cranked, the spring opens the choke a slight amount. This design is used on Chrysler built cars.

Water-Heated Choke

In addition to using exhaust heat to control the operation of the carburetor choke, recent models of the Lincoln car also use the coolant from the engine water jacket. The design is such that as long as the water in the water jacket remains higher than a specified value, the choke will not be in operation, Fig. 22-11.

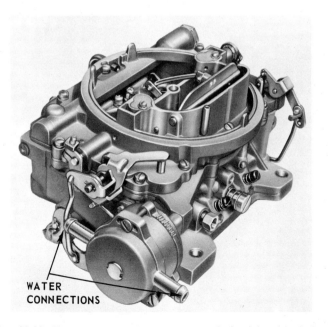

Fig. 22-11. Note water connections to provide heat for the choke and preventing choke from closing as long as coolant is warm.

Electric Choke

The electric automatic choke control as adapted to Zenith carburetors is a part of the carburetor assembly, Fig. 22-12. On downdraft carburetors, manifold vacuum is supplied to the vacuum choke cylin-

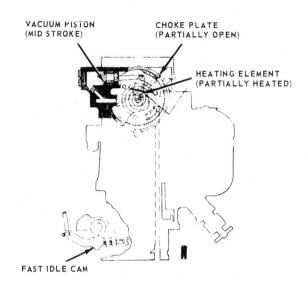

Fig. 22-12. Details of Zenith electric choke which is in the partly open position.

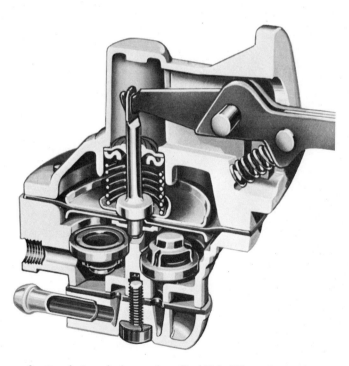

Sectional view, fuel pump from Ford V-8, 221 cu. in. engine.

der bore through an internal vacuum channel. The heat for operating the thermostat spiral spring is provided by an electric heating element in the thermostat chamber. A fast idle cam and rod connected to the throttle shaft provide fast idle during warm-up.

Quiz - Manual, Automatic Chokes

1. Is a lean mixture or a rich mixture required to start a cold engine?
2. What two methods are used to control the operation of a choke?
3. Where is the heat used to operate an automatic choke usually obtained?
4. When thermostatic coil is mounted on side of carburetor, how is heat supplied?
   a. Electrically
   b. Through tubing which passes through the exhaust manifold
   c. From hot water obtained from the radiator
5. Explain how air velocity is used in some chokes to aid in the operation of the choke.
6. What provision is made in carburetor linkage to prevent stalling during the warm-up period of an internal combustion engine?
7. In the cross-over type automatic choke, where is the thermostatic coil located?
   a. On the side of the carburetor
   b. In a well in the exhaust manifold
   c. In the hot water jacket of the engine
8. What is the major disadvantage of the manually operated choke?

ENGINE MANIFOLDS

The intake manifold connects the carburetor or carburetors to the intake ports of the engine. The exhaust manifold connects the exhaust ports of the engine to the exhaust pipe or pipes, which in turn lead to the muffler. Originally, because of the characteristics of the fuel being used, intake manifolds were of simple construction. However, in order to insure satisfactory distribution of present day fuels and keep the fuel vaporized, heat is supplied to the intake manifold. This is accomplished by surrounding a part of the intake manifold with a jacket which is supplied with heat from the exhaust manifold.

The difficulty in designing intake manifolds is to provide each cylinder with the same quality and quantity of fuel. As pointed out in the section on fuels, gasoline is a mixture of various hydrocarbons, some of which vaporize more easily than others. Equal distribution of the fuel to each cylinder could be more easily attained if the gasoline consisted solely of easily vaporized fuel. In order to keep the different components that form gasoline vaporized, heat is applied to aid in the vaporization. Heat tends to reduce the volumetric efficiency of the engine; that is, smaller amounts of the combustible mixture will reach the cylinder and in that way power will be reduced.

Manifold Heat

On in-line engines, heat is applied to the intake manifold by surrounding a central section with a heat jacket, Fig. 23-1, through which hot exhaust gases are directed. Another design is to have a small section of the intake manifold in contact with the exhaust manifold.

On V-8 engines, where the intake manifold is situated between the two banks of cylinders, special passageways are included in the design of the manifold. These passageways conduct hot gases from the exhaust manifold close to the intake passageways, to provide the necessary heat.

In order to regulate the amount of heat reaching the intake manifold from the exhaust, a thermostatic valve is provided. These valves and their operation are described in detail on page 237.

Unequal Distribution

Even with this aid to vaporization the mixture in the intake manifold is not completely vaporized. As a result the quantity and quality of fuel reaching each cylinder varies. As a result some cylinders will develop more power than others and some cylinders will have a greater tendency to detonate than others. This condition varies with the speed of the engine and it is necessary to design and adjust the carburetor so as to provide an adequate mixture for what would otherwise be the weak cylinder. The other cylinders will then receive a mixture that is too rich.

Fig. 23-1. Intake manifold with gasket. The square section at the center is the heat jacket supplied with hot exhaust gases from the exhaust manifold which is bolted directly to it by the studs.

There are several reasons why the fuel reaching each of the cylinders varies in quality and quantity. First of all, when the throttle valve of the carburetor is partly open, the flow of air and fuel is directed against one side. The choke valve will also affect the distribution. Of even greater importance is that the heavy particles of the fuel mixture have greater inertia than the lighter particles. As a result, the heavier particles will tend to continue moving past a branch in the manifold. The cylinder supplied by that branch will therefore, not receive its full quota of such heavy particles but will receive an excess of lighter particles. Similarly, some cylinders will re-

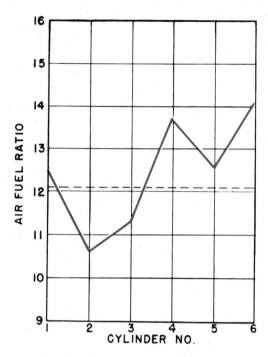

Fig. 23-2. *Note how the air-fuel ratio varies in the different cylinders, with No. 2 receiving a very rich mixture and cylinders No. 4 and 6 receiving lean mixtures.*

characteristics and shape of the intake manifold that the composition of the fuel, the heat supplied, engine speed, etc. will seriously affect fuel distribution.

From other studies it is learned, that as a result of variations in fuel distribution, explosion pressures developed in a six cylinder engine may vary from a low 125 lb. per sq. in. to a maximum of 310 lb. per sq. in. In one case it was found cylinders three and four developed the minimum pressure, cylinder six the maximum, and cylinders one, two and five approximately 280 lb. per sq. in. each. Increasing the rate of fuel supply improved the condition up to a certain point, and further increases resulting in cylinders three and four producing an explosive pressure of 310 lb. per sq. in. and the other cylinders developing only 235 lb. per sq. in.

In order to improve the distribution of fuel to the engine cylinders and thereby increase the power, many engines are equipped with carburetors of two or four throats. In addition, some engines will be equipped with more than one carburetor. For example; two four-throat carburetors are often used on V-8 engines. Three dual carburetors have been also used on V-8 engines.

ceive greater quantities of tetraethyl lead than others. Obviously those cylinders receiving the leanest mixture and/or least amount of tetraethyl lead will have the greatest tendency to knock.

In Fig. 23-2, the variation in air-fuel ratio of the fuel reaching each of the cylinders of a particular manifold and the variation in the motor octane rating of the fuel supplied each cylinder is shown in Fig. 23-3. It must be emphasized that in addition to the physical

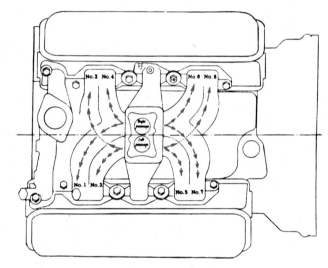

Fig. 23-4. *Manifold for dual carburetor on V-8 engine.*

Naturally special manifolds have to be used for such installations. In Fig. 23-4, the path of the fuel mixture in a manifold designed for a V-8 using a dual carburetor is shown. A V-8 manifold fitted with three dual carburetors is shown in Fig. 23-5, while Fig. 23-6 shows a more conventional installation of a four-throat carburetor on a V-8 engine.

In order to equalize pressures existing in the two sections of the manifold, it is necessary that they be interconnected. This is usually done by cutting a groove in the flange of the carburetor where it is bolted to the manifold.

Racing engines or other high performance engines are often fitted with one carburetor for every pair of

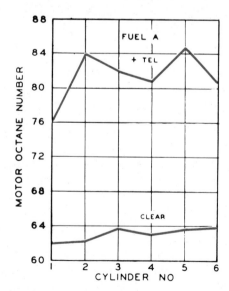

Fig. 23-3. *Illustrating the variation in octane rating of the fuel reaching the different cylinders of a six cylinder engine. The upper curve is for fuel with tetraethyl lead (TEL), while the lower curve is for clear gasoline. Data from experiments made by Sun Oil Co.*

cylinders. One carburetor for every cylinder has also been used. The carburetor and manifold of a four cylinder Offenhauser racing engine are shown in Fig. 23-7. Note that in this design, the manifold extends beyond the branches leading to the end cylinder.

General Design Of Manifolds

Manifolds for passenger cars and commercial vehicles are usually made of cast iron or aluminum while manifolds for racing engines are made either of cast aluminum or built-up of aluminum tubing. In other than racing cars the walls of the manifold are approximately 1/8 in. thick.

The number of outlets to the manifolds is dependent on the number of cylinders and the arrangement of valves. For example, each cylinder may have its individual intake and exhaust port, Fig. 23-1. A more usual arrangement is to have some of the ports Siamesed, that is, a single port supplies two cylinders.

For example a six cylinder in-line engine may be designed so that both end ports are exhaust and the ends of the intake manifold connect to Siamese intake ports; all other ports, both intake and exhaust, being connected to individual branches of their respective

Fig. 23-7. Offenhauser engine showing the manifold with two carburetors.

manifolds. With such an arrangement, the exhaust manifold would have six branches while the intake has four. See Fig. 23-8. By having as many Siamese ports as possible, there would be four exhaust ports and three intakes on a six-cylinder engine.

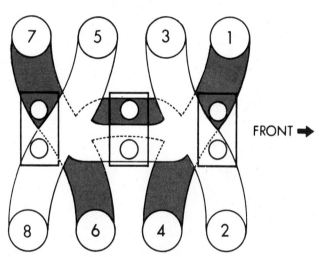

Fig. 23-5. Manifold designed for three dual carburetors on a V-8 engine.

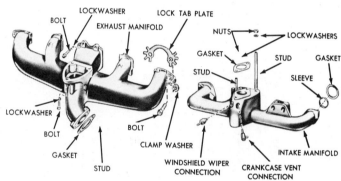

Fig. 23-8. Manifold assembly for in-line six cylinder engine.

Eight cylinder engines (both V-type and in-line), when fitted with a dual carburetor have the manifolds so designed that each carburetor throat supplies alternate cylinders in the firing order. The usual firing order of an in-line eight is 1-6-2-5-8-3-7-4, number 1 cylinder being at the front. In such engines all the intake ports are usually Siamese and the engine will have four intake ports, one for each pair of cylinders. One throat of the carburetor will then supply the four inner cylinders and the other throat will supply the two cylinders at each end of the engine.

On a V-8 with dual carburetion, Fig. 23-4, one throat of the carburetor will supply the end cylinders on the left bank and the two central cylinders on the right bank. The other throat of the carburetor supplies the central cylinders on the left bank and the end cylinders on the right bank. For example the firing order

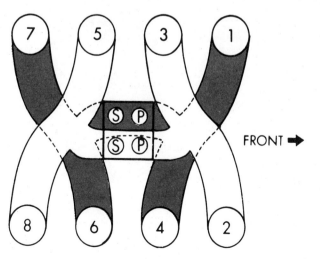

Fig. 23-6. Four-throat carburetor on V-8 engine. The "S" and "P" represent the primary and secondary throats of the carburetors.

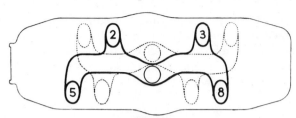

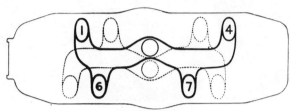

— FIRING ORDER —
LEFT HAND BARREL OF CARBURETOR
5-8-3-2

— FIRING ORDER —
RIGHT HAND BARREL OF CARBURETOR
1-4-6-7

Fig. 23-9. Illustrating fuel distribution of V-8 with a firing order of 1-5-4-8-6-3-7-2 equipped with a dual carburetor.

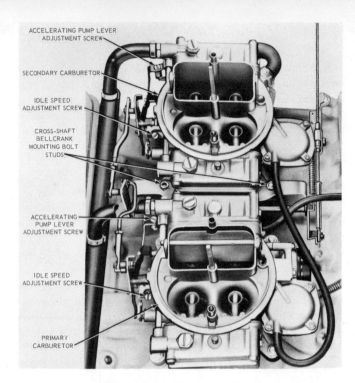

Fig. 23-10. The dual Holley 4 venturi carburetor installation, for the 427 cu. in. Ford, consists of two 4-barrel carburetors mounted on a special aluminum manifold.

of the Ford V-8 is 1R, 1L, 4R, 4L, 2L, 3R, 3L, 2R, or 1, 5, 4, 8, 6, 3, 7, 2. One throat of the carburetor will supply 1L, 7L, 6R, and 4R. The other will supply 8R, 3L, 5L, and 2R, Fig. 23-9.

The intake and exhaust manifolds on most engines are separate castings, Fig. 23-8. In the case of V-type engines, the intake manifold is placed in the V formed by the cylinders, while separate exhaust manifolds are bolted on each side of the cylinder block. On in-line engines, the two manifolds are placed together on the

DODGE CHARGER 3, sleek, experimental two-seater, has no doors or windows that open. Jet-aircraft-type canopy swings open, steering wheel-instrument cluster pod moves up and out of way, and seats elevate to admit driver and passenger. Outside air enters driver-passenger area through scoops at base of windshield, circulates in compartment and exhausts through rear bulkhead port.

one side of the engine. However, on some engines, the intake manifold is built into the cylinder block where it is wholly or partly surrounded by water in the cooling system. In this way the temperature of the manifold throughout its length, is maintained at substantially the same temperature, regardless of weather. As a result, carburetion and distribution are improved. Essentially the same economy is obtained regardless of air temperatures. See also Fig. 23-10.

A radical departure from conventional manifold design is shown in Fig. 23-11. In this design, the arms of the manifold make long sweeping curves from the carburetor to the cylinder block. The purpose of the design is to provide more equal distribution of fuel to the individual cylinders, and reduce the variation in octane rating and air fuel ratio of the fuel reaching the various cylinders.

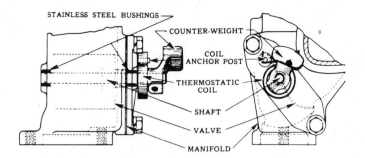

Fig. 23-12. Details of manifold heat control valve. Note stainless steel bushings and balance weight.

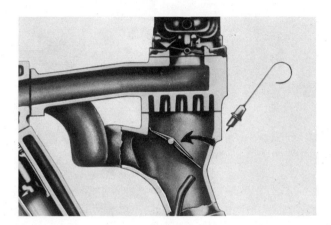

Fig. 23-13. The manifold heat control valve is indicated by the arrow. It is in the position it assumes when the engine is hot.

Fig. 23-11. Note the manifold on this Plymouth engine.

Manifold Heat Control

The purpose of a carburetor is to deliver a metered amount of atomized fuel mixed with air, to the manifold. However, regardless of how well mixed and vaporized the fuel mixture is as it leaves the carburetor, its characteristics are changed as it passes through the manifold. Cold surfaces in the manifold will cause some of the vaporized fuel to condense, and changes in direction of flow will, through inertia, cause some portions of the mixture to settle out. These conditions have been observed by using glass manifolds.

The problem is further complicated by the characteristics of the fuel itself. Formerly, when the fuel was highly volatile, the problem was not so difficult. With today's fuels which are relatively nonvolatile, it is necessary to supply heat to obtain better vaporization and more equal distribution of the fuel to each cylinder. Heat to the intake manifold is most needed when the manifold is cold, and also when the engine is idling, in which case the suction on the carburetor is low and the fuel is not sprayed very finely. It is important that a minimum of heat reach the carburetor

as excess heat would tend to vaporize the fuel before it reaches the carburetor jets, causing vapor lock and flooding.

In order to supply heat to, and also regulate the amount of heat reaching the intake manifold, a thermostatically controlled heat valve is installed. Details of such heat control valves are shown in Figs. 23-12, 23-13, and 23-14.

This device known as a manifold heat control valve, is built into the exhaust manifold. It is so

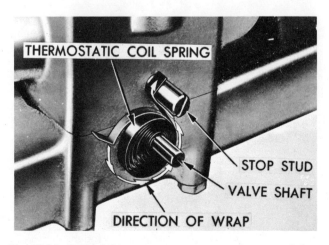

Fig. 23-14. Typical thermostatic spring as used to control the position of the manifold heat control valve.

designed that when the engine is cold, a maximum amount of heat is directed against an area of the intake manifold. As the engine reaches operating temperature, the thermostat changes the position of the

Fig. 23-15. Arrows point to the exhaust crossover on this V-8 intake manifold.

valve, so the exhaust gases are no longer directed against the intake manifold, but are directed directly to the exhaust pipe and mufflers.

Fig. 23-16. Note the unusual exhaust manifolds on this high performance Dodge engine.

Fig. 23-13, shows the location of a manifold heat control valve on an in-line six cylinder engine. In this case, the valve is in the position it assumes

when the engine has reached operating temperature, and the exhaust gases are not directed to the intake manifold, but into the exhaust pipe. With a cold engine, the valve will have rotated in a clockwise direction, directing the gases against the lower surface of the intake manifold. Note how the lower surface of the intake manifold is finned, to increase the area exposed to hot gases.

A typical thermostatic coil spring as used on a manifold heat control valve is shown in Fig. 23-14. The thermostat is mounted on the outside of the exhaust pipe or manifold, and is provided with a counter-balance weight, see Fig. 23-12. Note in Fig. 23-12, the valve shaft is mounted on stainless steel bushings.

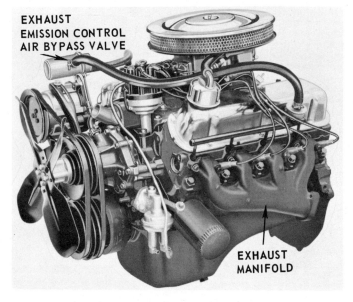

Fig. 23-17. Unusually large exhaust manifold on this 289 cu. in. Ford engine.

This is important because of the high temperatures and acids of the exhaust, there is a strong tendency for these valves to become rusted in position.

In the case of V-8 engines, in order to supply heat to the intake manifold, a passage is provided to carry exhaust gases from one side of the intake manifold to the other. This is known as the exhaust crossover and is shown in Fig. 23-15. The heat control valve, located in one of the exhaust manifolds, then directs the exhaust gases through this crossover passage during the warm-up period.

It is particularly important that the manifold heat control valve be kept free and not rusted in position. Due to rust and corrosion, it is apt to become "frozen" in position. If it becomes "frozen" so that no heat is directed to the intake manifold, fuel will not be properly vaporized and fuel economy will drop. If the manifold heat control valve is "frozen" so heat is directed all the time to the intake manifold, vapor lock will result, and maximum power will not be developed.

To insure free operation of the manifold heat control valve, special oils, usually containing graphite are employed. To free a stuck valve, penetrating oils may be used, and the valve shaft should be tapped back and forth with a light hammer.

Exhaust Manifolds

As has been indicated, exhaust manifolds take many forms and in recent designs the trend is strongly toward increasing their internal dimensions so as to reduce resistance to the flow of exhaust gases and by reducing the back pressure, performance is improved. This is particularly noticeable in the high performance engines. A Dodge design is shown in Fig. 23-16, and the 289 cu. in. Ford, in Fig. 23-17. The intake and exhaust manifolds of the GMC V-6, Fig. 12-1b, is also of interest. Attention is also called to the exhaust pipes of the Ford Race Engine, shown on page 120.

Quiz - Engine Manifolds

1. What is the purpose of the intake manifold?
2. Why is heat applied to the intake manifold?
3. Where is the intake manifold on a V-type engine located?
   a. In the V, between the two banks of cylinders
   b. On each side of the engine, on the outside
   c. On the front of the cylinder block
4. On an in-line type engine where is heat usually applied to the intake manifold?
   a. At the center of the manifold
   b. At the rear of the manifold
   c. At the front of the manifold
5. What causes unequal distribution of fuel?
6. Do all cylinders receive fuel of the same octane rating?
7. Which cylinders of a V-8 engine do the barrels of a dual carburetor supply?
   a. Both barrels supply all cylinders
   b. The left barrel supplies the cylinders on the left side of the engine, and the right barrel supplies the right hand cylinders
   c. The right hand barrel will supply center cylinders on the right bank of cylinders and end cylinders on left bank. The left hand barrel will supply the center cylinders of left bank of cylinders and end cylinders on right bank.
8. The manifold heat control valve is so designed for what purpose?
9. Why are carburetors of more than one throat used on some multicylinder engines?
10. Why are some intake manifolds built into the cylinder block where they are completely surrounded by water?

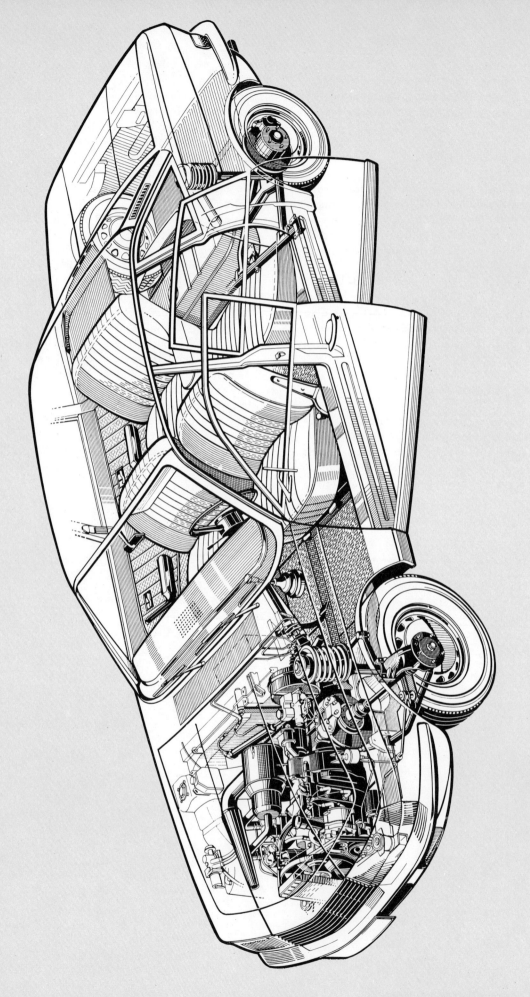

NSU Motorenwerke AG has produced a new and larger Wankel-engined car. The front-wheel-drive NSU Ro 80 is a 5-seater saloon powered by a 130 hp rotary combustion engine. It has selective-automatic gearbox, dual circuit braking system for four-wheel disc brakes, independent suspension and rack-and-pinion hydraulic servo-assisted steering.

AIR CLEANERS

Air that is drawn into a carburetor and mixed with fuel must be as free from dirt as possible. If this is not done, the dust acts as an abrasive and under extreme conditions, the resulting wear will reach such proportions that it soon becomes necessary to recondition the engine.

To reduce the amount of dust entering the carburetor, an air cleaner is installed at the air entrance of the carburetor so all air is screened and filtered. In addition to filtering the air, the air cleaner is also designed to act as a silencer to reduce the noise of the air rushing into the carburetor.

There are several different types of air filters in common use today.

1. Oil wetted mesh cleaner.
2. Oil bath cleaner.
3. Paper element cleaner.
4. Polyurethane cleaner.

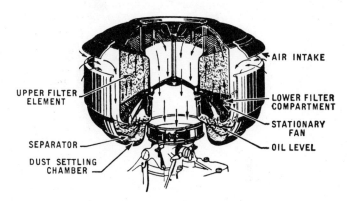

Fig. 24-2. Oil bath type air cleaner.

Oil Wetted Type

The oil wetted mesh cleaner, Fig. 24-1, is one of the older type cleaners. In this design, air passes through a copper mesh screen which has been wetted with engine oil. This type cleaner is not as efficient as some of the others, and has the disadvantage of soon becoming clogged with dust with the further result that air flow is restricted, and the air-fuel ratio is then seriously affected. In addition, relatively large portions of extremely fine dust particles are not removed from the air stream.

Where an oil wetted mesh cleaner is used, it is important that the copper screen be washed in kerosene or other solvent, and then dipped in engine oil at frequent intervals, the frequency depending on dust conditions in the area of operation. Manufacturers recommend that this cleaning operation be done at least every 1,000 miles.

Oil Bath Type

In the oil bath type air cleaner, Fig. 24-2, which is more efficient than the oil wetted mesh cleaner, the direction of the incoming air is reversed and directed over the surface of the oil bath. This causes a large portion of the dust to be retained in the oil bath. The air is then passed through an oil wetted copper mesh screen, through the silencer, and into the carburetor.

The usual recommendation for servicing the oil bath type cleaner is to clean it every 5,000 miles.

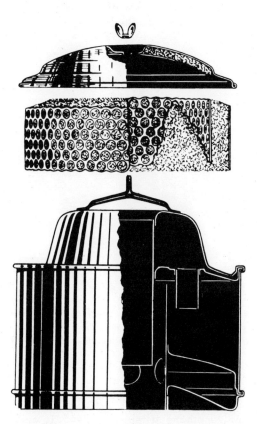

Fig. 24-1. Oil filter of the oil wetted, copper mesh type.

The wire-mesh portion of the unit is cleaned in the same manner as the oil wetted mesh cleaner previously described. The oil bath portion of the cleaner is serviced by emptying the oil and scraping the dirt from the bottom of the reservoir. Then the reservoir is refilled with SAE 40 engine oil.

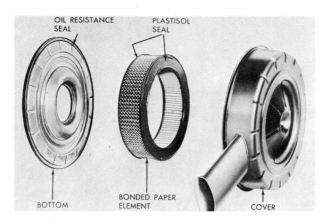

Fig. 24-3. Paper element, or dry-type air cleaner.

Paper Element Type

The paper element type cleaner is of more recent development and is highly efficient. The filter element consists of special paper which has been formed into an accordion-pleated ring and sealed top and bottom with a plastic ring, Fig. 24-3. The element can be cleaned by removing it from its housing and tapping it against some hard surface to shake off accumulated dirt. This type cleaner element should never be immersed in cleaning solution. Special testing equipment, Fig. 24-4, is available for testing the element.

Another type of paper element air cleaner, known as a heavy-duty dual-stage cleaner, consists of a re-

Fig. 24-3b. Individual open stacks are provided for this high performance engine.

placeable oil wetted paper inner filter surrounded by a glycol wetted polyurethane foam outer filter. The polyurethane element should be washed in solvent and reoiled using SAE 30 engine oil every 12,000 miles or 12 months.

A special type used on some high performance cars is shown in Fig. 24-3a. It will be noted that a single air cleaner is provided for three carburetors. This provides some protection against dust entering the engine through the carburetor. It is preferred to the open stack type, Fig. 24-3b, which provides no resistance to the free flow of air but does not prevent dust from entering the engine.

Fig. 24-4. One form of tester for checking the condition of dry-type air cleaner. Air is forced through the cleaner, and the amount of restriction is indicated by the height of the ball in the tube.

Polyurethane Type

The polyurethane filter, Fig. 24-5, is also a recent development and is highly efficient. The filtering ele-

Fig. 24-3a. A single air cleaner for three carburetors on high performance engine.

ment consists of the polyurethane filtering element which is supported in a perforated metal ring. This element is cleaned after removing it from the housing, by washing in kerosene or mineral spirits. Hot degreasers should not be used. The excess solvent should be squeezed out, and after dipping in engine oil, the filter element is replaced in the air cleaner housing. As the polyurethane element is easily torn, the manufacturers advise that the element should never be shaken, swung or wrung to remove excess solvent or oil.

Fig. 24-5. Polyurethane type of filter being cleaned in kerosene.

Hot and Cold Air Intake

To reduce variations in carburetion due to changes in temperature of the air, some carburetors are equipped with a thermostatically controlled air inlet temperature device. The air inlet duct mechanism consists of a valve plate, thermostat, adjustable thermostat rod, two springs and a retaining clip.

The air received from the air duct passes through a silencing chamber in the air cleaner body and then through the filter element. Leaving the filter element, the air passes down into the carburetor.

The temperature of the air entering the air cleaner is thermostatically controlled by the carburetor air duct assembly. Air from the engine compartment, or heated air from a shroud around the exhaust manifold is available to the engine.

A thermostatic bulb in the air duct is exposed to the incoming air. A spring-loaded valve is connected to the thermostatic bulb through linkage. The valve plate spring holds the valve in the closed position (heat on) until the thermostatic bulb overcomes the valve tension.

During engine warmup period, when the air entering the air duct is less than 75 deg. F., the thermostat is in the retracted position and the valve plate is held in the "heat on" position, thus shutting off the air from the engine compartment. As the air temperature passing the thermostatic bulb approaches 85 deg. F., the thermostat starts to pull the valve down and allows the cooler air from the engine compartment to enter the air cleaner. When air temperature reaches 105 deg. F., the valve will be in the "heat off" position so only engine compartment air will enter the air cleaner.

This system was modified and improved and forms part of the exhaust emission control system which is described in the chapter on that subject.

Quiz - Air Cleaners

1. Name four types of air cleaners.
2. Where is the air cleaner installed?
   a. Between the carburetor and the manifold.
   b. At the air entrance of the carburetor.
   c. On the carburetor air bleed.
3. Which type of air cleaner is usually considered to be more efficient, the oil wetted type, or the oil bath type?

4. What precautions should be taken when cleaning a polyurethane type filter element?
5. How should a paper element type of air filter be cleaned?
   a. Washed in cleaning solvent.
   b. Cleaned by blowing out the dirt with compressed air.
   c. Tapping against some hard surface.

The new 350 cu. in. Buick engine. Available with either two or four-barrel carburetor.

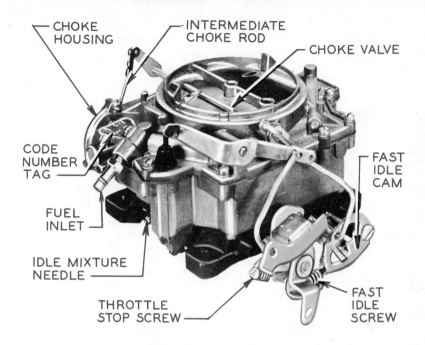

CHOKE HOUSING · INTERMEDIATE CHOKE ROD · CHOKE VALVE · CODE NUMBER TAG · FUEL INLET · IDLE MIXTURE NEEDLE · THROTTLE STOP SCREW · FAST IDLE CAM · FAST IDLE SCREW

Fig. 25-1. Showing some of the points that require adjustment on a carburetor. Note particularly the throttle stop screw, fast idle cam and screw, choke rod and idle mixture needle.

CARBURETOR
ADJUSTMENT, SERVICE

Adjusting Carburetors

Modern carburetors are accurately calibrated for the individual engines for which they are designed. Adjustments are provided for idling speed and the amount of fuel required for idling.

Formerly carburetors were provided with two and three adjustments so that the amount of fuel could be controlled throughout the complete range of engine speeds and conditions. Obviously such carburetors required considerable time and skill to adjust and only a fair degree of accuracy could be attained after prolonged road testing under all speeds and conditions.

Before adjusting any carburetor it is important that the ignition system be in good condition, and that the compression is equal in all the cylinders. It is also important that there be no leaks in the intake manifold, and the engine is at operating temperature. The carburetor must be clean internally, in good mechanical condition, and the float level must be correctly set.

Before attempting to adjust the idle mixture, it is necessary to first adjust the engine idling speed. This is particularly necessary on a vehicle fitted with an automatic transmission, for if the idling speed is too great, the car will tend to "creep" when the engine is idling, and the transmission is in "drive."

To adjust the idling speed, it is necessary to first bring the engine up to operating temperature and make sure the fast idle cam is not holding the throttle open. In addition, the choke must be fully open. With manual shift cars in "neutral," and automatic transmission cars in "drive," adjust the idle speed adjustment screw, or throttle stop screw, Fig. 25-1, to obtain the desired speed. This will vary slightly with different engines. In general, the idling speed for a car fitted with a manual transmission is specified at 475 rpm and automatic transmission at 425 rpm.

Today virtually all carburetors, with the exception of some models of the Tillotson carburetor, have an idle mixture adjustment only. On single-throat carburetors the adjustment, indicated by the arrow in Fig.

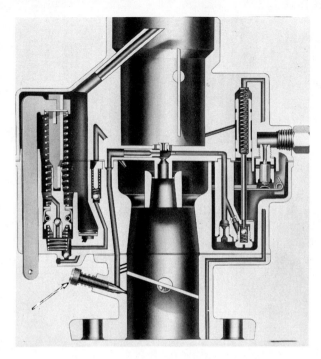

Fig. 25-2. The arrow points to the idle mixture adjustment on this Rochester carburetor.

25-2, is easily and quickly made by turning the adjustment to the position which gives maximum idling speed. Obviously the idle speed or throttle position must not be altered until after the idle mixture has been correctly set. The usual method of making the idle adjustment is to first set it approximately one turn open. With the engine running and at operating temperature, gradually open the adjustment until the engine falters. Then, turn the adjustment in until the engine operates smoothly.

Fig. 25-3. Vacuum gauge with hose for connecting to intake manifold.

A more accurate method is to attach a vacuum gauge, Fig. 25-3, to the intake manifold and then adjust the idle mixture to obtain the maximum reading on the vacuum gauge. A tachometer, to determine the speed of the engine, may also be used for this purpose.

Many factors, in addition to the condition of the engine, will affect the reading of the vacuum gauge. Compression ratio, carburetor and valve restrictions, and the speed at which the test is made, will all influence the reading. Vacuum readings for tune-up purposes are always made at idling speed.

In connection with engine vacuum readings, it is important to note that the vacuum decreases with an increase in altitude. Approximate vacuum readings for engines of different numbers of cylinders are given in the following table:

Elevation in Feet	Number of Engine Cylinders		
	Four	Six	Eight
Zero to 1000	18 to 20	19 to 21	21 to 22
1000 to 2000	17 to 19	18 to 20	19 to 21
2000 to 3000	16 to 18	17 to 19	18 to 20
3000 to 4000	15 to 17	16 to 18	17 to 19
4000 to 5000	14 to 16	15 to 17	16 to 18
5000 to 6000	13 to 15	14 to 16	15 to 17

Adjusting two or four-throat carburetors is slightly more difficult, as such carburetors are provided with two idle mixture adjustments. On such carburetors it is advisable to use the vacuum gauge or tachometer method of adjusting the carburetor, as a more accurate adjustment can be obtained.

Before making the idle mixture adjustment on a two or four-throat carburetor, Fig. 25-4, both idle adjustments should be turned in until they seat and and then backed out an equal amount. In most cases this should be one turn. Then, after starting the engine and it has reached operating temperature, the two adjustments are turned out equal amounts at a time, until the maximum reading on the vacuum gauge is attained. On most engines the best adjustment will be secured when both idle mixture adjustments are turned out equal amounts. However, in some instances slightly smoother idling will be secured by turning out one adjustment slightly more than the other. There should never be more than one quarter turn difference between the position of the two adjustments.

The procedure for adjusting four-throat carburetors is given with the detailed description of the individual makes. The procedure on such units is the same as only two idle mixture adjustments are provided.

Adjustments of carburetors can be checked by an analysis of the exhaust gases.

Other carburetor adjustments include such items as throttle linkage adjustment, fast idle cam, unloader adjustment, automatic choke adjustment, and accelerating pump adjustment. Some of these adjustments are made only in connection with a carburetor overhaul and adjustments vary with different installations.

In connection with throttle linkage adjustment, this is relatively critical on cars equipped with automatic transmissions and procedure and specifications vary with different makes and models. Unless the throttle linkage is correctly adjusted, trouble may be experienced in the shifts of the automatic transmission.

Fig. 25-4. The arrows indicate the two idle mixture adjustments on this four-throat carburetor. Adjustments on a two-throat carburetor are similar.

The fast idle cam, Fig. 25-1, must be adjusted in correct relationship to the automatic choke. The final adjustment is such that when the choke is fully open, the fast idle cam should not be holding the throttle open.

Unloaders are adjusted by means of special gauges on some cars, while on others, simple measurements are used.

Exhaust Emission Control Idle Adjustments

Accurate adjustment of the idle mixture and idle speed is particularly important on engines equipped with exhaust emission control systems. The instructions vary with different engines and different manufacturers. However, it is important that the engine be at full operating temperature, with the choke open, air cleaner thermostatic valve open on engines so equipped, hot idle compensator closed on carburetors so equipped, and air cleaner installed. In the case of automatic transmission equipped cars, the idle adjustment is made with the shift lever in "drive" position.

It must be remembered that it is possible to adjust the idle mixture so that it is too lean. While that would decrease the amount of carbon monoxide produced, the hydrocarbons would be increased.

The importance of accurately adjusting idle mixture and speed, is shown by the fact that Chevrolet has detailed instructions covering the adjustment on a decal affixed to the radiator shroud.

Most carburetors on engines with exhaust emission control equipment are fitted with devices which limit the range through which the idle mixture can be adjusted, Fig. 21-32 and Fig. 21-32a. Such limiters must not be removed or otherwise made ineffective.

Exhaust Gas Analyzers

In the unit devoted to fuels and their combustion, it was pointed out that for perfect combustion of one pound of fuel, 15.27 lb. of air is required. This is the theoretical relationship. However, in an internal combustion engine it is found that, to obtain maximum power, a definite air-fuel ratio is required which is different from the ratio that will give maximum economy.

If an engine is being operated with a lean mixture, (excessive amount of air), obviously the power developed will increase as more fuel is supplied. This increase in power with increase in fuel will continue until all of the oxygen in the air being supplied to the cylinder is consumed in the combustion of the fuel.

However, the fuel and air reaching the cylinders are imperfectly mixed. The mixture is diluted by exhaust gases that have remained in the cylinder, and the fuel reaching the cylinder ranges from a vapor to wet particles. It is, therefore, necessary to supply more fuel than is called for by theoretically perfect combustion. In general, maximum power is secured from air-fuel ratios of 14 to 1, and maximum economy with ratios of approximately 16 1/2 to 1.

While it is possible to measure the quantities of air and fuel entering an engine, it is a complicated process and limited to research laboratories. The same results can be obtained in the shop with relatively simple equipment, which analyzes the exhaust gases, Fig. 25-5.

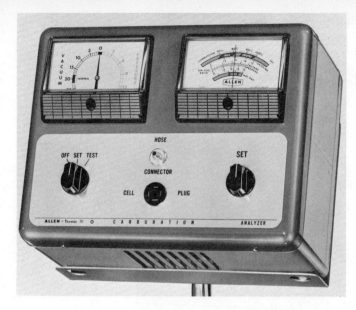

Fig. 25-5. Equipment used for analyzing exhaust gases. (Allen Electric)

There are several different types of exhaust gas analyzers in use. A frequently used type operates on the principle that the composition of the exhaust gas affects its ability to conduct heat.

Different gases will conduct heat from a heated surface at different rates. That is, their thermal conductivity varies and air is considered as having a thermal conductivity of one. Nitrogen, oxygen and carbon monoxide have a thermal conductivity of approximately the same as air, while carbon dioxide is about one half that of air, and hydrogen is seven times greater.

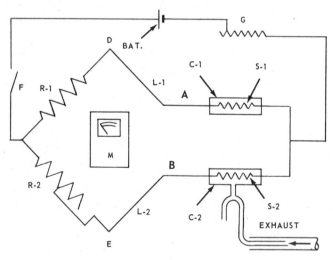

Fig. 25-6. Electrical circuit of exhaust gas analyzer.

It is this difference in thermal conductivity that is used in the analysis of exhaust gases. To do this, a Wheatstone bridge type of instrument is used, Fig. 25-6. This makes a comparison of the resistance of similar coils of platinum wire, one set of coils being suspended in exhaust gas, while the other is in air. Current is passed through the coils which causes them to heat. The gas surrounding the gas coils conducts away some heat, and thereby affects their resistance, which is indicated on the instrument. The amount or degree of temperature change is dependent upon the composition of the exhaust gas which, in turn, is dependent on the fuel and air entering the engine through the conductor. The instrument can, therefore, be calibrated to read directly the air-fuel ratio.

Hydrogen and carbon dioxide are the components of the exhaust gas that produce the reading on the meter. Hydrogen will cause the pointer to deflect toward the rich side, while carbon dioxide will deflect it toward the lean side.

When current flowing through "A" and "B" side of the Wheatstone bridge, Fig. 25-6, is the same, no current will be flowing through the meter M. When instrument is being calibrated for use, air is drawn through resistor cells C-1 and C-2 and the two sides of the bridge are balanced by means of variable resistance R-2. In use, exhaust gas from a pickup, Fig. 25-7, is passed through resistor cell C-2. The exhaust gas with its carbon dioxide will carry away more heat from the platinum resistor S-2 than air does from S-1. This will decrease resistance of S-2 and unbalance circuit so that current will flow through the meter. The amount of current will be in proportion to change in resistance of S-2, which in turn is in proportion to the amount of carbon dioxide in the exhaust gas.

There are two types of pickups used to get a sampling of the exhaust gas. One type, Fig. 25-7, has one side connected to the exhaust pipe, while the other is connected to the instrument. The other type is inserted in a flexible tube into the exhaust pipe and has the resistor cell S-2 right at that point.

Vapor Lock

Just as water turns to steam when it is heated, gasoline turns to vapor when sufficient heat is applied. When complete or partial interruption of fuel flow results from vaporization of the fuel, the carburetor system is said to be vapor locked. This condition may occur anywhere in the fuel line, the fuel pump, or in the carburetor itself.

Whether or not vapor is likely to form and cause vapor lock depends on the vapor pressure of the fuel; in other words, the ease at which it will vaporize. The standardized method of measuring or determining vapor pressure in the laboratory is known as the Reid method. U. S. Government specifications for motor gasoline require that the Reid vapor pressure at 100 deg. F. should not exceed 12 lb. per sq. in.

As the vapor of motor fuel occupies a greater volume than in liquid form, the amount of fuel flow will therefore be reduced. Under vapor lock conditions, loss in power and missing will occur and under extreme conditions, the engine will stop. After the fuel and carburetor system has cooled, the engine can be started without difficulty.

Carburetors are now designed with vents to overcome or reduce any tendency toward vapor lock. Car and engine manufacturers frequently place an asbestos gasket approximately 1/2 in. thick between the carburetor and manifold. This reduces the transmission of heat to the carburetor so that there is less tendency toward vapor lock in the carburetor. In addition, fuel pumps are placed so that they will be cooled by air blasts and shielded from the heat of the exhaust manifold. Also to reduce the possibility of vapor lock, fuel lines are placed as far as possible from the muffler and exhaust line.

Low pressure on the fuel will also promote vapor lock. A pusher type pump, located in the fuel tank, would therefore be better than the conventional suction type fuel pump.

In addition to design of carburetor, pump, and lines, vapor lock is also controlled by gasoline refineries. This is done by changing the vapor pressure. During winter months a fuel that is easily vaporized

Fig. 25-7. Equipment used to collect exhaust gas from tail pipe of vehicle.

is supplied so as to facilitate starting. During summer months when temperatures are high, engines are more easily started and a fuel that is not so easily vaporized is provided. However, during unseasonably warm weather in the spring and before refiners have supplied their summer grade fuel. It is not unusual to encounter difficulties from vapor lock.

Carburetor Icing

The formation of ice in carburetors is a problem which will occur under certain weather conditions. It is most likely to occur when the atmospheric temperature is between 28 and 55 deg. F., with the relative humidity between 65 and 100 percent. It usually occurs after the engine is started and before it has reached operating temperature, and the result is that the

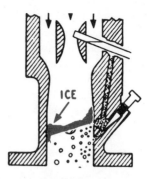

Fig. 25-8. Ice and frost will collect on throttle plate, restricting the flow of fuel from idling jets, when air temperature ranges from 28 to 55 deg. F. and the relative humidity ranges from 65 to 100 percent.

engine will stop or stall when operated at idling speed. Each time the engine stops it can be easily restarted, but when the engine speed is reduced to idling it will stop again.

The ice is formed at the edge of the throttle plate, Fig. 25-8, and will restrict the flow of the air-fuel mixture when the throttle plate is at or near the idle position, causing the engine to stop. The engine will start again without difficulty as it is necessary to open the throttle, which will permit the air-fuel mixture to flow to the engine.

The formation of ice results from rapid vaporization of the fuel which may lower the temperature, or the temperature may be reduced as much as 25 deg. F. This lowered temperature causes the moisture in the air to freeze, causing ice to form on the edge of the throttle plate, where the air speed is greatest.

As soon as the engine reaches operating temperature, the carburetor will be sufficiently warm so that it will be impossible for ice to form.

Fuel refiners use special additives which aid materially in overcoming this trouble. A faster than normal idling speed is of help in minimizing the trouble but adjustment of the carburetor fast idle linkage should be made with care. Many carburetors are now provided with a passage which conducts exhaust heated air around the area of the idle mixture ports, Fig. 21-20. In that way the possibility of carburetor icing is greatly reduced.

Carburetor Servicing

Because of the great number of different makes and types of carburetors in use, space limitations here will not permit us to give complete and detailed descriptive procedure on servicing and repairing all these units. However, there are certain basic points which should be observed when overhauling all carburetors.

First of all, manufacturers have provided kits of repair parts and gaskets for overhauling their carburetors. See Fig. 25-9. Most of the manufacturers include with those repair kits, the necessary illustrated instructions for replacing the parts.

As the carburetor is being disassembled, all parts should be placed in a convenient tray so that they can be washed in clean commercial carburetor cleaning fluid. All parts should be washed except such items as the accelerator pump diaphragm or plunger, the power valve diaphragm, and the anti-stall dashpot assembly. In other words, do not wash those parts

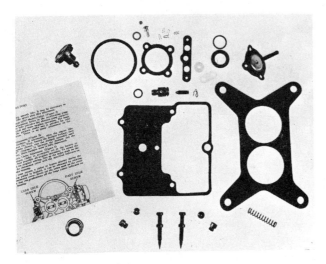

Fig. 25-9. Parts supplied in a typical carburetor repair kit. Note sheet from illustrated repair instruction folder on left.

made of fabric or rubber, which would be injured by the cleaning solution. After cleaning, all traces of the cleaning solution should be washed away with a stream of water, and the parts blown dry with compressed

Fig. 25-10. Using a straightedge to check gasket surface of carburetor for warpage.

air. Compressed air should be forced through all passages of the carburetor, to be sure they are thoroughly clean. Wire brushes should never be used; neither should fine wire be run through any jets as this may damage the ports.

Check the choke shaft for grooves, wear and excessive looseness or binding. Inspect the choke plate for nicked edges and the choke piston for ease of operation. Make sure the throttle shaft and its bearings are not worn. Worn parts should be replaced.

Inspect all parts such as the air horn throttle body, choke housing, etc., for cracks and other defects. Check all gasket surfaces for warpage, Fig. 25-10. This is particularly important on die castings.

Check the floats for leaks by holding them under water which has been heated to about 200 deg. F. Bubbles will appear if there is a leak present.

Inspect all gasket surfaces for nicks, and replace any parts that have been damaged.

Always install all of the parts contained in the repair kit. Set the float level with the gauge provided, Fig. 25-11.

Troubleshooting on Carburetors, Fuel Systems

Carburetors and fuel systems give many thousands of miles of trouble-free service and, while defective or poorly adjusted carburetors will seriously affect the economy and performance of the vehicle. Complete failure of the engine to operate seldom originates in the carburetor. Therefore, when the engine does not start or operate efficiently, it is advisable to first check ignition, compression and supply of fuel to the carburetor, before examining the carburetor.

If the ignition and compression prove to be in good operating condition, the first step is to examine the choke to make sure that with the engine cold, the choke is closed and, if the engine is hot, the choke is open. That condition is checked by removing the air cleaner and observing the position of the choke plate which will be visible on removal of the air cleaner.

If the operation of the choke proves to be satisfactory, the next step is to check for fuel to make sure it is reaching the carburetor. This can be accomplished by operating the carburetor linkage by hand. The fuel should spurt from the accelerator jets which can be noted by looking into the carburetor air intake. If no fuel is observed squirting from the accelerator jets, it indicates that there is no fuel in the carburetor float bowl. This is usually an indication that the fuel pump is inoperative, or that the fuel lines are clogged or otherwise defective. To check this condition, disconnect the fuel line at the carburetor and direct the line into a small receptacle. Crank the engine with the starter for a moment. Fuel should flow in spurts from the fuel line into the receptacle.

A defective fuel pump, or clogged fuel lines or lines with air leaks will prevent fuel from reaching the carburetor, provided of course, that there is fuel in the supply tank. In this connection, the fuel line extends from the top of the tank to within an inch of the bottom. Occasionally this line has broken so it does not reach the fuel unless the tank is virtually full of fuel.

To make sure the line connecting the fuel pump to the fuel supply tank is not clogged or leaking, disconnect it from the fuel pump and force compressed air through it. If the line is clear, the air will be heard bubbling through the fuel in the tank.

Air Leaks

Air leaks in the fuel line are more difficult to find and the usual method is to locate the trouble by elimination. In other words, first make sure the line is not obstructed and the fuel pump is in good condition. If no fuel is pumped from the supply tank, it is reasonable to assume that there are air leaks present.

The fuel line leading from the end of the main fuel line to the fuel pump is a frequent source of trouble. Being made of rubber it deteriorates on the inside and causes stoppage of the fuel. Being flexed by the movement of the engine on its rubber mountings, leaks may develop.

It is important to make sure nuts holding the carburetor to the manifold are tight, and the nuts holding the manifold to the cylinder block are secure. If the carburetor or manifold are loose, air leaks will result and carburetion will be affected as air will be drawn in, diluting the air-fuel mixture.

Troubles with the carburetor itself may be caused by worn linkage, dirt, incorrect fuel level, worn parts, or maladjustment.

Some carburetors are fitted with sight plugs in the side of the float bowl, so the fuel level can be determined without disassembling the carburetor. On such carburetors, the fuel should be level with the bottom edge of the plug hole. Worn external carburetor linkage can, of course, be determined by examination.

Carburetors are usually cleaned by first disassembling and washing the individual parts in special carburetor cleaning solutions. This gives the opportunity of inspecting and replacing any worn parts, and also resetting the fuel level. Special cleaning solutions are available, which will clean the interior of the carburetor while the engine is operating. Such solutions are used by disconnecting the regular fuel line at the carburetor, and connecting a can of the cleaning solution to the carburetor. The engine is then started and operated until a can (usually one pint) of the cleaning solution has been used.

Carburetor cleaning solutions are designed to not only dissolve the grease and dirt that accumulates on the outside of the carburetor, but also the gum which is of varnish-like consistency found on both the inside and outside of carburetors. Such gum is formed by heat acting on the fuel.

Carburetor Troubleshooting

While the basic causes of carburetor trouble will vary somewhat with different makes and designs of carburetors, the usual conditions or difficulties and their respective causes are outlined below.

Possible causes of poor performance generally result from too lean a mixture. If the carburetor is correctly adjusted a lean mixture and poor performance may result from the following:

 a. Air leaks at carburetor or manifold.
 b. Clogged carburetor air filter.
 c. Clogged fuel lines.
 d. Defective fuel pump.
 e. Incorrect fuel level.
 f. Automatic choke incorrectly set.
 g. Clogged fuel screen.
 h. Dirt in carburetor jets and passages.
 i. Worn or inoperative accelerating pump.
 j. Wrong or incorrectly set metering rod (Carter carburetor).
 k. Inoperative power valve, economizer or jet.
 l. Damaged or wrong size main metering jet.
 m. Worn idle needle valve and seat.
 n. Loose jets in carburetor.
 o. Defective gaskets in carburetor.
 p. Burned through or leaking heat riser.
 q. Clogged mufflers, ignition and poor compression should also be checked.
 r. Defective manifold heat control valve.
 s. Worn throttle shaft.
 t. Leaking vacuum lines to accessory equipment.

Poor Idling

Poor idling is usually caused by defective ignition system, leaking engine valves, or uneven engine compression. In the carburetor, the following should be checked:

 a. Incorrect adjustment of idle needle valve.
 b. Incorrect float level.
 c. Sticking float needle valve.

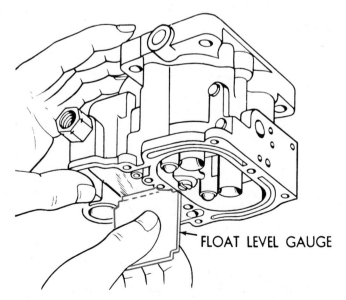

Fig. 25-11. Using a gauge to check the float level setting.

FLOAT LEVEL GAUGE

d. Defective gaskets between carburetor and manifold.
e. Defective gaskets in carburetor.
f. Loose carburetor to manifold nuts.
g. Loose manifold to block nuts.
h. Idle discharge holes partly clogged.
i. Defective automatic choke.
j. Loose jets in carburetor.
k. Leaking vacuum lines to accessory equipment.
l. Vacuum leaks which are partly compensated for by a rich idle adjustment.
m. Worn main metering jet.
n. Restricted or clogged air cleaner.
o. High float level.

Hard Starting

In addition to the fuel system troubles listed below, hard starting may be caused by use of engine oil that is too viscous, defective ignition system, low compression, weak starting battery, defective starting motor, excessive friction due to poorly fitted pistons and piston rings.

a. Incorrect choke adjustment.
b. Defective choke.
c. Incorrect float level.
d. Incorrect fuel pump pressure.
e. Sticking fuel inlet needle.
f. Improper starting procedure.

Poor Acceleration

Poor acceleration may be caused by defective ignition system, excessive engine or chassis friction, lack of compression, dragging brakes and incorrect carburetion. In the case of the carburetor, the following should be checked:

a. Accelerator pump incorrectly adjusted.

b. Accelerator pump inoperative.
c. Corroded or bad seat on accelerator bypass jet.
d. Accelerator pump leather hard or worn.
e. Clogged accelerator jets or passages.
f. Defective ball checks in accelerator system.
g. Incorrect fuel level.

Carburetor Floods

The usual causes of carburetor flooding are as follows:

a. Fuel level too high.
b. Stuck float needle valve.
c. Defective gaskets in carburetor.
d. Cracked carburetor body.
e. Excessive fuel pump pressure.

Excessive Fuel Consumption

There are many causes of excessive fuel consumption other than defective carburetion. Among such causes may be listed, poor engine compression, excessive engine friction, dragging brakes, misaligned wheels, clogged mufflers, defective ignition. The most usual cause of excessive fuel consumption is quick starts and high speed driving. In the carburetor and fuel system the following should be checked:

a. Adjustment of idle mixture.
b. Fuel leaks in carburetor or lines.
c. Clogged air cleaner.
d. High fuel level.
e. Defective fuel economizer.
f. Defective manifold heat control valve.
g. Defective carburetor gaskets.
h. Defective manifold gaskets.
i. Excessive fuel pressure.
j. Sticking fuel inlet needle.

Quiz - Carburetor Adjustment, Service

1. Which should be adjusted first?
   a. Ignition.
   b. Carburetor.
2. How is a vacuum gauge used when adjusting a carburetor?
3. Describe briefly the procedure for adjusting a single throat carburetor.
4. Describe briefly the procedure for adjusting a dual carburetor.
5. With other conditions remaining the same, where would you have the highest manifold vacuum?
   a. In a valley.
   b. At the top of a high mountain.
6. In general which engine has the highest intake manifold vacuum?
   a. Four cylinder engine.   c. Eight cylinder engine.
   b. Six cylinder engine.

7. For perfect combustion how many pounds of air are required to burn one pound of gasoline?
   a. 27.15 lb.
   b. 13.50 lb.
   c. 15.27 lb.
   d. 12.75 lb.
8. What is the advantage of analyzing the exhaust gas?
9. Do all gases conduct heat at the same rate?
10. On the Wheatstone bridge type of exhaust gas analyzer, which two gases produce the reading on the meter?
    a. Oxygen and carbon monoxide.
    b. Hydrogen and carbon dioxide.
    c. Carbon monoxide and carbon dioxide.
11. What causes vapor lock?

12. Ice forms at what point in the fuel system when the engine is first started?

    a. Fuel Pump.
    b. At the air inlet to the carburetor.
    c. At the edge of the throttle plate.
    d. In the fuel filter.

13. Which of the following parts should not be washed in carburetor cleaning solution?

    a. Carburetor float.
    b. Anti-stall dashpot.
    c. Idle needle valve.
    d. Accelerator pump diaphragm.
    e. Accelerator pump plunger.
    f. Carburetor float.
    g. Throat plate.

14. How can a float be checked for leaks?

    a. By inflating with air.
    b. Immersing in water at 120 deg.
    c. Immersing in water at 200 deg.
    d. Immersing in gasoline.

15. If an engine fails to start and the ignition system is in good condition and the fuel tank is full, what should be checked next?

    a. The position of the choke plate.
    b. The idle mixture adjustment.
    c. The float level.

16. List three causes for carburetor flooding.

17. List three causes for hard starting, which originate in the fuel system.

18. List five causes of excessive fuel consumption originating in the fuel system.

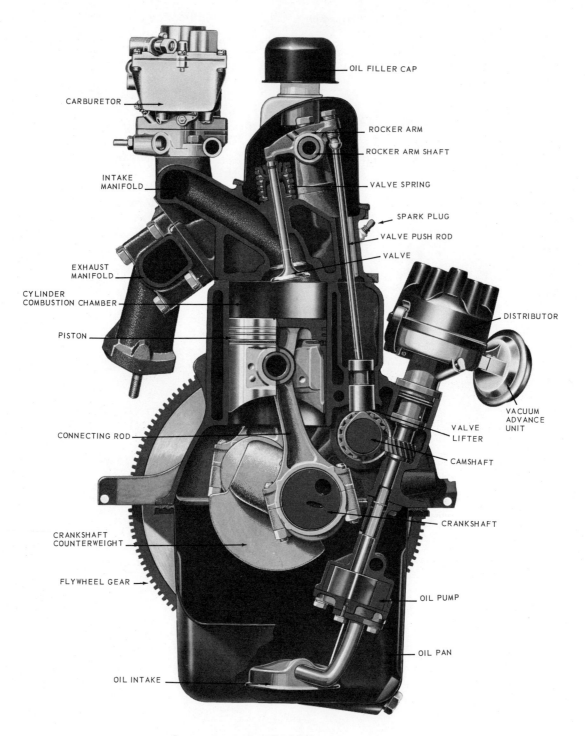

CARBURETOR

OIL FILLER CAP

ROCKER ARM

ROCKER ARM SHAFT

INTAKE MANIFOLD

VALVE SPRING

SPARK PLUG

VALVE PUSH ROD

VALVE

EXHAUST MANIFOLD

CYLINDER COMBUSTION CHAMBER

DISTRIBUTOR

PISTON

VACUUM ADVANCE UNIT

CONNECTING ROD

VALVE LIFTER

CAMSHAFT

CRANKSHAFT

CRANKSHAFT COUNTERWEIGHT

FLYWHEEL GEAR

OIL PUMP

OIL PAN

OIL INTAKE

Front section view, Ford Falcon, 144 cu. in., 6-cylinder engine, with principal parts identified.

FUEL
SUPPLY SYSTEMS

On engines such as used on lawn mowers, and many industrial engines, fuel is supplied to the carburetor by gravity feed. On automobiles, either mechanical or electrical pumps are used. In the case of the mechanical pump, it is operated by means of a cam on the camshaft of the engine. In some cases, the fuel pump is combined with a vacuum pump which is used to operate the windshield wiper. However, in recent years this practice is being superseded by using electric windshield wipers.

Fig. 26-2. External view of the fuel pump shown in Fig. 26-1.

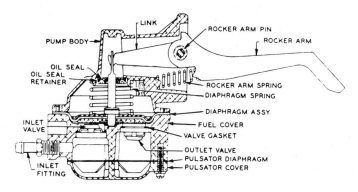

Fig. 26-1. Typical diaphragm type mechanical fuel pump. (AC Spark Plug Div.)

Fuel Pump Operation

A typical fuel pump is illustrated in Figs. 26-1 and 26-2. This type of fuel pump has a built-in air dome with a diaphragm to dampen out pulsations in the fuel stream. It is a diaphragm type pump, and is actuated by the rocker arm through a link and pull rod from a cam on the engine camshaft sprocket.

A rocker arm spring holds the rocker arm in constant contact with the eccentric or cam on the engine camshaft sprocket, so the rocker arm moves up and down as the camshaft rotates. As the arm swings downward, it bears against the shoulder on the link which is pivoted on the rocker arm pin. The link swings upward, pulling the diaphragm upward by means of the connecting pull rod. Upward movement of the fuel diaphragm compresses the diaphragm spring, and also creates a vacuum in the fuel chamber

under the diaphragm. The vacuum causes the outlet valve to close, and fuel from the gasoline supply tank to enter the fuel chamber through the inlet valve.

As the rotating eccentric on the camshaft permits the rocker arm to swing upward, the arm releases the fuel link. It cannot move the link downward. The compressed diaphragm spring then exerts pressure on the diaphragm, and the fuel in the chamber below the diaphragm. This pressure closes the inlet valve, and forces fuel out through the outlet valve to the carburetor.

As the fuel diaphragm is moved downward only by the diaphragm spring, the pump delivers fuel to the carburetor only when the pressure in the outlet line is less than the pressure maintained by the diaphragm spring. This condition arises when the carburetor float needle valve is not seated, and the fuel line from the pump to the carburetor float chamber is open. When the needle valve is closed, and held in place by the pressure of the fuel on the float, the pump builds up pressure in the fuel chamber until it overcomes the pressure of the diaphragm spring. This pressure results in almost complete stoppage of diaphragm movement until more fuel is needed.

The air dome with diaphragm in the bottom of the fuel pump provides a pocket in which fuel under pressure can compress a certain volume of air. When the pressure is relieved (pump on suction stroke) the pocket of compressed air pushes the fuel on to its destination. The air dome minimizes flow pressure variations and increases pump output.

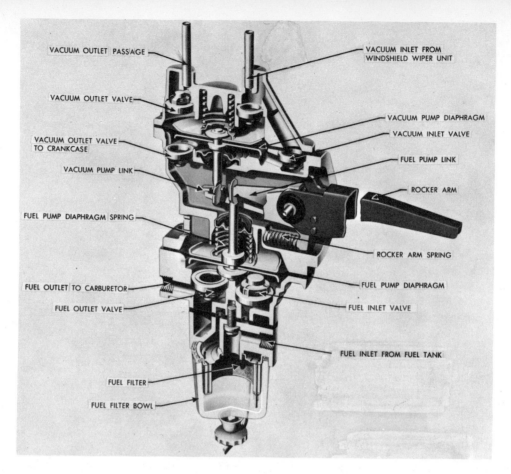

VACUUM OUTLET PASSAGE
VACUUM INLET FROM WINDSHIELD WIPER UNIT
VACUUM OUTLET VALVE
VACUUM PUMP DIAPHRAGM
VACUUM INLET VALVE
VACUUM OUTLET VALVE TO CRANKCASE
FUEL PUMP LINK
VACUUM PUMP LINK
ROCKER ARM
FUEL PUMP DIAPHRAGM SPRING
ROCKER ARM SPRING
FUEL OUTLET TO CARBURETOR
FUEL PUMP DIAPHRAGM
FUEL OUTLET VALVE
FUEL INLET VALVE
FUEL INLET FROM FUEL TANK
FUEL FILTER
FUEL FILTER BOWL

Fig. 26-3. Sectional view of combination fuel and vacuum booster pump.

Fuel and Vacuum Pump

A combination fuel and vacuum pump is shown in Fig. 26-3. The operation of the fuel section of this pump is similar to the one just described. The vacuum pump section operates as follows:

The vacuum booster portion of the pump is shown in Fig. 26-4. As the rocker arm forces the diaphragm up against spring pressure, the outlet valve opens, forcing the air in the upper chamber out through the exhaust port. At the same time a vacuum is created in the lower chamber. This causes air to be drawn from the windshield wiper motor through the inlet port on the booster, into the upper inlet chamber and then through the lower inlet valve into the lower chamber. On the return stroke, spring pressure forces the diaphragm downward expelling the air in the lower chamber through the lower outlet valve. This now creates a vacuum in the upper chamber which again draws the air from the wiper motor into the inlet chamber, and through the upper chamber inlet valve into the upper chamber. This type of vacuum booster makes it possible to supply vacuum to the windshield wiper motor on both up and down strokes of the diaphragm.

An exploded view of a mechanically operated fuel pump is shown in Fig. 26-5. Basic operation of this pump is similar to that of the previous pump.

Permanently Sealed Fuel Pump

The Carter permanently sealed fuel pump is shown in Fig. 26-3a. This is a mechanically operated pump, actuated by means of the fuel pump rocker arm and an eccentric on the camshaft. To disassemble, first scrape away the staking mark and remove the rocker arm retaining plug. Release the tension on the rocker arm pin by pressing the arm downward against the diaphragm and rocker arm spring pressure, or remove rocker arm spring and allow the rocker arm pin to fall out. Remove the rocker arm.

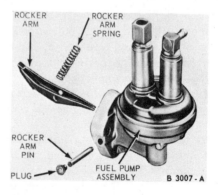

ROCKER ARM
ROCKER ARM SPRING
ROCKER ARM PIN
PLUG
FUEL PUMP ASSEMBLY
B 3007-A

Fig. 26-3a. Mechanically operated and permanently sealed fuel pump. (Carter)

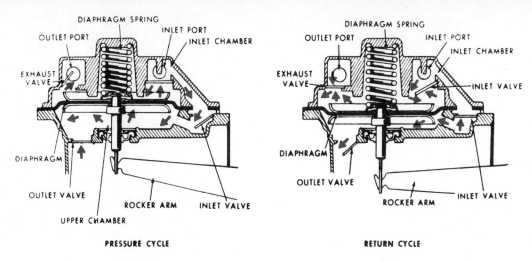

PRESSURE CYCLE

RETURN CYCLE

Fig. 26-4. Showing details of operation of vacuum portion of fuel pump illustrated in Fig. 26-3.

Diagnosing Troubles of Mechanical Fuel Pumps

Fuel pumps give many miles of trouble-free service. When they no longer pump fuel in sufficient quantities they should be replaced with a new or rebuilt unit.

To determine if the fuel pump is at fault, first make sure the supply tank has a sufficient quantity of fuel. If the fuel supply is satisfactory, disconnect the fuel supply line at the carburetor, and direct the fuel line into a small container. Then with the ignition turned off, crank the engine by means of the starter. If the fuel pump is in good condition, strong spurts of fuel will come from the supply line. If no fuel is pumped or only a small quantity, the pump is probably defective and should be replaced, provided of course that the fuel lines are not clogged, or the fuel line between the pump and the supply tank does not have an air leak. In general, a mechanical fuel pump as designed for passenger car use will pump approximately one quart of fuel in one minute at 500 rpm, engine speed.

In this connection, a flexible fuel line is often used to connect the pump with the end of the rigid fuel line leading to the supply tank. These flexible fuel lines, after a year or two of service, may develop air leaks, or the interior may swell and obstruct the flow of fuel.

An infrequent trouble is when the fuel pump supplies too much fuel. Excessive pressures are usually caused by insufficient flexing of the diaphragm. Such a condition would result in flooding of the carburetor.

Fuel pumps may be tested with suitable pressure gauges. The gauge is connected to the outlet side of the pump and, when the engine is cranked by the starter the gauge should register 3 to 5 lbs. pressure. The length of the hose connecting the gauge to the fuel pump should not exceed 6 in., otherwise inaccurate readings may result. Another test can be made by directing the flow from the pump into a pint or quart measure. With the engine operating at idling speed, a pint of fuel should be pumped in approximately 45 seconds. The fuel in the carburetor float bowl is sufficient to operate the engine for a long enough period to make such a test. The vacuum side of the pump can be checked by connecting a vacuum gauge to the intake connection. With the engine operating at idle speed, the vacuum should be a minimum of 10 in.

When the vacuum pump of a combination fuel pump is defective it will usually be disclosed by a slowing up of the action of the windshield wiper when the car is ascending steep hills, or whenever the throttle is fully open as when rapidly accelerating.

When the vacuum diaphragm is punctured, there will be a direct line from the engine crankcase, through the vacuum pump to the intake manifold. The engine vacuum will then draw oil from the crankcase

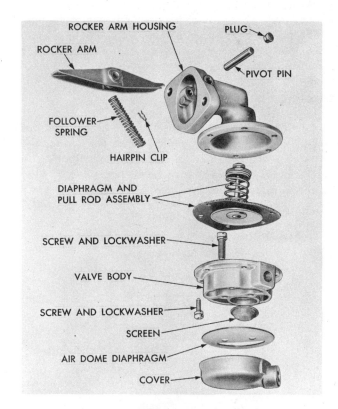

Fig. 26-5. Exploded view of mechanically operated fuel pump. (Autolite)

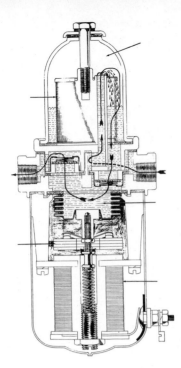

Fig. 26-6. Sectional view of Autopulse electric fuel pump. Arrows show path of fuel.

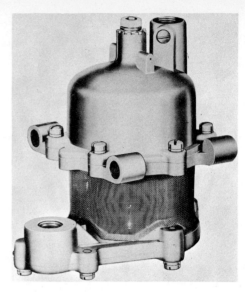

Fig. 26-8. The pusher type fuel pump, developed by Carter Carburetor Corp. is operated by an electric motor and submerged in the fuel in the supply tank. (Copyright by Carter Carburetor Corp. All rights reserved.)

to the engine and excessive oil consumption will result. A rough check on this condition can be made by disconnecting the vacuum line leading from the pump to the intake manifold. This should be disconnected at the lower end after the engine has been running for a short period. If oil drips from the tubing the vacuum diaphragm is punctured.

Within the fuel pump there are usually five points where wear would affect the performance of the pump. These points are: worn linkage, worn valves or seats, worn pull rod, and punctured fuel diaphragm, and punctured vacuum diaphragm.

Electric Fuel Pumps

Electrically operated fuel pumps are of two basic types: the suction type which draws the fuel from the tanks in a manner similar to the mechanically operated pumps; and the pusher type pump which is placed in the bottom of the fuel supply tank, and pushes the

Fig. 26-7. Construction of Bendix electric fuel pump.

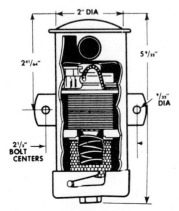

fuel to the carburetor. Autopulse and the Bendix electric fuel pumps are shown in Figs. 26-6 and 26-7 respectively. Both of these are of the suction type.

An advantage of the externally mounted electric pump which draws the fuel from the supply tank is that several pumps can be installed so, not only can larger quantities of fuel be supplied to the carburetor, but, in addition, in the event that one pump should fail, the others would continue to supply fuel.

An important advantage of the electrically operated fuel pump is that there is a considerable reduction in the tendency toward vapor lock. The reason for this is that it can be mounted on the dash or any other relatively cool spot under the hood. Whereas the mechanical pump, because it is driven mechanically by the engine, will operate at a higher temperature and will therefore be more apt to produce vapor lock. In addition, the electric pump will supply fuel to the carburetor as soon as the ignition is turned on.

The pusher-type pump has the advantage that the fuel in the supply line is under pressure and consequently there is reduced tendency toward vapor lock. There are no valves between the pump and the carburetor and therefore the fuel drains back into the tank when the engine is stopped, thereby eliminating a pressure buildup and consequent hard starting of a hot engine. The delivery of the fuel is steady and nonpulsating.

The pusher type unit made by Carter Carburetor Corp., Fig. 26-8, utilizes a centrifugal type unit driven by an electric motor and, being submerged in the fuel, the fuel acts both as a coolant and a lubricant.

In-Tank Electric Fuel Pump

The in-tank electric fuel pump, Fig. 26-8a, delivers fuel to the carburetor through the vapor separator which includes an additional outlet for the fuel line. On

270

Fuel, Supply Systems

Fig. 26-8a. Details of in-tank electric fuel pump. (Carter)

engine start, current is delivered through a special by-pass circuit. Current passes through the oil pressure switch to the pump, delivering full 12V to the pump. When the engine starts, the current will pass through a resistor, cutting voltage to 8-1/2 to 10V. This pump is serviced as an assembly.

Servicing the Autopulse

When fuel pump trouble is suspected, disconnect the fuel line at the carburetor, and direct the fuel line from the pump into a small container. Turn on the ignition switch, and then place a finger over the end of the fuel line. If pump stops or clicks very infrequently, the pump and fuel line connections are satisfactory. Remove the finger from the outlet side of the fuel line and, if ample fuel flows, the pump is operating satisfactorily. Always be sure that electrical connections are in good condition and that the correct voltage is reaching the unit.

Stewart-Warner Electric Pump

This electrically operated fuel pump, Fig. 26-9, is of the diaphragm type which is operated by the action of an electromagnet and rocker arm and pin. Electric

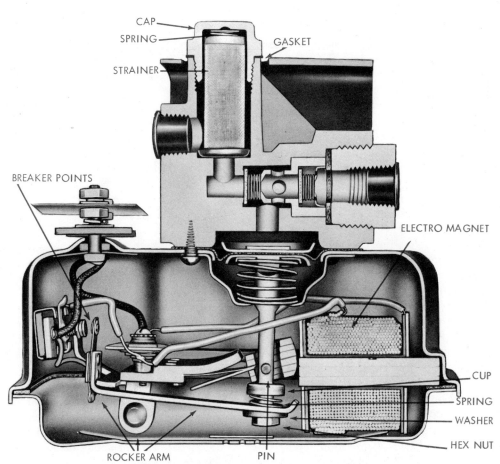

Fig. 26-9. Details of Stewart-Warner electric fuel pump.

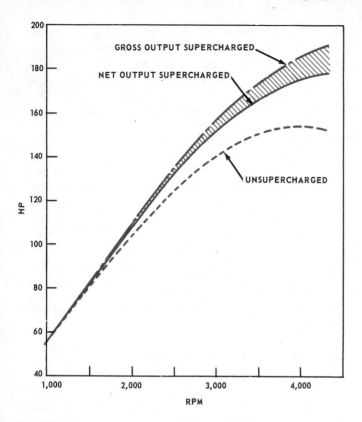

Fig. 26-10. *Comparison of power developed by a nonsupercharged engine and an engine equipped with a mechanically driven supercharger.*

half the power will therefore be developed under such conditions. Superchargers are therefore used on aircraft to maintain power at high altitudes.

Basically a supercharger is a compressor and a supercharged engine will have a higher overall compression than it had as a result of the volume of the combustion chamber and the displacement of the cylinder. This higher overall compression will increase the tendency toward detonation of spark ignition engines. When a supercharger is used on an automobile, fuel of higher than standard octane rating is required in order to overcome detonation.

When installed on a Diesel engine, only air is blown into the cylinders and the tendency toward detonation is reduced.

Superchargers are designed to develop from 4 to 20 lb. pressure. Obviously the greater pressure they develop the more mixture or air will be carried to the cylinders. The power required to drive the supercharger increases rapidly, and may be as much as 50 hp per lb. of air per second. A supercharged engine will burn more fuel than when it is unsupercharged, and the increase in power is not proportional to the increase in fuel consumed.

current to the armature is opened and closed by means of tungsten and platinum breaker points. As the current is opened and closed, the rocker arm causes the diaphragm to move up and down to produce the necessary vacuum to draw the fuel from the supply tank.

Superchargers

The power developed by an internal combustion engine is largely dependent on the amount of combustible mixture reaching the cylinders. Manifolds, carburetors and the size of valves and valve ports are all important factors in determining the amount of combustible mixture reaching the cylinders. In order to overcome the friction losses in the intake system and also to aid in scavenging the cylinders of burnt gases, superchargers are used to blow the combustible mixture into the cylinders of spark ignition engines. In the case of Diesel engines only air is blown into the cylinders. See Fig. 26-10.

Superchargers were first developed for racing cars, and other high performance engines. They have also found wide application on aircraft. In the latter case, the power of an engine falls rapidly as the airplane attains altitude, because of the decreased density of the air. As the air density decreases, smaller amounts of air will be drawn into the cylinders until at an altitude of 18,000 feet only one half the charge will reach the cylinder as at sea level. Only one

Fig. 26-11. *Rootes type supercharger.*

Types of Superchargers

There are two general types of superchargers, the Rootes type and the centrifugal. The Rootes type blower consists of two rotors. In most designs each rotor has two lobes and in shape resembles a figure eight. However, some Rootes type superchargers are fitted with rotors of three or more lobes. A unit with three lobes is shown in Fig. 26-11. The shafts of the two rotors are interconnected through gearing and operate at the same speed. Its action is similar to the gear type oil pump. The rotors do not quite touch each other and there is also a slight clearance between the rotors and the surrounding housing. In operation, air enters the housing by the action of the rotors, and passes between the lobes of the rotors and the housing. The air is then forced out through the outlet opening of the unit.

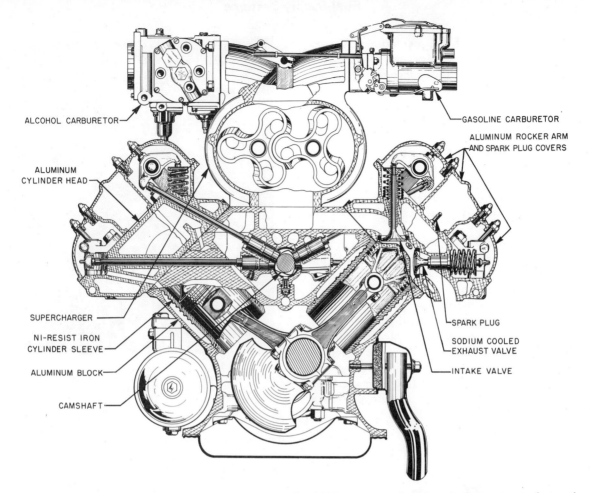

Fig. 26-12. Rootes type supercharger installed on Buick XP300 experimental engine. Carburetors are of aircraft pressure type, one for premium gasoline and the other for alcohol. Intake manifold is designed with minimum bends or obstructions to permit easy flow from supercharger to combustion chambers.

With the Rootes type blower, the rate of delivery varies slightly faster than the speed of rotation, because the leakage decreases as the speed increases. Above a certain minimum speed the amount of super-

charging is almost constant. Rootes type blowers are driven at from one to two times engine speed. An installation of a Rootes type supercharger on the Buick XP300 engine is shown in Fig. 26-12.

The centrifugal type supercharger consists of an impeller rotating at a high speed inside a housing.

Clearance between the blades and the housing must be kept at a minimum and as speed of rotation is approximately five times engine speed, it can easily attain a speed of 25,000 rpm. It is therefore essential that the rotor be accurately balanced, both statically and dynamically. Furthermore, the rotor blades must be made strong enough so that the centrifugal force at high speeds will not cause them to stretch and strike the housing.

On racing car installation, Fig. 26-13, the air from the impeller first passes to a diffuser, where the force of the moving air is converted to static energy. The diffuser consists of a ring-shaped housing containing blades or vanes. Coolers are also used to reduce the temperature of the air. This is important as the act of compressing the air will increase its temperature. The warm air entering would reduce the efficiency of the engine. The coolers consist of several lengths of finned tubing.

Fig. 26-13. Arrow points to centrifugal type of supercharger installed on old type race engine.

The rate of delivery of the centrifugal supercharger increases as the square of the speed of rotation. As a result, very little supercharging is obtained at lower speeds and the variation between different speeds is large. Carburetion is more difficult with a centrifugal supercharger than with a Rootes type unit.

Location of Supercharger

Superchargers can be placed either between the carburetor and the manifold or at the air inlet of the carburetor.

Racing cars usually have the supercharger between the carburetor and the manifold. This has the advantage that the fuel can be supplied to the carburetor by the same system as is used in conventional carburetion. If the supercharger is placed ahead of the carburetor, the fuel must be supplied under sufficient pressure to overcome the added air pressure at the carburetor fuel nozzles. When the carburetor is placed between the supercharger and the engine, it is necessary to connect the carburetor float chamber and the outlet side of the supercharger with a pressure equalizing tube.

Fig. 26-15. *Details of turbocharger as installed on 215 cu. in. aluminum V-8 Oldsmobile engine.*

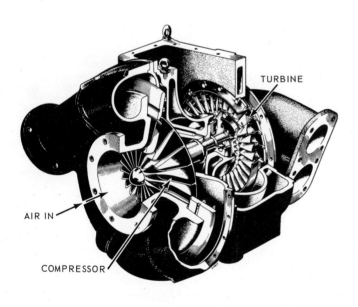

Fig. 26-14. *A turbo-charger with an axial flow type turbine driving a centrifugal blower. The turbine is on the right and the blower on the left.*

TURBINE

AIR IN

COMPRESSOR

Turbocharger

Most superchargers in the past have been driven mechanically by means of gearing to the crankshaft. Another method is to have the supercharger driven by the force of the exhaust gases, Fig. 26-14. In that way the power needed to drive the unit mechanically is saved.

A turbocharger installed on a 215 cu. in. Olds-

mobile engine is shown in Fig. 26-15. This aluminum V-8 engine with conventional four-barrel carburetor develops 185 hp @ 4800 rpm. When equipped with the turbocharger the horsepower was increased to 215.

In addition to the turbocharger, the design includes the injection of special fluid (Turbo-rocket fluid). This is injected in proportion to the octane requirements of the engine. In other words, during sudden acceleration and under full throttle conditions, this fluid is injected and increases the octane value of the air-fuel mixture reaching the engine. This makes it possible to operate the engine with its 10.25 to 1 compression ratio with ordinary premium grade gasoline.

By studying Fig. 26-15, it will be noted that the exhaust gases (curved arrows) after leaving the cylinder are directed against the vanes of the turbine, causing it to rotate. The supercharger is mounted on the other end of the turbo-shaft and forces the air-fuel mixture (dotted arrows) into the intake manifold and on into the combustion chamber. The turbo-rocket fuel (solid arrows) is injected into the intake manifold under low vacuum conditions.

The turbocharger, as installed on some Cummins diesel engines, is shown in Fig. 26-15a. The Cummins turbocharger consists of a turbine wheel and a compressor wheel separately incased, but mounted on, and rotating with a common shaft. The turbine side of the turbocharger mounts to the exhaust manifold outlet flange and the compressor wheel side connects with the air intake manifold. Lubrication and cooling is obtained from filtered engine oil through flexible lines of tubing.

Power to drive the turbine wheel, which in turn drives the compressor wheel, is obtained from energy

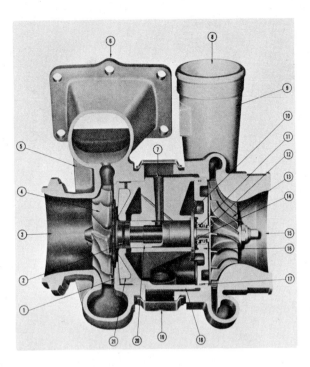

Fig. 26-15a. Details of the Cummins turbocharger as used on diesel engines. 1—Heat shield. 2—Piston ring seal. 3—Exhaust out. 4—Turbine wheel. 5—Turbine casing. 6—Exhaust in. 7—Oil in. 8—Air to engine. 9—Compressor casing. 10—Bearing insert. 11—Oil seal. 12—Sleeve. 13—Compressor wheel. 14—Thrust washer. 15—Air in. 16—Seal plate. 17—Seal ring. 18—Bearing housing. 19—Oil out. 20—Bearing. 21—Insulation pad.

of exhaust gases. The rotating speed of the turbine wheel changes as the energy level of exhaust gases change so engine is supplied with enough air to burn fuel for its load requirements.

Ramming Effect

By means of an air scoop attached to the carburetor inlet, Fig. 21-37, a slight supercharging effect can be obtained. This ramming effect has been used on aircraft and race engines. The dynamic pressure resulting from the movement of the vehicle is then added to the normal charging pressure. At normal touring speeds the ramming effect is of little consequence. However, the resultant pressure increases with the square of the speed.

Reduced Back Pressure

Greatly aiding the effect of the supercharger and the turbocharger is a reduction in back pressure from the exhaust system and also a reduction in resistance to air flow in the fuel induction system.

Back pressure is reduced by improved muffler design and the use of individual exhaust headers for each cylinder as shown in the Ford 427 cu. in. high performance engine, Fig. 26-16. Note also the air cleaner designed for minimum restriction of air to the carburetor.

Fuel Gauges

There are two general types of fuel gauges in use today: the thermostatic type, and the balancing coil type.

Thermostatic Type Gauge

The thermostatic type of fuel gauge consists of a sending unit located in the fuel tank, and the gauge or registering unit located on the instrument panel. In addition, there is a voltage regulator unit which is designed to maintain an average value of 5.0 volts at the gauge terminals. It is compensated for temperature variations and is provided with an adjustment which controls the rate at which the contacts make and break and in that way controls the voltage supplied to the gauge system.

The gauge pointer is controlled by a bimetallic arm and heating coil, Fig. 26-17. The sending unit in the fuel tank is a rheostat that varies its resistance depending on the amount of fuel in the tank.

Fig. 26-16. To reduce exhaust back pressure, individual exhaust headers are provided on this high performance 427 cu. in. Ford engine. Also note special air cleaner for carburetors.

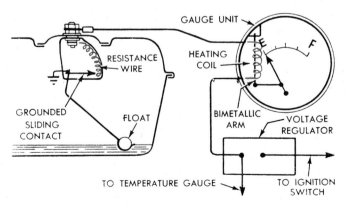

Fig. 26-17. Thermostatic type of fuel gauge.

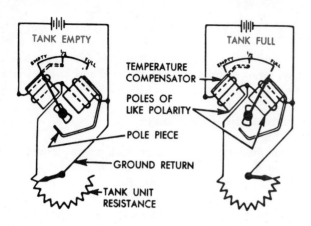

Fig. 26-18. *Circuits of AC fuel gauge. Conditions for tank empty are shown at the left, while full position is shown at the right.*

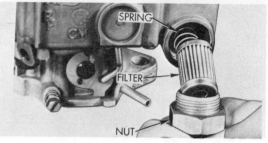

Fig. 26-19. *Above. Ceramic type fuel filter. Fig. 26-19a. Below. Installing a paper element type filter in a carburetor.*

When the fuel tank is empty, the grounded sliding contact, Fig. 26-17, is at the end of the resistance wire of the rheostat. With all of the resistance in the circuit, only a small amount of current will flow through the heating coil of the gauge unit, which will then register zero. When the tank is full, the float rises with the fuel, moving the grounded contact toward the beginning of the resistance coil. More current will therefore flow through the heating coil and the bimetallic arm of the gauge unit will deflect the pointer to the "Full" position.

The AC Balanced Coil Type Gauge

The AC fuel gauge used by General Motors cars and trucks, as well as some independent manufacturers, is of the electrically operated balanced coil type and consists of a dash unit and a tank unit, Fig. 26-18. The dash unit is made of two coils placed at 90 degs. to each other. An armature and pointer assembly is mounted at the intersection of the center line of the two coils. To prevent vibration of the pointer, the armature is provided with a dampening device.

The tank unit of the AC fuel gauge consists of a rheostat with a movable contact arm. Position of the contact arm is controlled by a float which rests on the surface of the fuel. To prevent splashing of the fuel from seriously affecting the movement of the float, a torque washer and spring are used.

The tank unit is grounded out of the gauge circuit when the fuel tank is empty and the float is in its lowest position. Current then passes only through the coil on the empty side of the dash unit as the "full coil" is of higher resistance, and the pointer is pulled to indicate zero. As fuel is added to the supply tank, there is corresponding rise of the float. Movement of the rheostat arm places resistance in the circuit, so that current will now flow through the "full" coil. As a result, the pointer will be attracted so that it indicates the quantity of fuel in the tank.

As an increase or decrease of battery voltage will affect both coils equally, the accuracy of the gauge will not be affected. Compensation for temperature variation is also provided.

Fuel Filters

Because of the small size of jets and apertures in the carburetor through which the fuel passes, it is essential that only clean fuel be supplied. Fuel filters are installed in the fuel line between the fuel pump and the carburetor. These filters are of various types and construction and are designed to filter out all solid matter and any water that may be present. Filters are so designed that they can be quickly disassembled and easily cleaned. A strainer of copper mesh is usually incorporated in the design of the fuel pump. In addition, some fuel pumps have effective filters built into the units. In many cases the filter is built into the carburetor. A ceramic type filter is shown in Fig. 26-19 and a paper element type filter in Fig. 26-19a.

Filters use many different materials to filter the fuel. Ceramic, Fig. 26-20, a series of copper disks, Fig. 26-21; copper screening; and impregnated fibre disks are used. As the fuel pump delivers a pulsating flow of fuel, some fuel filter designs include an air dome which smooths out the pulsations, and a steady flow of fuel is supplied to the carburetor.

As the accumulations of dirt and water in the filter tend to restrict the flow of fuel, it is essential that the unit be disassembled and cleaned periodically. This is usually done twice a year, in the spring and in the fall.

Examination of the filter will quickly show how it is disassembled. Frequently the filter bowl is held in place by a bale wire and screw, Fig. 26-20. Loosening the screw will permit slipping aside of the bale wire, after which the filter bowl can be removed, then

Fig. 26-20. A ceramic element is used in the Carter fuel filter. (Carter Carburetor Corp.)

Fig. 26-21. Illustrating the path of the fuel through a fuel filter produced by AC Spark Plug Div., General Motors Corp.

the filter element. The filter element should be washed in acetone or a good carburetor cleaning solution. Filter elements of the copper disk type should then be blown dry with compressed air. Replacement elements are available in case the original element is damaged or otherwise defective.

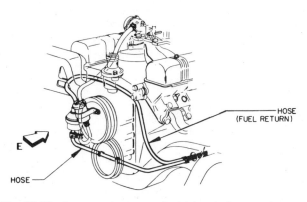

Fig. 26-22. Can type throwaway fuel filter with vapor drain.

When reassembling a filter it is important to use a new gasket between the bowl and the body of the unit to insure against leakage. If the top of the filter is a die casting, this should be checked for warpage. If found to be warped, a complete new unit should be installed.

A can type throwaway type fuel filter is also used on many vehicles. In some cases the fuel filter has a special metering outlet at the top so that any vapor which forms is bled off and returned to the gas tank through a separate line, Fig. 26-22.

Liquefied Petroleum Gas

A mixture of gaseous petroleum compounds, principally butane and propane, together with small quantities of other similar gases, is known as liquefied petroleum gas. This is frequently abbreviated as LPG

Fig. 26-23. LPG installation on a truck.

Fig. 26-24. Zenith LPG system installed on a tractor.

or LP gas. It is used for cooking, heating, and as a fuel for internal combustion engines. In the latter case, it is found principally in large trucks and tractors, as shown in Figs. 26-23 and 26-24.

Chemically it is similar to gasoline as it consists of a mixture of compounds of hydrogen and carbon. However, it is a great deal more volatile and at usual

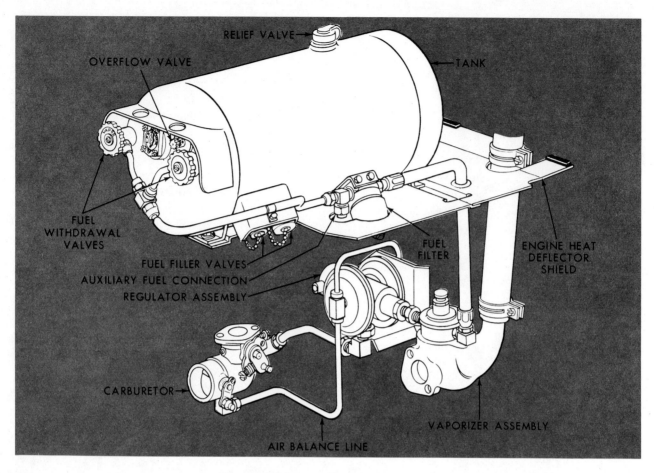

Fig. 26-25. Layout of Zenith LPG system.

atmospheric temperatures it is a vapor. For that reason, when used as a fuel for internal combustion engines, a special type of carburetor is required.

For storing and transporting, LPG is compressed and cooled so that it is a liquid and, depending on conditions, approximately 250 gallons of LPG form one gallon of liquid. Because of the pressure it must be stored in strong tanks. The boiling point of propane is approximately 44 deg. F. below zero, Fig. 20-1a.

At temperatures below their boiling points, butane and propane exert no pressure, but as their temperature increases, the pressure increases rapidly. For example, at 40 degs. F., liquid propane will have a pressure of 65 lbs., while butane will have a pressure of about 3 lbs. Then at 65 degs. F., the pressure of propane will have increased to 100 lbs. and butane to 15 lbs.

LPG gas is becoming more widely distributed as an increasing number of trucks and tractors are being fitted with the necessary equipment. In addition to its lower cost, LPG has the advantage of having a high octane value. Pure butane has a rating of 93, while propane is approximately 100. The octane rating of LPG will, therefore, range between these two values, depending on the proportion of each gas used.

As it is a dry gas, LPG does not create carbon in the engine and does not cause dilution of the engine oil. Therefore, its use reduces valve grinding, cylinder and ring wear, and other engine maintenance. The oil changes for the engine can be made at less frequent intervals because it is such a clean burning fuel.

In order to get maximum power and other advantages from the use of LPG, it is generally advisable to have the engine designed especially for its use. However, many satisfactory conversions of conventional gasoline engines have been made. Such conversions are usually made with an engine designed for use with premium fuel, i.e. a compression ratio of about 10 to 1.

Other advantages claimed for LPG are easy cold weather starting, lack of objectionable exhaust odor, elimination of evaporation, and spillage losses.

This means that a pressure tank must be used and the entire fuel system be kept sealed to avoid loss.

Operation of LPG System

Briefly the operation of an LPG system on an internal combustion engine is as follows: the gas leaves the supply tank, Fig. 26-25, as a liquid at high pressure and a vaporizer, or regulator is required to allow this liquid to expand into a gas at low pressure before the engine can use it. These vaporizers are usually mounted near the engine and usually being water jacketed, are connected to the engine water circulation system to avoid frosting of the internal parts in cold weather.

A filter is also connected into the line between the tank and the vaporizer-preferably near the vaporizer to filter out any possible contaminators in the fuel.

From the vaporizer, the dry gas, at low pressure, is piped to the mixing valve which is used in place of a carburetor. In Fig. 26-26, the conventional gasoline carburetor has been converted to use LPG. The engine starts and operates under control of the throttle valve, just the same as when gasoline is used in a carburetor.

It is desirable to have a cold intake manifold when using LPG so the manifold heating arrangements are usually blocked off.

the supply tank and is known as the liquid withdrawal system, Fig. 26-26a.

In the tank vapor system all regulators operate on gas, while in the liquid withdrawal system, the first regulator works on liquid, with the second on gas. Liquid withdrawal systems include a positive action vaporizer. This unit is supplied with heat from the engine.

On some gasoline engines that are coverted to LPG, the original carburetor is used. In such cases the carburetor body is drilled and a tube is inserted into the venturi. The location of the opening of the tube corresponds to the opening of the main discharge. A similar arrangement is used on installations designed to operate on either gasoline or LPG.

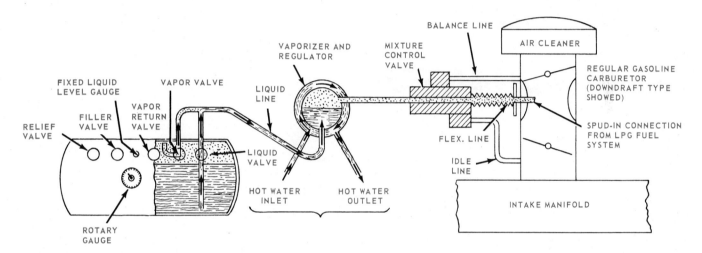

Fig. 26-26. *Schematic drawing of LPG carburetion system. This system, designed by the A. O. Smith Co., converts the conventional gasoline carburetor to use LPG.*

LPG Carburetor Systems

The differences between the LPG and gasoline carburetion systems are basically mechanical and arise from the different characteristics of the two fuels.

As LPG in the supply tank is under pressure, a fuel pump is not required. Being under relatively high pressure, the fuel first passes through a pressure reducing regulator which operates from a coil spring working against a diaphragm. This regulator reduces the pressure to between 10 and 3 lbs. per sq. in.

From the primary regulator, the LPG passes to the secondary regulator which is also a diaphragm type regulator. Because of reduced pressure, the fuel reaching the secondary regulator is a vapor and the secondary regulator reduces the pressure so that it is the same as atmospheric pressure, and the fuel is delivered to the carburetor where it is mixed with the correct proportion of air.

There are two main types of LPG carburetion systems. One system, known as the vapor withdrawal system, takes the vapor from the top of the supply tank. The other type draws liquid fuel from the bottom of

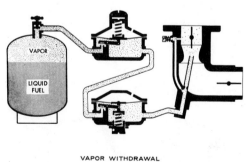

VAPOR WITHDRAWAL

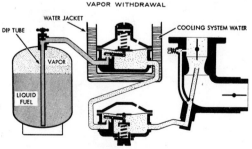

LIQUID WITHDRAWAL

Fig. 26-26a. *Illustrating two types of LPG fuel and carbureting systems.*

Another design known as the adapter type carburetor, consists of an air-fuel mixing unit. This is installed between the gasoline carburetor and the air cleaner. No throttle plate is provided in the adapter carburetor, as the throttle on the gasoline carburetor is used.

Obviously when a conversion installation is made which permits operating on either gasoline or LPG, special shut-off valves are installed as both fuels cannot be used simultaneously. These valves may be either manually or electrically controlled. In addition, there is a main shut-off valve at the LPG tank, Fig. 26-27. This is hand operated and is needed when the supply tank is filled.

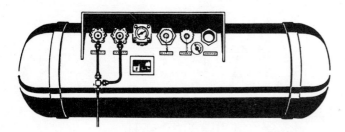

Fig. 26-27. *Typical horizontal fuel supply tank for* **LPG** *with control valves and gauges.*

A combined vaporizer and pressure reducing device is shown in Fig. 26-28. This device takes the liquid butane-propane under tank pressure, and converts it into a dry gaseous fuel at slightly below atmospheric pressure, and regulates the flow of this gas through the carburetor in the correct volume and pressure to meet the demands of the engine at all speeds and loads.

In Fig. 26-28, the various parts are as follows: (A) Combination LPG and gasoline carburetor; (B) Gasoline inlet to carburetor; (C) Gasoline float lock; (D) Easy starting choke; (E) Air inlet to carburetor;

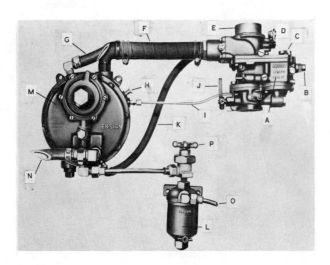

Fig. 26-28. *The Model-R Ensign regulator unit is a combined vaporizer and pressure reducing device.*

(F) Connection between LPG regulator and carburetor carrying LPG vapor; (G) Hot water supply from engine water jacket to supply heat to regulator M; (H) Idle adjusting screw on regulator; (I) Supply line for idling mixture; (J) Carburetor throttle lever; (K) Balance line; (L) Filter for LPG; (M) Ensign regulator unit type R; (N) Water return line to pump; (O) LPG line to supply tank; (P) LPG shut-off valve.

Details of the Ensign model R LPG regulator unit are shown in Fig. 26-29. In this unit, liquid LPG from the supply tank enters the regulating unit at fuel inlet (1) and is filtered at (2). Flow of liquid through high pressure valve (3) is controlled by pressure regulator diaphragm (4), lever (5), and spring (6). Major expansion of the liquid occurs within the space surrounding the high pressure valve (3). Expanded LPG enters coil (7) which is surrounded by hot water from the engine water jacket. Vaporized LPG leaves the coil at main valve (8) at slightly below atmospheric pressure for passage to the carburetor through outlet (9). Control of the outlet pressure is accomplished by operation of the large regulator diaphragm (10), lever (11), and spring (12).

Hot water from the engine cooling system enters the regulator at (13). Hot water then flows over the vaporizer coil (7) through outlet (14) and back to the intake side of the engine water pump.

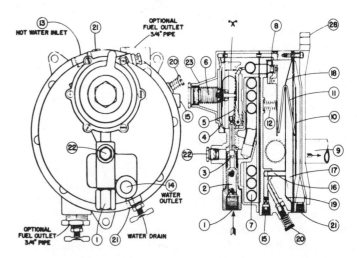

Fig. 26-29. *Details of* **LPG** *regulator produced by Ensign Carburetor Company.*

LPG for idling is taken at (15), via tube (16) from the LPG vapor reserve chamber (17) which is located behind partition plate (18). Fuel enters this zone through orifice (19) and the idle adjustment is made at (20).

An atmospheric vent (21) on back cover plate behind diaphragm (10) is connected to the carburetor air horn pitot tube and is known as the balance line. Its purpose is to automatically reduce the flow of LPG vapor from the regulator unit to compensate for air cleaner or other air entrance losses.

Details of a carburetor for LPG gas are shown in Fig. 26-30. This is a Bendix unit and a final stage regulator is built into the assembly as well as "back-suction" type of economizer.

Fuel pressure at the fuel inlet (1) is controlled by the primary regulator in the fuel system. The force exerted by the fuel valve spring (8) on the fuel valve

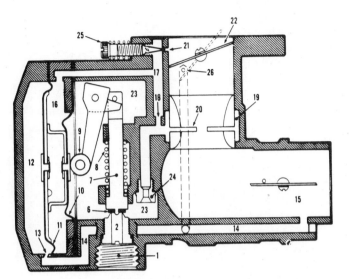

Fig. 26-30. One type of Bendix LPG carburetor.

assembly (7) is such that a pressure of 20 psi would be necessary to raise the valve. The travel of the fuel valve (7) is controlled by the movement of diaphragms (10) and (11) which are responsive to pressure variations at key points in the carburetor. An adjustable valve seat is provided to have a specific starting position for the diaphragm lever (9).

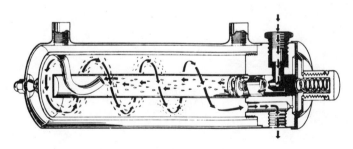

Fig. 26-31. Details of the type J & S LPG vaporizer.

The diaphragm chamber (12) receives its ventilation through the orifice (13) and channel (14) from the air intake (15) of the carburetor. Diaphragm chamber (16) communicates directly with the two pressure areas in the throttle body of the carburetor. Through channel (17), orifice (18) and annulus (19) it reaches venturi throat (20). Through channel (1) and adjustable idling orifice (21) it connects with the area beyond the throttle plate (22).

The pressure transmitted to the diaphragm chamber (16) will vary with the position of the throttle plate. Thus, whichever of the two areas produces the lower pressure, will be most influential in the movement of diaphragms (10) and (11). The position of these two diaphragms controls the pressure in fuel chamber (23).

If the adjustment (25) were seated, the pressure across diaphragm (11) would be the same as the pressure difference between the air intake and the throat of the venturi. At idle this difference would not be enough to cause the diaphragms to open the fuel inlet valve. By opening the adjustment (25) there will be sufficient pressure difference to cause fuel to flow.

Details of a vaporizer are shown in Fig. 26-31. In this unit, produced by the J & S Carburetor Company, the liquid flows into the vaporizer at the left end and is indicated by the arrows. When passing through the regulator the pressure of the liquid is reduced to approximately 7 lbs. This reduction in pressure results in part of the liquid being vaporized. The vapor and the balance of the liquid pass through the inner tube and are discharged from it at the right end. At this point, the mixture is given a whirling motion which keeps the liquid in contact with the walls of the vaporizing chamber, and is vaporized as it travels toward the outlet.

When the demand for gas by the engine is reduced, the balanced regulator which is placed between the vaporizer and the carburetor (on the J & S system) closes. The liquid butane-propane that is in the vaporizer and in contact with the heated wall of this chamber, will continue to build pressure. This pressure causes the liquid to be expelled from the vaporizing chamber into the inner chamber where it is out of contact with the hot walls of the vaporizing chamber. It is withdrawn as the engine continues to consume gas for idling.

Quiz - Fuel Supply Systems

1. On lawn mower engines, how is fuel usually supplied to the carburetor?
2. On modern passenger cars, what two methods are used to drive the fuel pumps?
3. For what purpose is the vacuum pump built into some types of fuel pumps?
   a. To operate the pistons in automatic chokes.
   b. Operate windshield wipers.
   c. Aid in pumping fuel.
4. What is a major cause of excessive fuel pump pressure on a mechanical type fuel pump?
   a. Insufficient flexing of the diaphragm.
   b. Clogged fuel cleaners.
   c. Clogged line to the fuel supply tank.
5. How much pressure should the conventional mechanical type fuel pump develop?
   a. 5 lbs.   c. 15 lbs.
   b. 10 lbs.

6. In 45 seconds, how much fuel should be pumped by the average mechanical type fuel pump?
   a. 1 pint.
   c. 3 pints.
   b. 2 pints.
   d. 32 ounces.
7. What is the average vacuum developed by a vacuum pump that is built into a fuel pump?
   a. 5 in.
   c. 10 in.
   b. 7-1/2 in.
   d. 18 in.
8. What is a major advantage of using an externally mounted electrically operated fuel pump?
9. Name two main types of mechanically driven superchargers.
10. Which type of internal combustion engine will tend to detonate more?
   a. Supercharged.
   b. Nonsupercharged.

11. What is a major advantage of the turbosupercharger over the mechanically driven type?
   a. Little or no power required to drive it.
   b. Develops more pressure.
12. Name the two general types of fuel gauges.
13. Name two types of materials used in fuel filters.
14. Liquefied petroleum gas is a mixture of:
   a. Butane and propane.
   b. Propane and heptane.
   c. Methane and octane.
   d. Butane and methane.
15. Is the boiling point of propane higher or lower than zero degrees Fahrenheit.
16. Does LPG have a high or low octane rating?
17. Does LPG produce more or less carbon in an engine than gasoline?

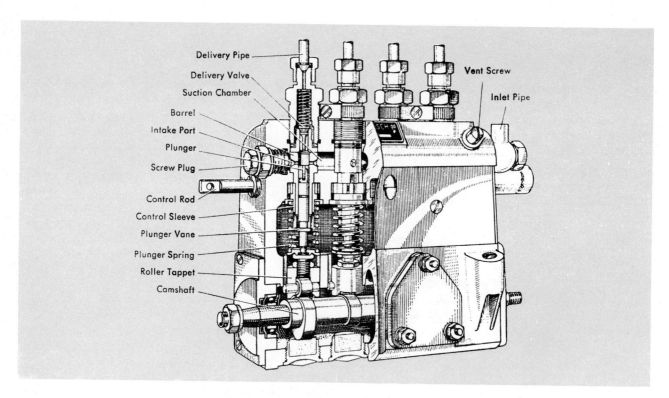

Fig. 27-1. American Bosch type APE Diesel injection pump for four cylinder engine.

FUEL
INJECTION

Diesel Injectors

As described in the unit on engine fundamentals, a Diesel engine compresses air, and at the point of maximum compression, fuel is injected into the combustion chamber. Ignition takes place as a result of the high temperature which has been created.

To force fuel into the combustion chamber of a Diesel engine requires a pump and an injector. Because of high pressures existing in the combustion chamber at the time of injection, the injection system must develop pressures well in excess of the combustion chamber pressure.

A Diesel fuel injection system in delivering the fuel to the combustion chamber must fulfill five main requirements:

1. Meter or measure the correct quantity of fuel injected.
2. Time the fuel injection.
3. Control the rate of fuel injection.
4. Atomize the fuel into fine particles.
5. Properly distribute the fuel in the combustion chamber.

There are two different methods of fuel injection: air injection and mechanical or solid injection.

In the air injection system, a blast of air from an external source forces a measured amount of fuel into the cylinder.

In the solid injection system which is now used almost exclusively, fuel is forced into the cylinder by direct pressure on the fuel.

In the automotive field, there are four basic types of solid fuel injection systems:

1. Multiple unit.
2. Unit injection.
3. Distributor.
4. Pressure-time.

The multiple pump or unit fuel system includes in addition to the usual tank and cylinders, a low-pressure fuel transfer pump, a separate assembly mounted on the side of the engine containing an individual high pressure pump for each cylinder which meters and distributes pressurized fuel to the injectors, also an injector for each cylinder.

Bosch Diesel System

The American Bosch Arma Corporation has fuel injection pumps for single cylinder engines and also multi-cylinder engines. These are available in two basic series; the APE series and the PS series. The APE series for a four cylinder Diesel is shown in Fig. 27-1. Each pump element is made up of a plunger and a barrel, Fig. 27-2. The plunger is so accurately fitted in the barrel that it will provide a seal without special packing even at high pressures and low speed. The plunger jacket is milled out along a helical line providing for the control helix on the plunger. The barrel has two opposing radial holes through which the fuel oil reaches the delivery chamber of the barrel, Fig. 27-2. In the compression stroke, the pump plunger is actuated by a cam; in the suction stroke, by the plunger spring. The valve is closed by a spring-loaded delivery valve connected with the delivery pipe to the respective nozzles in the cylinder. To vary the quantity of fuel delivered by the pump, the pump valve has a control sleeve on the upper end of which a toothed quadrant is clamped. A control rod meshes with the tooth quadrant so the pump plunger can be rotated during operation.

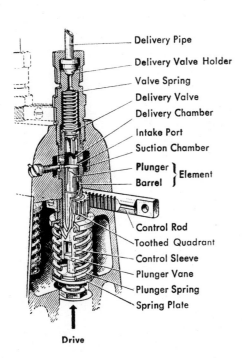

Delivery Pipe
Delivery Valve Holder
Valve Spring
Delivery Valve
Delivery Chamber
Intake Port
Suction Chamber
Plunger } Element
Barrel }
Control Rod
Toothed Quadrant
Control Sleeve
Plunger Vane
Plunger Spring
Spring Plate
Drive

Fig. 27-2. Sectional view of Bosch pump element.

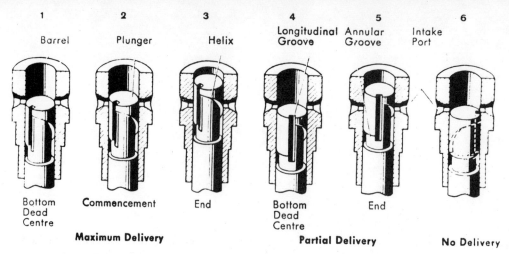

1	2	3	4	5	6
Barrel	Plunger	Helix	Longitudinal Groove	Annular Groove	Intake Port

Bottom Dead Centre	Commencement	End	Bottom Dead Centre	End	
Maximum Delivery			**Partial Delivery**		**No Delivery**

Fig. 27-3. Rotation of plunger controls quantity of fuel delivered.

Various positions of the plunger are shown in Fig. 27-3.

In its upward movement, the plunger closes the intake port, as shown at 2, and forces the fuel through the delivery valve to the delivery pipe. Delivery stops as soon as helix and inlet port coincide, as the delivery chamber of the barrel is from that moment connected to the suction chamber through the longitudinal and annular grooves. The fuel is thus forced back into the suction chamber. If the plunger is turned sufficiently far for the longitudinal groove and inlet port to meet, as shown at 6, Fig. 27-3, the fuel in the delivery chamber is not subjected to pressure, and no fuel will be delivered.

The injection nozzle used in the multiple unit Diesel system, as made by Bosch, is designed to control the mixture formation in the combustion chamber. Bosch nozzles are either of the pintle type or the hole type.

The operation of the nozzle is controlled by the fuel pressure. As soon as this pressure, during the delivery stroke of the injection pump, exceeds the tension of the pressure spring in the nozzle holder, the pressure acting on the pressure taper of the nozzle needle causes the latter to be lifted off its seat, and the fuel to be injected into the combustion chamber.

The nozzle opening pressure (which is adjustable) is determined by the initial tension of the pressure spring in the nozzle holder, Fig. 27-4. The needle stroke is limited by the plane surface on the nozzle holder.

When injected, the fuel takes the following path: delivery pipe, through the connector and pressure passage of the nozzle holder, Fig. 27-4, then through groove and passage of nozzle, through injection hole or holes of nozzle and into combustion chamber of the engine.

Fig. 27-4. Details of Bosch nozzle holder with pintle type nozzle, (left).

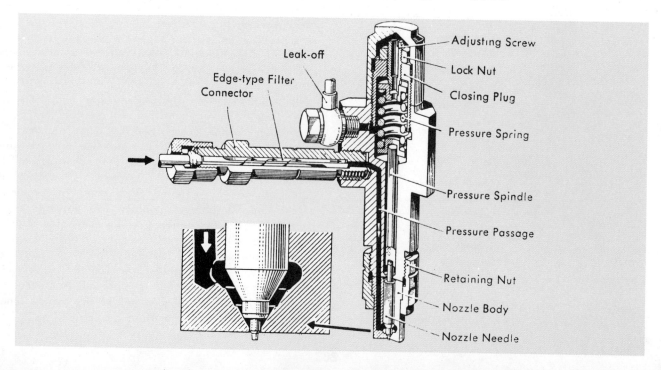

The importance of delivering only absolutely clean fuel to the nozzles cannot be overemphasized. Because of the closely fitted parts, any foreign matter of microscopic size can cause malfunctioning and wear of the parts. Consequently, two or more filters are usually installed, Fig. 27-5. The first, or primary filter, is designed to remove the larger and heavier particles and is often of the cleanable metal edge type. The final filter should be capable of removing particles down to 3 to 5 microns (0.00012 to 0.00020 in.).

American Bosch Series
PS Fuel Injection Pumps

The American Bosch PS series of fuel injection pumps, Fig. 27-5a, is built to three main types; PSB, PSJ and PSU. They are all similar in that each utilizes a single hardened steel plunger which reciprocates for pumping action and rotates continuously for distribution of the fuel to the discharge outlets.

The design eliminates the need for individual fuel adjustments for each cylinder. Fuel is injected during the high velocity portion of the plunger stroke and

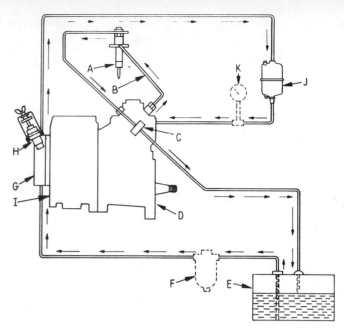

Fig. 27-5. Schematic diagram of American Bosch PSJ fuel system. A—Injection nozzle. B—High-pressure fuel line. C—Overflow valve. D—Injection pump. E—Fuel tank. F—Primary filter. G—Supply pump. H—Operational hand priming pump. I—Governor housing. J—Final filter. K—Fuel oil pressure gauge, if used.

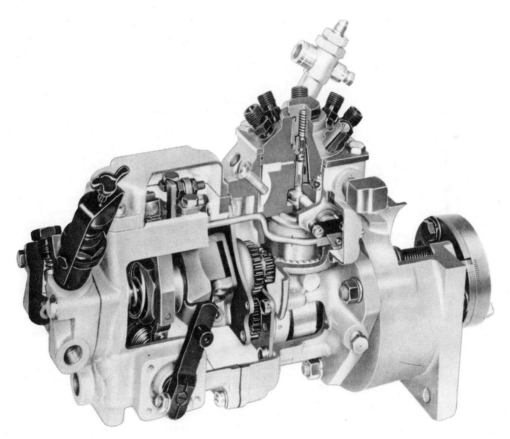

Fig. 27-5a. American Bosch series PSJ fuel injection pump, with external timing device.

fuel metering employs precise port opening and port closing principles.

PS series pumps are connected to the engine lubricating system for complete lubrication of the camshaft, bearings, tappets, lower portion of the plunger and governing mechanism. The upper portion of the plunger is lubricated by the high-pressure fuel. The manufacturers claim the PS series is particularly adapted to multifuel engines.

Fuel delivery is also regulated by a single, positive acting delivery valve with a relief piston which automatically closes at the end of each delivery cycle because of spring action and a drop in pressure in the fuel metering system. This insures a sharp fuel cut-off and prevents nozzle secondary injections and dribble which tend to produce nozzle carbonizing.

Uniform regulation from low idle to full load is provided by a mechanical centrifugal governor which automatically adjusts the fuel up to a preset maximum for positive engine torque control and peak engine operating efficiency. A separate lever, operating directly against the governor fulcrum lever, moves the fuel metering sleeve to no-fuel position for shutoff.

The fuel supply pump is of the gear type and is driven directly from the end of the governor shaft. An overflow valve is provided to return the excess fuel to the supply tank.

A schematic drawing of the PSJ fuel system is shown in Fig. 27-5.

General Motors Diesel Injection System

The General Motors Diesel operates on the two-cycle principle, and has a unit injector fuel system. In this system a single unit measures the amount of fuel to be injected under varying conditions of speed and load, builds up the high pressure needed to inject

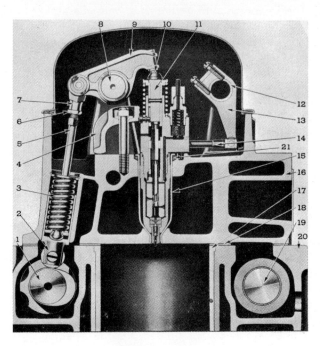

Fig. 27-7. Cross section of General Motors Diesel cylinder head and fuel injector.

the fuel into the combustion chamber which is filled with air at an approximate pressure of 1,000 lbs. per sq. in., and atomizes the fuel. There is no central metering or pressure pump and, therefore, high pressure fuel distributing lines are eliminated.

In the General Motors unit injection system, high pressures exist only at the tip of the injector. Each injector is complete. After repair work, or having run dry, it is not necessary to prime the G.M. injector.

The complete fuel system, Fig. 27-6, consists of the fuel supply tank, fuel line, fuel filters, fuel pump, fuel line manifold, and the fuel injector. A separate injector is provided for each cylinder. From the supply tank, fuel is drawn through the first fuel strainer or filter by the fuel pump. The fuel is then forced through the second filter to the fuel intake manifold which supplies fuel to the individual injectors. The surplus fuel is returned through the outlet manifold to the supply tank.

The cross-sectional view of the engine, Fig. 27-7, shows the injector mounted in the cylinder head and Fig. 27-8 shows the details of the injector.

In the G. M. unit injector, Fig. 27-8, fuel is supplied to the injector at approximately 20 lbs. per sq. in. and enters the body (24) through the filter cap (21). The fuel then passes through the filter (23) and fills the chamber (27) between the bushing (13) and the spill deflector (14). The plunger (26) operates up and down by means of the engine camshaft, push rods, and rocker arms. The plunger (26) operates in a bushing which is connected to the fuel supply in the annular chamber by means of the ports (12) and (29).

The motion of the injector rocker arm is transmitted to the plunger (26) by means of the follower

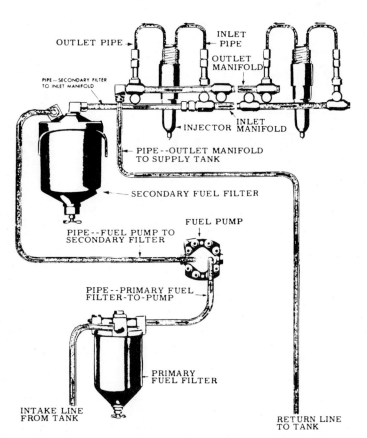

Fig. 27-6. Complete fuel system of General Motors two-cycle Diesel engine.

(1) which bears against the return spring (3). By means of the gear (6), and rack (7), the plunger can be rotated. An upper and lower helix are machined into the lower end of the plunger for the purpose of metering fuel. As the plunger is rotated, the relation of the two helices with the ports (12) and (29) is changed.

As the plunger moves downward, the fuel in the injector high-pressure cylinder is first displaced through the ports (12) and (29), back into the supply chamber (27), until the lower edge of the plunger

the desired amount of fuel which remains under the plunger for injection into the combustion chamber.

The various positions of the plunger from no injection to full injection are shown in Fig. 27-9. Full injection is obtained with the control rack pushed completely in. In that position the upper port is closed shortly after the lower port has been covered. In that way a full effective stroke and maximum injection is produced. When the control rack is pulled out completely, the upper port is not closed by the helix until after the lower port is uncovered. As a result, all of

1. FOLLOWER.
2. FOLLOWER GUIDE.
3. PLUNGER SPRING.
4. FOLLOWER PIN.
5. STOP PIN.
6. GEAR.
7. RACK.
8. SEAL RING.
9. GEAR RETAINER.
10. UPPER HELIX.
11. METERING RECESS.
12. UPPER PORT.
13. BUSHING.
14. SPILL DEFLECTOR.
15. SPACER.
16. CHECK VALVE.
17. VALVE SEAT.
18. VALVE.
19. VALVE SPRING.
20. VALVE STOP.
21. FILTER CAP.
21A. GASKET-FILTER CAP.
22. FILTER SPRING.
23. FILTER ASSEMBLY.
24. INJECTOR BODY.
25. INJECTOR NUT.
26. INJECTOR PLUNGER.
27. FUEL CHAMBER.
28. LOWER HELIX.
29. LOWER PORT.
30. SPRAY TIP.

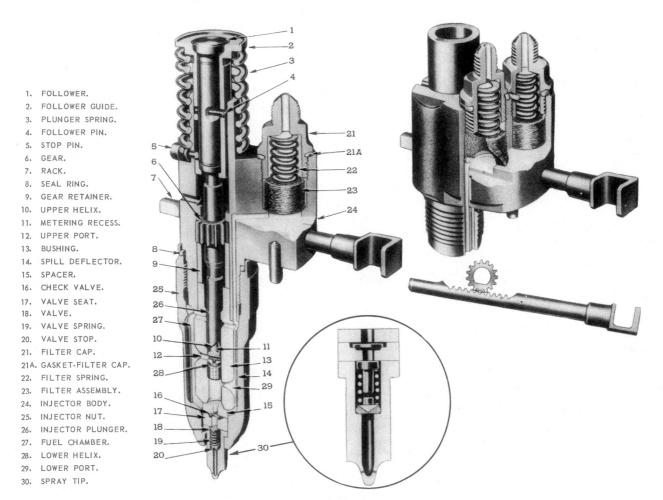

Fig. 27-8. Details of General Motors injector.

closes the port (29). The remainder of the oil is then forced upward through the central passage in the plunger into the recess between the two helices. From there it can still flow back into the supply chamber until the upper helix closes the upper port (12).

At this point, both upper and lower ports are closed. The fuel remaining under the plunger is then forced through the spray tip and into the combustion chamber of the engine. Changing the position of the helices by rotating the plunger, retards or advances the closing of the ports, and the beginning and ending of the injection period, at the same time controlling

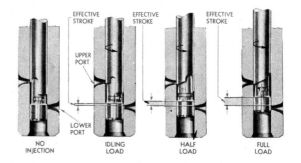

Fig. 27-9. Four positions of the plunger from no injection to full injection of the General Motors injector.

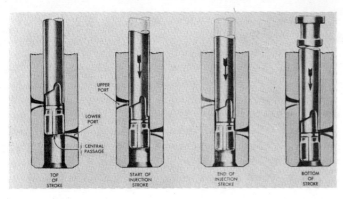

Fig. 27-10. Four positions for downward travel of the General Motors injector.

the fuel charge is forced back into the supply chamber and no injection of fuel occurs.

The four positions for the downward travel of the plunger are shown in Fig. 27-10. On the downward travel of the plunger, the metered amount of fuel is forced through the valve assembly, through the check valve (16), Fig. 27-8, and against the spray tip valve (18).

When sufficient pressure has been built up on the fuel, the spray tip valve is lifted from its seat and the fuel is forced through the small orifices in the spray tip (30) and into the combustion chamber. The check valve (16) prevents air leakage from the engine combustion chamber into the injector in case the valve (18) is accidently held open by a particle of carbon or

dirt, thus permitting the injector to continue to operate until the foreign matter works through the valve. On the upward return movement of the plunger, the high pressure cylinder is again filled with fuel through the ports. The constant circulation of fresh fuel oil in the fuel supply chamber (27) helps maintain even operating temperatures. In addition, all traces of air are eliminated.

Each injector control rack is operated by a lever on a common control shaft. This, in turn, is linked to the governor and the throttle. These levers can be rotated independently on the control shaft by the adjustment of two screws which permit a uniform setting of the injector racks.

Cummins Pressure Time System

The Cummins PT system for Diesel engines operates on the pressure time principle which is based on the fact that by changing the pressure of a liquid flowing through a pipe, the amount of liquid coming out the open end is changed. Increasing the pressure increases the amount of liquid delivered. The Cummins PT system consists of the fuel pump (with governor), the supply and drain lines and the injectors, Fig. 27-11.

The fuel pump, Fig. 27-12, is made of three main units. (1) A gear pump, which draws fuel from the supply tank and delivers it under pressure through the pump and supply lines to the individual injector. (2) The pressure regulator which limits the pressure

Fig. 27-11. Fuel flow diagram of the Cummins pressure time system.

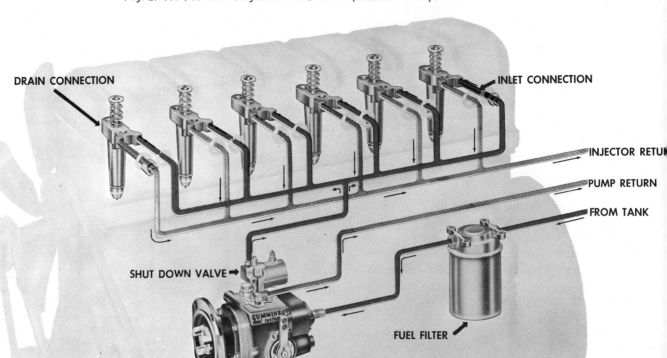

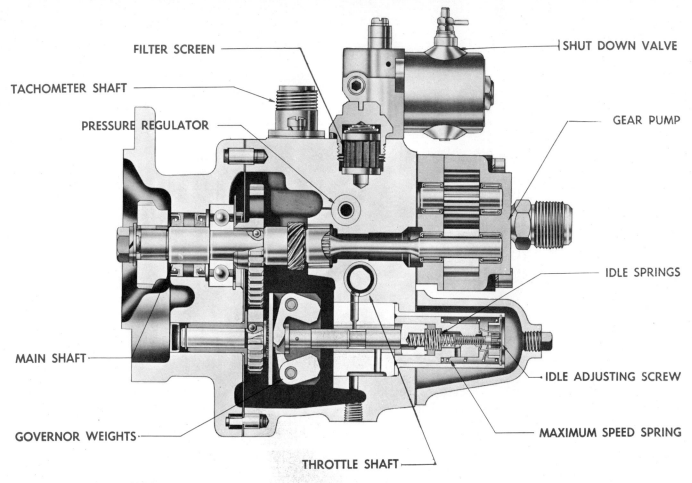

FILTER SCREEN

TACHOMETER SHAFT

PRESSURE REGULATOR

SHUT DOWN VALVE

GEAR PUMP

IDLE SPRINGS

MAIN SHAFT

IDLE ADJUSTING SCREW

GOVERNOR WEIGHTS

MAXIMUM SPEED SPRING

THROTTLE SHAFT

Fig. 27-12. Cross section of Cummins PT pump with idling and high speed mechanical governor.

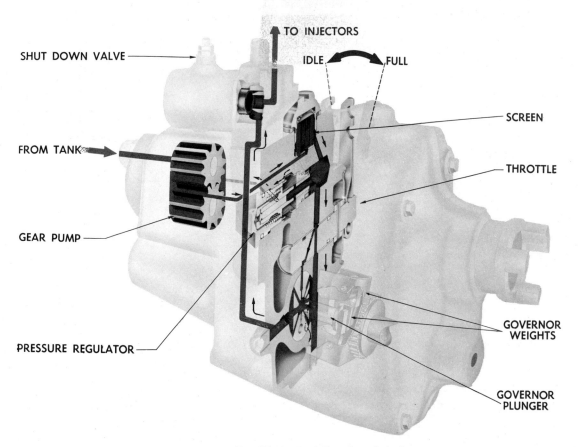

TO INJECTORS

IDLE   FULL

SHUT DOWN VALVE

SCREEN

FROM TANK

THROTTLE

GEAR PUMP

GOVERNOR WEIGHTS

PRESSURE REGULATOR

GOVERNOR PLUNGER

Fig. 27-13. Fuel flow through fuel pump.

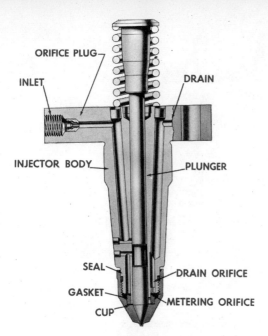

Fig. 27-14. Cross section of Cummins injector.

Cummins Injectors

The injector used with Cummins Pressure Time Diesel System is shown in Fig. 27-14. Fuel circulates through the injector at all times, except during a short

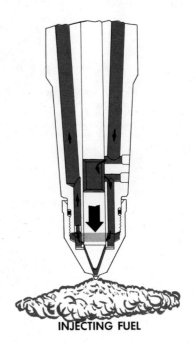

INJECTING FUEL

Fig. 27-15. Fuel flow through injector while injecting fuel.

of fuel to the injectors. (3) The governor and throttle which act independently of the pressure regulator to control fuel pressure to the regulators. The fuel pump is driven at crankshaft speed.

The gear pump is located at the rear of the fuel pump, Fig. 27-12, and consists of a single set of gears which pick-up and deliver fuel throughout the system, Fig. 27-11.

The pressure regulator is a bypass valve to regulate the fuel under pressure to the injectors.

Fuel for the engine flows past the pressure regulator to throttle shaft, Fig. 27-13. The fuel passes around the shaft to the idle jet in the governor. For

period following injection into the combustion chamber. From the inlet connection, fuel flows down the inlet passage of the injector, around the injector plunger, between the body end and cup, up the drain

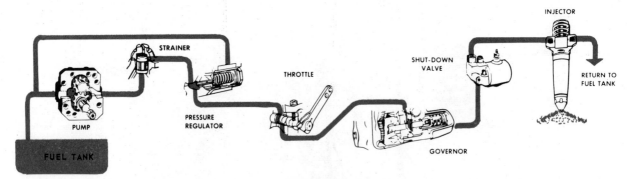

Fig. 27-16. Pressure flow diagram of the Cummins Pressure Time System.

operation above idle, fuel passes through the throttling hole in the shaft and enters the governor through the primary jets.

Mechanical governor action is provided by a system of springs and weights, Fig. 27-13. The governor maintains sufficient fuel for idling and second; it cuts off fuel above maximum rated speed. Different types of governors are available for different engine requirements.

passage to the drain connections and manifold and back to the supply tank. As the plunger comes up, the injector feed passage is opened and fuel flows through the metering orifice into the cup. At the same time, fuel flows past the cup and out the drain orifice. The amount of fuel entering the cup is controlled by the fuel pressure against the metering orifice and fuel pressure is controlled by the fuel pump. During injection, Fig. 27-15, the plunger comes down until

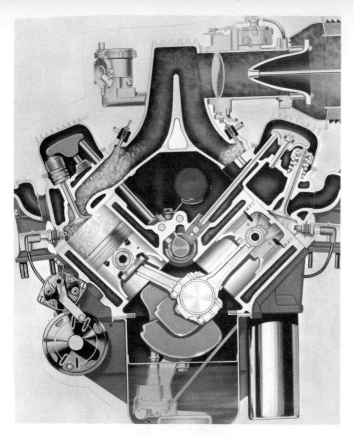

Fig. 27-17. *Fuel injection system installed on Chevrolet engine as optional equipment.*

the orifice is closed, and the fuel in the cup is injected into the cylinder. While the plunger is seated in the cup, all fuel flow in the injector is stopped.

The flow diagram of the Cummins Pressure Time System is shown in Fig. 27-16.

Cummins Metering Pump Injection System

Another Cummins system, known as the distributor type employs a metering pump to measure each charge of fuel which is delivered at low pressure to the injectors by means of a distributor.

The injectors build up pressure of the fuel and inject it into the engine combustion chamber.

The Cummins Diesel fuel pump, as used in the distributor system, performs four functions:

1. Draws fuel from the supply tank.
2. Measures or meters the fuel in equal charges for each cylinder.
3. Distributes and delivers the metered fuel at the correct instant to the individual injectors in the engine.
4. Provides a governor for control of idling and maximum engine speeds.

Fig. 27-18. *Fuel injection system installed on Chevrolet with parts identified.*

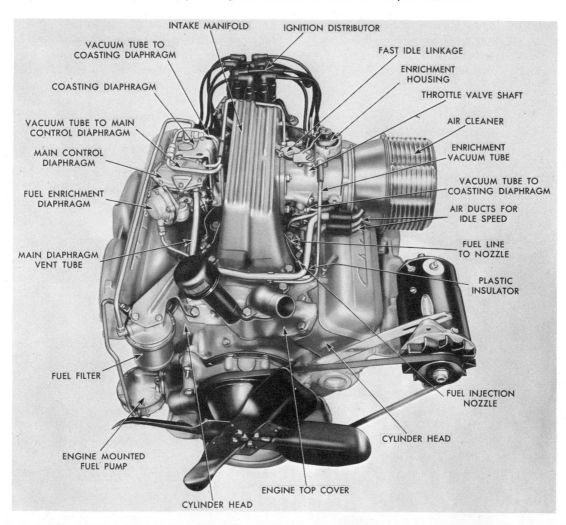

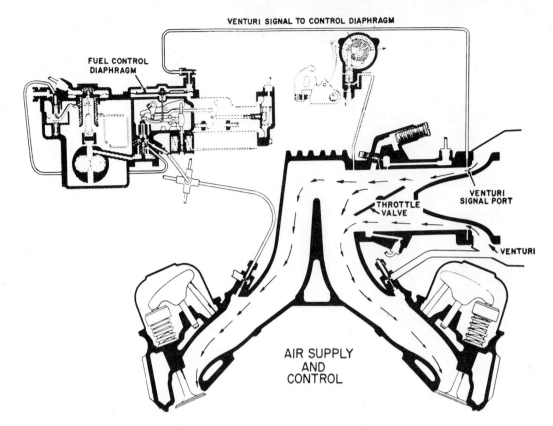

FUEL CONTROL DIAPHRAGM

VENTURI SIGNAL TO CONTROL DIAPHRAGM

THROTTLE VALVE

VENTURI SIGNAL PORT

VENTURI

AIR SUPPLY AND CONTROL

Fig. 27-19. Schematic view of Chevrolet fuel injection system showing airflow and control system.

The Cummins metering pump injection system (not illustrated) although still used on a number of install- ations, has been superseded by the Pressure Time System, described on preceding pages.

Gasoline Injection

A system of gasoline injection is somewhat differ- ent from a Diesel injection system. The gasoline en- gine is also a good vacuum pump--which the Diesel engine is not-- so it is customary to inject the gasoline into the inlet manifold near the inlet valve, and allow the cylinder vacuum to suck the fuel into the cylinder.

Because the gasoline is not thus injected into the cylinder against the compression pressure, as in a Diesel, the pump can use a lower pressure than the Diesel and is therefore known as a low-pressure sys- tem.

The injection is of two types; the constant or "dribble" system where a very small stream of fuel runs constantly into the intake manifold while the engine is running, and the timed or intermittent system where a shot of fuel is supplied on the suction stroke of each cylinder.

The constant supply system does not need to be timed, but the intermittent system is timed with the crankshaft in the same manner as the ignition dis- tributor.

One of the first gasoline injection systems was developed by Robert Bosch in Germany for Mercedes

racing cars and was an adaptation of the Bosch Diesel fuel pump previously described herein. The fuel was injected near the inlet valves and was timed.

A number of American racing cars use fuel injec- tion of the constant type and find it satisfactory for racing purposes. Both the constant and intermittent types are used to some extent on American passenger cars.

Among the advantages listed for fuel injection are:
1. Increased power.
2. Higher torque.
3. Improved fuel economy.
4. Quicker cold starting.
5. Faster warm-up.
6. No need for manifold heat.
7. Lower intake temperatures.

A typical gasoline injection system as used by Chevrolet is shown in Figs. 27-17 and 27-18. This is of the constant flow type. Details of operation are shown in Fig. 27-19. A similar system was used by Pontiac.

Mercedes-Benz Diesel System

The Diesel system used on the Mercedes-Benz passenger cars such as the model 200D, Fig. 27-20, uses a glow plug to insure quicker starting. This is necessary as the compression temperature of a Diesel is approximately 1300 deg. to 1600 deg. F. When starting a cold engine, however, compression temperatures are only approximately 575 deg. F. Such a temperature is not sufficient to ignite the fuel. Glow plugs are therefore installed to provide the additional heat required for starting, Fig. 27-21. The glow plugs receive the necessary power from the starting battery as shown in Fig. 27-22, and a switch is provided so that the glow plug is disconnected as soon as the engine starts.

The complete injection system is shown schematically in Fig. 27-23 and it will be noted the fuel feed pump is driven by the injection pump and draws fuel through the prefilter and forces the fuel through the fuel union filter into the suction end of the injection pump, Fig. 27-1. The plungers of the injection pump elements force the fuel through the pressure valves and then into the injection nozzles which operate at an

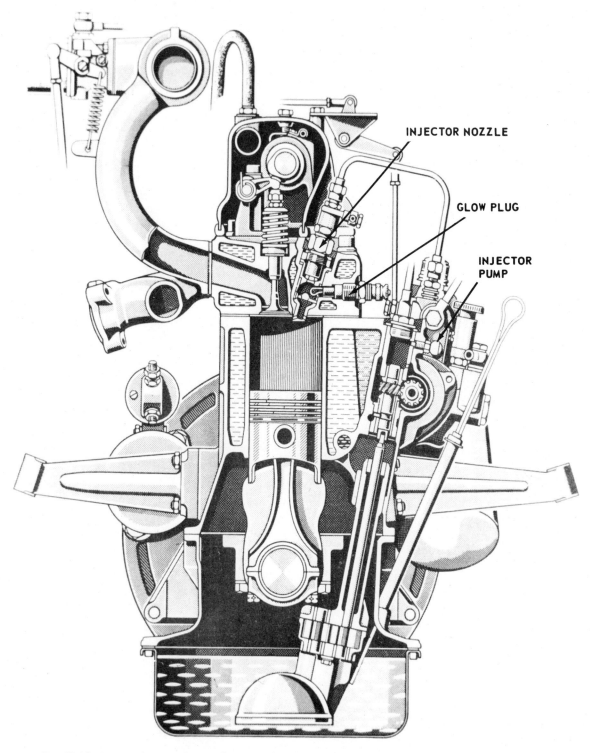

INJECTOR NOZZLE

GLOW PLUG

INJECTOR PUMP

Fig. 27-20. Sectional view of Mercedes-Benz diesel engine. Note location of glow plug which provides necessary heat for starting.

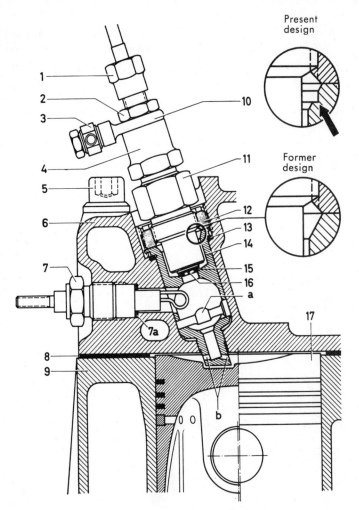

Fig. 27-21. *Details of injector nozzle and glow plug. 1-Line to fuel supply. 2-Hexagon nut. 3-Fuel leak line. 4-Nozzle holder. 5-Cylinder head screw. 6-Cylinder head. 7-Glow plug. 7a-Sealing ring. 10-Fitting. 11-Nozzle holding nut. 12-Threaded ring. 13-Sealing ring. 14-Precombustion chamber. 15-Seal. 16-Nozzle needle. 17-Piston.*

opening atm. pressure of 110 to 120. These nozzles spray the fuel into the precombustion chamber and into the main combustion chamber.

The fuel feed pump always delivers more fuel than is needed and the surplus fuel returns to the fuel tank through the bypass valve and the fuel return valve. Any fuel leaking at the injection nozzles also flows back to the fuel tank through the drip-fuel line to the fuel return line.

The injection pump is of Bosch manufacture and designated as the model M. This is a smaller version of the older units such as illustrated in Fig. 27-1. It is featured by suction space scavenging and the fuel in the suction chamber is constantly under pressure. This pressure is produced by the fuel pump and the excess fuel scavenges the entire suction chamber. The method of transfering the control rod travel is also different than on previous models. This travel is no longer affected by means of a toothed control rod. With the new design, when the control rod is moved, the lever with its control sleeve is also moved through the clamping piece on the control rod, transmitting the movement on the control sleeve and on the pump plunger. The pump plunger is now seated on the roller tappet. The advance stroke is adjusted by exchanging rollers on the tappet and the feed quantity can be adjusted by lateral movement of the clamping pieces on the control rod.

Mercedes Gasoline Injection

Manifold fuel (gasoline) injection and port fuel injection are both used on Mercedes-Benz cars. Currently the models 220SE and 300SE are equipped with the manifold type of fuel injection, while the model

Fig. 27-22. *Wiring diagram of glow plug circuit.*

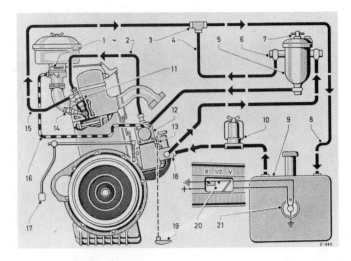

Fig. 27-23. *Schematic diagram of Mercedes-Benz Diesel system. 1-Throttle duct. 2-Injection pressure line. 3-T-section. 4-Bypass line. 5-Main filter. 6-Bypass valve. 7-Bleeder screw. 8-Return line. 9-Fuel tank. 10-Prefilter. 11-Injection nozzle. 12-Injection pump. 13-Adjusting lever. 14-Glow plug. 15-Drip-fuel line. 16-Vacuum line. 17-Accelerator. 18-Fuel feed pump. 19-Start and stop control. 20-Fuel gauge. 21-Fuel gauge transmitter.*

230SL is equipped with the port type of fuel injection.

As the name implies, fuel is injected directly into the manifold with the one type and in the other it is injected into the valve port directly under the intake valve head, Fig. 27-24.

The injection valve used in the manifold type of injection system is shown in Fig. 27-25 while the injection pump and complete system is shown in Fig. 27-26. In this system of injection, the pump injects finely atomized fuel into the intake manifold for three cylinders at one time. As a result fuel may not always be injected during the intake stroke with the intake valve open. But injection takes place at various times, although the time does not vary for any one cylinder. Since the camshaft of the injection pump turns at half crankshaft speed, but has double cams, fuel is injected at every turn of the crankshaft. As a result, the fuel quantity for any one cylinder is injected in two equal parts.

In the port injection system, Fig. 27-21, the principal of "jerk" injection has been retained, but the nozzles no longer inject into the intake manifold, but into the port of the intake valve. During the injection process, which coincides with the suction stroke of the piston, part of the atomized fuel is injected into the combustion chamber past the opened valve. During this process, the atomized fuel takes up heat from the cylinder. The electric starting valve is arranged in the middle of the intake manifold in such a way that the fuel jets are directed toward the individual intake ports.

Roosa Master Fuel Injection Pump

The Roosa Master fuel injection pump is a single cylinder, opposed plunger, inlet metering, distributor type unit, Fig. 27-27, and is used largely in high speed Diesel engines. The main components are: drive shaft,

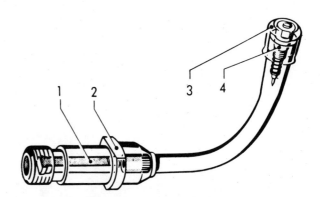

Fig. 27-25. Detail of injection valve as used in Mercedes-Benz gasoline injection system. 1-Filter. 2-Retainer. 3-Locking cap. 4-Valve insert.

distributor rotor, transfer pump, pumping plunger, internal cam ring, hydraulic ring, end plate, and governor.

It is a self-lubricated unit with the filtered fuel it pumps. There are no spring-loaded lapped surfaces, no ball bearings, no gears and most accessories are built in.

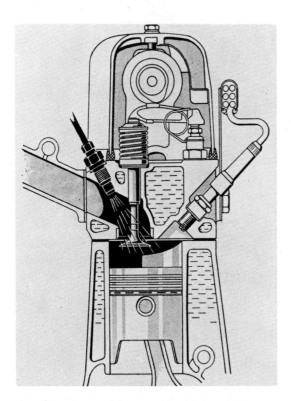

Fig. 27-24. Sectional view of Mercedes-Benz gasoline injection system. Note location of spray nozzle.

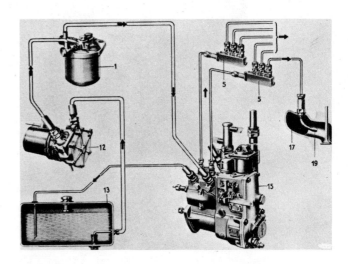

Fig. 27-26. Fuel flow system of Mercedes-Benz gasoline injection system. 1-Fine fuel filter. 5-Fuel distributor fittings. 12-Fuel feed pump. 13-Fuel tank. 15-Injection pump. 17-Intake manifold. 19-Injection valves.

The rotating members revolve on a common axis and are the drive shaft, distributor rotor (containing the plungers and mounting the governor) and the transfer pump.

Fuel is drawn from the supply pump into the inlet strainer (1), Fig. 27-27, by the vane type fuel transfer pump (2). Excess fuel is bypassed through the regulating valve (3) back to the inlet side. The flow thus bypassed increases in proportion to the speed, and the regulating valve is designed so transfer pressure also increases with speed.

pumping cylinder, as at idling, the plungers move out very little. As additional fuel is admitted, the plunger stroke increases to the maximum quantity as limited by leaf spring arrangement (12).

At this point (charging) of the cycle, the rollers (13) are in the "valley" or relieved part of the cam (14) between lobes. The fuel is trapped in the cylinder for

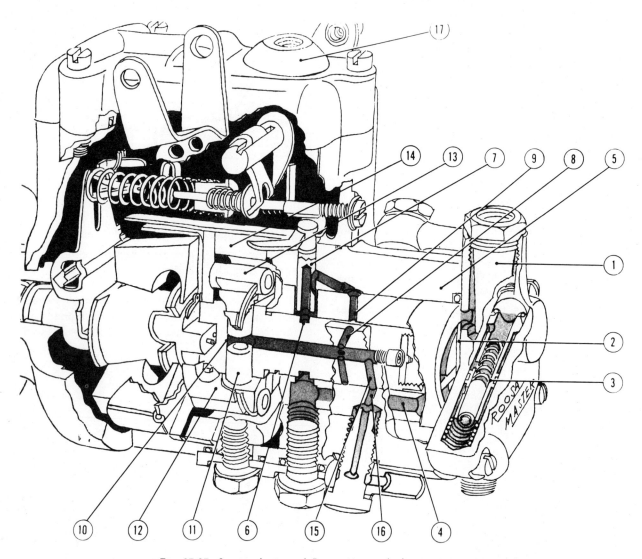

Fig. 27-27. Sectional view of Roosa Master fuel injection pump.

Fuel, under transfer pump pressure, is forced through the axial passage (4) into the head (5), into an annular groove (6) milled around the rotor shank. The fuel flows around the groove and through the metering valve (7) in a quantity determined by engine demands. As the rotor revolves, one of its charging ports (8) comes into register with passage (9), permitting the fuel (still under pump pressure) to enter the axial passage (10). The inflowing fuel forces the plungers (11) outward, a distance proportionate to the quantity to be injected on the following stroke.

If only a small amount of fuel is admitted into the

a very short interval after charging is complete. This is caused by the fact that the charging port has passed out of registry with passage (9) and the rotor discharge port (15) has not yet come into registry with an outlet port (16) in the hydraulic head.

Further rotation of the rotor brings its discharge port into registry with an outlet port at which point the rollers simultaneously contact the opposing cam lobes and the plungers are forced toward each other. The fuel trapped between the plungers is forced from the pump through one of the outlet ports into an injection line.

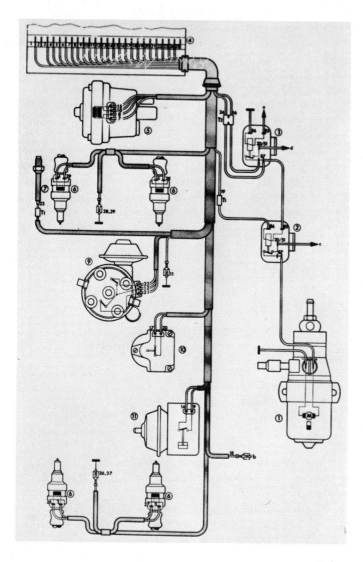

Fig. 27-27. Main components of the VW electronic fuel injection system. 1-Electric fuel pump, 2-Pump relay, 3-Main relay, 4-Electronic control unit, 5-Pressure sensor, 6-Injectors, 7-Temperature sensor, 9-Distributor with trigger contacts, 10-Throttle switch, 11-Pressure switch.

VW Electronic Fuel Injection System

The electronic fuel injection system installed on some models of the Volkswagen was developed by Bosch of Germany. The system was devised to help meet the need for exhaust emission control. The system provides accuracy both in fuel metering and in the mixture distribution to the individual cylinders.

Each cylinder is provided with a solenoid operated injector valve through which the fuel is injected intermittently to the intake ports. The firing order of the VW engine is 1-4-3-2. The injector valves of each two cylinders which follow one another in this firing order are operated simultaneously. That is, the injector valves of cylinders 1 and 4 and those of cylinders 3 and 2 operate together.

In operation, Fig. 27-27, current is supplied to a control unit (4) via a main relay (3) and to an electric

fuel pump (1) via a pump relay (2). A time switch in the control unit activates the fuel pump for 1 to 1-1/2 seconds after ignition is turned on to permit build up of fuel pressure. Fuel injectors (6) are kept under constant pressure of 28 psi so amount of fuel injected depends on length of time injectors are kept open and is metered according to engine requirements.

Engine speed and intake manifold pressure are used primarily as the input signals to the electronic control system. The ignition distributor houses trigger contacts that signal to control unit when more fuel is to be injected. The throttle valve (10) cuts off supply of fuel during deceleration.

An electrically driven fuel pump forces fuel into the pressure line, through a filter to the ring main. The pressure regulator connected to the ring main maintains pressure at approximately 28 psi. Surplus fuel returns to the supply tank through a special line. The ring main feeds fuel to the electromagnetic injectors by way of fuel distributor pipes.

The intake air distributor, Fig. 27-28, keys the air supply to four intake manifolds (1) and to the four cylinders of the engine. The amount of air required by the fuel injection system is controlled during engine operation by the throttle valve in the intake air distributor (2). Since the throttle valve is connected to the accelerator pedal it is completely closed during idle, and intake air must pass through an idling circuit that includes an adjusting screw (7) which controls engine idling speed.

The idling circuit supplies sufficient air at normal operating temperatures. However, at lower temperatures more air is required and an auxiliary air regulator (8) supplies it. This regulator is a rotary valve in an auxiliary air line from the air cleaner. On-off positions are controlled by an oil temperature sensor.

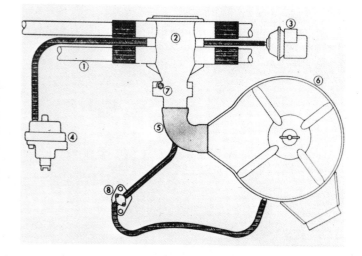

Fig. 27-28. Air system of VW electronic fuel injection system. 1-Intake pipes, 2-Intake air distributor, 3-Pressure switch, 4-Pressure sensor, 5-Elbow, 6-Air cleaner, 7-Idle air screw, 8-Auxiliary air regulator.

Variations in barometric pressure have no influence on the mixture richness of this system. The pulse generator in the distributor (9) supplies information about the angular position of the crankshaft and thus determines the injection timing which is constant at 15 deg. crank angle after top center, under all operating conditions.

There are no adjustments to be made on this system, nor is matching to the individual engine necessary. Specialized equipment is available for checking the system. However, the fuel system should be checked for leaks and pinched lines, especially at the tank, pump, filter and pressure regulator. The fuel filter should be replaced every 6000 miles. To make this change, pinch the fuel hose between filter and tank with a clamp. Also clamp hose between Y connector and pump. Remove old filter, then install new filter with arrow facing pump. Then remove clamps.

The air filter is of the oil reservoir type which should be cleaned and refilled with new SAE 30 oil every 6000 miles.

Trigger contacts of the distributor are nonadjustable. Make sure all electrical connections are clean and tight. Set engine idle speed. Adjust idling air adjusting screw, Fig. 27-28, with engine at operating temperature. Idling speed is specified at 850 rpm.

Quiz - Fuel Injection

1. On the compression stroke, what does a Diesel engine compress?
   a. Air.
   b. Air-fuel mixture.
   c. Diesel fuel.
2. What are the four basic types of Diesel fuel injection used on automotive engines?
3. What five requirements must a Diesel fuel injection system fulfill?
4. In the Bosch system what does the rotation of the pump plunger control?
   a. The quantity of the fuel delivered.
   b. Timing of injection.
   c. Compression.
5. What type engines are the General Motors Diesel?
   a. Four cycle.
   b. Two cycle.
   c. Sleeve valve.
6. What type of injector system is used on the General Motors Diesel engine?
7. How many high pressure distributing lines are used on a four cylinder General Motors Diesel engine?
   a. Four.   b. Eight.   c. None.
8. After repair work, or having run dry, is it necessary to prime a General Motors injector?
9. In the General Motors system, fuel is supplied to the injector at what pressure?
   a. 5 lb.
   b. 10 lb.
   c. 15 lb.
   d. 20 lb.
10. In the Cummins PT Diesel system what method is used to increase the flow of fuel?
    a. Increased pressure.
    b. Increased size of jet.
    c. Rotation of plunger.
11. Does fuel flow all the time in the Cummins injector?
12. In a gasoline injection system, the injection pressures are higher or lower than in a Diesel System?
13. Name two types of gasoline injection systems.
14. The injection pump on an American Bosch gasoline injection system is driven at what speed?
    a. Engine speed.
    b. Half engine speed.
    c. Twice engine speed.
15. In the Volkswagen fuel injection system, fuel is injected into the combustion chamber.
    True or False?
16. Injector valve for cylinders one and two operate together in the Volkswagen injection system.
    True or False?

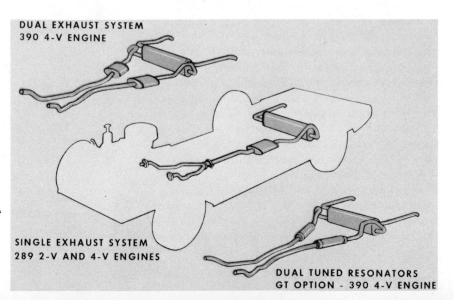

Fig. 28-1. Three different types of exhaust systems. Also see Fig. 28-2. (Mercury)

EXHAUST
SYSTEMS

The exhaust system of an automotive engine consists of the exhaust manifold, exhaust pipe, muffler and tail pipe. See Figs. 28-1, and 28-2. It is designed to conduct the burned gases (or exhaust) from the engine, silence the noise of the exhaust, and conduct it to the rear of the vehicle.

In such cases, a completely separate exhaust system may be provided for each side of the engine. Or, the two sides may be joined together by means of a "cross over pipe."

Regardless of the individual design, the passageways forming the manifold are made as large in size

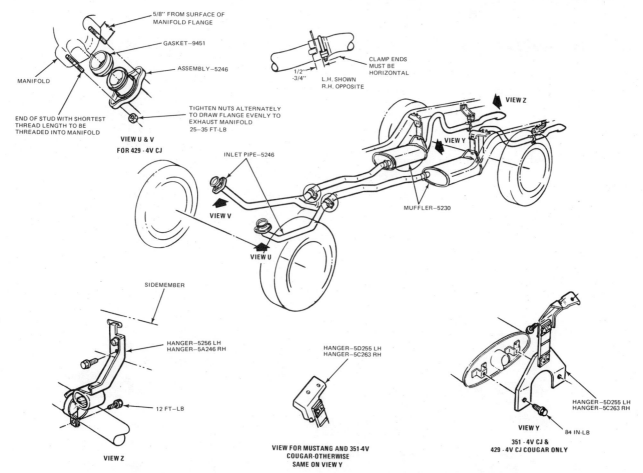

Fig. 28-2. Dual exhaust system on V-8 engine, showing details of hangers and connections.

Exhaust Manifold

Exhaust manifolds are of many different types. On an in-line engine the manifold is usually bolted to the side of engine, Fig. 28-2, while on V-8 engines, separate manifolds are provided for each side of the "V."

as practical in order to reduce the resistance to the flow of the burned gases. Included in the design of the exhaust manifold is the manifold heat valve, which together with special passageways, conducts heat to the intake manifold in order to improve the vaporization of the fuel. This will be discussed in detail later.

Mufflers

In order to reduce the noise of the exhaust of an internal combustion engine, exhaust gases from the engine are passed through a muffler, Fig. 28-3. The muffler is so designed that the gases are expanded slowly, and are also cooled before they are discharged into the tail pipe and the atmosphere. In addition, the design must be such that there is a minimum of back pressure developed. Back pressure prevents free flow of the exhaust gases from the engine, and as a result, not all of the burned gases will be expelled, or exhausted from the cylinders. Such unexpelled gases dilute the incoming combustible gases, and as a result, the power of the engine is reduced.

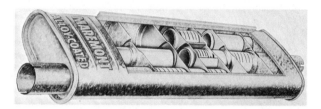

Fig. 28-3. Special layers of aluminum, cadmium, lead and zinc alloys coatings are used to protect this muffler against corrosion.

On an automotive vehicle, the engine first exhausts into the exhaust manifold, Fig. 28-2. The gas then passes through the exhaust pipe into the muffler. From the muffler it passes into the tail pipe and from there into the atmosphere at the rear of the vehicle.

A certain amount of expansion and cooling of the exhaust gas is provided for in the design of the exhaust manifold and exhaust pipe. Usually these are designed to provide from two to four times the volume of a single cylinder of the engine. The additional expansion is then provided for in the muffler.

Muffler Design

The design of the muffler varies with different manufacturers. One type is known as the straight through type, Fig. 28-4. In this design, a straight path is provided for the gases which extends from the front to the rear of the unit. A centrally located pipe with perforations is provided. Surrounding this pipe is a sheet metal shell, approximately three times the diameter of the pipe. In some instances, the space between the outer shell and inner pipe is open and in other cases it is filled with steel wool or some other heat-resistant sound deadener and porous material.

Another type of muffler reverses the flow of the exhaust gases, Fig. 28-4, and has the advantage of conserving space. The double shell and two shell are still other forms of modern mufflers.

In order to reduce the noise of the exhaust below that attained by a single muffler, many systems are equipped with two mufflers in each line, Fig. 28-1. Such construction is particularly necessary on cars with a long wheel base and powered with a high output engine. The additional unit is usually known as a resonator.

Back Pressure

In Fig. 28-5, the loss in engine power due to back pressure from the exhaust system is shown. It will be noted that as the speed of the vehicle increases, back pressure also increases. Note also for a given car speed, the loss in power increases very rapidly with the increase in back pressure. For example; with 2 lbs. back pressure at 70 mph, the power loss is 4 hp and when the back pressure is 4 lbs. the power loss has increased to 8 hp.

Similarly, fuel consumption is increased as muffler back pressure increases. This is shown graphically in Fig. 28-6.

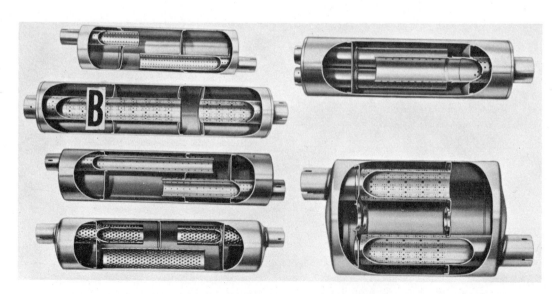

Fig. 28-4. Different types of muffler construction. Muffler B is a straight through, while the others are variations of the reverse flow type of construction.

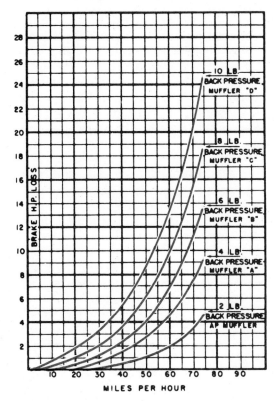

Fig. 28-5. Showing the loss in horsepower due to exhaust back pressure.

Care must be exercised that there are no dents in the exhaust system that would tend to obstruct the free flow of the exhaust gases, as any obstruction would reduce power and fuel economy.

Corrosion Of Exhaust System

Mufflers, tail pipes and exhaust pipes wear out due to corrosion which occurs on both the inside and outside. The rusting that occurs on the outside is due to rain, snow and humidity. In some northern metropolitan sections this external rusting is accelerated by the use of salt on icy road surfaces.

By far the greatest amount of corrosion occurs inside the exhaust system particularly in the muffler, because for every gallon of fuel burned, approximately an equal quantity of water is formed. This water, produced by the combustion of the fuel, passes through the exhaust system. Mixed with acids also formed in the combustion process, the interior of the exhaust system is quickly rusted.

Until the exhaust system has reached operating temperature, much of the moisture will condense on the cool surfaces and collect in the muffler. Then as the muffler becomes hot, the collected moisture will be evaporated and be forced out of the tail pipe. Engineers have found that condensate boils at 202 to 210 deg. F. Mufflers must therefore be operated at or above that temperature to dispel the condensate. On short drives the muffler will not reach that temperature, and will corrode rapidly.

In addition to the action of corrosion, mufflers and the rest of the exhaust system will wear out and become less effective due to the accumulation of carbon, loose parts, leaks, etc. In order to reduce the tendency toward corrosion, most manufacturers are using some form of rust-resisting coatings and/or special alloys in the construction of their mufflers and pipes. In addition, stainless steel is also being used. Other manufacturers are using a ceramic coating on the interior of the mufflers and pipes.

Exhaust Gas Is Deadly

It is imperative that no leaks occur in the muffler and exhaust system, the reason being that exhaust gases contain carbon monoxide. This is a deadly poison. When it finds its way into the interior of the ve-

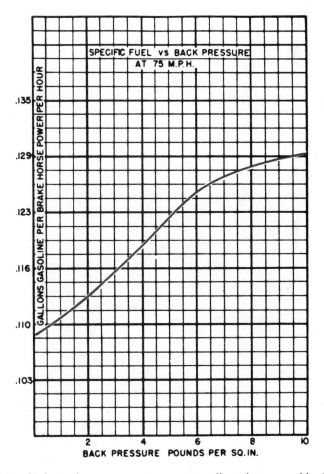

Fig. 28-6. Fuel consumption increases rapidly with increased back pressure.

hicle it causes headache, drowsiness, nausea and as the quantity is increased, unconsciousness and finally death results.

Surveys show that 5 percent of the cars on the road contain sufficient carbon monoxide to cause drowsiness and seriously impair driver judgment and reflexes.

301

Any exhaust leaks that occur in the exhaust system, from the exhaust manifold back to the tail pipe, should be repaired immediately or new parts should be installed.

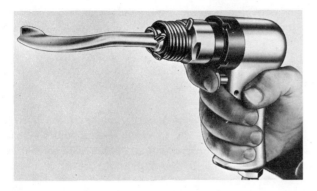

Fig. 28-7. One type of pneumatic muffler gun designed for muffler and pipe removal work.

Just as exhaust gas is dangerous to the occupants of a vehicle, so is it dangerous to mechanics working in a repair shop. Engines should never be operated in a closed garage, unless adequate ventilation is provided. In large shops, special ventilating ducts are provided. These ducts are connected to the tailpipe of the engine so the exhaust is conducted outdoors.

type of service in which the vehicle is used. If the car or truck is used mostly for short trips, it is not unusual for the tail pipe to require replacement in less than 10,000 miles. This is particularly true in the case of dual exhaust systems on V-8 engines. The reason is that as the exhaust is divided into two separate lines, they do not attain as high a temperature as would be the case in a single exhaust system. Operating at a lower temperature, less moisture is evaporated and consequently more rusting occurs.

As shown in Fig. 28-2, the exhaust system consists of the exhaust manifold, the exhaust pipe, the muffler and tail pipe. The joint between the manifold and the exhaust pipe is usually of the flange and gasket type. Brass nuts on steel bolts are usually used to hold the flanges together as the brass will not rust on the steel and is therefore more easily dismantled.

The usual construction of the exhaust pipe is to make the lower end slightly larger in diameter than the opening in the muffler. The muffler opening can then be slipped into the end of the exhaust pipe. A clamp is placed around the end of the exhaust pipe, and when tightened, the two parts are held securely together. The connection between the tail pipe and the muffler is of similar construction. Metal or combination metal and fabric straps, are used to hold the muffler and pipes securely in place.

To remove a muffler and tail pipe, the clamps and supporting straps are first removed. As the

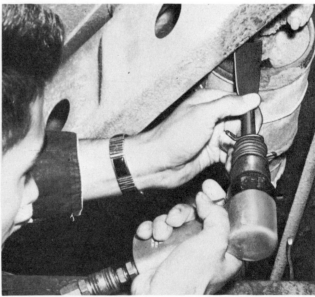

Fig. 28-8. Using a pneumatic muffler gun to cut through muffler pipes to speed removal.

Servicing Exhaust Systems

Because of the rusting that occurs in exhaust systems, it is frequently necessary to replace the various parts. The muffler and tail pipe are the parts replaced most frequently. Their life is largely dependent on the

pipes usually have rusted to the muffler it is usually difficult to separate the joints. If any of the parts are to be used again, penetrating oil should be used liberally on the joints before attempting to pull them apart. In most cases, the parts are not to be used again and consequently they can be cut apart. Hacksaws can be used for that purpose, but power driven tools such as those shown in Fig. 28-7 and Fig. 28-8 will do the job much more quickly. To speed the job

Fig. 28-9. *Special tool being used to expand end of pipe to facilitate installation of new muffler.*

of installation, it is frequently necessary to expand the end of a pipe or muffler so that it can be more easily assembled. A special expanding tool is shown in Fig. 28-9.

Quiz - Exhaust Systems

1. What four major parts form the exhaust system on an automobile?
2. On an in-line engine where is the exhaust manifold usually attached?
3. What effect does back pressure have on the operation of an engine?
   a. Reduces power of the engine.
   b. Increases power of the engine.
   c. Increases the amount of carbon monoxide.
4. What is a major factor in the rusting of a muffler?
   a. Short distance driving.
   b. Long distance driving.
   c. High speed.
5. What material is used in making the nuts used to bolt together the flange between the manifold and exhaust pipe?
   a. Cast iron.
   b. Steel.
   c. Castellated.
   d. Brass.
6. The forward end of the muffler is larger or smaller than the end of the exhaust pipe?

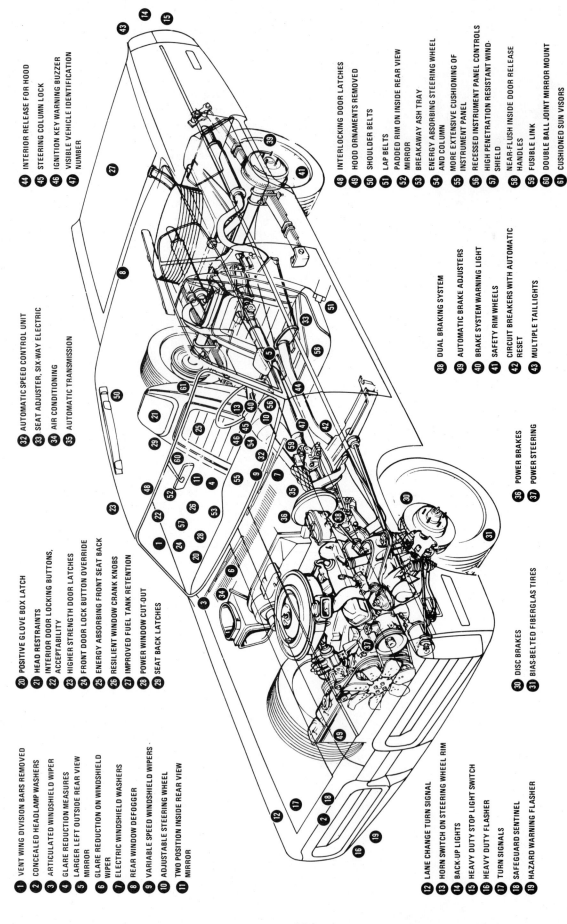

1. VENT WING DIVISION BARS REMOVED
2. CONCEALED HEADLAMP WASHERS
3. ARTICULATED WINDSHIELD WIPER
4. GLARE REDUCTION MEASURES
5. LARGER LEFT OUTSIDE REAR VIEW MIRROR
6. GLARE REDUCTION ON WINDSHIELD WIPER
7. ELECTRIC WINDSHIELD WASHERS
8. REAR WINDOW DEFOGGER
9. VARIABLE SPEED WINDSHIELD WIPERS
10. TWO POSITION INSIDE REAR VIEW MIRROR
11. ADJUSTABLE STEERING WHEEL

12. LANE CHANGE TURN SIGNAL
13. HORN SWITCH ON STEERING WHEEL RIM
14. BACK-UP LIGHTS
15. HEAVY DUTY STOP LIGHT SWITCH
16. HEAVY DUTY FLASHER
17. TURN SIGNALS
18. SAFEGUARD SENTINEL
19. HAZARD WARNING FLASHER

20. POSITIVE GLOVE BOX LATCH
21. HEAD RESTRAINTS
22. INTERIOR DOOR LOCKING BUTTONS, ACCEPTABILITY
23. HIGHER STRENGTH DOOR LATCHES
24. FRONT DOOR LOCK BUTTON OVERRIDE
25. ENERGY ABSORBING FRONT SEAT BACK
26. RESILIENT WINDOW CRANK KNOBS
27. IMPROVED FUEL TANK RETENTION
28. POWER WINDOW CUT-OUT
29. SEAT BACK LATCHES

30. DISC BRAKES
31. BIAS-BELTED FIBERGLAS TIRES

32. AUTOMATIC SPEED CONTROL UNIT
33. SEAT ADJUSTER, SIX-WAY ELECTRIC
34. AIR CONDITIONING
35. AUTOMATIC TRANSMISSION

36. POWER BRAKES
37. POWER STEERING

38. DUAL BRAKING SYSTEM
39. AUTOMATIC BRAKE ADJUSTERS
40. BRAKE SYSTEM WARNING LIGHT
41. SAFETY RIM WHEELS
42. CIRCUIT BREAKERS WITH AUTOMATIC RESET
43. MULTIPLE TAILLIGHTS

44. INTERIOR RELEASE FOR HOOD
45. STEERING COLUMN LOCK
46. IGNITION KEY WARNING BUZZER
47. VISIBLE VEHICLE IDENTIFICATION NUMBER

48. INTERLOCKING DOOR LATCHES
49. HOOD ORNAMENTS REMOVED
50. SHOULDER BELTS
51. LAP BELTS
52. PADDED RIM ON INSIDE REAR VIEW MIRROR
53. BREAKAWAY ASH TRAY
54. ENERGY ABSORBING STEERING WHEEL AND COLUMN
55. MORE EXTENSIVE CUSHIONING OF INSTRUMENT PANEL
56. RECESSED INSTRUMENT PANEL CONTROLS
57. HIGH PENETRATION RESISTANT WINDSHIELD
58. NEAR-FLUSH INSIDE DOOR RELEASE HANDLES
59. FUSIBLE LINK
60. DOUBLE BALL JOINT MIRROR MOUNT
61. CUSHIONED SUN VISORS

Strong emphasis on safety for past several years has spearheaded development of many safety-oriented features. Head restraints, rear window defogger, automatic brake adjusters, energy absorbing steering wheel and column and other safety related items are shown in this phantom view of a 1972 Plymouth Fury.

EXHAUST EMISSION CONTROL

There are many factors contributing to pollution of the air we breathe.

Hydrocarbons (HC's) and oxides of nitrogen (NO_x) are important ingredients of smog which is a combination of smog and smoke from automobiles and industry. In mild quantities smog burns the eyes; in excessive quantities it causes death. Hydrocarbons and oxides of nitrogen along with carbon monoxide are all emitted from the automobile exhaust and from the crankcase breather.

California was the first state to limit the amount of carbon monoxide and hydrocarbons which were permissible emissions from the automobile exhaust system. California set the limit at 275 ppm (parts per million) for hydrocarbons and 1.5 percent carbon monoxide. Since that time the Federal government has also enacted laws limiting such emissions.

To meet these requirements crankcase ventilating systems have been redesigned and alterations to engines, carburetion and ignition systems have been made.

Crankcase Emission Control Systems

Crankcase emission control systems are a development of the familiar crankcase ventilating system, Fig. 29-1. In that design, air enters through the oil filler cap. After passing through the crankcase, (as shown by the arrows) it leaves through the draft or vent tube with its opening below the engine. In that way the movement of the air past the open end of the tube provides a suction which helps draw the fumes from the crankcase.

So that these fumes are not ejected into the atmosphere, the emission control system is arranged so that the ventilating air after passing through the crankcase is directed first into the rocker arm cover chamber. From there the fumes are drawn into the manifold and then into the combustion chamber. This system is known as the positive crankcase ventilating system or crankcase emission control system.

One such system, classified as the open type, is shown in Fig. 29-2. It will be noted that air enters the oil filler cap in the normal manner and after passing through the crankcase and rocker valve cover chamber, it passes through the oil control valve and into the intake manifold. From there it mixes with the carburetor mixture and is burned again in the combustion chamber.

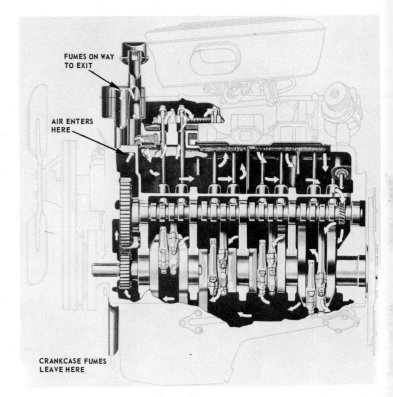

FUMES ON WAY TO EXIT

AIR ENTERS HERE

CRANKCASE FUMES LEAVE HERE

Fig. 29-1. Note path of air through the crankcase to carry away engine blow-by and help maintain proper oil temperature.

Naturally, the connecting tubing and flow control valve must be kept clean. A quick check of the condition of the system can be made by removing the ventilator valve and cap from the rocker cover. If the valve is not plugged, a hissing noise will usually be heard as the air passes through the valve, and a

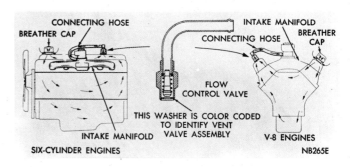

CONNECTING HOSE
BREATHER CAP
INTAKE MANIFOLD
CONNECTING HOSE
BREATHER CAP
FLOW CONTROL VALVE
THIS WASHER IS COLOR CODED TO IDENTIFY VENT VALVE ASSEMBLY
INTAKE MANIFOLD
SIX-CYLINDER ENGINES
V-8 ENGINES
NB265E

Fig. 29-2. Open type of positive crankcase ventilation. Note air intake is through oil filler cap.

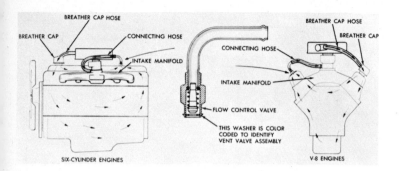

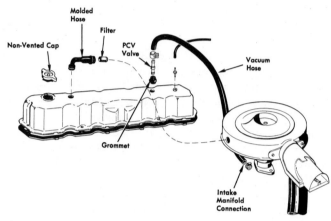

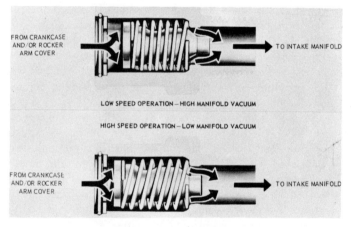

the intake manifold vacuum is very high. The high vacuum overcomes the tension of the spring, Fig. 29-6, and moves the valve to the low flow position. With the valve in this position, all the ventilating air passes through the restricted passage in the valve. With the

Fig. 29-3. Closed type of pressure crankcase ventilation. Note air intake is from the carburetor air filter.

strong vacuum should be felt when a finger is placed over the valve inlet. Also, a strong suction should be felt at the oil filler pipe.

Another crankcase ventilating or emission control system, but classed as the "closed" type, and built primarily for cars destined for California, is shown in Figs. 29-3 and 29-4.

EMISSION CONTROL

Fig. 29-5. Typical "closed" type crankcase ventilating system is shown in American Motors 6-cylinder engine application. Note non-vented oil filler cap and location of PCV valve.

valve in this position, there is minimum ventilation. As the engine speed increases and manifold vacuum decreases, the spring forces the valve out of the passage and to full-open position, thereby increasing airflow.

Fig. 29-4. Closed crankcase ventilating system on Ford truck engine. Note connection with carburetor air filter.

Fig. 29-6. Details of Ford regulator valve operation.

Comparing this system with that shown in Fig. 29-2, (the open type) it will be noted that air for the system first passes through the carburetor air filter before entering the oil filler cap, which is of the closed type. Other designs provide a separate air filter for the system. From that point on, the system is similar to the open type.

Servicing is also similar in that all connecting tubing and air filters must be kept clean and in good operating condition.

The purpose of the pressure control valve, located between the valve cover and the manifold, Fig. 29-5, is to prevent excess airflow during idling. During idle,

A plugged PCV system can cause condensation of the blow-by gases in the crankcase, resulting in the formation of acids, sludge and oil dilution. A plugged PCV valve can also cause oil to be drawn into the oil filter.

Exhaust Emission Control

In addition to the crankcase ventilating system or crankcase emission control system, as it is more rightly called, it is also necessary to limit the emission of the hydrocarbons and carbon monoxide that issue from the exhaust pipe in order to comply with federal regulations.

While there are many different types of systems designed to control the emission of these noxious gases from the exhaust, they can be grouped into two broad classes:

1. Those designed to reduce or eliminate the formation of those harmful pollutants in the engine.
2. Those designed to destroy or otherwise alter the pollutants after they have been formed.

The difficulties to overcome in the solution of the problem can be appreciated by considering the many different conditions that affect the production of these pollutants. These include:

1. Air-fuel ratio.
2. Spark advance.
3. Combustion chamber design.
4. Quantity of combustion chamber deposits.
5. Manifold vacuum.
6. Displacement of the cylinder.
7. Type of transmission.
8. Valve timing.
9. Exhaust back pressure.
10. Engine speed.
11. Maintenance.
12. Temperature.

Chrysler researchers point out that reduction of hydrocarbon and carbon monoxide emission of the order of 60 percent, appear to be possible by regular maintenance. A rough calculation shows that adjustments of carburetion would show an approximate reduction of 60 percent carbon monoxide.

Early experimentation showed that as the fuel mixture was made leaner, hydrocarbon concentration was reduced. General Motors engineers Jackson, Wiese and Wentworth found that with an air-fuel ratio of 10 to 1, over 1200 ppm of hydrocarbon existed. Whereas when the mixture was leaned to 18 to 1, the concentration dropped to less than 400 ppm. Also of interest is their data which relates to hydrocarbon production and fuel economy. At 30 mph and a 10 to 1 air-fuel ratio, the hydrocarbon emission was .250 lb. per hr. and fuel economy was 12 mpg. Then with an air-fuel ratio of 16 to 1, fuel economy jumped to 21 mpg and the emission dropped to .05 lb. per hr.

This information presented at a recent meeting of the Society of Automotive Engineers by the General Motors researchers also dealt with the effects of ignition timing. They pointed out that 11 mpg economy and approximately .010 lb. per hr. hydrocarbon emission was obtained when the ignition timing was 10 deg. BTC. When the timing was advanced to 50 deg. BTC, hydrocarbon emission increased to .075 lb. per hr. and fuel economy soared to 21 mpg. These researchers also found that as combustion chamber deposits increased, exhaust hydrocarbons also increased.

While retarding the spark decreases hydrocarbon concentrations in the exhaust, it has little effect on carbon monoxide production. However, by leaning, the mixture reduces both hydrocarbon and carbon monoxide emissions.

E. Bartholomew of the Ethyl Corp., in a paper presented before the Society of Automotive Engineers, pointed out that manifold vacuum at constant engine speed over the full range, from full throttle to about 20 in. of vacuum, has little effect on concentration of hydrocarbon in the exhaust when air-fuel ratio and spark advance are constant. On the other hand, when the air-fuel ratio is constant and the spark advance is that required to produce a constant percentage of maximum attainable torque, concentration of hydrocarbons rises with increase in manifold vacuum. As vacuum is increased beyond approximately 15 in., the rate of emission rise becomes much more rapid. When the pattern of spark advance is that furnished the normal distributor, which includes retard in the lower range of manifold vacuum, emission rises rapidly with increase in manifold vacuum. If power enrichment is provided, the rate of rise is less marked.

Like other investigators, Bartholomew also found that the rate of low exhaust emission is much more difficult when the engine is connected to a manual transmission instead of an automatic transmission. In considerable measure, the unfavorable effect of manual transmission is attributable to its tendency to maintain high engine speed on deceleration for a longer period when the throttle is closed. With closed throttle there is high manifold vacuum, with consequent increased possibility of misfire, and backfire. In general, cars having automatic transmissions require less complicated carburetors for achievement of low level combustible emission.

Cars with engines having low combustion chamber surface area relative to volume, have correspondingly low exhaust hydrocarbon concentrations, was reported by Charles Scheffer of the General Motors Corp. before the Society of Automotive Engineers. Combustion chamber surface area relative to volume increases with compression ratio and number of cylinders, and it decreases with the long stroke and larger displacement.

The amount of unburned hydrocarbons is proportional to the combustion chamber surface area. These unburned hydrocarbons mix with the burned volume to form a hydrocarbon concentration in the exhaust according to Scheffer's research. Therefore, the ratio of the surface area to chamber volume, S/V, is an important engine design feature relating to exhaust hydrocarbons. Low S/V engines would be expected to have correspondingly low exhaust hydrocarbon concentration.

Compression ratios have a great effect on hydrocarbon emissions. One major benefit derived from low compression ratios is that the lower compression ratio engine has a larger clearance volume and therefore a larger volume of residual gas which would trap more of the hydrocarbon rich portion of the exhaust and result in less hydrocarbon concentration at the tail pipe. The lower compression engine also has a higher exhaust temperature. However, changes in surface to volume ratio had no effect on exhaust carbon monoxide concentration.

Other researchers have attacked the problem by developing methods of supplying additional air to the carbon monoxide and hydrocarbon emissions as they leave the combustion chambers. This is accomplished by pumping air into the exhaust manifold through jets placed at each exhaust port, Fig. 29-7. This method requires the use of a special air pump driven by a belt from the crankshaft, as well as manifold jets, check valves, connecting tubing, etc.

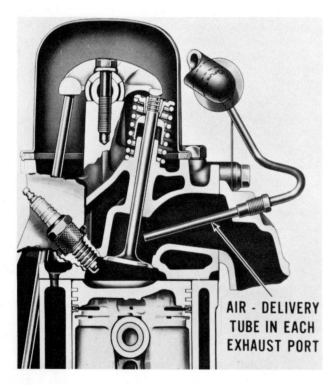

AIR - DELIVERY
TUBE IN EACH
EXHAUST PORT

Fig. 29-7. Showing location of air delivery tube at exhaust port. (Rambler)

From a chemical angle, this method oxidizes or burns the hydrocarbons and carbon monoxide by supplying the needed oxygen, converting these gases to other nonharmful gases.

As the problems associated with the reduction of hydrocarbons and carbon monoxide exhaust emissions by treatment of the exhaust gases became clear, Chrysler engineers decided to eliminate the problem at its source, if possible, by improvements in the engine.

Chrysler engineers, in addition to studying the effects of air-fuel ratio, spark timing, manifold vacuum, crankcase ventilation, also found that the use of retarded spark timing during idle and low engine speeds caused a substantial increase in engine heat rejection. As a result, it was necessary to increase the cooling capacity in most of their engines to handle this larger heat load. However, the higher coolant temperatures reduced hydrocarbon emissions. With the engine idling at 800 rpm, it was found that, with the original engine, the heat rejection was 750 Btu per minute. Whereas with the altered engine, the heat rejection was 900 Btu per minute. At the same time the hydrocarbons dropped from 200 ppm to 170 ppm.

Exhaust Emission Control Systems

There are several different methods in current use to control the emissions of hydrocarbons and carbon monoxide. In general, there is a trend to eliminate the problem at its source by alteration of the engine design, carburetion and ignition.

Ford IMCO System

The Ford IMCO (Improved Combustion) exhaust emission control system is designed to reduce the amount of carbon monoxide and hydrocarbons formed in the engine combustion chamber. This design is used on Ford cars provided with the Cruise-O-Matic transmission, except on certain Mustang and Fairlane models.

To attain the desired objectives, engine design modifications have been made which promote more complete combustion of the air-fuel mixture in the combustion chamber. Major design changes include: alteration of the camshaft, reduced compression ratio, revised intake manifold, as well as changes in

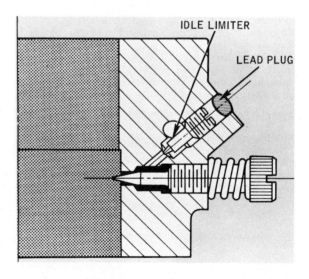

IDLE LIMITER

LEAD PLUG

Fig. 29-8. One method of limiting idle mixture adjustment in order to prevent excessively rich mixtures. (Ford)

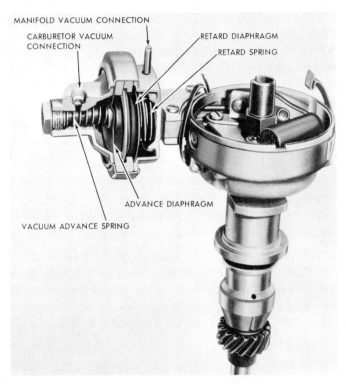

Fig. 29-9. Autolite dual diaphragm ignition distributor design to provide special retardation of spark at idle speeds and during deceleration.

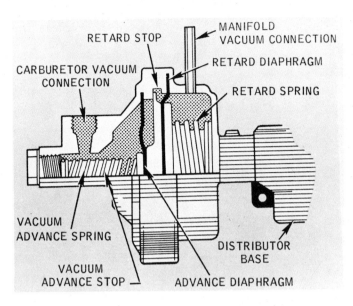

Fig. 29-10. Details of diaphragm assembly. One diaphragm provides the normal advance, while the other provides special retardation at low speeds and during deceleration.

the carburetor and ignition system. Carburetor idle screws are equipped with limiters, Fig. 29-8, and carburetors are calibrated to obtain the desired air-fuel ratio.

The distributor, Fig. 29-9, is of the dual advance type and is provided with two diaphragms. The spark is at the normal position for starting; but when the engine speed drops to idling, the spark is automatically retarded. The outer, or advance, diaphragm, Fig. 29-10, controls the spark advance in the usual manner as the single diaphragm does on conventional distributors. The other diaphragm works in the opposite direction to retard the spark at idling and during periods of deceleration. Calibrated coil springs bear on the vacuum sides of both diaphragms to supply resistance to the actual force of the vacuum. Only the outer diaphragm is linked to the distributor breaker plate. The link passes through the center of the inner diaphragm. The inner diaphragm serves to position a return stop for the outer diaphragm to govern the amount of spark retard when spark advance vacuum is reduced.

In addition to changes in calibration, the carburetors are equipped with plastic limiters, or an internal limiter, making it impossible to increase the richness of the mixture beyond a predetermined point, Fig. 29-8.

Retarding the spark and controlling the air-fuel ratio significantly reduces the emission of noxious fumes from the exhaust, keeping them within the desired limits.

Ford Thermactor Emission System

This system, Fig. 29-11, is composed of the following major parts:
1. Air pump incorporating a relief valve.
2. Air distribution manifolds with check valve.
3. Cylinder heads with air injector tubes.
4. Exhaust backfire suppressor valve.
5. For some engines revised distributor and carburetor.

The air inlet manifold distributes fresh air from the air pump to individual exhaust ports in the cylinder head. The cylinder head with air injection tubes provides for introduction of air into the exhaust port near

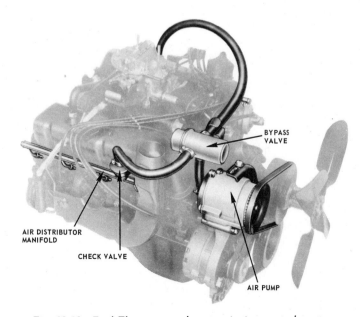

Fig. 29-11. Ford Thermactor exhaust emission control system.

the exhaust valve seat. This location most efficiently mixes exhaust gases and air for effective burning of the hydrocarbons and carbon monoxide according to Ford engineers.

Air injection into the exhaust system increases exhaust system back pressure, both by increasing the

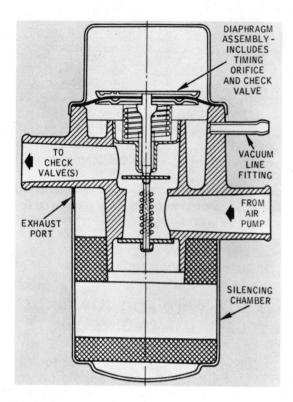

Fig. 29-12. Sectional view of Ford Thermactor air bypass valve.

gas volume and by increasing its temperature. By relieving the pump pressure during maximum engine operating conditions, the relief valve reduces the horsepower loss due to the exhaust emission control system.

The Thermactor bypass valve, Fig. 29-12, under normal acceleration and road conditions, permits air to flow from the pump to the Thermactor air manifold check valve. But when the intake manifold vacuum rises to a high value (idling and deceleration), this high vacuum acts on a diaphragm in the bypass valve assembly to reposition a spring loaded two-plate valve and divert the airflow to the atmosphere through an air silencing chamber at the bottom of the valve. This action continues for a brief interval until pressures on both sides of the diaphragm equalize through a calibrated bypass timing orifice in the diaphragm.

By interrupting Thermactor air delivery during deceleration, the bypass valve prevents backfiring which might otherwise occur due to increased burning of the enriched exhaust mixture. Since the bypass valve can also control Thermactor system air pressure, it eliminates the need for the relief valve which was included in the 1967 installation.

Check valves located in the diaphragm allow any increase in air pressure within the diaphragm chamber to equalize immediately. This effectively compensates for transient vacuum conditions.

Servicing the Ford Thermactor

In cases of backfiring, if the air bypass valve is suspected as being the cause, remove the hose to the air manifold check valve(s) at the air bypass valve connection. With the transmission in neutral and the parking brake on, start the engine and permit it to idle. There should be a definite flow of air from the disconnected hose.

To simulate the air bypass cycle, pinch off the small intake manifold vacuum supply line to the valve for about five seconds. Then release it. When the hose is released, airflow through the bypass valve should diminish or stop for a short period. This interval may vary in length as the time is dependent on engine vacuum and the length of time the hose was shut off.

While the valve may check off in that test, there still may be a leak in the diaphragm area that would render the unit unfit for service. To test for such an air leak, disconnect the intake manifold supply hose at the bypass valve. Insert a T-connection in the disconnected end of the hose and connect a vacuum gauge to one of the remaining ends of the T-connection and a short length of tubing to the other end of the connection. Plug the open end of the hose.

Note the vacuum reading with the engine warm and at normal idling speed. Remove the plug from the end of the tubing and connect it to the vacuum hose fitting on the bypass valve. After a full minute, note the gauge reading. If the gauge reading is less than before, an air leak is indicated.

GM Controlled Combustion System

In essence, the C.C.S. system increases combustion efficiency through different carburetor and distributor calibration and higher engine operating temperatures. Complete effectiveness of the system, as well as full power and performance, depends on idle speed and idle mixtures being set according to specifications.

The C.C.S. system includes no additional units other than a special air cleaner assembly. In general, the carburetors are calibrated leaner and the timing retarded during low speed and deceleration. However, the system is designed specifically for each engine-transmission-rear axle combination.

The thermostatically controlled air cleaner is designed to keep the air entering the carburetor at approximately 100 deg. F. when underhood temperatures are less than 100 deg. F. By keeping the air at 100 deg. F. or more, the carburetor can be leanly calibrated to reduce hydrocarbon emission, minimize carburetor icing, and improve engine warm-up characteristics.

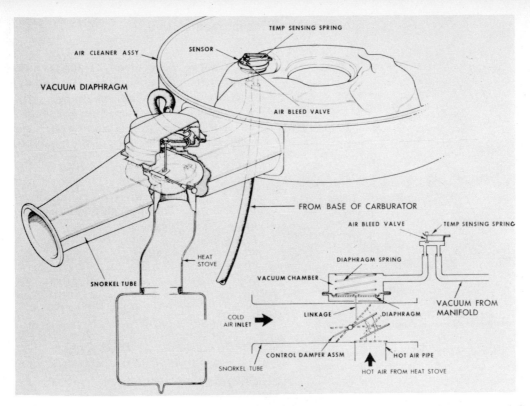

Fig. 29-13. General Motors Controlled Combustion System, as installed on some models of Chevrolet engines.

The thermostatically controlled air cleaner system is composed of a special air cleaner and a heat stove. The heat stove is a sheet metal case surrounding the exhaust manifold that traps the heat generated from the manifold and uses it to heat the air going to the carburetor.

The air cleaner primarily consists of a body, filter element, sensor unit, vacuum diaphragm assembly, damper door and connecting hoses and links, Figs. 21-36 and 29-13.

The sensor unit is mounted in the body of the air cleaner on the clean air side of the filter. The sensor unit regulates (depending on the temperature of the air passing it) the amount of vacuum supplied to the vacuum diaphragm. The vacuum diaphragm (depending on the amount of vacuum supplied to it by the sensing unit) opens the damper door, allowing heated air from the heat stove to enter the cleaner and shuts off the passage for ambient air. The damper door is fully open (all warm air) at 8 in. of mercury and fully closed (ambient air only) at 6 in. of mercury or less. The vacuum signal measured at the diaphragm assembly will not be the same as actual engine vacuum, as the thermostatic control valve in the sensor unit provides a controlled vacuum leak for regulation of the supply signal. A bimetal strip accomplishes the temperature sensitive controlled vacuum leak.

To attain the desired retarded spark during idle, the Controlled Combustion System uses "ported" spark advance, with the vacuum take-off just above the throttle valve, so that there is no vacuum advance at closed throttle. However, there is vacuum advance as soon as the throttle is opened slightly.

Because of the greater heat rejection to the coolant during idle with no spark advance, some engines are likely to overheat if allowed to idle for an extended period. For that reason, some engines are provided with a thermo-vacuum switch located in the coolant passage. There are three connections to this vacuum switch. One connection is to the intake manifold, another to the "ported" vacuum source and the third connection is to the distributor vacuum advance unit.

When the engine coolant is at normal temperature, the thermo-vacuum switch supplies "ported" vacuum to the distributor. However, should the coolant temperature rise above 220 deg. F., full intake manifold vacuum will be supplied to the distributor even at closed throttle, thereby advancing the spark, increasing engine rpm, and causing the temperature to drop.

Servicing the C.C.S. system is basically a precision tune-up job, with special care being taken in adjusting the idle mixture and idle speed. The sensor unit requires no adjustment. It is also important that the cooling system thermostat be of the 195 deg. type.

Chrysler Cleaner Air Package

The method developed by the Chrysler Corp. engineers to limit the emission of carbon monoxide and hydrocarbons from the engine includes improvements in the engine, carburetion and ignition systems. All alterations are designed to reduce the formation of the noxious gases. No means is provided to alter the gases in the exhaust after having been formed in the engine, as do some of the other methods.

311

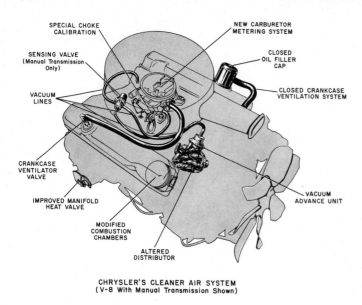

CHRYSLER'S CLEANER AIR SYSTEM
(V-8 With Manual Transmission Shown)

Fig. 29-14. Chrysler Cleaner Air System is designed to limit the production of noxious gases within the combustion chamber.

for a large percentage of total emission. As these were part load conditions, it was possible to select lean mixtures for such conditions.

Similarly, emissions were reduced by retarding the spark during idling and deceleration. The results from such modifications are shown in Fig. 29-15.

	IGNITION TIMING		PERCENT CHANGE FROM STANDARD
	10 DEG. BTDC	5 DEG. ATDC	
RPM	500	550	+10
Fuel-Air Ratio	.085	.071	−16
HC	495	185	−63
CO	7.4	1.1	−85
CO_2	10.4	14.1	
O_2	0.1	0.3	
Airflow	35 lb./hr.	54 lb./hr.	+54
Fuel Flow	3.0 lb./hr.	3.8 lb./hr.	+27

Fig. 29-15.

The "Cleaner Air Package," Fig. 29-14, as it is called, is described as an exhaust emission control system which produces satisfactory emission levels by the use of optimum combinations of air-fuel mixture and spark timing. Modifications of existing carburetors and ignition distributor, Fig. 29-14, together with a new distributor vacuum control valve constitute the basic C.A.P. system.

Chrysler research showed that highest concentrations of hydrocarbons and carbon monoxide were obtained during idle and deceleration. Emission during the 0 to 25 mph and from 15 to 30 mph also accounted

Chrysler's Cleaner Air System

Chrysler's 1972 engines incorporate many emission controls which, when coupled with internal engine modifications, constitute their Cleaner Air System. This system features an evaporative emission control system with a charcoal canister and an overfill limiting valve, Fig. 29-16.

Special emission control devices for California cars include; exhaust port air injection, exhaust gas recirculation and solenoid vacuum control. Lower emission standards in California require special equipment which, generally, appears in full production the following year.

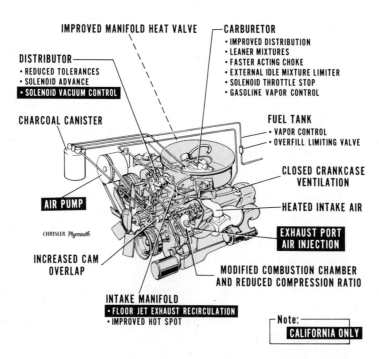

Fig. 29-16. Features of Chrysler's Cleaner Air System are called out. California — only items for 1972 are bordered in black.

General Motors A.I.R. System

The General Motors Air Injector Reactor system (A.I.R.) as installed on the Cadillac and some of the other General Motors cars, reduces the amount of hydrocarbons and carbon monoxide in the exhaust gases by injecting air directly into the exhaust port of each cylinder. The air added to the hot gases causes further oxidation of the gases before they enter the exhaust pipe.

The equipment, Fig. 29-17, used in this system consists of a belt driven pump located with the front accessory group, a rubber formed air hose, a metal tubing manifold between the cylinder heads, and specially designed cylinder heads that incorporate air passages to the rear of each exhaust valve. There is a diverter valve and silencer on the A.I.R. pump to control pressures within the system and a check valve to protect hoses and pump from hot gases. The manufacturers caution against operation of the vehicle with the drive belt disconnected.

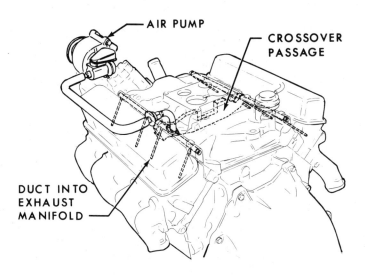

AIR PUMP

CROSSOVER PASSAGE

DUCT INTO EXHAUST MANIFOLD

BUICK'S AIR INJECTION REACTOR

Fig. 29-17. Air Injection Reactor (A.I.R.) system on GM cars is similar to arrangement shown on 1972 Buick engine. System is composed of air pump, check valve, rubber hose with fittings, integrally cast passages in intake manifold and cylinder heads. In operation, air is pumped into exhaust ports to mix with exhaust gases and cause HC and CO particles to burn up.

The carburetor used with this system is a specially calibrated Quadrajet 4MV carburetor. The idle mixture screws have an extra long needle taper to provide finer adjustment.

As is the case with other exhaust emission control systems, tune-up specifications must be carefully followed. In case of failure of the air supply, the trouble may be caused by loose or broken drive belt, leaks in hose or connections, diverter valve failure, check valve failure or pump failure. Noises in the system may result from leaks, loose parts, failure of diverter valve or check valve or pump.

Oldsmobile's TCS System

Another General Motors emission control system, which was featured first on 1970 Oldsmobile engines, is the Transmission-Controlled Vacuum Spark Advance (TCS) system, Fig. 29-18. It serves to retard spark timing in neutral or low gear. When the automatic transmission shifts to a higher gear, a pressure switch in the transmission signals a vacuum solenoid on top of the engine to permit the distributor vacuum advance mechanism to advance spark timing. On manual transmission applications, the signal is controlled by gear shift position.

Exhaust Gas Recirculation

Among the more recent developments in emission control is the Exhaust Gas Recirculating (EGR) system. It is designed to control nitrogen oxide (NOx) emissions. Basically, the EGR system recirculates a metered amount of exhaust gas into the air-fuel mixture in the combustion chambers where it slows down the combustion process and absorbs heat. Since NOx is produced by high temperatures, the EGR system serves to reduce temperatures and NOx emissions.

Buick, for 1972, utilizes a special intake manifold and a metering valve to do the EGR job, Fig. 29-19. Passages in the intake manifold route exhaust gases from the exhaust manifold to a metering valve. On acceleration, the valve opens and meters a small amount of exhaust gas to the intake area below the carburetor. This dilutes the air-fuel mixture before it enters the combustion chambers. The valve permits a proportionately greater flow of exhaust gases as the acceleration rate climbs.

Solenoid Controls

Several car manufacturing divisions of General Motors have incorporated an antidieseling solenoid in the carburetor linkage. This device avoids engine dieseling, or run-on, by permitting the throttle valve to close after the ignition is switched off. The dieseling problem was brought on by the increased engine idle speeds and higher operating temperatures required for better emission control.

So the antidieseling solenoid is a means of holding the throttle lever at a higher idle speed when energized (850 rpm, for example). It allows the lever to contact the slow idle cam (approximately 600 rpm) when de-energized.

A simple electrical test will establish whether or not the solenoid is operable. As mentioned, it should be energized with the ignition ON, de-energized with the ignition OFF.

Evaporative Emission Controls

Evaporative Emission Controls prevent the escape of gasoline vapors from the fuel tank and carburetor, whether or not the engine is running, Fig. 29-20. Most vehicles built during and since the 1971 model year use an activated charcoal canister to trap the vapors when the engine is shut off. On restarting, a flow of filtered air through the canister purges the vapors from the charcoal. The mixture goes through one or more tubes feeding into the carburetor and/or carburetor air cleaner, and it is burned in the engine.

The fuel tank cap has a pressure-vacuum relief valve which permits air to enter the tank as the fuel level goes down. The conventional vented gas cap cannot be used on cars equipped with an Evaporative Emission Control System.

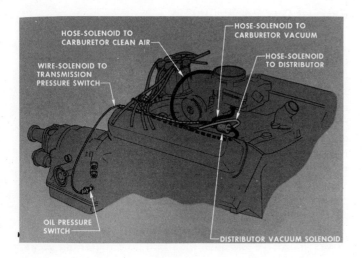

Fig. 29-18. *Oldsmobile's* TCS *system helps control emissions by retarding spark timing in neutral and low gear while permitting normal advance in high gear.*

Emission control service involves various operational checks, including tests of exhaust gases by means of gas analyzers. Generally, a complete engine tune-up, coupled with necessary adjustments or replacement of emission control devices, will bring HC, CO and NOx readings back to the acceptable levels engineered into the vehicle when it was built.

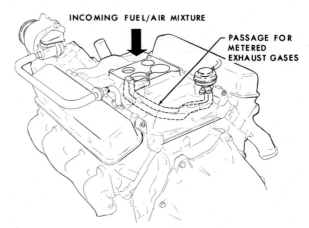

BUICK'S EXHAUST GAS RECIRCULATION

Fig. 29-19. *Exhaust gas recirculation aids in reducing the formation of oxides of nitrogen, an air pollutant now under stringent new car emission standards.*

EVAPORATIVE EMISSION CONTROL SYSTEM

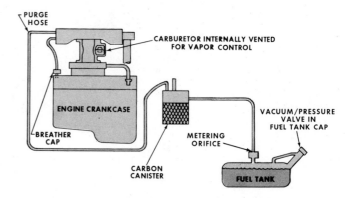

Fig. 29-20. *Schematic depicts elements of Ford's Evaporative Emission Control system. Charcoal canister stores vapors until they are recycled to combustion chambers.*

Quiz - Exhaust Emission Control

1. What is the purpose of the pressure control valve placed between the valve cover and the manifold in the crankcase ventilating system?
   a. Provide extra air for idling.
   b. Prevent excess airflow during idling.
2. The Chrysler Cleaner Air Package injects air into the exhaust manifold. True or False?
3. Retarding the spark at idle increases the emission of hydrocarbons. True or False?
4. On cars equipped with automatic transmissions, it is more difficult to control the emission of exhaust gases. True or False?
5. The amount of unburned hydrocarbons is proportional to combustion chamber surface area. True or False?
6. In the new Autolite distributor, how many diaphragms are provided to control the spark?
   a. One.   b. Two.   c. Three.
7. Is additional equipment needed in the Ford Thermactor Emission System? Yes or No?
8. Is heated air provided in the GM Controlled Combustion System? Yes or No?

FUNDAMENTALS OF ELECTRICITY, MAGNETISM

Electricity plays a vital role in the operation of modern automotive vehicles. Car manufacturers switched from 6-volt to 12-volt systems in 1955 and 1956 to cope with the growing number of electrical systems and components. And, more recently, there has been experimentation with 24-volt systems for possible use in passenger cars to meet increased electrical demands.

These demands include: starting, lighting and ignition systems; horns, turn signals and emergency 4-way flashers; control circuits for automatic transmissions and overdrive units; windshield wipers and washers; fuel gauge, cigarette lighters and multiple instrument panel convenience and warning lamps; radio, heater, clock and many other electrically operated accessories such as power windows, power seats, speed control unit and stereo tape player.

It follows logically that anyone who expects to successfully maintain, repair and trouble shoot today's vehicles must have a thorough knowledge of the fundamentals of electricity.

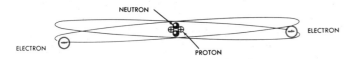

Fig. 30-1. Electrons rotate about central core of atoms, much as earth and other planets rotate about sun.

Static Electricity

The ancient Greeks had a word for it: "Electric" is derived from a Greek word meaning amber, because they found that by rubbing a piece of amber with a piece of silk, bits of paper, straw and dry leaves were attracted to it. Later experiments showed that the same effect can be produced by rubbing a rod of glass or hard rubber with a handkerchief. In fact, many other nonmetallic materials are found to have this property called static electricity.

For example, if a rod of hard rubber is rubbed with a piece of fur and then held close to a pith ball suspended on a thread, the pith ball will be attracted

to the rod. But if allowed to touch it, the ball will spring away. Then if a glass rod, rubbed with a piece of silk is held close to the same pith ball, it will attract the ball, but after contact is made it too will be repelled.

Attraction And Repulsion

Further experiments show that all electrified materials behave either as glass or rubber. Glass is said to have a POSITIVE charge and hard rubber a NEGATIVE charge. It was also discovered that two strips of hard rubber electrified by rubbing with fur would repel each other. Two glass rods behaved in a similar manner. However, when an electrified rod of rubber was suspended near an electrified rod of glass, they would attract each other.

From that simple experiment came one of the most important laws of electricity: Similarly charged bodies repel each other, while oppositely charged bodies attract each other. This law also applies to magnets, which will be covered later.

Electron Theory Of Electricity

In spite of the fact that people have experimented with and controlled the use of electricity for scores of years, no one can explain just what electricity is. During that time, many different theories have been advanced as to the nature of electricity. Today, the electron theory is generally accepted.

In essence, it proposes that all matter (the earth, rocks, minerals, chemicals, elements, etc.) consists of tiny particles called molecules. These molecules, in turn are made of two or more smaller particles called atoms. These atoms are further divided into even smaller particles which are called protons, neutrons and electrons.

These particles (protons, neutrons and electrons) are the same in all matter, regardless of whether it is a gas, a liquid or a solid. The different properties or characteristics of the matter result from the arrangement and number of protons, neutrons and electrons which form the atoms of which matter consists.

The proton has a natural positive charge of electricity. The electron has a negative charge, while the neutron has no charge at all but adds weight to the matter.

Central Core Of Atom

Protons and neutrons form the central core of the atoms about which the electrons rotate, Fig. 30-1. Electrons carry small negative charges of electricity which neutralize the positive charges of the protons.

The simplest atom of all is the hydrogen atom, which consists of one positively charged proton and one negatively charged electron, Fig. 30-2. Other atoms, such as those forming copper, iron or silicon, are much more complicated. Copper, for example, has 29 electrons circling about its nucleus in four different orbits. See Fig. 30-3.

Size Of Atom

It is difficult to conceive the size of the atom. The mass of the electron is about .000,000,000,000,000, 000,000,000,000,911 of a gram. Assuming the size of a proton in an hydrogen atom is the size of a baseball and located in Kansas City, then the orbit of the electron would reach from the Atlantic coast to the Pacific.

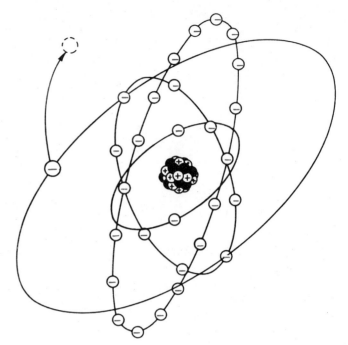

Fig. 30-3. Copper atom consists of 29 electrons circling about its nucleus of neutrons and protons in 4 different orbits.

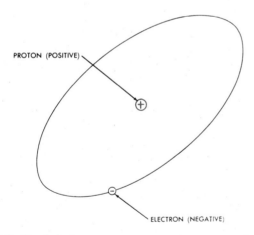

Fig. 30-2. Simple hydrogen atom consists of one positively charged proton and one negatively charged electron.

So, along with the extremely small size of the electrons and protons, they are separated by relatively vast distances. An appreciation of this distance between the proton and electron is necessary to understand the flow of electricity.

Insulators

In most elements, the nucleus is composed of protons and neutrons which are surrounded by closely held electrons which never leave the atom. These are

called bound electrons. When this type of electron predominates in an element or compounded material, the material is an insulator or a nonconductor of electricity.

Conductors

In other types of material the nucleus is surrounded by another group of electrons which can be made to move from one atom to the other when electricity is applied, Fig. 30-3. Electrons of this type are known as free electrons and the materials are called conductors of electricity.

Speed Of Electricity

The speed of electricity is 186,000 miles per second. However, that does not mean that the electrons travel from one end of the circuit to the other at that speed. Actually, the forward movement of the electrons is no more than a drift. Free electrons, available as the result of overlapping electron orbits in conducting materials, are pulled from one atom to another, and temporarily rotate about each new center.

Electron Drift

The rate at which the free electrons drift from atom to atom determines the amount of current flow. In order to create a drift of electrons through a circuit, it is necessary to have an electrical pressure, which is called voltage.

In other words, electric current is a flow of electrons, and the more electrons in motion, the stronger the current. The greater the concentration of electrons at a battery or generator terminal, the higher the pressure between the electrons. The greater this pressure is, the greater the flow of electrons.

Volts -- Amperes --- Ohms

The pressure between the electrons is measured in volts, while the flow of electrons (current) is measured in amperes.

Opposing the flow of electrons is the resistance of the conductors, which is measured in ohms. Some materials offer greater resistance than others: iron more than copper; copper more than silver. The length of the connecting wiring also contributes to the amount of resistance in a circuit. And, finally, the size of the wiring is also a resistance factor since a conductor of small diameter will offer greater resistance to the flow of electrons than will a conductor of large diameter.

Ohm's Law

There is a definite relation between the voltage, the resistance and the current flowing in an electrical circuit. This relationship is known as Ohm's Law which states that the voltage impressed on a circuit is equal to the product of the current in amperes and the resistance in ohms. When given in a mathematical formula it is written:

$$E = IR$$

where E is the voltage, I the current in amperes and R the resistance in ohms. Transposing the factors of this equation, it may also be written:

$$R = \frac{E}{I} \text{ or}$$

$$I = \frac{E}{R}$$

Ohm's Law is used extensively in checking and troubleshooting electrical circuits and parts in automobiles. For example: the current flowing through the field coils of a 12V generator is 1.5 amperes. What is the resistance of the coils? Answer: 8 ohms.

Studying Ohm's Law reveals that if the resistance of a circuit increases, while the voltage remains constant, the current will decrease. For example, if the connections at a starting battery are loose or corroded, a high resistance will be caused. The result will be that there will be insufficient current reaching the starting motor, lights or other units to provide proper operation.

Types Of Circuits

There are three general types of electrical circuits: series, Fig. 30-4; parallel, Fig. 30-5; and a combination of the two, which is known as series-parallel, Fig. 30-6. All circuits, regardless of type,

consist of a source of electricity (a generator or a battery), various pieces of electrical equipment or devices, and the necessary electrical conductors which connect the equipment or devices to the source of electrical power.

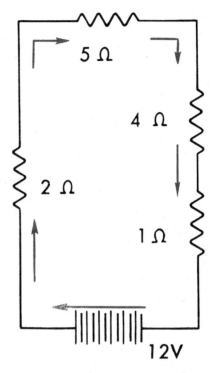

Fig. 30-4. In a series circuit, total resistance is sum of individual resistances shown by Greek letter Omega.

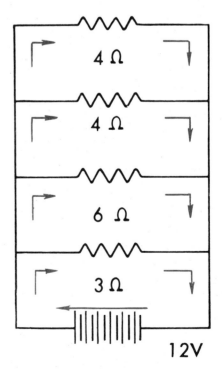

Fig. 30-5. Note how current divides through different branches of this parallel circuit.

317

In a series circuit, Fig. 30-4, the current passes from the generator or battery to each of the devices in turn, and then to the other terminal of the generator. In that way, the current has only one path to flow. The amount of current will be the same in all parts of the circuit.

In parallel electrical circuits, Fig. 30-5, there will be more than one path for the current to flow. In such circuits one terminal of each device is connected to a common conductor leading to one terminal of the battery or generator, and the remaining terminals of each device are connected to another common conductor, which in turn is connected to the other terminal of the source of electrical power.

The series-parallel circuits, Fig. 30-6, are those which have some electrical devices connected in series and others in parallel.

To find the total resistance of the series circuit, all that is necessary is to add the resistance of each device. In Fig. 30-4, the total resistance would be 12 ohms. The current flowing would then be found by applying Ohm's Law. In this case the current would be 12 volts divided by 12 ohms, which equals 1 ampere.

In parallel electrical circuits, there are several paths for the current to take, and consequently the total resistance of all the devices will be less than the resistance of any single device. To find the total resistance of a parallel circuit, the following formula is used:

$$R = \frac{1}{\frac{1}{R_1} + \frac{1}{R_2} + \frac{1}{R_3} + \frac{1}{R_4}} \text{ etc.}$$

Using the values shown in Fig. 30-5 and substituting in the above formula we have:

$$R = \frac{1}{\frac{1}{4} + \frac{1}{4} + \frac{1}{6} + \frac{1}{3}}$$

$$R = \quad 1 \text{ ohm}$$

The total current flowing through the circuit will be 12 divided by 1, or 12 amperes. The current flowing through any single branch of a parallel circuit is found by dividing the voltage by the resistance of that particular branch. In Fig. 30-5, the current flowing in each branch would be 3,3,2 and 4 amperes. Adding these gives 12 amperes, which checks with the value found for the total circuit.

To make the calculations for a series-parallel circuit, the procedure is to treat each portion separately. Then having calculated the resistance of each parallel portion, those resistances are then added as would be the case in a simple series circuit.

In Fig. 30-6, the resistance of the upper parallel circuit becomes 3 ohms, the parallel circuit on the left of the diagram is 6 ohms. Adding these values to

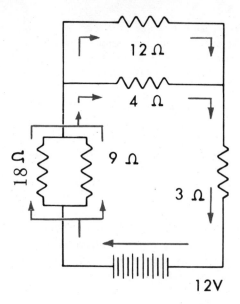

Fig. 30-6. A series-parallel circuit has some electrical devices connected in series, others in parallel.

3 ohms of the series circuit on the right side of the diagram makes a total of 12 ohms. Which incidentally is the same as the total resistance of the series circuit shown in Fig. 30-4.

Voltage Drop

The decrease in voltage as current passes through a resistance is known as the voltage drop, and the sum of the individual drops in voltage is equal to the total voltage impressed on the circuit. Ohm's Law is used to calculate the voltage drop in different parts of a circuit. In Fig. 30-4, as was previously pointed out, there is 1 ampere of current flowing. And as the

MAGNETIC FIELDS

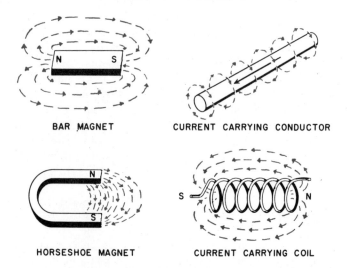

Fig. 30-7. Note that lines of force leave magnet or loop of wire at north pole, reenter at south pole.

voltage drop is equal to E = IR, the voltage drop across each of the resistances would be 1 x 2 = 2, 1 x 5 = 5, 1 x 4 = 4 and 1 x 1 = 1. Adding these drops in voltage we have 2 + 5 + 4 + 1 = 12 volts, which checks with the voltage impressed in the circuit.

Electrical Work And Power

The electrical unit for measuring work is called the joule. One joule is equal to one ampere flowing for one second under the pressure of one volt.

To clarify this, it is necessary to understand that work is done when energy is expended, and is calculated as the product of the force and the distance through which it acts in overcoming resistance. Power is the rate of doing work.

An electrical force may exist without work being done and is the condition which exists between the terminals of a battery when no equipment is connected to the terminals of the battery, current will flow and work will be done.

Power is the rate at which work is done, or:

$$\text{Power} = \frac{\text{work}}{\text{time}}$$

$$\text{Electrical power} = \frac{\text{electrical work}}{\text{time}}$$

The watt is the electrical unit of power and is equal to one joule of electrical work per second. Then:

$$\text{Watt} = \frac{\text{Joules}}{\text{Seconds}} = \frac{\text{Volts x Amperes x Seconds}}{\text{Seconds}}$$

Therefore: Watts = Volts x Amperes

For example: If in an automotive lighting circuit, the current is 36 amperes and the voltage is 12, then the number of watts is 36 x 12 = 432 watts.

The unit for measuring mechanical power is the horsepower and experimentally it has been found that one horsepower is equal to 746 watts.

Magnetism

Magnetism, like electricity, is still a mystery. We know many laws governing its behavior and have applied it in the automotive field to starting motors, electric generators, ignition coils, voltage and current regulators, etc. However, no one knows just what magnetism is.

The effects of magnetism were first discovered when it was found that pieces of iron ore from certain parts of the world would attract each other and also other pieces of iron. In addition it was found that fragments of this ore when suspended in air would always point toward the North Star. The end of the piece of ore that pointed toward the north was called the "north pole" and the other end the "south pole."

The space surrounding a magnet and in which its effect can be noted, is known as its magnetic field, Fig. 30-7. This field is strongest close to the magnet, and gets progressively weaker as the distance from the magnet is increased.

The area or extent of the magnetic field can be determined by means of a compass, which will also show the direction of the lines of force. In Fig. 30-7 note how the lines of force leave the north pole of the magnets (and the coil) and re-enter at the south pole. Also note on the horseshoe magnet how the lines of force are more concentrated and stronger in the area immediately between the two poles of the magnet.

Theory Of Permanent Magnets

While the effects, direction and extent of magnetic fields are easily studied, there is no actual knowledge as to why certain materials have magnetic properties and others do not. However the electron theory is generally accepted as giving the best explanation.

As previously explained in the unit on Fundamentals of Electricity, an electron carries a charge of negative electricity and is constantly moving in an orbit about the proton. It is therefore assumed that a known charge of electricity moving in an orbit is the same as a current of electricity flowing through the conductor. Thus, an electron moving in a fixed circular orbit creates a magnetic field, Fig. 30-8, which has a north pole on one side of the orbit and a south pole on the other. It is believed that more substances do not show magnetic properties because the orbits of the various electrons are so arranged that the magnetic fields cancel each other.

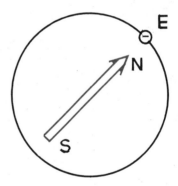

Fig. 30-8. An electron moving in a fixed circular orbit, creates a magnetic field.

In iron, cobalt and nickel (which are magnetic substances) the electron orbits align themselves in parallel planes, and in the same direction when placed in a magnetic field, as shown in Fig. 30-9. This arrangement of the electron-created magnets produces a strong magnetic effect.

It is also interesting to note that soft iron will lose virtually all of its magnetic effect as soon as it is removed from the magnetic field. Hard steel will retain its magnetic characteristics for a long and indefinite period. Special alloys of tungsten, chromium and cobalt produce magnetic fields of considerably greater strength than other materials, and will also retain their magnetism for a longer period. Such alloys are used to form the magnets used in ignition magnetos and other specialized electrical equipment, where a strong magnetic field is required. Magnetic lines of force seem to penetrate all substances, and are deflected only by magnetic materials, or by another magnetic field. There is no insulator for magnetism or lines of force.

Another interesting property of magnets is that when a magnet is cut in two, the individual pieces of the magnet will each have north and south poles, as shown in Fig. 30-9.

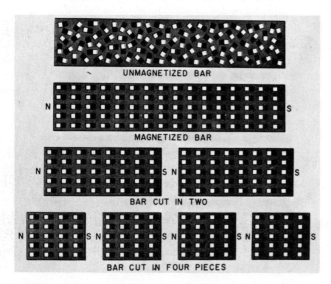

Fig. 30-9. In magnetic substances, electron orbits align themselves in parallel planes and in same direction when placed in a magnetic field.

Attraction And Repulsion

When two permanent magnets are so placed that the north pole of one is close to the south pole of another magnet, they are found to attract each other. Also if the magnets are placed with similar poles close together, they are found to repel each other, as shown in Fig. 30-10. This attraction and repulsion of magnets is of great importance, and forms a fundamental law of magnetism, namely: Like poles of magnets repel each other, and unlike poles attract each other.

Producing Magnets, Magnetic Fields

By stroking a piece of hardened steel with a natural magnet, it will be found that the piece of steel will soon become a magnet. Steel railroad tracks laid in a north-to-south direction are found to be magnetized as the result of lying parallel to the magnetic field of the earth.

However, much stronger magnets and magnetic fields can be produced by electrical means. Placing a piece of steel in any strong magnetic field will cause it to become magnetized.

A magnetic field surrounds any conductor carrying an electrical current. The discovery of that fact resulted in the development of much of our electrical equipment. Such a field of force is always at right angles to the conductor, as can be shown by placing a magnetic compass close to a conductor of electricity. This is illustrated in Fig. 30-11. Since a magnetic force is the only force known to attract a compass needle, it is obvious that a flow of electric current produces a magnetic field similar to that produced by a permanent magnet. When making this experiment, direct current should be passed through the conductor. Alternating current should not be used as the magnetic field will change with each alteration of the current.

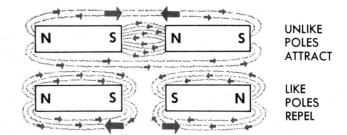

Fig. 30-10. Lines of force leaving north pole of one magnet, will enter south pole of an adjacent magnet since all lines are in same direction. Lines leaving similar poles are repelled as they have opposite direction.

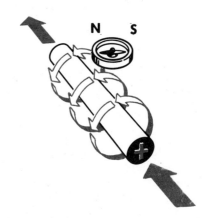

Fig. 30-11. A magnetic field surrounds any conductor carrying an electrical current, and field is at right angles to conductor.

Not only is the field of force at right angles to the conductor, but the field of force also forms concentric circles about the conductor, as shown in Fig. 30-12. Also, as the current in the conductor is increased, the field of force is increased. Doubling the current will double the strength of the field of force.

Left Hand Rule

It is important to know the direction of the lines of force that surround a conductor. The direction of the lines of force is dependent on the direction the current is traveling in the conductor. To determine

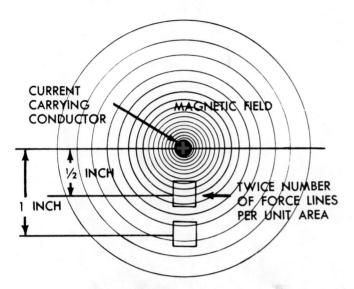

Fig. 30-12. A magnetic field forms concentric circles around a conductor carrying an electric current.

the direction of the lines of force, grasp the conductor with the left hand, and with the thumb extended in the direction the current is flowing. The fingers will then indicate the direction in which the lines of force

Fig. 30-13. Fingers of left hand around conductor show direction of lines of force and extended thumb shows direction of current in conductor.

surround the conductor, Fig. 30-13. The same rule can be used to determine the direction the current is flowing, after having first determined the direction of the magnetic field by means of a compass.

Strengthening The Field

As pointed out previously, the magnetic field surrounds the conductor which is carrying an electric current. If this conductor is formed into a loop, Fig. 30-14, the lines of force on the outside of the loop spread out into space, but the lines of force on the inside of the loop are confined and crowded together, thereby increasing the density of the lines of force in that area. As a result of this crowding together of the lines of force, a much greater magnetic effect is produced with the same amount of current flowing.

One side of the loop will be a north pole, and the other side will be a south pole. By increasing the number of loops, the magnetic field will be greatly increased. This will be discussed in greater detail later. By winding the loops or coils on a core of soft iron, the field is still further intensified.

MAGNETIC FIELD AROUND A LOOP

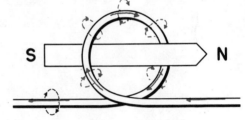

MAGNETIC FIELD AROUND A COIL

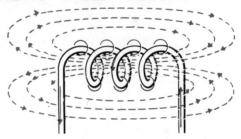

Fig. 30-14. Illustrating magnetic field surrounding a single loop carrying current, and field surrounding a coil of wire.

Combining Magnetic Fields

It is important to know the result when two magnetic fields are brought together. In Fig. 30-7 and Fig. 30-10, the fields of horseshoe magnets and the fields resulting from similar and from unlike poles were shown. The resultant magnetic fields surrounding adjacent conductors are also of interest.

The current flowing in opposite directions in two adjacent and parallel conductors is a typical condition, Fig. 30-15. In these illustrations, the + mark on the end of the conductor indicates that the current is moving away from the reader, and the • in the end of the conductor indicates that the current is coming toward the reader.

Chevrolet's 307 cu. in. V-8 features a carburetor hot air system. In operation, heat from exhaust manifold is ducted to air cleaner snorkel. Thermostat, control valve and damper blend hot and cold air entering carburetor for better air-fuel vaporization.

A field of force will surround each conductor, and the direction of the field can be quickly determined by applying the left hand rule. As shown in B, Fig. 30-15, the field will be clockwise around one conductor and counterclockwise around the other. However, the area between the conductors, the lines of force are moving in the same direction.

As the amount of current is the same in both conductors, the total number of lines between the conductors is the same as the total number of lines

MAGNETIC EFFECT OF PARALLEL CONDUCTORS

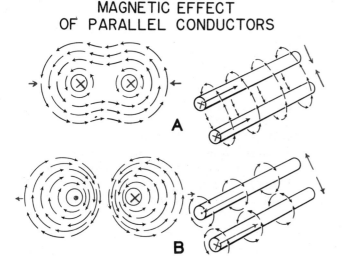

Fig. 30-15. With current flowing in same direction in two conductors (A), resultant magnetic field tends to draw conductors together. If current is flowing in opposite direction (B), magnetic field will force conductors apart.

outside the conductors. As the distance between the conductors is very little and limited, the lines of force will be very much crowded in that area. In other words, the density of the magnetic field will be greater between the conductors than it will be beyond the conductors. This condition is known as a case of unbalanced density, which will cause forces to act on the conductors.

When current is moving in opposite directions in the two parallel conductors, the unbalanced density will tend to force the conductors apart. If the current is moving in the same direction in the two parallel conductors, the unbalanced density will tend to draw the conductors closer together. These conditions are shown in Fig. 30-15.

As was illustrated in A, Fig. 30-15, two parallel conductors carrying current in the same direction will tend to move closer together. In such a condition, the two conductors are acting basically like a single conductor, carrying a current equal to the sum of the two currents. As a result, twice the number of lines of force are created, as would be produced by either conductor with its original current. When several more current-carrying conductors are placed side by side,

Fig. 30-16. When several current-carrying conductors are placed side by side, magnetic lines of force join and surround all conductors.

the effect as shown in Fig. 30-16, is produced. Here the lines of force join and surround all of the conductors. Such a magnetic pattern is obtained in a section of a generator field coil, a starter solenoid or an ignition coil.

The strength of the magnetic field surrounding a coil of wire is in direct proportion to the number of turns of wire in the coil, and the strength of the current. The product of the amperes flowing times the number of turns of wire, is a means of calculating the magnetizing force created, and is known as the ampere-turns.

Determining Polarity

To determine the magnetic polarity of any coil or electromagnet when the direction of current flow is known, the left hand rule for coils may be used. To apply this rule, grasp the coil with the left hand so that the fingers extend in the direction the coil is wound and in the direction of current flow, Fig. 30-17. The thumb will then point toward the north pole created by the current flow through the coil. It must be remembered that both the direction of current flow, and the direction of coil winding, will determine the polarity of a coil. This is particularly important when connecting field coils of a generator together.

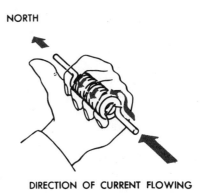

NORTH

DIRECTION OF CURRENT FLOWING

Fig. 30-17. Left-hand rule for coils may be used to determine polarity of a current-carrying coil.

Magnetic Conductivity

The conductivity of air for lines of force has been adopted as standard, and air is rated as having a permeability of one. Permeability of a substance is defined by Kelvin as "the ease with which lines of force may be established in any medium as compared with a vacuum." Briefly, it is the magnetic conductivity of a substance.

When a soft iron core is inserted in a coil to form a true electromagnet, Fig. 30-18, the magnetic flux or lines of force will be increased several hundred times. By means of the better conductor for the lines of force (the use of the iron core) more lines of force are created.

The field coils in generators and starters, regulator windings on iron cores and ignition coils all use this same principle.

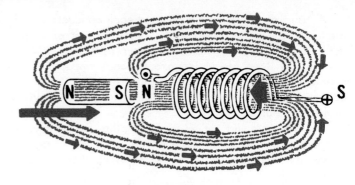

Fig. 30-19. A solenoid usually consists of a tubular coil of wire and an iron core which is free to move into coil when current is applied.

Solenoids

A solenoid is a tubular coil of wire with an air core, and is designed to produce a magnetic field. In most cases the solenoid also includes an iron core that is free to move in and out of the tubular coil, Fig. 30-19. Movement of the iron core is then used to operate some mechanism or switch. In the automotive field, it is usually used to shift a starting motor drive into engagement with the flywheel ring gear. When a solenoid is used to close the contacts of an electrical switch, it is called a magnetic switch.

In Fig. 30-19, it will be noted that the south pole of the iron core is adjacent to the north pole of the coil. The polarity of the movable iron core is induced by the lines of force from the coil. Because the adjacent poles of the coil and the core are of opposite polarity, there is an attraction which draws the movable core into the center of the coil whenever current flows.

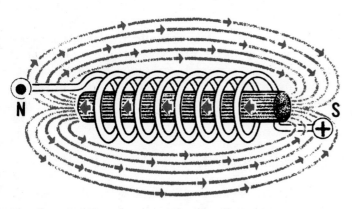

Fig. 30-18. Magnetic field of a coil can be strengthened by winding coil on a core of soft iron to form an electromagnet.

Quiz - Electricity, Magnetism

1. How will an electrified piece of rubber react when placed close to an electrified piece of glass?
   a. Attract.
   b. Repel.
2. How do similarly charged electrified bodies react to each other?
   a. Attract.
   b. Repel.
3. What tiny particles form an atom?
4. Electrons have what type of electrical charge?
   a. Positive.
   b. Negative.
5. The nucleus of an element consists of:
   a. Protons and neutrons.
   b. Atoms and electrons.
   c. Neutrons and electrons.
6. Electrons in a conductor are:
   a. Bound.
   b. Free.
7. State Ohm's Law.
8. What is the total resistance in a series circuit having four individual resistances of four ohms, ten ohms, five ohms and two ohms?
9. Write the formula for determining the total resistance of a number of resistances in a parallel circuit.
10. If in an automotive circuit there is a current of 6 amperes and the voltage is 12, how many watts are there?
11. How many watts are there in one electrical horsepower?
    a. 764.   c. 746.
    b. 464.   d. 674.
12. What is the name of the area surrounding a magnet?
13. Which of the following are magnetic substances?
    a. Iron.   c. Nickel.
    b. Brass.   d. Lead.
14. The magnetic field of force surrounding an electrical conductor is in what direction?
    a. Parallel to the conductor.
    b. At right angles to the conductor.

15. When you place the fingers of your left hand around a current-carrying conductor, with extended thumb showing direction of current, what does direction of the fingers indicate?

16. If you insert an iron core in a coil of wire carrying current, will the field be:
    a. Strengthened.
    b. Weakened.

17. Will the magnetic force tend to separate two parallel conductors carrying current in the same direction, or tend to pull them together?
    a. Separate.
    b. Attract.

18. How much will the field be strengthened if you insert a magnetic core in a coil of wire carrying current?
    a. Twice.
    b. Reduce it.
    c. Several hundred times.
    d. Fifty times.

19. When using the left-hand rule as applied to a current-carrying coil, what does the direction of the thumb indicate?
    a. The direction of the current.
    b. North pole.   c. South pole.

20. Where is a solenoid used in a modern automobile?

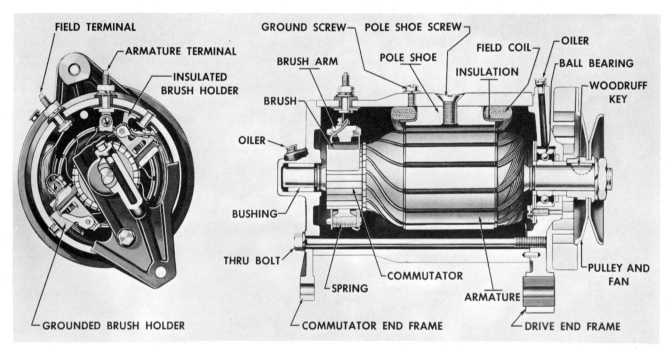

Fig. 31-1. Cutaway view shows major parts of direct current shunt wound generator.

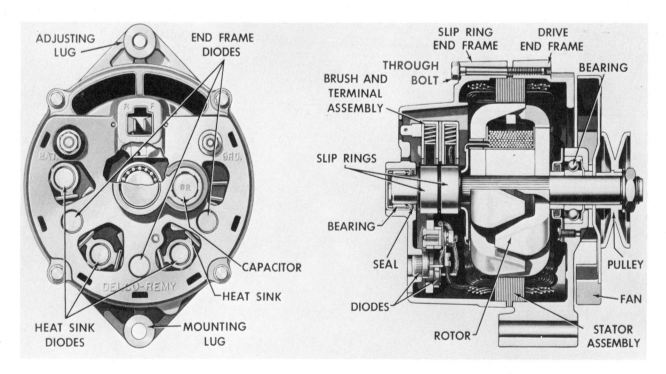

Fig. 31-2. This Delco-Remy AC generator (alternator) is typical of those used on General Motors cars.

ELECTRIC GENERATORS
AND ALTERNATORS

An automotive generator of electricity, Figs. 31-1 and 31-2, is a machine that converts mechanical energy supplied by the engine into electrical energy used to maintain the storage battery in a fully charged condition, and to supply electrical power for the ignition system and accessory equipment.

strated by connecting the ends of a loop of wire to a sensitive electrical measuring instrument and moving the loop through a magnetic field.

Actually, a voltage can be produced either by moving the coil of wire through a stationary field, or by keeping the coil stationary and moving the magnetic

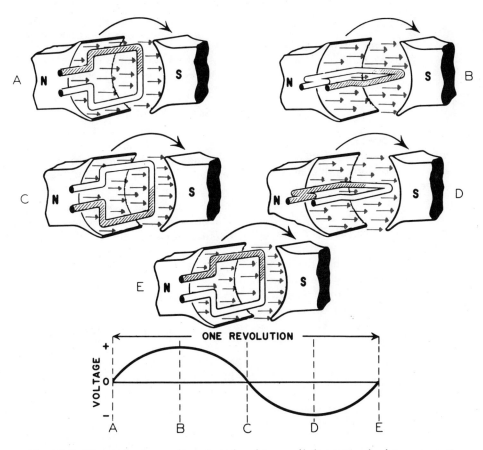

Fig. 31-3. Illustrating how voltage is induced in a coil that is revolved in a magnetic field. Curve at bottom shows variation of voltage for each position of revolving coil.

Electromagnetic Induction

The operation of automotive electric generators is based on the principle that when a coil of wire is moved through a magnetic field, a voltage will be induced or generated in the coil. This can be demonduced through a magnetic field, a voltage will be induced or generated in the coil. This can be demon-

field. In general, then, voltage is induced in a coil whenever there is a change in the lines of force passing through the coil.

The lines of force being cut by a rotating coil are shown in Fig. 31-3. When the coil is in a vertical position as shown at A, Fig. 31-3, the lines of force surrounding the conductor are balanced; that is, for that instant, no lines of force are being cut. Therefore, no voltage will be induced in the coil. As the coil approaches position B, Fig. 31-3, an increasing number of lines of force will be cut and the generated voltage will increase until it reaches a maximum at position B. After passing position B, the voltage will start to decrease as fewer lines of force are being cut, and will become zero when position C is reached. As rotation is continued, another maximum will be reached at position D. However, the lines of force are now being cut in the opposite direction to that of position B, so the current generated will flow in the opposite direction. Since the current keeps changing its direction as the loop of wire is rotated, it is called an alternating current. The variations in the value and direction of the generated voltage are shown in the lower portion of Fig. 31-3.

To make use of the electrical energy that is being generated, each end of the coil is connected to a ring which rotates with the coil of wire. Contact with these rotating rings is made by brushes which bear against the rings as shown in Fig. 31-4. Note the direction of the generated voltage as shown by the voltmeter connected to the brushes and also the curve at C, Fig. 31-4.

Alternating Current

All automotive generators produce alternating current (AC) which, in turn, must be rectified or converted to direct current (DC) to satisfy the needs of the storage battery and the various DC electrical systems and accessories.

In an alternating current generator, or alternator as it is more commonly called, Fig. 31-2, the magnetic field is rotated and voltage is generated in the stationary coils. Rectifiers are built into the alternator to limit current flow to one direction only and thereby provide direct current at the output terminal.

Alternators and matched voltage regulators are used on all late model passenger car engines. Advantages of this type of charging system will be covered later.

Direct Current Generator

A direct current generator operates basically in the same manner as an alternator in that it produces alternating current. However, the DC generator works on the principle that voltage is generated in a coil, or coils, of wire (armature) as it is rotated in a stationary magnetic field. And, instead of using a rectifier to convert the AC to DC, a mechanical switch (brushes and commutator) is provided.

The commutator is a segmented portion of the armature which, in turn, is composed of many coils, each connected to a bar or segment of the commutator, Fig. 31-5. The field poles are secured to the frame

with heavy screws, and the armature is carried in bearings mounted in the end plates. Commutator brush holders vary among reaction, swivel and box types. Long bolts are used to hold the end plates securely against the main frame.

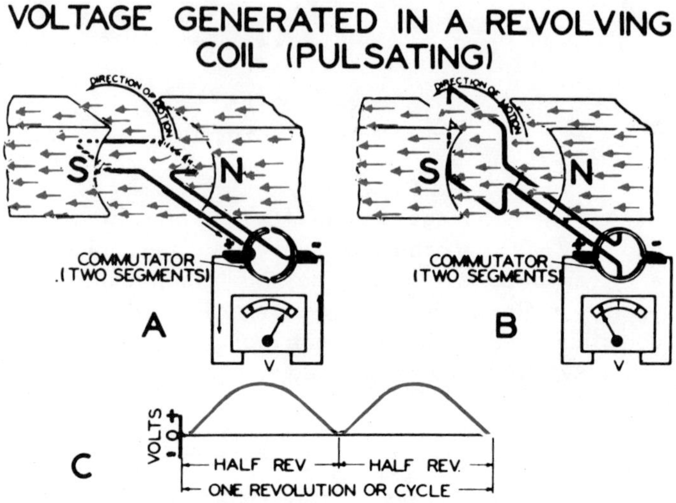

VOLTAGE GENERATED IN A REVOLVING COIL (PULSATING)

Fig. 31-4. By use of a commutator, induced voltage always flows in same direction, although it pulsates in a single-coil setup like this.

Some armatures are supported by two ball bearings, while others use a ball bearing at the drive end and a plain bushing at the other end. Both types of bearings are provided with hinge-cap oilers for lubrication, although many DC generators are fitted with oilless plain bushings and ball bearings of the type which require no lubrication.

Most generators incorporate a cooling fan, which usually forms part of the driving pulley. On some generators, the field frame is engineered with openings so the brushes and commutator can be inspected.

Operating Principles

To illustrate the operating principles of DC generators, Fig. 31-4 shows a simple armature with a single coil revolving in the magnetic field. Since there is only a single coil in the armature, there are only two segments in the commutator which rotates with

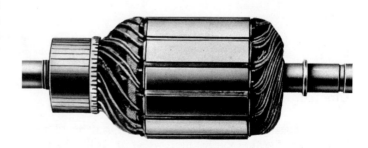

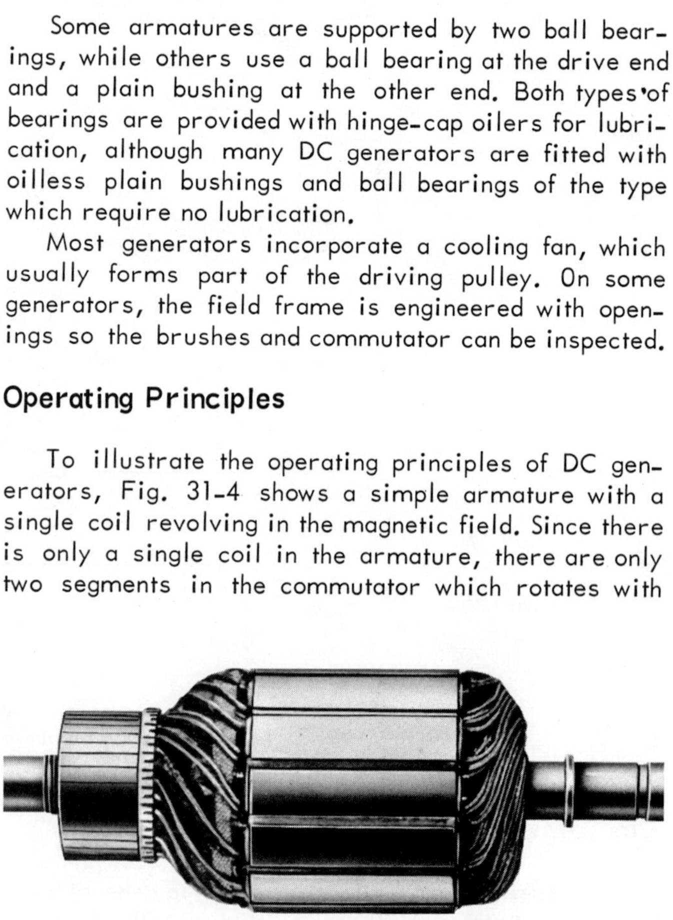

Fig. 31-5. Generator armature is provided with many coils, and commutator bars or segments are connected to ends of each coil.

the coil. Each segment of the commutator is insulated from the other, and an end of the rotating coil is connected to each segment.

As the commutator revolves with the armature coil, first one segment of the commutator is connected to the right-hand brush, then the other. The result is that one brush will always be positive and the other negative.

To describe this action in greater detail, as the armature coil approaches the position shown at A, Fig. 31-4, the voltage generated will approach a maximum, and the current will be leaving the right-hand brush as shown, pass through the external circuit and return by way of the left-hand brush. As the armature coil reaches the position shown at B, Fig. 31-4, the voltage will be zero. However, the rotating coil, with its commutator bar, is again about to cut through the magnetic field in the same direction as it did 180 deg. previously. The result is that current will again flow from the right-hand brush.

The commutator changes the alternating current generated within the armature to direct current as it leaves the brushes. While the current will always flow in the same direction, it will rise and fall in value. This is shown at C, Fig. 31-4, and is known as a pulsating current, resulting from the fact that the voltage will be maximum when the armature coil passes through a magnetic field of maximum density, and drops to zero where the field is at zero density.

The strength of the voltage induced in the rotating coil is proportionate to the strength of the magnetic field, the speed with which the conductor or coil is moved through the field, and the number of turns of wire used to form the coil. Therefore, in order to increase the voltage induced in the coil, the magnetic field is strengthened, the number of turns of wire in the coil is increased, and the speed of rotation of the coil is increased.

Also, in order to eliminate the two peaks of current per revolution, Fig. 31-4, as is obtained with a single coil armature, generator armatures are wound with many coils, each coil being connected to its individual commutator bar, Fig. 31-5.

As a result of using many coils to form the armature, the number of peaks of voltage will be equal to the number of coils used, as shown by the graph of the generated voltage, Fig. 31-6.

In addition to increasing the number of turns of wire in the armature, the generated voltage can be increased by using electromagnets to form the field instead of permanent magnets as were used in Fig. 31-4. In addition, the number of field poles can also be increased.

These coils may be connected in series, parallel (shunt) or series-parallel with the armature. Most automotive passenger car generators are of the shunt type, Fig. 31-7, while the once-popular third-brush generator is now used mainly in tractor applications.

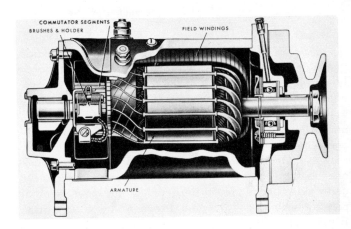

Fig. 31-7. This direct current "B" circuit generator is typical of those used on Ford cars before 1963.

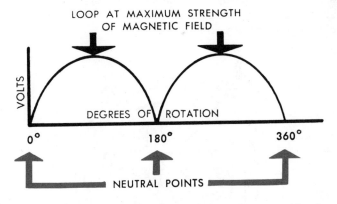

Fig. 31-8. In armature wound for 2-pole generator, neutral points are located midway between poles.

Armature Reaction

Also important in the design and servicing of generators and motors is armature reaction. This is the effect of the magnetic field created by the current-carrying conductor of the armature upon the magnetic field created by the field coils.

In Fig. 31-4, it was shown that in a generator with two field poles, no voltage was induced in the rotating coil when it was in the vertical position. This region is known as the commutating zone and lies at the neutral point, Fig. 31-8.

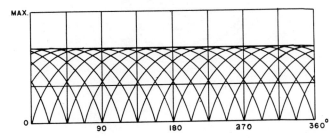

Fig. 31-6. By using many coils in armature, and a commutator, a constant, direct voltage is produced.

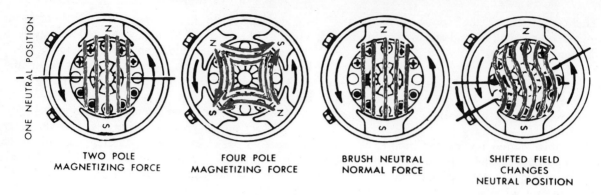

TWO POLE
MAGNETIZING FORCE

FOUR POLE
MAGNETIZING FORCE

BRUSH NEUTRAL
NORMAL FORCE

SHIFTED FIELD
CHANGES
NEUTRAL POSITION

ONE NEUTRAL POSITION

Fig. 31-9. Illustrating neutral position for different types of generators, and effect of shifted field.

In an armature wound for a two-pole generator there are two neutral points, one located approximately midway between each of the two poles. All the armature conductors on one side of the neutral point have voltage generated in the same direction, Fig. 31-9, and all the conductors on the opposite side have voltage generated in the opposite direction.

Generators with more than two field poles have one neutral point for each field pole. Many automotive generators have four field poles and four neutral points, which are located between the field poles, Fig. 31-9.

However, the magnetic field set up by the armature will react on and distort the magnetic field set up by the field coils. As a result the neutral point will not be midway between the pole pieces, but will be shifted, and the direction of the shift will be in the direction of armature rotation.

Fig. 31-11. Simulating magnetic field formed after combining fields of armature and field coils of generator.

The field resulting from the combination of the armature field and that produced by the field coils is shown in Fig. 31-11.

With a change in the field and a consequent shift of the neutral position, a new location of the brushes

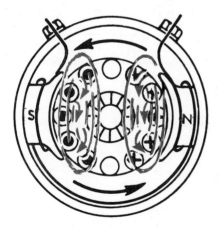

Fig. 31-10. Showing magnetic field surrounding coils of armature when current flows through coils.

In Fig. 31-10, the magnetizing force from the armature is shown. It must be remembered that all the current flowing through the external circuit passes through the armature, and this may range from a fraction of an ampere to maximum. As a result, the magnetic field surrounding the armature will also vary in intensity.

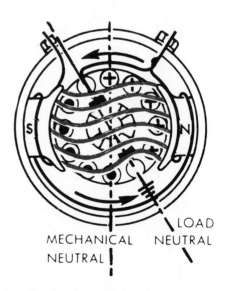

MECHANICAL
NEUTRAL

LOAD
NEUTRAL

Fig. 31-12. Now brushes have been shifted to load neutral position to avoid high current being short-circuited between brush and commutator bars.

becomes necessary. Otherwise, the armature coil being commutated would be generating voltage, and a high current would be short circuited between the commutator bars and the brush. This would cause a heavy arc to form, which would cause burning and rapid wear of the brush and commutator.

Fig. 31-12 shows the brushes shifted to the load neutral. Note that this new position is in the direction of armature rotation.

At a constant speed and load there is an ideal location for the brushes so that there will be no arcing. However, as generator speed and load vary over a wide range, the ideal commutating point (and consequently the brush location) will vary also. For that reason, generator designers select a brush position which will give the minimum arcing for average operating conditions.

Shunt Wound Generators

One of the difficulties of DC generator operation is that at low speeds output is limited. This is a serious difficulty because the starting battery would not receive a charge at idling and low speed operation. In addition, there would be insufficient current for the operation of other electrical equipment. That is the main reason why the third brush generator was replaced by the shunt type generator.

The shunt type generator has the field coils connected directly to the main brushes, thereby shunting off some of the generator's own armature output. While the shunt type generator provides improved low speed characteristics, some external means of controlling generator output must be provided. Such controls prevent the generator from exceeding its rated capacity of voltage and current.

Consideration of Fig. 31-13, will show that as the armature, battery and field are all in parallel, the current through each branch of the circuit will then

vary with their resistance. As the resistance of the battery is much less than the field, most of the current from the armature will pass through the battery, and only a small amount through the field. If the resistance of the battery is increased, more of the current will be forced back through the shunt field because its resistance has not been changed.

This increase in field current will increase the number of lines of force that the armature coils can cut, and the voltage will be increased.

If additional load is placed in parallel on the generator, as shown in Fig. 31-14, the total resistance of the load will be reduced, with the result that the current through the load will be still further increased and consequently the current through the generator field will be still further reduced. This in turn decreases the generated voltage.

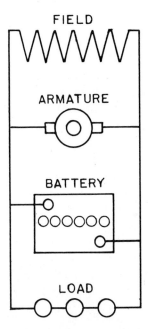

Fig. 31-14. Placing additional load on generator reduces resistance of load.

As was previously pointed out, shunt wound generators are provided with current and voltage regulators which prevent current and voltage from exceeding predetermined values. Such means of regulation will be discussed in a later section.

Shunt Generator Circuits

There are two major types of shunt generator circuits. One is known as the "A" circuit, Fig. 31-15, and the other is known as the "B" circuit, Fig. 31-16.

To understand the difference between these two generator circuits it is necessary to explain briefly the operation of the regulator which is used to control the output.

Regulators consist basically of spring-loaded contact points and a resistance. The contact points are

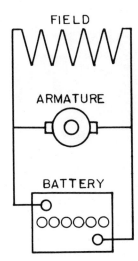

Fig. 31-13. With armature, field and battery in parallel, current through each branch of circuit will vary with resistance of each.

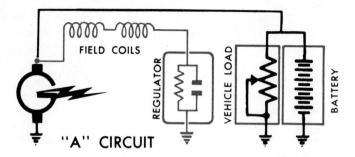

Fig. 31-15. In "A" type generator circuit, regulator resistance is inserted between field and ground when regulator points are open.

The "A" circuit is used primarily on Delco-Remy equipped passenger cars, whereas the "B" circuit is used on Ford built passenger cars. There is no particular advantage of using one circuit or the other.

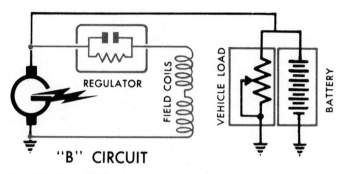

Fig. 31-16. In "B" type generator circuit, regulator inserts resistance between insulated side of circuit and field coil.

opened electromagnetically by means of a winding. When the points are open, the resistance is automatically connected to the field coils of the generator, thereby reducing the amount of current flowing in that circuit. This in turn reduces the strength of the magnetic field and lowers the output of the generator. When the points are closed, the resistance is shorted out of the circuit so the field current is increased and the generator output rises.

In the generator circuitry shown in Fig. 31-15, the regulator resistance is inserted between the field and the ground, when the regulator points are open. This is known as an "A" circuit generator, which can be identified by noting that the field coil lead is connected to the insulated brush inside the generator, and that the field circuit is grounded at the generator regulator.

Third Brush Generators

Third brush generators make use of the fact that the magnetic fields set up by the field coils and the armature coils react on each other, strengthening the field at some points and weakening it at others. This reaction is used to control the output of third brush generators.

In third brush generators, Fig. 31-17, it will be noted that instead of both terminals of the field wind-

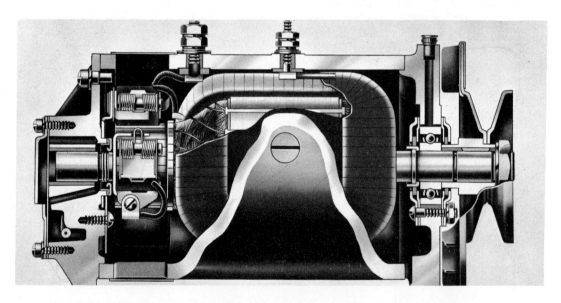

Fig. 31-17. Sectional view reveals inner construction of typical third brush generator now used mainly in tractor applications.

In the "B" circuit generator, shown in Fig. 31-16, the field coil lead is connected to the grounded brush inside the generator or to the generator frame. With this type of generator, the field circuit is connected to the insulated brush through the regulator.

ings being connected directly to the brushes, one end of the field winding is connected to the third brush, while the other end of the field winding is connected to the ground. The position of the third brush is adjustable, and its position controls the voltage applied to the circuit. In this way the output of the generator can be controlled.

The two main brushes, Fig. 31-18, are located at the neutral points on the commutator where there is maximum voltage, and as the third brush is positioned between the two main brushes it picks up less than the maximum available voltage.

Moving the third brush in the direction of armature rotation (toward the adjacent main brush) will increase the voltage across the field circuit, and the current through the field windings is thereby increased, Fig. 31-18.

Increasing the field current also increases the magnetic field strength, which in turn increases the output of the generator. Moving the third brush away from the adjacent main brush (against armature rotation) reduces the voltage across the field circuit, and results in lower generator output, Fig. 31-19.

It is also important to note that the voltage developed in the armature windings between the third brush and the ground brush, decreases as fewer magnetic lines of force are cut by the armature conductors when the lines of force shift from their neutral position, Fig. 31-18. This decrease in voltage forces less current through the field windings. As a result,

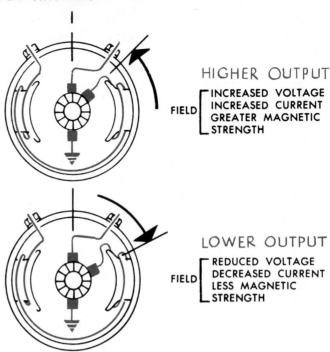

Fig. 31-19. Effects of shifting adjustable brush of third brush generator is shown and described.

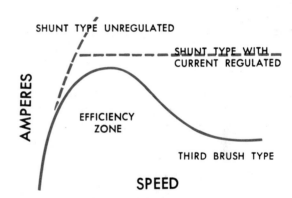

Fig. 31-20. Output of shunt and third brush generators is compared at different speeds.

the voltage across the main brushes is reduced, which in turn results in less pressure to cause current to flow through the load circuit.

In that way, the third brush generator regulates its own current output without an external current regulator. However, some means of controlling the voltage is needed.

Fig. 31-20 illustrates the current output of shunt and third brush type generators. Note how the current provided by the third brush unit decreases as the speed goes up.

Special Generator Circuits

As the current through the armature and fields of a DC generator increases, there is a corresponding increase in the strength of the magnetic field, and also greater distortion and shifting of the field.

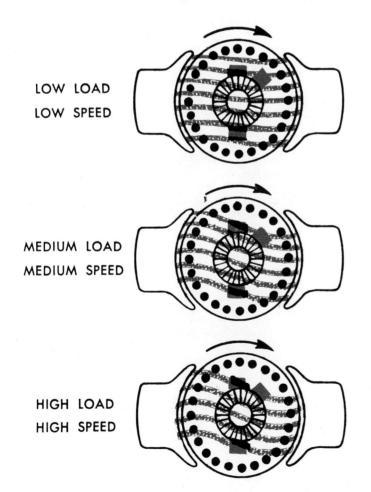

Fig. 31-18. Note how magnetic field shifts with rotational speed and load on third brush generator.

On some generators, for trucks or buses which have a heavy electrical load, the shift of the magnetic field is so great that some special means are required as compensation. These means are used on variations of the basic shunt wound generator and include the interpole-generator, the reverse-field generator, and the split-field generator.

Interpole Generators

The mechanical neutral position of the magnetic field is midway between the field poles of the generator. At that point, the armature conductor, connected to the brushes through the commutator, will have zero current flow as the voltage at that point is changing from one direction to the other, Fig. 31-8. However, because the magnetic field has shifted from the neutral point, the armature conductor will still be generating voltage, and there is a flow of current when the conductor is shorted by the brushes.

It is therefore essential, if commutator arcing is to be reduced or eliminated, that the armature coil does not cut through lines of force during commutation. This can be accomplished by installing an "interpole," Fig. 31-21, which will tend to neutralize the magnetic field of the armature coils.

This interpole is a narrow pole piece mounted on the generator frame between the two regular pole pieces, Fig. 31-21. It is wound with heavy bar copper since it is connected in series with the armature and all the armature current passes through it. The number of turns of wire in the interpole coil are chosen to produce sufficient ampere-turns in the opposite direction to counteract the magnetic field created by the current flowing through the armature. Since the amount of current flowing through the armature and the interpole is always equal, the correct amount of correction will always be present. As a result the magnetic field between the poles will remain in a straight line, and brushes will be located exactly on the mechanical neutral point.

Bucking Field Generators

One method of obtaining current at low generator speeds is to have additional turns of wire on the armature to obtain the higher voltage needed under such a condition.

However, when the speed is great, only a weak magnetic field is required to obtain the desired voltage. In fact, sufficient field strength will be provided by the residual magnetism of the field coils. But this voltage cannot be controlled. Even though the contact points of the voltage regulator open and insert resistance into the field coil circuit, voltage will continue to increase.

Voltage of this type of generator is controlled by means of a bucking field coil, Fig. 31-22. This is a shunt field coil of high resistance which is wound on

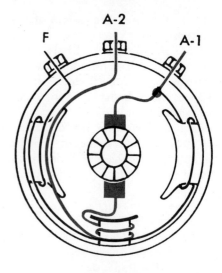

INTERPOLE

Fig. 31-21. An interpole is one method of reducing arcing at generator brushes.

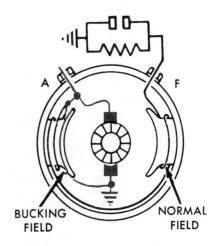

Fig. 31-22. A bucking field coil is wound in reverse direction of other field coils and controls generated voltage.

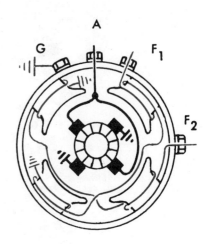

Fig. 31-23. A split field generator is designed to supply current at low speeds.

one field coil and connected directly across the armature. The winding is connected in the reverse direction to the normal field winding, and its magnetic field opposes the normal field.

At low speeds, when normal field current is large, the opposing effect of the bucking field is not large in comparison to that of the main field. At higher generator speeds, when the current in the regular or main field circuit is reduced by the voltage regulator, the opposing effect of the bucking field is greater than the residual magnetic field, and practically all of the lines of force are cancelled. As a result the generated voltage will drop.

In that way, the current flow through the main field coils can be controlled by the regulator, and the effects of the residual magnetism can be controlled by the bucking field. Normal generator voltage will then be maintained.

field coils is designed for maximum allowable field coil current. The split field generator has approximately twice the field strength of a generator having only one field coil.

This type of generator is frequently used on buses operating in cities, where long periods of idling and slow operating speeds are normal conditions.

Alternating Current Generators

An alternating current generator (alternator), Fig. 31-24, consists of two major parts: a stator in which the voltage is generated, and a rotor which provides the magnetic field. The stator consists of three sets of windings assembled around the inside circumference of a laminated core. This core forms parts of the exterior frame of the generator, and provides a path for the flow of the magnetic flux between two adjacent

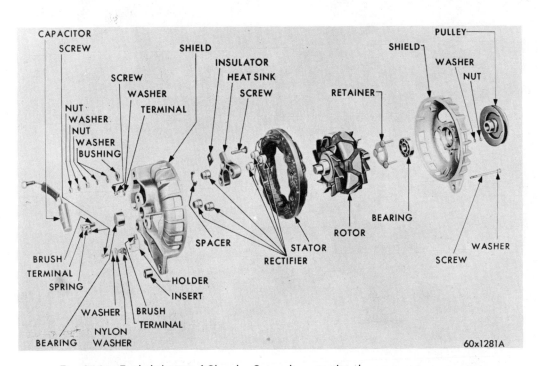

Fig. 31-24. Exploded view of Chrysler Corp. alternator details component arrangement.

Split Field Generators

Another method of providing sufficient voltage at low engine speeds to supply current for the load circuit is by means of the split field generator, Fig. 31-23.

The split field generator has two field circuits within the generator. By increasing the magnetic field strength with an added field coil circuit, the voltage necessary to provide current for the load circuit can be reached at a much lower speed.

The stronger field necessary for developing voltage at low speeds is accomplished by splitting the field circuit into two separate circuits, each controlled by its own voltage and current regulator. Each set of

poles of the rotor. The front and rear cases of the alternator are generally held together by "through bolts" and are well vented at both ends. A fan mounted on the front of the rotor shaft draws air through the cases for cooling. The cases support the bearings, usually a sealed thrust ball bearing at the front and an axial roller bearing at the rear.

When the rotor revolves within the stator, the alternate north and south magnetic poles created are strengthened by current flowing through concentric windings on the rotor shaft. These field windings are energized by current from the starting battery by way of the brushes and slip rings. See Fig. 31-25.

An alternator will produce an appreciable amount

Under hood shot which illustrates how modern V-8 engines "fit" engine compartment, yet offer reasonably good accessibility to battery, alternator, V-belt, hoses, spark plugs, etc. for service. With this Chrysler 340, the most difficult service point is the rear mounted distributor.

of current at low speeds and, in contrast to the conventional direct current generator, which will develop little or none. See Fig. 31-26. If a smaller pulley is installed on a DC generator in an attempt to increase its speed in relation to engine speed, the centrifugal force created at higher engine speeds will throw the wires from the rotating armature.

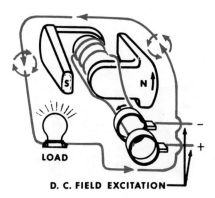

Fig. 31-25. Current for field excitation of alternator is supplied through slip rings from battery.

Another major advantage of the alternator is that the magnetic field (which is rotating) carries only 2 to 3 amperes of current, and the voltage is generated in the stationary coils. This field current is supplied through slip rings and, consequently, no arcing will occur at the brushes. Whereas, with the DC generator, 25 to 45 amperes pass through the brushes from the commutator - arcing is difficult to overcome - and rapid commutator and brush wear results.

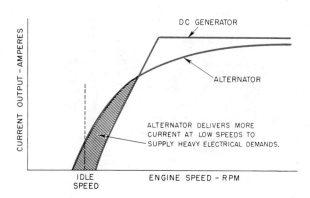

Fig. 31-26. Output of direct current generator and alternator is compared from idle to high speed operation.

In the illustration of a simplified alternator, Fig. 31-3, only a single conductor, or loop, and the voltage generated is shown. An alternator with all the conductors connected in series would produce a similar wave of alternating voltage and is known as a single phase alternator. Alternators used for automotive purposes, however are of the three phase type. That is, three separate windings are provided in the stator

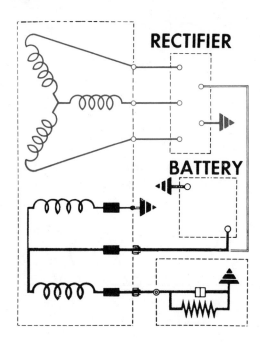

Fig. 31-27. Note in typical alternator wiring diagram how stator windings form a "Y."

which are usually connected as shown in Fig. 31-27. Each of these windings then generates a separate voltage, Fig. 31-28. On some alternators, the three stator windings are connected to form a triangle. This is called a "Delta" winding.

Field Excitation

To strengthen the magnetic field, the field circuit on the rotor is connected to the battery or the direct current side of the rectifier, Fig. 31-25. This connection is made through brushes and solid slip rings mounted on the shaft of the rotor. The direct current voltage of the system is controlled by varying the amount of field current which excites the generator.

To provide voltage control at high speed, many alternators have a reverse field winding. Electrically, this reverse winding is a high resistance shunt winding connected in parallel with the main field winding.

The reverse winding is so wound and connected that when the generator is charging, current flow in the reverse winding creates a magnetic field which opposes that created by current flow in the main winding.

Rectifiers

Since alternating current cannot be used to charge a starting battery or provide current to produce the magnetic field in an alternator, it is necessary to change the alternating current produced in the stator to direct current. This conversion is done by means of a rectifier, a device which permits current to flow through it in only one direction. When the three-phase output of an alternator is passed through the rectifier,

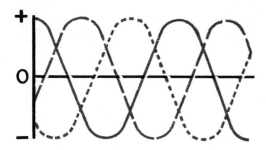

Fig. 31-28. Each winding of stator generates a separate voltage to make alternator a three-phase unit.

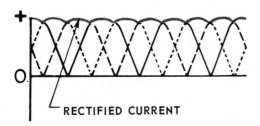

RECTIFIED CURRENT

Fig. 31-29. Rectifier permits current to pass through in one direction only. In illustration, rectified three-phase current is shown with effective voltage in red.

instead of the voltage of each phase ranging from positive to negative and back to positive again, only the voltage in one direction will pass through. The result is as shown in Fig. 31-29. Note that while the voltage of each phase ranges from zero to maximum, the combined voltages of all the phases varies very little.

Types of Rectifiers

Different types of rectifiers in use include:
1. Magnesium-copper sulphide.
2. Selenium.
3. Silicon diode.

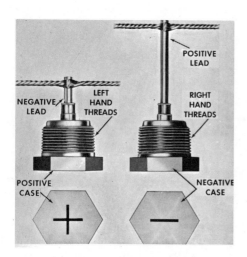

Fig. 31-30. In some applications, silicon diode rectifiers carry positive and negative markings.

Magnesium-Copper Sulfide Rectifier

The plates of magnesium-copper sulfide rectifiers have a comparatively high current carrying capacity per unit of area, but three volts is the maximum each plate can stand. For that reason, this type rectifier is used only on alternators of 6V capacity.

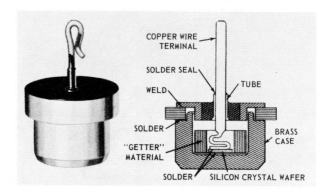

Fig. 31-31. Diode shown is from Ford Autolite alternator. Note silicon crystal wafer at end of copper wire.

Selenium Rectifiers

The rectifier plates used in the selenium rectifier have a comparatively low current capacity per unit of area, but operate satisfactorily at higher voltages and can therefore be used on 12V alternators.

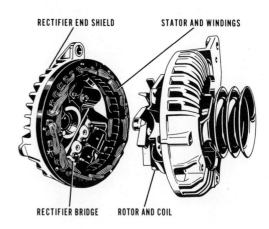

Fig. 31-32. Late model Chrysler-built alternator has heavy-duty rectifiers, or diodes, mounted in a bridge that is bolted to end frame of alternator.

Silicon Rectifier

The silicon rectifier, or silicon diode rectifier, Figs. 31-30 and 31-31, is the most recent type of rectifier to be developed. Because of its small size, it is often built into the end frame of the alternator. Whereas other types of rectifiers are relatively large in size and are therefore mounted externally, Fig. 31-32. In the automotive type alternator, three positive silicon rectifiers are used, and three negative rectifiers of the same construction. Generally, these are mounted directly on one end of the alternator, Fig. 31-24, three being mounted in the frame, and three in a bracket or "heat sink" which is attached to but insulated from the end frame.

Some silicon diodes, Fig. 31-30, are plainly marked with a + or - sign to identify the polarity of the case. On an alternator to be used on a negative grounded system, the negative case diodes are mounted into the slip ring end frame, and the positive case diodes are mounted in the heat sink. Diodes with a negative case have positive polarity leads, while positive case diodes have negative polarity leads. Some alternators produced for foreign vehicle applications (positive ground systems) have positive diodes mounted in the slip ring end frame and negative diodes in the heat sink.

Certain alternators, Ford Autolite for example, Fig. 31-33, utilize two steel diode plates (heat sink), each containing three diodes. The plates are insulated from each other and are of opposite polarity. The complete assembly is attached to the rear housing of the alternator by means of four mounting studs in the outer plate. The inner plate (positive) also contains the alternator output terminal.

In any case, the six diodes change alternating current from the stator windings to a flow of direct current at the output terminal of the alternator. Thus the rotor (magnetic field), stator (conductors) and diodes

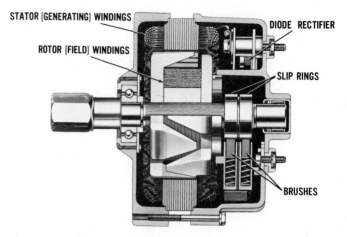

Fig. 31-33. Cutaway view of Ford Autolite alternator shows how diode rectifiers are placed in separate plates bolted to rear housing.

(rectifiers) act as a team to produce the direct current electricity to keep the battery fully charged and to supply electrical energy to the vehicle's current-consuming devices.

Quiz - Electric Generators

1. For what purpose is the automotive generator used?
2. What happens when a coil of wire is moved through a magnetic field?
3. When rotating a coil of wire through a horizontal magnetic field, maximum voltage will be produced in what position of the coil?
   a. Horizontal.
   b. Vertical.
4. Why are cooling fans incorporated in the design of modern automotive generators?
5. In a direct current generator, voltage is generated in which unit?
   a. Armature.
   b. Field.
   c. Stator.
   d. Regulator.
6. In a direct current generator, what device is used to change alternating current to direct?
   a. Commutator.   c. Transistor.
   b. Rectifier.
7. What three methods can be used to increase the strength of the generated voltage?
8. What is armature reaction?
9. In an armature wound for a two-pole generator, how many neutral points are there?
   a. Two.   b. Four.   c. Six.

10. Which type of generator has the better low speed characteristics?
    a. Shunt.
    b. Third brush.
11. In the A-type generator circuit, where is the regulator resistance inserted?
    a. Between the field and the ground.
    b. Between the insulated side of the circuit and the field coil.
    c. Shunted across the armature.
12. In the B-type generator circuit where does the regulator insert the resistance?
    a. Between the insulated side of the circuit and the field coil.
    b. Shunted across the armature.
    c. Shunted across the field.
13. When the third brush is moved in the direction of armature rotation, is output increased or decreased?
    a. Increased.
    b. Decreased.
    c. No change.
14. Does the current output of a third-brush generator increase or decrease with the speed of rotation?
    a. Increase.
    b. Decrease.

15. What is the purpose of an interpole in a generator?
    a. Increase output.
    b. Decrease arcing at the brushes.
    c. Maintain constant voltage.
16. What is the purpose of a bucking field generator?
    a. Control the voltage.
    b. Increase the output.
    c. Strengthen the magnetic field.
17. What is a major advantage of an alternator over a direct current generator for automotive service?
18. In most alternators, the voltage is generated in which part of the unit?
    a. Rotor.
    b. Stator.
19. In most alternators, what is the name of the part which supplies the field?

20. In an alternator, what is the name of the part which changes the current from alternating to direct?
    a. Converter.
    b. Commutator.
    c. Rectifier.
21. What kind of current is supplied to the field of an alternator?
    a. Direct.   b. Alternating.
22. For what purpose is a diode used on a modern automotive alternator?
23. How many windings are there in a Y-type stator?
    a. One.
    b. Two.
    c. Three.
    d. Five.

Late model Pontiacs have an integral charging system, capable of producing 50 amps. at engine idle speed and 80 amps. at normal cruising speed. Regulator is built in (arrow).

GENERATOR AND ALTERNATOR TESTING AND SERVICING

To obtain maximum life from a DC generator, regular inspection and maintenance procedures should be followed. Periodic lubrication, where required, inspection of brushes and commutator, and testing of brush spring tension are essential. In addition, it is important to check electrical connections for clean, metal-to-metal contact and tightness.

Lubrication

The trend has been toward the production of generators that are lubricated at the time of manufacture for approximately 50,000 miles of maintenance-free operation. These generators are not fitted with hinged cap oilers, and call for lubrication only when the generator is disassembled for major service.

However, when generators do have hinged cap oilers, Fig. 32-1, observe the following lubrication recommendations:

1. On generators containing bushing-type bearings, lubricate bushings at every lubrication period with a few drops of medium viscosity engine oil.
2. Lubricate ball bearing-equipped generators with 8 to 10 drops of medium viscosity engine oil. Do not over oil, since this may wash out grease packed in the bearing which could get on the commutator and brushes. In addition, excess oil will tend to rot electrical insulation.

Inspection

In general, check and inspect the condition of DC generators every 10,000 miles. However, if the car is operated in areas where there is excessive dust, at high speeds, or if most of the operation is at high electrical load, the inspection should be at more frequent intervals.

Begin by visually and manually inspecting the condition of all starting and charging system cables, clamps, wires and terminal connections. See that the generator drive pulley is tight on the shaft, and that the drive belt is in good condition and adjusted to proper tension, Fig. 32-2. Also make sure that the starter, generator and voltage regulator are securely mounted to insure good ground circuits.

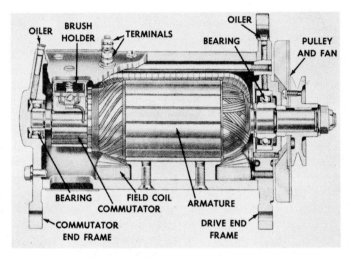

Fig. 32-1. Cross-sectional view of DC generator shows major elements, including bearings in end frames and hinge cap oilers.

On-Car Commutator Service

Remove the cover band, if the generator is so equipped, and inspect the commutator, brushes and electrical connections. If the commutator is dirty or slightly rough, sand it with number 00 sandpaper or by means of a special sanding tool. Never use emery cloth on a commutator.

Fig. 32-2. Generally, a deflection of 1/2 to 3/4 in. will provide correct tension of generator belt. However, if other accessories are being driven, factory specifications should be followed.

To sand a commutator, wrap the end of a flat piece of soft wood with a strip of number 00 sandpaper. Then, with the generator in operation, hold the sandpaper against the commutator and move it back and forth so that the entire surface of the commutator is sanded. Sandpaper in rolls designed especially for sanding commutators can be secured from automotive parts jobbers.

If the commutator is rough and pitted, or inaccessible for on-car service, the generator must be removed, disassembled and serviced on the bench. See the procedure for overhauling generators in another section.

Further Inspection

After inspecting and sanding the commutator, blow clean the interior of the generator with compressed air. If the brushes are worn down to one-half their original length, they should be replaced. The amount of wear can be determined by comparing it with a new brush. Lift the brushes in the brush holder to see that they are free to operate, and test the tension of the brush springs, Fig. 32-3. If tension is too great, rapid brush and commutator wear will result; if too weak, arcing will result. If the generator has been operated under excessive loads, it will overheat and possibly cause the brush springs to lose their strength. This condition will usually be revealed by a burned or blue appearance of the spring. Such springs should be replaced.

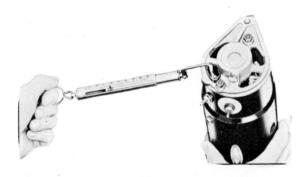

Fig. 32-3. Test tension of brush springs with a spring scale to insure that brushes make good contact with commutator.

Inspect the inner surface of the generator cover band for tiny globules of solder. If any solder is found, it indicates that the generator was producing excessive current and melted the solder used in connecting the armature wires to the commutator bars. In these cases, the armature must be replaced or the connections resoldered, Fig. 32-4.

Beyond these simple points of inspection, electrical tests are called for. However, since there are two basic types of generator-regulator circuits used in the automotive field, and since some tests vary slightly with the two types of generators, correct identification is imperative.

Identifying "A" and "B" Generators

The "A" circuit generator (sometimes known as the standard) has the field grounded through the regulator, Fig. 31-15, while the "B" circuit (sometimes called heavy-duty) has the field grounded within the generator, Fig. 31-16. A sure method of identification is to disconnect the field wire from the generator field terminal, taking care not to let this wire touch the ground. Connect a voltmeter from the generator field terminal to the ground, then, with the engine operating at a fast idle, a voltage reading indicates that the generator is the "A" circuit type. If no reading is indicated, the generator is a "B" circuit and is of the heavy-duty type.

Fig. 32-4. If generator has overheated and "thrown solder," connections between armature coils and commutator must be resoldered - or armature replaced.

Another method of determining the type of generator is to note the connection between the field and the brushes (on generators which have a removable cover band). If the generator field coil lead is connected to the insulated brush inside the generator, then the generator is of the "A" circuit type. If the generator field coil is connected to the grounded brush or the generator field frame, then the generator is the "B" circuit type.

Electrical Tests

CAUTION: On all cars with double contact regulators, NEVER GROUND the generator field with the regulator connected to the generator. This will instantly burn the upper set of contact points on the regulator. Double contact regulators are usually found on cars equipped with air conditioning and other electrical equipment which imposes a heavy load on the generator.

Testing Shunt Generator Output "A" Circuit

To test the current output of an "A" circuit shunt-type generator, connect an ammeter as shown in Fig. 32-5. On systems with double contact regulators, disconnect the lead from the field terminal of the regulator, then ground it. Start the engine and gradual-

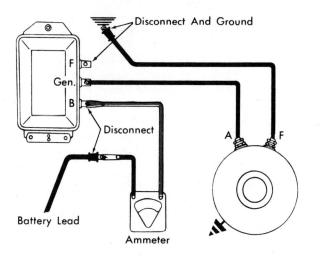

Fig. 32-5. Connect an ammeter in charging system as shown to test current output of "A" circuit generator.

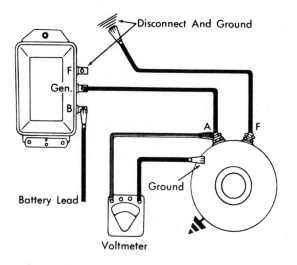

Fig. 32-6. Install a voltmeter in charging system as indicated to test voltage output of "A" circuit generators.

ly increase engine speed until the ammeter indicates at least 25 percent above the rated output of the generator. If the output does not reach this specified value and increase steadily, it should be checked further to determine the cause of the low output.

A voltage output test should be made to determine that all the windings in the armature are still operating, and the insulation of the field windings are in good condition. Connect a voltmeter as shown in Fig. 32-6. Make sure all lights and accessories on the vehicle are turned off. Speed up the engine until the voltmeter indicates in excess of 16V on 12V systems and 8V on 6V systems. Do not operate the engine at this speed for more than a second or two as it will damage the generator. If those voltages are not reached, disconnect wire from regulator to generator armature terminal. If correct voltage is then attained, the starting battery is defective. If the correct voltage is not attained with the battery out of the circuit, the generator should be overhauled.

Testing Shunt Generator Output "B" Circuit

Disconnect the regulator armature and field wires at the generator. Connect a jumper wire from the generator armature terminal to the generator field terminal, Fig. 32-7, also the positive lead of a 0-50 ampere ammeter to the generator armature terminal. Start the engine and, while it is idling, connect the ammeter negative lead to the positive lead of the battery.

Run the engine at 1500 rpm and read the current output on the ammeter. The generator should reach or exceed its specified output. Disconnect test leads as soon as the test is completed to prevent overheating the generator.

Generator Circuit Resistance Test

Excessive resistance in the charging circuit will cut down current to the battery, or increase generator voltage. The check for the insulated side of the charging circuit is as follows: connect the ammeter and voltmeter as shown in Fig. 32-8. The generator field control is a 25 ohm, 25 watt unit with an open position. Start the engine and operate at fast idle. Adjust the generator field control knob until the generator charges at 20 amp. If necessary, turn on some lights in order to obtain that value. The voltmeter should not read more than 0.7 volts. If voltage exceeds that amount, there is excessive resistance in the circuit. Voltage drop from armature terminal of generator to armature terminal of regulator should not exceed 0.2 volts; from armature terminal of regulator to battery terminal of regulator 0.2 volts; across test ammeter and leads 0.25 volts; from end of disconnected battery wire to ungrounded post of battery 0.15 volts.

To check the generator circuit resistance of the generator ground circuit, connect the instruments as shown in Fig. 32-9. With the engine at fast idle, adjust the generator field control knob to obtain a charging rate of 20 amperes. The voltage should not exceed 0.1 volt.

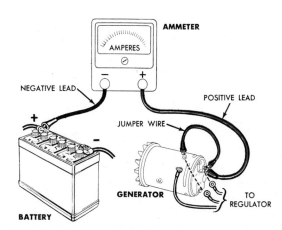

Fig. 32-7. Connect an ammeter and a jumper wire as shown to check output of "B" circuit generators.

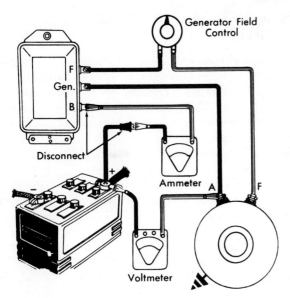

Fig. 32-8. *Here is recommended method of making circuit resistance test, using a voltmeter and an ammeter.*

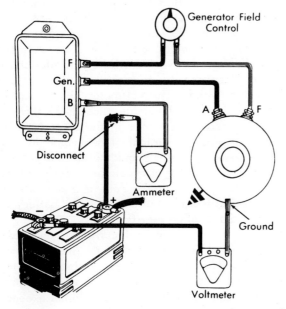

Fig. 32-9. *Connect voltmeter and ammeter in circuit as indicated to test resistance of generator ground circuit.*

No Output

If, as the result of tests it is found that no current is being generated, remove the cover band (if so equipped) and check the brushes, commutator and internal connections.

If the brushes are making good contact with the commutator and the cause of the trouble is not apparent, use a test lamp, Fig. 32-10, to locate the trouble. The procedure is as follows:

1. First disconnect the leads from the generator terminals. Insert a piece of paper or other insulation between the grounded brush and the commutator. Check for grounds with the test lamp, between the generator main brush or "A" terminal and the generator frame. If the generator is an "A" circuit type, disconnect the field ground lead before making this test. If the lamp lights, it indicates that the generator is internally grounded. The location of the ground can be found by raising and insulating all the brushes from the commutator and checking the brush holders, armature, commutator and fields separately.

   If a grounded field is found, check the regulator contact points since a grounded field may have permitted an excessive field current which burned the regulator contact points. Burned regulator points should be cleaned or replaced as required.

2. If the generator is not grounded, check the field circuit for an open circuit with a test lamp. To make this test on an "A" circuit generator, the test lamp is connected to the armature and field terminals of the generator. On "B" circuit generators, the test lamp is connected to the field terminal and the ground. If the test lamp does not light, the field circuit is open. A lighted test lamp indicates a continuous circuit, but does not indicate a short circuit.

3. If the field circuit is not open, check for a short circuit in the field by connecting a battery of the specified voltage and an ammeter in series with the field circuit. If the current flowing is not in accordance with the value given in the specifications, new field coils should be installed.

   If a shorted field coil is found, the regulator contacts should be checked, since a shorted field may have permitted excessive field current which would cause the regulator contacts to burn.

4. If the preceding tests have not located the trouble, check the armature for open circuits. Open circuited commutator bars will arc each time they pass under the brushes, so that the bars will soon be badly burned and pitted. It is usually advisable to replace the armature. However, if the commutator bars are not badly burned, and the "open" in the armature is at the point where it is soldered to the commutator bar, the repairs can be easily made, Fig. 32-4. If any doubt exists, the armature can be tested for open circuit.

Another method of determining whether a no-charge condition is caused by the generator or regulator is one frequently used for systems fitted with single contact regulators of either "A" or "B" circuits. On "A" circuit systems, the procedure is to use a jumper wire to connect the field terminal of the generator to ground. Then, with the engine operating at a fast idle, a charge on the instrument panel indicator signals that the generator is satisfactory, and the regulator is defective.

In the case of "B" circuit systems, the procedure is to connect the armature terminal of the regulator to the field terminal. Then, with the engine operating at a fast idle, a charge on the instrument panel indicator shows that the regulator is defective. No charge indicates that the generator is defective.

In the methods just outlined, the jumper wire cuts the regulator out of the circuit.

Low or Unsteady Output

If a low or unsteady output is produced by the generator, the following checks and corrections should be made:

1. Check for a slipping generator drive belt. Adjust belt tension, or replace drive belt.
2. Examine generator brushes and/or brush springs. Sticking brushes or weak brush spring tension will prevent good contact with the commutator. This will usually be accompanied by arcing at the brushes. Sand commutator and replace brushes and/or brush springs.
3. Inspect generator for dirty, out-of-round, or high-mica commutators. Turn commutator in a lathe, undercut mica and replace brushes.

Excessive Generator Output

When tests show that the generator output is excessive (as shown in chapter devoted to current and voltage regulators), even after the "F" terminal has been disconnected, the trouble is the generator itself. This being the case, the procedure to be followed in locating the trouble will depend on which type generator-regulator circuit the system uses.

Remember, the two basic circuits differ essentially in which part of the circuit the regulator inserts resistance. In "A" circuit generators, the field circuit is grounded through the regulator, Fig. 31-15, while "B" circuit generators have the field grounded internally, Fig. 31-16.

On "A" circuit generators, an accidental internal ground in the field circuit would prevent current regulation so that excessive generator output may result. On that type of circuit, an internally grounded

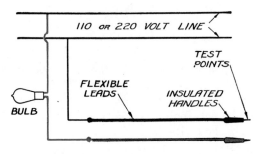

Fig. 32-10. A test lamp can be fabricated for use in making electrical tests of continuity and open circuits.

field circuit which would cause excessive output may be located by means of a test lamp by connecting it between the "F" terminal and the generator frame.

When making this test, disconnect the leads from the "F" terminal and lift the brush to which the field lead is connected. If the test lamp lights, the field is internally grounded. A ground of this kind frequently results from a wearing away of the insulation on the field lead. This can be repaired easily by taping the lead. It is also possible to make a repair when a ground has occurred at the pole shoes. To make such a repair, remove the field coils, reinsulate, then reinstall them.

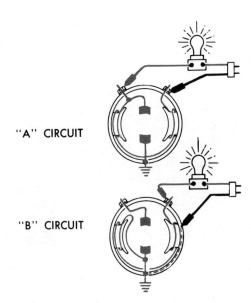

Fig. 32-11. Use test lamp to test generator field circuits: if lamp lights, field circuit is continuous; if it does not, field is open.

On "B" circuit generators, the only cause for excessive output (with lead disconnected from "F" terminal) would be a "short" between the field circuit and the insulated main circuit. To repair this condition, simply reinsulate and relocate the leads.

Noisy Generators

The operation of a generator in perfect condition should be virtually noiseless. However, noise will result from improperly seated brushes, a worn commutator, worn bearings, or loose generator mounting or drive pulley.

Testing for Grounded Field

A test lamp, Fig. 32-10, is used to determine if the field circuit is grounded. All internal field coil connections must be disconnected. On "A" circuit generators, raise both brushes. On "B" circuit generators raise both brushes and also disconnect field from grounded brush. Place one test point on generator frame and other on field terminal. If lamp lights, field is grounded. If it does not light, there is no ground. A short circuited field coil will have little effect on generator output.

Check for Open Circuits or Shorts

If no ground is indicated, check field coils with test light for open circuit. This can be done by placing test points on ends of field coil leads in turn, Fig. 32-11. If test lamp does not light, an open circuit is indicated. If lamp lights, the field circuit is continuous, but this does not eliminate the possibility of a short circuit.

A short in a field coil is most easily detected by comparing the current draw of the field coil with the value listed in the specifications of that particular generator. To do this, connect the field coil in series

Fig. 32-12. Test for short circuit in armature by rotating it on a growler while holding a strip of steel over each coil in turn.

with a battery (6V or 12V in accordance with the particular generator) and an ammeter. If the current indicated by the test is higher than the specified value, a short is present, and new field coils should be installed.

Fig. 32-13. Check for grounded armature coils by touching test lamp prods to armature shaft and any commutator bar.

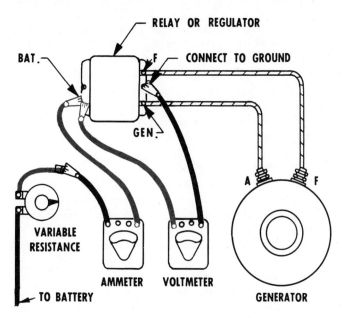

Fig. 32-14. Here is test hookup for checking output of third brush generator. If generator is equipped with a regulator, field terminal must be grounded.

Testing the Armature

The armature is tested for shorts by placing in a growler, Fig. 32-12. A short circuit will cause a short strip of steel to vibrate when it is held over the armature core. While making the test, the armature is rotated slowly in the jaws of the growler in order to check all of the coils of the armature.

The armature is checked for grounds by means of a test lamp, Fig. 32-11. The procedure is to touch the armature shaft with one point of the test set and any one of the commutator bars with the other point, Fig. 32-13. If the lamp lights, a ground is indicated and the armature should be replaced.

Third Brush Generator Output

An ammeter, voltmeter, and variable resistance are used to check the output of the third brush type generator. The ammeter and variable resistance are connected in series into the charging circuit at the relay or regulator "BAT" terminal and the voltmeter between that same terminal and the ground, Fig. 32-14. If the generator is equipped with a regulator, the "F" terminal must be grounded temporarily with a jumper lead to eliminate the action of the regulator while the test is being made.

With the generator at operating temperature, increase the generator speed to the value given in the manufacturer's test specifications. Then adjust the variable resistance to obtain the specified voltage and note the current indicated on the ammeter. If generator is checked with fully charged battery in circuit, variable resistance may not be required. Variable resistance is needed to increase voltage to specified value.

When checking a generator with a manually or thermostatically controlled field resistance, make sure the field resistance is shorted out of the field circuit before attempting to adjust the generator output.

On many third brush generator models fitted with voltage regulators, the position of the third brush is not adjustable. When the third brush is adjustable, the output is increased by moving the brush in the direction of armature rotation. The usual construction of the third brush permits adjustment after loosening one or more clamping screws. Some models have the clamping screw accessible on the outside, while other designs have the clamping screw on the inside of the commutator end frame.

Check brushes for wear. If worn to less than one-half the original length, they should be replaced.

5. Remove ball bearing from commutator end of armature shaft, using a puller designed for that purpose, or press bearing from end frame of generator.
6. Remove generator pulley attaching nut from armature shaft, then take off pulley and fan.
7. Disengage armature from drive end frame assembly, using a puller, or press if off.
8. Unscrew bearing retainer plate screws and lift retainer plate and gasket from end frame, if so equipped.

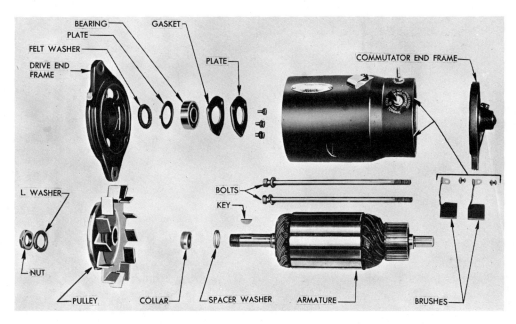

Fig. 32-15. *Exploded view of DC generator reveals two long through bolts which hold end frames to main frame.*

Third brush generators must never be operated on open circuit as this would result in burning out the generator. Neither should they be adjusted above the specified maximum output.

Servicing Generator

Place the generator in a bench vise, using the vise as a holding fixture only, taking care not to damage the frame.

Disassembly:
1. Remove two through bolts, Fig. 32-15.
2. Remove generator commutator end frame by prying between field frame and commutator end frame with two screwdrivers.
3. Pull drive end frame and armature assembly from field frame, Fig. 32-16.
4. Inspect brush holders and frame, making sure they are not loose and are correctly aligned.

9. Remove field and armature terminal nuts, washers and bushings, then push terminal studs through frame.
10. Unscrew pole screw from each shoe, and remove coil as an assembly. This can be done

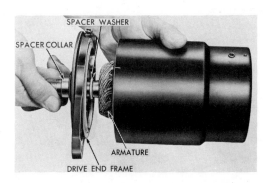

Fig. 32-16. *Scribe end frame and main frame before disassembling generator to insure correct alignment of frames on reassembly.*

Fig. 32-17. *Turn down a rough or scored commutator on a lathe. Remove only enough stock to clean up surface.*

with aid of pole shoe spreader and screwdriver held into screw slot by means of a lever.

11. Clean and inspect component parts for wear or damage. Correct as required.

Service:

1. Turn down commutator on a lathe, Fig. 32-17, and undercut mica so that it is 1/32 in. below surface of commutator bars, Fig. 32-18.
2. Make sure that new brushes are free in brush holders. Using end frame to support brushes and armature shaft, sand brushes to conform to commutator: place a strip of number 00 sandpaper between the commutator and brush; with light pressure on brush, withdraw sandpaper. This operation must be repeated until contact surface of brush fits curvature of commutator.
3. Install new ball bearing on commutator end of armature shaft, or in end frame.
4. Replace grease and oil seals, as required, and refill grease reservoir half-full, if so equipped.

Reassembly:

1. Reassemble pole shoes and field coils in generator frame, and install pole screws.
2. Reinstall field and armature terminal studs, terminal nuts, washers and bushings.
3. Place drive end frame on armature shaft and install generator pulley, band and attaching nut.
4. Perform tests outlined earlier for locating opens, shorts and grounds in armature and field coils.
5. Reassemble armature and end frames into generator frame and field coils, dropping brushes in place on commutator.
6. Install through bolts and nuts.

Polarizing the Generator

After a generator has been disconnected, tested or repaired, it should be polarized to make sure it has the correct polarity with respect to the battery in the circuit. If this is not done, the generator may be damaged and, in addition, the relay contacts may be burned and a rundown battery result. The method of polarizing a generator will depend on whether the generator field is grounded through the regulator ("A" circuit) or is internally grounded ("B" circuit).

On "A" circuit generators, Fig. 31-15, after reconnecting leads, momentarily connect a jumper wire between "GEN" and "BAT" terminals of the regulator. This permits a momentary surge of current to pass through the generator which will polarize it correctly.

To polarize "B" circuit generators, Fig. 31-16, disconnect the lead from the field terminal of the regulator and momentarily touch that lead to the regulator battery terminal. The resulting surge of current will correctly polarize the generator.

On cars with double contact regulators, disconnect field lead from regulator and ground it. Then momentarily place jumper lead from battery to the generator armature terminal.

Fig. 32-18. *After turning commutator, undercut mica between bars by utilizing a special undercutting attachment on lathe.*

Generator Bench Test

Whenever possible after a generator has been overhauled, it should be tested to make sure its output comes up to specifications. This is most easily done on a test bench designed for that purpose, Fig. 32-19.

Generator test benches provide means for rotating the generator armature at varying speeds. Field current controls, ammeter, voltmeter and tachometer are also provided. Most generator test benches also provide means for checking the voltage regulator.

Alternator System Inspection

Alternator-equipped charging systems also require regular inspection and maintenance. As with DC generator systems, the frequency of inspection depends on operating conditions. High-speed operation, high temperatures, dust and dirt all tend to increase wear on alternator components.

Inspect alternator systems visually and manually at approximately 5,000-mile intervals to make sure that brushes, slip rings and bearings are in good operating condition. Also test the battery's state of charge and the condition of starting and charging system cables, wires and connections. Check for tightness of alternator and regulator mounting bolts to insure good ground circuits. Look over the alternator drive belt for signs of wear or slippage, and see that the tension adjustment is correct. Alternator drive belt tension is more critical because the inertia created by the rotor is greater than that produced by the armature of a DC generator, Fig. 32-20.

On-Car Testing

Alternator testing and service call for special precautions since the alternator output terminal is connected to the battery at all times:

1. Use care to avoid reverse polarity when performing battery service of any kind. A surge of current in the opposite direction could burn out the alternator diodes (silicon rectifiers) and damage vehicle wiring.

2. Do not purposely or accidently "short" or "ground" system when disconnecting wires or connecting test leads to terminals of alternator or regulator. For example, grounding of the field terminal at either the alternator or regulator will damage the regulator. Grounding of the alternator output terminal will damage the alternator and/or charging circuit.

3. Never operate an alternator on an open circuit. With no battery or electric load in circuit, alternators are capable of building high voltage (50 to over 110 volts) which may damage diodes and could be dangerous to anyone who might touch the alternator output terminal.

4. Do not try to polarize an alternator. Polarity of the alternator system cannot be lost or changed, so attempts to polarize the system serve no purpose and may cause damage to diodes, the wiring harness, or other system components.

Maintenance is minimized by the use of prelubricated rotor bearings and long brushes in most modern alternators. If a problem exists, such as low output or overcharging, check for a complete field

Fig. 32-20. Adjust alternator drive belt tension to manufacturer's specifications. Good operating condition and correct tension must be maintained.

circuit (rotor) by placing a large screwdriver on the alternator rear bearing surface. If the field circuit is complete, there will be a strong magnetic pull on the blade of the screwdriver which indicates that the field is energized. If there is no field circuit, a modern alternator will not charge because it is excited by battery voltage.

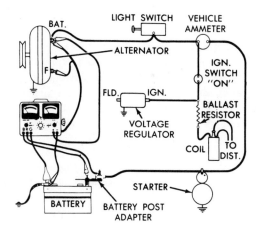

Fig. 32-21. Make test connections as shown to check current output of alternator at specified speed and voltage.

Current Output Test

Make the following test connections, Fig. 32-21, to measure an alternator's ability to produce its rated output at specified speed and voltage at normal operating temperature:

1. Connect a tachometer to engine at distributor primary terminal of ignition coil and ground.

2. Disconnect battery ground cable.

3. Disconnect battery positive cable and install a battery post switch to positive battery post and connect test ammeter leads to switch terminals. (This switch protects ammeter.)

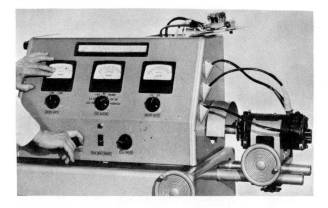

Fig. 32-19. Special test benches are available for making off-car tests of generator and regulator.

4. If a battery post switch is unavailable, disconnect alternator lead wire at solenoid and connect ammeter to disconnected wire and to solenoid terminal.
5. Disconnect field lead at alternator and regulator, and connect a jumper wire from field terminal of alternator to battery terminal of alternator.
6. Connect a voltmeter across battery.

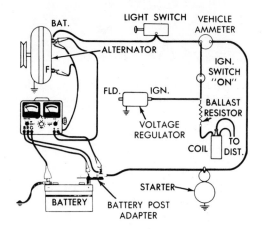

Fig. 32-22. If current output is low, make circuit resistance tests of alternator to pinpoint cause.

Then follow this test procedure:
1. Close battery post switch and start engine. Open battery post switch for tests.
2. Increase engine speed to 1500 rpm and rotate tester control knob to limit voltage to 15 volts.
3. Observe ammeter. If no output is indicated, stop test. If reading is within 5 amps. of rated output, system is satisfactory. (Approximately 3 amps.

are utilized for full field excitation, 1 1/2 amps. for ignition system and 1/2 amp. for instruments – all hidden from ammeter.)
4. Complete test as quickly as possible to avoid damage to automatic transmission.

Circuit Resistance Tests

If the current output test indicates a malfunction in the alternator system, make circuit resistance tests, Fig. 32-22, to determine whether the trouble is in the circuit or in the alternator.

Make an insulated circuit resistance test as follows:
1. Install battery post switch and connect ammeter test leads to switch.
2. Disconnect field lead at alternator and regulator, and connect a jumper wire from field terminal of alternator to battery terminal of alternator.
3. Connect positive voltmeter lead to alternator battery terminal and negative voltmeter lead to positive battery cable clamp.
4. Close battery post switch and start engine. Open switch and increase engine speed until ammeter reads 20 amps.
5. Observe voltmeter reading. Excessive resistance in insulated circuit is indicated if reading exceeds 0.3 volts on vehicles equipped with a charge indicator lamp, or 0.7 volts on vehicles equipped with an ammeter.

To test for excessive resistance in ground circuit:
1. Connect battery post switch, ammeter and field jumper as in insulated circuit test.
2. Connect negative voltmeter lead to alternator frame and positive voltmeter lead to battery negative post.

Fig. 32-23. Exploded view of Chrysler Corp. alternator shows relationship of components, and how stator and rotor are sandwiched between shields.

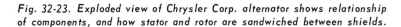

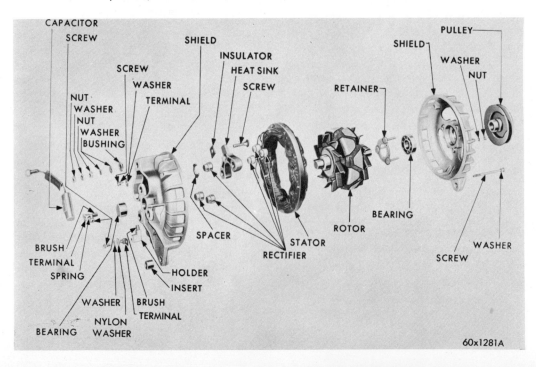

3. With engine operating, adjust engine speed to produce 10 amps. from alternator.

4. If voltmeter reading indicates more than 0.3 volts, there is excessive resistance in ground circuit of alternator system.

Alternator Removal and Disassembly

If the alternator system fails to meet current output specifications, yet passes the circuit resistance tests, remove the alternator from the vehicle for disassembly and bench tests, Fig. 32-23.

Remove the ground cable from the negative post of the battery. Disconnect the leads from the alternator output terminal (BAT.) and from the field terminal (FLD.). Disconnect the ground lead. Unscrew the mounting bolts and adjusting arm bolts. Slip off the drive belt, or belts, and remove the alternator from the engine.

To disassemble the unit: Scribe marks on front and rear housings to aid reassembly. On Chrysler and Motorola and Leece-Neville alternators, remove the brushes before separating the housings, Fig. 32-24. Also remove the isolation diode from Motorola units at this time.

Remove the through bolts and separate the housings by lightly tapping the front case, or by prying gently between the front case and the stator (stator should remain with rear housing). When housings come apart, remove the brush assemblies from Ford Auto-Lite and Delcotron alternators.

Use a puller to remove the pulley from the rotor shaft on Chrysler units. Other alternator rotors can be supported in a vise for removal of the drive end shaft nut, pulley and fan.

On Chrysler alternators, pry the drive end bearing retainer spring from the shield, then support the shield and tap the rotor shaft through the bearing.

On Motorola units, remove the split ring washer, and separate the rotor and bearing from the drive end housing. On other alternators, support the rotor in a vise, attach a suitable tool to the drive end housing, pull the housing and bearing from the rotor shaft. Special tools are available to pull or press bearings from the rotor shaft or housing.

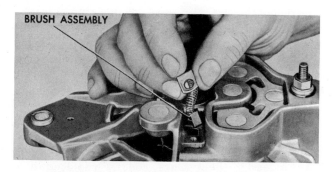

Fig. 32-24. *Remove brushes from Chrysler Corp. alternator as shown before separating shields, or housings.*

Fig. 32-25. *Test rotor for open circuit by using test lamp and touching test prods to each slip ring.*

Rotor Tests

To review: The rotor consists of a field coil wound around a shaft and enclosed between two multi-poled end pieces. The field winding is insulated from the shaft and connects to two slip rings at the rear of the shaft. One ring is contacted by the insulated brush; the other by the ground brush. Current passes through the insulated brush, through the field winding and back to ground through the ground brush.

To test the rotor for an "open circuit": Connect test lamp leads to each slip ring. If the lamp lights, the circuit is complete, or closed, Fig. 32-25.

To test for a "short circuit": Connect one test lamp lead to the rotor shaft and the other to one of the slip rings. The lamp should not light, showing that there is no connection or "short" between the windings or slip rings and the rotor shaft.

If the rotor fails either test, replace it.

Stator Tests

The stator consists of three windings wound around the inside of a circular laminated core and connected to each other at one end. The other end of each winding is connected to a set of two diodes, one positive and one negative, all insulated from the core. Tests for "opens" are made between the windings and ground to the core.

To test for an open circuit: Connect one test lamp lead to the stator core and, with the other lead, prod each of the three stator leads. The lamp should not light, showing no connection, or completed circuit, between the core and windings.

To test the stator windings for continuity: Contact each of the three stator leads in turn, two at a time, Fig. 32-26. The lamp should light, showing a complete circuit, or good continuity.

Replace the stator if it fails either of these two tests.

Fig. 32-26. Check stator windings for continuity by touching test lamp prods to two stator leads at same time.

Fig. 32-27. Test negative diodes as shown; change test lead to output terminal of alternator to check positive diodes.

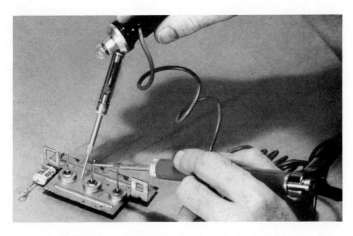

Fig. 32-28. Check condition of individual diodes by using test lamp and touching prods to diode base and its lead.

Diode Tests

A diode is a silicon rectifier connected to a terminal and mounted in a heat sink. It will allow current to pass through in one direction only, within its capabilities. As long as the current passes through the system in the proper direction and within the limitations set by the manufacturer, a diode will function properly. In doing its job, it prevents a battery from draining its current back through the alternator.

A diode will fail if the current passing through exceeds its limitations. And it will fail if a surge of current is applied to its reverse side. It will also fail if it is subjected to excessive heat due to a poor solder joint, a loose crimp connection at the lead, or a loose fit in the heat sink.

Several testers permit diode testing without removing the stator leads; others require that the leads be disconnected. To make the test: Clip one test lead to the output terminal of the alternator and the other to each of the positive diodes in turn. The meter readings should fall in the "good" band and in relatively the same area. To test the negative diodes, move the test lead from the output terminal to ground on the housing and touch the other test lead to each negative diode in turn. Again, the meter readings should be in the "good" zone and relatively close, Fig. 32-27.

To test individual diodes: Connect one test lamp clip to the diode base and one to the diode lead. Then reverse the connections: The lamp should light only once, Fig. 32-28. If the lamp lights both times, the diode is shorted. If it does not light at all, the diode is open.

An isolation diode is used in Motorola alternators to provide a solid state switch to control the charge-discharge light on the dash, and to automatically connect the voltage regulator to the alternator and battery terminal when the alternator is operating. It also is designed to eliminate electrical leakage over the alternator insulators. Testing procedures are the same as for the rectifying diodes in the alternator end housing and heat sinks.

Making Necessary Repairs

Occasionally, the slip rings on the rotor shaft require service. Slip rings that merely need cleaning can be polished with 00 sandpaper or a 400 grain polishing cloth. Slightly scored rings can be turned true on an armature lathe, but only enough stock should be removed to clean up the marks.

Diode replacement can be handled by disconnecting, cutting or unsoldering the lead, then pressing out the defective unit. Use special diode removing tools and support the housing from the inside, Fig. 32-29. Some diodes in heat sinks can be replaced as an assembly; others mounted in the end housing must be replaced on an individual basis.

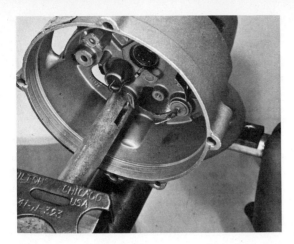

Fig. 32-29. Usually, defective diodes must be pressed out of rear case while supporting it to avoid distortion.

Install the through bolts, tightening them evenly. Check rotor rotation for freedom of movement and seating of brushes on the slip rings. Output tests of the reconditioned alternator can be made on a special generator-alternator test bench before reinstallation on the engine (or on-car output tests covered earlier can be repeated after reinstallation).

Reinstall the alternator on the engine. Adjust drive belt tension, but do not pry against the stator section of the alternator. Connect the lead wires to the field terminal, battery terminal and ground. Reconnect the ground cable to the negative post of the battery. The alternator will be polarized when the ignition switch is turned on.

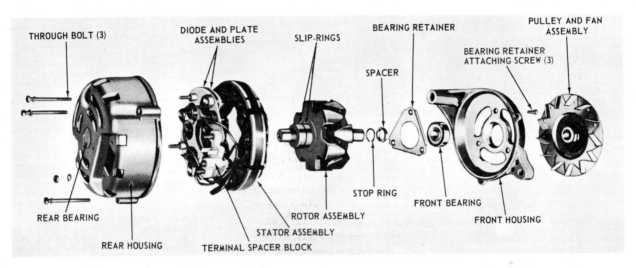

Fig. 32-30. Exploded view of Ford Autolite alternator gives details needed for performing correct disassembly and reassembly.

Reassembly and Reinstallation

After all bench tests have been completed, defective parts replaced and diodes connected to stator leads, the parts can be reassembled in reverse order of disassembly, Fig. 32-30. Make sure that replacement bearings are fully seated in the housings.

Position the front housing on the rotor shaft and press it in place. On Chrysler alternators, press the pulley on the rotor shaft until the hub just touches the inner race of the front bearing, Fig. 32-31. Assemble the fan, pulley and drive end shaft nut on other alternators, tightening the nut approximately 50 ft. lbs.

Install the brushes before assembling the two housings, using a straight stiff wire or thin welding rod pushed through the end housing to retain the brushes in the holder until reassembly of the housings is completed.

Align the scribe marks made on the housings and carefully install the rear housing on the front housing. See that the brushes are not damaged by the slip rings, then slip out the stiff wire or welding rod and allow the brushes to seat on the slip rings.

Quiz - Generator and Alternator Testing, Servicing

1. How often should a generator be inspected?
   a. Every 1,000 miles.
   b. Every 5,000 miles.
   c. Every 10,000 miles.
   d. Every 20,000 miles.
2. What material should be used when cleaning a commutator?
   a. No. 80 sandpaper.
   b. Very fine emery paper.
   c. No. 00 sandpaper.
   d. Powdered Carborundum.
3. After turning a generator commutator in a lathe, what additional operation is required?
4. Why is the tension of generator brush springs important?
5. If the inner surface of a generator cover band is found to be covered with globules of solder, what is indicated?
   a. Generator has been operating at excessive speed.

Fig. 32-31. Install drive pulley on Chrysler Corp. alternator by means of a press, while rotor is properly supported.

   b. Generator was producing excessive current.

   c. Generator was not polarized.

6. Where is the field circuit of a "B" type generator grounded?
   a. Within the generator.
   b. Outside the generator.

7. What caution must be observed when checking output of shunt generator equipped with double contact regulator?
   a. Never ground generator field with regulator connected to generator.
   b. Always be sure that field is grounded.
   c. Use a jumper between field and armature.

8. When checking the output of "B" circuit generators, where should the jumper be connected?
   a. From armature to field terminal.
   b. From armature to ground.
   c. From field to ground.

9. List three causes for low or unsteady output of a generator.

10. If tests show that generator output is excessive, even after F terminal has been disconnected, where will the trouble be?
   a. In the regulator.
   b. In the generator.
   c. Poor ground connection.
   d. Discharged battery.

11. To test the field circuit of an "A" circuit generator for an open circuit, where should the test prods of the test lamp be placed?
   a. One on field terminal, other on ground.
   b. One on field terminal, other on armature.
   c. One on armature terminal, other on ground.

12. When checking third brush generator output, where is the ammeter connected?
   a. In series into the charging circuit at "BAT" terminal of the regulator.
   b. In shunt across the battery.
   c. Into the field circuit between generator and regulator.

13. How would you polarize an "A" type generator?

14. How would you polarize a "B" type generator?

15. When checking for a grounded stator, one prod of the test lamp is touched to the frame and the other to each of the stator leads in turn. If the lamp lights, what is indicated?
   a. A ground.
   b. A short circuit.
   c. An open circuit.
   d. Circuit is in good condition.

16. What instrument is used to check silicon diode rectifiers?
   a. Ammeter.
   b. Voltmeter.
   c. Ohmmeter.
   d. Oscilloscope.

17. What is usual procedure for removing a defective diode from the end housing of an alternator?
   a. Unscrew it.
   b. Press it out.
   c. Unsolder it.

18. How would you polarize an alternator?
   a. Connect a jumper lead between output and field terminals of alternator.
   b. Disconnect wire from field terminal of alternator and touch that wire to output terminal.
   c. An alternator does not need to be polarized.

GENERATOR AND ALTERNATOR REGULATORS AND RELAYS

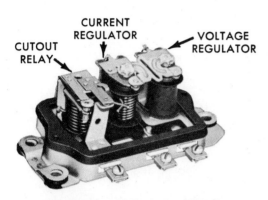

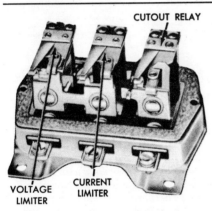

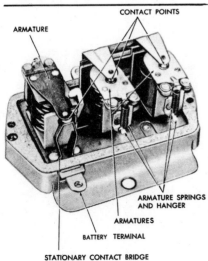

Fig. 33-1. Some typical three unit DC generator regulators are shown: Top. Delco-Remy. Center. Ford. Bottom. Autolite. Each consists of a cutout relay, current regulator and voltage regulator.

In order to control the output of an automotive generator, the charging system is provided with a regulator. Basically, a regulator is an automatic switch which controls generator output so that excessively high voltage and current will not damage the battery, generator or other units of the system.

Such regulation is needed on both shunt-wound direct current generators and on alternating current generators, or alternators, since output will continue to increase as generator speed increases. With the regulator in the system, output is maintained at a constant rate, Fig. 31-20.

DC Generator Regulator Operation

The DC generator regulator, Fig. 33-1, controls the voltage and the current by automatically cutting additional resistance in or out of the field circuit of the generator. Varying the resistance of the field circuit will alter the amount of current passing through the generator fields. This, in turn, changes the strength of the magnetic field, and in that way the generator output is regulated.

Again reviewing generator-regulator circuitry, there are two methods of connecting the additional resistance in the field circuit. In one circuit, the resistance is inserted between the field windings and the ground, Fig. 33-2. This is known as the "A" or standard-duty circuit. In the other, additional resistance is connected into the field circuit between the insulated brush and the field windings, Fig. 33-3. This is known as the "B" or heavy-duty circuit.

During the last ten years that car manufacturers utilized DC charging systems, "A" circuit generator regulators were installed on General Motors and Chrysler Corpration passenger cars and light trucks, while "B" circuit regulators were used on Ford-built passenger cars and light trucks, and on American Motors cars.

Regulators used on most DC generator-equipped passenger cars consist of three elements: cutout relay, voltage regulator, and current regulator, Fig. 33-1. However, in some applications using a third brush generator (farm tractors, for example), only a cutout relay is used. Others utilize a cutout relay and step-voltage control unit. Later installations incorporate

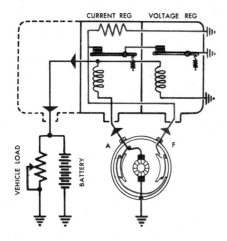

Fig. 33-2. On standard-duty "A" circuit generators, field coil is connected to insulated brush and is grounded through regulator.

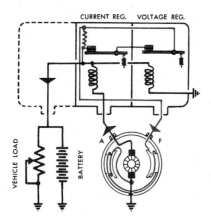

Fig. 33-3. On heavy-duty "B" circuit generators, field coil is connected to insulated brush, which grounds field circuit through generator.

a cutout relay and vibrating voltage regulator, or a cutout relay and combined current-voltage unit. It can be seen by these various regulators that all direct current generators require a cutout relay in the charging system.

Cutout Relay

The purpose of the cutout relay is to prevent the battery from discharging through the generator when the engine is stopped or is turning at slow speed. In operation, this relay closes the circuit between the generator and the battery when generator speed is high enough to develop sufficient voltage to charge the battery. It opens the circuit when generator speed is too low to develop charging voltage.

As shown in Fig. 33-4, the cutout relay is provided with two windings assembled on a single core. One winding consists of a few turns of heavy wire which is in series with the charging circuit, while the other winding is a shunt winding of many turns of fine wire which is shunted across the generator.

The windings and core of the cutout relay are assembled in a frame, and a flat steel armature with a contact point is attached to the frame by a flexible hinge, Fig. 33-5. When the generator voltage builds up to a value great enough to charge the battery, the cutout relay armature is pulled down. This closes the contacts, and current from the generator then passes through the series winding, adding to the magnetism that is holding the armature down and the points closed. When the generator stops or slows down, current begins to flow from the battery to the generator through the series winding which reverses the magnetic field of the relay. This releases the armature, opens the points, and breaks the circuit between the battery and the generator.

Voltage Regulator

The purpose of the voltage regulator is to prevent the circuit voltage from exceeding a predetermined safe value, and also to maintain a constant voltage in the system. As a result, when the battery needs charging, it automatically cuts resistance out of the field circuit, thereby increasing the flow of current in that

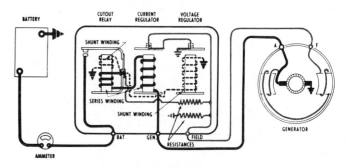

Fig. 33-4. Diagram of Delco-Remy three unit "A" circuit regulator shows: series windings in cutout relay and current regulator in solid black; shunt windings in cutout relay and voltage regulator in dashed black; field circuit and resistors in red.

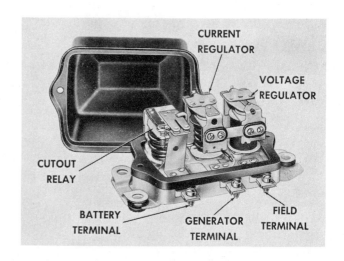

Fig. 33-5. This three unit, single-contact regulator is a typical Delco-Remy assembly used on many "A" circuit systems.

circuit, with the further result that output is increased. When the battery becomes fully charged, the resistance is cut into the field circuit, so that the charging rate is decreased.

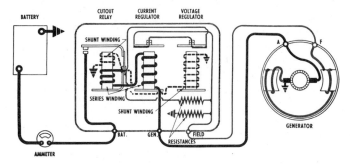

Fig. 33-6. Diagram of three unit "B" circuit Delco-Remy regulator shows: series windings in cutout relay and current regulator in solid black; shunt windings in cutout relay and voltage regulator in dashed black; field circuit and resistors in red.

The battery will actually regulate its own charge, within certain temperature limits, if the voltage in the circuit is kept at a constant value. This occurs because opposing or counter voltage of the battery increases as the battery comes up to charge. A constant-system voltage becomes less and less able to overcome this increasing counter voltage so that the charge rate to the battery automatically tapers off.

Some voltage regulators have a single shunt winding of many turns of fine wire, which is connected across the terminals of the generator, Fig. 33-4. Others have two windings assembled on a single core: a high resistance shunt winding consisting of many turns of fine wire, and a low resistance series winding consisting of a few turns of heavy wire. As shown in the diagram, Fig. 33-6, the shunt winding is shunted across the generator, while the series winding is in series between the generator field circuit and the regulator contact points.

Operation of a typical voltage regulator is as follows: When the generator reaches the voltage for which the regulator is adjusted, the magnetic field produced by the winding, or windings, overcomes the tension of the armature spring and pulls the armature down, separating the contact points. This inserts a resistance into the generator field circuit so that the generator field voltage and current are reduced, along with a weakening of the magnetic field of the regulator shunt winding which permits the contact points to close. With the points closed, the generator field circuit is grounded, so that generator current and voltage increase, and the cycle is repeated. This opening and closing of the contact points occurs from 50 to 200 times per second and, by maintaining a constant voltage, the generator supplies varying amounts of current in accordance with the requirements of the battery and electrical load.

Current Regulator

The current regulator is a magnetic switch which operates in the charging circuit to protect the generator from overload by limiting current output to a safe value. Usually, the current regulator is the center unit mounted on the base of a three unit regulator, Figs. 33-4 and 33-6. It has a series winding of a few turns of heavy wire, and the entire output of the generator passes through this winding. When the current regulator is not working, the tension of the spiral spring holds the armature away from the core so the points are in contact. In this position, the generator field circuit is completed to ground through the regulator contact points in series with the voltage regulator contact points.

When the generator current output reaches the value for which the unit is set, the magnetic pull draws the armature down, opening the contact points. This inserts a resistance into the generator field circuit, reducing the field current output. This in turn reduces the pull on the armature of the current regulator, allowing the spiral spring to pull the armature up and close the contact points. This grounds the generator field circuit, causing the generator output to again increase. This cycle is repeated from 30 to 50 times per second, limiting the generator output so it does not exceed its rated maximum.

Resistances

The current and voltage regulator units use one or two common resistances, Fig. 33-6. One is inserted in the field circuit when either the current or voltage regulator unit operates. The second resistance is connected between the regulator field terminal and the cutout relay frame, which places it in parallel with the generator field coils. The sudden reduction in field current, occurring when either the current or voltage regulator contact points open, is accompanied by a surge of induced voltage in the field coils as the magnetic field changes in strength. These surges are partly dissipated by the two resistors and reduce the arcing at the contact points.

Temperature Compensation

Cutout relays, voltage regulators and current regulators are usually wound with copper wire, and the resistance of these windings increases as they become warm. It is therefore necessary to compensate for this change in resistance, otherwise the degree of "magnetic pull" exerted by these windings would vary and cause the voltage and current settings to change.

In most designs, the necessary temperature correction is provided by means of a bimetallic hinge on the armature of the relay or regulator, Fig. 33-5. This bimetallic hinge appears to be made of a thin strip of spring steel. Actually it is made of two thin layers of different metals which are fused together. These metals have different rates of expansion as the result of heat. Thermostatic action takes place as the hinge gets hot; one side expands more than the other, causing the hinge to bend. This type of hinge applied to the regulator or relay armature tries to bend with increasing temperature and reduces the tension of the spring. Change of spring tension compensates for the increased resistance of the copper windings as the temperature goes up and the regulator will now operate at the same or slightly lower voltage.

Regulator Polarity

Most regulators are designed for use with systems having the negative terminal of the battery grounded. Using the wrong polarity regulator on a system will cause the regulator contacts to pit badly and shorten its life. Regulators are clearly marked on their base to indicate the system for which they are designed.

Delco-Remy Three Unit Regulators

The Delco-Remy three unit single contact regulator, used mostly on General Motors passenger cars, is the "A" circuit type and grounds the field circuit in the regulator. This type regulator has only a single winding on the voltage regulator unit as compared to the two windings used on the two unit regulator and some three unit regulators. Because of this difference in winding on the voltage unit, there is a difference in the method of checking and adjusting the voltage setting.

This regulator, Fig. 33-5, is of the single contact point type, Fig. 33-4.

When checking and adjusting the three unit Delco-Remy regulator, follow this procedure:

    a. Bring voltage regulator to operating temperature.

    b. Check voltage regulator.

    c. Check cutout relay.

    d. Bring current regulator to operating temperature.

    e. Check current regulator.

VOLTAGE REGULATOR ADJUSTMENT: To adjust air gap, push down on armature until contact points are just touching. Measure the air gap between the armature and winding core, Fig. 33-7. Adjust by loosening contact mounting screws and moving mounting bracket as required. Manufacturer's specifications must be consulted.

VOLTAGE SETTING: There are several methods of making this setting. The following is known as the "fixed 1/4 ohm resistance method" and can be used for either 6 or 12 volt systems, using single contact regulators.

Make connections as shown in Fig. 33-8. Bring regulator up to operating temperature by operating generator at 3500 rpm (generator) for 15 minutes.

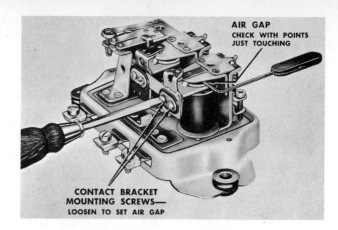

Fig. 33-7. Follow procedure illustrated here to adjust air gap on Delco-Remy voltage regulator.

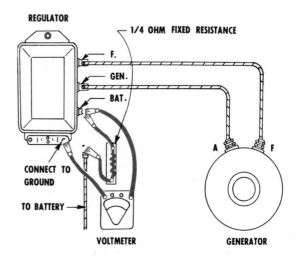

Fig. 33-8. Connect fixed resistance and voltmeter leads, as illustrated, to check voltage regulator settings of "A" circuit Delco-Remy charging system.

Fig. 33-9. Adjust voltage regulator by turning adjusting screw clockwise to increase voltage, counterclockwise to reduce voltage of Delco-Remy regulators.

Regulator cover must be in place. It is not necessary to measure the current while test is being made, but it is important that no load other than ignition be on the generator. Cycle the generator by reducing its

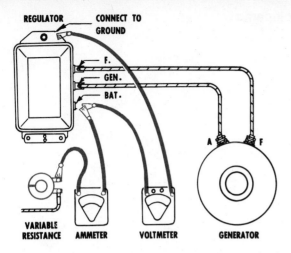

Fig. 33-10. Connect variable resistance and voltmeter leads, as shown (in red), to check voltage regulator setting of "A" circuit Delco-Remy charging system.

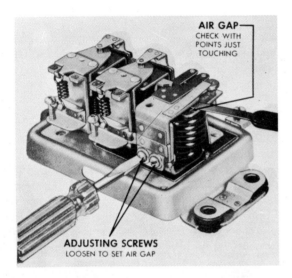

Fig. 33-11. To set air gap of cutout relay in Delco-Remy regulators, raise or lower armature — with battery disconnected.

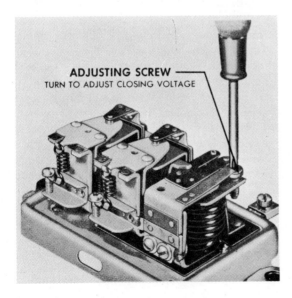

Fig. 33-12. Adjust closing voltage of cutout relay by turning screw clockwise to increase voltage, counterclockwise to lower voltage.

speed until the contacts of the cutout relay open. Then bring generator back to 3500 rpm. (Engine about 1500 rpm.) Note reading on voltmeter.

Adjust voltage setting by turning adjusting screw, Fig. 33-9. To increase voltage, turn screw clockwise. After each setting, recycle generator.

VARIABLE RESISTANCE METHOD: Make connections as shown in Fig. 33-10. Start generator and adjust variable resistor to 1-10 amps. Operate generator at specified speed for 15 minutes. Cycle the generator as previously explained and adjust voltage setting as shown in Fig. 33-9. Test specifications are given for a normal room temperature of 80 deg. If regulator is adjusted at room temperature higher than 80 deg., set voltage 0.1 volt less than specified normal setting for each 10 deg. above 80 deg. For lower room temperatures, set voltage setting 0.1 volt more for each 10 deg. below 80 deg.

CUTOUT RELAY ADJUSTMENT: The cutout relay requires three checks and adjustments. These are air gap, point opening, and voltage required to close the contacts. When adjusting the air gap and the point opening, it is necessary to disconnect the battery.

The air gap is measured when the armature is held down so that the contact points are closed. To adjust, loosen the adjusting screws and raise or lower the armature until the desired gap is obtained, Fig. 33-11. Be sure the points are in alignment and the adjusting screws are tightened when the adjustment is completed.

The point opening or gap between contacts is adjusted by bending the upper armature stop.

A voltmeter is needed to check the voltage at which the points of the cutout relay close. The voltmeter is connected from the "GEN" terminal of the regulator to ground. When making the test, increase generator speed slowly until sufficient voltage is produced to close the relay contacts. To adjust the closing voltage, turn the adjusting screw clockwise to increase the closing voltage and counterclockwise to lower the closing voltage, Fig. 33-12. After each adjustment, the generator should be stopped and then its speed increased slowly to check the closing voltage.

The manufacturer's specifications should be followed closely when making any of these adjustments.

CURRENT REGULATOR ADJUSTMENT: It is necessary to check the air gap and the current setting of current regulators.

The air gap check and adjustment is made in the same manner described for the voltage regulator.

To check the current regulator setting, the voltage regulator must be prevented from operating. One method is shown in Fig. 33-13. The procedure is to insert a screwdriver through the hole in the regulator base, with the screwdriver firmly contacting the regulator base and the shield at the same time. When making the current setting, connect an ammeter in series with the regulator battery terminal and the wire disconnected from that terminal. Turn on all lights and accessories and operate the generator at specified speed for 15 minutes with the cover in place. Short the voltage regulator by inserting the screwdriver through the base. Cycle generator and note current setting. Adjustment is made by turning screw controlling spring tension of current regulator.

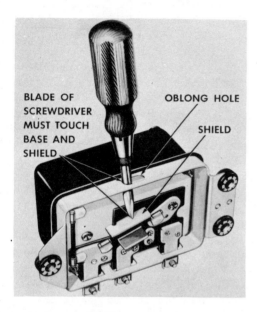

Fig. 33-13. To keep Delco-Remy voltage regulator from operating while checking current regulator setting, insert screwdriver through hole in regulator base as indicated.

Another method of adjusting the setting of the current regulator is known as the jumper lead method. This method is used only on current regulators without temperature compensation. An ammeter is connected into the charging circuit as in the previous test and a jumper lead is placed across the voltage regulator points, Fig. 33-14. With all the lights and ac-

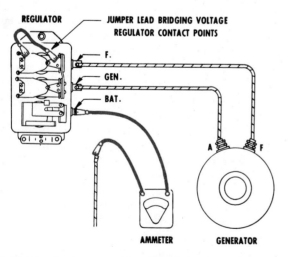

Fig. 33-14. To check setting of certain Delco-Remy current regulators, place jumper lead across voltage regulator points and connect ammeter as illustrated.

Fig. 33-15. Clean large, flat voltage regulator points on Delco-Remy regulators with a spoon or riffler file. Use crocus cloth on cutout relay points.

cessories turned on, operate generator at specified speed and note current setting. Adjust spring tension of current regulator to limit current to desired value. Make final adjustment by increasing tension.

Check for Oxidized Regulator Points

Oxidized regulator points may be the cause of low generator output or discharged starting battery. The following check should be made to determine if single contact regulator points are oxidized: Connect an ammeter in the charging circuit and turn on the headlights. Operate the generator at a speed which will produce a charge rate of 5 amps. Using a short jumper lead, connect the field terminal of the regulator to the ground. If the generator output increases more than 2 amps., oxidized regulator contact points are indicated, and they should be cleaned.

Cleaning Delco-Remy Regulator Points

Regulator contact points will not operate indefinitely without some attention and the great majority of regulator trouble can be overcome by simple cleaning of the current and voltage regulator points, plus occasional adjustment. The large flat points should be cleaned with a spoon or riffler file. On some negative grounded regulators which have the flat contact point on the regulator armature, loosen the upper contact bracket mounting screws so that the bracket can be tilted to one side, Fig. 33-15. On positive grounded regulators, the flat point is in the upper contact bracket so the bracket must be removed for cleaning the points. A flat file cannot be used successfully to clean the flat contact points since it will not touch the center where wear is most apt to occur. Emery cloth or sandpaper must never be used to clean contact points.

Remove all oxides from contact points. It is not necessary to remove any pitting or cavities that may have developed.

Cutout relay contact points are of soft material and should not be cleaned with a riffler file. These should be cleaned with crocus cloth or fine abrasive material. Points should then be cleaned with fresh commercial solvent to remove any foreign material.

Delco-Remy Double Contact Regulator

Because of increased electrical load, many cars, particularly those equipped with air conditioning, are provided with regulators of the double contact type, Fig. 33-16.

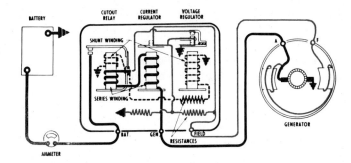

Fig. 33-17. Lower set of voltage regulator points controls voltage at low speeds, upper set of points provides control at high speeds.

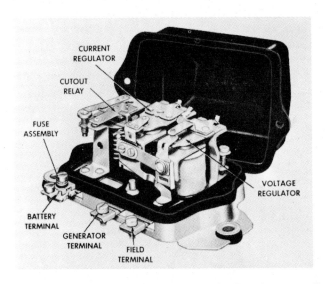

Fig. 33-16. Double contact regulators by Delco-Remy are so-called because voltage regulator unit has two sets of contact points.

On all cars with double contact regulators, NEVER GROUND the generator field with the regulator connected to the generator. This will instantly burn the upper set of contact points of the regulator.

Before polarizing the generator of a system fitted with a double contact regulator, always insulate the brushes from the commutator.

The instruction given previously for checking current output, voltage output, testing for ground in generator, generator circuit resistance test, and generator ground circuit test are also applicable to double contact regulator systems.

OPERATION: Regulators of the double contact type are similar to the single contact unit just discussed. However, the voltage regulator unit of a double contact type generator regulator is provided with two sets of points instead of one to accommodate the high field current used in the generator, Fig. 33-17.

The lower set of contacts limits the generator voltage at low speeds as vibration of the contacts intermittently inserts resistance in the generator field circuit. When the speed is increased, the lower set of points can no longer control the voltage and the armature closes the upper set of points. A vibrating action takes place on the upper contacts to regulate the volt-

age at high speeds. The upper set of contacts alternately places a short circuit across the generator field circuit, or inserts resistance in the circuit, thus limiting the voltage to a predetermined value.

CUTOUT RELAY TESTS: Connect a voltmeter between the generator terminal of the regulator and the ground, Fig. 33-18, and a 25 ohm, 25 watt rheostat that has an open position, between the field terminal of the regulator and the field lead from the generator. Set the engine on fast idle and the rheostat turned to position of maximum resistance. Slowly turn out the resistance until the cutout relay points close and note the voltage. Set to specified voltage by turning adjusting screw on cutout relay clockwise to increase the setting, counterclockwise to decrease the setting.

Slowly turn rheostat to obtain specified amperage reading. Then slowly increase resistance, noting how far the ammeter will move below zero, before the relay opens up and returns the needle to zero. This reading is the opening amperage of the cutout relay, and it is the amount of reverse current discharged from the battery to generator that is required to open the points. If reverse current is between 1 and 6 amps.,

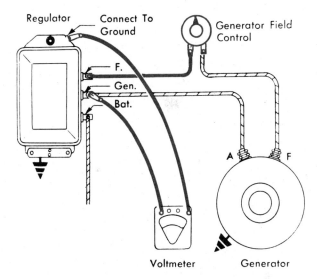

Fig. 33-18. To test cutout relay closing voltage of Delco-Remy double contact regulator, connect voltmeter leads and variable resistance unit, as illustrated.

the cutout relay is operating normally. The only adjustments are the air gap and the point opening. Adjust the air gap by loosening the two screws in back of relay; raise or lower armature as required, Fig. 33-19. Point opening can be adjusted by bending the upper armature stop.

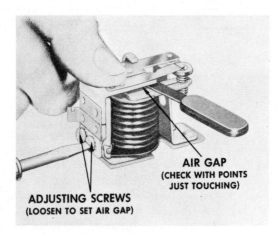

Fig. 33-19. Set air gap of cutout relay by raising or lowering armature as required. Check specifications.

CURRENT REGULATOR TEST: Connect a 1000 watt carbon pile resistor, ammeter and variable resistance unit, as shown in Fig. 33-20. Speed up engine to approximately 2,000 rpm and at the same time, add enough load to bring current regulator into operation. As speed of generator increases and additional load is added, ammeter will move up scale to a maximum reading. From this point, increasing or decreasing the load will lower the ammeter reading. Ammeter reading should fall within specified amperage range.

To adjust current setting, turn adjusting screw of current regulator clockwise to increase setting.

Final setting should always be made by increasing spring tension. After each adjustment and before taking reading, replace regulator cover and cycle the generator.

To adjust air gap, push current regulator armature until contact points just close. Adjust the gap by moving the contact mounting bracket up or down as required.

VOLTAGE REGULATOR TESTS: Never ground generator field with regulator connected to generator. This will instantly burn up the upper set of contact points when the system is operated.

To check voltage regulator, make connections shown in Fig. 33-21. Then with the variable resistance turned to position of minimum resistance, operate generator at a medium speed, or a higher speed, so that regulator is operating on upper set of contacts. Operate at that speed for 15 minutes. Regulator cover must be in place. Cycle generator by turning the var-

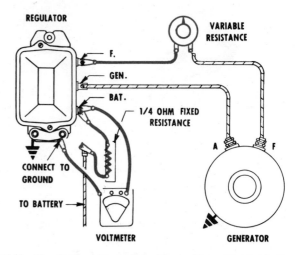

Fig. 33-21. To check setting of double contact voltage regulator, connect voltmeter leads, fixed resistance and variable resistance as indicated.

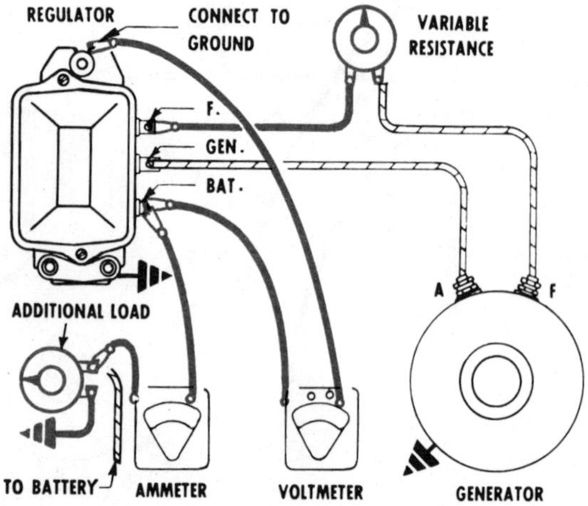

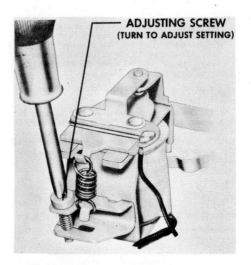

Fig. 33-22. Adjust voltage regulator by turning screw clockwise to increase voltage, counterclockwise to reduce voltage.

Fig. 33-20. To check setting of current regulator in Delco-Remy double contact regulators, connect ammeter leads, 1,000 watt resistor and variable resistance unit as shown.

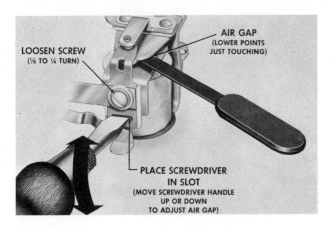

Fig. 33-23. Adjust voltage regulator air gap by raising or lowering armature as required.

Fig. 33-23. If it is found necessary to make this air gap adjustment, the voltage setting of both sets of contacts must be rechecked. Air gap should be measured with contact points just touching.

Other Delco-Remy Controls

A single unit cutout relay assembly, Fig. 33-24, is used with third brush generators on some farm tractors to open and close the circuit between the generator and battery. In applications like this, the cutout relay is often mounted on top of the generator.

To test and adjust the single unit relay, follow the same procedure used on the cutout relay of two and three unit Delco-Remy regulators – with one exception. That is, to adjust closing voltage, bend the armature spring post up to increase closing voltage, bend it down to decrease closing voltage. After each adjustment, stop the generator, then slowly increase its speed and recheck the closing voltage setting, using a voltmeter connected from the "GEN" terminal of the relay to ground.

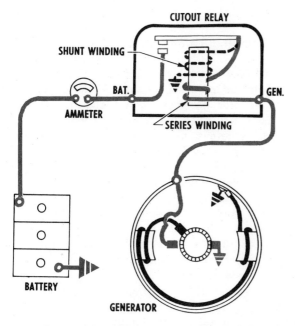

Fig. 33-24. Circuits of single unit cutout relays include: relay series winding and charging circuit in red; cutout shunt winding in dashed black; generator field circuit in solid black.

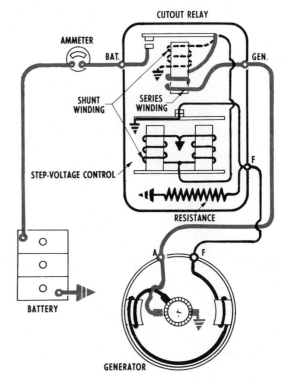

Fig. 33-25. Step-voltage control unit utilizes: cutout relay series winding in red; cutout shunt winding in dashed black; step-voltage control shunt winding and resistance unit in solid black.

iable resistance to open position momentarily, then slowly decrease resistance. Regulator should be operating on upper contacts between specified voltages.

Increase generator field control slowly until regulator begins to operate on lower set of contact points. The lower set should operate at specified voltage below the upper set of contacts.

To adjust the voltage setting while operating on the upper set of points, turn the adjusting screw on regulator clockwise to increase voltage setting, Fig. 33-22. Final setting should always be made when increasing the tension on spring.

The difference in voltage between operation of the upper set of contacts and the lower contacts can be increased by slightly increasing air gap, and decreased by slightly decreasing the air gap. This adjustment can be made while the regulator is operating,

Cutout relays having fixed or variable resistance are also used in certain third brush generator applications. This type of relay controls generator output by inserting resistance in the field circuit. On some installations, this added resistance is utilized under light load conditions, then it is cut out of the circuit when the headlights are turned on.

Step-voltage control units are another type of relay that automatically inserts resistance in the field circuit of "A" circuit generators, Fig. 33-25. The step-voltage control assembly consists of a conventionally wired cutout relay and a step-voltage unit having two shunt windings placed on two cores, a flat steel armature, contact points and a field resistance unit. The contact points remain open to keep the resistance in the circuit to reduce generator output as long as the battery retains a satisfactory charge. When battery voltage drops, the contact points close, field resistance is shorted out and generator output is increased to its maximum.

Two Unit Regulators

The Delco-Remy two unit regulator for use with third brush generators consists of a conventional cutout relay and a voltage regulator unit, Fig. 33-26. Whereas the step-voltage control unit simply cuts resistance in and out of the field circuit; the voltage regulator unit used in the two unit regulator prevents voltage from exceeding a specified maximum. In operation, the points vibrate as in three unit regulators.

Fig. 33-26. In Delco-Remy two unit regulator applications, voltage regulator limits voltage output to a specified maximum.

Combined current-voltage regulators are used with both third brush and shunt type generators with "A" circuits, Fig. 33-27. Construction of these regulators features a cutout relay and a combination current-voltage regulator. The relay is conventional, but the current-voltage unit has three windings on one core and is designed to control both the battery charge rate and circuit voltage. This regulator is more suited than two or three unit regulators for use on farm tractors and stationary engines where the equipment operates for long periods under little electric load.

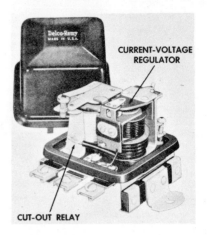

Fig. 33-27. Late type Delco-Remy two unit, combined current-voltage regulators are equipped for screw adjustment, while older models are fitted with adjustable spring hangers.

Single Winding Relays

Other relays include:
1. Solenoid relays used in conjunction with starter solenoids to prevent the starting motor from operating when the engine is running.
2. Horn relays used to close the circuit between the horns and battery when the horn ring or button is depressed.
3. Telltale relays used in connection with indicator lights on the dash to warn of a malfunction in a particular electrical circuit, Fig. 33-28.
4. Buzzers in which the contact points "buzz" to signal that an abnormal condition exists in the circuit (for example, a preset speed has been exceeded).

These relays utilize a single core with single winding and an armature arrangement which controls the operation of a set of contact points to open and close the circuit being controlled.

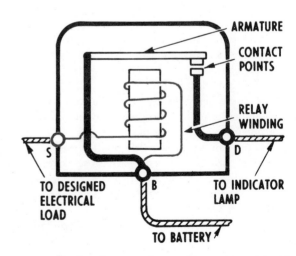

Fig. 33-28. Telltale relays are designed to make and break current flow to an indicator light on dash when a malfunction occurs in circuit.

Fig. 33-29. Autolite two charge regulators utilize a two-step voltage control which closes contacts when system is at rest, opens contacts when charging circuit is sufficiently energized.

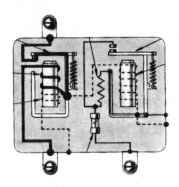

Fig. 33-30. When Autolite two charge voltage regulator contact points are open, a resistance is placed in generator field circuit.

Autolite Two Charge Regulator

The two charge (TC) regulator, Fig. 33-29, is used in connection with a third brush generator to reduce generator output when required. In almost every case, the two charge regulator is mounted on the same base as the cutout relay.

Contact points in TC regulators, Figs. 33-29 and 33-30, ground the generator field circuit when the points are open, and insert a resistance in the field circuit when closed.

One of the TC regulator contacts is mounted on a stationary bridge, while the other is mounted on a movable magnetic armature, Fig. 33-29. An electromagnet with many turns of fine wire is shunted across the generator output. The amount of magnetism developed in the electromagnet therefore depends on the voltage of the generating system. Spring tension is provided to hold the contacts together, until sufficient current flows through the shunt winding to pull the contacts apart. When the voltage reaches the value for which the voltage regulator is adjusted, the magnet in the voltage regulator overcomes the spring tension and pulls down the armature, opening the contact points, Fig. 33-30. This inserts the resistance in the field circuit, which reduces output by approximately 50 percent and generator voltage is reduced.

Most Autolite two charge regulators have a fuse

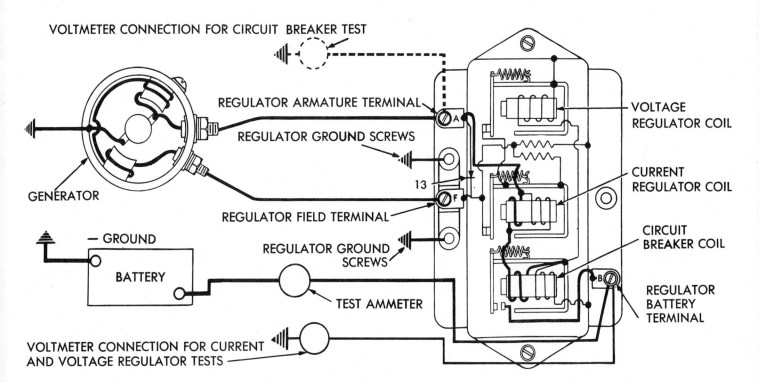

Fig. 33-31. Design of charging system circuitry differs among manufacturers. Compare this Autolite diagram with Delco-Remy, Figs. 33-4 and 33-6.

mounted on the base. It is connected in the generator field circuit and protects the field against excessive field current, which would happen if an open circuit occurred in the charging circuit.

A quick test on a two charge regulator is to connect an ammeter in series with the lead from the battery and disconnect the field lead. If the regulator is defective, the output will drop off.

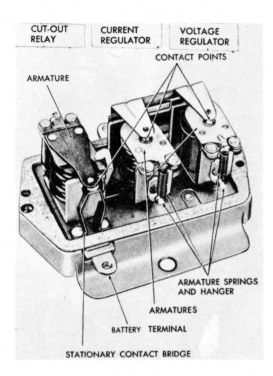

Fig. 33-32. Used mainly on Chrysler Corporation cars with DC charging systems, Autolite three unit regulators locate battery terminal on one side, armature and field terminals on other side of regulator.

Autolite Three Unit Regulator

While both Delco-Remy and Autolite generators and regulators are "A" circuit type, there are some detailed differences between the two. The Autolite current regulator is provided with both a series and shunt winding, Fig. 33-31, whereas the current regulator used in most Delco-Remy systems has only a series winding. In addition, there is a difference in terminology. On the Autolite unit, the regulator terminal which is connected to the generator is marked A or ARM, with the latter designation plainly embossed on the cover of the unit. Delco-Remy calls this same terminal "GEN." Another difference is in the location of the terminals, with Autolite placing the battery terminal on one side of the regulator and the armature and field connections on the other, Fig. 33-32.

Another and major difference is in the type of temperature compensation. To correct for the effects of heat on the operating characteristics of the regulator windings, Autolite units have a nickel-iron

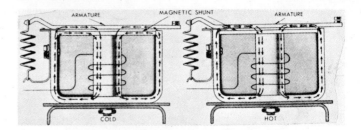

Fig. 33-33. Magnetic shunt used on most Autolite regulators bridges top of yoke just below armature. When cold, it bypasses some magnetism so that a higher voltage is required to operate armature. As shunt becomes heated, it loses its magnetic properties and all magnetic lines of force act on armature.

magnetic bypass on the voltage regulator unit, Fig. 33-33. This shunt bypasses some of the magnetic flux when the unit is cold and allows most of the flux to act on the voltage regulator armature when the unit is hot. Thus, when the coil is hot and produces less flux per volt, the magnetic shunt allows most of the flux to act on the armature. The change in winding resistance is overcompensated to allow the regulator to operate at a higher voltage under cold operating conditions. This is necessary because it requires a higher voltage to charge a battery when its electrolyte is at a low temperature.

Three Unit Regulator Tests

Before making any tests on the Autolite regulator, the units should be in operation at least 15 minutes in order to bring the regulator to operating temperature. Final tests must be made with the cover in place and with the unit mounted in the same position it occupies on the vehicle. Each time an adjustment is made and the cover replaced, the generator should be cycled. Autolite suggests two ways of cycling the generator:

1. Vary generator speed: Drop speed to zero and return to test rpm.
2. Varying generator voltage: Use field rheostat to drop voltage to near zero, and return to regulated amount by gradually turning rheostat to "all out."

CUTOUT RELAY TEST: Connect instruments as shown in Fig. 33-34. Operate generator at approximately 1,500 to 2,000 rpm. Turn rheostat to increase generator voltage. At the instant the cutout relay contacts close, the voltmeter will show a slight dip. The highest voltage before the "dip" occurs is the closing voltage of the cutout relay.

To check the opening of the cutout relay, use same connections shown in Fig. 33-34. Turn the field rheostat until the ammeter reads 10 to 15 amps., then reduce the amperes slowly with the field rheostat. Observe the discharge amperage just before the contacts open. If the opening and closing of the cutout relay points do not check with specifications, remove the cover and make adjustments.

To adjust the closing voltage, change the spring tension by bending the lower spring hanger, Fig. 33-1. Increasing tension raises the closing voltage.

To adjust the opening amperage, increase or decrease the contact gap by bending the stationary contact bridge, Fig. 33-35. Decreasing the gap lowers the opening amperage. Be sure to keep the points in alignment.

VOLTAGE REGULATOR TEST: Connect instruments as shown in Fig. 33-36. In this test the 1/4 ohm resistance may be used for both 6 and 12V systems. Operate the generator at approximately 3,000 rpm. The indication on the voltmeter will be the operating voltage of the voltage regulator. If this does not agree with specifications, remove the cover and adjust the voltage unit spring tension by bending the lower spring hanger. Increasing the tension raises the operating voltage. Replace cover quickly; cycle the generator.

CURRENT REGULATOR TEST: To test the operating current of the regulator, make the connections shown in Fig. 33-37. Operate the generator at approximately 3,000 rpm. Adjust the carbon pile until maximum amperage is obtained on the ammeter. This is the output at which the regulator is adjusted. If this does not agree with specifications, remove the cover and adjust the current regulator spring tension by bending the lower spring hanger, Fig. 33-1. Increasing the tension raises the operating current. If a carbon pile is not available, the battery may be partly discharged by operating the starting motor 15 seconds at a time. Then start the engine and operate the generator at approximately 3,000 rpm and note the ammeter reading. This will be the operating current of the current regulator.

CONTACT POINT SERVICE: On Autolite regulators, the circuit breaker or cutout relay contacts are both made of coin silver. The upper contact and lower contact of both voltage and current regulators are made of dissimilar metals. These are basically two different alloys of silver. It is very important that

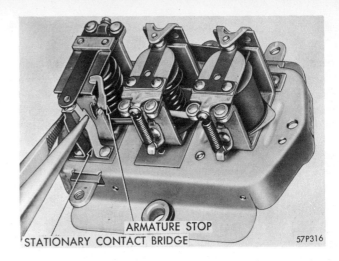

STATIONARY CONTACT BRIDGE   ARMATURE STOP

Fig. 33-35. Set cutout relay opening amperage of Autolite regulators by readjusting contact point gap by squeezing or spreading stationary contact bridge.

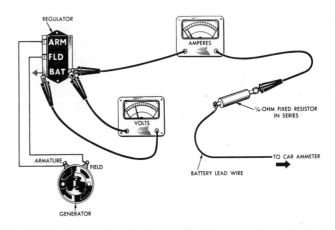

Fig. 33-36. Connect fixed resistor and voltmeter and ammeter leads as illustrated to test operating voltage of Autolite voltage regulator.

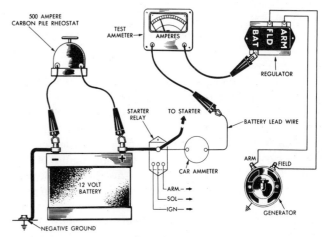

Fig. 33-37. Attach ammeter test leads and carbon pile rheostat to Autolite system as shown to check operating current of regulator.

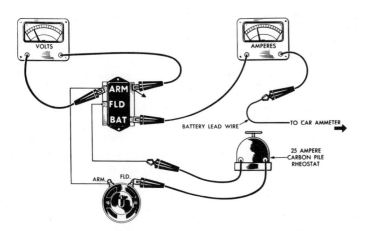

Fig. 33-34. Connect test leads as indicated to check closing voltage and opening amperage of cutout relay, or circuit breaker, in Autolite three unit regulators.

these contacts be installed in their proper relation according to the grounding of the system in which they are used. If the wrong contacts are installed, or if a regulator of the opposite polarity is used, transfer of metal and arcing of the contacts will be greatly increased, resulting in shorter contact life. Armatures and stationary contact brackets of all positive ground units are cadmium plated. Armature and stationary contact brackets of negative units are copper plated.

To clean Autolite regulator contacts, use a No. 6 American Swiss cut equaling file. Filing must be done parallel with the armature. Do not use emery

not go in. Adjustment is made by bending the brass armature stop on top of the unit, Fig. 33-38.

VOLTAGE AND CURRENT REGULATOR: The air gap on these units is checked at the instant the contacts barely separate. The most accurate way to check the voltage and current regulator air gaps is to connect a test lamp in series with the current and voltage regulator contacts, Fig. 33-38.

CHECKING AND ADJUSTING REGULATOR AIR GAPS

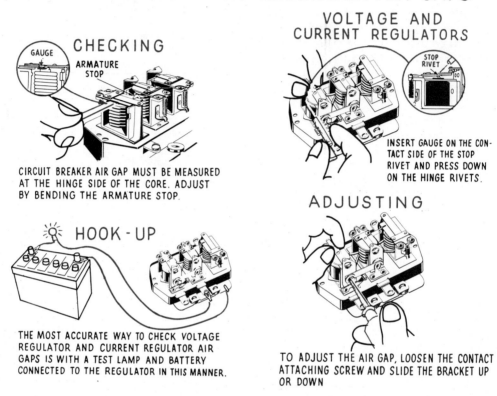

CHECKING

CIRCUIT BREAKER AIR GAP MUST BE MEASURED AT THE HINGE SIDE OF THE CORE. ADJUST BY BENDING THE ARMATURE STOP.

HOOK-UP

THE MOST ACCURATE WAY TO CHECK VOLTAGE REGULATOR AND CURRENT REGULATOR AIR GAPS IS WITH A TEST LAMP AND BATTERY CONNECTED TO THE REGULATOR IN THIS MANNER.

VOLTAGE AND CURRENT REGULATORS

INSERT GAUGE ON THE CONTACT SIDE OF THE STOP RIVET AND PRESS DOWN ON THE HINGE RIVETS.

ADJUSTING

TO ADJUST THE AIR GAP, LOOSEN THE CONTACT ATTACHING SCREW AND SLIDE THE BRACKET UP OR DOWN

Fig. 33-38. These sketches illustrate proper method of checking and adjusting air gaps of Autolite three unit regulators.

cloth or sandpaper. After filing, the contacts should be cleaned by placing a narrow strip of linen tape between the contacts, then saturate the tape with carbon tetrachloride, drawing the wet portion of the tape back and forth between the contacts. Finally a dry portion of the tape should be used between the contacts.

AIR GAP ADJUSTMENT: The air gap on Autolite regulators is the air space between the armature and the winding core. If the air gap is too wide or too narrow, the magnetic effects and the spiral spring action will be upset. Furthermore, improper air gaps interfere with the temperature compensation of the units. Once correctly adjusted, there will be little change throughout a long period of operation.

CIRCUIT BREAKER: The circuit breaker, or cutout relay, air gap is checked with the contacts open. A two step flat gauge is used. The smaller end of the specified gauge should just slide between the core and armature, and the large portion of the gauge should

With the regulator at rest, both sets of contacts are closed and the lamp should light. A special pintype gauge having two specified dimensions is used for checking. With the smaller gauge inserted between the armature and the core on the contact side of the stop rivet, press down on the two hinge rivets. This causes the armature to move down against the gauge and the contact spring will follow. The contact points should open slightly as indicated by the lamp dimming or going out. Next, insert the larger gauge, and press down on the hinge rivets. The light should burn normally, indicating that the contacts are still closed.

If the air gap is out of adjustment, loosen the contact adjusting screw, Fig. 33-38, and slide the bracket up or down as required. Be sure to keep the contacts aligned to insure maximum contact life.

Voltage and current regulator contact assemblies are the same, and the air gaps are checked in the same manner.

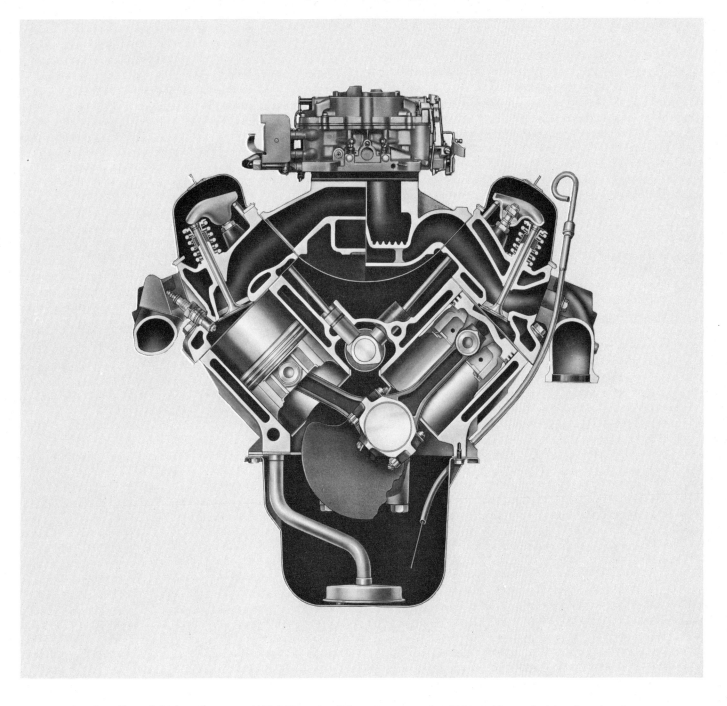

American Motors' high performance AMX 390 cu. in. V-8 engine is rated at 315 hp with standard four-barrel carburetor. Bore is 4.17; stroke is 3.57. Compression ratio is 10.2 to 1. Note cast depressions in top of pistons for valve clearance.

Ford Regulators

With the exception of a double contact Delco-Remy regulator used on some Ford cars equipped with air conditioning, all Ford regulators are of the "B" circuit type which ground the field inside the generator. The double contact regulator made by Delco-Remy grounds the field in the regulator. Other regulators used on Ford-built automobiles are made by Ford, Bosch or Autolite. The old 6 volt systems have the positive side of the battery grounded, while 12 volt systems have the negative side of the battery grounded.

Ford regulators consist of the familiar three units: Cutout relay, current regulator and voltage regulator. The units operate in a manner similar to units previously described.

TEMPERATURE COMPENSATION: The armature hinge of these regulators is of bimetal construction, and is built into armature hinge. The temperature sensitivity of the bimetal causes the voltage regulator setting to change according to temperature. Therefore, it is necessary to establish a normal or stabilized regulator operating temperature to coincide with the specified setting. The temperature of the surrounding air for this setting is 70 to 80 deg. F. The regulator temperature for this or any other setting is defined as the temperature of the regulator after one-half hour of operation on the car, or after the regulator has been heated until it becomes stabilized.

Ambient Temperature °F.	Voltage Regulation Setting (Volts)				
	Standard Regulator (Ford and Bosch)	40 amp. Low Cut In (Autolite)	30 amp. Low Cut In, 50 amp. and 60 amp. (Bosch)		60 amp. (Ford)
			Lower Stage	Upper Stage	
25	15.1-15.9	14.3-15.2	14.4	15.1	15.5
35	15.0-15.8	14.3-15.2	14.3	15.0	15.4
45	14.9-15.7	14.3-15.1	14.3	15.0	15.3
55	14.8-15.6	14.3-15.0	14.2	14.9	15.2
65	14.7-15.5	14.3-14.9	14.2	14.8	15.1
75	14.6-15.4	14.2-14.9	14.1	14.8	15.0
85	14.5-15.3	14.1-14.8	14.0	14.7	14.9
95	14.3-15.1	14.1-14.7	14.0	14.7	14.8
105	14.2-15.0	14.0-14.7	13.9	14.6	14.6
115	14.1-14.9	14.0-14.6	13.9	14.5	14.5
125	13.9-14.7	13.9-14.5	13.8	14.5	14.4
135	13.8-14.6	13.8-14.4	13.7	14.4	14.3
145	13.6-14.4	13.8-14.4	13.7	14.4	14.2

Fig. 33-39. Ford voltage regulator temperature compensation chart reveals broad range of voltage settings at ambient temperatures from 25 to 145 degs. F.

For correct voltage regulator adjustment, first be sure that the regulator has reached normal operating temperature; then make the voltage adjustment setting coincide with the temperature of the surrounding air, which is the under hood temperature. Specifications are shown in Fig. 33-39. To measure the temperature, a special thermometer, Fig. 33-40, is clamped to the case of the regulator. When a regulator is being checked on a workbench, the temperature would be the room temperature. The procedure is to clip the

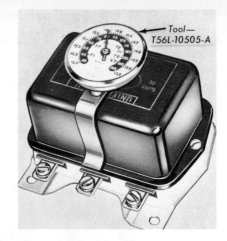

Fig. 33-40. Since voltage settings vary with temperature changes, Ford recommends use of a special thermometer so stabilized operating temperature can be established before adjustments are made.

thermometer to the regulator case and mount a small fan 15 in. from the regulator. The fan will provide sufficient airflow to assure stabilization of the regulator at the temperature indicated by the thermometer.

The following tests apply to all "B" circuit regulators:

CUTOUT RELAY TEST: Start the engine and run it at approximately 1500 rpm. Make connections as shown in Figs. 33-41 and 33-42. Decrease the resistance in the field circuit, and the voltage output of the generator as indicated by the voltmeter, will increase until the cutout relay closes. The cutout closing will be indicated by a rise of the ammeter needle and a dip of the voltmeter needle. The maximum voltage at the time the voltmeter needle dips will be the closing voltage of the cutout relay.

To adjust the cut-in voltage, bend the adjusting arm, Fig. 33-43, upward to increase the voltage on Ford-built units. On the Bosch unit, Fig. 33-44, bend the cutout spring adjusting arm upward to decrease the cut-in voltage.

VOLTAGE REGULATOR TEST: Make the connections as shown in Figs. 33-41 and 33-42. Reduce resistance in field circuit to zero. The ammeter should

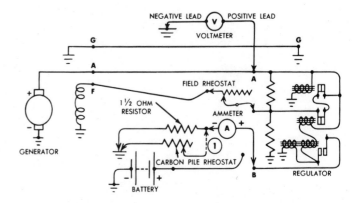

Fig. 33-41. How test equipment connects into charging circuitry is clearly illustrated in this wiring diagram of a Ford DC generator equipped system.

show an approximate 10 amp. load. Read the voltage regulation on the voltmeter scale. Speed the engine momentarily to see if voltage remains regulated. If the regulator voltage is not within the limits set by the specifications for the ambient temperature, com-

To increase the voltage setting, increase the spring tension by bending the adjustment arm upward, Fig. 33-43. On the Bosch heavy-duty unit, Fig. 33-44, bend the voltage limiting spring upward to decrease the voltage setting.

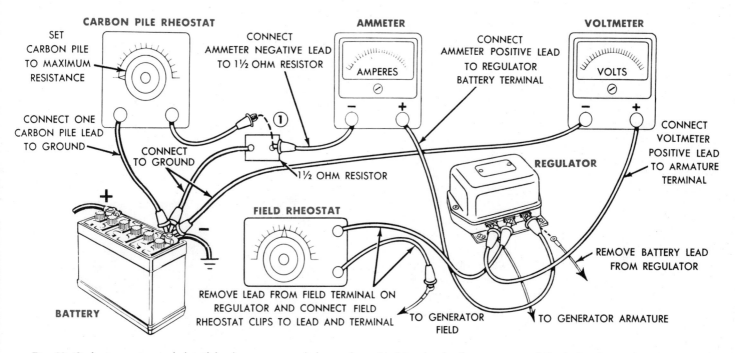

Fig. 33-42. *Instruments needed and hookup recommended are shown in this sketch of arrangement of Ford charging system components.*

pute the difference as a positive or negative correction. Remove the regulator cover, and make a new voltage regulator test. Adjust the new setting up or down by the amount of the correction computed.

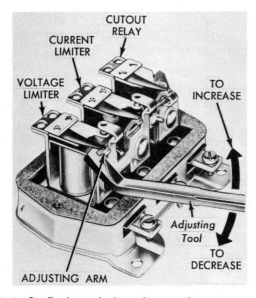

Fig. 33-43. *On Ford standard regulators, adjusting arms are provided as a means of adjusting voltage regulator and current regulator units.*

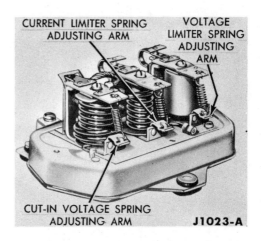

Fig. 33-44. *On Bosch heavy-duty regulators, bend adjusting arm upward to decrease voltage or amperage output, downward to increase output.*

CURRENT REGULATOR TEST: Connect the carbon pile rheostat across the 1 1/2 ohm resistor (6V systems use 3/4 ohm resistor), Figs. 33-41 and 33-42. With the engine speed at 1500 rpm, slowly decrease the resistance of the rheostat until the voltmeter reading drops to 13V, (6V systems 6.5V). The ammeter will indicate the setting of the current regulator.

Remove all test leads except the voltmeter leads. Install the battery and field leads on the regulator terminals. Run the engine at 1500 rpm and read the voltage regulation under battery load on the voltmeter. The voltmeter will usually be low when the engine is first started, because the battery is partly discharged. After a few minutes of operation, the voltage will rise to the original value.

If the current limit is less than specified, increase the spring tension by bending the current regulator adjusting arm upward, Fig. 33-44.

Foreign Car Regulators

The regulators used on imported cars are basically the same as those used domestically. However, there is considerable confusion because of the many different systems of lettering used to identify the different connections. In addition, some regulators will have five or more terminals. In such cases, the additional terminals are connections for various accessories and form a sort of terminal block. These additional terminals are usually marked A-1, A-2, etc.

On the British Lucas units, battery terminals are marked B or A, the field F, the armature D, and the ground D. European Bosch regulators are marked D or F for field, D+ or + for armature, while the battery terminal is marked 51. On Italian electrical systems, the field is marked 67, the ground 31, the armature 51 and the battery 30.

British Lucas and Italian systems generally have the field grounded internally, while the Bosch and the French Ducellier and Cibie units have the field grounded externally. The generator should always be first checked to determine its type, before proceeding with any tests.

Regulators for Alternators

Regulators most commonly used in AC charging systems are the electromagnetic type and the transistor type. Carbon pile regulators are also used, but mainly in heavy-duty, high-output applications.

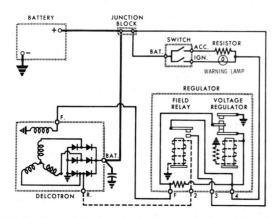

Fig. 33-45. Most alternator equipped cars use an electromagnetic regulator assembly having a double contact voltage regulator unit.

In electromagnetic regulators, Fig. 33-45, the voltage regulator unit limits voltage output by controlling the amount of current applied to the rotating field (alternator rotor). The field relay, on regulators so equipped, connects the alternator field windings and voltage regulator windings directly to the battery. In some cases, it also serves as an indicator lamp relay. The conventional cutout relay is eliminated by the diodes in the alternator; the current limiter (regulator) is eliminated by the current-limiting characteristic of alternator design.

Transistor regulators have no moving parts and, consequently, have a long life. These regulators usually consist of transistors, diodes, resistors and a capacitor which work together to regulate alternator field current and thereby limit output voltage to a safe value.

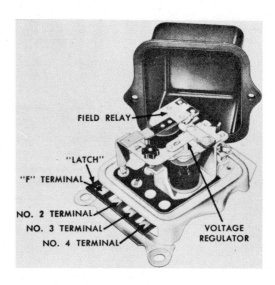

Fig. 33-46. Many late model General Motors cars utilize a Delcotron AC generator in conjunction with a two unit, double contact regulator.

Delco-Remy Alternator Regulators

Delco-Remy regulators utilize a voltage regulator unit to limit voltage output of "Delcotron" AC generators to a preset value. This unit is incorporated in single, two or three unit electromagnetic regulators in many standard equipment applications. The single unit regulator is used only in circuits with an ammeter. The two unit, double contact regulator is suitable for use in circuits containing either an ammeter or indicator lamp. The three unit, double contact regulator contains a voltage regulator, field relay and indicator lamp relay. Regulator terminals are of the slip-connection type. Slots in the regulator base are keyed to mating surfaces of a connector on the wiring harness to insure correct connections. Since the regulator terminals are the slip-on type, a special adapter must be used during testing so that test connections can be made.

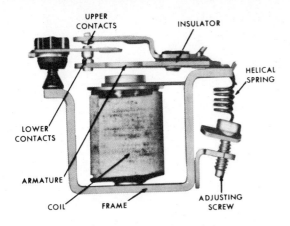

Fig. 33-47. Double contact regulators have upper and lower contacts on a movable armature with stationary contacts mounted on a contact arm in between.

Two Unit, Double Contact Regulators

Most late model General Motors Corporation cars are equipped with a Delco-Remy two unit regulator, Fig. 33-46. A double contact voltage regulator unit and a field relay unit make up the regulator assembly. If an indicator lamp is used in the charging circuit, it lights when the ignition switch is turned on, goes out when the Delcotron begins to produce charging voltage. If the indicator lamp lights when the Delcotron is in operation, trouble exists in the charging system.

The voltage regulator actually has many stages of operation. A typical Delco-Remy two unit, double contact regulator, Fig. 33-47, will operate as follows:

1. The field relay points close when the engine starts and the Delcotron stator windings put out a voltage. As soon as the points close, the field current is supplied directly from the battery instead of through the ignition switch and resistance wire, Fig. 33-45.

2. When engine speed is low and the battery or accessories need a lot of current, the lower contacts of the voltage regulator unit remain closed to allow full field current (approximately 2 amps.) to flow.

3. As engine speed increases, or the load lessens, the lower contacts vibrate between open and closed position to reduce field current to between 2 amps. and 3/4 amp.

4. When the speed and load requirement reach a point where exactly 3/4 amp. field current provides the needed output, the voltage regulator armature will "float" between the upper and lower contacts. In this situation, the entire field current passes through a resistor that limits current to 3/4 amp.

5. When engine speed is high and load is low, increased voltage in the charging circuit will cause the voltage regulator armature to be drawn down, closing the upper set of contacts to ground the circuit and no field current will flow.

6. As engine speed is reduced and the load again calls for a small charge, the upper contacts will vibrate and field current will flow at from 0 to 3/4 amp., depending on the rate of vibration.

Erratic operation of any alternator regulator could be caused by dirty or pitted contact points. To clean the contacts, fold over a sheet of very fine silicon carbide abrasive paper and rub it against another piece of abrasive paper to wear off the sharp edges. Then pull it between the contacts to clean them. Maintain this cleanliness during tests. When checking point gaps, for example, be sure that blade of feeler gauge is absolutely clean.

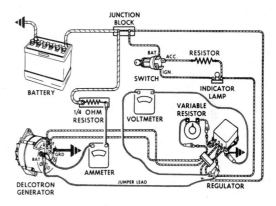

Fig. 33-48. To check voltage of Delco-Remy two unit regulators, connect a test adapter, ammeter, voltmeter, 1/4 ohm resistor, 25 watt variable resistor and jumper lead as indicated.

Two Unit Regulator Tests and Adjustments

To test and adjust the voltage regulator setting, make the test connections as shown in Fig. 33-48. Turn the variable resistor to the "no resistance" position and operate the Delcotron for approximately 15 minutes at 1500 rpm with the regulator cover in place. Turn off all accessories and lights, then proceed as follows:

1. Cycle Delcotron: turn variable resistance to "full resistance" position; disconnect leads at No. 2 and No. 4 terminals of wiring harness connector; reconnect both of these leads; return variable resistance to "no resistance" position.

2. Accelerate engine to approximately 2500 rpm; check voltmeter reading, and compare with manufacturer's specifications. (Typical setting is 13.8 to 14.6 at 85 deg. F.)

3. To adjust voltage setting, turn adjusting screw, Fig. 33-49. Always turn screw clockwise to make final setting to be sure spring holder is seated against head of screw.

4. If specified voltage setting cannot be made, check point opening between upper contacts with lower contacts touching, Fig. 33-50. Check

specifications. If adjustment is necessary, bend upper contact arm to obtain correct setting.

5. Cycle Delcotron and recheck voltage setting with cover in place. (When removing and installing cover, remove No. 4 lead at harness connector and jumper wire from Delcotron battery terminal.)

Fig. 33-49. To adjust voltage setting of voltage regulator unit, turn adjusting screw clockwise to increase voltage, counterclockwise to decrease voltage.

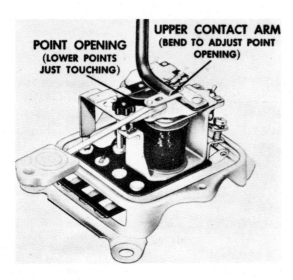

Fig. 33-50. If voltage cannot be set by turning adjusting screw, readjust point gap to specifications by bending upper contact arm.

6. Slowly increase resistance with engine operating at 2500 rpm until regulator begins to operate on lower set of contacts.
7. Take voltage reading and compare with specifications.
8. To adjust voltage setting while operating on lower set of contacts, increase voltage by turning nylon nut to enlarge air gap between arma-

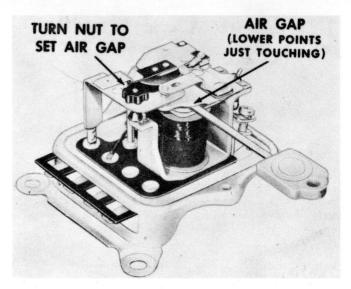

Fig. 33-51. If voltage setting is still out of specification, reset air gap by turning nylon nut on contact support.

ture and core; decrease voltage setting by turning nut to reduce air gap, Fig. 33-51.

9. If air gap adjustment is necessary, be sure to recheck voltage setting while regulator is operating on upper contacts.

To check closing voltage of the field relay, make test connections shown in Fig. 33-52. Turn the variable resistor to "full resistance" position with the ignition switch "off," then slowly decrease resistance and watch voltmeter for closing voltage of relay. If necessary, adjust closing voltage setting by bending heel iron of field relay unit, Fig. 33-53.

Single and Three Unit Regulator Adjustments

Test connections for checking the voltage settings on single unit, double contact regulators are as shown in Fig. 33-48, except that leads No. 2 and No. 4 are left disconnected. Compare tests results with specifications. Adjustments are made as indicated in Figs. 33-49 and 33-51.

Test connections for checking the voltage settings on three unit, double contact regulators are shown in Fig. 33-54. Test procedures and adjusting methods are similar to those used on two unit voltage regulators. However, on some models, air gap adjustment is made by sliding the contact support bracket up or down.

Three unit regulators are fitted with an indicator lamp relay unit. If the lamp and relay are good, the lamp will light when the ignition switch is turned on, go out when the engine starts. However, if the lamp stays lit after the engine starts, the relay may be defective or the system may have a malfunction. To check, make connections shown in Fig. 33-55. Operate the engine and check voltage reading. If it is more than 5 volts, the indicator lamp relay is defective. If it is less than 5 volts, the trouble is elsewhere in the

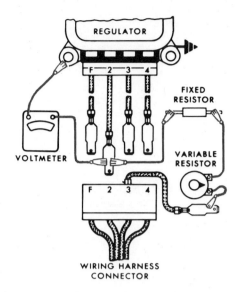

Fig. 33-52. To test field relay closing voltage, connect a 100 ohm variable resistor, a 60 ohm fixed resistor and voltmeter test leads to test adapter.

system. The air gap of the relay can be adjusted by bending the upper contact support; the opening voltage can be adjusted by bending the heel iron as in field relay adjustment, Fig. 33-53.

Delco-Remy Transistor Regulator

Each of the various models of Delco-Remy transistor is matched to the generator field circuit it must control and to the vehicle application. Inner construction is similar, but the various models are not interchangeable, Fig. 33-56. Basically, the transistor is "switched" on and off to control generator field current. The frequency of switching depends on generator

Fig. 33-53. To adjust field relay closing voltage, bend heel iron, then turn variable resistor to "no resistance" position and recheck voltage.

speed and accessory load, with the possibility that the "on-off cycle" may be repeated as often as 7,000 times per second.

To test the voltage regulator setting, operate the engine at approximately 1500 rpm for 15 minutes with the low beam headlights "on." Place a thermometer

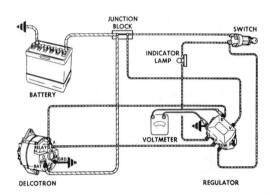

Fig. 33-54. Make these test lead connections to check voltage setting of Delco-Remy three unit regulator used on some General Motors cars.

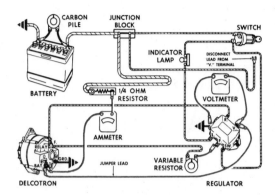

Fig. 33-55. To test indicator lamp circuit of three unit regulators, connect voltage leads to regulator (R) terminal and ground.

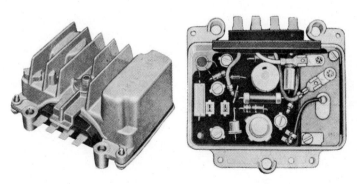

Fig. 33-56. Late model Delco-Remy transistor regulators are similar, but internal construction differs. They are not interchangeable.

1/4 in. from the regulator cover. Connect voltmeter test leads to regulator terminal No. 3 and to ground, and compare the voltmeter reading with the manufacturer's specification for the normal voltage setting at indicated ambient temperature. (Typical setting is 13.9 to 14.7 volts at 85 deg. F.) Adjust voltage regulator as required.

An external adjustment is provided on some models, Fig. 33-56, to permit tailoring generator output to individual driving needs. If adjustment is necessary, remove the access plug from the regulator cover. Note the position of the adjusting screw slot with regard to lines cast on the regulator cover, Fig. 33-57.

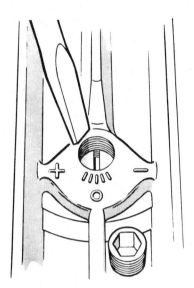

Fig. 33-57. With pipe plug removed from transistor regulator, turn adjusting screw carefully to obtain higher or lower voltage setting as required.

For an undercharged battery, turn the adjusting screw one notch clockwise to increase regulator voltage 0.3 volt. For an overcharged battery, turn the screw one notch counterclockwise to reduce regulator voltage 0.3 volt. Check for improved battery condition over a reasonable length of time, then repeat the one-notch adjustment if necessary.

On transistor regulators with an internal adjustment, remove the regulator from its mounting with all wiring and voltmeter leads attached to No. 3 terminal and ground. Take off the bottom cover and turn the adjusting screw clockwise to lower regulator voltage, counterclockwise to raise it, Fig. 33-58. (Adjusting screw is very sensitive, should be turned only a few degrees.) Then reinstall the cover, remount the regulator on the vehicle, and retest the voltage regulator setting.

Autolite Alternator Regulators

Most late model Ford Motor Company cars utilize an electromagnetic, two unit alternator regulator consisting of a field relay and a double contact voltage limiter (regulator), Fig. 33-59. As is generally the case with alternator-equipped charging systems, a cutout relay and a current regulator are not needed.

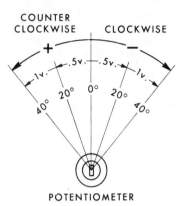

Fig. 33-58. Some Delco-Remy transistor regulators have an internal adjustment to raise or lower voltage. With bottom cover plate removed, turn adjusting screw as marking dictates.

The field relay connects the battery and alternator output to the field circuit when the engine is running. The double contact voltage limiter controls the amount of current supplied to the rotating field. At low engine speed and with a load applied, the upper contacts of the voltage limiter are closed, full system voltage is applied to the field and maximum field current will flow. At high engine speed and with little or no load, the lower contacts are closed and no current flows to the field. A resistor is connected from the field terminal to ground to absorb electrical surges when the voltage limiter armature vibrates on the contacts or floats between them.

On Ford cars with charge indicator lights on the dash, battery current flows through the indicator light and a parallel resistor, and through the voltage limiter contacts to the field coil. When the ignition switch is

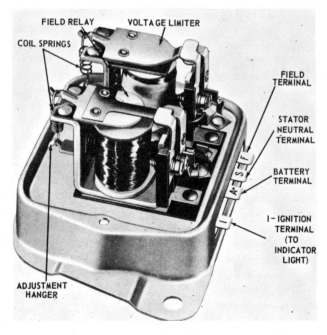

Fig. 33-59. Ford Autolite electromagnetic alternator regulators have two control units and four slip-on terminals coded as shown.

turned "on," this small current permits the alternator to start charging. On cars with ammeters, closing of the field relay contacts connects battery and alternator output to the field through the voltage limiter contacts.

Autolite Alternator Regulator Adjustments

Certain gap adjustments may be checked before electrical tests are performed. If an adjustment is required, it should be made with the regulator removed from the car.

With the upper contacts of the voltage limiter closed, bend the lower contact bracket to obtain a .017 to .022 in. gap at the lower contacts, Fig. 33-60.

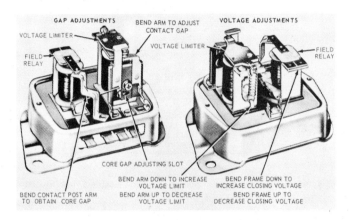

Fig. 33-60. Gap and voltage adjustments are pointed out in front and rear views of typical Autolite regulator.

Adjust the core gap with the upper contacts closed. Loosen the lock screw 1/4 turn; insert a screwdriver in the adjustment slot and adjust the core gap to a .049 to .056 in. clearance between the armature and the edge of the core closest to the contacts. Tighten the lock screw and recheck the core gap.

To adjust the field relay, place a .010 to .018 in. feeler gauge on top of core close to the contacts and hold the armature down on the gauge. Then bend the contact post arm until the bottom contact just touches the upper contact.

Voltage Tests and Adjustments

Make the voltage limiter test with the regulator cover in place and with regulator at normal operating temperature (run engine 20 minutes with hood down). Connect test leads as shown in Fig. 33-61, then proceed as follows:

1. Close battery switch, start engine, then open switch.
2. Operate engine for 5 minutes at 2,000 rpm.
3. With no resistance in circuit, ammeter should indicate less than 10 amps. with tester control set at 1/4 ohm position.

4. Cycle the regulator (turn ignition switch off, close adapter switch, start engine, open adapter switch).
5. Check voltmeter reading and reading on thermometer mounted on regulator. Compare readings with these specifications:

   50 deg. - 14.3 to 15.0 volts.
   75 deg. - 14.1 to 14.9 volts.
   100 deg. - 13.9 to 14.7 volts.
   125 deg. - 13.8 to 14.6 volts.

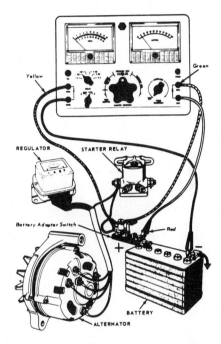

Fig. 33-61. To make a voltage limiter test on an Autolite regulator, install a battery adapter switch and connect volt-amp. test leads as illustrated.

6. Make the following voltage limiter adjustments as necessary: Bend the spring arm "down" to increase the voltage setting, "up" to decrease voltage, Fig. 33-60.

To test the field relay, connect test leads as shown in Fig. 33-62. With the engine at normal operating temperature, proceed as follows:

1. Slowly rotate field resistance control from off position while observing relay contacts and noting voltmeter reading as contacts closed.
2. Make the following field relay closing voltage adjustment if necessary: Bend the relay frame "down" to increase closing voltage, "up" to decrease closing voltage, Fig. 33-60.

Transistorized Regulator Adjustments

The Autolite transistorized voltage regulator, Fig. 33-63, controls alternator voltage output electronically with the use of transistors and diodes rather than by means of a vibrating armature relay. The voltage

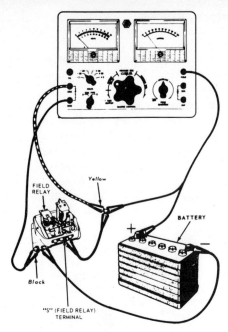

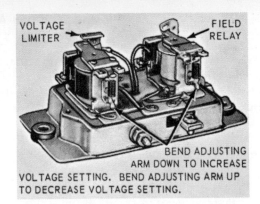

Fig. 33-62. To make a field relay test on an Autolite regulator, disconnect regulator terminal plug, install jumper wire and connect volt-amp. test leads as shown.

Fig. 33-64. Some Ford models are produced with Leece-Neville alternator regulators as standard equipment. Test procedures and adjustments are similar to Autolite except as noted here.

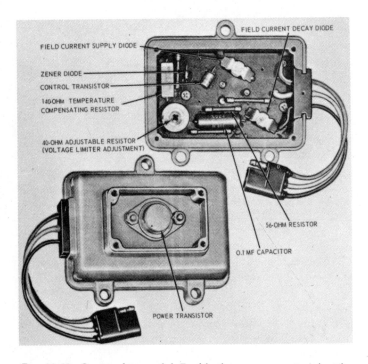

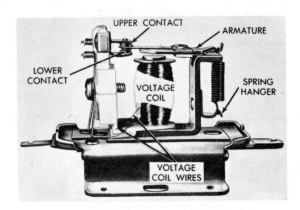

Fig. 33-65. Chrysler cars are equipped with a single unit alternator regulator. Later units have plastic bracket arrangement with upper and lower stationary contacts attached.

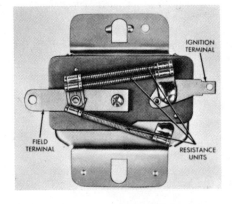

Fig. 33-63. Certain late model Ford-built cars are equipped with Autolite transistorized voltage regulators. Bottom cover must be removed for access to 40 ohm adjustable resistor.

Fig. 33-66. Bottom view of late-type Chrysler alternator regulator reveals three resistance units, two of which are connected in series with field circuit.

sensing element is a zener diode which changes its resistance to suit voltage requirements. The field relay unit is mounted separately.

The only adjustment on the transistorized unit is the voltage limiter setting. With the regulator at normal operating temperature, remove the mounting screws and take off the bottom cover of the regulator. Adjust the 40 ohm adjustable resistor to obtain the correct voltage setting, Fig. 33-63.

Leece-Neville Alternator Regulator Adjustment

Follow the same general core gap and contact point gap settings as on the Autolite unit. However, field relay and voltage limiter voltage setting are made by bending the adjusting arms, Fig. 33-64. The Leece-Neville unit used on Ford cars with an ammeter charge indicator has 3 terminals; the unit used with a charge indicating light has 4 terminals.

Chrysler Alternator Regulator

Chrysler Corporation cars utilize a single unit, double contact voltage regulator connected into the field circuit between the battery and field terminal of the alternator. The "IGN" terminal of the regulator is connected to the coil side of the ignition switch so that the field circuit is completed only when the switch is turned "on."

The "double contacts" are mounted on a plastic bracket attached to the regulator frame, Fig. 33-65. A fusible wire connects the upper contact bracket to the "IGN" terminal, another fusible wire connects the lower contact bracket to ground. Three resistance units are used: 2 in parallel with the upper contacts, the other connected between the "FLD" terminal and ground, where it serves to reduce arcing at the regulator contacts, Fig. 33-66.

When the ignition switch is turned "on," battery voltage energizes the coil winding and magnetic force pulls down the armature. If battery voltage is low, the magnetism will not overcome the spring tension holding the upper contacts closed, and maximum current will flow through the rotor field coil.

As battery voltage goes up, so does the magnetic strength of the voltage coil. This overcomes armature spring tension, opens the upper contacts and field current flows through the regulator "IGN" terminal and the two resistors in parallel with it. This circuit reduces field current and, in effect, alternator output voltage. When engine speed is high and electrical load requirements are low, battery voltage increases and the strengthened voltage coil pulls the armature down

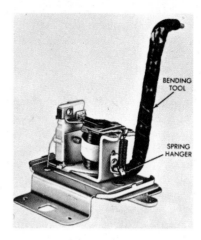

Fig. 33-68. To adjust upper contact voltage setting, bend spring hanger with an insulated bending tool which adjusts spring tension on armature plate.

high or low points, the armature vibrates (opening and closing the contacts) to limit battery voltage and, therefore, alternator output voltage.

Chrysler Regulator Tests and Adjustments

Normalize alternator regulator temperature by operating regulator under a 10 amp. load for 15 minutes. Then make the test connection shown in Fig. 33-67 and proceed to test upper contacts:
1. Close battery post adapter bypass switch and start engine.
2. Open bypass switch while making tests.
3. Operate engine at 1250 rpm and rotate tester control knob until ammeter reads 15 amps.
4. Cycle system: rotate field control knob from "direct" to "open," then back to "direct."
5. Take voltmeter reading and compare with specifications.

If upper contact voltage setting is not within specifications, remove the regulator and its mounting, take off the regulator cover and adjust the setting:
1. Use an insulated bending tool, Fig. 33-68, to bend regulator lower spring hanger "down" to increase voltage setting, "up" to decrease voltage setting.
2. Reinstall, connect and retest regulator after each adjustment of lower spring hanger.
3. If this adjustment fails to bring voltage setting within specifications, measure lower contact gap. It should be .014 in. Bend lower stationary contact bracket if necessary.

To test lower contacts:
1. Increase engine speed 2200 rpm.
2. If test ammeter reads over 5 amps., rotate tester knob to 1/4 ohm position.
3. Cycle system.
4. Read voltmeter for voltage setting of lower contacts and compare with manufacturer's specifications.

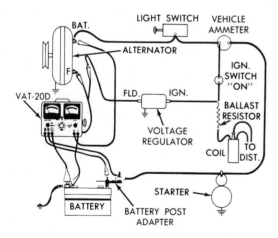

Fig. 33-67. Voltage regulator test on Chrysler regulators calls for installation of battery post adapter switch and volt-amp. tester having field control unit.

to close the lower contacts. The current path, then, is through the lower contacts to ground, bypassing the alternator field coil and causing output voltage to drop.

As is the case with other electromagnetic regulators, when electrical load requirements reach certain

5. Voltage should increase not less than 0.2 volt or more than 0.7 volt above the voltage setting of upper contacts.

6. If voltage is still out of specifications, check air gap, Fig. 33-69: insert a .048 in. wire gauge between regulator armature and core of voltage coil next to stop pin on armature. Press down on armature until it contacts wire gauge, and upper contacts should just open.

7. Repeat air gap test with .052 in. wire gauge. Press down on armature until it contacts wire gauge. Upper contacts should be closed.

8. If air gap adjustment is necessary, loosen bracket screw and move bracket up or down to obtain proper setting. If difference between voltage settings is less than 0.2 volt, adjust air gap to .052 in. If difference is more than 0.7 volt, adjust air gap to 0.48 in. Tighten bracket screw and recheck adjustment.

Adjusting Voltage - Replacing Fusible Wire

Specifications for the voltage setting of Chrysler alternator regulator give a tolerance of 1 volt from low setting to high setting at temperatures indicated. In cases involving unusual driving habits, the voltage setting can be increased or decreased .3 volt at a time. A reasonable service period should be allowed between adjustments to permit a careful observation of battery condition under the new setting.

If visible inspection shows that the fusible wire has "blown," a new wire can be installed if this special soldering procedure is followed:

1. Cut fuse wire above solder connection at base and unwind wire from top bracket.

2. Tin end of fuse wire with resin core solder.

3. Hold tinned end of wire into recessed rivet at base of regulator and against old piece of fused wire that remains.

4. Let a drop of molten solder fall on these parts and cool to form a good solder joint.

5. Pull fuse wire up to remove slack and wrap it around bracket.

6. Solder coiled wire to bracket and cut off excess wire.

Essex Regulator on Chrysler Cars

An Essex-built regulator is used on some late model Chrysler cars, Fig. 33-70. It too, is a single unit, double contact regulator, but in contrast to the Chrysler regulator, the "lower" contact mounted on the armature is connected to the "IGN" terminal. The upper contact mounted on the armature is connected to ground by a flexible wire.

This arrangement calls for the Chrysler regulator test procedure in reverse, that is: for Essex regulators, merely transpose Chrysler alternator upper

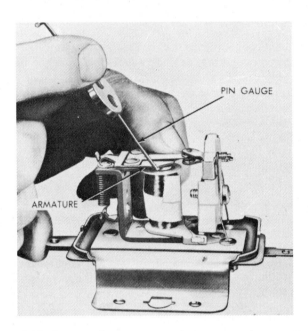

Fig. 33-69. Air gap adjustment is vital to correct voltage regulator settings. Carefully check upper and lower contact point openings while holding wire gauge in place.

and lower contact test procedures. In addition, the Essex regulator has an adjustment opening in the regulator cover. If the lower contacts voltage setting must be changed, use a screwdriver to turn the adjustment screw clockwise to increase voltage, counterclockwise to decrease voltage.

Quiz - Generator and Alternator, Regulators and Relays

1. When the battery is low in charge, what does the regulator do?
   a. Cuts resistance out of the generator field circuit.
   b. Cuts resistance into the generator field circuit.
   c. Cuts resistance into the armature circuit.

2. In an "A" circuit generator, the voltage regulator inserts resistance at what point in the circuit?
   a. Between the field windings and the ground.
   b. Between the insulated brush and the field.
   c. Between the armature and the ground.

3. In a "B" circuit generator, the voltage regulator inserts resistance at what point in the circuit?
   a. Between the field windings and the ground.
   b. Between the insulated brush and the field.
   c. Between the field and the ground.

4. What is the purpose of the cutout relay?
   a. Prevent battery from discharging through the generator.

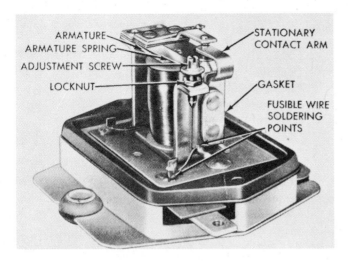

ARMATURE
ARMATURE SPRING
ADJUSTMENT SCREW
LOCKNUT
STATIONARY CONTACT ARM
GASKET
FUSIBLE WIRE SOLDERING POINTS

Fig. 33-70. Essex alternator regulators ground field circuit when lower contacts close rather than through upper contacts as in Chrysler regulator operation.

b. Cut the battery out of the circuit.
c. Cut resistance out of the field circuit.

5. What is the purpose of the voltage regulator?
   a. Maintain a constant charging rate.
   b. Prevent the circuit voltage from exceeding a predetermined value.
   c. Prevent battery from discharging through the generator.

6. What is the purpose of the current regulator?
   a. Protect the generator from overload.
   b. Maintain a constant charging rate.
   c. Prevent battery from discharging through the generator.

7. In a current regulator, how much of the current passes through the winding?
   a. All of the current.
   b. 75 percent.
   c. 50 percent.

8. Why is temperature compensation needed on a voltage regulator?

9. Is is necessary to consider the polarity of the electrical system when selecting a voltage regulator?

10. When checking the voltage setting of a voltage regulator, where is the voltmeter connected?
    a. To the battery terminal of the regulator and to the ground.
    b. To the ground and the armature terminals.
    c. To the field and battery terminals.

11. What three adjustments should be made on a cutout relay?

12. When checking the voltage at which cutout relay points close, where should the voltmeter be connected?
    a. To battery and ground connections.
    b. To generator terminal of the regulator and ground connections.
    c. To generator and battery connections.

13. When checking the setting of a current regu-

lator, should the voltage regulator be operating?

14. Why are double contact regulators used on some installations?

15. Why are two sets of points used on some voltage regulators?
    a. Because of higher field current.
    b. Because of higher armature current.
    c. Because of heavy-duty battery.

16. A step-voltage control unit is usually used on what type of generator?
    a. "A" circuit.
    b. "B" circuit.
    c. Third brush.

17. If the charging rate remains high, when the F lead is disconnected from the step-voltage control unit, what is indicated?
    a. Generator is in good condition.
    b. Voltage control unit is defective.
    c. Generator field circuit is grounded.

18. The two unit regulator is usually used with what type of generator?
    a. "A" circuit generator.
    b. "B" circuit generator.
    c. Third brush generator.

19. What type of temperature compensation is used on Autolite regulators?

20. What type generator-regulator circuit is used on most Ford cars?
    a. "A" circuit.
    b. "B" circuit.

21. On an Italian regulator, what does the number 30 signify?
    a. Battery.
    b. Armature.
    c. Field.

22. How do Delco-Remy electromagnetic regulators limit voltage output?

23. What type of AC generator-regulator is used on most late model General Motors cars?
    a. Single unit.
    b. Two unit.
    c. Three unit.

24. What method of adjustment is used on voltage regulator unit of Delco-Remy two unit alternator regulator?
    a. Adjust spring tension.
    b. Bend heel iron.
    c. Raise or lower mounting bracket.

25. How do you adjust closing voltage of the field relay unit of a Delco-Remy two unit alternator regulator?
    a. Adjust spring tension.
    b. Bend heel iron.
    c. Raise or lower mounting bracket.

26. What job does the transistor do in a Delco-Remy transistor regulator?

27. Are Delco-Remy transistor regulators adjustable?

28. What is the "makeup" of an Autolite alternator regulator?
    a. Voltage regulator and current regulator.
    b. Voltage regulator and field relay.
    c. Current regulator and field relay.
29. What two important requirements must be met before you can adjust any Autolite regulator?
30. What is the name of the voltage sensing element used in an Autolite transistorized regulator?
31. How do you adjust the voltage setting of a Leece-Neville regulator used on Ford cars?
    a. Adjust spring tension.
    b. Raise or lower mounting bracket.
    c. Bend adjusting arms.
32. What type alternator regulator is used on most late model Chrysler-built cars?
    a. Single unit.   b. Two unit.   c. Three unit.

33. Do Chrysler alternator regulators use a double contact voltage regulator unit?
34. What is the purpose of using a battery post adapter switch when testing Chrysler alternator regulators?
    a. It sells more switches.
    b. It simplifies "cyling" the system.
    c. It makes it easier to connect test leads.
35. What is the best way to replace a fusible wire in Chrysler regulators?
    a. Unsolder "blown" wire, resolder new one in place.
    b. Snip off "blown" wire, resolder new one in place.
    c. Replace entire regulator.
36. Do Essex regulators used on Chrysler cars call for exactly the same test procedures as Chrysler regulators?

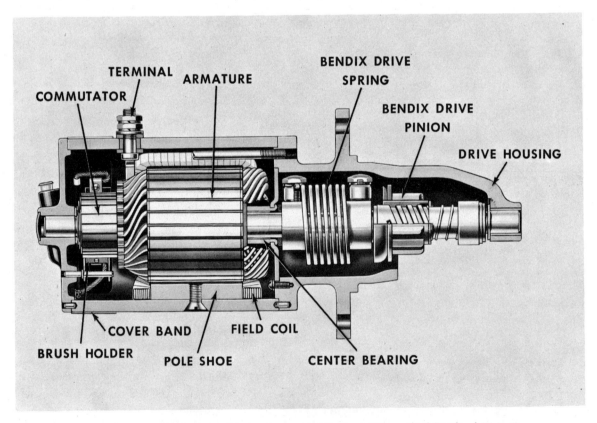

Fig. 34-1. Component parts of Delco-Remy starting motor and standard Bendix drive unit.

STARTING MOTOR
FUNDAMENTALS

The starting motor, Figs. 34-1 and 34-2, is an electric motor designed specifically for cranking internal combustion engines at speeds which will permit starting.

manent magnet, as in Fig. 34-3, the flow of current in the conductor will cause a magnetic field to encircle the conductor in a clockwise direction (left-hand rule applies).

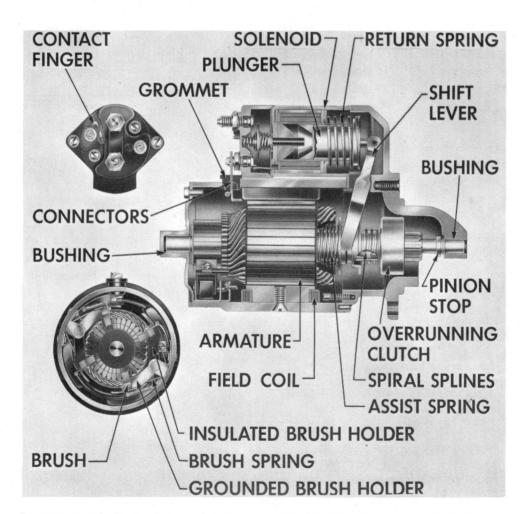

Fig. 34-2. Sectional and end views of starting motor with solenoid and overrunning clutch drive unit.

Electric motors of this type operate on the principle that a current-carrying conductor will tend to move from a strong magnetic field to a weak magnetic field. To illustrate, if a single current-carrying conductor is placed in a magnetic field created by a per-

This circular magnetic field will tend to cancel out and weaken those lines of force between the poles of the permanent magnet BELOW the conductor. At the same time, both fields will combine ABOVE the conductor to create a strong magnetic field. In effect,

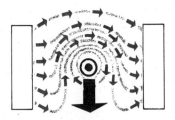

Fig. 34-3. When a current-carrying conductor is placed in a magnetic field, conductor will tend to move in direction indicated.

there is more magnetism above the conductor and less below it. Then, as the distorted lines of force tend to straighten out, they exert a downward thrust on the conductor.

Rotary Motion

To see how downward thrust is converted into rotary motion, the conductor is bent into a loop as shown in Fig. 34-4. The rotating part is known as the armature. It will be noted that the ends of the loop are connected to two semicircular brass bars called the commutator. The magnetic field of the two magnetic poles is created by two electromagnets. Current for the electromagnets, which in this case are called field coils, is provided by a battery. Tracing the circuit from the battery, it will be seen that the armature coil and the field coils are connected in series. In other words, when the circuit is completed, current flows from the battery, through the armature winding, through the field coils and back to the battery.

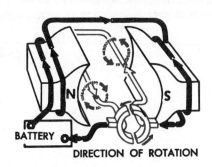

Fig. 34-4. Drawing depicts simple electric motor using single loop of wire for an armature. Note direction of current flow and field around conductor.

The current flowing through the field coils produces a strong magnetic field which flows from the north pole (on the left) to the south pole (on the right). At the same time, current flowing through the armature coil produces a circular magnetic field to surround the conductor as shown by the arrows, Fig. 34-4. This circular magnetic field is in a clockwise direction on the left-hand conductor of the armature, and counterclockwise around the right conductor. Note that the current in the left-hand side of the armature coil is flowing toward the commutator, which is the

same direction as shown in Fig. 34-3. This results in a downward thrust on the conductor. As the current is flowing in the opposite direction in the right-hand side of the armature coil, the thrust will be in the opposite direction, or upward, Fig. 34-5.

The combination of the two thrusts causes the armature to rotate. This rotation will continue, for as the armature coil passes the vertical position, the commutator, which rotates with the armature, will automatically connect the armature coil so the current will continue to flow away from the commutator in the right hand, and toward the commutator in the left-hand coil.

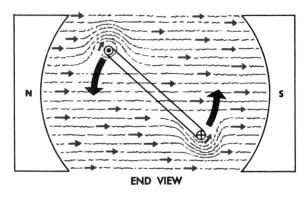

END VIEW

Fig. 34-5. Lines of force react to distortion of magnetic field to create a downward thrust at left and upward thrust at right, causing armature coil to rotate.

The tendency for a current-carrying coil to move when placed in a magnetic field can be easily demonstrated by means of a permanent magnet, a battery and some wire as shown in Fig. 34-6. After connecting the battery to points A and B, reverse the connections of the battery, and the wire bent in the form of a yoke will then swing in the opposite direction. Turning the horseshoe magnet over from its original position will also change the direction of thrust on the yoke.

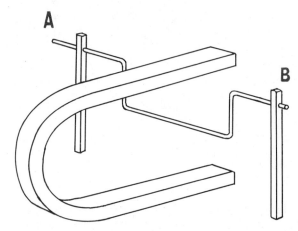

Fig. 34-6. Simple equipment shown will demonstrate basic principle of electric motor. Connecting battery to end of loop of wire, at A and B, will cause loop to swing.

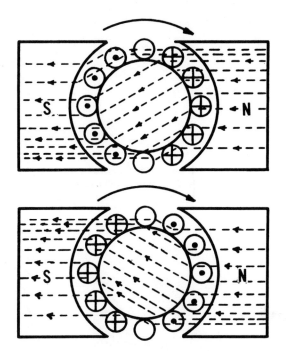

Fig. 34-7. Field distortion caused by armature reaction in a motor is shown in top drawing. Reaction in a generator is diagrammed below.

Counter Voltage

As was pointed out in the unit on the Fundamentals of Electricity, when any conductor is moved through a magnetic field, a voltage will be induced in the conductor. This condition also occurs in a motor, when the conductor is being supplied with current. However, the voltage induced in the conductor (by virture of the fact that it is cutting magnetic lines of force) will be in the opposite direction to the voltage that is being supplied to the motor. Such voltage is known as a back voltage, or counter electromotive force, (EMF).

Effect of Counter EMF

The effect of the counter EMF is to limit the current in the armature, and as the speed of the armature increases, the counter EMF also increases. As it is opposed to the voltage applied to the motor, it has the effect of decreasing the effective voltage. As a result, the voltage that is forcing current through the armature is the difference between the applied voltage, and the counter EMF. Actually this counter EMF is the same voltage the armature would develop, if it were operated as a generator.

Armature Reaction

Armature reaction in motors is similar to armature reaction in generators. However, the current in a motor armature is opposite to that of a generator rotating in the same direction, Fig. 34-7. As a result, the armature reaction in a motor is similar in principle to that of a generator, which is explained in de-

tail in the unit dealing with the fundamentals of generators. The difference lies in the fact that the current in the armature, moving in the opposite direction, will magnetize the armature core in the opposite direction. Since the direction of the field current is the same in both machines, the reaction of the two magnetic fields in each case, will be in opposite directions. A comparison of the armature reactions of a motor and a generator is shown in Fig. 34-7.

Speed and Torque Characteristics

A reason for using a series-wound motor for cranking internal combusion engines is that it has extremely high torque. Torque varies with the strength of the magnetic field and the current in the armature. With the armature and field coils in series, any increase in current will produce an increase in the strength of the field. As the load on the motor increases, the current through the fields and armature will also increase. As a result, the torque will keep increasing as the load increases. This is shown in Fig. 34-8.

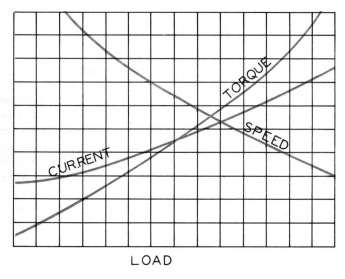

LOAD

Fig. 34-8. Chart curves illustrate that increased load on a series motor will cause its speed to drop, while current and torque will rise.

The speed of a series-wound motor will vary with the load. For any given load which a certain series motor is driving, there will be a certain definite speed. With heavy loads, series-wound motors will operate at a relatively slow speed. With a light load, such motors will operate at very high speeds. The explanation is as follows:

Any armature always tends to operate at such a speed that the voltage used in overcoming its resistance, plus the counter EMF, will be equal to the voltage being applied to the motor. At heavy loads the current, and the voltage consumed in overcoming internal resistance, will be large. Consequently, the armature will not have to rotate at very high speed to produce the required counter EMF to equal the applied voltage. However, under light loads, the motor speeds up, inducing a higher counter EMF and decreasing the current through the field and armature coils. This weakens the strength of the field, causing a further increase in armature speed, which again decreases the counter EMF.

With no load, the speed of a series-wound motor will continue to increase to such an extent that centrifugal force will destroy the armature. Series-wound motors as used for cranking internal combustion engines should therefore never be operated without a load except under controlled conditions.

In addition to using series-wound motors for cranking purposes, they are also used to operate convertible top mechanisms.

Cranking Motor Internal Circuits

While the basic characteristics of the series-wound motor is used in all cranking motors, there are many modifications of the method of connecting the field coils to each other and to the armature. Some variations in the internal circuits of cranking motors are shown in Figs. 34-9 and 34-10.

Fig. 34-9 (left) shows a four-pole, two-field coil design which is used on many motors. The two windings are connected in parallel to each other, and in series with the armature, permitting the high current to divide in equal amounts and pass through each field winding. All of the current then passes through the armature, with the result that high cranking torque is produced. The two poles which have no windings serve to complete the magnetic circuits.

The starting motor in Fig. 34-9 (center) has four field coils on four poles. With this setup, one half of the current flows through one pair of windings to one of the insulated brushes, and the other half flows through another pair of windings to the other insulated brush. The current then combines at the commutator and goes through the armature. Four field coil windings of low resistance create stronger magnetic fields and produce starting motors with greater torque and cranking ability.

A variation of this principle of dividing the current is found in starting motors having six poles and six field windings paired off three ways, Fig. 34-9 (right). In this motor, one third of the current flows through each of three pairs of field windings to one of three insulated brushes. Increasing the number of circuits through the starting motor keeps resistance low, so that high horsepower can be developed for use in heavy-duty service.

As mentioned earlier, a starting motor with all field coils connected in series, Fig 34-10 (left), would crank up to an extremely high top free speed if not controlled. With this in mind, shunt connections are used on many 12V starting systems, Fig. 34-10 (center

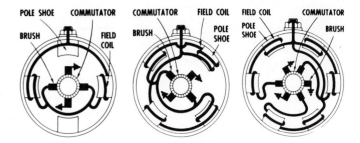

Fig. 34-9. Three typical starting motor circuits include: Left. Four-pole, two-field coil design. Center. Four-pole, four-field coil design. Right. Six-pole, six-field coil design.

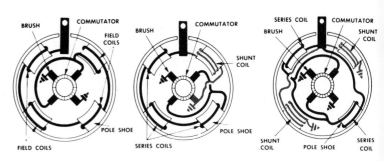

Fig. 34-10. Four-pole starting motor circuits also in use are: Left. Four-field coils all in series. Center. Three series field coils and one shunt field coil. Right. Two series field coils and two shunt field coils.

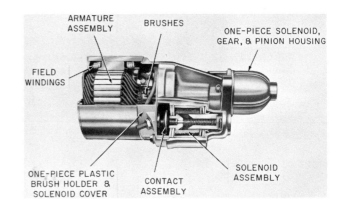

Fig. 34-11. Reduction gear starter used on late Chrysler Corporation engines has an armature-to-engine crankshaft ratio of 45 to 1.

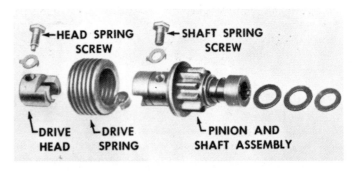

Fig. 34-12. Exploded view of standard Bendix drive shows construction features and location of head spring screw, which is key to disassembly of starter drive.

and right). Two, or three, heavy field coils are connected in series and carry current to the armature. The remaining field coil, or coils, are shunt coils connected between the starting motor terminal and ground. The shunt coil has two purposes, first to assist the series coils to build up and maintain a high magnetic field, and second to prevent excessive motor speed and noise, when the armature is not subjected to cranking load.

When the motor is cranking the engine, heavy current flows through the series windings to form the magnetic field. The ampere turns in the shunt field provide additional strength under this condition. When the engine starts, the load on the starter immediately drops. Less current flows through the armature and series field, which makes this field weaker, and would result in high rotational speed if the shunt field was not used. The shunt field continues to produce its maximum field strength so that the motor is held to a safe speed.

Starter Drive Control Circuits

The starting motor armature must revolve at a fairly high speed to produce sufficient torque to rotate the engine. In order to accomplish this, the starter is fitted with a small drive pinion which meshes with gear teeth on the engine flywheel. The gear reduction is approximately 15 to 1. That is, the starter armature revolves 15 times for each revolution of the flywheel, except when special reduction gear motors are used, Fig. 34-11.

As soon as the engine starts, its speed is much greater than the cranking speed, and if the starter drive pinion remained engaged with the flywheel, the starter speed would be excessive. For example, if the engine speed was 1,000 rpm, the starter speed would be 15 times as great or 15,000 rpm. Such a speed would ruin the armature and to prevent this, various mechanisms have been developed which permit the gears to mesh during the cranking period but which demesh the gears as soon as the engine is started.

Starter Drives

A starting motor equipped with a standard Bendix drive is shown in Fig. 34-1, and an exploded view of the drive unit is shown in Fig. 34-12. The Bendix drive provides an automatic means of engaging the drive pinion with the flywheel ring gear for cranking the engine and for automatic disengagement of the starter pinion after the engine starts.

The drive pinion is mounted on a threaded sleeve or hollow shaft which has spiral threads that match the internal threads in the drive pinion. The sleeve is a loose fit on the starter motor armature shaft. One end of the sleeve is bolted to the Bendix drive spring, while the other end of the drive spring is keyed and bolted to the armature shaft through the drive head.

When the starter is not in operation, the pinion is in the position shown in Fig. 34-1, and the pinion is not meshed with the flywheel ring gear. As soon as the circuit is completed to the starter, the starter armature begins to revolve, and being a series-wound motor its speed increases very rapidly. The threaded drive sleeve picks up speed with the armature as it is driven through the drive spring. However, the drive pinion being a loose fit on the sleeve, does not pick up speed instantly. The result is that the sleeve turns within the pinion, forcing the pinion along the shaft and into engagement with the flywheel ring gear. The action is similar to holding a nut stationary and turning a screw into it so that the nut would move from one end of the screw to the other. As the drive pinion reaches the stop on the end of the sleeve, it must then rotate with the sleeve and the armature so that the engine is cranked. The drive spring compresses slightly to absorb the shock of engagement.

As the engine starts, the flywheel will spin the drive pinion more rapidly than the armature and threaded sleeve are turning, with the result that the pinion is backed out of mesh with the flywheel ring gear.

Some Bendix drive units are provided with a small anti-drift spring between the drive pinion and the pinion stop which prevents the pinion from drifting into mesh when the engine is running. Another design uses a small anti-drift pin and spring inside the pinion which provides sufficient friction to keep the pinion from drifting into mesh.

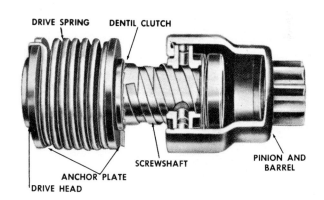

Fig. 34-13. Folo-Thru Bendix Drive must not be disassembled. Remove faulty unit by screwing pinion out to drive position, then force pin from shaft and slide unit from armature shaft. Install new assembly.

The Bendix "Folo-Thru" drive, (see Fig. 34-13), is designed to hold the drive pinion in mesh with the flywheel ring gear until a predetermined engine speed is reached. In operation, a spring-loaded detent pin locks the pinion in the engaged position. When the engine starts and reaches a given rpm, centrifugal action will force the detent pin out of the notch and allow the pinion to demesh from the flywheel.

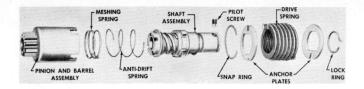

Fig. 34-14. Barrel-type Bendix drive mounts on an extra long armature shaft to facilitate inboard meshing of drive pinion with engine flywheel ring gear.

Barrel Type Drive

Starting motors are sometimes equipped with barrel type drive units as shown in Fig. 34-14. In this design the drive pinion, as it meshes, moves toward the starting motor and for that reason is referred to as an inboard drive. The barrel which is integral with the drive pinion is assembled on the spiral sleeve of the shaft assembly. The end of the spiral sleeve is attached to the inner end of the drive spring by an anchor plate. The other end of the spring is attached to the

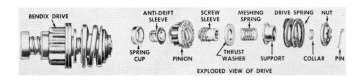

Fig. 34-15. Compression-spring Bendix drive is also designed for inboard meshing. In operation, pinion forces screw sleeve back against the drive spring to absorb shock of engagement.

armature shaft through the end of the drive shaft assembly. The action of the barrel type Bendix unit is similar to that of the standard unit. As the armature begins to rotate, the drive spring and sleeve pick up speed with the armature. The barrel and drive pinion assembly do not pick up speed instantly, with the result that the pinion moves into mesh with the flywheel ring gear. After the engine starts, the pinion is spun out of mesh.

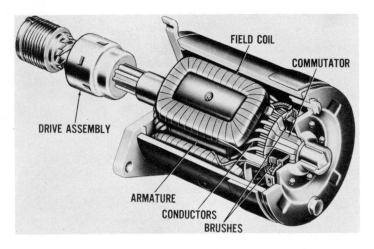

Fig. 34-16. Autolite starting motor used on late model Ford engines has barrel-type drive unit. Note typically long armature shaft.

Starting motors on some late model Ford engines utilize barrel type drive units, Fig. 34-16. Another type of drive used by Ford is called "Positive Action Drive." This mechanism features a movable pole which is connected to a fork that slides the drive gear into engagement with the flywheel, Figs. 34-17 and 34-18.

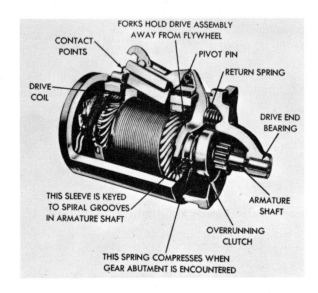

Fig. 34-17. Starting motor, used on late model Lincoln Continentals, features Positive Action Drive via a starter drive actuating lever.

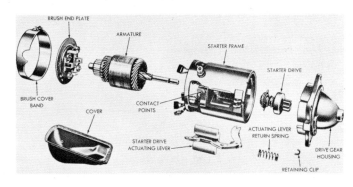

Fig. 34-18. Exploded view of Positive Action Drive starter shows relationship between actuating lever and starter drive unit.

Compression Spring Type Bendix Drive

The operation of a compression spring type inboard Bendix drive is somewhat different from the standard and barrel types. In the compression spring type, Fig. 34-15, meshing of the drive pinion forces the screw sleeve back against the drive spring through the thrust-washer and support so that the drive spring is compressed to absorb the shock of engagement.

For heavy-duty cranking, a friction clutch type Bendix drive is used. This type of drive operates in much the same manner as other Bendix drives, except that it uses a series of spring-loaded clutch plates which slip momentarily under shock of engagement.

FORD THERMACTOR EXHAUST CONTROL SYSTEM

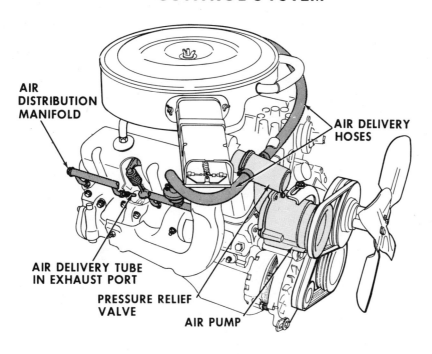

AIR DISTRIBUTION MANIFOLD

AIR DELIVERY HOSES

AIR DELIVERY TUBE IN EXHAUST PORT

PRESSURE RELIEF VALVE

AIR PUMP

FORD IMCO EXHAUST CONTROL SYSTEM ELEMENTS

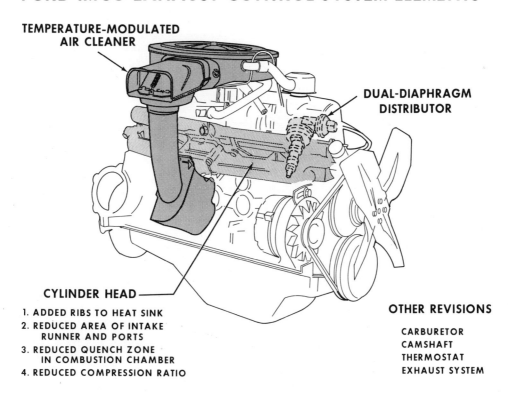

TEMPERATURE-MODULATED AIR CLEANER

DUAL-DIAPHRAGM DISTRIBUTOR

CYLINDER HEAD

1. ADDED RIBS TO HEAT SINK
2. REDUCED AREA OF INTAKE RUNNER AND PORTS
3. REDUCED QUENCH ZONE IN COMBUSTION CHAMBER
4. REDUCED COMPRESSION RATIO

OTHER REVISIONS

CARBURETOR
CAMSHAFT
THERMOSTAT
EXHAUST SYSTEM

Exhaust emissions from late model cars generally are controlled by air injection into exhaust ports (Thermactor) or by engine modifications that are customized to each power plant for improved combustion (IMCO). Ford's two approaches to solving the emission problem are shown.

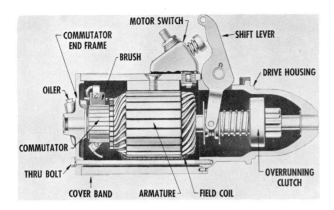

Fig. 34-19. *This Delco-Remy starting motor is fitted with a manually operated overrunning clutch. Pedal operates switch and also shifts drive pinion into mesh.*

Overrunning Clutch

The overrunning clutch is designed to provide positive meshing and demeshing of the starter drive pinion and the flywheel ring gear. A mechanically operated unit is shown in Fig. 34-19, while a solenoid operated unit is illustrated in Figs. 34-20 and 34-21.

The overrunning clutch starter uses a shift lever which slides the clutch and drive pinion assembly along the starter armature shaft so that it can be engaged and disengaged with the flywheel ring gear. The clutch transmits cranking torque from the starter to the flywheel gear, but permits the pinion to overrun (run faster) the armature once the engine has started. This protects the starter armature from excessive speed during the brief interval that the drive pinion remains enmeshed and the engine has started.

The overrunning clutch, details of which are shown in Fig. 34-22, consists of a shell and sleeve assembly which is splined internally to match the splines on the starter armature shaft. In that way, both the shell and sleeve assembly and armature shaft must turn together. A pinion and collar assembly fits loosely into the shell, and the collar is in contact with four hardened steel rollers which are assembled into notches cut in the inner face of the shell. The notches taper inward slightly so that there is less room in the end away from the rollers than in the end where the rollers are shown in Fig. 34-22. The rollers are spring-loaded by small springs and plungers.

When the shift lever is operated, the clutch assembly is moved along the armature shaft until the pinion meshes with the flywheel ring gear. If the teeth should butt instead of mesh, the clutch spring compresses so that the pinion is spring-loaded against

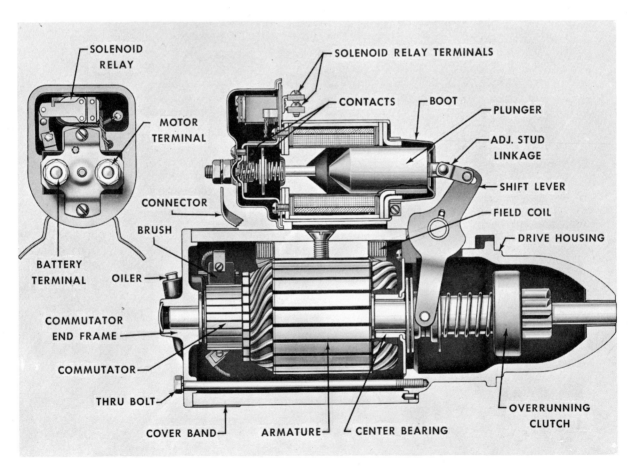

Fig. 34-20. *Cutaway view of Delco-Remy starter gives details of solenoid operated overrunning clutch. At left is end view of solenoid and solenoid relay with cover removed.*

the ring gear teeth. Then as the armature starts to rotate, the gears are forced into engagement.

As movement of the shift lever is completed, the starter switch is closed so that the starter armature begins to rotate. This rotates the shell and sleeve as-

When the engine starts to operate, it tries to drive the starter armature through the pinion. This causes the pinion to rotate with respect to the shell so that it overruns the shell and armature. The rollers are

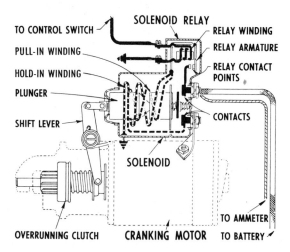

Fig. 34-21. *Schematic reveals details of wiring circuit of solenoid relay and solenoid incorporated in starting motor shown in Fig. 34-20.*

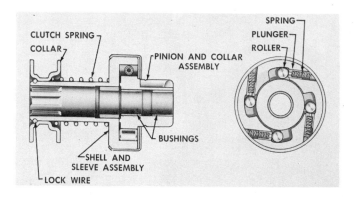

Fig. 34-22. *Sectional view of overrunning clutch reveals details of construction and location of rollers in clutch.*

sembly, causing the rollers to jam tightly in the smaller sections of the shell rotator. The rollers will then jam between the pinion collar and the shell so that the pinion is forced to rotate with the armature and crank the engine.

turned back toward the larger section of the shell notches where they are free and the pinion is therefore permitted to overrun.

This protects armature for the instant that car operator leaves starter switch closed or until automatic controls take over so that shift lever is released. The shift lever spring then pulls the overrunning clutch drive pinion out of mesh with the ring gear. Movement of the shift lever also opens the starting motor switch.

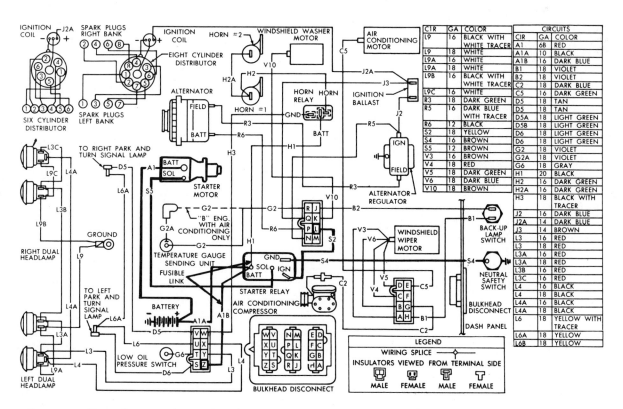

CIR	GA	COLOR
L9	16	BLACK WITH WHITE TRACER
L9	18	WHITE
L9A	16	WHITE
L9A	18	WHITE
L9B	16	BLACK WITH WHITE TRACER
L9C	16	WHITE
R3	18	DARK GREEN
R5	16	DARK BLUE WITH TRACER
R6	12	BLACK
S2	16	YELLOW
S4	16	BROWN
S5	12	BROWN
V3	16	BROWN
V4	18	RED
V5	18	DARK GREEN
V6	18	DARK BLUE
V10	18	BROWN

CIR	GA	COLOR
A1	6B	RED
A1A	10	BLACK
A1B	16	DARK BLUE
B1	18	VIOLET
B2	18	VIOLET
C2	18	DARK BLUE
C5	16	DARK GREEN
D5	18	TAN
D5	18	TAN
D5A	18	LIGHT GREEN
D5B	18	LIGHT GREEN
D6	18	LIGHT GREEN
D6	18	LIGHT GREEN
G2	18	VIOLET
G2A	18	VIOLET
G6	18	GRAY
H1	20	BLACK
H2	16	DARK GREEN
H2A	16	DARK GREEN
H3	18	BLACK WITH TRACER
J2	16	DARK BLUE
J2A	16	DARK BLUE
J3	14	BROWN
L3	16	RED
L3	18	RED
L3A	16	RED
L3A	18	RED
L3B	16	RED
L3C	16	RED
L4	16	BLACK
L4	18	BLACK
L4A	16	BLACK
L4A	18	BLACK
L6	18	YELLOW WITH TRACER
L6A	18	YELLOW
L6B	18	YELLOW

Fig. 34-23. *Typical engine electrical system, used on late model Chrysler Corporation cars, shows circuitry and electrical connections of starting motor, solenoid, neutral safety switch and fusible link.*

Starting Motor Control Circuits

There are various types of controls used with starting motors. Typical circuits are shown in Figs. 34-23 and 34-26. The simplest control is a pedal or switch which, when operated, connects the starter directly to the battery so that cranking takes place. On overrunning clutch, Fig. 34-19, or Dyer drive starters, the pedal not only operates the starter switch but it also shifts the drive pinion into mesh with the flywheel ring gear.

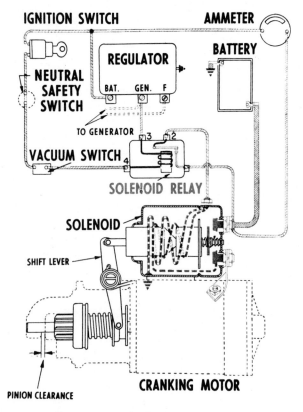

IGNITION SWITCH   **AMMETER**
REGULATOR   **BATTERY**
NEUTRAL SAFETY SWITCH
BAT.   GEN.   F
TO GENERATOR
VACUUM SWITCH
SOLENOID RELAY
SOLENOID
SHIFT LEVER
PINION CLEARANCE
CRANKING MOTOR

Fig. 34-24. Wiring circuit of starting motor relay and solenoid illustrates how added protection is afforded by completing solenoid relay winding circuit through generator on older Buick engines.

On installations where long battery cables would be required, or when more automatic control is desired, a magnetic switch or solenoid is connected in series with the ignition switch. When the switch is turned to the "start" position, the magnetic winding becomes connected to the battery so that the magnetic switches are operated and the circuit between the battery and starter is completed.

On starters with an overrunning clutch, Fig. 34-20, the solenoid is sometimes used with a solenoid relay as well as a vacuum switch. Turning on the ignition switch and then depressing the accelerator pedal completes the circuit to the solenoid relay. The relay winding is energized so that the relay contacts close. Closing the relay points connects the solenoid windings directly to the battery so that the solenoid is operated. The solenoid shifts the drive pinion into mesh with the flywheel ring gear, and also closes heavy contacts which complete the circuit from the starting motor to the battery. The vacuum switch opens the solenoid circuit after the engine starts.

One type of installation, Fig. 34-24, provides added protection against operating the starter while the engine is running, by completing the solenoid relay winding circuit through the generator. When the engine is running, the generator voltage is approximately the same as the battery, so that even though the vacuum switch contacts remain closed, there would be no voltage through the relay winding and the relay would not operate.

The solenoid switch on a starting motor not only closes the circuit between the battery and the cranking motor, but also shifts the starter pinion into engagement with the flywheel ring gear. This is accomplished by means of linkage between the solenoid plunger, and the shift lever on the starter. When the circuit is completed to the solenoid, current from the battery passes through two separate windings, known as the "pull-in" and "hold-in" windings. The combined magnetic field of these windings pull in the plunger so the drive pinion is shifted into mesh, and the main contacts of the solenoid switch are closed, Fig. 34-21.

Different size wires are used on the two windings, but approximately the same number of turns. The heavy pull-in winding is used to complete the plunger movement, but when the air gap is decreased, the hold-in winding is sufficient to retain the plunger. The closing of the main switch contacts closes the circuit between the battery and the starter and at the same time shorts out the pull-in winding.

When the control circuit is opened, after the engine is started, current no longer reaches the hold-in winding. However, current flows from the battery through the main switch contacts, through the pull-in winding (in reverse direction) and then through the hold-in winding to the ground. With the same number of turns of winding in both coils and the same current, the magnetic forces are equal but opposed and counteract each other. Tension of the return spring then causes the plunger to return to the "at rest" position and break the circuit.

Should cranking continue after the control circuit is broken, it would probably be caused by shorted turns in the pull-in circuit or a misalignment of the solenoid resulting in binding of the plunger. Low voltage or an open circuit in the hold-in winding will cause an oscillating action of the plunger. Check for a complete circuit of the hold-in winding as well as the condition of the battery whenever chattering of the switch occurs.

Whenever a solenoid is replaced, it is necessary to adjust the pinion travel. The clearance should be 1/8 to 3/16 in. The exact clearance will vary slightly with different starter designs.

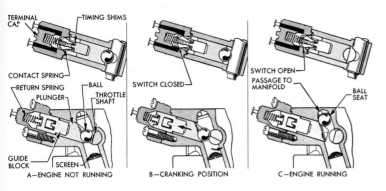

Fig. 34-25. *Ball-type vacuum switch built into carburetor prevents starter from being operated while engine is running. Flat spot on throttle shaft serves as an operating cam.*

VACUUM SWITCHES: Vacuum switches are used on some installations to provide a safety factor in the circuit so that the starter cannot be operated while the engine is running and also to provide more automatic control of the starting motor. There are two major types of vacuum switches, the diaphragm type and the ball type.

The ball type, Fig. 34-25, is built into the carburetor and is also known as the carburetor starter switch or the accelerator vacuum switch. The switch consists of a stainless steel ball, plunger, guide block, W-shaped contact spring and return spring housed in a passage in body flange which is closed by a terminal cap containing two contacts.

When the engine is not running and throttle is closed, the ball rests on lower end of switch plunger and bears against a flat spot on the throttle shaft and the contacts are not closed. When the accelerator is depressed with the engine stopped and ignition switch turned on, the flat spot on the throttle shaft acts as a cam to push the switch ball and guide block upward until the contact spring closes both contacts in the terminal cap, closing the circuit and putting the cranking system into operation. After the engine starts running and the throttle is in the idle position, manifold vacuum causes the ball to move upward against a seat in the throttle body and the switch return spring pushes the contact spring and plunger down to separate the switch contacts opening the solenoid switch relay circuit, Fig. 34-24, at that point.

The diaphragm type of vacuum switch has a spring-loaded flexible diaphragm in a housing, one side of which is open to the intake manifold. The other side of the diaphragm is linked mechanically to switch contacts. Linkage is also made to the accelerator pedal so that when the ignition switch is turned on and the accelerator is depressed, the vacuum switch contacts are closed to complete the circuit to the starter solenoid relay. After the engine has started and vacuum has developed in the manifold, the vacuum moves the diaphragm in the vacuum switch and locks the switch contacts in the open position. This stops the starting motor and prevents further operation until the engine has stopped.

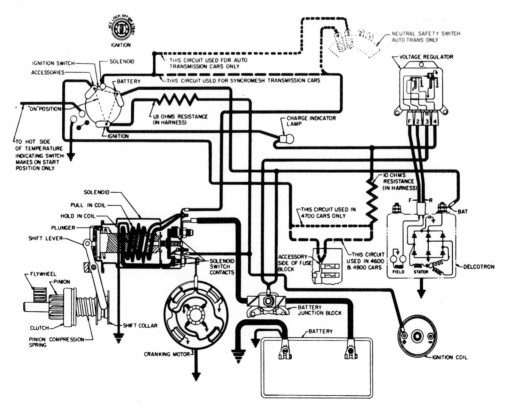

Fig. 34-26. *Starting system, used on late model Buick engines with automatic transmission, incorporates neutral safety switch connected in control circuit between ignition switch and solenoid.*

NEUTRAL SAFETY SWITCH: All cars equipped with an automatic transmission are provided with a neutral safety switch. The purpose of this switch is to eliminate the possibility of starting the engine while the transmission lever is in a position to drive the car. As shown in Fig. 34-26, it is connected in series between the ignition switch and the solenoid. On some installations, the transmission shift lever may be placed in either "park" or "neutral" position before the circuit to the starter is completed, and in other installations, it must be placed in "park" position only.

Starter Service

Checking the starting motor periodically is important in order to reduce roadside failures. The frequency of the inspection is dependent on the type of operation. In normal passenger car service, the motor should be inspected every 10,000 miles of operation. In door-to-door delivery service or other forms of operation, a more frequent inspection is desirable. Batteries and cables should be inspected every 5,000 miles.

To inspect the starting motor, the cover band should be removed, and the condition of the commutator and brushes noted. If the commutator is dirty it should be cleaned with a strip of No. 00 sandpaper, which is held against the commutator while the armature is rotating. To prevent the motor from overheating, it should not be operated for more than 15 seconds at a time. If the commutator is rough, pitted, or out-of-round, or if the mica is high, the starting motor should be disassembled and the commutator reconditioned in a lathe. Mica on starting motor commutators

should be undercut 1/32 in. If there are spots of solder on the interior surface of the cover band or starter housing, it indicates that the motor has overheated due to excessively long periods of cranking. This may cause open circuits at the commutator riser bars and consequent failure. Each time an open-circuited bar passes under a brush, severe arcing will occur so that the commutator bar will be badly pitted.

Brushes should make good clean contact with the commutator and should have the specified spring tension. Brushes should also have free movement in the brush holders and if worn more than one half their length, they should be replaced.

The starting motor must be securely bolted to the engine and the drive must operate freely. If the motor is fitted with oilers, it should be oiled with a few drops of light engine oil.

At approximately 25,000 mile intervals, the starting motor should be completely disassembled, cleaned, inspected, and tested. The armature and field windings should not be cleaned in any grease-dissolving solution nor by any high temperature grease-removing solution as that would damage the insulation.

If the starting motor is equipped with a Bendix type drive, Fig. 34-1, the drive should be cleaned with kerosene and lubricated with a trace of light engine oil on the spiral sleeve. Excessive oiling must be avoided.

The overrunning clutch type drive, Figs. 34-2 and 34-20, must never be cleaned with high temperature or grease-dissolving solution. The drive pinion on the overrunning clutch should turn freely in the overrunning direction and should not slip in the driving direction.

TROUBLE SHOOTING: STARTING SYSTEM

TROUBLE: STARTER CRANKS ENGINE SLOWLY

Possible Cause	Correction
1. Discharged battery or defective cell.	1. Make specific gravity and load tests--recharge or replace battery.
2. Excessive resistance in starter.	2. Disassemble and check for bent armature, or armature dragging on field poles--straighten or replace armature.
3. Excessive resistance in cranking circuit.	3. Make voltmeter or ohmmeter checks at cable connections, solenoid or relay, and at ground connections--repair or replace units as required.
4. Engine oil too heavy for prevailing temperature.	4. Change oil to suit conditions.
5. Excessive engine friction.	5. Check for tight-fitting engine bearings, pistons, rings, etc.

Fig. 34-27. This chart spells out common problems that could cause engine to crank slowly. Sequence of tests and corrections are shown.

TROUBLE: STARTER INOPERATIVE

Possible Cause	Correction
1. Loose or corroded battery terminals.	1. Clean battery posts and cable clamps--tighten clamps securely.
2. Discharged battery.	2. Recharge battery.

3. Dead battery.
4. Open starting circuit.

5. Inoperative solenoid or relay.

6. Faulty ignition switch.
7. Defective starter.

8. Inoperative neutral safety switch (cars with automatic transmission).

3. Replace battery.
4. Check cable connections, ignition switch, solenoid or relay and wiring--repair as required.
5. Use heavy jumper cable to bypass unit--replace faulty solenoid or relay.
6. Replace switch.
7. Disassemble starter and inspect parts--repair or replace starter.
8. Check operation of switch--adjust or replace switch.

TROUBLE: STARTER TURNS BUT DRIVE DOES NOT ENGAGE

Possible Cause	Correction
1. Broken teeth in flywheel ring gear.	1. Replace ring gear.
2. Rusted starter drive shaft.	2. Clean, lubricate shaft.
3. Defective starter drive.	3. Replace drive unit.

TROUBLE: STARTER DOES NOT DISENGAGE

Possible Cause	Correction
1. Faulty ignition switch.	1. Replace switch.
2. Short circuit in solenoid.	2. Replace solenoid.
3. Stuck solenoid contact switch plunger.	3. Repair solenoid.
4. Broken solenoid plunger spring.	4. Replace spring or solenoid.
5. Faulty starter relay.	5. Replace relay.

Fig. 34-28. Trouble shooting chart simplifies sequence of checks required to pinpoint cause if engine will not crank.

Starting Motor Tests

There are many ways of testing a starting motor to determine its operating condition. Begin by making on-car tests, follow up with stall and no-load tests, then pinpoint the cause of the problem with bench tests.

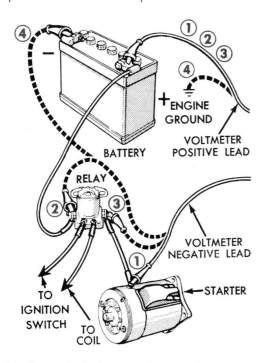

Fig. 34-29. To test for high resistance in starting system, use low-reading voltmeter (0.1V calibrations) to test voltage drop at points indicated.

On-Car Starting Motor Tests

The following tests will help determine whether or not the starting motor must be removed for stall and no-load tests:

STARTING CIRCUIT TESTS: Excessive resistance in the starting circuit can be located by using an expanded-scale voltmeter to test voltage drop across the various points shown in Fig. 34-29. Remove the primary lead from the ignition coil and crank the engine.

Maximum allowable voltage drop is as follows:
1. With voltmeter connected to positive post of battery and to starter terminal - 0.5.
2. With voltmeter connected to positive post of battery and to battery terminal of starter relay - 0.1.
3. With voltmeter connected to positive post of battery and to starter terminal of starter relay - 0.3.
4. With voltmeter connected to negative terminal of battery and to ground - 0.1.

AMPERAGE DRAW TEST: To test starting motor on the car under load:
1. Engine must be at normal operating temperature.
2. Connect test equipment to starting circuit as shown in Fig. 34-30.
3. Remove primary lead from ignition coil and adjust variable resistance to its maximum resistance to keep current from flowing through ammeter.

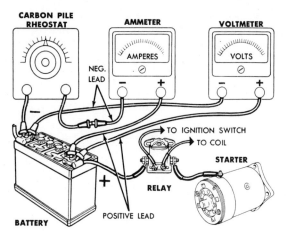

Fig. 34-30. *To test starter on-car under load (amperage draw), make test lead connections as shown and crank engine.*

4. Then crank the engine for no more than 15 seconds and note the exact reading on the voltmeter.
5. Stop cranking and adjust variable resistance until voltmeter indicates same voltage as obtained while starter cranked engine.
6. The ammeter reading will then indicate amperage draw of starting motor under load.
7. Compare this reading with manufacturer's specifications (usually 150 to 200 amps.).

Stall and No-Load Tests

The stall test is made to determine the resistance of the starting motor by testing current draw at a specified voltage with the armature locked. The no-load test is made to determine:
1. How fast the armature will revolve.
2. The amount of current draw at a specified voltage.

STALL TEST: Clamp the starting motor in a vise and proceed as follows:
1. Install a locking wedge between starter drive housing and drive pinion. See Fig. 34-31.
2. Connect high current-carrying variable resistance and an ammeter in series with starter and a battery.

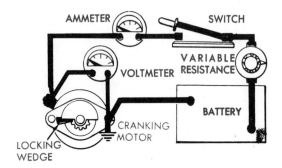

Fig. 34-31. *To test starter under stalled conditions, make connections as indicated and install a locking wedge at drive pinion.*

3. Adjust the variable resistance unit to full-resistance position.
4. See that battery is charged to above-normal battery voltage so it can supply proper test voltage as controlled by variable resistance unit.
5. With voltmeter connected across starter terminals, close circuit and adjust resistance until given voltage is obtained at starter.
6. Note amount of current draw on ammeter. It should fall within manufacturer's specified limits.

For example, if specifications call for testing at 4.0, adjust the variable resistance control to obtain this value and take an ammeter reading. A typical current draw specification for this test might be: minimum, 400 amps.; maximum, 450 amps.

NO-LOAD TEST: Connect the test equipment as shown in Fig. 34-32, using a tachometer attached to the end of armature shaft and omitting the locking wedge for this test:
1. Adjust variable resistance control to obtain given voltage value.
2. Starter will run at no-load speed.
3. Read ammeter and tachometer and compare these readings with specifications. Typical test specifications might read: voltage, 11; amperage draw, 90; rpm, 1925 to 2400.

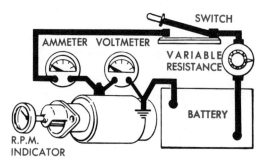

Fig. 34-32. *To make no-load test on starter, connect test leads as shown and attach tachometer to armature shaft to provide a means of controlling engine rpm.*

Bench Tests

When stall or no-load tests indicate that trouble exists in the starting motor, the following bench tests should be performed to pinpoint the cause:

ARMATURE AND FIELD OPEN CIRCUIT TEST: An open circuit armature may sometimes be detected by examining the commutator for evidence of burning. The spot burned on the commutator, is caused by an arc formed every time the commutator segment connected to the open circuited winding passes under a brush.

An open circuit test of the field can be made by means of a 110V test lamp, or by connecting a volt-

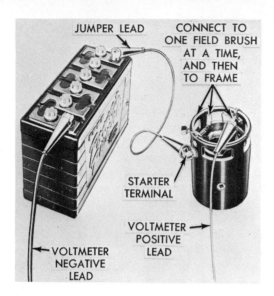

Fig. 34-33. *To make open circuit test of field windings of starting motor, connect voltmeter leads and jumper lead to points indicated.*

meter and battery as shown in Fig. 34-33. As starters have several windings, it will be necessary to check each winding separately. If the lamp fails to light, or if no reading is obtained on the voltmeter, the field winding is open and will have to be repaired or replaced.

ARMATURE AND FIELD GROUNDED CIRCUIT TEST: This test will determine if the winding insulation has failed, which would permit a conductor to touch the starter frame or armature core. It can be made with a 110V test lamp, or by using a voltmeter.

To test the armature by means of a test lamp, touch one test prod to the armature shaft and touch the other prod to each commutator bar in turn. If the lamp lights, the armature windings are grounded.

To make the test with a voltmeter, connect a jumper lead from the positive post of the battery to the armature shaft. Connect the voltmeter leads to the negative post of the battery and to each commutator bar in turn. See Fig. 34-34. If any voltage is indicated, the windings are grounded.

To test for grounded field circuit windings, connect a jumper lead from one terminal of the starter to one post of the battery. Contact the other post of the battery with a test prod and see that the brushes are away from the frame of the starting motor. Then touch the other test prod to the field frame of the starting motor. If the lamp lights, or if any voltage is indicated on the meter, the field windings are grounded.

Analyzing Test Results

If the starting motor produces correct amperage draw at specified voltage under the stall test--and if, under no-load conditions, it rotates at normal rpm at specified voltage and amperage draw--the starting motor is in good condition.

However, if trouble is indicated, consider the following:

1. If starting motor fails to rotate under no-load tests and shows high amperage draw, there may be direct ground in armature or field windings or "frozen" armature shaft bearings.

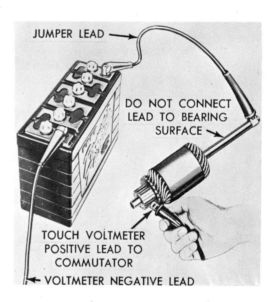

Fig. 34-34. *To test for grounded circuit in armature, make above connections and use voltmeter positive lead to probe each commutator bar in turn.*

2. Low no-load speed and a high amperage draw indicate a dragging armature, worn bearings, tight or dirty bearings.
3. Low no-load speed and a low current draw, point to high resistance in starting motor. One of the field windings may be "open," or other causes could be broken brush springs, badly worn brushes, high insulation between the commutator bars, extremely dirty or oily commutator.
4. High no-load speed and high current draw is a sign of "shorted" field windings.

Quiz - Starting Motor Fundamentals

1. In which direction does a current-carrying conductor tend to move when placed in a magnetic field?
   a. From strong magnetic field to weak one.
   b. From weak magnetic field to strong one.

2. Describe the reaction between the field formed around a current-carrying conductor and the field of a permanent magnet.
3. To what are the ends of an armature coil connected?

397

4. Describe the operation of a starting motor.
5. In an electric motor, the rotating coils are cutting magnetic lines of force, thereby generating voltage. In which direction does the current flow?
   a. In the same as the applied voltage.
   b. Opposed to the applied voltage.
6. Why is a series-wound motor used for cranking an internal combustion engine?
   a. Higher speed.
   b. Higher torque.
   c. Constant speed.
7. On a light load, a series-wound motor will rotate at what speed?
   a. Low speed.
   b. High speed.
   c. Normal speed.
8. As the load on a series motor increases, will the current through the armature and fields increase or decrease?
   a. Increase.
   b. Decrease.
   c. Remain the same.
9. What is the purpose of the shunt field coil used in conjunction with series coils on some cranking motors?
10. What is the approximate gear ratio between the cranking motor pinion and the engine flywheel ring gear?
    a. 1 to 1.
    b. 15 to 1.
    c. 50 to 1.

11. Why is it necessary for the starter pinion to disengage from the flywheel as soon as the engine starts?
12. What is the purpose of the Bendix drive?
13. Describe the operation of an overrunning clutch as used on a starter.
14. For what purpose is a solenoid used in a starting circuit?
15. What is the purpose of the vacuum switch?
    a. Prevent the starter from being operated while the engine is running.
    b. Prevent vacuum in intake manifold from exceeding a certain value.
    c. Switch vacuum from one point to another.
16. Where is the ball type vacuum switch located?
    a. On the starter.
    b. Built into the carburetor.
    c. Built into the intake manifold.
17. On what type chassis is a neutral safety switch found and what is its purpose?
18. Give four reasons why a starting motor may fail to crank an engine.
19. There are six tests described for use with cranking motors. Name four of them.
20. Under load, approximately what current will be flowing through a 12 volt starting motor?
    a. 50 amps.
    b. 150 amps.
    c. 300 amps.
21. A burned commutator is usually an indication of what condition?

ENGINE
IGNITION

Battery Ignition Systems

The ignition system on an internal combustion engine provides the spark which ignites the combustible mixture in the combustion chamber.

The modern ignition system, operating from a battery, consists of the battery, ignition coil, distributor, condenser, ignition switch, spark plugs, resistor and the necessary low and high tension wiring. Fig. 35-1 shows a wiring diagram of a typical ignition system.

The purpose of ignition coil, Fig. 35-2, is transforming or stepping up the 6 or 12V from the battery to the high tension voltage of approximately 20,000V

Fig. 35-1. Diagram of ignition circuit.

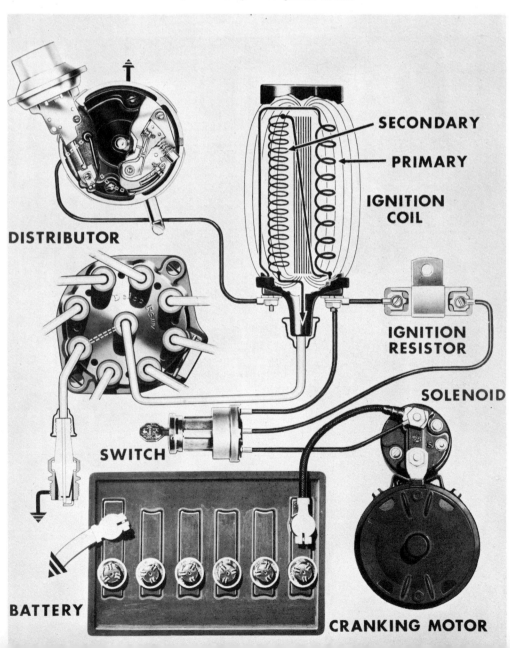

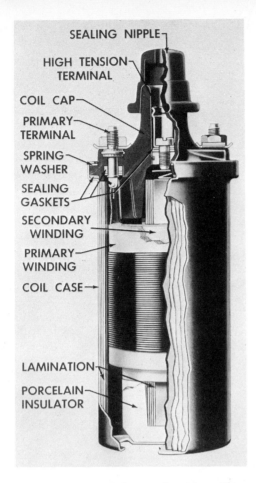

Fig. 35-2. Sectional view of ignition coil.
(AC Spark Plug Division)

SEALING NIPPLE
HIGH TENSION TERMINAL
COIL CAP
PRIMARY TERMINAL
SPRING WASHER
SEALING GASKETS
SECONDARY WINDING
PRIMARY WINDING
COIL CASE
LAMINATION
PORCELAIN INSULATOR

Fig. 35-4. Ignition condenser with mounting bracket.

respective cylinders of the engine and also has a mechanism which controls the point at which the breaker points open, thereby advancing or retarding the spark in accordance with engine requirements.

The purpose of the ignition condenser, Fig. 35-4, is to reduce arcing at the breaker points and thereby prolong their life.

The spark plug, Fig. 35-5, provides the gap in the combustion chamber across which the high tension electrical spark jumps to ignite the combustible charge.

The purpose of the ignition switch is to connect and disconnect the ignition system from the battery so the engine can be started and stopped as desired.

required to jump the spark plug gap located in the combustion chamber.

The ignition distributor, Fig. 35-3, has several functions. It opens and closes the primary ignition circuit, it distributes the high tension current to the

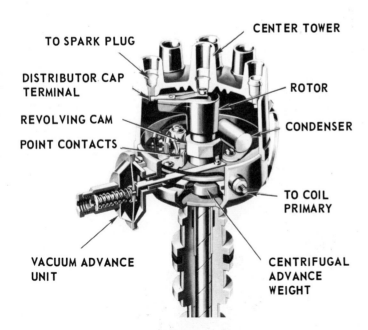

TO SPARK PLUG
CENTER TOWER
DISTRIBUTOR CAP TERMINAL
ROTOR
REVOLVING CAM
CONDENSER
POINT CONTACTS
TO COIL PRIMARY
VACUUM ADVANCE UNIT
CENTRIFUGAL ADVANCE WEIGHT

Fig. 35-3. Sectional view of late type Autolite distributor.

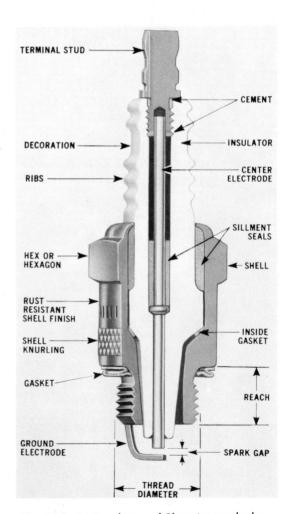

TERMINAL STUD
CEMENT
DECORATION
INSULATOR
CENTER ELECTRODE
RIBS
SILLMENT SEALS
HEX OR HEXAGON
SHELL
RUST RESISTANT SHELL FINISH
SHELL KNURLING
INSIDE GASKET
GASKET
REACH
GROUND ELECTRODE
SPARK GAP
THREAD DIAMETER

Fig. 35-5. Sectional view of Champion spark plug.

When the ignition switch is closed, Fig. 35-1, and the ignition distributor contacts also closed, current will flow from the battery, through the primary of the ignition coil, the distributor contact (breaker) points to the ground connection and back to the battery. The current flowing through the primary winding of the ignition coil produces a magnetic field in the coil. When the distributor contact points open, the magnetic field collapses and the movement of the magnetic field induces current in the secondary winding of the coil. As there are many more turns of wire in the

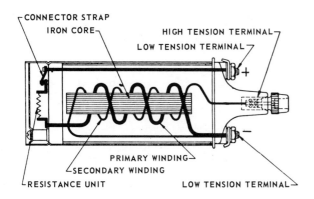

Fig. 35-6. Details of ignition coil, showing the primary and secondary windings and terminals.

secondary than there are in the primary, the voltage is increased up to 20,000V. The distributor then directs this high voltage to the proper spark plug where it jumps the gap. The heat of this spark ignites the fuel in the combustion chamber. The burning fuel expands and forces the piston down. Downward motion of the piston in turn rotates the crankshaft.

Ignition Coils

The ignition coil, Figs. 35-2 and 35-6, is a pulse transformer and is designed to step up the low primary voltage as received from the battery and generator of 6 or 12V to approximately 20,000V. It is composed of a primary and a secondary winding and core of soft iron. The primary winding is made up of approximately 200 turns of relatively heavy wire (approximately No. 18 gauge) and the secondary winding may have as many as 22,000 turns of fine wire, (approximately No. 38 gauge). The usual construction is to have the secondary winding wound around the soft iron core and the primary winding surround the secondary. The purpose of the core is to concentrate the magnetic field. This assembly is usually placed in a steel case with a cap of molded insulating materials which carries the terminals. Many coils have their windings immersed in oil. This is done to improve insulation and reduce the effects of moisture. In addition such coils can better withstand corona effects and heat.

When the ignition switch, Fig. 35-1, is closed and the distributor contact points are closed, the current flows through the primary winding of the ignition coil. The current produces a magnetic field around the coil windings. However, this does not occur instantly as it takes time for the current and consequently the magnetic field to reach its maximum value which is determined by either the resistance of the coil winding or the length of time the distributor contacts are closed. In general, the current does not reach the maximum as the contacts remain closed for such a short time, particularly at higher engine speeds.

When the breaker points begin to open, the primary current will tend to continue flowing. This is a natural condition in a winding which is increased by means of the iron core. Without an ignition condenser, the induced voltage causing this flow of current would establish an arc across the contact points and the magnetic energy would be consumed in this arc. As a result the contact points would be burned and normal ignition would be impossible. The condenser prevents this arc by providing a place for the current to flow, thus quickly checking the flow of current. As a result of this action, the magnetic field produced and sustained by the current flow will quickly collapse. It is this rapid collapse of the magnetic field, cutting the windings of the coil, which induces the high voltage in both the primary and secondary windings.

Ignition coils must also be designed to withstand moisture, the heat developed in the windings, and the corona effects. Coils are therefore filled with an insulating material such as oil or paraffin-like material. In addition to providing insulation, the oil or other material must provide rapid heat dissipation and keep corona effects to a minimum. Oil has the advantage that, being a liquid, it automatically heals itself if any breakdown in insulation occurs.

To prevent coils from absorbing moisture, they are hermetically sealed. The outer housing of some makes of coils are finned to increase their cooling.

Heavy-duty coils are built with larger cores and also provided with greater insulation. The higher inductance of such coils limits top speed performance to 4,000 engine rpm, but their life is materially longer.

Voltage Variations and Requirements

Engine speed, compression pressures, carburetor mixture ratios, spark plug temperatures, width and shape of plug gap will all affect the voltage required to produce a spark at the plug gap.

As previously pointed out, the length of time the ignition points are closed (which in turn is dependent on engine speed) will affect the voltage produced by the coil. However, there is a wide range between maximum and minimum voltages produced at low engine speeds, Fig. 35-7. This range in voltage is caused by increased tendency toward arcing under

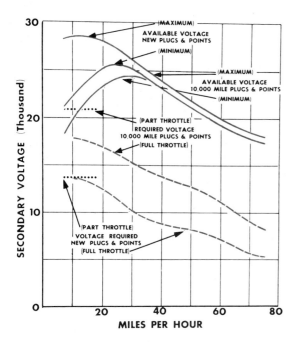

Fig. 35-7. *Variation of ignition voltage under different conditions.*

Negative High Tension Polarity

Most ignition manufacturers specify negative polarity as negative polarity of the high tension outlet of the ignition coil is considered as a means of conserving electrical energy. This is due to the fact that the center electrode of the spark plug is the hottest part of the plug. When the center electrode is connected to the negative high tension voltage, the spark gap becomes ionized more readily and thus forms a lower resistance path for the spark. A lower voltage is therefore required to fire the same plug gap.

A simple means of testing coil polarity on a car can be made with a voltmeter. The positive lead is connected to a good ground and the negative lead is connected to spark plug terminal of No. 1 cylinder. With this connection, the voltmeter is across the coil high tension windings. Run engine at idling speed. If voltmeter indicates "up" scale, the coil has a negative polarity.

An ordinary lead pencil can be used to check polarity. Insert the pencil point in the gap between the end of the ignition cable and the spark plug terminal. If the flare appears on the plug side, the polarity is correct.

Ignition Condensers

Ignition condensers are provided to prevent an arc at the distributor contact points when the points first open. This is accomplished by providing a place where current can flow until the contact points are fully open.

Condensers are made of alternate sheets of metal foil and insulation. The sheets of foil are of slightly smaller area than the insulating sheets and, as shown in Fig. 35-8, alternate sheets of foil are connected to one terminal of the condenser, while the remaining sheets of foil are connected together to provide the other terminal. The condenser is connected directly across the distributor contact points.

Condenser action requires a high quality insulation between the sheets of foil and in automotive condensers. The sheets of foil and insulation are in the form of long narrow strips which are then rolled to form a compact cylinder.

In order to eliminate the possibility of moisture entering the condenser, they are hermetically sealed.

The capacity of a condenser is measured in microfarads and is proportional to the total area of the foil and inversely proportional to the thickness of the insulating sheets which are called the dielectric. In other words, the thinner the dielectric the greater the capacity of condenser. Ignition condensers usually vary in capacity from .15 to .25 microfarad.

Loosened or corroded connections will increase the series resistance of a condenser which will cause it to be slow in taking a charge. This in turn causes high voltage and arcing at the distributor contact points. In general a resistance up to .5 ohm does not seriously affect ignition performance.

such conditions. Whenever an arc occurs at the breaker points, the voltage induced in the secondary winding is reduced. Obviously when such voltage reaches the minimum required to jump the gap at the plug, missing will occur.

New distributor contact points, correctly installed, make possible the maximum voltage from the coil secondary. New plugs have the lowest firing requirements and after use the electrodes of the plugs become worn and eroded and a higher voltage is required to jump the gap. After approximately 10,000 miles of operation, the points will also be covered with oxide which will lower the minimum voltage available at low speeds. In addition plug gaps often increase as much as .015 in. (approximately 50 percent).

It is therefore necessary that a margin of voltage be available over and above that required to fire a plug under ideal conditions. Install the coil as close to the distributor as possible to greatly aid ignition conditions. In addition, the distributor should be centrally located in respect to the engine so that spark plug leads will be as short as possible. Coil terminals must be connected correctly so as to insure negative polarity at the high tension terminal.

Keeping all high tension leads as short as possible reduces the electrostatic capacity of the system and thereby increases the voltage available at the plugs.

A higher voltage is also required when carburetor mixtures are lean. Such voltage may be as much as 40 percent higher than normal requirements. The highest voltage requirements exist at low engine speed under very light acceleration. Missing under such conditions is a direct indication that there is insufficient voltage available to fire the plug.

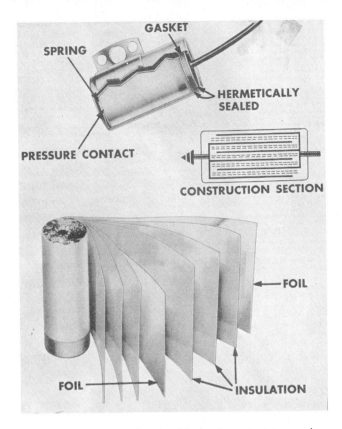

Fig. 35-8. Construction details of Delco-Remy ignition condenser.

If the tungsten transfers from the positive to the negative point, Fig. 35-10, reduce condenser capacity, move distributor-to-coil leads closer together, move these leads away from ground or lengthen condenser lead.

Fig. 35-10. High condenser capacity causes transfer of metal from positive to negative breaker point.

This arcing at the contact points causes transfer of tungsten from one breaker point to the other, so that a tip builds up on one point while a pit forms on the other. The direction in which the tungsten transfers can be used as basis for trouble shooting and correction of the pitting. If the material transfers from the negative to the positive point, Fig. 35-9, one or more of these corrections can be made: Increase condenser capacity, shorten condenser lead, separate distributor-to-coil low and high tension leads, move these leads closer to ground.

Vibrator Type Ignition Coil

The vibrator type of ignition coil, Fig. 35-11, consists of the conventional primary and secondary windings and soft iron core. In addition, it is provided with a set of contact points which are connected in

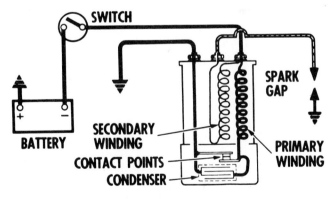

Fig. 35-11. Circuit of vibrator type ignition coil.

series with the primary winding and are mounted so that the magnetic field from the core will pull the movable or vibrating point away from the stationary point and, in that way, the primary circuit is opened and closed.

Vibrating type ignition coils were used for many years in the early days of the industry and popularly known as the Model-T coil. Today they are used primarily for starting Diesel engines.

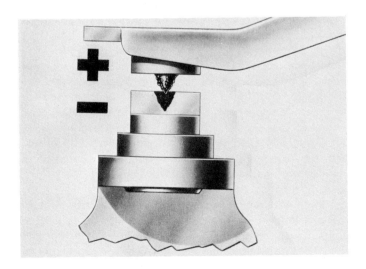

Fig. 35-9. Low condenser capacity causes transfer of metal from negative to positive breaker point.

These coils are constructed with the primary next to the core and the secondary on top of the primary. As a result, it is necessary to make the coil case of insulating material.

In operation, current flows through the primary winding and creates a magnetic field, which attracts the armature carrying one of the sets of contact points. This causes the contact points to separate and open the primary circuit. This in turn causes the magnetic field to collapse, releasing the armature so that the points close, reestablishing the flow of current through the primary winding. This cycle is repeated at a rate dependent on the stiffness of the armature spring. Each time the magnetic field is built up and collapses, current is induced in the secondary winding and a stream of sparks will jump between the secondary leads when they are held close together. A condenser is connected across the vibrator contacts to prevent an arc from forming and bringing the current flow to an abrupt stop.

On the Model-T Ford and other engines using the vibrator type coil, a secondary lead was connected to a spark plug and the other lead grounded. One coil was provided for each cylinder and the distributor handled primary current only.

On Diesel engines the stream of sparks is used to ignite a spray of oil in the intake manifold, in order to obtain easier starting under low temperature conditions.

Ignition Distributors

The ignition distributor is designed to make and break the primary ignition circuit, and also to distribute the high tension current to the proper spark plug at the correct time. It is driven at one half crankshaft speed on four-cycle engines, and is usually driven by the camshaft, though in some cases an accessory shaft is used. In order to keep high tension leads as short as possible, it is desirable to have the distributor centrally located in respect to the engine. However, in many designs the distributor is mounted at the front or rear of the engine.

Detailed construction of the ignition distributor varies considerably with different manufacturers. Basically, it consists of a housing into which the distributor shaft and centrifugal weight base assembly are fitted with suitable bearings. In most cases, these bearings are of the bronze bushing type, though heavy duty distributors frequently employ ball bearings. In low-priced distributors, the shaft will turn directly in the cast iron housing of the distributor.

Details of a recent model Delco distributor are shown in Fig. 35-12. A window in cap is provided for easy adjustment of the breaker point gap, while cap is in position. The circuit breaker plate located below the centrifugal advance mechanism uses the outer diameter of the main shaft bushing for its bearing surface. A retainer clip in the upper shaft bushing holds the movable plate in position. The contact set is attached to the movable breaker plate. A vacuum advance control unit, attached to the distributor housing is mounted under the movable breaker plate. The rotor serves as a cover for the centrifugal advance mechanism which consists of an automatic cam actuated by two centrifugal weights.

As the breaker cam is rotated, each cam lobe passes under the breaker lever rubbing block. This causes the breaker points to separate. As these are connected in series with the primary winding of the ignition coil, current will pass through that circuit when the points are closed. When the points open, the magnetic field collapses and a high tension voltage is induced in the secondary winding of the ignition coil.

The usual design is to provide one lobe on the breaker cam for each cylinder of the engine. A six-cylinder engine will therefore have a six-lobe cam in the distributor, and an eight-cylinder will have an eight-lobe cam, Fig. 35-12. As a result, every revolution of the breaker cam will produce one spark for each cylinder of the engine.

On a four-cycle engine, each cylinder fires every other revolution. The distributor shaft must therefore revolve at one half crankshaft speed. On a two-cycle engine the distributor shaft would revolve at the same speed as the crankshaft.

After the high tension surge is produced in the ignition coil by the opening of the breaker points, the current passes from the coil to the center terminal of the distributor cap which is mounted on top of the distributor housing. From that point, it passes down to the rotor which is mounted on top of the breaker cam and revolves with it. The current passes along the rotor, and jumps the minute gap to the cap electrode under which the rotor is positioned at that instant. This cap electrode is in turn connected by high tension wiring to the spark plug. As the rotor rotates, it distributes current to each of the cap terminals in turn, Fig. 35-1.

Spark Advance

In order to obtain efficient operation of an internal combustion engine, throughout the range of speed and operating conditions, it is essential that the spark occur at the correct instant. That instant will vary according to engine load and speed. Mechanism is, therefore, provided to automatically advance and retard the spark as conditions require. On automotive engines two methods are usually provided: these are by centrifugal force and engine vacuum.

When the engine is idling the spark is usually timed to occur just before the piston reaches the top of the compression stroke. Under idling conditions or, when driving at a sustained speed under part throttle conditions, cylinders take in only part of the full charge. As a result, compression pressures are relatively low, and as a consequence combustion is slow and must be started earlier. At higher engine speeds, there is a shorter interval of time for the mixture to ignite and expand. Therefore, in order to obtain the maximum amount of power at higher speeds, it is necessary to have the spark occur slightly earlier in the engine cycle. This is accomplished by means of the centrifugal advance mechanism, Figs. 35-12 and 35-13. In Fig. 35-12 the advance mechanism is above

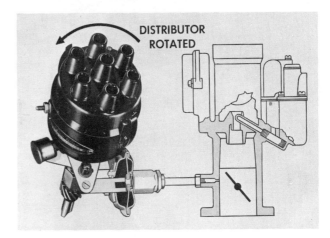

Fig. 35-14. Vacuum advance mechanism on a Delco-Remy distributor which rotates the distributor in its mounting.

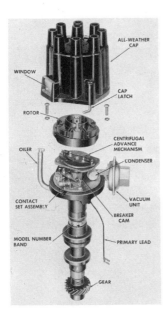

Fig. 35-12. Details of typical Delco-Remy distributor.

the contact set assembly, and in Fig. 35-13 it is below the ignition breaker plate. The mechanism consists of two weights, which the centrifugal force developed by the rotating shaft tends to throw outward against the tension of springs. The faster the distributor shaft

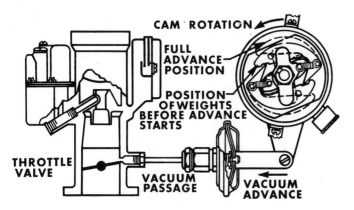

Fig. 35-13. Diagram showing details of centrifugal and vacuum advance mechanism. (Delco-Remy)

rotates, the greater the centrifugal force, and the greater the movement of the advance weights. The movement of the weights is transmitted to the breaker cam so that the cam is rotated to an advanced position

in respect to the distributor drive shaft In other designs, the cam is integral with the distributor shaft, and the movement of the centrifugal weights will rotate the breaker plate around the axis of the distributor shaft.

The amount of centrifugal advance required varies considerably for each make and model of engine and is determined experimentally on a dynamometer. Under part throttle operation, the intake manifold is high and, therefore, a smaller amount of mixture is sucked into the engine and compression pressure is low. With lower pressures, the mixture does not burn as rapidly, and to obtain maximum efficiency under such conditions, the spark should be advanced more than that obtained by the centrifugal mechanism. This additional advance is obtained by means of the vaccum advance mechanism.

Vacuum Advance

The conventional vacuum advance mechanism, Fig. 35-13, utilizes the vacuum in the intake manifold to provide the additional spark advance required under part throttle operation and has a spring loaded diaphragm connected by linkage to the ignition distributor. The spring loaded side of the diaphragm is airtight and is connected by tubing to a point on the atmospheric side of the carburetor throttle, when the throttle is in the idling position. With the throttle in the idling position, there is virtually zero vacuum at the point where the vacuum spark control connection is made. However, as soon as the throttle is opened, it swings past the opening of the vacuum passage and the vacuum can then act on the diaphragm of the spark advance mechanism. This causes the diaphragm to deflect and its motion is transmitted by linkage to the distributor. In some designs, the distributor is rotated on its mounting, Fig. 35-14, while in other designs the breaker plate is rotated.

The amount of movement is of course proportional to the amount of vacuum. At any particular engine

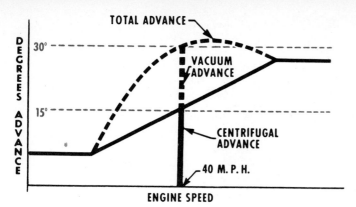

Fig. 35-15. Typical centrifugal and vacuum advance curves.

speed there will be a definite amount of spark advance resulting from the operation of the centrifugal advance and also from the vacuum advance mechanism.

For example, Fig. 35-15 shows that the centrifugal advance at 40 mph supplies 15 deg. spark advance. If the throttle is only partly opened, an additional vacuum advance of up to 15 deg. may be obtained. However, if the throttle is opened completely, the manifold vacuum will approach zero with the result that there will be no spark advance provided by the vacuum spark advance mechanism. Another curve or chart of spark advance showing the rapid decrease in vacuum advance between 20 percent engine load and full load is shown in Fig. 35-16.

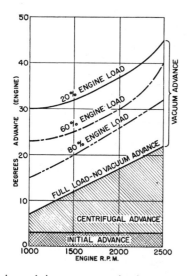

Fig. 35-16. A chart of the engine spark advance on a typical V-8, high compression engine, showing the rapid decrease in vacuum advance between 20 percent engine load and full engine load. Spark advance requirements will vary with different engines.

Factors Governing Spark Advance

ENGINE LOAD:
 Less Load - Combustion is slower and more spark advance required.
 More Load - Combustion is faster and less spark advance required.

ENGINE SPEED:
 Low Speed and Load - Combustion slower and more spark advance required.
 Low Speed and Full Load - Combustion faster and less spark advance required.
 High Speed and Full Load - Combustion slower and more spark advance required.

ENGINE TEMPERATURE:
 Cold Engine - Combustion slower and more spark advance required.
 Hot Engine - Combustion faster and less spark advance required.

CYLINDER BORE:
 Larger Bore - Combustion slower and more spark advance required.
 Smaller Bore - Combustion faster and less spark advance required.

COMPRESSION RATIO:
 Low Compression Ratio - Combustion slower and more spark advance required.
 High Compression Ratio - Combustion faster and less spark advance required.

CHARACTER OF FUEL:
 Low Volatile Fuel - Combustion slower and more spark advance required.
 High Volatile Fuel - Combustion faster and less spark advance required.

AIR-FUEL MIXTURE:
 Lean Mixture - Combustion faster and less spark advance required.
 Rich Mixture - Combustion slower and more spark advance required.

KNOCK RATING OF FUEL:
 High Octane Fuel - Combustion slower and more spark advance required.
 Low Octane Fuel - Combustion faster and less spark advance required.

In addition to the above factors which affect spark timing, there are several others which include the shape of the combustion chamber, location of the spark plug, carbon accumulation in the combustion chamber, equality of fuel and distribution to the individual cylinders.

Cam Angle

Cam angle or dwell angle is the number of degrees through which the distributor cam rotates, while the ignition points are closed. It is directly related to the breaker point gap. Decreasing the breaker point gap will increase the cam angle. In a six-cylinder engine the average cam angle is 36 deg. As there are 60 deg. of cam rotation devoted to firing each cylinder of a six-cylinder engine the points are open for 24 deg. and closed for 36 deg. The cam angle of an eight-cylinder engine is approximately 31 deg. while on a four-cylinder engine the cam angle would be about 41 deg.

The breaker point gap or cam angle must be set very accurately. If the cam angle is too small, there will be insufficient time for the current to pass through the primary winding of the ignition coil, and a weak spark will result. If the cam angle is too great, the breaker points will not open far enough so that they will tend to stick together, and misfiring will result. The best method of adjusting the breaker points, is by means of a dwell meter, though many mechanics will use a thickness gauge.

Ford Loadomatic Advance

Spark advance on the Ford Loadomatic distributor, Fig. 35-17, is controlled entirely by vacuum. The demands of the engine are satisfied by the action of the breaker plate, which is controlled by a vacuum actuated diaphragm working against the action of two calibrated breaker plate springs. The breaker plate is free to rotate on the shaft upper bushing. The diaphragm moves the breaker plate in a counterclockwise direction to advance the spark, and the springs move the plate in a clockwise direction, to retard the spark. The degree of spark advance is determined by the strength of the vacuum acting on the diaphragm.

Vacuum is transmitted to the distributor diaphragm from three interconnected passages in the carburetor, Fig. 35-17. Older designs used only two passages in the carburetor and did not have a spark valve. The opening of one passage is in the throat of the venturi, and the openings of the other two passages are in the throttle bore, just above the closed throttle plate.

All manifold vacuum passes through a spark control valve located in the carburetor throttle body, Fig. 35-17. Under steady part open throttle operation, the spark valve is held open against the pressure of a calibrated spring. A combination of atmospheric pressure outside of the spark valve diaphragm, and manifold vacuum from within, holds the spark valve open. When accelerating, manifold vacuum momentarily drops below a predetermined point, and the calibrated spring closes the spark valve shutting off the manifold vacuum to the distributor, which prevents excessive spark advance. Vacuum from the venturi prevents full spark retard. As engine speed approaches the throttle setting, manifold vacuum increases sufficiently to open the spark valve, and allow a higher vacuum to operate the diaphragm in the distributor.

At high engine speed, manifold vacuum falls and the valve closes. This prevents loss of venturi vacuum due to bleed back caused by lower manifold vacuum. This assures full spark advance at high engine speeds.

The spark valve operates in a similar manner to provide an intermediate spark retard, whenever the load on the engine is increased to a degree where normal road load spark advance would be too great, and the wide open throttle retard would reduce the efficiency of the engine.

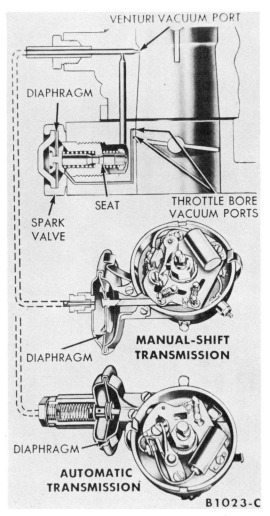

Fig. 35-17. Ford Loadomatic distributor as used on cars with manual shift transmission and with automatic transmission.

On Ford cars using the Loadomatic distributor and automatic transmission, the operation is somewhat different. Vacuum to the distributor is transmitted in the same manner to the distributor, as is used with the manual shift transmission. However, the distributor used with the automatic transmission has three spark advance systems, Fig. 35-17. At part throttle operation, there is a rapid spark advance which is controlled by the breaker plate spring. A stop in the vacuum chamber allows steady advance at steady part throttle operation. Additional advance at higher speeds, is controlled by calibration shims, located between the spring and vacuum connection in the diaphragm housing.

Distributor Service

Complete distributor service includes not only the replacement of the distributor breaker points, but also the testing and replacement, when necessary of the condenser, rotor, distributor cap, distributor cam, centrifugal and vacuum advance mechanism and distributor shaft bearings.

Fig. 35-18. Late type distributor tester.
(Sun Electric)

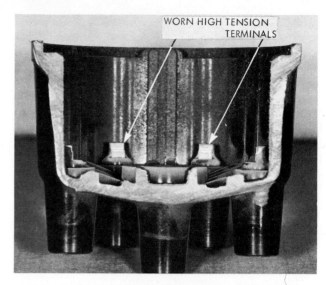

Fig. 35-19. Part of distributor cap cut away to show eroded condition of firing points.

To properly test a distributor to make sure all parts are functioning correctly, distributor testing equipment as shown in Fig. 35-18 is required. Such equipment will check the spacing or dwell of the ignition points, the degree of advance at various speeds, wear of the distributor cam as indicated by the regularity and spacing of the sparks.

DISTRIBUTOR CAPS:

These should be carefully checked to make sure that sparks have not been arcing from point to point within the cap. Neither should there be any cracks in the cap, and both interior and exterior must be clean and free from dirt. The firing points should not be eroded, Fig. 35-19, and the interior of the towers must be clean and free from corrosion. If necessary, the interior of the towers can be cleaned by means of a round wire bristle brush. When cleaning distributor caps, care must be exercised not to use any cleaning solution that would injure cap which is usually made of some form of Phenol-resin.

There are two principal methods of holding the distributor cap in place on the distributor housing.

Fig. 35-20. Illustrating parts of a distributor. (Delco-Remy)

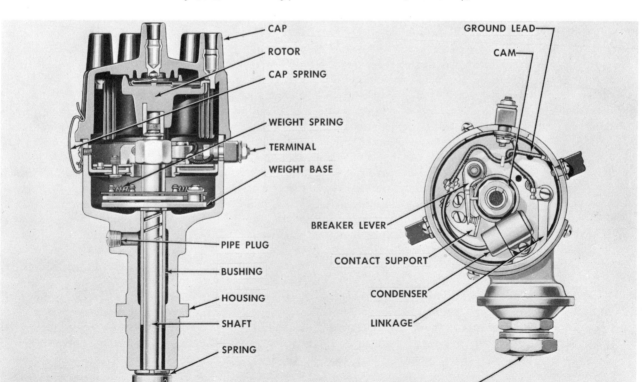

One is by means of external clips or cap springs, Fig. 35-20, and the other is by means of a latch as shown in Fig. 35-21. The former is easily removed by pulling back the clips, permitting the lifting off of the cap from the distributor housing. In the case of the latch, the cap is removed by inserting a screwdriver in upper slotted end of cap retainer, press down and turn until the latch is disengaged.

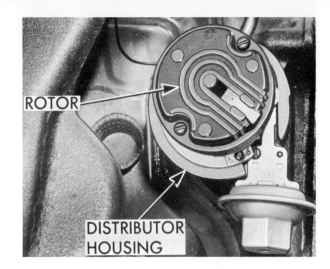

Fig. 35-23. This type rotor is attached to top of distributor shaft by means of two screws.

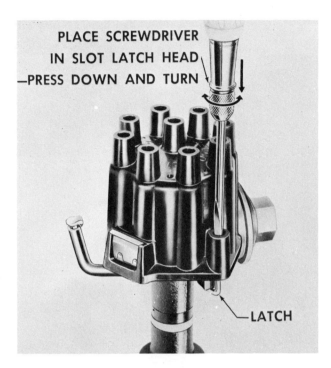

Fig. 35-21. Method of removing distributor cap from one type of Delco-Remy distributor.

high tension spark. Most rotors are designed simply to carry the high tension current. However, some are designed to include a resistor for the suppression of radio and TV interference.

Rotors are mounted on the upper end of the distributor shaft, Fig. 35-20, and in most cases all that is necessary to remove them is to pull them off. In that connection, the rotor must have a snug fit on the end of the shaft. On another design, two screws are used to attach the rotor, Fig. 35-23, to a plate on the top of the distributor shaft.

DISTRIBUTOR SHAFT:

There should not be more than .002 in. side clearance between the shaft and its bearings. The gear and its coupling or drive must be tight on the end of the shaft, and not be worn. When replacing bushings in the distributor housing, these should be removed by a special puller or press, Fig. 35-24, and most manufacturers recommend that the bushings be bur-

ROTORS:

Rotors are designed to distribute the high tension current to the towers of the distributor cap. They are provided with some sort of spring connection to the center tower or terminal and this spring must have

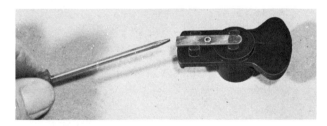

Fig. 35-22. Firing end of rotor must not be worn.

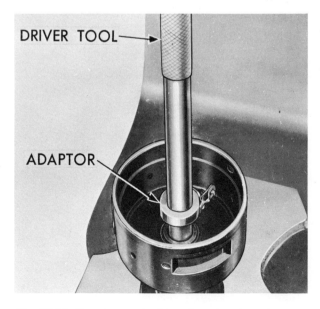

Fig. 35-24. Pressing out bushings from distributor housing.

ample tension to provide good electrical contact. The firing end of the rotor, Fig. 35-22, from which the high tension spark jumps to each of the terminals in turn should not be worn in any way, as any wear or irregularity will result in excessive resistance to the

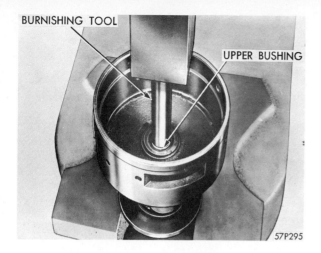

Fig. 35-25. Some types of distributor shaft bushings must be burnished after installation.

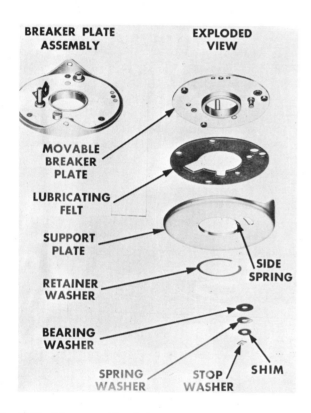

Fig. 35-26. The assembly of the center bearing breaker plate is shown in the upper left and exploded view is on the right.

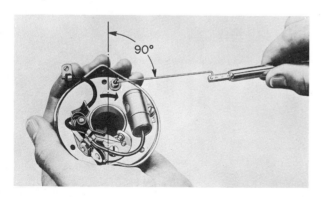

Fig. 35-27. Measuring tension on movable plate.

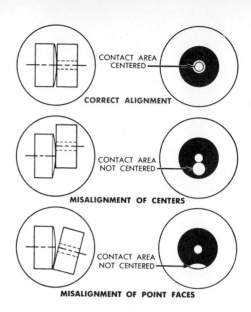

Fig. 35-28. Ignition breaker points must be accurately aligned for efficient operation and long life.

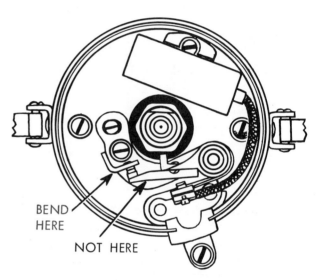

Fig. 35-29. To align ignition breaker points, bend only the stationary point bracket. Special bending tools are available for the purpose.

nished after installation, Fig. 35-25. However, the porous bushings used in many Delco-Remy units are manufactured to exact size and should not be reamed, scraped or filed. Some bushings should be soaked in engine oil prior to installation.

BREAKER PLATE:

The bearings of the breaker plate must not be worn and must operate smoothly. In the case of the Delco-Remy center bearing breaker plate, Fig. 35-26, by means of a spring balance, the spring tension can be measured, Fig. 35-27.

BREAKER CAM:

The breaker cam must be smooth and not worn. Any inaccuracies will be disclosed when the assembled distributor is tested on the distributor tester, Fig. 35-18, by an examination of the spark pattern. On assembly the cam should be given a very light coating of special grease.

INSULATORS:

Insulators at primary lead connection, Fig. 35-30, should be checked to make sure they are in good condition, and there is no possibility of any grounds.

BREAKER POINTS:

Breaker points must be centered and in accurate alignment, Fig. 35-28. Misalignment of breaker points will severely reduce their life and result in misfiring.

When aligning breaker points, only the stationary point bracket should be bent, Fig. 35-29. Never attempt to bend the movable breaker arm.

Breaker points are fastened to the breaker plate by means of a lock screw, Fig. 35-30, or the two attaching screws, Fig. 35-31. To remove the breaker point assembly shown in Fig. 35-30, after removing the distributor cap and rotor, remove the screw holding the condenser to the breaker plate, and disconnect the condenser lead together with the breaker arm spring. Remove the lock screw, permitting the lifting up of the point assembly from the pivot post. Some recent Delco breaker points have the condenser attached directly to the breaker plate.

For distributor shown in Fig. 35-31, procedure is similar except contact assembly is held in position by two screws. Note in this design, breaker points form a single assembly, and according to the manufacturer, there is no need to align the points. The only adjustment required is that of cam dwell (gap).

The installation of breaker points or contact point assemblies, is accomplished in the reverse order. To adjust the breaker point gap, or dwell, an eccentric adjustment screw is provided, Fig. 35-30. This moves the position of the stationary point in relation to the movable point, thereby altering the gap between the two. When setting the gap, the rubbing block on the

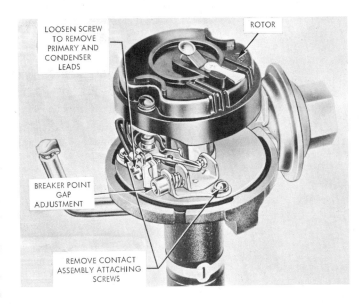

Fig. 35-31. *External adjustment type distributor with cap removed.*

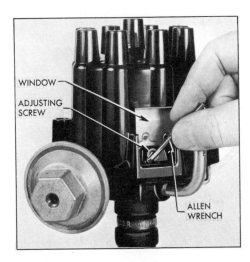

Fig. 35-32. *Adjusting cam angle, or breaker point gap, on external adjustment type distributor.*

movable arm must be on a high point of the distributor cam. The gap is adjusted to a specified width. When setting the gap, a blade of a thickness gauge of the correct thickness, is placed between the points and the gap is adjusted by turning the eccentric screw. Instead of an eccentric screw, some distributors have a notched hole in the breaker plate in which a screwdriver is inserted.

In the case of the distributor shown in Fig. 35-31, the point gap is adjusted by means of screw as shown in the illustration which moves the stationary point backward or forward as required. In that way, alignment of the points is not altered. The adjustment is controlled by inserting an Allen-type wrench into the hexagon hole in the adjustment. This adjustment can be made without removing the distributor cap, as the cap is provided with a window, Fig. 35-32, through which the adjustment can be reached with the Allen

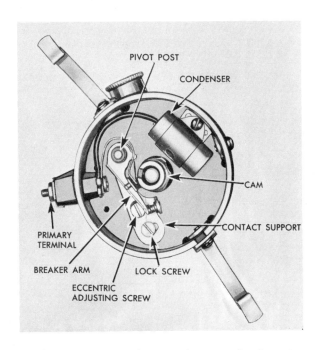

Fig. 35-30. **Note eccentric adjustment for setting breaker point gap.**

wrench. This permits making the adjustment while the engine is running to the specified dwell angle of 30 deg. for an eight cylinder engine. Another method can be used if a dwell meter is not available. Connect a test lamp in series in the primary lead. Rotate the distributor shaft until the rubbing block is on the high point of one of the cams. Then turn adjusting screw, Fig. 35-32, until lamp lights. Then back off on the adjustment one-half turn.

Dirty and slightly pitted ignition breaker points can be dressed with a few strokes of a fine-cut contact point file. The file must be free of dirt and oil. Care must be taken to keep the surfaces of the points parallel. In most cases it is advisable to install a new set of contact points.

BREAKER ARM SPRING TENSION:

Breaker arm spring pressure must fall between specified limits. (Usually 19-23 oz.) Weak spring tension will result in chatter and missing at high speeds, while excessive tension will cause excessive wear of the points, rubbing block and distributor cam. Contact point pressure should be checked with a spring gauge hooked to the end of the breaker lever and pull exerted at 90 deg. The reading should be taken just as the points separate. The pressure should be adjusted by bending the breaker lever spring. To decrease the pressure, pinch the spring carefully, Fig. 35-33. To increase the pressure, the lever must be removed from the distributor, so the spring can be bent away from the lever.

Fig. 35-33. Illustrating method of decreasing pressure of breaker arm spring.

CAM ANGLE:

Cam angle or dwell, as it is also called, is the number of degrees of cam rotation from the instant the ignition breaker points close until they open again. It is controlled entirely by the width of the breaker point gap. Decreasing the width of the breaker point gap, increases the cam angle.

To measure the cam angle, special equipment is required. A cam angle meter is included in the design

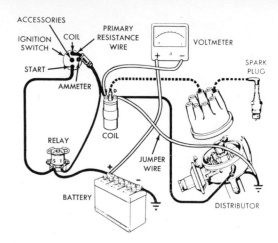

Fig. 35-33a. Ford ignition system showing primary resistance wire. Voltmeter is connected to check voltage at coil.

of a distributor tester as shown in Fig. 35-18. When checking the cam angle, the instructions accompanying the equipment should be followed. Cam angle of six cylinder engines is approximately 40 deg., and for eight cylinder engines approximately 30 deg. However, the specifications for the individual ignition system should be followed.

IGNITION RESISTOR:

In most 12V systems and some 6V systems, a resistor is connected in series with the primary circuit of the ignition coil during normal operation, Fig. 35-1. However, during the cranking period, the resistor is cut out of the circuit so that full voltage is applied to the coil. This insures a strong spark during the cranking period, and in that way quicker starting is provided. Contacts on the cranking motor solenoid are used to cut the resistor out of the primary circuit during the cranking period. The ignition coil and its windings are designed to operate efficiently at a voltage lower than full battery voltage, so that when full battery voltage is applied, a hotter than normal spark is provided. It must also be remembered, that during the cranking period, the excessive load applied on the battery, will reduce the voltage reaching the ignition system. If full battery voltage was used continually for normal operation, the coil would quickly burn out.

On older systems, the resistor was of the block type shown in Fig. 35-1. Recently a wire type resistance is being used to connect the coil to the battery, Fig. 35-33a.

There are two types of wire used for this resistance. Prestolite and Chrysler use a wire that is sensitive to heat. As the temperature of the wire increases, so does its resistance. As a result, when the engine reaches operating temperature, its resistance is such that six volts are applied to the coil.

The resistance of the Delco Remy and Ford resistance wire is not affected by heat. However the starting circuit is designed so as long as the starting motor is operating, full battery voltage is applied to the coil. When the starter is not cranking the engine, the resistance wire is cut into the circuit to reduce

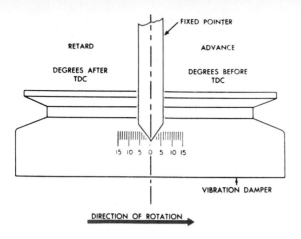

Fig. 35-34. *Typical of timing marks on vibration damper.*

Fig. 35-35. *Ignition timing light with special advance control. Note meter for indicating amount of advance.*

the voltage applied to the coil.

If the engine fires when the ignition switch is turned on, but stops when the switch is released to running position, it usually indicates that the resistor is defective and should be replaced.

At no time should the resistor be shorted out of the circuit as that would supply continuous full voltage to the coil and burn it out.

Resistors and resistor wires should be checked whenever the breaker points are burned or when the ignition coil is burned out. With the ignition switch turned on, the voltage reading from the resistor side of the coil to the ground should be approximately 5 to 7V, unless other specifications are available. Resistance of resistor as used on 12V systems is approximately 1.5 ohms.

Ignition Timing

The ignition must be accurately timed so that the spark occurs in the combustion chamber at the correct instant. Incorrectly timed ignition results in loss of efficiency and power. If the spark occurs too early, both fuel economy and power will be sacrificed. If the

spark occurs too late, preignition with attendant "pinging" occurs, and if continued, the engine will be damaged. The time that the spark occurs varies considerably in different engines and for that reason factory specifications should be carefully followed. The occurrence of the spark is timed in relation to the position of number one piston, unless otherwise specified, and is listed as so many degrees before top center. This is abbreviated BTC or BTDC, and the top center referred to, is at the end of the compression stroke.

Timing marks are placed on the flywheel, the vibration damper at the front of the engine or on the fan pulley. Typical timing marks are shown in Fig. 35-34.

To time the ignition of an engine, the ignition breaker points should just start to open, as the piston of number one cylinder approaches top dead center on its compression stroke. The most accurate method, and the one most frequently used, is to use a stroboscopic type of timing light, Fig. 35-35. The timing light is connected to the battery and to Number One spark plug. The beam is then directed to the timing marks, and with the engine running, the light will flash each time the spark occurs. The timing marks will have the appearance of standing still so that the

Fig. 35-36. *Details of dual advance distributor used on some Ford engines. This design includes both centrifugal and vacuum advance.*

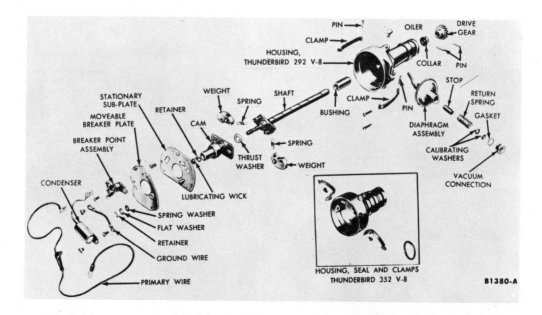

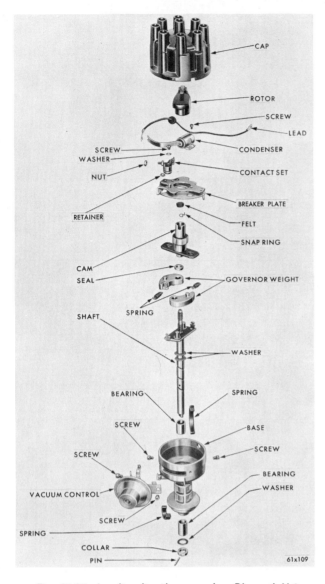

Fig. 35-37. *Autolite distributor used on Plymouth V-8.*

In the Autolite distributor shown in Fig. 35-37, note that the distributor cam is not integral with the shaft, but is a separate unit. A felt wick is provided in the top of the distributor cam for lubrication.

Special Distributors

The ignition distributors used on most cars have a single set of breaker points and cam lobe for each cylinder of the engine. At higher engine speeds, the breaker points of such distributors remain closed a very short time, with the result that there is very little time for the coil to build up. This difficulty can be overcome to a degree by means of twin ignition distributors or double alternate distributors. Twelve volt ignition is another method of providing a better spark at high speeds and is discussed in another section.

Twin ignition distributors, Fig. 35-38, are built as though they were two complete distributors combined into a single unit. This type has two complete and independent ignition systems--two ignition coils and two sets of breaker points, and two spark plugs for each cylinder. Usually the two sets operate simultaneously so the spark at both plugs in the cylinder occurs at the same instant. However, they can be designed so one set of breaker points opens slightly before the other in order to offset a lag in combustion.

Double alternate distributors, Fig. 35-39, have two breaker arms that operate alternately. This permits a cam to be used that has half as many lobes as there are cylinders. In some installations the two sets of breaker arms are connected to a single ignition coil, while in other cases, two coils and a special cap and rotor are used. In that way, each set of contacts remains closed for a longer interval and with separate coils, there is greater time for the coil to be saturated.

time the spark occurs is easily noted. The specified timing mark should coincide with the index mark. If not, the clamp screw of the distributor is loosened, and the distributor rotated to the correct position. Moving the distributor housing against shaft rotation advances the timing, and with shaft rotation retards timing.

Distributor Types

In addition to the distributors previously illustrated and discussed, there are several others used on vehicles. Fig. 35-36 shows the dual advance distributor used on some Ford engines. On this distributor, centrifugal advance is decreased by bending a spring post (located below the breaker plate) away from the distributor shaft. Vacuum advance on this distributor is controlled by shims placed behind the vacuum diaphragm spring. Adding washers will decrease the advance.

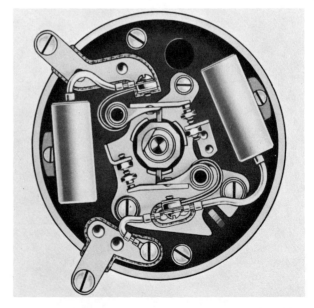

Fig. 35-38. *Breaker plate for twin ignition distributor.*

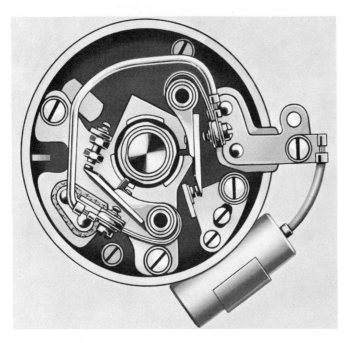

Fig. 35-39. Breaker plate for double alternate distributor using a single coil. (Autolite)

Before attempting to synchronize the breaker contacts of twin ignition distributors, Fig. 35-38, it is important that each set of contacts has the same gap. The fixed contacts are mounted on the breaker plate, while the adjustable contacts are mounted on the subplate. The distributor is then mounted on a test stand, and an indicator light lead is connected to each primary terminal. Operate the distributor in the correct direction and observe if the two sets of lights are synchronized. If not, loosen the screws holding the subplate and rotate the subplate until the two lights are exactly synchronized.

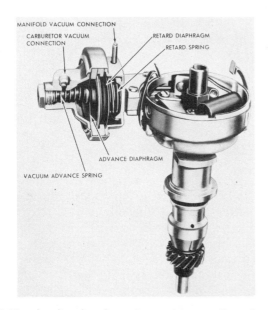

Fig. 35-39a. Autolite distributor designed especially to limit production of noxious exhaust gases. Note the two diaphragms.

The double alternate distributor with 45 deg. spark, Fig. 35-39, has one set of contacts on the mainbreaker plate assembly and another set of contacts on the subplate. The first step in synchronizing the breaker points is to set the gaps exactly the same. The assembly is then mounted on a test fixture and when operated there should be a 45 deg. interval between the opening of one set of contacts and the opening of the other. Adjustment can be made by adjusting the position of the subplate which is controlled by an eccentric.

The distributor, shown in Fig. 35-40, is similar to that shown in Fig. 35-39, except that two coils are used and the breaker contacts are not 45 deg. apart. The interval between the contacts varies with the angle of the V of the engine cylinders. A test fixture is required when shychronizing the breaker points of such a distributor. As in the other types of distributors, both sets of contact points are adjusted to the same specified gap. Then with the distributor mounted in a testing fixture, the subplate is adjusted to obtain the firing interval specified for that particular distributor.

Exhaust Emission Control Distributors

As explained in the chapter on Control of Exhaust Gases, the Autolite system uses a special distributor with two diaphragms, Fig. 35-39a. By such means the spark is retarded the correct amount while idling, and during deceleration, and also provides the correct advance for acceleration and other types of driving.

One diaphragm, Fig. 35-39a, controls the spark in the same manner as the conventional distributor. That is the outer or advance diaphragm. The inner or retard diaphragm works in the opposite direction to retard the spark at slow engine speeds and during deceleration.

Calibrated coil springs bear on the vacuum sides of both diaphragms to supply resistance to the actuating force of the vacuum. Only the outer diaphragm, Fig. 35-39b, is linked to the distributor breaker plate. The link passes through the center of the retard diaphragm without touching it. The inner diaphragm serves to position a return stop for the outer diaphragm to govern the amount of spark retard when spark advance vacuum is reduced.

The dual diaphragm assembly is designed to provide the distributor with two distinct spark retard stops _ a normal retard of 6 deg. BTC, and an additional 12 deg. retard ATC. The normal retard gives the desired spark time for starting, while the additional retard position provides a setting suitable for more complete combustion and minimum contaminant emission after starting.

The vacuum sides of the two diaphragms are at either extreme of the diaphragm housing so they provide opposing operating forces. Carburetor vacuum from a port above the throttle plate is supplied to the outer diaphragm. Vacuum from the intake manifold,

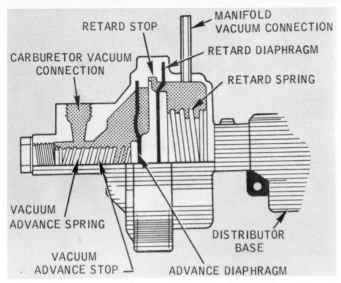

Fig. 35-39b. Schematic drawing of Autolite dual diaphragm distributor. Note connections for manifold and carburetor vacuums.

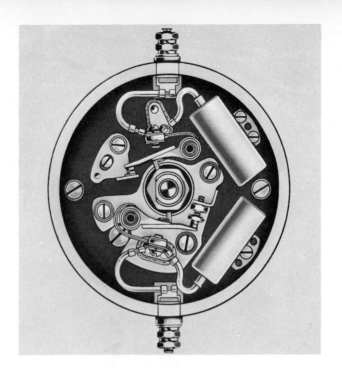

Fig. 35-40. Breaker plate for double alternate distributor using two ignition coils. (Autolite)

or below the throttle plate, is supplied to the inner or retard diaphragm.

During cranking, there is no vacuum and consequently both diaphragms are at rest, Fig. 35-39b, and the diaphragm link holds the breaker plate in the normal retard position until the engine starts.

When the engine runs at idle or fast idle, carburetor vacuum is weak and the manifold vacuum is strong. The manifold vacuum then moves the diaphragm against the resistance of the retard spring until the retard stop is reached. At the same time the vacuum advance spring is stronger than the carburetor vacuum, and the advance diaphragm is moved against the retard diaphragm plate. In this position the diaphragm plate turns the breaker plate to retard the ignition timing another 12 deg.

As the carburetor throttle is opened, carburetor vacuum is increased. This causes the advance diaphragm to move away from the retard diaphragm against the tension of the advance spring, pulling the link and the breaker plate with it to advance the spark. At speeds above 1400 to 1600 rpm, the advance diaphragm functions like the conventional diaphragm.

As in previous models of Autolite distributors, the centrifugal advance controls the position of the cam in relation to the distributor shaft to provide basic full power setting. The diaphragm assembly functions to increase the degree of advance for better engine efficiency under normal loads at steady speeds.

When timing an engine equipped with an Autolite distributor with the dual diaphragms, remove both vacuum lines from the distributor and plug the manifold vacuum line. Attach the timing light to the engine and with the engine idling at 550-600 rpm check the initial timing and make any needed adjustments. Quick checks on the centrifugal advance mechanism can be made in the usual manner by "reving" up the engine. Then, with the vacuum hose from the carburetor reconnected, there should be further advance if the vacuum advance is functioning.

To check the vacuum retard, return the engine speed to 550-600 rpm and reconnect the manifold vacuum to the distributor. If the retard diaphragm is working, the spark timing should retard after the manifold vacuum hose is reconnected.

Delco Unitized Ignition

A Unitized ignition system available on some General Motors vehicles (1972 Pontiac Grand Prix SJ for example) has only one component and 9 connections, compared to 12 components and 21 connections on the conventional unit. The unitized ignition system incorporates the coil, distributor, electronic amplifier, wiring and spark plug wires.

A magnetic pickup assembly located over the shaft, Fig. 35-40a, contains a permanent magnet, a pole piece with internal teeth, and a pickup coil. When the teeth of the timer core are rotating inside, and the pole piece lines up with the teeth, an induced voltage in the pickup coil signals the all electronic module to open the ignition coil primary circuit. The primary current decreases and a high voltage is induced in the ignition coil secondary winding, which is directed through the rotor and high voltage leads to fire the spark plugs.

The magnetic pickup assembly is mounted over the main bearing on the distributor housing, and is made to rotate by the vacuum control unit, thus providing vacuum advance. The timer core is made to rotate about the shaft by conventional advance weights, thus providing centrifugal advance.

When making compression checks on the engine, disconnect ignition switch connector from the Unit Ignition System. No periodic lubrication is required. Engine oil lubricates the lower bushing and an oil-

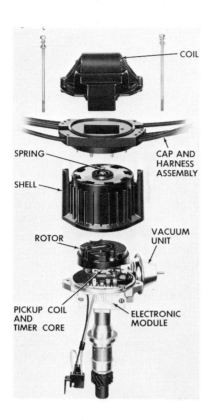

Fig. 35-40a. Details of the Unitized Ignition system as installed on some Pontiac engines.

filled reservoir provides lubrication for the upper bushing.

Firing Order

In order to reduce engine vibration and secure an even flow of power, the cylinders of internal combustion engines must fire in the correct sequence.

When describing the firing order of different engines, the cylinders are numbered. On in-line engines, Number One cylinder is the one immediately behind the timing gears. The remaining cylinders are in numerical order. On V-8 engines, the usual practice is to call the first cylinder on the left bank Number One and the first cylinder on the right bank would be Number Five in the case of an eight cylinder engine, or Number Seven in the case of a twelve cylinder engine.

The firing order of in-line six cylinder engines in the United States is 1-5-3-6-2-4. On eight cylinder in-line engines the usual firing order is 1-6-2-5-8-3-7-4. The Dusenberg and some European straight eights are exceptions.

The most popular firing order of a V-8 is 1-8-4-3-6-5-7-2. Other firing orders used on V-8 engines are: 1-6-2-5-8-3-7-4, 1-5-4-2-6-3-7-8, and 1-8-7-3-6-5-4-2.

The firing order of four cylinder in-line engines can be either 1-3-4-2 or 1-2-4-3. Firing order on the four cylinder, horizontal opposed, Volkswagen engine is 1-4-3-2, with Number One cylinder being marked on the rim of the distributor.

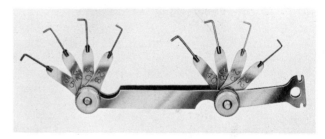

Fig. 35-42. Spark plug gap gauge, with gap adjuster at right end. The various gauges are of the wire type for more accurate measurement of the gap.

Spark Plugs

The spark plug in a spark ignition engine provides the gap across which the high tension voltage jumps, creating a spark which ignites the compressed mixture of air and fuel.

The spark plug, Fig. 35-41, consists of a center electrode which is connected to the ignition coil secondary through the distributor. The center electrode is insulated from the spark plug shell by means of a molded insulator resembling porcelain. The side electrode protrudes from the bottom edge of the spark plug shell and is so positioned that there is a gap between it and the center electrode. This gap is known as the spark plug gap, the size of which is adjusted by bending the side electrode. Fig. 35-42 shows a combined spark plug gauge and a tool for adjusting the gap by bending the side electrode.

Spark plug gaps range from approximately .020 in. to .040 in. and they must be carefully set in accordance with manufacturer's specifications. The size of the

Fig. 35-41. Sectionalized Autolite spark plug with power tip.

gap is dependent on the compression ratio of the engine, and characteristics of the combustion chamber and the ignition system. In general, there is a trend toward wider spark plug gaps made possible by improved ignition systems. At one time a gap of .025 in. was virtually standard on all engines. Today, however, many manufacturers specify gaps of .030, .035 or .040 in. The advantage of the wider gap is that it includes more mixture than a narrow gap and consequently there is better opportunity to ignite it.

The shell of the spark plug is threaded so it can be easily replaced. The following thread sizes are used: 1/2 in. pipe thread, 7/8 in., 10 mm., 14 mm., and 18 mm.

The 1/2 and 7/8 in. sizes are now obsolete in the automobile field, but are still used on some engines in the marine field.

Currently in automobile engines, the usual sizes are 14 and 18 mm.

In addition to having the correct size thread, it is important that the spark plug extend into the combustion chamber the correct amount. The correct point for the spark plug electrodes in the combustion chamber is determined by the engine manufacturer. Installing plugs with a longer reach than specified will place the electrodes further in the combustion chamber. This may result in the valves or piston striking the spark plug. If a plug with a short reach is installed so that the spark plug electrodes become partly sheltered by the spark plug hole in the cylinder head, engine roughness and missing will probably result.

Heat Range

Spark plugs must be designed so the temperature of the firing end of the plug is high enough to burn off any carbon or other combustion deposits. But it must not get so hot as to cause preignition or deterioration of the insulator or electrodes. This is difficult as the temperature of the spark plug tip varies greatly with different engines and with different operating conditions. Engineers of the AC Spark Plug Division of General Motors Corp., point out that in conventional automotive service, the center wire temperatures range from a low of 200 degs. C. at 10 mph to a high of 800 degs. C. at 80 mph.

The temperature of the spark plug insulator is dependent on the characteristics of the spark plug itself and also on the burning fuel in the combustion chamber. The latter temperature will of course vary with the design of the engine, compression ratios, cooling system, and air-fuel ratio.

As the tip of the spark plug absorbs heat from the burning fuel, the heat travels up the insulator to the spark plug shell, to the cylinder head, and then to the water jacket. The path the heat travels is shown in Fig. 35-43. The heat absorbed by the insulator increases as the temperature in the combustion chamber increases. More heat will be absorbed as the area of the insulator exposed to the hot gases is increased.

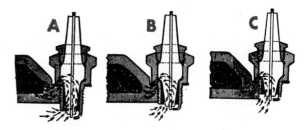

Fig. 35-43. Illustrating the path that heat must take from the tip of the spark plug to reach the water jacket of the engine. The longer the path, the hotter the plug. Spark plug (A) is a hotter plug than plugs (B) or (C).

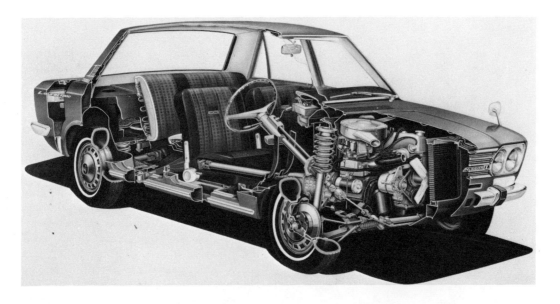

Datsun 1800 (Nissan Laurel in Japan) has unit body on 103 in. wheelbase with independent suspension at all four wheels. Featured are strut-type front suspension, rack and pinion steering, in-line overhead-camshaft four-cylinder engine rated at 105 hp.

Booster-Gap

Turbo-Action

Fig. 35-44. Special Champion spark plug with booster or series gap which affords protection against low temperature fouling so plug continues to fire under severe fouling conditions.

More heat will be absorbed by the spark plug shown on the left of Fig. 35-43, than the one on the right as the area of its tip exposed to the combustion chamber is greater.

If the path the heat must follow to reach the cooling system is short, the tip will have a lower temperature than if the path is long. Plugs with long paths for the heat to travel are known as hot plugs, while spark plugs with short paths for the heat to travel are known as cold plugs.

In addition to the length of the path traversed by the heat in reaching the cooling system, the material of

which the insulator is made and also its shape will affect its temperature. As a result, some spark plug insulators have a narrow neck just above the tip. Another design will have recessed tip sections which more readily follow temperature changes in the combustion chamber. Other designs provide increased volume, between the shell and the insulator, which permits more effective charge cooling, Fig. 35-44. Another design has the tip of the insulator protruding beyond the end of the shell for improved heat characteristics.

The heat range of any spark plug is its ability to transfer heat from the firing end up through the insulator, gasket and shell to the cylinder head and water jacket. Heat range is also known as the "Thermal Characteristic." Fig. 35-44a shows typical heat flow in an automotive type spark plug. A spark plug designed for the Mazda rotary engine is shown in Fig. 35-44b. Note the unusual dual firing points.

Fig. 35-44b. Note the twin firing points on this spark plug designed for a Wankel rotary engine.

Engine designers select spark plugs which will give good performance for average driving conditions. However, if the engine is operated for long periods under approximately full load conditions, the standard equipment spark plug will operate at too high a temperature and preignition will result. It is, therefore, necessary to install a colder plug, which will carry off the greater heat more rapidly.

On the other hand, if the engine is operated for long periods of slow speed at part throttle opening, the standard equipment plug will tend to foul. That is, the insulator tip will become covered with carbon and other products of combustion. The result will be that the high tension voltage will leak across the accumulations (because of their lower resistance) rather than jump the gap at the electrodes. A hotter plug (one with a longer heat path) should then be used.

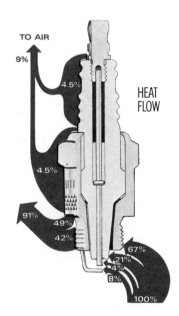

TO AIR

9%

4.5%

HEAT FLOW

4.5%

91%

49%

42%

67%

21%

4%

8%

100%

Fig. 35-44a. Illustrating the heat flow from a spark plug.

Spark Plug Fouling

As pointed out in the preceding paragraphs on "Heat Range," there is a tendency for products of combustion to accumulate on the portion of the insulator of the spark plug within the combustion chamber. As a result there are three types of spark plug fouling:

1. Carbon fouling.
2. High speed or lead fouling.
3. Oil and carbon fouling.

Fig. 35-45. Example of carbon fouled spark plug which results from prolonged low speed operation and excessively rich carburetor mixture.

Carbon fouling, Fig. 35-45, results primarily from extended low speed operation and when the carburetor mixture is excessively rich. Carbon fouling, which causes missing or roughness, is usually relatively soft black soot which is easily removed from the spark plug.

Fig. 35-46. High speed or lead fouling results from the fuel additives and prolonged high speed driving.

Lead fouling, Fig. 35-46, results from the tetraethyl lead used in the fuel to improve its antidetonating characteristics and is caused by extended high speed operation. Spark plugs with lead fouling will

Fig. 35-47. Example of oil and carbon fouling which results from excess oil reaching the combustion chamber.

frequently operate satisfactorily at low and medium loads. But when full load is applied, missing will occur. This results from the higher temperatures melting the accumulations of lead salts, thus increasing their electrical conductivity so that the plug will be shorted out.

Lead compounds added to gasoline have a particularly bad effect on some spark plug insulators. They react with the silica in the insulator to form lead silicate glass which has a low melting point, and which at high temperatures, is a relatively good conductor of electricity. For that reason a spark plug may give satisfactory operation under light loads, but fail when full loads and high combustion chamber temperatures are reached.

In some cases of lead fouling, it is possible to operate the engine at a speed just below the point where missing will occur. Then by gradually increasing the speed (always keeping below the missing speed) it will be possible to burn off the lead fouling and full throttle operation attained.

Lead fouling will sometimes appear as a heavy crusty formation; in other instances it will be tiny globules. The form it takes will depend on fuel, operating conditions and time.

The third type of fouling, Fig. 35-47, is found on engines that are badly worn so excess oil reaches the combustion chamber, either past the piston rings or past the valve guides.

Another condition that affects spark plug operation is the condition of the gap across which the spark jumps. In Fig. 35-48, is shown a spark plug with extreme electrode erosion resulting from the plug having been used too long. High capacity of the system also affects electrode life. (See paragraph on spark plug gaps.)

Voltage Required to Jump Gap

There are many factors which will affect the voltage required to jump a certain gap. Among these factors may be included the shape of the electrodes forming the gap, the conductivity of the gases in the gap, temperature, pressure, and the air-fuel ratio existing within the gap. W. A. Bychinsky of the AC

Fig. 35-48. Abnormal erosion of electrodes results from extreme plug temperatures. Make sure that plug has correct heat range and that plug is seated firmly on new gasket.

Spark Plug Division of General Motors Corp., gives the data shown in Fig. 35-49. It will be noted that the voltage required to jump a gap increases rapidly until 12,000V is needed to jump a gap of .060 in. The measurements were made in a conventional automotive engine at road load.

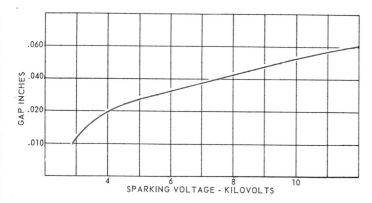

Fig. 35-49. Voltage required to jump different size gaps.

As pointed out in the section on distributors, the current delivered to the plugs is dependent on the current flowing in the primary, and this decreases as the engine speed increases. The voltage at the plug is also dependent on the cleanliness of the spark plug electrode. For example, an ignition system that is capable of delivering 20,000V to a clean plug may be able to deliver only one half that amount to a plug that is partly fouled. This results from the fact that it takes appreciable time for the voltage to build up to a value where it can jump the plug gap. This is explained as follows: When the ignition breaker points are closed, energy is stored in the ignition coil in the form of the magnetic field. Then when the breaker points open, the magnetic field collapses, causing the high voltage. This high voltage is not reached instantaneously, but it is built up to a maximum and then drops to zero. This requires an appreciable length of time (electrically speaking) or about 1/20,000 second. Thus, the voltage increases until it reaches such a value that it is capable of jumping the gap at the spark

plug. However, if the plug is partly fouled, some current will flow across the coating on the insulator. In other words, the accumulation on the insulator acts as a shunt across the gap. This loss of current reduces the peak voltage so that in the case of a badly fouled plug the voltage may not build up to a value that will jump the gap.

W. A. Bychinsky points out in a paper presented before the Society of Automotive Engineers that the faster the high tension voltage is built up, the less effect fouling will have. One method of attaining fast electrical buildup condition is by means of high frequency ignition systems. Another is by means of a series gap. However, the construction of reliable series gaps is difficult, but considerable progress is being made in that direction.

Spark Plug Gaps

Spark plug gaps do not remain constant, but increase in size, the amount of increase being dependent on mileage, chemical characteristics of the fuel, combustion chamber temperatures, and particularly the action of the electrical spark which tears off portions of the electrode. The electrical characteristics of the ignition system also affect the rate of wear of the spark plug electrodes. In this connection, the electrical capacity of the ignition coil and the wiring is an important factor. Systems with high capacity will cause more rapid gap wear than systems with low capacity. For example, aircraft ignition systems are electrically shielded. This increases the capacity of the system and accelerates the wear of the electrodes. Inserting a resistor in or near the spark plugs will tend to counteract this condition. Resistors reduce the peak current which passes through the electrodes when the capacity of the system is being discharged.

The standard spark plug gap varies with different engines. For example, the recommended gap on many American cars is .035 in., while on European cars it is often less than .025 in.

Experimentally it has been determined that the combustion process in an engine is independent of the spark. In other words, if a spark is obtained at the plug gap, it will ignite the mixture and the minimum amount of energy required in the spark to start combustion is only a small part of the total energy available.

However, in actual practice some engines operate better with wider spark plug gaps than others and many engineers are in agreement that the explanation is in the characteristics of the air-fuel mixture in the vicinity of the plug gap. The air-fuel mixture in different parts of the combustion chamber of different engines varies considerably. This is due to the form of the combustion chamber, the turbulence imparted to the mixture, and the amount of burned gases remaining in the combustion chamber from the previous cycle of operation.

Installation of Spark Plugs

Before installing a spark plug, it is important to make sure it is clean (if a used plug is being installed) and that the gap is adjusted in accordance with the manufacturer's specifications. When adjusting the gap, the side electrode only should be bent. Never bend the center electrode, as that will crack the insulator.

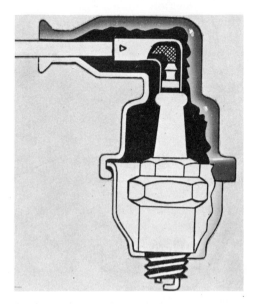

Fig. 35-50. Spark plug insulator and terminal protected by special nipple.

After adjusting the gap, make sure the threads of both the spark plug and the threads in the engine are clean, and not encrusted with carbon and dirt. Also clean the surface of the cylinder head against which the spark plug gasket seats. This is important, for if dirt is present at that point, compression leaks may occur, and in addition, the dirt acts as a heat insulator and the spark plug will run hot and faulty operation result. In addition it is important to clean the threads with a thread chaser, Fig. 35-50a. Only with clean threads can accurate torque readings be obtained.

Fig. 35-50a. Special thread chaser for cleaning threads in spark plug holes. (AC Spark Plug Div.)

When tightening a spark plug, a torque wrench should be used. While most spark plugs should be tightened to 25 to 30 ft. lbs. torque, there are many exceptions and the manufacturer's specifications should be consulted. Spark plugs should be tightened to the degree that the gasket (if used) is just crushed. When spark plugs are replaced, new gaskets should always be used.

The external portion of the spark plug insulator, together with the terminal, should always be covered with a rubber nipple made for that purpose. This prevents accumulation of dust and moisture on the insulator which would permit the high tension voltage to leak across from the terminal to the ground shell or body of the plug. Without such nipples secondary voltage is greatly reduced. A spark plug and terminal protected with a special rubber nipple is shown in Fig. 35-50.

Cleaning Spark Plugs

Special equipment is available for cleaning spark plugs, such as shown in Fig. 35-51. However, when the spark plug electrodes become worn, the spark plugs should be replaced as it takes a higher voltage to jump across worn electrodes even though the gap has been adjusted to the correct size.

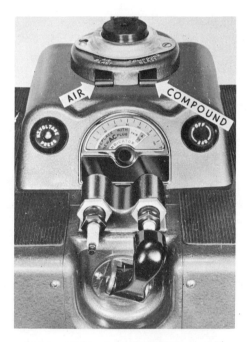

Fig. 35-51. Combined spark plug cleaner and tester.

Spark Plug Life

Under favorable operating conditions, the life of a spark plug ranges from 5,000 to 10,000 miles. Beyond that mileage, they should be replaced.

Steadily raising compression ratios and increased quantities of tetraethyl lead in the fuel to raise its octane ratings, have made the conditions under which the spark plug operates increasingly severe.

Spark plug life can be materially extended by frequent cleaning and regapping. As the electrodes be-

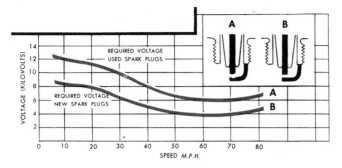

Fig. 35-52. *Comparison of voltage required to fire new and old plugs.*

come worn, they should be filed until the end of the center electrode is flat and smooth, and the surface of the side electrode is parallel to the end of the center electrode. Higher voltages are required to a fire a spark plug with worn electrodes. As shown in Fig. 35-52, considerably higher voltage is needed to fire a used spark plug than a new plug. This is particularly true at low speeds where the difference may be as much as 4,000V.

Testing Spark Plugs

Fig. 35-51 shows a combined spark plug cleaner and tester. In this unit, the plug is cleaned by blasting the firing end with an abrasive compound. The ability of the plug to fire is then tested under compression.

The tester or analyzer shown in Fig. 35-53 is of the oscilloscope type and is connected to the ignition

Fig. 35-53. *Special oscilloscope type spark plug tester, which checks operation of plugs in the engine.*

circuit. Then with the engine running the behavior and operation of the spark plug is shown on the screen of the oscilloscope. Pictures are provided on the instrument so that comparison can be made of the plug being tested with specific conditions.

Magnetos

A magneto is a self-contained device which generates and distributes electricity for igniting the combustible mixture in the combustion chamber of the internal combustion engine. The magneto not only generates the electricity, but it also steps up the low voltage to a high tension voltage and distributes it to the various cylinders at the correct instant. It does this without the aid of a battery. Some magnetos are of the low tension type, generating a low voltage which is then stepped up to a high voltage by means of a separate coil. High tension magnetos produce voltage of sufficient value to jump the spark plug gap without any external coil.

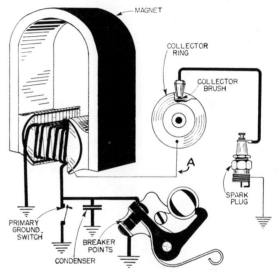

Fig. 35-54. *Diagram of shuttle wound high tension magneto. The lead to the high tension winding on rotor is shown at A.*

Magneto Ignition Advantages

Magneto ignition systems have several advantages. First of all, they do not require any battery or other source of current. Secondly, the intensity of the generated voltage does not decrease with the engine speed, but increases.

Magnetos were used extensively on automobiles during the early years of the industry, but they have been superseded by battery ignition, one reason being that to start an engine that is equipped with a magneto, relatively higher speeds are required than is the case with battery ignition. Magnetos are extensively used on trucks, tractors and small motors as used for lawn mowers. They are also used on internal combustion engines for industrial power. Magnetos are particularly popular for internal combustion engines, where a battery is not needed for starting or lighting. The recent development of permanent magnets of greatly increased strength has materially improved their performance.

Principles of Operation

As previously pointed out in the section devoted to the fundamentals of electricity, electricity can be generated by revolving a coil of wire in a magnetic field. In the conventional generator, the magnetic field is produced by passing some of the generated current through coils of wire (field coils) which in turn produce the magnetic field. In other words, the magnetic field is produced electrically. In the case of the magneto, the magnetic field is produced by means of permanent magnets. Until recently the magnets used in magnetos were made of high quality carbon steel. Beginning in 1935, special alloy steels were developed which have greatly improved magnetic characteristics over the carbon steel formerly used. Magnets made of such special alloys are not only stronger for the same size, but also retain their magnetism for much longer periods. The alloys used on modern magnets are usually tungsten, chromium and cobalt.

Types of Magnetos

There are two ways in which magnetos may be classified. Originally they were classified as to the type of current they produced--low tension or high tension. The low tension magneto developed a low voltage and required an external coil to step up the voltage. The high tension magneto incorporated the coil in the magneto itself.

The other method of classifying magnetos takes into consideration the portion of the magneto which is revolved. Magnetos, which have the windings on an armature which is revolved in a magnetic field, are known as shuttle wound magnetos, Fig. 35-54. In the inductor type magneto, both the coil and magnet are mounted in stationary positions and movement of the magnetic field is obtained by breaking and reestablishing the magnetic field, Fig. 35-55. The third type of magneto is known as the revolving magnet design. This has been made possible by the new magnetic steels and in this design the coil, together with a short magnetic circuit, is mounted in a stationary position and one or more magnets are revolved between the pole pieces of the magnetic circuit. Some manufacturers also classify this construction as the induction type.

Low Tension Magnetos

The low tension magneto was the first type of magneto and is still used extensively on industrial engines. In this construction the permanent magnets are U-shaped, with the armature, carrying a single primary winding, revolving between the pole pieces.

As explained in the section devoted to the fundamentals of electricity, revolving a coil of wire in a magnetic field will cause current to flow in the coil, and this current is of the alternating type. The arma-

ture winding is connected to the primary winding of an ignition coil, and breaker points which revolve with the armature are timed to open the circuit at peak voltage. This interruption of the primary current produces a high tension current in the secondary winding of the coil (see ignition) which is carried back to the distributor rotor on the magneto where it is directed to the proper spark plug.

Breaker points on a low tension magneto can be connected either in series with the armature winding or in parallel. In the series connection, the magneto serves simply as a current source and the value of the current is relatively low, because the resistance of the primary winding of the coil is included in the circuit. However, when the breaker points are in parallel with the armature winding, a heavier current flows through

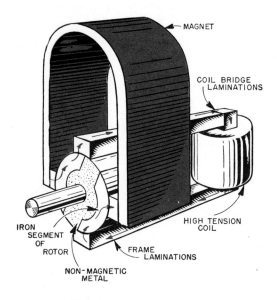

Fig. 35-55. Rotary inductor type magneto.

the armature as the resistance of the primary winding of the coil is no longer included in the circuit. Then when the breaker points open, this heavy current surges through the primary winding of the coil, with a strong inductive effect. The result is that the magnetic field of the coil is built up very rapidly.

Examples of low tension magnetos in current use are the Bendix L A and L A R magneto made by the Scintilla Magneto Div. of the Bendix Aviation Corp., and the series M R B magneto produced by the American Bosch Corp.

Bendix Low Tension Magnetos

The Bendix Scintilla low tension magnetos are of the rotating magnet type and are designed to generate and distribute low tension voltage through low tension cables to individual coils, one located adjacent to each spark plug. The current is stepped up to a high voltage by the individual coils and then conducted to the spark plug by a short length of high tension cable at the proper firing interval of the cylinder. The L A and L A R series magnetos, Fig. 35-56, are of the base mounted type and are available for 2, 3, 4, 5, and 6 cylinder engines. The L A R magneto is equipped with an electrical connector mounted in the cover and containing seven socket connections to simplify and speed installation.

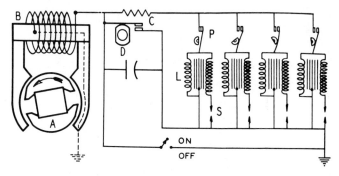

Fig. 35-57. Diagram of Bendix Scintilla low tension magneto circuit types L A and L A R.

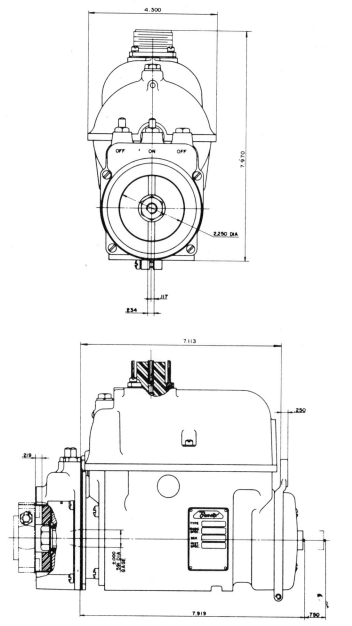

Fig. 35-56. Details of Bendix type L A R low tension magneto.

The principle of operation is as follows: The two pole rotating magnet has a North and South pole and magnetic flux passes from the North pole through the coil core and back to the South pole. As the magnet is turned, the polarity continually changes, thereby producing flux reversals in the coil core. The number of flux reversals during one complete revolution is equal to the number of poles on the magnet.

Rotation of magnet (A), Fig. 35-57, causes flux changes in the magneto coil core. These in turn generate low tension current in the magneto coil (B). At the position of the magnet, where this current is greatest, the breaker contacts (C) are opened by the cam (D). This causes the current to seek a new path by way of a 1 ohm resistance wire (used to reduce point arcing) to the distributor contact points (P) and the primary winding of the external coil (L) which is mounted adjacent to the spark plug (S) on the engine. Note that Fig. 35-57 applies to a four cylinder application. The rapid rise in current through this winding induces a high voltage in the secondary winding of the external coil (L), causing a spark to jump the gap at the spark plug (S).

The ground terminal on the magneto is electrically connected to the ignition switch. When the switch is in the "OFF" position, this wire provides a direct ground for the primary current. This prevents the interruption of the primary current when the contact points open, and as a result high voltage is not induced in the secondary winding of the external coil.

American Bosch Low Tension

The American Bosch low tension magneto is known as the series MRB and is of the shielded type for use with large stationary engines requiring exceptionally long ignition cables. If high tension magnetos were used on such installations, the high tension cables would be of extreme length and the resulting high capacitance of the high tension circuit would seriously reduce the efficiency of the ignition system. By using a low tension magneto and placing the ignition coil or coils close to the spark plugs, the capacity of the high tension circuit is kept at a minimum and ignition is improved. Energy losses, corona effects and high capacitance charges are eliminated. In addition, fire hazards are reduced, and radio and TV interference is also greatly reduced. Spark plug life is materially extended.

These magnetos are of the inductor type, with stationary coil, magnets and breaker.

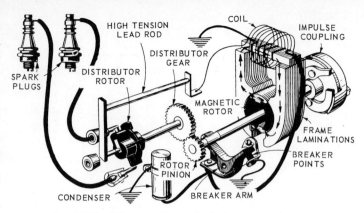

Fig. 35-58. Schematic diagram of rotating magnet magneto.

High Tension Magnetos

The high tension magneto differs from the low tension magneto in that it generates high tension electricity within itself and distributes it to the various spark plugs. No external ignition coil is used, as in the case of the low tension magneto.

In the conventional high tension magneto, the armature is wound with primary and secondary windings, corresponding to the windings of an ignition coil, Fig. 35-6. These windings on the armature revolve in the magnetic field set up by permanent magnets. As the coils or windings pass through the magnetic field, cur-

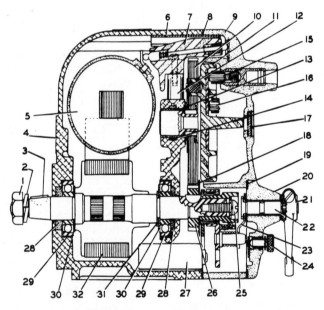

Fig. 35-59. American Bosch type MJB rotating magnet magneto. (1) Nut drive shaft. (2) Lock washer. (3) Key. (4) Magneto housing. (5) Coil. (6) High tension conductor insulation .(7) High tension conductor. (8) Distributor plate gasket. (9) Distributor plate. (10) Distributor gear. (11) Distributor rotor. (12) Distributor gear bracket. (13) Distributor gear shaft bearing. (14) Bearing wick. (15) Distributor plate brush. (16) Distributor plate brush. (17) Observation window. (18) Indicating disk. (19) End cap gasket. (20) End cap. (21) Timing lever. (22) Timing lever shaft. (23) Timing lever bracket. (24) Short circuit screw. (25) Cam fastening screw. (26) Magnet rotor gear. (27) Condenser. (28) Felt washers. (29) Ball bearing. (30) Grease retaining washers. (31) Equalizing washer. (32) Magnet rotor.

rent is generated, and when it reaches its maximum, the breaker points (shunted across the primary winding) open. This induces a current in the secondary windings. As there are more turns of wire in the secondary than in the primary, the voltage is increased in value. The end of the secondary is connected to a collector ring. From there the high tension voltage passes to a distributor and from there to the individual spark plugs.

A variation of the original high tension magneto, in which the coil, condenser and breaker points were rotated, is to rotate a portion of the primary winding, while the remainder of the primary, together with the secondary, contact points, and condenser are stationary. The rotating portion of the primary is wound on the armature and is connected through a collector ring to the stationary primary. The primary circuit is completed through the breaker points to the ground.

High tension magnetos are provided with a safety gap which is shunted across the terminal of the high tension winding and the ground. In this, the insulation of the secondary winding is protected from excessive voltage, which would occur if a wire should become disconnected from a spark plug and there would be an incompleted circuit. A spark would then occur at the safety gap, and excess strain on the secondary insulation would be avoided.

Rotary Inductor Magnetos

In the rotary inductor type magneto, Fig. 35-55, both the magnet and coil are stationary and current is induced in the primary winding by rotating one or both legs of the magnetic circuit. When only one leg of the magnetic circuit is broken, the magnetic flux in the coil alternates from maximum to minimum, but does not undergo complete reversal when both legs of the magnetic circuit are interrupted.

Rotating Magnet Magnetos

The introduction of the more powerful permanent magnets of special alloy steel made possible the design of magnetos in which the magnet was revolved. Such magnetos are known as rotating magnet magnetos, and have virtually replaced the original design with stationary U-shaped magnets.

In the rotating magnet design, the coil, condenser and breaker points are stationary with the result that the design is simplified, of more sturdy construction, and moving connections are eliminated. In addition, tests and repairs are more easily made. Smaller and more compact units are also made possible with reduction in cost.

A schematic drawing of a rotating magnet magneto is shown in Fig. 35-58. Rotation of the magnetic rotor produces an alternating magnetic flux or field which cuts the stationary primary winding each time it increases and decreases. As a result, alternating electric currents are induced in the primary circuit during the period the circuit is completed through the closed breaker points. As the density of the magnetic field varies, the strength of the current induced in the primary circuit also varies and reaches a maximum value each time a complete magnetic flux reversal occurs in the magnetic circuit.

The current induced in the primary winding produces a magnetic field which surrounds the secondary winding. This field reaches its maximum when the cur-

insure constant change of air throughout the magneto. The ball bearings (20) supporting the magnet shaft are packed in high temperature grease and require no further attention for at least a year of normal operation. The distributor bushing (14) is of the oilless composition type.

The type PA4, Bendix Scintilla magnet, shown in Fig. 35-60, is of the rotating magnet type. High tension current is produced in the secondary winding as previously described. One end of the primary winding

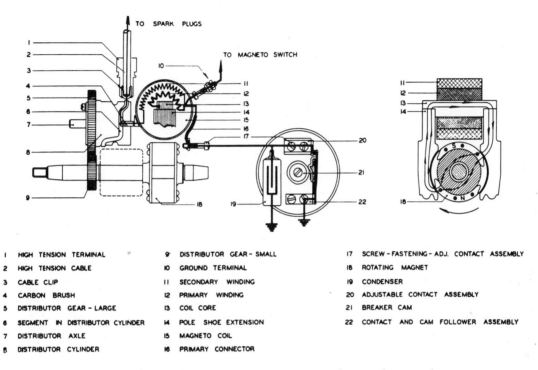

1	HIGH TENSION TERMINAL	9	DISTRIBUTOR GEAR - SMALL	
2	HIGH TENSION CABLE	10	GROUND TERMINAL	
3	CABLE CLIP	11	SECONDARY WINDING	
4	CARBON BRUSH	12	PRIMARY WINDING	
5	DISTRIBUTOR GEAR - LARGE	13	COIL CORE	
6	SEGMENT IN DISTRIBUTOR CYLINDER	14	POLE SHOE EXTENSION	
7	DISTRIBUTOR AXLE	15	MAGNETO COIL	
8	DISTRIBUTOR CYLINDER	16	PRIMARY CONNECTOR	

17	SCREW - FASTENING - ADJ. CONTACT ASSEMBLY
18	ROTATING MAGNET
19	CONDENSER
20	ADJUSTABLE CONTACT ASSEMBLY
21	BREAKER CAM
22	CONTACT AND CAM FOLLOWER ASSEMBLY

Fig. 35-60. Details of Bendix type PA4, rotating magnet magneto, showing electric and magnetic circuits.

rent in the primary winding reaches its maximum. At the instant of maximum current in the primary winding, the breaker points are caused to open by the action of the breaker cam. This stops the flow of current in the primary circuit and causes the collapse of the magnetic field. The collapsing lines of force then induce a current in the secondary circuit and, as the ratio of turns in the secondary is high compared to those in the primary, a high tension voltage is produced.

The self-induced voltage produced in the primary winding, resulting from the collapsing magnetic field, is absorbed by the condenser which is shunted across the breaker points. In effect this action promotes a more rapid collapse of the primary field and at the same time reduces arcing at the breaker points.

An example of the rotating magnet magneto is American Bosch type MJB magneto, Fig. 35-59. In this magneto the coil windings (5), condenser (27), and interrupter are stationary, while the magnets (32) are rotated. The screened ventilators on each side of the housing (4) and the fan action of the magnet rotor (32)

(12) is grounded to the magneto housing, while the other end is connected to the insulated contact point. When the contact points (20) are closed, the primary circuit is completed, permitting current to flow in the primary winding. One end of the secondary winding (11) is connected to the insulated end of the primary winding, while the other end terminates at the high tension insert in the coil. High tension current in the secondary winding is conducted to the center of the distributor cylinder (6) by means of the carbon brush (4). From there it is conducted to the segments of the distributor cylinder and then to the electrodes of the high tension cable terminals (1). High tension cables then carry it to the individual spark plugs.

The ground terminal (10) on the type PA4 Bendix Scintilla magneto is electrically connected to the ignition switch. When the switch is in the "OFF" position, this wire provides a direct path to ground for the primary current, preventing interruption of the current when the points open. As a result, high voltage will not be induced in the secondary circuit.

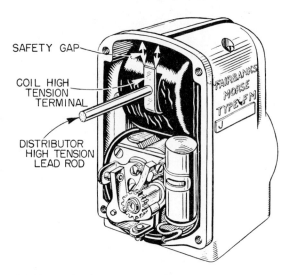

SAFETY GAP

COIL HIGH
TENSION
TERMINAL

DISTRIBUTOR
HIGH TENSION
LEAD ROD

Fig. 35-61. Fairbanks Morse type FM, rotating magnet magneto.

A Fairbanks Morse type FM magneto with cover removed is shown in Fig. 35-61. Note gear for rotating magnet and breaker cam. These are built in a variety of designs for engines of various sizes and compression ratios.

Flywheel Magnetos

Flywheel magnetos, Fig. 35-62, are of the revolving magnet type and are used extensively for ignition on small internal combustion engines used on lawn mowers, garden tractors, outboard motors, etc. For the most part, flywheel magnetos are used on single cylinder engines, but are also used occasionally on two and four cylinder engines.

The theory of operation is similar to that of the rotary magneto. In the typical flywheel magneto the magnet is mounted on the outer rim of the flywheel which revolves around the stationary ignition coil,

condenser and breaker point assembly. As the ends of the magnet pass by the pole pieces, an alternating magnetic flux is established through the ignition coil and current is generated in the primary circuit during the period that the breaker points are closed. A cam located on the crankshaft opens the points when the primary current is at a maximum. Interruption of the current causes the magnetic field to collapse, which in turn induces a high tension voltage in the secondary winding.

A WICO flywheel magneto for single cylinder engines is shown in Fig. 35-63. A type K1-503 Bendix Scintilla magnet, also for use on single cylinder engines, is shown in Fig. 35-64, and Fig. 35-65 gives the details of a flywheel type magneto for two cylinder engines. This is also of Bendix Scintilla manufacture. Note that it consists basically of two complete ignition systems with individual coils, breaker points and condensers.

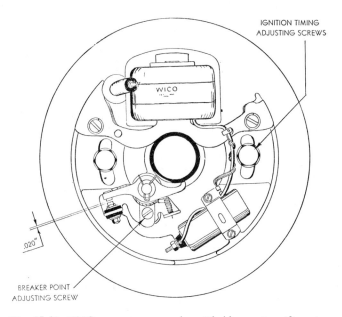

IGNITION TIMING
ADJUSTING SCREWS

.020"

BREAKER POINT
ADJUSTING SCREW

Fig. 35-63. WICO magneto as used on Gladden series 40 engines.

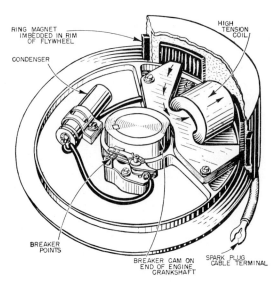

RING MAGNET
IMBEDDED IN RIM
OF FLYWHEEL

CONDENSER

HIGH
TENSION
COIL

BREAKER
POINTS

BREAKER CAM ON
END OF ENGINE
CRANKSHAFT

SPARK PLUG
CABLE TERMINAL

Fig. 35-62. Flywheel type magneto.

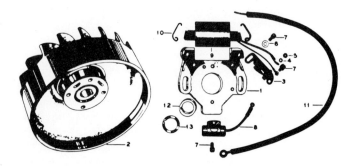

Fig. 35-64. Bendix Scintilla type K1-503 flywheel magneto for use on single cylinder engines. (1) Magneto mounting flange. (2) Flywheel and magnet assembly. (3) Breaker point assembly. (4) Lock washer. (5) Nut. (6) Washer. (7) Screw and lock washer. (8) Condenser. (9) Ignition coil. (10) Coil clamp. (11) High tension lead. (12) Breaker cam. (13) Washer.

Magneto Spark Advance

In order to advance the timing of the spark in accordance with different engine speeds and loads, both manual and automatic spark advance are used on magnetos. However, the manual advance is virtually obsolete.

by means of a centrifugally controlled spark advance rotor, Fig. 35-66. This depends for its action on two spring loaded pawls which are held close to the center of the rotor at low speeds and gradually swing outward as engine speed increases. Outward movement of the pawls is transferred by linkage to the breaker camshaft with the result that the cam changes its

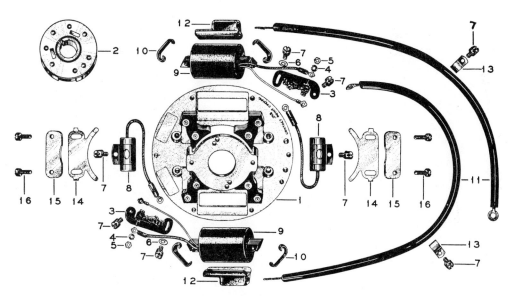

Fig. 35-65. Bendix Scintilla type K2A-1 flywheel magneto for two cylinder engines. (1) Magneto mounting flange. (2) Rotating magnet. (3) Breaker point assembly. (4) Lock washer. (5) Nut. (6) Washer. (7) Screw and lock washer. (8) Condenser. (9) Ignition coil. (10) Coil core clamp. (11) High tension lead. (12) High tension insulator. (13) Clamp. (14) Magneto flange tension spring. (15) Flange tension spring plate. (16) Screw and lock washer.

As the magneto produces an ignition spark at the instant the breaker points open, the spark timing can be advanced or retarded through a limited range by shifting the point at which the breaker points open. This is accomplished by rotating the plate on which

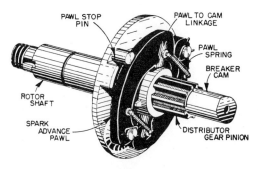

Fig. 35-66. Details of spark advance mechanism used on magnetos.

the breaker points are mounted through an arc of approximately 10 deg. However, the amount of advance or retard that can be obtained by such a method is definitely limited, as the intensity of the ignition spark decreases rapidly as the points are opened farther away from the point of maximum current.

Automatic spark advance on magnetos is obtained

relative position in respect to the drive shaft. In that way the spark timing is advanced. The degree and rate of spark advance is controlled by a pawl stop and the strength of the springs holding the centrifugal weights.

It should be pointed out that in general, magnetos are used on engines which are operated through a relatively small range of speeds and therefore do not require as wide a range of spark timing as is used on current passenger car engines.

Impulse Couplings

In order to intensify the spark while the engine is being cranked, magnetos on certain installations are provided with an impulse coupling. In addition, the impulse coupling automatically retards the spark during the starting period in order to prevent engine back firing.

There are many different types of impulse couplings. However, the basic principles of the different types are similar. These different types of design may be listed as follows: pivoted pawl type and sliding pawl type.

The pivoted pawl type which is shown in Fig. 35-67 has each pawl securely fastened to the hub plate, its movement being confined to a turning action in an arc about its pivot point. In the sliding pawl design, Fig. 35-68, the pawls are free, but move in a guide which restricts their movement to a straight line. Basically the impulse coupling acts as a mechanical reservoir to store the energy which is available at a low rate during the engine cranking period. This

speeds, a pawl on the hub engages a pin mounted on the magneto frame preventing further movement of the magneto rotor, while the engine half of the coupling continues to rotate. This relative change in position winds up the connecting spring. Then, at the time of ignition, the pawl is released and the drive spring snaps

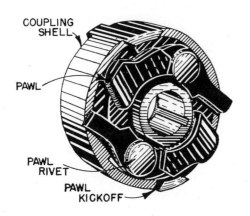 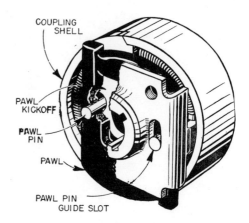

Fig. 35-67. *Left. Pivoted pawl type of impulse coupling.* Fig. 35-68. *Right. Sliding pawl type impulse coupling.*

accumulated energy is then released to the magneto at the instant that the spark is required to ignite the charge in the cylinder. The impulse coupling is arranged so the energy is released to provide a retarded spark during the starting period.

A shell and hub connected together with a strong spring form the basic parts of the impulse coupling. The shell is fitted to the engine drive shaft, while the hub is rotated by the magneto shaft. At cranking

the magneto rotor forward through its firing position. As the engine starts to operate under its own power, centrifugal force acts on the pawls to draw them into position where they do not engage the coupling stop pin, and the impulse coupling then acts as a solid drive member.

By selecting different numbers of pawls and stop pins, the impulse coupling can be designed to operate engines with different numbers of cylinders.

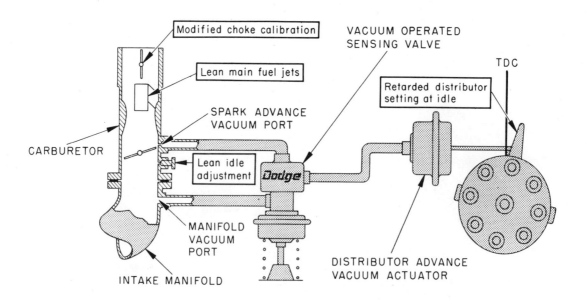

Chrysler's Cleaner Air System (CAS) of engine exhaust emission control leads to more complete burning of air-fuel mixture in combustion chambers. Drawing graphically shows system used in late model manual transmission-equipped cars.

Transistor Ignition System

The output of a conventional ignition system is limited by the amount of current in the primary circuit, and this in turn, is limited by the amount of current that can be interrupted by the conventional tungsten contact points. This is approximately 5 amp. for reasonable contact life. Another factor limiting the output is the period the contact points remain closed and as the engine speed increases, this time becomes increasingly short.

To overcome these problems, the transistor ignition system has been developed.

The transistor is a solid metallic device with the ability to switch large currents through the action of a very small control or relay current. The switching action of the transistor involves no moving parts and can be instantaneous through proper circuit design.

Basically there are four types of transistor ignition systems:

1. A transistor is used to make and break the ignition primary circuit, with the transistor control circuit triggered by the conventional distributor breaker points. This is known as the contact controlled transistor system, Fig. 35-69.

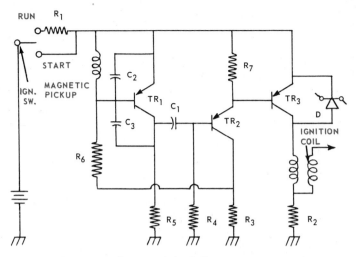

Fig. 35-69a. Circuit diagram of the full transistor ignition system, using a pulse generator in place of the regular breaker points.

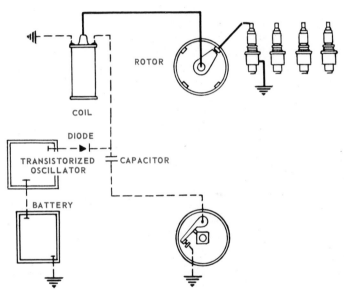

Fig. 35-69b. Capacitor discharge circuit.

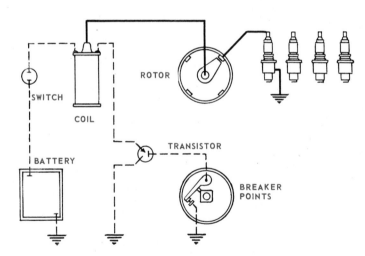

Fig. 35-69. Basic units of contact control ignition system.

2. The full transistor system using a pulse generator to trigger the transistor and eliminating the breaker points. This is known as the magnetic controlled transistor system, Fig. 35-69a.

3. The capacitor discharge system, Fig. 35-69b, using the conventional distributor breaker points to trigger the spark discharge. This is known as the contact controlled capacitor discharge system.

4. The capacitor discharge system, Fig. 35-69c, using a pulse generator to trigger the spark

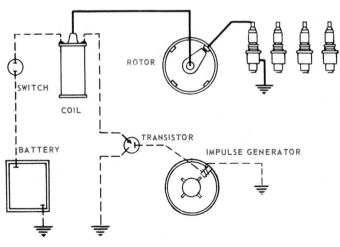

Fig. 35-69c. Magnetically controlled transistor system which eliminates the breaker points.

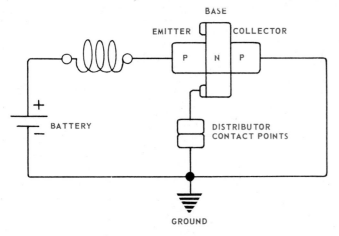

Fig. 35-69d. *Diagram of simple transistor ignition system using the conventional breaker points.*

discharge. This eliminates the distributor breaker points and is known as the magnetic controlled capacitor discharge system.

Briefly a transistor is a solid metallic device with the ability to switch large currents through the action of a very small or relay current. The switching action of the transistor involves no moving parts and can be made instantaneous through proper circuit design.

In the transistor of the PNP type (positive-negative-positive) there is a current going to the emitter, Fig. 35-69d, where it flows to and through the collector under the control of the base circuit. The base circuit has a negative bias and when the contact points in the circuit-to-ground are closed, it will permit current to flow. But when the contact points interrupt the base circuit, this also interrupts the flow of current from the emitter to the collector.

The current flow through the emitter and the collector is interrupted entirely by electronic means, as there is no motion of any kind, with no switch contacts or moving blades. It is this action which makes the transistor so well suited for ignition systems as it breaks the circuit so rapidly no condenser is required and there is no arcing.

The transistor may be compared to a horn relay in that a small current is used to control a heavy current. In the case of the transistor there are no moving parts, and it acts with virtually no time lag.

Contact Controlled System

The transistor ignition used by Ford is an example of the contact controlled system, Fig. 35-69e. The ignition coil primary in the transistor system is designed to draw 12 amp. peak current or approximately 5.5 amp. average current, as indicated on a conventional ammeter, in order to provide high spark plug voltage at the higher engine speeds.

The transistor is connected between the battery and the coil and is used to make and break the coil primary circuit.

The distributor breaker points are used to control the transistor. The 7.1 to 7.9 ohm resistor connected between the distributor and the transistor is in the wiring harness and limits the transistor control current to 0.5 amp. This low current greatly reduces pitting and wear of the distributor points.

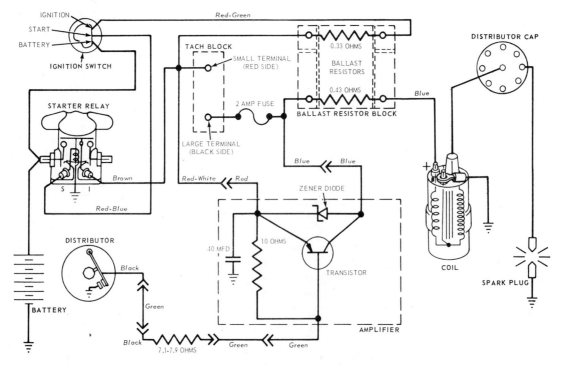

Fig. 35-69e. *Transistor ignition system circuit as installed on Ford vehicles. Note breaker points.*

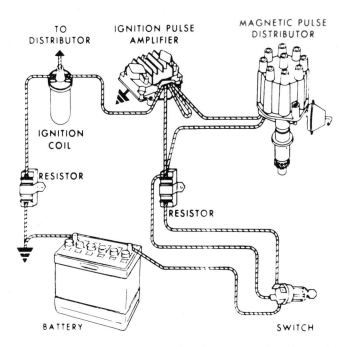

TO
DISTRIBUTOR

IGNITION PULSE
AMPLIFIER

MAGNETIC PULSE
DISTRIBUTOR

IGNITION
COIL

RESISTOR

RESISTOR

BATTERY

SWITCH

Fig. 35-69f. Note magnetic pulse distributor as used on this Delco transistor ignition system.

The amplifier assembly is mounted under the instrument panel to protect the parts from engine heat. A ceramic ballast resistor block and a tachometer connector block are mounted in the engine compartment. A 2 amp. fuse between the large black terminal of the tach block and the coil primary circuit prevents the transistor from being damaged by the application of external devices other than testing equipment.

The tachometer block is used to connect a tachometer or dwell meter into the circuit. Do not connect either of those instruments into the circuit in any other manner.

Most of the contact controlled transistor ignition systems on the market include one or two ballast resistors, which must be in balance with the rest of the circuit. Therefore, the original ballast resistor must be bypassed. This can be done by running a new conductor from the ignition switch in those cases where the ballast resistor is in the wiring harness. Or, if the resistor is readily accessible, a jumper wire over the unit can be used.

Magnetic Pulse Transistor

An example of the magnetic pulse transistor ignition system is produced by Delco and used by Pontiac. It features a specially designed magnetic pulse distributor, an ignition pulse amplifier and a special coil. The other units of the system are of standard design and include resistors or resistance wire, switch and battery, Fig. 35-69f.

The internal construction of the distributor differs greatly from conventional design. An inner timer core replaces the conventional breaker cam. The timer core has the same number of equally spaced projections or vanes as there are engine cylinders.

The timer core rotates inside a magnetic pickup assembly which replaces the conventional breaker plate, contact point set and condenser. The magnetic pickup assembly consists of a ceramic permanent magnet, a pole piece and a pickup coil. The pole piece is a steel plate having equally spaced internal teeth with one tooth for each engine cylinder.

This steel plate rotates inside a stationary pole piece. The pickup coil mounted under the pole piece picks up variations in the magnetic flux as the teeth on the rotor and stationary piece alternately have their teeth in and then out of alignment. This varying magnetic flux, weak as it is, causes a tiny current impulse to operate the transistor. The distributor rotor and cap are the same as in a conventional system.

The magnetic pickup assembly is made to rotate by the vacuum control unit and in that way, vacuum advance is provided. The timer core is made to rotate about the shaft by conventional advance weights to provide the centrifugal advance.

The ignition pulse amplifier consists primarily of transistors, resistors, diodes and capacitors with a printed circuit.

A wiring diagram for a typical magnetic pulse transistor ignition system is shown in Fig. 35-69f. There are two resistors used in this circuit. The resistor connected directly to the switch is bypassed during cranking. The other resistor is always in the circuit.

When the engine is not running and the switch is closed, the current flows through a part of the circuit shown in red, Fig. 35-69g. The current flows from the battery through the switch and resistor R-7 to the amplifier. From there it flows through transistors TR-1 and TR-2, resistors R-1, R-2 and R-3, the coil primary and resistor R-8 to the ground. The condenser C-1 is charged with positive voltage toward transistor TR-2.

When the engine is running, the induced voltage in the pickup coil causes transistor TR-3 to conduct, resulting in current flow in the circuit shown in red, Fig. 35-69h. This condition exists until the charge on the condenser C-1 is dissipated through resistor R-2. When that occurs, the circuit reverts to the conditions shown in Fig. 35-69g.

Resistor R-4 is known as a feedback resistor and its function is to turn TR-3 off, when TR-2 returns to the "on" condition. Resistor R-1 is a biasing resistor which allows transistor TR-1 to operate. The Zener diode D-1 protects transistor TR-1 from high voltages which may be induced in the primary winding, while condensers C-2 and C-3 protect transistor TR-3 from high voltages which appear in the system.

The Holley pulse generator is a simple unit. For a rotor it utilizes the original distributor cam and has a single pickup magnet pole surrounded by a coil

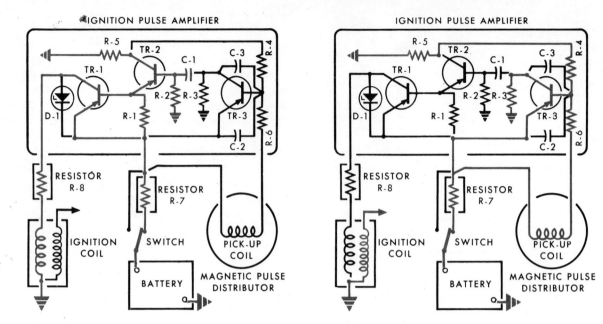

Fig. 35-69g. Left. *Internal wiring diagram of ignition pulse amplifier, showing current flow in red with switch on and engine not running.* Fig. 35-69h. Right. *Internal wiring diagram of ignition pulse amplifier, showing current flow in red when spark plug fires.*

winding. The pole piece is located so that its end is spaced .005 to .010 in. from the lobes of the distributor cam. Thus no rotor is needed to be supplied with the conversion kit. It is only necessary in the distributor to remove the breaker plate and substitute the pulse generator and adjust the proper spacing from the breaker cam.

The capacitor discharge system using a contact controlled capacitor, and the capacitor discharge system using a pulse generator to trigger the spark are not currently used by any of the car manufacturers and will therefore not be discussed at this time.

Chrysler Electronic Ignition

The basic circuits of the Chrysler Electronic Ignition system introduced in 1972 are shown in Fig. 35-69h. The primary circuit consists of the battery, ignition switch, compensating side of the dual ballast resistor, primary winding of the ignition coil, the power switching transistor of the control unit and the vehicle frame acting as a ground.

The secondary circuit consists of the ignition coil secondary winding, distributor cap and rotor, spark plugs and vehicle frame.

The compensating resistance serves the same purpose as in the contact ignition system, that is to maintain constant primary current with variation in engine speed. While starting, this resistance is bypassed, applying full battery voltage to the ignition coil; the compensating resistance is in series with both the control unit feed and the auxilliary ballast circuits, Fig. 35-69i and Fig. 35-69j.

In addition to the two basic circuits there are the pickup circuit, control unit feed circuit and auxilliary ballast circuits.

Two circuits are used to operate the circuitry of the control unit. These are the auxilliary ballast circuit which uses the 5 ohm section of the dual ballast resistor and the control unit feed circuit.

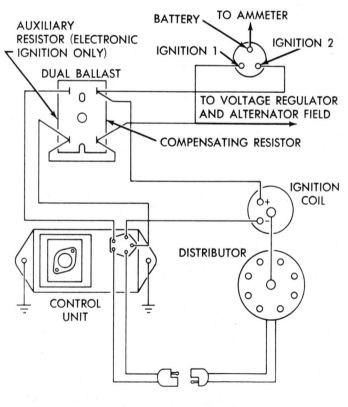

Fig. 35-69h. *Wiring diagram of Chrysler electronic ignition.*

The pickup circuit is used to sense the proper timing for the control unit switching transistor, Fig. 35-69i and Fig. 35-69j. The reluctor rotating with the distributor shaft produces a voltage pulse in the magnetic pickup each time a spark plug is to be fired. This pulse is transmitted through the pickup coil in the power switching transistor in the control unit, and causes the transistor to interrupt the current flow through the primary circuit. This break in the primary circuit induces a high voltage in the secondary coil and fires a spark plug.

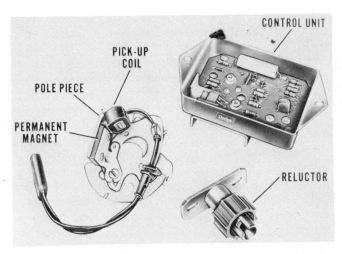

Fig. 35-69j. Magnetic pick-up components and control unit.

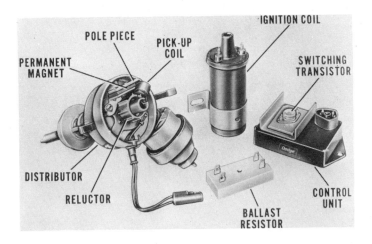

Fig. 35-69i. Electronic ignition system components.

The length of time that the switching transistor blocks the flow of current to the primary circuit is determined by the electronic circuitry in the control unit. This determines the "dwell." Dwell is not adjustable. Even though it may be read with a dwell meter, there is no means provided to change it. However, changes are not necessary.

The magnetic pickup and the control unit have replaced the function of the breaker points and unlike the breaker points, show no signs of wear. Therefore periodic checks of timing and dwell are not necessary. Ignition maintenance is reduced to inspection of wiring, and cleaning and changing of spark plugs as needed.

Ignition Circuit Tests

If the checks indicated under Trouble Shooting show that the ignition system is at fault, the following checks may be made to help locate the trouble. All tests are to be made with the lights and accessories off, and in the order shown. If the engine starts, but immediately stops when the starting switch is turned off, steps one to four may be omitted. Connections for the various connections of the voltmeter are shown in Fig. 35-70, in which meter connections are shown by dotted red lines. Values apply to 12V systems.

1. Check all connections in primary and secondary circuit.

2. Remove secondary coil lead from distributor cap. Hold 1/4 in. from engine while cranking and observe if spark occurs. If spark occurs, check distributor cap, rotor and spark plug wiring.
3. Connect voltmeter as shown at V-1, Fig. 35-70. Reading should be 1V maximum, while cranking engine. If no reading is obtained, trouble may be: Open ignition circuit used during cranking. Ignition switch not closing ignition circuit during cranking. Ground in circuit from coil terminal to ignition switch. Ground in coil.
4. Connect voltmeter as shown at V-2. Ignition switch on, breaker points open. Meter should show normal battery voltage. If not, trouble

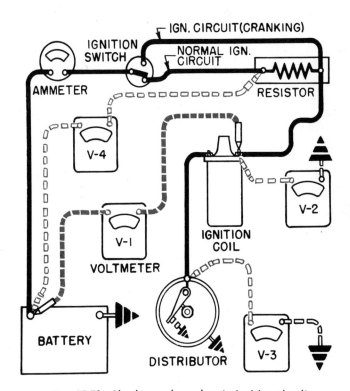

Fig. 35-70. Checking voltage drop in ignition circuit.

may be: Low battery. Breaker points not open. Ground in circuit from coil to distributor. Ground in distributor. Ground in coil. Ground in ignition circuit used during cranking or in lead connecting coil to resistor.

5. Connect voltmeter as shown at V-2, ignition switch on, points closed. Meter reading should be 5 to 7V. If higher than 7V: Contacts may not be closed. A loose connection in distributor. Distributor not grounded to engine. Faulty breaker points. Loose connection between distributor coil and distributor. Resistor out of circuit due to shorted or incorrect wiring. Starting contacts of ignition switch may stay closed. Resistor has too little resistance. Resistance should be within specified value. If meter reading is less than 5V, trouble may be: Loose connection from resistor through ignition switch to battery. Loose connection between resistor and coil. Resistance is open or has too much resistance.

6. Connect voltmeter as shown as V-3, ignition switch on and points closed. Meter reading should be 0.2 maximum. If not: Contacts are not closed. Loose connection in distributor. Distributor not grounded to engine. Defective breaker points. The voltage drop across the ignition breaker points should not exceed 0.125V.

7. Connect voltmeter as shown as V-4. Ignition switch on and points closed. Meter reading should not exceed 0.7V. If not, check for loose connection from resistor through ignition switch circuit to battery.

8. If these checks fail to find cause of trouble, remove coil distributor and resistor and check separately. Also check wiring harness.

Ignition Trouble Shooting

Engine Will Not Start

(Also see starting and fuel system troubles)
Weak battery.
Excessive moisture on high tension wiring and spark plugs.
Cracked distributor cap.
Faulty coil.
Faulty condenser.
Coil to distributor high tension lead not in place.
Loose connections or broken wire in low tension circuit.
Faulty ignition breaker points.

Hard Starting

Faulty or improperly gapped spark plugs.
Faulty or improperly adjusted breaker points.
Loose connections in primary circuit.
Defective high tension cables.
Low capacity condenser.
Faulty distributor cap or rotor.

Engine Misfires

Dirty or worn spark plugs.
Damaged insulation on high tension wires.
High tension wires disconnected.
High tension wires incorrectly routed to plugs.
Defective distributor cap.
Poor cylinder compression.
Breaker points incorrectly adjusted.
Weak breaker point spring.

Quiz - Engine Ignition

1. List the various units found in the modern ignition system.
2. What is the purpose of the ignition coil?
3. What is the voltage at the secondary of the ignition coil?
   a. 5,000 volts.
   b. 12 volts.
   c. 110 volts.
   d. 20,000 volts.
   e. 100,000 volts.
4. In addition to opening and closing the primary ignition circuit, what else does an ignition distributor do?
5. What is the purpose of the ignition condenser?
6. What is the purpose of the spark plug?
7. Describe briefly the construction of an ignition coil.
8. With the closing of the ignition switch, describe what happens in an ignition system.

9. Which is higher, ignition voltage at:
   a. High speeds?
   b. Low speeds?
   c. The same at all speeds?
10. When an arc is produced at the ignition breaker points, is the voltage induced in the secondary higher or lower than without an arc?
    a. Higher.
    b. Lower.
    c. The same.
11. Which requires the greater voltage to jump the gap, an old worn plug, or a new plug?
    a. New plug.
    b. Old plug.
    c. Same in either case.
12. What advantage is there in installing the ignition coil close to the distributor?
13. Is there any advantage in keeping the high tension leads as short as possible?

14. What advantage is there in having the high tension outlet of the ignition coil negative?

15. Describe the lead pencil test for determining the polarity of the ignition system.

16. Describe briefly the construction of an ignition condenser.

17. The capacity of an ignition condenser is measured in what units?
    a. Volts.
    b. Farads.
    c. Joules.
    d. Microfarads.
    e. Ampere turns.

18. If metal is transferred to the positive point of ignition breaker points, is the condenser too large or too small?
    a. Too small.
    b. Too large.

19. On what type of engine is a vibrator type ignition coil used, and for what purpose?

20. On a four-cycle engine at what speed is the distributor driven?
    a. Engine speed.
    b. Half engine speed.
    c. Twice engine speed.

21. On a two-cycle engine, at what speed is the distributor driven?
    a. Engine speed.
    b. Half engine speed.
    c. Twice engine speed.

22. On a typical distributor, how many lobes are there on the breaker cam for a six cylinder engine?
    a. Three.   b. Six.   c. Twelve.

23. The rotor in a distributor distributes the current to the various spark plugs. From where does it receive the current?

24. What engine conditions will affect the time that ignition should occur?

25. When the engine is idling, when is the spark usually timed to occur?
    a. Before top center.
    b. After top center.
    c. Before bottom center.

26. At higher engine speeds, why is it necessary to have the spark occur earlier?

27. At what point in the intake system is the vacuum advance connected?
    a. Atmospheric side of the carburetor throttle.
    b. Engine side of the carburetor throttle.
    c. Vacuum side of the fuel pump.

28. As load on an engine is increased, is more or less spark advance required?
    a. More spark advance.
    b. Less spark advance.

29. What is cam angle?

30. When cam angle is small, will there be more or less time for current to pass through the primary circuit?
    a. More time.   b. Less time.

31. In the Ford Loadomatic distributor, how is the spark advance controlled?
    a. By centrifugal force only.
    b. By vacuum only.
    c. By a combination of vacuum and centrifugal force.

32. What points can be checked with a modern distributor testing equipment?

33. When aligning breaker points, which part of the assembly should be bent?
    a. The stationary point.
    b. The movable point.

34. Why is a resistor used in the primary ignition circuit?

35. There are two general types of resistors used in the primary ignition circuit. One is a single unit or block type and is mounted on the fire wall of the engine. What is the other type?

36. What is the approximate resistance of the resistors used in the primary circuit?
    a. 18 ohms.
    b. 25 ohms.
    c. 1.5 ohms.
    d. 15 ohms.

37. List two places where timing marks are placed on an engine.

38. In the dual advance distributor used on some Ford engines how is the vacuum advance controlled?

39. Give the firing order of an in-line six cylinder engine.

40. Give a firing order of a V-8 engine.

41. What is meant by the heat range of spark plugs?

42. At high speeds what is the approximate temperature of the center wire of a spark plug?
    a. 212 deg.
    b. 400 deg.
    c. 800 deg.
    d. 3,200 deg.

43. Which plug is termed the hotter: a plug with a long path for the heat to travel, or a plug with a short path?
    a. Long path.
    b. Short path.

44. What three types of fouling are spark plugs subject to?

45. An ignition system that is capable of delivering 20,000 volts to a clean spark plug, may be able to deliver only half that amount to a fouled plug. Why?

46. Why are wider spark plug gaps favored over narrow gaps?

47. Give two reasons why the surface of the cylinder head against which the spark plug seats must be clean.

48. What are some advantages of magneto ignition?

49. What method is used to produce the magnetic field in a magneto?

50. When reconditioning a spark plug, what should be done to the center electrode?

51. Give two classifications of magnetos.

52. In the inductor-type magneto where are the coil and magnet mounted?
    a. Both in stationary positions.
    b. The magnet rotates and the coil is stationary.
53. In a rotating magnet magneto, which of the following parts rotate and which are stationary? Coil. Condenser. Breaker points.
54. Describe the operation of a flywheel-type magneto.
55. What is the purpose of an impulse coupling?
56. In a transistor-type ignition system, what does the transistor do?
    a. Transforms the battery voltage to high voltage.
    b. "Switches" on and off the primary current.
    c. Distributes the high tension current.
57. Give five causes originating in the ignition system, why an engine will not start.
58. Give five causes originating in the ignition system, why an engine will be hard to start.
59. Give five causes originating in the ignition system, why an engine misfires.
60. The capacitor discharge system uses breaker points. True or False?
61. What type is the Delco transistor ignition system?
    a. Pulse type.
    b. Capacitor discharge system.
    c. Magneto controlled system.
    d. Contact controlled system.
62. What type is the Ford transistor ignition system?
    a. Pulse type.
    b. Capacitor discharge system.
    c. Magnetic controlled type.
    d. Contact controlled type.
63. In the Autolite distributor designed to reduce harmful exhaust gas emission, carburetor vacuum is connected to which diaphragm?
    a. Advance diaphragm.   b. Retard diaphragm.
64. The ignition primary resistance wire used by Chrysler is not sensitive to heat.
    True or False?
65. How many connections are there to the Delco Unitized Ignition system?
    Four
    Nine
    Twenty-one
    Five
66. Is full battery voltage applied to the coil during cranking in the Chrysler electronic ignition system?
    Yes
    No

LIGHTS, LIGHTING CIRCUITS, WIRING, AND HORNS

Many modern cars have in excess of 20 different lights ranging from the small indicator lamp drawing approximately .25 amp., to the large sealed beam head lamp drawing in excess of 8 amp. for six volt units to over 4 amp. for the twelve volt type.

A typical sealed beam head lamp is shown in Fig. 36-1. In these lamps the filament, reflector and lens form a single unit. As the unit is completely sealed, the reflector never becomes tarnished, and as a result, the light output is not seriously affected by age. The filament is correctly focused in relation to the reflector and the lens at the time of manufacture, and consequently there is no need to focus these lamps. However, it is necessary to aim them correctly, to provide maximum illumination on the road, and at the same time avoid blinding approaching drivers.

Fig. 36-2. Unhooking spring from retainer ring of sealed beam head lamp.

Fig. 36-1. Cutaway view of modern sealed beam headlight.

Removing Sealed Beam Units

Removal of the sealed beam unit from the car is simple. The procedure is to first remove the head lamp door screws, permitting removal of the door. Unhook the spring from the retainer ring, Fig. 36-2. Then, remove screws indicated in Fig. 36-3. These screws hold the retaining ring, and should not be confused with the adjusting screws which are adjacent and which are shown in Fig. 36-6. The aiming screws should not be turned unless it is necessary to aim the lights. After removing the retainer ring and sealed

beam unit, Fig. 36-4, the lamp is separated from the wire connector, Fig. 36-5.

In most cases the screws for vertical aiming are at the top of the unit, and the horizontal aiming screws are at the side, Fig. 36-6. However, in some instances the vertical adjustment is placed at the bottom.

Fig. 36-6 shows a number "1" embossed in one lamp and a number "2" in the other. These are to identify the lamps, the number "2" being for outboard mounting and number "1" for inboard mounting. The outboard lamps have two filaments and a three-blade terminal, while the number "1" lamp has only a single filament and a two-blade terminal. The latter provides the high intensity reach down the highway, and the off focus of No. 2 lamp, illuminates the side of the road.

Fig. 36-3. Removing screws securing retaining ring.

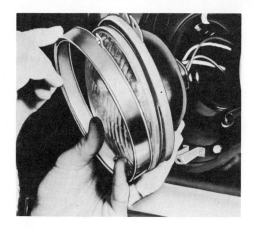

Fig. 36-4. *Removing sealed beam lamp and retaining ring.*

Aiming Headlights

The three guide points formed in the front of the lens glass on sealed beam units are used in aiming these units. See Fig. 36-5, detail at the right of the photo. Special headlight aiming equipment is available. With some types, aiming may be done in daylight without turning on the lights. The equipment is provided with an accurate level, so it is not necessary for the vehicle to be on a level floor.

Fig. 36-5. *Disconnecting sealed beam unit.*

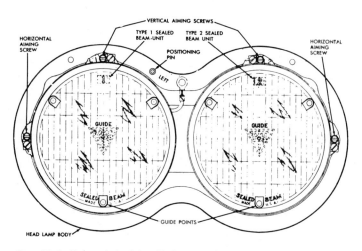

Fig. 36-6. *Typical dual headlight installation. No. 1 headlight on left and No. 2 on right. Note aiming screws and guide posts for aiming.*

Headlights may also be aimed by using a wall layout, as shown in Figs. 36-7 and 36-8. In using this set-up, the floor must be level and the tires correctly inflated. Fig. 36-7 shows how to establish the horizontal

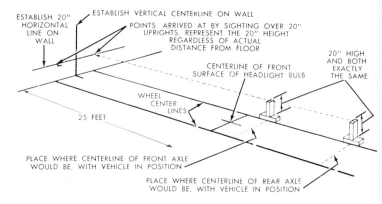

Fig. 36-7. *Floor and wall layout for headlight aiming.*

and vertical reference lines which are required. The horizontal centerline of the headlight, B, Fig. 36-8, is established by subtracting 20 in. from the actual measured height of the headlight lens center from the floor, and adding this dimension to the 20 in. reference line which was obtained by sighting over the uprights as shown in Fig. 36-7. Headlight vertical centerlines (dimension A), should be drawn on the layout, using measurements obtained from the car. Fig. 36-8 shows

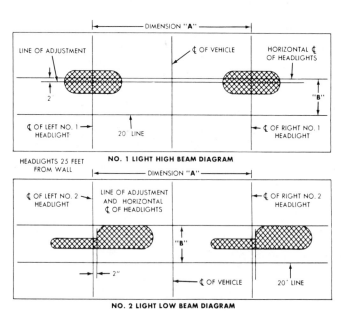

Fig. 36-8. *Wall diagrams for aiming headlights.*

diagrams for both high and low beams. The 2 in. dimension indicated should be changed as needed to meet your local and state requirements.

When focusing a sealed beam headlight, the adjustment at the top of the retaining ring, Fig. 36-6, will

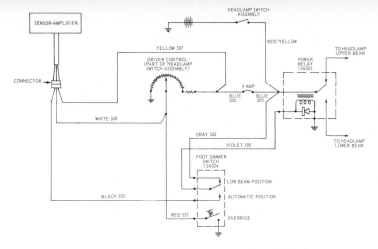

Fig. 36-8a. Wiring diagram of automatic headlight dimmer.

raise or lower the light beam, while the adjustment at the side will swing the beam to the right or the left. These adjustments are reached after the outer decorative ring has been removed.

Head Lamp Dimming

Most vehicles today are provided with a dual headlighting system. Each dual head lamp includes two sealed beam units, Fig. 36-6. The No. 2 lamp is provided with two filaments, one filament being used for "dim" lights and city driving. For country or "high beam" driving the other filament of No. 2 lamp is used together with the No. 1 sealed beam lamp. A dimmer switch in the toe-boards permits selection of the required illumination.

On vehicles which are provided with only two headlights, each light has two filaments similar to the No. 2 light and a dimmer switch, Fig. 36-9, is provided so that either high beam or low beam filament can be cut into the circuit.

Automatic Headlight Dimming

Some vehicles are equipped with a device to automatically dim the headlights. In the case of Ford built vehicles this is a driver-operated electronic device which automatically switches the headlights from high to low beam in response to light from an approaching vehicle or lights from the taillights of a vehicle being overtaken.

Major components of the system are: sensor-amplifier unit, power relay, driver sensitivity control and an interconnecting wire harness.

The sensor-amplifier combines a light-sensing optical device and a transistorized amplifier into a single unit with sufficient power to operate a power relay for switching the headlight beams. A precalibrated level assembly is attached as a part of the sensor-amplifier unit for setting the correct vertical aim. The unit is adjusted and completely sealed at the factory.

The power relay contains a diode for damping purposes to protect the sensor-amplifier. Be sure to observe proper polarity when connecting to prevent

burn out of diode.

The foot switch is a special dimmer override type that replaces the standard foot dimmer. With the foot switch in the automatic position, a slight downward pressure on the switch provides upper beam regardless of amount of light on the sensor-amplifier lens. A wiring diagram of the system is shown in Fig. 36-8a.

Lighting Circuit

The modern lighting circuit, Fig. 36-10, includes the battery, frame, all the lights and various switches that control their use. The lighting circuit is known as the single-wire system as it uses the car frame for the return.

The complete lighting circuit of the modern passenger car can be broken down into individual circuits, each having one or more lights and switches. In each separate circuit, the lights are connected in parallel, and the controlling switch is in series between the group of lights and the battery. As an example, the parking lights are connected in parallel and controlled by a single switch. In some installations, one switch controls the connection to the battery while a selector switch determines which of two circuits is energized. The headlights with their upper and lower beams, are an example of such a circuit.

Fig. 36-9. Typical circuit of headlight dimmer circuit.

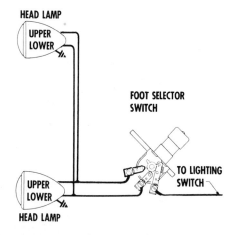

In some instances, such as the dome lights, several switches may be connected in parallel so that any switch may be used to turn on the light.

When studying the wiring diagram, all light circuits can be traced from the battery, through the ammeter to the switch (or switches) to the individual light.

Headlight Doors

Headlamp doors are a feature of several cars. There are two general types of such doors; one is electrically operated by a series wound motor, and the other by a vacuum powered motor.

Chrysler built cars with headlamp doors are provided with electrically operated doors using a series wound motor with two field coils. This is mounted behind the center of the grille and has a worm gear drive and internal limit switches. A relay and circuit breaker assembly is mounted to the instrument panel lower reinforcement, left of the steering column.

To open the headlamp doors in the event of an electric failure, first disconnect the motor electric leads. Then, rotate the hand wheel located at the lower end of the motor clockwise as indicated by the decal on the radiator yoke until the headlamp doors are completely open.

Electrical causes of operational failure include faulty motor, defective wiring or connections, malfunctioning of motor limit switch and circuit breaker failure, and faulty headlamp switch or relay.

Mechanical trouble includes: Torsion bar disconnected; crank screws missing; torsion bar twisted; stripped drive gear; rubber bumpers worn or missing; door pivot bushings worn, missing or dry; door rubbing against grille; torsion spring missing.

The system powered by the intake manifold vacuum is used on some General Motors cars. In this system the headlamps are in a barrel housing that is pivoted through a linkage system which is actuated by a vacuum powered cylinder push rod. The light switch controls not only the electrical circuit, but also the vacuum circuit which controls the headlight door operation. An 800 cu. in. reserve tank supplies vacuum for operation of the doors when the engine is stopped. Its capacity is sufficient to operate the headlight doors through one up-and-down cycle without the engine operating.

There is one power cylinder for each headlight door and a relay valve controls the vacuum to the power cylinders. So that the doors can be operated by hand in order to replace bulbs and for aiming, a manual valve is also provided. The manual switch must be pushed in before the doors can be operated by the headlight switch. The headlight door can be opened from the front of the car by pushing on the housing directly under the doors until the housing locks in the open position. The headlights should be aimed only when there is at least 20 in. of vacuum in the system.

Head Lamp Service Kinks

Short life or frequent burning out of head lamps results from excessive voltage. This in turn may result from loose or corroded electrical connections in the battery circuit or the generator charging rate may be set too high. The setting of the voltage regulator should also be checked.

Dim lights result from low voltage, and this in turn, may be caused by loose or corroded terminals in the lamp circuit. Or, the generator charging rate may be too low, the battery may be defective, or the voltage regulator may be set incorrectly.

The wiring in lighting circuits should be inspected periodically for loose and corroded connections, and chafed insulation. The connections at junction blocks and wire connections should be especially checked. Switches, bulb sockets, lamp shells, reflectors and lenses should also be inspected for loose mounting and corrosion.

In order to overcome the effects of rust on old cars, it is frequently necessary to solder a lead to a

Fig. 36-10. Example of modern wiring diagram. (1972 Fury)

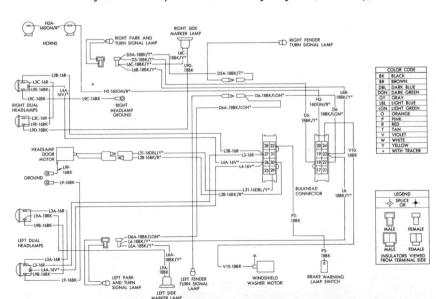

Fig. 36-11. *Typical fuse block. These are usually mounted behind the instrument panel.*

lamp socket case and ground the other end of the lead on the frame.

The voltage drop between the various lamp sockets (not the holder, reflector, or shell) and the ground, should be measured with a low-reading voltmeter. Each light should be turned on when making this test for high resistant ground connections. If any reading is obtained on the voltmeter, it is an indication that there is resistance present, and shell and socket must be carefully cleaned to obtain a good electrical connection.

Another test to be made is checking the voltage drop between the battery and each individual lamp. To make this test, connect a long voltmeter lead to the ungrounded starting battery terminal, and a test probe on the other lead of the voltmeter. Turn on the lights and touch the voltmeter probe to the insulated terminal of each lamp. The voltage drop should be less than 0.6 volt. If the voltage drop is greater than that amount, follow the circuit back through the switch and ammeter

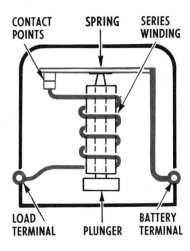

Fig. 36-12. *Wiring diagram of current limit relay. Note that contact points and relay winding are in series.*

to locate the part of the circuit in which the loss occurs. If the loss in voltage is due to a defective ammeter or switch, the part should be replaced. Usually the loss will be found at a terminal or connecting sleeve. In such cases, cleaning and tightening will overcome the trouble.

Fuses and Overload Relay

A fuse block, Fig. 36-11, or current limit relay, Fig. 36-12, is usually connected between the battery and the main lighting switch. The fuse block or relay is usually mounted on the back of the instrument panel.

When a short circuit or overload occurs in a circuit, the fuse burns out and opens the circuit, so that no further damage will result. The thermal overload relay operates by heating a strip or bimetal on which a contact is mounted. When a short circuit occurs, the excessive current heats the bimetal, causing it to bend and open the contacts. This opens the circuit, until the bimetal cools after which the contacts again close, completing the circuit. This cycle continues until the short is removed.

Another form of current limit relay uses a solenoid to control a set of contact points. There are two types, the vibrating and lockout type. On the vibrating type, excessive current will cause the relay to vibrate, and also cuts down the amount of current flowing so that excessive current cannot flow and cause damage.

In the lockout type, the contact points are held open by a separate winding connected between the points. A small current continues to flow through this winding, but the electrical equipment is rendered inoperative.

The current limit relay, Fig. 36-12, has a heavy series winding and a pair of contacts. Within the winding is a steel plunger, and above, a flat spring with one of the contact points and a brass button on it. When load requirements are not excessive, the current through the series winding is completed through the closed contact points. When there is a short circuit causing a high current, the magnetic field built by the series winding, is strong enough to move the plunger, which in turn strikes the brass button on the spring, forcing the contact points apart. As soon as the contacts open, current ceases to flow, and the plunger moves to its original position, permitting the contact points to close again. The resulting vibrating action keeps the current from becoming excessive. The lockout type current limit relay has an additional winding connected across the contact points which maintains the points in the open position, as long as the abnormal circuit condition exists.

Light Relays

Because of the limited voltage available in automotive lighting circuits, it is necessary to keep the resistance of the connecting wires to a minimum. A big aid in this is the use of heavier gauge wire. How-

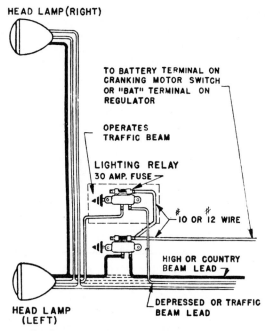

HEAD LAMP (RIGHT)

TO BATTERY TERMINAL ON CRANKING MOTOR SWITCH OR "BAT" TERMINAL ON REGULATOR

OPERATES TRAFFIC BEAM

LIGHTING RELAY
30 AMP. FUSE

#10 OR #12 WIRE

HIGH OR COUNTRY BEAM LEAD

HEAD LAMP (LEFT)

DEPRESSED OR TRAFFIC BEAM LEAD

BASE OF RELAYS MUST BE GROUNDED

TWO BEAM LIGHTING SYSTEM WITH RELAYS IN COUNTRY AND TRAFFIC BEAM CIRCUITS

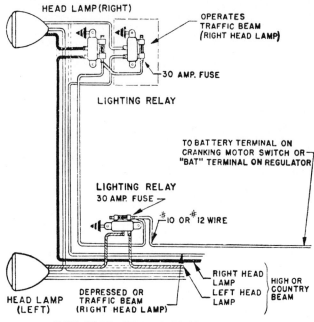

HEAD LAMP (RIGHT)

OPERATES TRAFFIC BEAM (RIGHT HEAD LAMP)

30 AMP. FUSE

LIGHTING RELAY

TO BATTERY TERMINAL ON CRANKING MOTOR SWITCH OR "BAT" TERMINAL ON REGULATOR

LIGHTING RELAY
30 AMP. FUSE

#10 OR #12 WIRE

HEAD LAMP (LEFT)

DEPRESSED OR TRAFFIC BEAM (RIGHT HEAD LAMP)

RIGHT HEAD LAMP
LEFT HEAD LAMP
HIGH OR COUNTRY BEAM

BASE OF RELAYS MUST BE GROUNDED

MULTIPLE BEAM LIGHTING SYSTEM WITH A RELAY IN EACH BEAM CIRCUIT OF RIGHT HEAD LAMP AND HIGH OR COUNTRY BEAM CIRCUIT OF LEFT HEAD LAMP

Fig. 36-13. Lighting relay circuits.

ever, the cost of such wire is high and, as a consequence, light relays are used to reduce the voltage loss. The relay can be placed in a position that decreases the length of the wiring, thereby reducing the voltage losses. The relay also eliminates the necessity of the main switch carrying all of the current and, therefore, eliminates the voltage loss due to burned switch contacts.

The wiring diagram for a typical lighting relay is shown in Fig. 36-13. Two lighting relays provide control of both high and low beams. When the lighting switch is placed in the high beam position, the winding of the lower relay is connected directly to the battery. The contacts of the lower relay will then close so the circuit from the battery to the high beam filaments is completed. When the selector switch is operated to obtain the depressed beam, the winding of the upper relay is connected to the battery, closing the relay points to connect the low beam filaments to the battery. At the same time, the winding of the lower relay is disconnected from the battery.

Lighting Wire Sizes

In order to conserve current, lighting wire must be of adequate size. The voltage loss in a length of wire is equal to the product of the current flowing and the resistance of the wire. Voltage loss or drop is also known as the IR drop. Keeping the resistance of the wire to a minimum will, therefore, keep the IR drop to a minimum. As the resistance of a length of

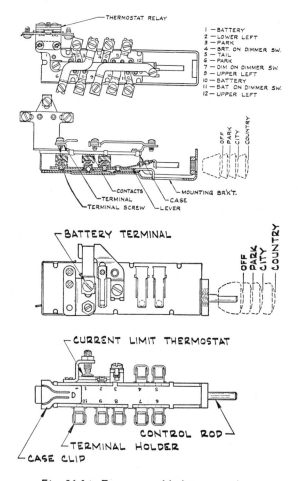

THERMOSTAT RELAY

1 —BATTERY
2 —LOWER LEFT
3 —PARK
4 —BRT. ON DIMMER SW.
5 —TAIL
6 —PARK
7 —DIM ON DIMMER SW.
8 —UPPER LEFT
9 —BATTERY
10 —BATTERY
11 —BAT ON DIMMER SW.
12 —UPPER LEFT

OFF PARK CITY COUNTRY

CONTACTS
TERMINAL
TERMINAL SCREW
MOUNTING BR'K'T.
CASE
LEVER

BATTERY TERMINAL

OFF PARK CITY COUNTRY

CURRENT LIMIT THERMOSTAT

CONTROL ROD
TERMINAL HOLDER
CASE CLIP

Fig. 36-14. Two types of lighting switches.

wire decreases as its diameter increases, it is advisable to use wire of relatively large cross section. In general, nothing smaller than No. 16 gauge wire should be used for lights of small candle power; for headlights and other lights of high candle power, wire of still larger gauge is required.

Lighting Switches

Originally, individual switches are provided for each light. On modern cars, a single switch unit is provided, Fig. 36-14, with individual switches being provided for special purpose lights such as dome lights, fog lights, etc. The modern switch provides control of such lights as head, fender, tail, side and instrument panel in a single unit.

In most vehicle installations, it is customary to arrange the wiring circuits so head, side, parking, and taillights are controlled simultaneously by one switch to insure meeting legal lighting requirements.

The main lighting switch may be of either the "push-pull" or "push-pull with rotary contact" type. A typical switch will have three positions: "off," "dim," or "parking" and "bright." Some switches also contain a rheostat to control the brightness of the instrument panel lights. The rheostat is operated by rotating the control knob, thus separating it from the push-pull action of the main switch.

Main lighting switches may also include a fuse block for protection of the lighting circuits. Another type combines light control with generator output control. This is accomplished by incorporating a resistor in the design, which will be cut in or out of the generator field circuit, by changing from one switch position to the other.

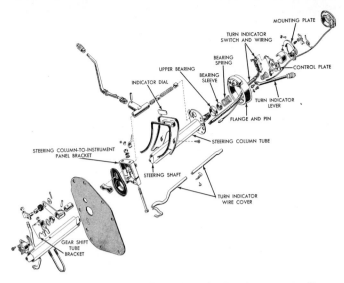

Fig. 36-15. Turn signal switch and related parts. (Ford)

left rear of the car, signaling a left turn. Moving the switch upward will light the lights on the right (front and rear), signaling a right turn. With the switch in a position to indicate a turn, the lights are alternately turned off and on by an interrupter or flasher included in the circuit.

Stoplight Switch

In order to signal a stop, a brake pedal operated switch is provided which operates the stoplight or lights at the rear of the vehicle. In some installations the stoplight switch is at the end of the brake master cylinder so that the contacts are closed by increasing brake fluid pressure, Fig. 36-16. In other installations, Fig. 36-16a, it is operated directly by movement of the brake pedal.

WIRE SIZE FOR LIGHTING CIRCUITS

Total Candle Power		Wire Gauge (for length in feet)							
6V	12V	3 Ft.	5 Ft.	7 Ft.	10 Ft.	15 Ft.	20 Ft.	35 Ft.	50 Ft.
3	6	18	18	18	18	18	18	18	18
8	16	18	18	18	18	18	18	18	18
15	30	18	18	18	18	18	18	16	16
30	60	18	18	18	18	18	16	14	14
40	80	18	18	18	18	16	16	14	12
50	100	18	18	18	18	16	14	12	12
60	120	18	18	18	18	14	14	12	10
80	160	18	18	16	16	14	12	10	10
100	200	18	18	16	16	12	12	10	8

Direction Signal Switches

The direction signal switch, Fig. 36-15, is installed just below the hub of the steering wheel. A manually controlled lever projecting from the switch, permits the driver to signal or indicate the direction of the turn he is about to make. Moving the switch handle down will light the light bulbs on the left front and the

Electric Wires and Cables

Wires and cables, usually made of copper are used to carry electricity to the various electrical devices, and equipment on passenger cars and trucks. It is of the greatest importance that wires and cables be of the correct size and have the proper insulation. If the diameter of the wire or cable is too small, its resistance will be too great, and valuable voltage will be lost in overcoming the increased resistance. This in turn will result in poor operation of the particular electrical unit. In the case of lights, they will not provide maximum illumination. In the case of starting motors, lower cranking speeds will result.

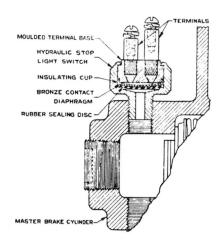

Fig. 36-16. Stoplight switch installed on hydraulic brake master cylinder.

Cable size and length determines its resistance. The smaller the diameter of the wire or cable, the greater its resistance, Fig. 36-17. Also, the longer the cable or wire, the greater its resistance will be

Wire and cable sizes are expressed by a gauge number, which indicates the cross-sectional area (not diameter) of the conductor. The cross-sectional

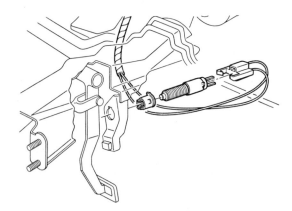

Fig. 36-16a. Details of stoplight switch mounted on brake pedal.

area of wires is given in circular mils. A circular mil is a unit of area equal to the area of a circle one mil in diameter. A mil is a unit of length equal to .001 in. Thus a wire 10 mils in diameter has a cross-sectional area of 100 circular mils (or 78.54 sq. mils.)

In the case of cables, Fig. 36-17, which are made up of a number of strands of wire, the cross-sectional area of the cable is equal to the circular mil area of a single strand, times the number of strands.

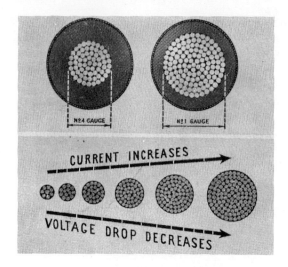

Fig. 36-17. Illustrating the gauge of electric cable and the effect of gauge size on voltage drop.

Special gauges, Fig. 36-18, are available for measuring the gauge size of wires. If such gauges are not available, the diameter can be measured by means of a micrometer. Then by checking the diameter obtained in that manner with the accompanying wire table, Fig. 36-19, its gauge size can be determined.

To determine the gauge size of a cable, count the number of strands. Then measure the diameter of a single strand with a micrometer. In the wire table, de-

Fig. 36-18. Typical gauge used for measuring the size of wire.

termine the area in circular mils for that diameter wire. Then multiply the area of the single wire in circular mils by the number of strands in the cable. Locate in the table the area in circular mils that is closest to that value. The gauge size corresponding to the total area in circular mils will be the gauge size of the cable.

When comparing cables it must be remembered that the external diameter of a wire or cable has nothing to do with its current-carrying capacity, Fig. 36-20. Thick insulation will make a small gauge wire look much larger. It is therefore important that only the size of the metal conductors be compared, and the way to do that is by means of a wire gauge, or by a micrometer.

Wire Diameter Inches	American Wire Gauge	Circular Mil Area
.4600	0000	211600
.4096	000	167800
.3648	00	133100
.3249	0	105500
.2893	1	83690
.2576	2	66370
.2294	3	52640
.2043	4	41740
.1620	6	26250
.1285	8	16510
.1019	10	10380
.0808	12	6530
.0640	14	4107
.0508	16	2583
.0403	18	1624
.0319	20	1022
.0284	21	810.1
.0253	22	642.4
.0225	23	509.5
.0201	24	404.0
.0179	25	320.4
.0159	26	254.1
.0142	27	201.5
.0126	28	159.8
.0112	29	126.7
.0100	30	100.5
.0089	31	79.7
.0079	32	63.2
.0070	33	50.1
.0063	34	39.7
.0056	35	31.5
.0050	36	25.0

Fig. 36-19. Wire gauge table.

Battery Cables

Because the starting motor, when cranking an engine, will draw approximately 150 amp., it is imperative that the cable connecting the battery to the starter be of sufficient gauge to carry such heavy current. For that reason, it is usually made of No. 1,

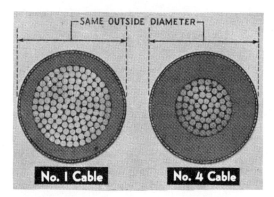

Fig. 36-20. The outside diameter of the cable insulation is no gauge of its current carrying capacity. In the illustration both cables have the same outside diameter, but the No. 1 cable has much less resistance and greater carrying capacity than the No. 4 cable.

or No. 2 gauge cable. The cable connecting the battery to the ground must also carry the same current. However, as it is grounded, there is no need to have it insulated. It is often made in the form of a flat woven wire strap.

Because of their proximity to the battery and consequent possibility of corrosion, it is important that the cables make good electrical contact with the cable terminals, and that the terminals make good electrical contact with the battery terminals. Any looseness or corrosion between the cable and its terminal, or between the cable terminal and the battery, will result in high resistance and consequent voltage drop.

High resistance between cables and their terminals can be checked easily by means of a voltmeter. With a current of approximately 20 amp. flowing, connect one terminal of a voltmeter to cable, the other to cable terminal. The voltage drop should then be approximately 0.1 volt. Voltage drop in starter to ground circuit should not be more than 0.1 volt.

Formerly, it was common practice to replace cable terminals when they were badly corroded. Most mechanics today will replace the entire cable.

High Tension Cable

In order to carry the high voltage to the spark plugs with minimum loss, it is essential that the high tension cables be covered with ample insulation which must withstand heat, cold, moisture, oil, grease, chafing and corona.

Corona is an electrical phenomenon which is not readily visible, but is one of the worst enemies of high tension cable as it deteriorates rubber very rapidly.

The passage of high tension electricity through a cable builds up a surrounding electrical field. The electrical field liberates oxygen in the surrounding air to form ozone which will attack the rubber insulation if it is not properly protected. This ozone causes the rubber to deteriorate and lose its insulating qualities. Electrical losses result, which in turn will seriously weaken the spark at the plug gap. High quality ignition cable is designed to withstand the effects of corona, also heat, cold, oil, grease and moisture. In recent years great improvements have been made in the insulation of high tension cables.

High tension cable is available in cut lengths designed for installation on the different makes and models of engines. However, in many cases the mechanic makes up the cable set, using the original cable as a guide in cutting the desired lengths. When installing new cable, the individual pieces should be cut as short as possible, but sufficient length should be provided so that sharp bends are avoided. In addition, it is advisable to separate the individual cables as much as possible. Short cables, well spaced, reduce the electrical capacity of the system and thereby improve ignition.

Insulating nipples should always be used at both ends of the ignition cable to reduce leakage and losses due to moisture.

When checking high tension cables, both the insulation and the terminals should be carefully examined. If the cable is carried in a conduit, it should be removed so the entire length of cable can be examined. If the insulation is hard or brittle, it should be replaced. The usual method of checking the insulation is to bend to a small circle, Fig. 36-21, and note if any cracks appear in the insulation. If the end of the copper cable has receded so the insulation extends beyond, it is probably not making good contact with the terminal. In such cases, it is probable that the entire cable has deteriorated and should be replaced.

The spark plug cables should be removed from the distributor cap sockets and each socket should be thoroughly cleaned. Frequently, these sockets have become corroded. It is important that all corrosion is removed, otherwise engine performance will be seriously affected. When replacing the cables, be sure they are pushed to the bottom of the sockets in the distributor. If this is not done, the spark will jump the air gap and cause corrosion and burned contacts.

Resistor Ignition Cable

To reduce interference with radio and TV reception, automotive ignition systems are provided with resistance in the secondary circuit. This may be in the form of a resistance unit built into the rotor, or distributor cap, resistance in the spark plugs, or special resistor-type ignition cable may be used. The latter form is being used currently.

Some resistor cable is made of parallel strands of linen thread covered with braided rayon thread. This core is then impregnated with graphite to make it a conductor for the high tension current. For insulation, a rubber-like substance that is virtually impervious to oil and heat is used. However, such cable has very little tensile strength and could easily be broken if pulled. When the conductor is broken a spark would jump across the gap and the conductor would eventually disintegrate and misfiring would result.

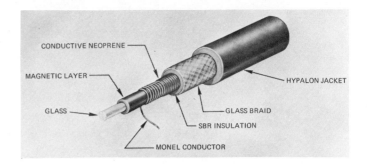

Fig. 36-21a. An ignition cable of the wire wound magnetic core type.

It is therefore important not to pull on the cable when disconnecting a spark plug. Instead, the rubber boot covering the end of the cable and the spark plug insulator should be grasped and pulled when disconnecting a spark plug. Also the insulation should not be punctured when making a connection when timing an engine as this would probably also sever the conductor with eventual failure resulting. Resistor cable formerly had a resistance of approximately 4000 ohms per foot. Currently, SAE specifications for ignition resistance cable call for 3000 to 7000 ohms per foot for low resistance (LR) cable and 6000 to 12,000 ohms per foot for high resistance cable (HR) cable.

High resistance cables are now available with conductors made of monel metal which is wound around a magnetic core, Fig. 36-21a. This has a resistance of 4000 to 7000 ohms per foot.

Another type of high resistance cable is a hypalon jacketed cable, Fig. 36-21b. This uses a metallic conductor that terminates in a high resistance of alloy wire wound on a ceramic core. The end of the cable is provided with a spark plug protector.

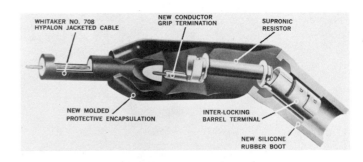

Fig. 36-21b. Metallic conductor type cable with the resistor element built into the terminal end.

Fig. 36-21. If cracks appear in the insulation when it is given a sharp bend, it should be discarded.

Chrysler has adopted for their electronic ignition system, a silicone jacketed cable with a nonmetallic conductor which is of the distributed resistance type. The silicone jacketing may withstand 350 deg. F for 192 hours without cracking.

When terminals are applied to resistor type cable,

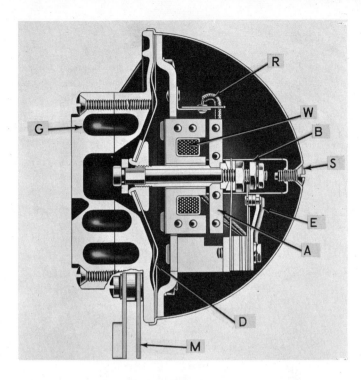

Fig. 36-22. Details of types HB, HC, HF and HG Autolite horn. A—Armature. B—Circuit breaker adjusting screw. D—Diaphragm. E—Circuit breaker. G—Sound ducts. M—Mounting springs. R—Resistor. W—Winding.

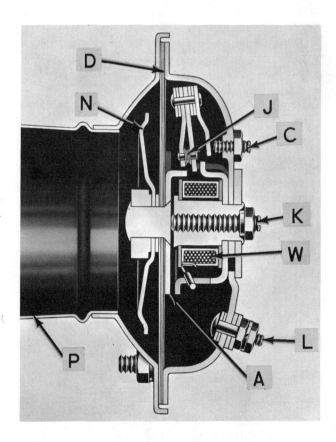

Fig. 36-23. Types HA, HD and HK Autolite electric horn. A—Armature. C—Circuit breaker adjusting screw. D—Diaphragm. J—Contacts. K—Striker screw. L—Horn terminal. N—Ringer disk. P—Projector. W—Winding.

the center staple should be driven into the center of the core to prevent over center arcing.

Positioning Ignition Cable

Care must be taken when replacing high tension ignition cables to install them in their original position. Not only must they be connected to the correct spark plug, but they must also be placed in the correct point in their respective brackets. If this is not done, cross firing will result and maximum power will not be attained.

Basically the wires should be so located in their brackets that the cables for cylinders next in firing order are as far apart as possible. For example: If the firing order is 1-5-4-2-6-3-7-8, the cables for cylinders four and two should be separated as much as possible as cylinder No. 2 fires immediately after cylinder No. 4.

Horns and Warning Signals

Most modern horns consist of a diaphragm, see Figs. 36-22, 36-23, and 36-24, which is vibrated by means of an electromagnet. When the electromagnet is energized, it pulls on an armature that is attached to the diaphragm. Movement of the armature flexes the diaphragm, and opens a set of electrical contacts. As the contacts are in series with the circuit, the current will be turned off and on at a high rate.

The tone and character of the horn signal is largely dependent on the manner in which the movement of the diaphragm is utilized and also on the stiffness of the diaphragm.

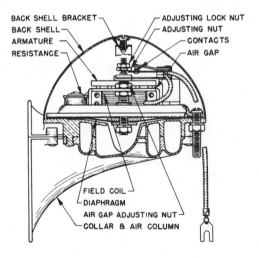

Fig. 36-24. Sectional view of typical horn. (Delco-Remy)

Some types of horns have a resistance connected in series with the magnet winding, Fig. 36-22, or a condenser connected across the horn contacts. As a result, arcing at the points is greatly reduced and point life increased.

The horn should be inspected periodically. Dust and other foreign matter should be wiped from the outside of the horn and projector. If it is rusted or corroded, it should be removed for overhaul. Naturally all mounting bolts and electrical connections should be tight. If the horn is not operating, the fuse and wiring should be inspected. Also if a horn relay is being used, that too should be checked.

To test whether a horn is inoperative, connect a jumper wire from the battery to the horn terminal. If the horn still does not operate, provide a good ground for the horn. If the horn then operates, it indicates that the ground connection is at fault.

Two-wire horns will not operate with only the battery jumper wire in place, but require a second jumper wire connecting the other horn terminal to the ground. If horns operate with these test, trouble will be found in the relay, wiring, or horn button.

The usual cause for continuous operation of the horn is a ground in the wiring leading from the horn button to the horn or horn relay.

Because of the relatively heavy current required to operate a horn, the wire selected for horn circuits should be No. 12 or larger.

Horns that are inoperative or do not have the correct tone, should be removed for inspection after making sure the difficulty is not in the wiring relay or connections.

The diaphragm of the horn, Figs. 36-22, 36-23 and 36-24, must be free of cracks, and not dented or deformed in any manner. Also make sure the resistor and condenser are in good condition.

When inspecting the horn contact points, care must be exercised not to force them apart as that would result in bending the contact spring. Contact points that are rough and pitted should be replaced, or cleaned and polished with crocus cloth, then washed clean with carbon tetrachloride. On some types of horns, replacement of the contacts necessitates replacement of the entire back assembly.

After cleaning or replacing the contact, and other defective parts, the horn is reassembled, but the horn dome and bracket are left off until after the horn is adjusted. All gaskets must be in place and flange screws and circuit breaker mounting screws must be tight. Make sure the nut on the projector side of the diaphragm is tight. To keep resistance to a minimum, all electrical connections within the horn must be soldered.

The adjustment of the armature gap is critical, and must be in accordance with the specifications for that particular make and model of horn. This gap ranges from .025 to .040 in. Rags or other material should not be stuffed into the projector to muffle the sound as this changes the frequency of vibration and also will give a false current reading when checking the current drawn by the horn. Clamping the flange in a vise will alter tension on the diaphragm, affecting its tone, and there is also the possibility of breakage.

Horn Relays

The horn relay is connected into the horn and battery circuit, Fig. 36-25, to make a more direct connection between the horn and the battery. In that way, the voltage drop in the wiring from the horn to battery is eliminated and higher voltage is available for operating.

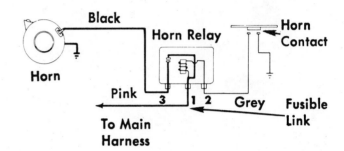

Fig. 36-25. Typical horn and horn relay circuit.

The horn relay consists of a winding on a core above which an armature is placed. The armature is provided with a contact point which meets a stationary contact point.

A typical horn circuit is shown in Fig. 36-25. When the horn button is depressed, the circuit from the battery to the horn relay is completed, and the relay contact points are closed. As shown in the diagram, when the contacts are closed, current direct from the battery is supplied to the horns.

Because of the low price, many mechanics will not attempt to repair a defective horn relay, but will install a new unit. However, there are only three checks and adjustments required: the air gap, point opening, and closing voltage. The air gap and contact point opening checks should be made with the battery disconnected.

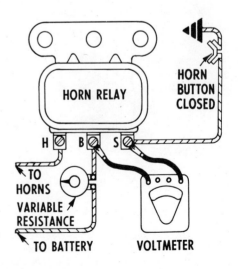

Fig. 36-26. Checking closing voltage of horn relay.

Unless the relay has been misadjusted, the air gap will seldom require adjustment. This air gap varies with different models of Delco-Remy relays and ranges from .015 to .045 in. On Autolite units, the adjustment ranges from .012 to .020 in. The air gap is checked with the contact points just touching and adjustment is usually made by bending the lower point support.

The contact point opening is measured with a thickness gauge, and adjusted by bending the armature upper stop. On Autolite units the contact point gap is usually .026 in., while on Delco-Remy units, the set-ting ranges from .020 to .045 in.

To check the closing voltage of the horn relay, a voltmeter is connected to battery and horn button terminal of the relay. Also a variable resistance of 10 ohms is connected in series between the horn relay and the battery, Fig. 36-26. Then, with the horn button depressed, the resistance is decreased and the voltage noted at which the contacts close. Bending the armature spring post down increases the closing voltage, while bending it up will decrease the voltage at which the contacts close.

Quiz - Lights, Lighting Circuits, Wiring, Horns

1. How much current does a sealed beam lamp on a 12 volt circuit draw?
   a. 8 amps.
   b. 4 amps.
   c. 12 amps.
2. How is the light output of a sealed beam headlight affected by age?
   a. Decreases rapidly.
   b. Not seriously affected.
   c. Improves with age.
3. How are the wires connected to a sealed beam head lamp?
   a. Pull apart, bayonet type connector.
   b. Soldered connections.
   c. Screw type connectors.
4. How many terminals are on the outboard lamp of a dual head lamp system?
   a. Three.
   b. Two.
   c. One.
5. What provision is made on modern sealed beam head lamps to assist in aiming the unit?
6. When aiming a sealed beam head lamp, what does the adjustment at the top of the retaining ring control?
   a. Vertical control of beam.
   b. Swing beam from side to side.
7. In the single wire system of automotive lighting, what is used for the return of the current to the battery?
8. Give two causes of excessive voltage in the lighting circuit.
9. What is the permissible voltage drop between the battery and the lamp?
   a. 12 volts.
   b. 0.6 volts.
   c. 1.0 volts.
10. What is the purpose of the fuse or overload relay in the lighting circuit?
11. The current limit relay has a single winding of very heavy wire. How is it connected in the circuit?
    a. Parallel.
    b. Series.
    c. Shunt.
    d. Series-parallel.

12. What is the purpose of the light relay as used in the head lamp circuit?
13. Which size wire can carry greatest amount of current? No. 16 gauge or No. 4 gauge?
14. What is the purpose of the rheostat used on some types of lighting switches?
15. On cars equipped with hydraulic brakes, where is the stoplight switch usually located?
16. Define the term circular mil.
17. What is the diameter of No. 16 gauge wire?
    a. .0508 in.
    b. .0805 in.
    c. .0160 in.
18. What size cable is commonly used to connect the starting motor?
    a. No. 1 or No. 2.   b. No. 000.   c. No. 36.
19. High tension ignition cables should be placed as close together as possible. True or False?
20. Give a simple test for checking condition of insulation on high tension ignition cable.
21. What is the purpose of ignition resistor cable?
    a. Improve the spark at the spark plugs.
    b. Reduce interference with radio and TV sets.
22. What causes the diaphragm on a modern horn to vibrate?
23. What is the purpose of the condenser in the horn?
    a. Reduce arcing at the contacts.
    b. Reduce the resistance.
24. What is the approximate range of gap of the armature on an electric horn?
    a. .025 to .040 in.
    b. .060 to .075 in.
    c. .005 to .010 in.
25. What is the purpose of the horn relay?
26. Where is the voltmeter connected when checking the closing voltage of a horn relay?
    a. To the battery and horn button contacts of the relay.
    b. To the battery and the horn contact of the relay.
    c. To the horn and the horn button contacts of the relay.
27. How are the automatic headlight doors on Chrysler cars operated?
    a. vacuum motor
    b. electrically

STORAGE BATTERIES

A lead-acid storage battery, such as shown in Fig. 36-27, is provided to supply a source of power for cranking the internal combustion engine. At the same time, it provides the necessary electrical energy for the ignition system. The battery also acts as a stabilizer to the voltage of the automotive electrical system. In addition it can, for a limited time, furnish current when the electrical demands of the vehicle exceed the generator output.

Fig. 36-28. Most modern batteries have covers made of hard insulating material which completely covers cell connectors. Side terminal design is another advance against tendency of battery to corrode.

Fig. 36-27. Typical starting battery, 12V, used for automotive starting and lighting.

The lead-acid storage battery is not a storage tank for electricity, but is an electrochemical device for converting chemical energy into electrical energy. The amount of electrical power in the storage battery is determined by the amount of chemical substances in the battery. When these substances have been used up, they are restored to their original chemical condition by passing an electric current through the battery. This recharging current must pass in the opposite direction to the discharging current.

Each cell of a lead-acid storage battery will produce approximately 2V. For a 6V battery three cells are therefore provided and for a 12V battery there are six cells, Fig. 36-28. In each case the cells are connected in series.

Each cell contains an element which is composed of a negative plate group and a positive plate group, Fig. 36-29. The plate is formed of lattice-like grids

of an alloy of lead and antimony, and the grids are filled with special lead-oxide pastes. These pastes, after processing to make them solid but porous, become the active materials of the battery after it has been charged.

Fig. 36-29. Cutaway section of automotive 12V battery.

452

The amount of current that can be produced by a storage battery is determined by the active area and weight of the materials in the plates, and by the quantity of sulphuric acid in the electrolyte. After most of the available active materials have been activated, the battery can produce little or no current, and is said to be discharged. Before it can provide current again it is necessary to restore the battery plates to their original chemical condition. This is accomplished by passing an electric current, from an external source, through the battery. The charging current must flow through the battery in a direction opposite to the current flow from the battery. This results in a reversal of the discharge chemical reactions in the storage battery, so the chemicals are restored to their original active condition.

The construction of an automotive type lead-acid storage battery, Fig. 36-29, is relatively simple. The positive and negative plates, Fig. 36-30, consist of special active materials contained in cast grids of lead-antimony alloy. These grids are rectangular, flat, lattice-like castings with relatively heavy frames and a mesh of vertical and horizontal wires. The positive plates contain lead peroxide which is chocolate brown color, while the negative plates contain sponge lead which is gray in color.

Each cell of a storage battery is made of alternate positive and negative plates. A plate group is made by welding (lead burning) a number of plates of the same polarity to a plate strap. The plate strap also includes a vertical terminal post, so the cell can be connected to the other cells forming the battery. Plate groups of opposite polarity are interlaced, so that negative and positive plates alternate. Usually negative plate groups contain one more plate than the positive plate group within the same cell. As a result there will be a negative plate on both sides of the plate group. The reason for this is that the chemicals forming the negative plates are not as active as those forming the positive plates. By providing the additional area, the chemical activity of the positive and negative plates are more nearly equalized. Each cell will, therefore, have an uneven number of plates and storage batteries are known as 13, 15, 17, etc., plate batteries. The greater the number of plates, or plate area, the greater the capacity of the cell, and the greater the current that will be available.

To insure against adjacent plates touching each other, separators are placed between them, Figs. 36-29 and 36-30. These separators are made of sheets of porous nonconducting material such as chemically treated wood, porous rubber, resin-impregnated fiber and glass fiber. Separators usually have ribs on one side facing the positive plate. This provides a greater volume of acid next to the positive plate and improves efficiency by increasing acid circulation. Some separators are also designed to aid in the reduction of loss of active material from the positive plate.

Battery separators must be chemically resistant

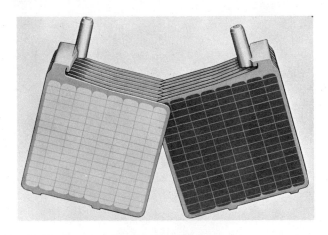

Fig. 36-30. Negative (left) and positive (right), storage battery plates, showing how the plates alternate. Note also the "feet" on the bottom edge of the plates which rest on the element rests formed on the bottom of the battery container. (Willard)

to sulphuric acid, and at the same time be mechanically strong. They must be porous enough to permit free passage of the electrolyte, and at the same time, prevent the active chemicals in the plates from touching each other through expansion.

The group of positive and negative plates are placed in each cell of the battery case. The lower edges of the cell groups rest on ribs or element rests, Fig. 36-29, and the spaces between the bridges are known as sediment chambers, where loosened material from the plates may accumulate without short circuiting the plates.

The battery container or case, in which the groups of plates are held, is of one piece molded type, usually of a hard rubber or bituminous composition. In addition to withstanding the action of sulphuric acid, it must be mechanically strong and not be affected by wide variations in temperature.

With the plates in place in the battery case, cell covers of molded hard rubber or similar material, are fitted over the terminal posts of the plate groups. Vents are provided in the covers, so the cells can be filled with electrolyte and, periodically, with water that has been lost through evaporation. In addition, the vents permit gases to escape.

There are many different types of vent caps. Some of the caps of recent design have materially reduced evaporation of water, so it requires replenishment only at long intervals.

After the covers are installed, the individual cells are connected together in series and finally asphaltic sealing compound is poured around the edges of the covers so that leakage is prevented.

Electrolyte

After the battery is completely assembled, it is filled with the electrolyte. In lead-acid storage batteries this is a fairly concentrated solution of sulphuric acid and water having a specific gravity of

1.290 at 80 deg. F. Specific gravity is the weight of a given volume of a liquid, divided by the weight of an equal volume of water at a temperature of 39.1 deg. F. When an electrolyte has a specific gravity of 1.290 it is 1.290 times as heavy as an equal volume of water, when both liquids are at the same temperature.

The specific gravity of a solution is measured by using a hydrometer, Fig. 36-31. This consists of a glass tube with a bulb syringe for sucking up samples of the electrolyte. Within the glass tube is a calibrated float. The depth to which the float sinks is a measure of the specific gravity of the solution. The float sinks further in solutions having a low specific gravity than it does in solutions having a high specific gravity.

The float is made of glass with a scale and its weight is accurately determined by the manufacturer, so it will indicate the specific gravity of the solution.

As temperature affects the specific gravity of a solution, it is necessary to take the temperature at the same time the specific gravity is taken. The more expensive hydrometers have a built-in thermometer so the temperature can be measured, and the necessary correction made. The temperature correction amounts to about .004 specific gravity for every 10 deg. F. change in temperature. The specific gravity of various percentages of sulphuric acid at various temperatures is shown in Fig. 36-32. Basically for every 10 deg. F. of electrolyte temperature above 80 deg., four gravity points (.004) must be added to the gravity reading. This compensates for the loss of gravity caused by

Fig. 36-31. Battery hydrometer with temperature correction.

Fig. 36-32. Specific gravities of various percentages of sulphuric acid at various temperatures.

Sulphuric Acid %	10	20	30	40	50	60	70	80	90	100	110	120	130
COMPLETELY DISCHARGED													
10.2			1.076	1.074	1.072	1.070	1.068	1.066	1.063	1.060	1.057	1.055	1.052
11.7			1.086	1.084	1.082	1.080	1.078	1.075	1.072	1.070	1.067	1.064	1.061
13.1			1.096	1.094	1.092	1.090	1.088	1.085	1.082	1.079	1.076	1.073	1.070
14.4		1.109	1.107	1.105	1.103	1.100	1.097	1.095	1.092	1.089	1.086	1.083	1.080
15.7		1.120	1.118	1.115	1.113	1.110	1.107	1.104	1.101	1.098	1.096	1.092	1.089
17.1		1.131	1.129	1.126	1.123	1.120	1.117	1.114	1.111	1.108	1.105	1.102	1.099
18.4		1.142	1.139	1.136	1.133	1.130	1.127	1.124	1.120	1.118	1.114	1.111	1.108
19.7	1.156	1.153	1.149	1.146	1.143	1.140	1.137	1.134	1.130	1.127	1.124	1.120	1.117
BARELY OPERATIVE													
21.0	1.166	1.163	1.160	1.156	1.153	1.150	1.147	1.143	1.140	1.137	1.133	1.130	1.127
22.3	1.177	1.173	1.170	1.167	1.163	1.160	1.157	1.153	1.150	1.146	1.143	1.140	1.136
23.5	1.187	1.183	1.180	1.177	1.173	1.170	1.167	1.163	1.159	1.156	1.152	1.148	1.145
ONE FOURTH CHARGED													
24.7	1.198	1.194	1.190	1.187	1.184	1.180	1.176	1.173	1.169	1.165	1.162	1.158	1.154
26.0	1.208	1.204	1.200	1.197	1.194	1.190	1.186	1.183	1.179	1.175	1.171	1.168	1.164
27.2	1.218	1.214	1.211	1.207	1.204	1.200	1.196	1.193	1.189	1.185	1.181	1.177	1.174
28.5	1.228	1.224	1.221	1.217	1.214	1.210	1.206	1.203	1.199	1.195	1.191	1.187	1.183
ONE HALF CHARGED													
29.7	1.238	1.234	1.231	1.227	1.224	1.220	1.216	1.212	1.208	1.204	1.200	1.196	1.193
31.0	1.249	1.246	1.242	1.238	1.234	1.230	1.226	1.222	1.218	1.214	1.210	1.206	1.202
32.2	1.259	1.256	1.252	1.248	1.244	1.240	1.236	1.232	1.228	1.224	1.220	1.216	1.212
THREE FOURTHS CHARGED													
33.3	1.270	1.266	1.262	1.258	1.254	1.250	1.246	1.242	1.238	1.234	1.230	1.226	1.222
34.5	1.280	1.276	1.272	1.268	1.264	1.260	1.256	1.252	1.248	1.244	1.240	1.236	1.232
35.8	1.290	1.286	1.282	1.278	1.274	1.270	1.266	1.262	1.258	1.254	1.250	1.246	1.242
FULLY CHARGED													
37.0	1.300	1.296	1.292	1.288	1.284	1.280	1.276	1.272	1.268	1.264	1.260	1.256	1.252
38.1	1.310	1.306	1.302	1.298	1.294	1.290	1.286	1.282	1.278	1.274	1.270	1.266	1.262
39.2	1.320	1.316	1.312	1.308	1.304	1.300	1.296	1.292	1.288	1.284	1.280	1.276	1.272

the expansion of the solution as its temperature increases. For every 10 deg. of electrolyte temperature below 80 deg., four gravity points must be subtracted from the gravity reading. This compensates for the gain in gravity due to the contraction of the liquid, as its temperature decreases.

Formerly 60 deg. and 70 deg. were used as the basis for measuring the specific gravity of storage battery electrolytes. More recently the American Association of Battery Manufacturers adopted 80 deg. as the standard for such measurements.

Chemical Action

The chemical actions that take place during charging and discharging of a lead-acid storage battery are shown in Fig. 36-33. In a charged condition, the positive plate material is essentially pure lead peroxide, the chemical symbol of which is PbO_2. This is chocolate brown in color. The active material of the negative plate is spongy lead, the chemical symbol being Pb, and is gray in color. The electrolyte is a solution of sulphuric acid, H_2SO_4, and water. The voltage of the cell depends upon the chemical difference between the active materials and slightly upon the concentration of the electrolyte.

When an electric load is connected to the battery, current will flow, and this current is produced by the chemical reactions between the active materials of the two kinds of battery plates and the sulphuric acid. As shown in Fig. 36-33, the oxygen in the PbO_2 combines with the hydrogen, H_2, from the sulphuric acid to form water, H_2O. At the same time the lead, Pb, in the lead peroxide combines with the SO_4, portion of the sulphuric acid to form lead sulphate, $PbSO_4$.

A similar action takes place at the negative plate where the lead, Pb, of the negative active material combines with the SO_4 of the sulphuric acid to form $PbSO_4$, lead sulphate.

While there is an electric load on the battery, lead sulphate is formed on both positive and negative plates in the battery, and the electrolyte becomes diluted with water.

As the discharge continues, the accumulation of lead sulphate in the plates, and the dilution of the electrolyte brings the chemical reactions to a halt. At low rates of discharge (small current), the reactions are more complete than at high rates, as more time is available for the materials to come into contact. When the chemical action can no longer take place, the battery is said to be discharged.

During charge, the chemical reactions are basically the reverse of those which occur during discharge. The $PbSO_4$, lead sulphate, on both plates is split up into Pb and SO_4, Fig. 36-33, while the water H_2O is split into hydrogen, H, and oxygen, O_2. The passage of the charging current, which is in the reverse direction to the discharging current, forces the SO_4 from the plates and combines with the H_2 to form H_2SO_4, sul-

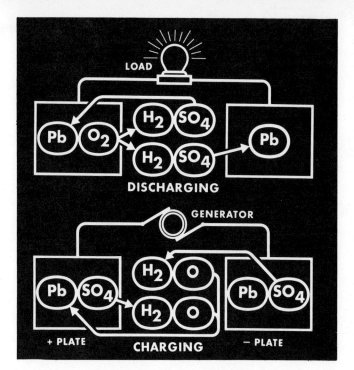

Fig. 36-33. Chemical action in a lead storage battery.

phuric acid. At the same time the oxygen O_2, enters into chemical combination with the lead at the positive plate to form PbO_2.

The specific gravity of the electrolyte decreases during discharge for two reasons. Not only is the sulphuric acid used up, but new water is formed. As the water is formed at the positive plates and diffuses slowly through the electrolyte, the positive plates are more likely to be damaged during freezing weather. When the battery is fully charged, the specific gravity of the solution increases, sulphuric acid is formed, and water is used up. As a result there is little danger of a fully charged battery freezing.

Specific gravity of the electrolyte may continue to rise for some time after a battery has been quick charged, as the newly formed acid requires time to diffuse from the plates to the electrolyte. Specific gravity readings taken while a battery is gassing will be erroneously low.

Voltage Variations

Battery voltage and specific gravity vary while the battery is being charged and it is important that these be checked. Starting batteries are designed to maintain a definite relationship between charging voltage and charging rate and any variation from standard conditions will result in unsatisfactory battery service.

The relationship between charging voltage and charging rate in a battery in various states of charge is shown in Fig. 36-34. From the chart it will be noted that as the specific gravity increases, the charging voltage must be increased if the same charging current is to be maintained.

The charging voltage is determined entirely by the battery until the charging voltage reaches the limit as

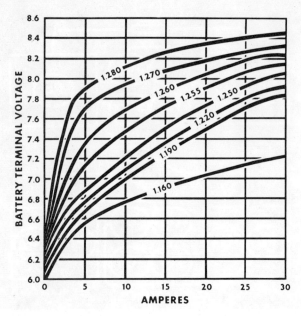

Fig. 36-34. Voltage variation with different battery conditions and charging rates. (6V system.)

set by the setting of the voltage regulator. Another point, shown by Fig. 36-34, is that the charging rate is reduced gradually if the charging voltage is limited. Whenever the charging voltage reaches the limit for which the regulator is adjusted, the voltage regulator operates to limit the voltage to that value. But as the battery comes up to charge, increased voltage is required to maintain the charging current at the same value. As additional voltage is no longer available, the charging current decreases, and in that way adjusts itself to the gradual change in the state of charge. For example, in a battery having a specific gravity of 1.220 and a charging voltage of 7.2, the battery will charge at approximately 12 amp., Fig. 36-34. When the specific gravity has increased to 1.250, the charging current will have dropped to 10 amp. and at 1.255 the charging current will be approximately 6 amp.

From Fig. 36-34, it can also be noted how a small change in charging voltage will greatly increase the charging current. For example, on a 1.250 battery increasing the voltage regulator setting from 7.2 to 7.5 will increase the charging current from 10 to 15 amp. A high final charging rate will often ruin a battery.

A battery in normal use tends to operate at lower and lower voltages for a given charging current. Batteries which have not been used for a long period, tend to operate at higher voltages for a given charging rate. Such batteries usually become discharged very quickly when placed in service. The maximum allowable setting of the regulator can be ineffective on such batteries as they tend to heat excessively when charged at higher rates. It is advisable to charge such batteries at a very low rate until there is no further increase in specific gravity readings.

Battery Voltage and Capacity

The open circuit voltage of a fully charged storage battery cell is 2.1 volt for acid of approximately 1.280 sp. gr. That is true regardless of the number of plates in the cell or their area. The voltage is determined only by the character of the chemicals in the plates and the specific gravity of the electrolyte. A 6V battery will therefore be made up of three cells, Fig. 36-27, connected in series and a 12V battery, Fig. 36-28, will consist of six cells.

The capacity, that is the amount of current it will deliver, depends on the number and area of the plates in the cell and also on the amount of acid present. In other words, cells having a large number of plates will deliver more current than cells having a smaller number. Automotive starting batteries are built with thin plates to provide maximum plate area in order that the electrolyte may have quick access to as much active plate area as possible.

Battery capacity drops rapidly as the temperature is reduced. The reason for this is that the battery is an electrochemical device and, as is the case with virtually all chemical actions, it is aided by heat. For example, as shown in Fig. 36-35, if the capacity of cranking power of a battery at 80 deg. is given as 100 percent, at 32 deg., the capacity will be only 65 percent and at 0 deg., only 40 percent.

Battery Ratings

There are two ratings for automotive starting and lighting batteries which have been incorporated in the standards of the Society of Automotive Engineers, the Association of American Battery Manufacturers and the United States Government.

The 20 hour rating in ampere hours indicates the lighting ability of the battery. The fully charged battery is brought to a temperature of 80 deg. F. and is then discharged at a rate equal to 1/20 of the published 20 hour capacity in ampere hours. For example, a battery rated by the manufacturer as a 6V 100 A. H. capacity would be discharged at 1.20 of 100 or 5 amp., until the voltage has dropped to 5.25 volts. The number of hours required for the discharge, multiplied by the rate of 5 amp., is its 20 hour rating, Fig. 36-36.

Cold Rating at 0 deg. F.: All 6 and 12V batteries of 80 ampere hours capacity and more, are discharged

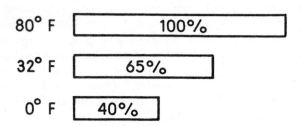

Fig. 36-35. Comparing the cranking power of a fully charged battery at different temperatures.

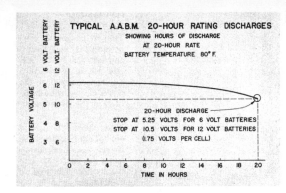

Fig. 36-36. Twenty hour rating discharges.

at 300 amperes, while 12V batteries of less than 80 ampere hours capacity are discharged at 150 amperes at a temperature of 0 deg. F.

These ratings indicate the cranking ability of a fully charged battery at low temperatures, and are expressed in two ways:

1. By the terminal voltage of a fully charged battery taken 5 seconds after the start of a discharge rate as indicated above with an electrolyte temperature of 0 deg. F.

2. By the number of minutes required for the battery to reach a terminal voltage equivalent to 1.0 volt per cell when discharged at the rate indicated above with an electrolyte temperature of 0 deg. F. at the start, Fig. 36-37.

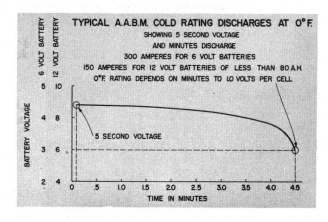

Fig. 36-37. Cold rating discharge test.

Battery Testing

There are several methods used to test the condition of a storage battery. In general, these include the measurement of the specific gravity by means of a hydrometer, Figs. 36-31 and 36-40, as previously described; measurement of cell voltage, Fig. 36-39; measurement of cell voltage during high discharge, Fig. 36-38.

Checking the condition of a battery with a hydrometer should not be done immediately after water has been added to bring the electrolyte to the desired level. Such measurements should be made before the

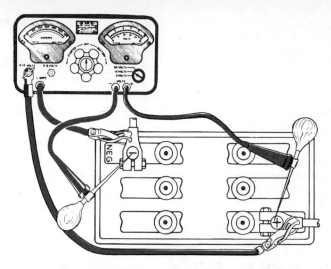

Fig. 36-38. High rate discharge connections.

Fig. 36-39. A voltmeter with 0.01 volt divisions is needed to make an open circuit test.

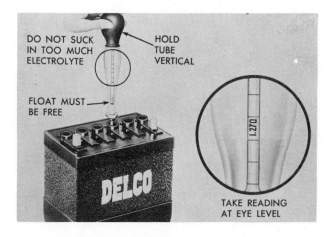

Fig. 36-40. Example of hydrometer being used to measure the specific gravity of the acid solution in a starting battery.

water is added, in order to obtain a representative sample. If the level is too low to obtain a sample, water should be added as needed, and then after the battery has been operated for a sufficient time to thoroughly mix the water with the electrolyte, the sample should be taken with the hydrometer.

Hydrometer readings should not be taken while the battery is gassing, as this would affect the accuracy of the reading.

As previously pointed out, when checking the specific gravity of a cell, it is also necessary to check the temperature of the electrolyte and make the necessary correction.

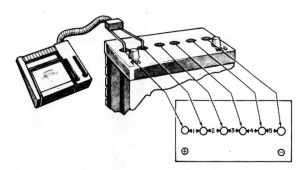

Fig. 36-40a. Checking a battery with a cadmium tester.

There are many different types of equipment available for making a high rate discharge test. The instructions accompanying the equipment should be followed. See Figs. 36-38 and 36-41. In general, such equipment operates on the principle of connecting a low resistance across each cell for about 30 seconds and measuring the voltage at the same time. Cells in good condition should give approximately 2V, although this will vary with different equipment. There should be less than 0.2V variation between cells.

Fig. 36-41. Hand type high rate discharge tester used for checking one cell at a time, on batteries with exposed cell connectors.

The light load battery test is claimed to be simpler and more conclusive than the hydrometer test. A voltmeter, having 0.01V divisions is needed, Fig. 36-39. The procedure is to place a load on the battery for 3 seconds by closing the starter switch. If engine starts, turn off ignition. Turn head lamps on (low beam), with lights still on, measure voltage of each cell. If any cell reads 1.95 volts or more and the difference be-

tween the highest and lowest cell is less than .05 volts, the battery is good. If any cell reads 1.95 volts or more, but there is a difference of 0.05 volts or more between the highest and lowest cell, the battery should be replaced.

If all cells read less than 1.95 volts, battery is too low to test. Recharge battery and repeat test. After testing, close openings in sealing compound made by prongs of tester.

Cadmium Test

Batteries with one piece hard covers cannot be checked by testing the voltage of the individual cells, as the cover cannot be pierced by the test prods. However, the individual cells of such batteries can be tested by means of a hydrometer or the complete battery can be tested under load, which requires a starter battery tester with a carbon pile rheostat. In addition, a new method known as the cadmium or cad-tip method has been devised which permits testing the individual cells.

The principle on which this tester operates is simple. The prod tips are one inch long cadmium tubes which contain an absorbent material which serves to keep the cadmium moist. When inserted into adjacent filler holes in the battery, the prods contact the electrolyte and carry electrical impulses to the voltmeter which is graduated to show the efficiency of the cell being tested.

If the readings of any two cells vary five scale divisions or more, the battery is at or near the point of failure.

Battery Water

Water for use in automotive batteries may be a good grade of drinking water, excluding mineral water. It is advisable to use distilled water, or other water that is free from impurities.

Check batteries that require excessive water, as this is usually an indication that the charging rate is too high.

Checking Cable Resistance

Battery cable and terminal connections may be tested with equipment comprising a voltmeter (5V maximum), ammeter of 300 or more capacity, and a carbon pile rheostat having a minimum capacity of 300 amp. connected in series with the ammeter.

Connections are as shown in Fig. 36-42, in which the ammeter and rheostat are connected in series within the case. Connect ammeter positive lead to battery terminal stud on junction block. Connect the negative lead to one side of the rheostat, and the other side of the rheostat to a ground on the engine. Attach the voltmeter leads to probes. Attach one voltmeter probe to terminal stud on junction block, and the other to the center of positive battery post. Adjust rheostat until ammeter reads 200 amp. Voltage drop should not exceed 0.2V. Repeat the test with the voltmeter connected to the ground and to the negative terminal of the battery. Reading should not exceed 0.2V. Be sure to turn off rheostat between each test.

Battery Charging

Only direct current can be used for charging batteries, and some method must be provided for controlling the amount of charging current. Before placing a battery on charge, the exterior of the battery and the terminals must be cleaned. In addition, the electrolyte must be brought up to the desired level. When charging batteries, the positive lead from the charger is connected to the positive terminal of the battery, and the negative lead from the charger is connected to the negative terminal of the battery. It is extremely important that the connections be correctly made; otherwise the battery will be ruined. If several batteries are to be charged at the same time and connected in series, the positive terminal of one battery should be connected to the negative terminal of the next battery. The positive terminal of the end battery of the series is then connected to the positive terminal of the charger, and the negative terminal of the series of batteries is connected to the negative terminal of the charger.

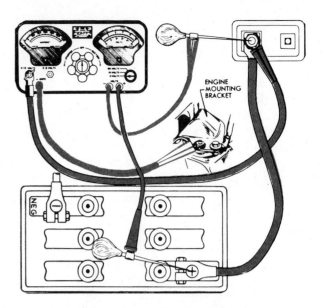

Fig. 36-42. Battery cable test connections.

The terminals of storage batteries are marked so they can be easily distinguished. The positive terminal is usually marked with a "P," "Pos," or "+." Negative terminals are marked "N," "Neg," or "-." In addition, the positive terminal of the battery is larger in diameter than the negative terminal. In case the markings have been erased, the polarity can be determined by dipping leads from the battery in a weak solution

Storage Battery Testing Chart

HYDROMETER TEST 80 DEG. F.	CONDITION	REMEDY
More than 1,300 Sp. Gr.	Specific Gravity too high	Adjust Specific Gravity
1.250 to 1.295	Probably Good	If variation among cells is less than 0.015 Sp. Gr., no correction is required. If greater than that amount, give high rate discharge test. If cells test O.K., recharge and adjust specific gravity of cells.
1.225 to 1.250	Fair	Battery should be recharged. Check operation of voltage regulator. Also check electrical system for loose connections, shorts, grounds and corroded terminals.
Less than 1.225	Poor	Recharge battery. Check voltage regulator, also electrical system for loose connections, shorts, grounds and corroded terminals.
Cells show more than .025 variation in Sp. Gr.	1. Short in low cell 2. Loss of electrolyte 3. Cracked cell partition	Recharge battery at approximately 7 amp. until gravity readings show no increase in three successive readings taken 1 hour apart. Adjust specific gravity of cell. Make a high rate discharge test 12 hours after charging. If more than 0.15V difference is shown on cell, battery is no longer serviceable.

of sulphuric acid. More gas bubbles will collect around the negative lead than around the positive. The same procedure can be used to determine the polarity of the charger.

Most commercial electricity is of the alternating type. In such cases it is, of course, necessary to convert the alternating current to direct, before it can be used for battery charging purposes. The usual methods used in converting alternating to direct current are motor-generators, tungar bulb rectifiers, and dry disk-type rectifiers.

Vent plugs on batteries with nonoverfill devices should be screwed tightly in place during charge.

To check the progress of the charge, hydrometer readings should be taken every hour. The battery is fully charged when the cells are gassing freely, and there is no increase in hydrometer reading for three successive hourly readings. Excessive charging will damage the battery, particularly the positive plates. Depending on the charging rate, most batteries can be charged in 12 to 16 hours. Batteries with sulphated plates will require a longer period.

Fig. 36-43. This battery charger provides six different charging rates and can be used for either six or twelve volt batteries.

Fig. 36-44. This charger can be moved to the car, and is electrically timed to turn off the charge at proper moment.

The constant current method of charging batteries is one method that is used extensively. That method is particularly advantageous where the condition of the battery is not known.

The charging rate varies with different conditions; however, a safe rate would be equal to 1/2 of the number of plates in the cell. For example, the charging current in amperes for a 13 plate cell would be 6 1/2 amp., for a 17 plate cell, 8 1/2 amp. When several batteries of different sizes are connected in series for charging, the charging current is determined by the size of the smallest battery in the series.

During charge, the temperature of batteries should be watched carefully. Should the temperature approach 125 deg. F., the charging rate should be reduced.

Many storage batteries are fitted with filler plugs of the nonoverfill type. In such cases, the electrolyte may be forced from the cell during charge when the vent plugs have been removed, so that a hydrometer reading can be taken. This tendency can be overcome by placing a small stick in the vent hole so that the nonoverfill device is held in the open position while taking hydrometer readings.

Constant Potential chargers, as the name implies, maintain the same voltage on the batteries throughout the period of the charge. As a result, the current is automatically reduced as the battery approaches full charge. Batteries in good condition will not be damaged by this method of charging. However, a badly sulphated battery may not come up to charge when the Constant Potential method is used. With this method of charging, battery temperature may rise rapidly, and it is important that frequent checks be made of the temperature.

High Rate Battery charging is a relatively new method. Prior to 1945 only low charging rates were advocated as it was believed that high rates would damage the battery plates. However, by using a high rate charger, batteries can be charged in approximately 30 minutes. As a result, the method has become popular as it permits charging the battery while the customer waits. In addition it has reduced or eliminated the necessity of a shop having on hand a number of batteries which may be rented to the car owner, while his original battery is being charged.

High charging rates can be used provided the tem-

Fig. 36-45. *One type of trickle charger designed particularly for the car owner. Other types are available for maintaining stocks of batteries in good condition.*

perature of the electrolyte does not exceed 125 deg. F., and does not cause excessive gassing and loss of electrolyte. In the case of export batteries, being made "wet" from the dry state, the maximum temperature should not exceed 110 deg. F.

Most high rate battery chargers, Figs. 36-43 and 36-44, are of the Constant Potential type and are designed to provide an initial charging rate of 40 to 70 amp. Some types of high rate chargers are equipped with a time cut-off or temperature limiting device, so that electrolyte temperature cannot exceed 125 deg. F. In other words, should the temperature reach 125 deg. F., the charger is shut off automatically.

Trickle chargers, Fig. 36-45, are designed to charge batteries at a rate of approximately 1 amp. They are used primarily for maintaining display and stocks of batteries in a fully charged condition. While the charging rate is extremely low, batteries can be damaged if left on a trickle charge for long periods. Common practice is to leave the batteries on a trickle charge during the day and take them off charge during the night. In that way danger of severe overcharging is eliminated.

Battery Repairing

Because of high costs of labor and parts, automotive storage batteries are today seldom repaired. Instead, the defective unit is replaced with a new battery. A battery in normal service and properly cared for will usually give satisfactory performance for 12 to 24 months; although it is not unusual for a battery to operate for even longer periods.

However, under some unusual conditions it may be necessary to disassemble a battery for examination to determine the cause of the failure. A battery in which the water level was not maintained is shown in Fig. 36-46.

Before opening a battery it is important to mark on the battery case the position of the positive and negative terminals. In addition, factory code markings should be recorded. Specific gravity readings of the individual cells should also be recorded for future reference.

If the battery case is cracked, or if the three cells are to be removed as a unit, the sealing compound is cut from the container walls with a hot putty knife. The three elements are then lifted from the case. Element shims should be kept with the elements to insure a snug fit when the cells are reinstalled.

To remove a single element, the cell connectors are cut with a hacksaw. Lead will tend to clog the teeth of the saw, but this can be prevented by first running the teeth of the saw through some sealing compound. The sealing compound, surrounding the cell, is then cut with a hot putty knife, permitting the cell to be pulled from the container.

Dry Charged Batteries

A dry charged starting battery contains no electrolyte until it is placed in service. The cell elements are given an initial charge on special equipment at the factory. They are then thoroughly washed and dried and assembled into battery cases.

A dry charged battery will retain its full charge indefinitely as long as moisture does not enter the cells. When ready for service, the electrolyte (shipped in individual plastic containers) is poured into each cell and the battery is ready for use.

Fig. 36-46. *This battery was ruined because the level of the electrolyte was not maintained.*

When filling a dry charged battery with electrolyte, the manufacturers advise that protective glasses be worn. The procedure is to remove the vent plugs and discard the white restrictors found in the vent openings. With the electrolyte container right side up, remove the lid, then unfold the top of the plastic bag which contains the electrolyte. Do not attempt to remove the plastic bag from the carton. The bag is sealed to the container, and any attempt to remove the bag may rupture it and spill the acid. Cut a small opening in a corner of the double-walled bag. A large opening will cause the acid to spatter. Using a glass or acid-proof funnel fill each battery cell with electrolyte as shown in Fig. 36-47. The cell is correctly filled to the split ring at the bottom of the vent well. After filling cells, wait five minutes, then if level has fallen, add electrolyte to bring to proper level.

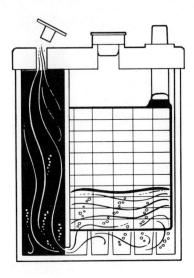

Fig. 36-48. In water-activated battery, water passing through acid-treated foam blocks (left) becomes electrolyte and activates plates (right).

Fig. 36-47. Filling a dry charged battery with electrolyte.

Water Activation

After a dry-charged battery has been activated with acid, it often requires a boost charge to meet industry standards. To combat this, several manufacturing techniques have been employed and several temporary sealing methods have been used to keep moisture from entering the dry-charged battery plates while the battery is in storage.

Recently, a sealed dry-charged, lead-acid battery has been developed that stores concentrated sulfuric acid in phenolic foam blocks apart from the battery plates. When the seals are broken and clear water is added, the battery can be placed in service immediately after activation. The need for a boost charge is minimized.

The new water-activated battery, Fig. 36-48, has six cells with higher plates that are closer together than those in conventional batteries. However, since the water-activated battery has a series of foam blocks alongside of, but separated from, the plates in each cell, the plates necessarily are narrower.

The foam blocks are treated with concentrated sulfuric acid and have vertical holes to aid in water distribution when the battery is activated. The water percolates through the foam blocks, diluting and mixing with the concentrated acid as it flows. The mixture of water and acid enters the plate area through slots in the partition at the base of the battery. The electrolyte formed rises over the plates, causing their activation.

The container and cover of the water-activated battery are made of fiberglass reinforced polyethylene, said to have high resistance to impact and vibration, particularly at low temperatures. The sealing feature of this battery involves sealing discs manufactured into both the vent and initial fill openings. When the battery is to be activated, the installer breaks the seals, activates all cells with water and then he permanently installs the initial fill caps. Future service is by way of the vent caps and openings.

Three-Piece Construction

Another recent breakthrough in battery manufacturing techniques is a three-piece battery design that contrasts sharply with conventional, two-piece box and top construction. This battery features straight-through the partition inter-cell connectors and heat-sealing of the elements (plates, separators and partitions) to the bottom of the sleeve and element rests of the reservoir to withstand vibration.

The battery is assembled in three basic pieces. The sleeve is injection molded with the inter-cell connectors as an integral part. Plates are automatically stacked into cells and loaded into the sleeve from the bottom as a single unit. The cell unit is then heat-sealed into the reservoir, keeping the plates, separators and partitions in register and imbedded into the bottom of the sleeve and element rests in 300 places.

Next the inter-cell connectors, plate straps and plates are welded together simultaneously and the top is heat-sealed on. Finally, post-burning torches automatically fuse the posts to the stub posts to a specific height. Throughout assembly, several vacuum and pressure leakage tests are made to guarantee against inter-cell leakage.

The three-piece battery has a polypropylene casing, and a polypropylene element protector is built in the sleeve mold to protect the plates from accidental damage by probes of testing instruments. In comparing the impact resistance of polypropylene against hard rubber, tests by the manufacturer at 0 deg. F. showed that the polypropylene casing is three times stronger. At 75 deg. F., polypropylene is said to be about 100 times as strong as hard rubber.

New Sodium Battery

With further development, the new Ford sodium-sulphur battery may play an important part in transportation of the future. This new battery can produce 15 times as much power as the familiar lead-acid battery of the same weight and which has so successfully provided power for starting, lighting and ignition for the present day automobile.

In the new Ford unit, positive sodium ions (1), Fig. 36-49, pass through the electrolyte to form sodium sulphide (2). Sodium electrons, which cannot get through, are channeled into the circuit, becoming the current (3). The electrons pass from the negative terminal through the motor (or other load) to the positive terminal, then into sodium sulphide (4), where they attract more positive sodium ions through the electrode. To charge the battery, the current is reversed.

The chemical process to charge and discharge is actually less complicated than that of the lead-acid battery which is described elsewhere in this text.

Unfortunately, there is no information available as to the performance that can be expected from this new sodium battery, but a 36 volt, 600 amp. lead-acid battery, such as is used in industrial trucks, weighs 1500 lb. A sodium-sulphur battery of the same capacity would therefore weigh one-fifteenth as much or 100 lb. From a power standpoint, the lead-acid battery has available 21,600 watts, or 29.0 hp. If a sodium battery of the same weight can provide 15 times as much power or 435 hp, that is a lot of power, but it must be remembered that an internal combustion engine of the same power weighs only about 500 lb.

While the major advantages of the new battery are high energy output and relatively inexpensive materials in construction, there are severe disadvantages, chief of which is high operating temperature. This means that while the car is in the garage, the battery would have to be heated to 800 deg. F. This results from the ceramic electrolyte which permits only sodium ions to flow through it and nothing else, but only as long as it is heated to 800 deg. F.

In that connection, it must be remembered that many chemicals and fuels of ignition temperatures less than that amount, are stored in the average garage. For example, the ignition temperature of benzene is only 780 deg. F. and acetylene 760 to 820 deg. F. Fire underwriters would probably view the new battery as a fire hazard and insurance rates would therefore be high.

Other batteries in the development stage include a General Motors unit using silver and zinc as reactants, and another using zinc and air which is being developed by General Dynamics Corporation.

A lithium-chlorine fuel cell, designed to convert chemical energy into electric energy is also under development by a General Motors division. At present, electrical propulsion by fuel cells is technically feasible, but size, weight and cost must be radically improved to make it practical for vehicles according to a General Motors spokesman.

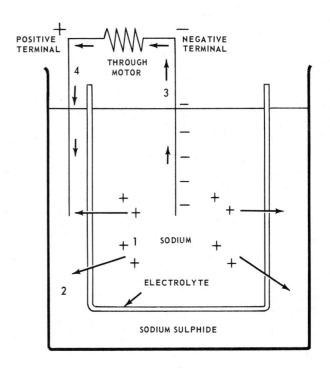

Fig. 36-49. The new Ford sodium-sulphur battery.

Electric Vehicles

In a Corvair converted to an experimental electric powered vehicle, using silver-zinc batteries, the car's range between charges is 40 to 80 miles, compared to 250 to 300 miles for a tank of gas. Weight of the power train of the electric powered vehicle is 1,230 lb. compared to 610 lb. for the conventional Corvair.

In a Corvair powered with the silver-zinc battery the performance was approximately the same as that of a conventional Corvair, but the battery was worn out after 100 recharges. It is also of interest that the silver-zinc powered vehicle weighed about 800 lb.

more than the gasoline powered Corvair. If the car were to be propelled by conventional lead-acid batteries, the batteries would weigh more than 2600 lb., which happens to be the approximate weight of a standard Corvair.

Quiz - Storage Batteries

1. What is a lead-acid storage battery?
   a. A storage place for electricity.
   b. A converter of chemical energy to electrical energy.
2. How much voltage can be obtained from a single cell of a storage battery?
   a. About 2 volts.
   b. About 6 volts.
   c. About 12 volts.
   d. Varies with size of plates.
3. What factors control the amount of current that can be produced by a single cell of a storage battery?
4. What is used to fill the positive plate grids of a storage battery?
   a. Lead peroxide.
   b. Sponge lead.
   c. Antimony oxide.
   d. Sulphuric acid.
5. Name three materials used to make plate separators in a storage battery.
6. What is the specific gravity of the electrolyte used to fill lead storage batteries?
   a. 1.290.
   b. 1.920.
   c. 1.450.
7. What instrument is used to measure the specific gravity of a liquid?
   a. Hygrometer.
   b. Barometer.
   c. Hydrometer.
   d. Gravometer.
8. The specific gravity reading of a storage battery is 1.290 at 90 deg. F. What is the correct specific gravity?
9. While a storage battery is discharging, what chemicals are formed from the lead peroxide and the sulphuric acid?
10. On a partly charged battery, the voltage-regulator setting is increased from 7.2 to 7.5 volts. How does that affect the charging current?
    a. Has no affect on charging current.
    b. Charging current increases.
    c. Charging current decreases.

11. How many cells in a 12 volt storage battery?
12. As the temperature drops, does a storage battery have more or less cranking power?
13. When making a high rate discharge test of a storage battery, what is the permissible voltage variation between cells?
    a. 0.2 volts.
    b. 0.02 volts.
    c. 0.6 volts.
14. When making a light load battery test, what is the permissible voltage variation between cells?
    a. 0.05 volts.
    b. 0.15 volts.
    c. 0.20 volts.
15. When charging a battery, to which terminal of the battery is the positive lead of the charger connected?
    a. Positive terminal.
    b. Negative terminal.
    c. Either terminal.
16. If the positive terminal of a battery is not otherwise marked, how can it be recognized?
17. What would be the normal safe rate for charging a 13 plate battery?
    a. 6 1/2 ampere.
    b. 13 ampere.
    c. 1.3 ampere.
18. When charging a battery by the high rate method, what is considered as being a safe temperature which should not be exceeded?
    a. 212 deg.   c. 80 deg.
    b. 125 deg.
19. When are trickle chargers used?
20. What is meant by a dry charged battery?
21. If the acid-treated foam blocks in a water-activated battery are separated from the plates, how does the electrolyte enter the plate area during activation?
22. During assembly of the new three-piece construction battery, the plates are loaded into the sleeve from the bottom so that all of the elements remain in register while the bottom of the sleeve is heat-sealed on.
    True or False?

SPEEDOMETERS

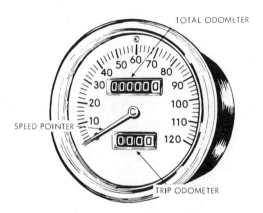

Fig. 36-50. *Typical speedometer with total and trip odometer.*

The speedometer used on automotive vehicles indicates the speed of the vehicle and also records the distance traveled.

A speedometer, as shown in Fig. 36-50, is driven by a flexible shaft, Fig. 36-51, connected with gearing within the transmission, or occasionally from the front wheel, Fig. 36-52.

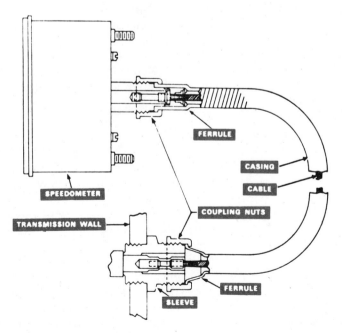

Fig. 36-51. *Details of speedometer drive from transmission.*

Speedometers are calibrated in miles per hour or in kilometers. When the instrument also records the distance traveled, this will be recorded in either miles or kilometers and that portion of the instrument is known as the odometer, Figs. 36-50 and 36-53. Most odometers record the total distance traveled, while some also record the distance of individual trips and therefore can be reset to zero when desired, Fig. 36-50.

To measure the speed of the vehicle and register the distance traveled requires a separate series of parts.

Fig. 36-52. *Method of driving speedometer from front wheel.*

Internal components of different makes and types of speedometers vary in appearance. The parts of a typical speedometer made by the AC Spark Plug Division of General Motors Corporation, is shown in Fig. 36-53.

Operation of a Speedometer

The speedometer and odometer are driven by a cable housed in a casing as shown in Fig. 36-51.

The cable is connected to a take-off gear at the

transmission or front wheel. This gear is designed for the particular vehicle model and takes into consideration the tire size and rear axle ratio. In most cases on transmission take-off, the speedometer is designed to convert 1,001 revolutions of the drive cable into a registration of one mile on the odometer. In other words, 1,001 cable revolutions in a minute, will result in a speed indication of 60 mph.

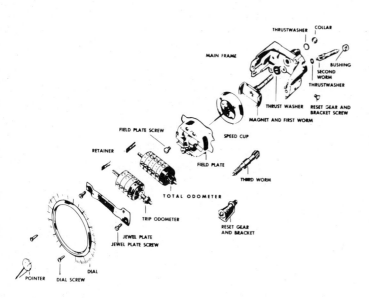

Fig. 36-53. Exploded view of typical speedometer made by AC Spark Plug Division of General Motors Corp.

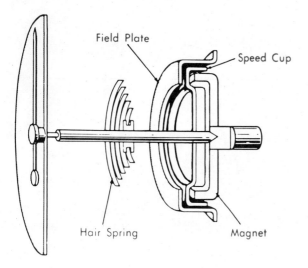

Fig. 36-54. Schematic drawing of speedometer showing speed cup, magnet, field plate, hairspring and pointer with dial.

Speed Indication

The speed indication of a speedometer or tachometer operates on the magnetic principle and includes a revolving permanent magnet which is driven by the cable connected to the transmission. Around this permanent magnet is a stationary field plate. Between the

magnet and field plate is a nonmagnetic movable speed cup on a spindle. The magnet revolves within the speed cup, Fig. 36-54.

The revolving magnet sets up a rotating magnetic field which exerts a pull on the speed cup making it revolve in the same direction. The movement of the speed cup is retarded and held steady by a hairspring attached to the speed cup spindle. The speed cup comes to rest at a point where the magnetic drag is just balanced by the retarding force created by the hairspring. An additional function of the hairspring is to pull the pointer of the instrument back to zero when the magnet stops rotating. There is no mechanical connection between the revolving magnet and the speed cup. As the speed of the magnet increases due to the movement of the vehicle, the magnet drag on the speed cup also increases and pulls the speed cup further around and in that way indicating a faster speed by the pointer on the face of the dial.

The magnetic field is constant and the amount of movement of the speed cup is at all times directly proportional to the speed at which the magnet is being rotated.

Temperature affect on the magnet is compensated by means of a special compensating alloy attached to the magnet.

These operating instructions apply to all magnetically driven speedometers including disk and indicating cylinder types.

Odometer Operation

Both trip and total odometers are driven through a series of gears originating from a special gear on the end of the first gear and magnet shaft, Fig. 36-55.

The total odometer usually has five figure wheels and a dummy wheel. The trip odometer has three figure wheels and a decimal wheel.

Both odometers are so constructed that when any wheel completes one revolution, it turns the wheel on the left 1/10 of a revolution.

The trip odometer mileage can be reset as desired by means of a reset mechanism and a special trip drive sleeve.

Resetting the Odometer

Note and record indicated mileage on the odometer. Note position and alignment of projecting ears of pinion carriers. Remove the odometer.

Hold the first odometer wheel on the extreme right (dummy or tenth wheel) between right-hand thumb and index finger.

With the left-hand index finger, rotate counterclockwise the first (to the left of dummy or tenth wheel) metal separator with slotted projection (pinion carriers).

Continue rotating the first carrier counterclockwise (looking at dummy wheel side of odometer assem-

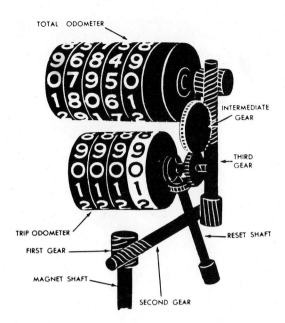

Fig. 36-55. Gear train of typical speedometer from magnet shaft to odometers.

bly) until the second figure wheel indicates the desired figure when in the odometer window opening.

Shift right-hand thumb and index finger to hold and keep in alignment the first figure wheel, the first pinion carrier and the second figure wheel.

With the left-hand index finger, rotate the second pinion counterclockwise until the third figure wheel indicates the desired figure when in the odometer window.

Proceed working from right to left until each figure wheel is in its desired position. Then reinstall the odometer in the instrument.

Inspection and Lubrication

TEST FOR TIGHT MECHANISM: Insert test cable and turn, Fig. 36-56. No binding or tightness should be felt. The test cable is a short length of conventional speedometer drive cable which is used to turn the mechanism of the speedometer by hand, Fig. 36-56. An initial fast spin of the test cable should swing the pointer of the instrument from zero to about half scale. From half scale the pointer should quickly return to zero. This indicates that the hairspring and magnet are in good working order. The same basic test also applies to the drum or indicator cylinder type of speedometer. The indicator cylinder should advance to at least 30 mph position and quickly return to zero.

TEST FOR CALIBRATION: Providing the instrument mechanism turns freely, place unit in test stand and run at various speeds. Compare readings of speedometer and test stand pointer movement.

Operate the speedometer in test stand and note the amount of noise. The noise level should be low enough not to be objectionable. Operate speedometer long

enough to record several miles. All figure wheels should be lined up evenly, except those wheels which may be operating.

If excessive grease was present in the speedometer head, the cable and casing should be cleaned.

Some speedometers are provided with a lubrication felt or wick. In such cases the wick should be saturated with special speedometer oil every 10,000 miles. Speedometer cables should be lubricated every 10,000 miles. To lubricate, disconnect cable at the instrument and draw cable from the casing. Coat the cable with special lubricant and replace. Coating should be light and not excessive.

Speedometer Trouble Shooting

Most difficulties encountered in the operation of speedometers usually originate in the drive cable. The cable may be broken, kinked, frayed or in need of lubrication. If the speedometer pointer wavers or fluctuates, the difficulty may be caused by either a kinked cable or the trouble may be in the speedometer head. The kinked cable rubs in its housing and winds up, slowing down the pointer. The cable then unwinds suddenly and the pointer jumps.

To check a cable for kinks, remove it from the casing and lay it on a flat surface. Then twist or rotate one end of the cable with the fingers. If the cable turns over smoothly it is not kinked. But if part of the cable turns over suddenly, it is kinked and should be replaced. As a comparison check, make the same test with a new cable.

Another method of testing a cable for kinks is to hold each end in your hands with the cable looped down in front of you. Then rotate the ends of the cable slowly with your fingers. If the cable is kinked it will "flop" and not turn smoothly.

Cables should be carefully inspected for fraying and wear. Cable fraying indicates excessively sharp

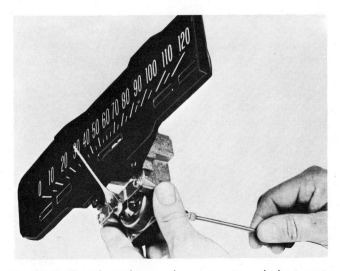

Fig. 36-56. Test for tightness of operation is made by inserting short length of cable in meter to spin the mechanism.

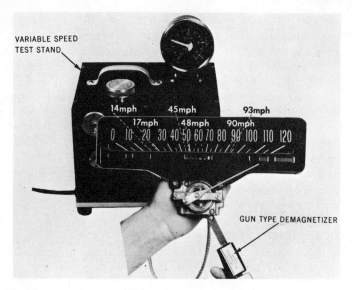

Fig. 36-57. One type of speedometer test stand with gun type demagnetizer.

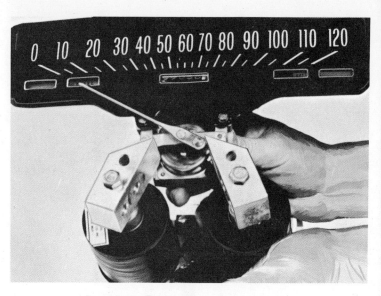

Fig. 36-58. Equipment used to magnetize the magnets of speedometer.

turns or a defective casing. If necessary, replace cable and casing assembly, and relocate and eliminate sharp turns.

Visually check cable tips for straightness. A cable that feels like a wet noodle should be replaced.

POINTER FLUCTUATES: May be caused by: Defective cable or casing. Worn or dirty spindle bearings. Excessive end play in magnet shaft. Dirt or grease on magnet or speed cup. Speed cup assembly rusted at spindle ends. Worn main frame magnet shaft bearing. Magnet shaft side play should not exceed .003 in. Bent speed cup spindle. Field plate not positioned correctly. Worn first, second, or third gears.

POINTER DOES NOT RETURN TO ZERO: May be caused by: Weak, broken or improperly adjusted hairspring. Pointer improperly set. Front jewel too tight. Dirt or grease in mechanism.

INCORRECT SPEED INDICATION: May be caused by: Dirty or grease-filled mechanism. Out of calibration. Out of balance pointer. Pointer balance may be checked by turning speedometer clockwise to different positions while it is running at a set speed. Indicated speed variation means that the pointer or speed cup is out of balance.

INCORRECT SPEED OVER HALF OF SCALE: May be caused by: Hairspring coils touching. Field plate eccentric with speed cup. Indicator drum out of balance.

EXCESSIVE NOISE: May be caused by: Too much end play in magnet shaft. Worn frame bearings. Worn gears.

INOPERATIVE ODOMETER: May be caused by: First gear stripped. Excessive end play in second gear. Second and third gears stripped, warped or worn. Damaged or binding idler gears.

ODOMETER READINGS INCORRECT: May be caused by: Worn second or third worm gears. Wrong transmission drive gear. Wrong tire size.

Calibrating the Speedometer

Calibration of a speedometer is the operation of mechanically balancing the torque of the magnet with the hairspring so that it checks with a test stand at least at three points on its dial scale, Fig. 36-57.

A speedometer test stand includes a method of rotating the speedometer at specified rates of speed. Also included, is a method of recharging the magnets and a demagnetizer, Fig. 36-58. As instructions for the operation and use of a test stand accompany the equipment, the procedure will not be included in this text.

Speedometer Cable Replacement

Speedometer cables break as the result of age, lack of lubrication, or because the cable casing has been installed so that it has sharp bends which results in excessive bending and flexing of the cable as it is revolved. In such cases the clamps holding the casing in position should be relocated so as to eliminate the sharp bends. When such bends are found in the casing, it may be necessary to replace same, which because of rough spots in the interior of the casing would tend to cause binding, friction and rapid wear of the cable.

Another cause of frequent breakage of the speedometer cable is excessive friction in the speedometer head. The test for such a condition has been described in a previous paragraph.

Replacement cables can be secured with both end tips in place or in kit form. In the latter case it is necessary to cut the cable to the desired length and attach the tip in place.

If a "tailor-made" cable is to be installed, the casing should be disconnected from the speedometer head, and the old cable withdrawn from the casing. If the old cable is broken, it will also be necessary to disconnect the casing at the transmission end so that the other section of the broken cable can be removed.

After withdrawing the old cable, spread a thin coat of speedometer cable grease evenly over the lower two-thirds of the new cable. Do not apply grease to the entire cable as that would result in the lubricant working up the cable and into the speedometer head and causing damage. After applying the lubricant to the cable, insert the cable into the upper end of the casing, lower end first. This will spread the grease evenly over the entire length of the cable.

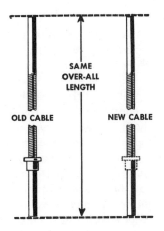

Fig. 36-59. New cable must have the same overall length as the original cable.

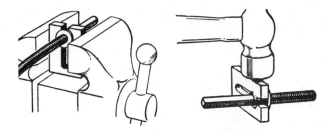

Fig. 36-60. Flexible speedometer cable can be staked to the tip by using the staking tool as shown.

Connect the upper end of the casing to the speedometer case, making sure that the cable tip engages correctly in the speedometer drive member. Tighten the ferrule nut. Then twist the lower end of the cable with your fingers to make sure it turns freely. A sharp twist of the cable should cause the speedometer needle to register. Finally, connect the lower end of the casing to the transmission, making sure that the cable engages in the speedometer driven gear.

When a cable kit is being used as a replacement,

the procedure is as follows: First cut the new cable the same length as that of the old cable, Fig. 36-59. Be sure to include the length of the tip which is to be staked on the cut end of the cable. Fit the new tip of correct shape to the cut end of the cable. Place the tip in the staking tool and squeeze the tool in the jaws of a vise or strike it a sharp blow with a hammer, Fig. 36-60. Finally, check the new cable for length against the original cable so as to be sure that the overall length is the same.

Quiz - Speedometers

1. How is the modern speedometer driven?
2. The modern speedometer shows only the speed of the vehicle. True or False?
3. On what principle does the speed indicating portion of the speedometer operate?
   a. Electronic.
   b. Mechanical.
   c. Magnetic.
   d. Electrical.
4. What means is used to control the pull on the speed cup?
   a. Hairspring.
   b. Mechanical brake.
   c. Magnetic brake.
5. Describe the operation of a speedometer.
6. What does an odometer record?
7. How is the odometer driven?
8. How many revolutions of the drive cable will register one mile on the meter?
   a. 101 revolutions.
   b. 1,001 revolutions.
   c. 3.77 revolutions.
   d. 4.01 revolutions.
9. Where do most troubles in a speedometer originate?
10. Describe the procedure for checking a speedometer cable for kinks.
11. Describe a method of checking a speedometer to see if there is any bind present.
12. What is the usual result of excessive friction in the speed cup bearing?
    a. Speedometer indicates higher than normal speed.
    b. Speedometer indicates lower than normal speed.
    c. Incorrect odometer readings.
13. Give two common causes why a speedometer cable becomes frayed.
14. Will excessive end play in the magnet shaft cause the speedometer pointer to fluctuate? Yes or No?

SPEED CONTROL
SYSTEMS

FORD AUTOMATIC SPEED CONTROL

The speed control system used on 1972 model Fords includes on OFF-ON switch, SET-ACC and COAST switches, servo (throttle actuator) assembly, speed sensor, amplifer assembly and the necessary wiring, linkage and vacuum connections. The switches are located in the steering wheel spokes. The amplifier assembly and speed sensor are located under the instrument panel. The servo assembly (throttle actuator) is attached to the dash panel under the hood on the Ford, Mercury and Meteor, and to the engine intake manifold on Thunderbird, Lincoln Continental and Continental Mark IV.

To operate the speed control system, the engine must be running and the vehicle speed between 30 and 80 mph. Manifold vacuum is constantly supplied when the engine is running. When the ON/OFF switch

in the steering wheel is actuated to the ON position, the system is made ready to accept a set speed signal.

Testing Ford Speed Control: A visual inspection is an important part of the system test. Check all items for abnormal conditions such as frayed wires and damaged vacuum lines. For the speed control to operate correctly it is necessary for the speedometer cables to be properly routed and securely attached to the components. Similarly all vacuum hoses must be securely attached and routed with no sharp bends or kinks. The servo (throttle actuator) and throttle linkage must operate freely and smoothly. The bead chain should have no more than 1/4 in. free play. Electrical connections must be complete and tight. The wiring harness must be properly routed. Look for frayed insulation, loose connections and shorts. Any problems revealed by visual inspection should be corrected before making any further tests.

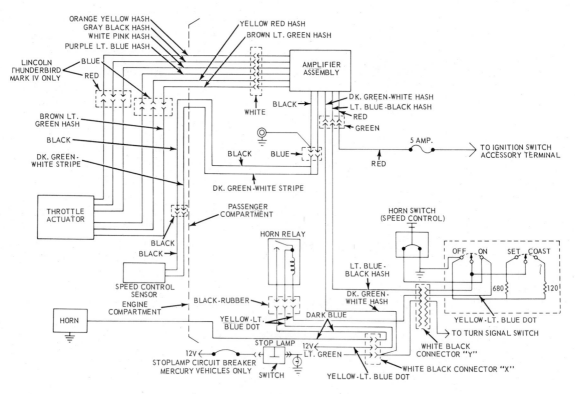

Fig. 36-61. Speed control system installed on 1972 Ford cars.

Control Switches Test: Disconnect the green connector going to the amplifier from the control switches. Then, check the lead (Lt. Blue-Black Hash) from the control switch as follows: Check for battery voltage at the lead (Lt. Blue-Black Hash) when the ON switch is depressed. Battery voltage should be available at the lead (Lt. Blue-Black Hash) coming from the control switches, Fig. 36-61.

Connect an ohmmeter between the Lt. Blue-Black Hash wire and ground. Check wire for continuity to ground when the OFF switch is depressed. If a resistance is found, the wiring slip rings or switch is probably at fault. Rotate the steering wheel back and forth and tilt the column up and down (if so equipped). If change in resistance is noted, clean the horn brush contacts and the ground brush. A good resistance must be obtained before making the remaing tests. Next, with an ohmmeter connected between the Lt. Blue-Black Hash wire and the ground, depress the set-speed switch. A reading of approximately 680 ohms should be indicated. With the ohmmeter still connected depress the coast switch. A reading of approximately 120 ohms should be indicated.

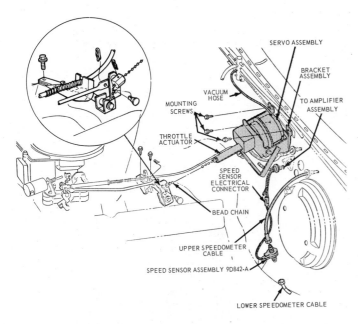

Fig. 36-62. Speed control sensor and servo assembly as installed on Ford Meteor and Mercury cars.

Speed Sensor Test: Disconnect the speed sensor wires from the amplifier assembly and connect an ohmmeter between the wire connector terminals (Dk. Green-White stripe and Black) at the speed sensor end. A reading of approximately 400 ohms should be obtained. A reading of zero ohms indicates a shorted coil and a maximum reading indicates an open coil. In either case replace the coil. If the ohmmeter records 400 ohms and the speedometer operates correctly within needle waver, the speed sensor is probably good. A speed sensor of known good quality can also be substituted to check for proper operation.

Servo-Assembly Test: Disconnect the ball chain from the carburetor. Separate the servo to amplifier connector. Connect an ohmmeter between the orange and gray wire leads at the servo connector. A resistance of approximately 85 ohms should be obtained. Connect the ohmmeter between the orange and white wires. A resistance of approximately 85 ohms should be obtained. Start the engine. With the servo disconnected from the amplifier, connect the orange lead

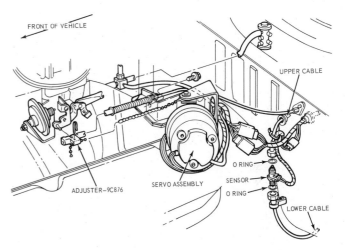

Fig. 36-63. Speed control sensor and servo assembly as installed on Lincoln Continental. Also typical of Thunderbird and Continental Mark IV.

of the servo to the battery positive terminal. Connect the white lead of the servo to the ground, and momentarily touch the gray lead of the servo to the ground. The servo throttle actuator should tighten the bead chain and open the throttle. The throttle should hold in that position or slowly release the tension on the chain. When the white wire is removed from the ground, the servo should immediately release the bead chain tension. Replace the servo if it fails to meet any of these tests. If the orange lead is shorted to either the white or gray leads, it may be necessary to replace the amplifier.

Amplifier Test: Do not use a test lamp to perform the following tests as excessive current draw will damage electronic components inside the amplifier. Use only a voltmeter of 5000 ohms/volt rating or higher.

ON Circuit Test: Turn on ignition switch and connect a voltmeter to the lead (Lt. Blue-Black Hash) at the amplifier (middle terminal) of green connector. The voltmeter should read 12 volts when the ON switch on the steering wheel is depressed and held. If voltage is not available, check the horn relay circuit and control switch test. Release the ON button; 12 volts should remain at the blue wire indicating the ON circuit is engaged. If the voltage does not remain, check for ground on the amplifier, fuse and/or circuit breaker and/or hang in a known good amplifier and recheck for a good ON ground.

OFF Circuit Test: With the ignition circuit on and the voltmeter connected to the Lt. Blue-Black Hash wire, depress the OFF switch on the steering wheel. Voltmeter on the blue wire should drop to zero indicating the ON circuit is deenergized. If the voltage does not drop to zero, perform the control switch test. If the switches check OK, hang in a known good amplifier and recheck the OFF circuit.

Linkage Adjustments: Adjust the bead chain to obtain 0.06 to 0.25 in. actuator arm free travel when the engine is at hot idle, Fig. 36-62 and Fig. 36-63. The adjustment should be made to take as much slack out of the bead chain as possible without restricting the carburetor lever from returning to idle. The tighter the bead chain the better the speed control system will perform. On vehicles equipped with a solenoid anti-diesel valve, be sure to perform this adjustment with the ignition switch in the ON position.

AC CRUISE MASTER CRUISE CONTROL

The speed control mechanism, produced by the AC Spark Plug division of General Motors Corporation, is generally known as the Cruise Master and is installed on many of the General Motors automobiles.

The major components of the Cruise Master are:
1. Push Button Control Switch Assembly. Mounted on the end of the turn signal handle.
2. Speed Transducer. Mounted at any convenient point in the speedometer cable line.
3. Power Unit. Mounted under the hood.
4. Cruise Release Brake Switch. Mounted on brake pedal bracket.
5. Cruise Release Brake Valve (vacuum). Mounted on brake pedal bracket.
6. Cable and Casing Assembly. Transducer to speedometer.

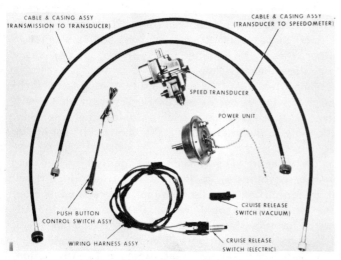

Fig. 36-65. Illustrating major components of Cruise Master System, as developed by the AC Spark Plug Div. of General Motors Corp.

The push button control switch assembly, Fig. 36-65, is used to engage the system and to adjust the speed downward.

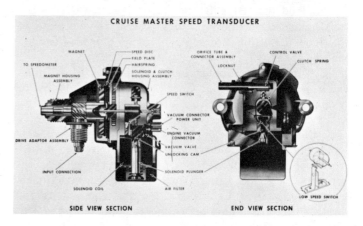

Fig. 36-66. Side and end views of Cruise Master Speed Transducer.

The speed transducer, Fig. 36-66, is a combination speed sensing device and control unit. When engaged it senses the underspeed or overspeed conditions and immediately activates the power unit to corrective throttle changes so that the set speed may be maintained.

The power unit, Fig. 36-67, is connected by bead chain to the carburetor throttle and is controlled by the speed transducer.

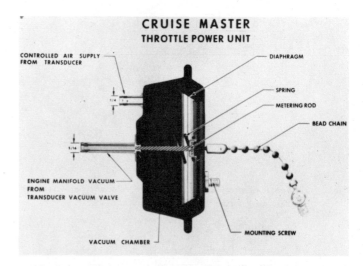

Fig. 36-67. Details of Cruise Master Throttle Power unit.

The cruise release brake switch, Fig. 36-68, is an electric switch which engages the system electrically when the brake pedal is pressed.

Cruise release brake valve is a vacuum valve which disengages system pneumatically when brake pedal is depressed and is an additional safety feature.

The cable and casing assemblies, Fig. 36-65, drive the transducer.

Operation of the System

When the operator pushes in the engage button partially, Fig. 36-68, the electric circuit in the transducer solenoid is completed through pin 1 and 3, Fig. 36-68, thus energizing the solenoid and engaging the cruise mechanism. When the button is released, it returns to its normal position and the electric circuit to the solenoid is completed through pin 1 and 2. The resistor R_1 reduces the current flow to a lower value so that the coil will not become overheated, but will maintain the solenoid in the engaged position.

When the button is pushed in fully and held (such as downward adjustment in "Operation") there is no connection between 1 and 2, or 1 and 3. Thus the system is de-energized. However, when the button is released, the electrical connection is first made between 1 and 3, and later through 1 and 2 which holds the system as previously described.

Energization of the transducer solenoid, Fig. 36-66, positions an unlocking cam which allows the clutch spring of valve, wire and spring assembly to grasp the rubber clutch fixed to the speed cup spindle assembly.

Theoretically, this behaves in the same manner as a speedometer pointer, that is, it moves either clockwise or counterclockwise according to the magnetic effect of the rotating magnet. This motion of the valve, wire and spring assembly changes the size of the openings in the orifice tube. The size of the window openings in its static condition is adjustable, Fig. 36-66. Simultaneously, operation of the transducer solenoid positions the vacuum valve within the transducer, connecting the engine vacuum directly to the power unit.

At the moment of engagement, engine vacuum is applied to the power unit diaphragm chamber through the metering rod aperture. Also at the same time, "air" enters through the transducer filter, passes through the preset window openings in the orifice tube and into the power unit. The balance of these two forces provide for initial throttle positioning.

Should the car approach an upgrade there would be a tendency for speed reduction. The cruise master keeps this at a minimum. When speed reduction occurs, the valve, wire and spring assembly moves in the direction which makes the window openings smaller, reducing the amount of air to the power unit thereby increasing the vacuum level in the power unit. This draws in the diaphragm and increasing the throttle angle via the connecting bead chain.

Conversely, if the car goes downgrade, there is a tendency to exceed the set speed. In this case, the valve moves in the direction which increases the size of the window openings. This admits a larger volume of air to the power unit, reducing the vacuum level and

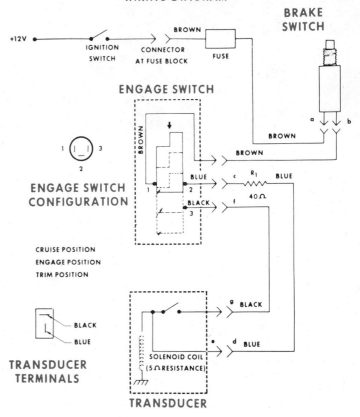

CRUISE MASTER
WIRING DIAGRAM

Fig. 36-68. Wiring diagram of Cruise Master.

in turn allowing the diaphragm to move out and reduce the throttle angle.

Both overspeed and underspeed tendencies are immediately corrected since a 3 mph speed change will result in a change in the size of the window openings capable of moving the power unit through its complete range.

Cruise Control Service

When making an electrical check out of the AC Cruise Control, Fig. 36-68, first check fuse and all connections.

To check the electric brake switch, connect an ohmmeter at points A and B on the brake switch. The meter should indicate infinity when the brake pedal is depressed and continuity when the pedal is released. The cruise release brake switch (electrical) is adjusted identically to the stoplight brake switch.

Check engage switch and connecting wiring as follows: Unplug button control connector (brown, blue and black wire) at electrical wiring harness connector and make the following tests. Connect ohmmeter between terminal No. 1 (brown wire) and terminal No. 2 (blue wire). Continuity shall be maintained until switch is depressed all the way. Then connect ohmmeter between terminal No. 1 (brown wire) and terminal No. 3

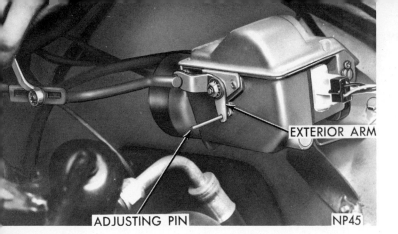

Fig. 36-69. Adjusting accelerator linkage on Plymouth Auto Pilot.

(black wire). No continuity should be shown. However, when button is depressed half-way, continuity should be indicated. When button is depressed all the way, no continuity should be shown.

To check the transducer solenoid coil, low speed switch, and wiring harness, Fig. 36-68, disconnect push button wire harness connector from main wire harness connector (brown, blue and black wires). Connect ohmmeter between point "C" (blue wire in main harness) and ground. The ohmmeter should read 45 ohms plus or minus 2 ohms.

If the resistance is greater than specified, check resistance of blue wire from C to D, which should be 40 ohms and resistance from point E to ground which should be 5 ohms. Replace either the wiring harness or solenoid if resistance is greater than specified. Also check black wire from F to G for continuity.

To determine the condition of the diaphragm, remove hoses from power unit and apply 14 in. of vacuum to either the vacuum tube opening (seal the other opening) and hold for one minute. The vacuum should not leak down more than 5 in. in one minute. If leak is detected replace the power unit.

GENERAL SERVICE: Clean transducer air filter in kerosene solvent and wet with SAE 10 oil at regular engine oil change intervals.

Adjust bead chain so that when the carburetor is on slow idle cam position, a slight amount of slack is present in bead chain.

Check vacuum hoses for kinking and signs of deterioration. Replace as needed.

If after doing the preceding service operations the car cruises under engagement speed, turn the orifice tube outward. If the car cruises at over the engagement speed, turn the orifice tube inward. Each 1/8 in. turn will change the car speed 1 mph. Test should be made at a speed of 50 mph.

Trouble Shooting

Cruise Master Will Not Engage: Trouble may be caused by blown fuse, defective engage switch, vacuum leak in power unit and/or brake switch and connecting lines, open in wiring harness, defective transducer.

Does Not Cruise At Engagement Speed: Trouble may be caused by incorrectly adjusted orifice tube.

System Hunts Or Pulses: Trouble may be caused by bead chain loose, kinked or deteriorated hoses, dirty air filter, defective and/or improperly positioned drive cables and/or casing assemblies.

System Does Not Disengage With Brake Pedal: Trouble may be caused by misadjusted or defective brake and/or vacuum switch.

System Applied Full Throttle When Engaged: Trouble may be caused by hoses interchanged at power unit.

Cannot Adjust Speed Downward With Engage Button: Trouble may be caused by defective engage switch or wiring.

Does Not Engage Or Engages At Lower Limits: May be caused by maladjusted transducer.

CHRYSLER-PLYMOUTH AUTO PILOT

The Auto Pilot, as installed on Plymouth automobiles, is a driver operated voluntary speed control device which can be used either as a warning signal to indicate that a preset speed has been reached, or as an automatic vehicle speed regulator.

The Auto Pilot instrument panel is used to set the Auto Pilot to the desired speed for existing driving conditions. When the preset speed is reached, the Auto Pilot provides a reaction pressure to the accelerator pedal pressure. Since the reaction pressure is low, five to seven pounds, the driver can override the setting by pressing the accelerator through the reaction pressure.

Operation of Speed Minder

Rotate thumb wheel control on the instrument panel to the desired speed indicated on the edge of the wheel and move the button from "OFF" to "ON" position. When the vehicle speed indicated on the thumb wheel is reached, reaction pressure is felt in the accelerator pedal. This reaction pressure may be relieved by moving the Auto Pilot button to the "OFF" position, or by turning the thumb wheel to maximum speed setting.

Automatic Speed Control

With the thumb wheel set to the desired speed, move the button to the "AUTO" position and release. The button will spring back to "ON" position and the panel light will be illuminated. When the vehicle speed indicated on the edge of the thumb wheel is reached, a reaction pressure will be felt in the accelerator pedal. The Auto Pilot is now in automatic control. No further control of the accelerator pedal is required. The Auto Pilot will automatically advance the acceleration for up hill operation and retard acceleration on down hill runs. Auto Pilot automatic control cancels instantly with the slightest brake pedal movement. Control of the vehicle then reverts to manual control. Disengagement of automatic control may also be accomplished by moving either the panel button to the "OFF" position or by turning off the ignition key.

Tests and Adjustments

Before attempting to adjust the accelerator linkage, the carburetor should be at the curb idle position with the choke fully open.

Operate the linkage by moving Auto Pilot exterior arm several times, Fig. 36-69, allowing the linkage to ease into normal position. Do not force linkage to close throttle.

Loosen locknut on Auto Pilot linkage rod and insert 1/8 in. diameter by 2 in. long gauge rod through hole in exterior arm and into hole in auto pilot housing. Then hold exterior arm and tighten locknut.

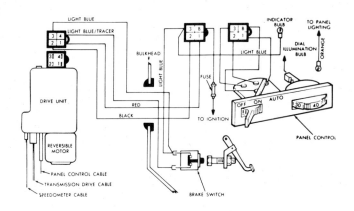

Fig. 36-70. Wiring diagram of Auto Pilot.

Electrical Tests

Turn ignition switch to accessory position, but do not start engine. Move control switch to "OFF" position. Touch one lead of 12V test lamp to terminal No. 1 (red wire) and second lead to a good ground, Fig. 36-70. If lamp fails to light, test for open circuit in red wire between Auto Pilot and ignition circuit.

Move control switch to "ON" position. Touch one lead of 12V test lamp to terminal No. 2 (black wire) and the other lead to a good ground. If test lamp fails to light, test for open circuit in black wire between Auto Pilot and ignition circuit.

Move control switch to "AUTO" position. Panel light should light and switch spring back to "ON," when switch is released.

Touch test lamp to a good ground and the other lead first to terminal No. 2, (black wire) and then to terminal No. 3. If lamp fails to light on No. 2 terminal, test for open circuit in black wire between Auto Pilot and ignition circuit. If test lamp fails to light

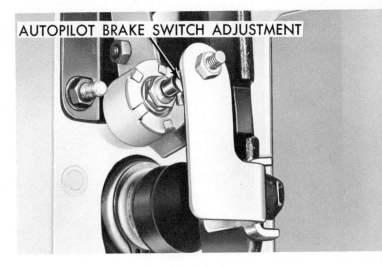

AUTOPILOT BRAKE SWITCH ADJUSTMENT

Fig. 36-71. Showing location of Auto Pilot brake switch adjustment.

when terminal No. 3 is touched, test for open circuit in light blue wire circuit from Auto Pilot to control switch.

If panel light on Auto Pilot control fails to light, check the light bulb.

Terminal No. 4 (light blue wire) is checked by grounding one lead of test lamp while the other lead is touched to terminal No. 4. If test lamp fails to light, test for open connection in light blue wire between Auto Pilot and Auto Pilot brake switch, Fig. 36-70. If circuit is open at brake switch, check switch adjustment. This adjustment must be accurately made. Adjust brake switch, Fig. 36-71, so that test lamp goes out with approximately 1/4 to 1/2 in. brake pedal movement.

Thumb Wheel Dial Adjustment

The Thumb Wheel is spring-loaded and may be adjusted without removal of the assembly from the instrument panel as follows: If speed is less than thumb wheel setting, rotate thumb wheel to extreme low speed end and slip the wheel (by increasing pressure in the same direction) the necessary amount to correct the calibration. Rotate the thumb wheel to the other extreme end for speeds higher than setting.

Quiz - Speed Control Systems

1. In the Ford speed control system where are the amplifier and sensor located?
   Under the instrument panel
   Under the hood
   On the steering column
2. For the Ford speed control system to be operating at what speed must the vehicle be traveling with the engine running?
   Less than 25 mph
   More than 80 mph

Between 30 and 80 mph

3. What free play should the bead chain have in the Ford Speed control system?
1/2 in.
1/4 to 1/2 in..
No more than 1/4 in.

4. The AC Cruise Master is found on what makes of vehicles?
a. Chrysler.
b. American Motors.
c. General Motors.
d. Ford.

5. In the Cruise Master Control System where is the transducer located?
a. At the end of the turn signal lever.
b. At any convenient point in the speedometer cable.
c. On the instrument panel.

6. The push button control switch in the Cruise Master System is designed to:
a. Adjust the speed downward.
b. Adjust the speed upward.

7. In the Cruise Master System the bead chain connects the carburetor throttle to what part of the system?
a. Power unit.
b. Push button control switch.
c. Cruise release brake switch.

8. The Plymouth Auto Pilot can be used either as a speed warning signal or an automatic vehicle speed regulator? True or False?

9. The Thumb Wheel on the Auto Pilot can be adjusted without removal from the instrument panel. True or False?

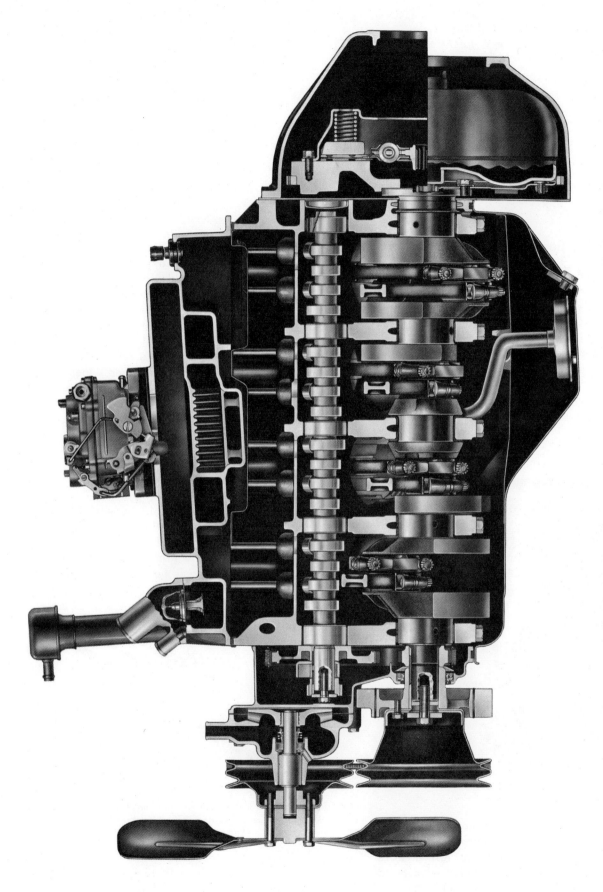

AMX 390 cu. in. V-8 has forged steel crankshaft and connecting rods, five main bearings, hydraulic valve lifters, and intake runner passages designed for high airflow efficiency. AMX car with 390 and automatic transmission accelerated from 0 to 60 mph in 6.5 sec. in quarter mile.

WINDSHIELD WIPERS, WASHERS

Vacuum Operated Wipers

Vacuum operated windshield wipers, Fig. 36-72, depend on the vacuum in the intake manifold for power. The device consists essentially of a piston within a cylinder. By means of valves, controlled by the position of the piston, first one end of the cylinder is connected to the intake manifold and then the other. In that way, the piston is moved back and forth within the cylinder. Movement of the piston causes the operating shaft to oscillate, which in turn swings the windshield wiper blade back and forth across the face of the windshield.

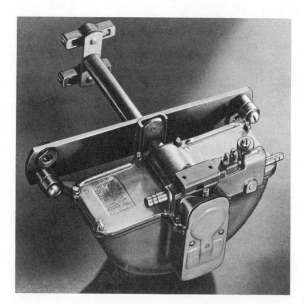

Fig. 36-72. Trico vacuum windshield wiper motor, with built-in control valve for operating windshield washer.

As explained in the section on carburetion and fundamentals of engine, intake manifold vacuum is maximum at idling speed and zero at full throttle operation. As a result, vacuum operated windshield wipers will not operate when the carburetor throttle is wide open. To overcome this difficulty, a vacuum

pump is incorporated in the fuel pump (see Fuel Pumps) so that there will always be vacuum available for operation of the windshield wiper.

Originally cars were only equipped with a single windshield wiper, Fig. 36-73. This was placed in front of the driver. In order to increase visibility and widen the range of vision, an additional wiper is placed on the opposite side of the windshield. This second wiper blade was at first operated by another wiper motor. More recently, both wiper blades are operated by a single motor with suitable linkage, Fig. 36-74, so that the wiper blades on both right and left sides of the windshield are synchronized.

Trouble Shooting on Vacuum Windshield Wipers

Failure of vacuum windshield wipers is usually caused by leaks or stoppage in the vacuum line. Leaks can usually be found by careful examination of the vacuum line and its connections, while stoppage can be located by blowing through the line with compressed air.

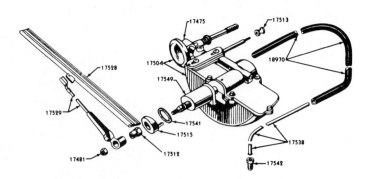

Fig. 36-73. Vacuum windshield wiper motor. Tubing for connecting to intake manifold is shown at 18970. Windshield wiper arm 17529, and wiper blade 17528.

If the motor itself is defective, it is usually replaced with a new unit, rather than repaired. Sluggish operation will occasionally be encountered on old units.

In such cases improved operation can be secured by disconnecting the vacuum line at the manifold and immersing the line in light machine oil. Then by moving the wiper blade back and forth across the windshield, oil will be drawn into the motor providing lubrication.

On twin windshield wipers, trouble may also be encountered in the transmission and link assemblies. The difficulty is usually the result of wear and in such cases the usual practice is to replace the worn parts. Adjustments are provided on some installations and in such cases, the adjustment should be checked.

Electric Windshield Wipers

Electric windshield wipers are usually operated by shunt or compound wound motors, Figs. 36-75 and 36-76. Both single and two-speed electric wipers are

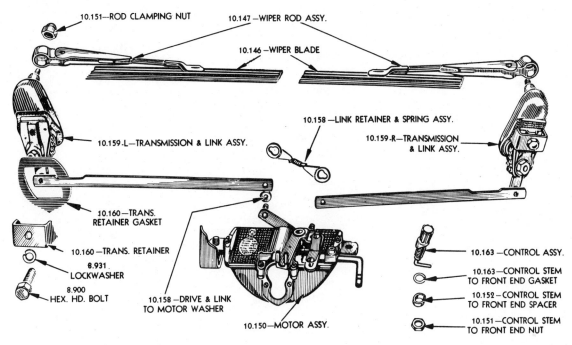

Fig. 36-74. Dual windshield wiper, showing motor, transmission and link assembly, wiper rod and wiper blades.

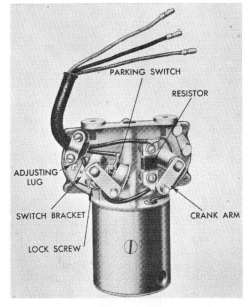

Fig. 36-75. Autolite windshield wiper motor provided with a parking switch and a special circuit that provides for a fixed parking position. Reciprocating motion is implied by the linkage between the cranks and the wiper arm pivots.

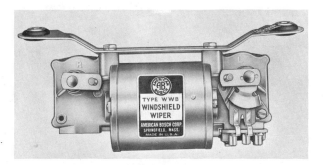

Fig. 36-76. American Bosch electric windshield wiper motor.

available. An exploded view of an Autolite electric windshield wiper is shown in Fig. 36-77.

In order that any electric windshield wiper may operate satisfactorily, it is essential that the motor, linkage and drive pivots operate freely, otherwise the operation of the assembly may be noisy or complete failure will result.

Fig. 36-78, illustrates the wiring diagram of an Autolite double-crank arm wiper. Two speeds are provided. At low speed the motor has full field current,

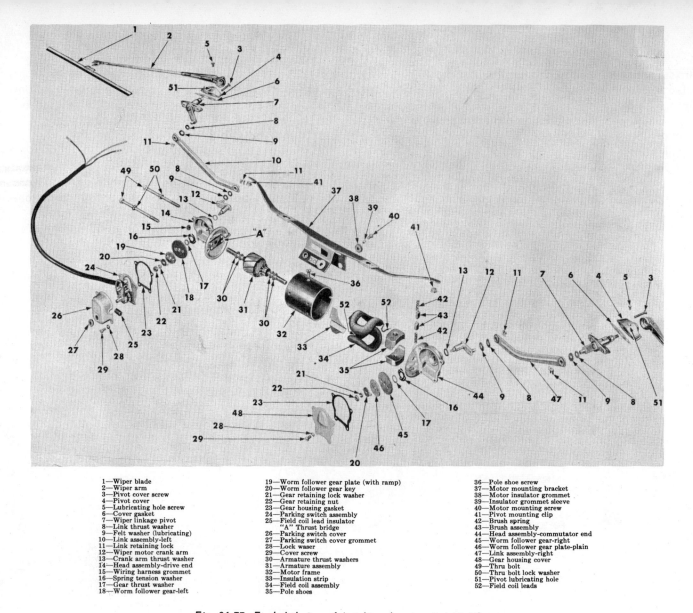

1—Wiper blade	19—Worm follower gear plate (with ramp)	36—Pole shoe screw
2—Wiper arm	20—Worm follower gear key	37—Motor mounting bracket
3—Pivot cover screw	21—Gear retaining lock washer	38—Motor insulator grommet
4—Pivot cover	22—Gear retaining nut	39—Insulator grommet sleeve
5—Lubricating hole screw	23—Gear housing gasket	40—Motor mounting screw
6—Cover gasket	24—Parking switch assembly	41—Pivot mounting clip
7—Wiper linkage pivot	25—Field coil lead insulator	42—Brush spring
8—Link thrust washer	"A" Thrust bridge	43—Brush assembly
9—Felt washer (lubricating)	26—Parking switch cover	44—Head assembly-commutator end
10—Link assembly-left	27—Parking switch cover grommet	45—Worm follower gear-right
11—Link retaining lock	28—Lock waser	46—Worm follower gear plate-plain
12—Wiper motor crank arm	29—Cover screw	47—Link assembly-right
13—Crank arm thrust washer	30—Armature thrust washers	48—Gear housing cover
14—Head assembly-drive end	31—Armature assembly	49—Thru bolt
15—Wiring harness grommet	32—Motor frame	50—Thru bolt lock washer
16—Spring tension washer	33—Insulation strip	51—Pivot lubricating hole
17—Gear thrust washer	34—Field coil assembly	52—Field coil leads
18—Worm follower gear-left	35—Pole shoes	

Fig. 36-77. Exploded view of Autolite electric windshield wiper.

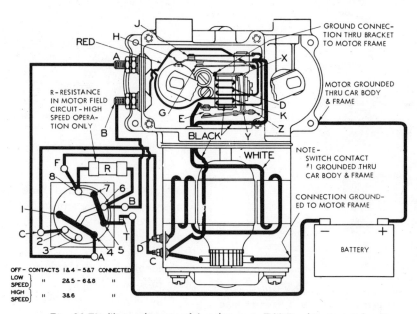

**Fig. 36-78. Wiring diagram of Autolite type E.W.B. electric wind-
shield wiper.**

while for high speed a resistance is inserted in the field circuit. The control switch is provided with three positions: "Off," "Low Speed," and "High Speed." When the dash control switch is turned to the "Off" position, the motor will continue to operate until a cam on the crank arm strikes the switch button, opening the circuit. Parking position of the blade is adjusted by moving the bracket on which the parking switch is mounted.

Noisy operation of electric wipers is sometimes caused by excessive end play of the motor armature. The amount of end play varies with different makes and types of installations. Noise will also be caused by incorrect relation between the motor and the linkage and pivot shaft assemblies. Elimination of excessive friction in the driving mechanism should reduce such noise.

Most windshield wiper motors are fitted with oilless type bushings and therefore do not require any lubrication. The gear box should be filled three-quarters full, before assembly, with special lubricant and all crank arm shafts should be greased their entire length.

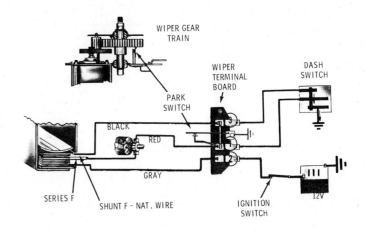

Fig. 36-79. Wiring diagram of GM windshield wiper with rectangular motor housing. Switch is in LO speed position. (General Motors Corp.)

GM Windshield Wipers

Two types of windshield wipers are used currently on General Motors cars. The nondepressed park

Electric Wiper Trouble Shooting Chart

CONDITION	POSSIBLE CAUSE	REMEDY
Wiper inoperative.	No current at wiper.	Check circuit and wiring.
	Defective dash switch.	Check dash switch mounting.
	Wiper unit latching mechanism binding.	Check latching mechanism, making sure it operates freely.
	Defective relay control.	Check relay control.
	Drive shaft seized.	Free up shaft or replace parts.
Wiper will not shut off.	Wiper latching mechanism binding.	Free up latching mechanism.
	Relay control switch defective.	Check relay control.
	Relay control coil grounded.	Eliminate ground.
	Drive pawl tab broken.	Replace drive pawl.
Excessive speed in high speed range but operates normally in low.	Resistor on wiper terminal board open.	Replace terminal board assembly.
Wiper operates in high speed only.	Defective dash switch.	Check switch for loose mounting and connections.
	Circuit between dash switch and wiper unit open.	Check circuit.
	Open shunt field on motor.	Check circuit.
Wiper operates in low speed only.	Defective dash switch.	Check switch and connections.
	Circuit between switch and wiper terminal grounded.	Check circuit for grounds.
Blades do not park.	Defective relay switch.	Replace switch assembly.
Intermittent operation.	Weak circuit breaker.	Replace motor case and brush assembly.
	Armature end play too tight.	Adjust end play.
Washer inoperative	Defective hose.	Replace hose.
	Defective dash switch.	Replace switch.
	Defective relay coil.	Replace relay coil.

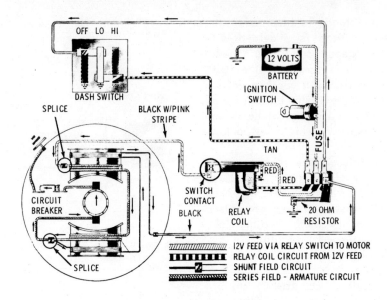

Fig 36-79a. Wiring diagram of General Motors windshield wiper
with round motor housing. Switch is in LO position.
(General Motors Corp.)

system uses a rectangular shaped motor with wiper blades that are visible above the hood line when in the parked position. The depressed park system incorporates a cylindrical motor and the wiper blades are parked below the hood line.

The two speed rectangular motor is a compound wound unit with a gear box containing a parking switch in addition to the gear train. The low speed circuit is shown in Fig. 36-79. Turning the wiper switch to the LO position completes the circuit through terminals No. 1 and No. 3 to the ground. Current then flows from the battery via the wiper terminal No. 2, through the series field and divides through the armature to the ground via wiper terminal No. 1, to

wiper switch. The other current passes through the shunt field to the ground.

The wiring diagram for the wiper with the round motor housing is shown in Fig. 36-79a. In the round two-speed motor the brush plate and circuit breaker assembly is attached to a field assembly in the end cap. The end cap and field assembly are serviced as a unit. The brush plate and circuit breaker must be detached from the field assembly in order to replace the armature. The motor has only two external leads.

Moving the wiper switch to the LO position, Fig. 36-79a, completes the relay coil circuit to ground at the wiper switch. With the relay coil energized, the relay contacts close completing the 12 volt circuit to the motor relay windings. Current then flows through the series field coil and divides, part passing through the armature to ground via the internal circuit breaker, and the other part through the shunt field coils.

Hidden Windshield Wipers

Many recent model cars have the windshield wipers hidden under an access door which is vacuum operated. The door is linked to a torsion bar housed in the plenum chamber and swings up and forward when the wiper system is in operation. Manifold vacuum is used to operate the system and a diagram is shown in Fig. 36-80.

Vacuum from the manifold is supplied to the vacuum reserve tank and then to the center terminal of the relay valve. When the wiper switch is in the "OFF" position, the solenoid is deactivated. The vacuum is then allowed to pass through the valve to the manual

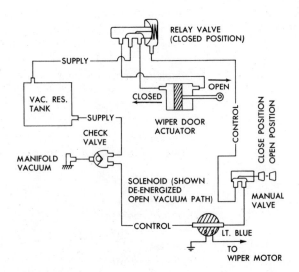

Fig. 36-80. Vacuum circuit for operation of access door to hidden
windshield wiper.

valve. The manual valve allows passage of the vacuum to the diaphragm portion of the relay valve.

Vacuum on the relay valve diaphragm pulls the internal valve to the right and opens a path for the vacuum at the center terminal (yellow) to pass into the red terminal circuit. From there it is routed to the left side of the wiper door actuator. Vacuum on this side of the actuator piston pulls the rod in and holds the acess door closed.

When the wiper switch is turned on, the solenoid is actuated and the control vacuum is stopped at the solenoid valve. The diaphragm spring then forces the internal valve to the left, completing the vacuum circuit to the opposite side of the windshield wiper access door actuator. The actuator rod then moves forward opening the door through the connecting linkage.

For manual operation of the door, the manual valve cuts off the vacuum to the relay valve. The manual valve must be in the "IN" position in order to close the door or return the system to automatic.

Quiz - Windshield Wipers

1. What is the major source of vacuum used to operate a windshield wiper?
2. Describe the basic operation of a vacuum windshield wiper.
3. How are two wiper blades operated when there is only one wiper motor?
   a. By means of suitable gearing.
   b. By means of linkage.
   c. Magnetically.
4. What is the most frequent cause of failure of the vacuum type windshield wiper?
   a. Leaks or stoppage in vacuum line.
   b. Excessive friction.
   c. Stripped gears.
5. Describe a method of overcoming sluggish operation of a vacuum type windshield wiper.
6. What type electric motors are usually used to operate electric windshield wipers?
7. What means are used to control the speed of the electric windshield wiper motor?
8. If armature of wiper motor has excessive end play, what is the usual result?
   a. Noisy operation.
   b. Motor speed will increase.
   c. Motor will fail to operate.
9. Do windshield wiper motors usually require lubrication? Yes or No?

WINDSHIELD WASHERS

Some types of electric windshield wipers also include windshield washer pumps. A wiring diagram of a modern three-speed windshield wiper, including the windshield washer pump, is shown in Fig. 36-81. This shows the circuit for low-speed operation of the wiper blade. It will be noted that the operation of the switch will cut in or cut out resistance to control the speed of the electric motor. This motor is of the series shunt type.

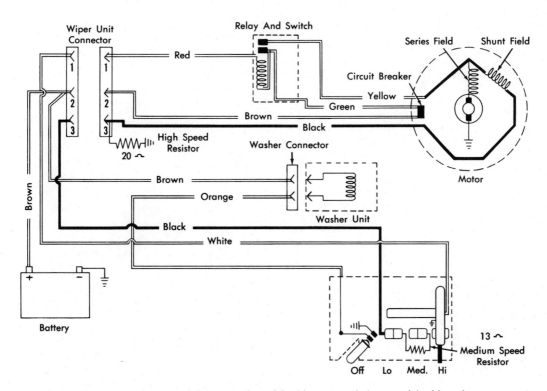

Fig. 36-81. Wiring diagram of three-speed windshield wiper including windshield washer pump.

The complete system consists of a wiper unit which contains the 12V DC motor, a gearbox section, a relay control, and a windshield washer pump. The unit drives two wiper transmission link arms, that connect the wiper unit assembly to the two individual wiper transmissions.

The wipers and washers are controlled by a three-way switch, located on the instrument panel. Some installations have single-speed, and others two-speed wipers. The washers are activated by a button integral with the switch. By depressing the washer button, the switch lever is mechanically moved to the "Lo" speed position. The washer relay coil is energized by the current flowing from the No. 2 terminal on the wiper unit connector, to the relay coil, and from there to the ground on the control switch.

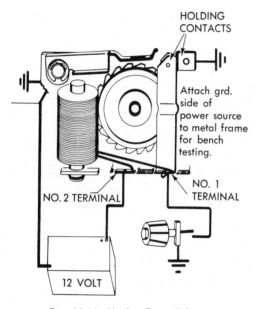

Fig. 36-82. Washer Pump Schematic.

The windshield washer, Fig. 36-82, which is designed for use with a single-speed wiper, uses a bellows type pump, Figs. 36-83 and 36-84. This pump is provided with a three lobe rotor cam, and it consists of a relay pump assembly, valve assembly and related parts assembled in a single unit which attaches directly to the gearbox of the electric windshield wiper.

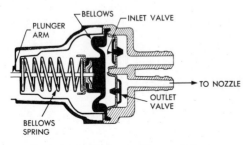

Fig. 36-83. Washer Bellows — Exhaust.

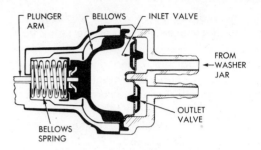

Fig. 36-84. Washer Bellows — Intake.

The washer pump is driven through gears by the wiper motor. Thus when the wiper is operated, the rotor cam of the washer is always turning with the wiper gear. As the rotor cam rotates, it actuates a spring-loaded roller and plunger arm assembly to which a ratchet arm is attached. The lever arm pin extends into the slot of a spring-loaded plunger arm. The spring-loaded plunger arm which is attached to the washer bellows, is held in the retracted position (spring compressed) by an eccentric on the ratchet wheel when the pump is idling.

While the pump is idling, therefore, the lever arm pin can move freely back and forth in the plunger arm slot and no pumping action occurs. The ratchet arm is prevented from rotating the ratchet wheel by a spring which prevents engagement, when the relay coil is not energized.

When the washer button on the instrument panel is pushed in to start the washer, the circuit to the washer pump relay coil is closed to the ground, Fig. 36-82. The relay then pulls the ratchet arm in against the ratchet wheel. The ratchet arm which was previously moving back and forth, now starts to rotate the ratchet wheel. Also a cam allows the contact points to close, which provides a ground circuit after the switch is released. As the ratchet wheel rotates,

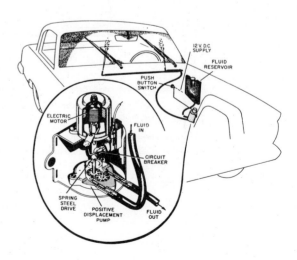

Fig. 36-85. An electrically operated windshield washer is available on some models of Chrysler cars.

the eccentric is moved away from the plunger arm tang, releasing the plunger arm for pumping action. The plunger arm being spring-loaded now moves in a direction toward the bellows and collapses the bellows, forcing the water in the bellows through the outlet valves in the nozzles, Fig. 36-83. At the same time, the edge of the plunger arm slot moves up tight against the lever arm pin. As the rotor cam is turned, each lobe actuates the lever arm which in turn pulls the plunger arm back compressing the spring. While the plunger arm is being pulled back, water is drawn in through the inlet valve, Fig. 36-84. The cycle is then started over again.

Electric Windshield Washer

Electrically operated windshield washers are installed on some models of Chrysler, Dodge and Plymouth cars. Fluid is gravity fed from a plastic reservoir and the pump assembly is located in the engine compartment, Fig. 36-85. A self-resetting circuit breaker mounted inside the pump will reset after a period of two minutes in the event of a frozen pump.

Quiz - Windshield Washers

1. What type pump is frequently used in the operation of a windshield washer?
   a. Piston type pump.
   b. Bellows type pump.
   c. Diaphragm type pump.
2. Which motor is used to drive the washer motor?
   a. Has individual motor.
   b. Is driven by wiper motor.
3. Describe the operation of the washer pump.
4. List three reasons for an inoperative windshield washer.

BATTERY CHARGING ...FAST CHARGE

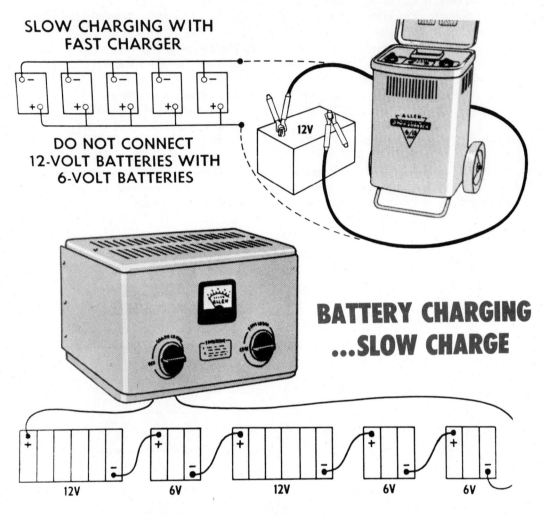

SLOW CHARGING WITH
FAST CHARGER

DO NOT CONNECT
12-VOLT BATTERIES WITH
6-VOLT BATTERIES

12V

BATTERY CHARGING
...SLOW CHARGE

12V   6V   12V   6V   6V

6 AND 12-VOLT BATTERIES MAY BE PLACED IN
SERIES ON THE SAME LINE WITH A SLOW CHARGER

METERS

Diagnosing troubles in electrical systems is one of the most important duties of the automotive electrician. With proper instruments connected in a circuit, he is able to determine where trouble exists, and whether adjustments are needed. In addition, electrical instruments enable him to make adjustments so the electrical equipment conforms to factory specifications. The basic instruments used by the automotive electrician are the ammeter for measuring the current in amperes, and the voltmeter for measuring the voltage or pressure. With the increased use of resistance type high tension ignition wiring, the use of the ohmmeter for measuring resistance, has become important. The oscilloscope is also becoming popular.

Meters must of course be accurate, and it must be remembered, that low-priced instruments seldom have the accuracy required. For example, voltmeter scales should be calibrated to 0.1 volt, and ammeters to 0.5 amp. It is not unusual to find instruments with scales indicating such accuracy, but because of design (such as low resistance) the readings will be in error.

Meter Design

Most modern ammeters and voltmeters used in the automotive service field are of the moving coil type, Fig. 37-1 and Fig. 37-2. These instruments consist of a permanent horseshoe or hoop-shaped magnet, and a movable coil. The pole pieces on the ends of the magnet are shaped to provide a uniform magnetic field.

Current flowing through the movable coil reacts with the magnetic field, causing the coil to rotate against the tension of a light spring, which is similar to the hairspring of a watch.

Relative movement of the coil is directly proportional to the current flowing through it. A pointer attached to the coil moves across a calibrated scale, and indicates the amount of current flowing through the coil.

The basic design of ammeters and voltmeters is the same. However, by studying Figs. 37-1 and 37-2, it will be noted that the ammeter is provided with a heavy shunt of low resistance connected across the movable coil. In addition, there is another resistance

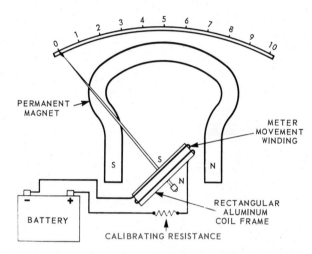

Fig. 37-1. Schematic drawing of a voltmeter. Note the calibrating resistance in series with the moving coil.

connected in series with one end of the shunt and the coil. This resistance is used for calibrating the instrument.

The voltmeter, Fig. 37-1, does not have a resistance shunted across the coil, and has only the calibrating resistance in series with the coil.

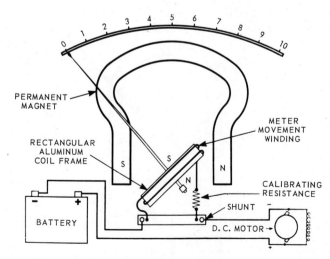

Fig. 37-2. Note that the ammeter has a heavy resistance connected across the moving coil and another resistance connected in series with the moving coil.

Ammeters are always connected in series with the circuit, Fig. 37-3, and voltmeters are always connected across (in parallel) the terminals of the device or circuit. See Fig. 37-3.

A single voltmeter can be designed to cover several different ranges of voltage. This is accomplished by varying the resistance in series with the movable coil. When this is done, a separate resistance is provided for each range of the instrument. The resistance is changed by means of a switch located on the instrument.

Ammeters also can be designed to cover several different ranges of current. This is done by providing several different shunts.

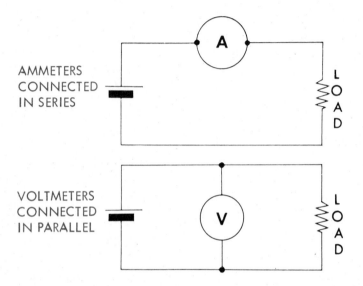

AMMETERS CONNECTED IN SERIES

VOLTMETERS CONNECTED IN PARALLEL

Fig. 37-3. Ammeters are always connected in series with the circuit to measure the current in amperes and the voltmeter is always connected in shunt or across the circuit to measure the voltage.

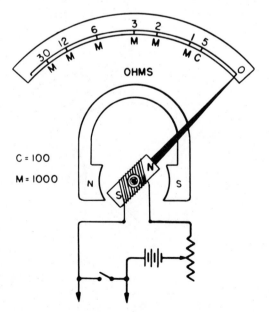

Fig. 37-3a. Details of ohmmeter. Note battery and adjustable resistance.

When using ammeters it is important that the leads provided by the manufacturer be used. Leads having a different resistance will seriously affect the accuracy of the instrument. This will be particularly noticeable when checking and adjusting voltage regulators.

A generally accepted standard for the maximum resistance of an ammeter is 0.1 v. drop across the ammeter terminals of the connected ammeter leads with 10 amp. flowing in the circuit. Therefore, the resistance would be .01 ohms.

The resistance of a good voltmeter is usually 100 ohms per volt.

In general, ammeters and voltmeters used for automotive service work should have an accuracy of one percent of full scale deflection. In addition, they should be compensated for changes in temperature.

Ohmmeter

The ohmmeter is an instrument designed to measure the resistance of an electric circuit or unit in ohms. In automotive service work it is used particularly to measure the resistance of resistors such as are used in the ignition circuit.

The basic ohmmeter consists essentially of a conventional D'Arsonval galvanometer such as is used in a voltmeter or ammeter. In the ohmmeter, Fig. 37-3a, in addition to the D'Arsonval unit, there is a calibrated resistance, a variable resistance and a self-contained battery. The leads used to connect the ohmmeter to the unit to be tested must also be mentioned as they are of special low resistance. As they are used when calibrating the instrument, they must be used when measuring the resistance of the circuit or unit.

Before using the ohmmeter, it first is necessary to standardize the battery voltage. This is done by joining the two instrument leads together so that there is essentially zero resistance. The variable resistance is then adjusted to bring the indicating needles to the zero mark on the dial.

When measuring the resistance of a circuit or piece of equipment, there can be no current flowing through it, other than that from the battery within the ohmmeter. Then to measure the resistance of a unit, the leads from the ohmmeter are simply connected to its terminals and the resistance in ohms is then read on the dial.

Tachometer

The tachometer is designed to indicate the speed in revolutions per minute of a rotating part. In automotive service work, it is a specially designed instrument as it is used exclusively to measure the speed of the engine.

The tachometer, as used in automotive service work, consists of a D'Arsonval galvanometer, a condenser, a single-pole double-throw relay and provision for calibrating the instrument for variation

Fig. 37-3b. Tachometer and dwell meter are combined in a single case.

in voltage of the instrument battery cell. Resistances are also included and which can be selected to allow for four, six or eight lobe distributor cams.

The tachometer, Fig. 37-3b, operates by charging a condenser by means of a self-contained flashlight battery or mercury cell, and then discharging the condenser through a D'Arsonval galvanometer. This is accomplished by the action of a single-pole double-throw relay, and the meter reading depends on the frequency of interruption. The higher the engine speed, the higher the rate of condenser discharge and charge.

One lead of the instrument is connected to primary connection on the distributor and the other to the ground. Then with the engine running, when the breaker points open, battery voltage from the vehicle ignition system which goes to the coil is applied to the relay. The relay armature will then contact the lower relay point and the meter battery cell will charge the condenser. When the breaker points are closed, practically no current is applied to the relay windings and the relay points will separate. This allows the condenser to discharge through the meter, and this action is repeated each time the points open and close.

Dwell Meter

The dwell meter is designed to measure the angle through which the distributor shaft turns while the distributor breaker points are closed. This is known as the dwell or cam angle. The dwell meter is often contained in the same case as the tachometer, Fig. 37-3b, however it does not operate from the charge and discharge of a condenser.

The dwell meter is operated by the voltage which is present across the breaker points. With the meter leads connected with proper polarity to the distributor primary and to the ground, open breaker points will

impose full battery voltage on the meter. Under this condition the meter will indicate zero percent of dwell.

With the breaker points closed, practically no voltage will be applied to the meter and it will therefore indicate 100 percent of dwell. In terms of degrees, 100 percent of dwell depends on the number of lobes on the distributor cam. For a four lobe cam, 100 percent dwell would be 90 deg., for a six lobe cam it would be 60 deg. and for an eight lobe cam it would be 45 deg.

Therefore when the breaker points are closed, the meter attempts to indicate 90, 60, or 45 deg., depending on the position of the lobe selector switch.

As the distributor rotates, the points will alternately open and close and the meter will then attempt to indicate alternately zero and 100 percent dwell. The inertia of the meter movement and the high capacity damping condenser connected across the meter will prevent rapid fluctuation of the indicating needle. As a result, the meter will indicate an average value. If the points remain closed longer than they remain open, this average value will be closer to 100 percent. If they are open longer than they are closed, the average value will be closer to zero. Automotive factories specify what the angle of dwell should be.

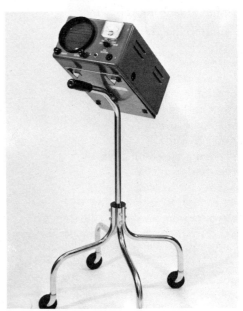

Fig. 37-4. Typical oscilloscope used for checking operation of ignition system.

The Oscilloscope

The oscilloscope, Fig. 37-4, is an electronic device which is used to visually observe and measure the instantaneous voltage in an electric circuit. Basically, aside from the vacuum tubes and circuitry required to operate it, the oscilloscope consists of a cathode-ray tube, and operates in much the same manner as a television set. The oscilloscope produces a graph-like picture showing voltage values with respect to time. This picture is generally referred to as the pattern or wave form.

This pattern or wave form, Fig. 37-5, is produced by the cathode ray or stream of electrons striking the face or screen of the tube, which is coated with a phosphorescent material. When the electrons strike this material, it gives off a brilliant glow, thus making it possible to see or trace the path of the ray as it moves across the screen.

In addition to being able to measure voltage in an electrical circuit, the oscilloscope can be used to determine the polarity of the voltage, which is indicated by the vertical movement of the ray. Thus, when connected to the secondary circuit of an ignition system, the voltage which is normally negative, will appear above the zero reference.

The oscilloscope wave form is controlled by the voltage in the electrical system to which it is connected. Oscilloscopes can also be connected to non-electrical components by means of special pickups known as transducers. These devices, which convert other forms of energy to electrical impulses, are used to observe engine compression and valve action, and locate noises and vibrations.

As an ignition system analyzer, the oscilloscope can be used to detect the following:

Spark plug firing voltage.
Coil action.
Condenser action.
Breaker point action.
Coil available voltage.
Reversed coil polarity.
Low voltage available.
Insulation leakage.
Worn spark plug electrodes.
Lean air fuel mixtures.
Excessive rotor gaps.
Breaks in high tension wiring.
Excessive primary circuit resistance.
Excessive secondary circuit resistance.
Poor rotor to cap contact.
Fouled spark plugs.
Grounded high tension wires.
Shorted coils.
Shorted condensers.
Defective breaker points.
Engine load on spark plug voltage.
Distributor point dwell.

Oscilloscope Wave Form

When studying the oscilloscope wave form or pattern, Fig. 37-5, consider it to be graphs of voltage with respect to time. The vertical displacement from the horizontal zero line (either up or down, depending on the polarity) represents voltage at any instant along the zero line. As oscilloscopes are used mostly in connection with the secondary circuit, as here it is the most informative, the screen is laid out in kilo-

volts to permit accurate voltage measurements of secondary circuit patterns.

Each part of the wave form represents a specific phase of ignition system operation, and is usually divided into three sections; firing section, intermediate section and dwell section.

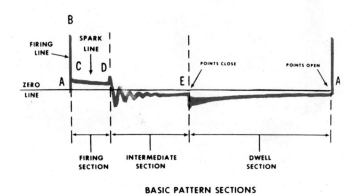

Fig. 37-5. Basic wave form of ignition system.

The firing section, Fig. 37-5, so called because it is during this period that the actual firing of the spark plug takes place. This section of the wave form is composed of only two lines. The firing line is the vertical line indicating the voltage required to overcome the rotor and spark plug gaps. The spark line is a horizontal line indicating the voltage required to maintain the spark and its duration. Point "A," Fig. 37-5, in the pattern, represents the instant at which the breaker points have opened. The resulting high voltage is indicated by the vertical rise from "A" to "B" in the pattern. The height at point "B" shows the voltage required to fire the plug and rotor gaps. This is often known as the firing or ionization voltage.

After the spark plug fires, there is a noticeable drop in secondary voltage to point "C." As the spark continues to bridge the gap, the spark voltage remains at a fairly constant low value until the spark stops at point "D."

The intermediate section, which immediately follows the firing section, is seen as a series of gradually diminishing oscillations, which just about disappear by the time the dwell section begins. Beginning at point "D," the remaining coil energy dissipates itself as an oscillating current, which gradually dies out as it approaches point "E." The oscillation results from the combined effects of the coil and the condenser, in dissipating this energy.

The dwell section represents the period of time during the ignition cycle in which the breaker points are closed. The dwell section begins at point "E," Fig. 37-5, when the breaker points close. Closing of the points causes a short downward line followed by a series of small rapidly diminishing oscillations. The dwell section continues until the points open at the beginning of the next wave form at point "A."

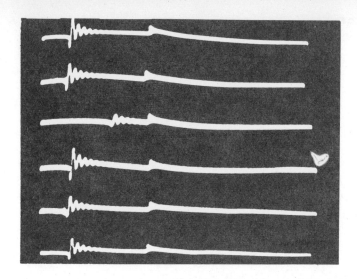

Fig. 37-6. This type oscilloscope places the wave form of each cylinder one above the other, for easy comparison. Note that No. 3 cylinder does not conform with the others. In this case a shorted spark plug is indicated.

Some oscilloscopes will show the wave form of each cylinder, one above the other, Fig. 37-6, while others will show the wave form of each cylinder, one after the other, Fig. 37-7.

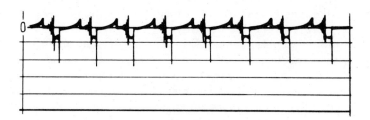

Fig. 37-7. Many oscilloscopes place the wave form of each cylinder one after the other as shown above.

In Fig. 37-6, all cylinders, except No. 3 are firing correctly. That cylinder has a shorted spark plug as indicated by the fact that the firing voltage (Line "A"-"B") Fig. 37-5, has not built up. Excessive spark plug gaps would be indicated when the firing line is longer than usual. When breaker points are defective or incorrectly gapped, the wave form of the dwell section will not follow the normal pattern. Each difficulty in the ignition circuit will show up in the wave form of the oscilloscope.

The oscilloscope does not replace existing equipment, but is used as an additional aid to trouble shooting. It will show in what area of the ignition system the trouble is occurring; regular metered equipment is then used to pin point the trouble. For this reason, oscilloscopes usually are incorporated in an engine analyzer test stand, Fig. 37-8, along with multi-range voltmeter, ammeter, tachometer, dwell meter, ohmmeter, alternator-regulator tester, vacuum-pressure gauges, combustion efficiency tester (exhaust gas analyzer) and timing light.

Infra-Red Testers

Emission standards and the need for a means of testing the amount of hydrocarbons and percentage of carbon monoxide in exhaust gases brought about the development of infra-red testers.

One infra-red unit, Fig. 37-9, utilizes nondispersive infra-red optical benches as sensing devices. The meter readouts of hydrocarbons and carbon monoxide result from the amount of energy these gases absorb, or block off, as they pass through a beam of infra-red light in each optical bench. The higher the concentration of either HC or CO, the higher the readout.

The tester is easy to operate. A probe is placed in the tailpipe of the test vehicle, and an exhaust gas sample is drawn through the tester by means of a positive displacement pump.

On its way to the infra-red optical benches, the gas sample is dried and filtered. The same sample then passes throught the infra-red light sources in both benches before being expelled. Output signals from both benches are fed to their respective meters by solid state amplifiers. The HC meter reads from 0 to 2000 in parts per million (ppm). The CO meter reads from 0 to 7-1/2 percent.

Two other meters are included in the tester instrument panel, the tachometer and the exhaust flow indicator. These instruments monitor engine speed and

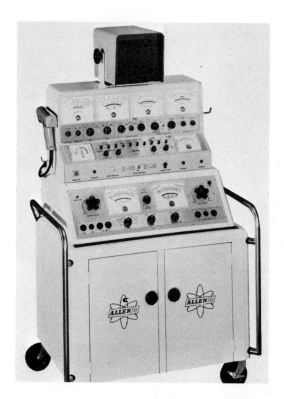

Fig. 37-8. This modern engine analyzer with oscilloscope is designed to test engine performance in minutes by means of a series of sequential tests. Unit is mobile and has a minimum number of test leads.

Fig. 37-9. Infra-red exhaust emission tester selectively measures levels of carbon monoxide and unburned hydrocarbons in sample of exhaust gas picked up by probe in tailpipe of car.

the passage of the exhaust gas sample through the unit.

The infra-red exhaust emission tester is more accurate than the combustion efficiency tester that operates with a thermal conductivity cell designed to measure the heat of the exhaust gases. This arrangement works fine, until the exhaust gas is too thin to heat the TC filament. Then the lean mixture cools the filament and the meter starts going the wrong way.

With the infra-red tester, the HC scale will back up the CO reading. The operator sets the carburetor air-fuel mixture and engine idle speed to bring the CO reading within the carbon monoxide limits allowed. Then he reads the HC meter. If it is lower than the established maximum, the engine is operating within emission standards. If the HC reading is high, further work or parts replacement is necessary.

Combinations and Consoles

In recent years combination testers have become quite popular. Volt-amp testers and tach-dwell meters lead the way. Latest ignition-charging system testers will test transistorized, capacitor discharge or conventional ignition systems. They work on 6, 12, 24, or 32V systems and on both AC and DC charging systems with only a single hook-up.

Console units incorporating engine analyzing instrumentation come in many "packages." Some are built up by adding individual or combination testers to the basic test stand. Others are unitized and put on wheels to provide mobility.

Most sophisticated of all is the master analyzer with computerized operation. Factory-approved specifications are fed into the unit for comparision with test results of the vehicle being diagnosed. Upon completion of a programmed series of tests, a readout is printed for the mechanic and the car owner. It contains both "specified" and "actual" readings for each test.

Quiz - Electric Meters

1. What type magnet is used in a conventional voltmeter?
   a. Electro-magnet.
   b. Permanent magnet.
2. In a voltmeter, is the calibrating resistance in series or in shunt with the movable coil?
   a. Series.
   b. Shunt.
3. What is the major difference between a voltmeter and an ammeter?
4. When using an ammeter, how should it be connected in the circuit?
   a. In series.
   b. In shunt.
5. When using a voltmeter, how should it be connected in the circuit?
   a. In series.
   b. In shunt.
6. When using an ammeter, why is it important to always use the leads provided by the manufacturer?
7. What is an oscilloscope used for?
8. What can the wave form shown on an oscilloscope screen tell about the ignition system of an automobile?
9. Name the three sections of the wave form shown by an oscilloscope.
10. If the wave form shown on an oscilloscope screen rises very little above the horizontal zero line, what is indicated?
11. Why is an oscilloscope usually incorporated in an engine analyzer?
12. The infra-red tester detects and measures the level of two emissions for which maximum allowable standards have been established. What are they?

SPRING SUSPENSION AND STEERING

The modern automobile has come a long way since the days when "just being self-propelled" was enough to satisfy the car owner. Improvements in suspension and steering, increased strength and durability of components, and advances in tire design and construction have made large contributions to riding comfort and driving safety.

Basically, suspension refers to the use of front and rear springs to suspend a vehicle's frame, body, engine and power train above the wheels. These relatively heavy assemblies constitute what is known as "sprung" weight. "Unsprung" weight, on the other hand, includes wheels and tires, brake assemblies, the rear axle assembly and other structural members not supported by the springs.

The springs used in today's cars and trucks are engineered in a wide variety of types, shapes, sizes, rates and capacities. Types include leaf springs, coil springs, air springs and torsion bars. These are used in sets of four per vehicle, or are paired off in various combinations, and are attached to the vehicle by a number of different mounting techniques.

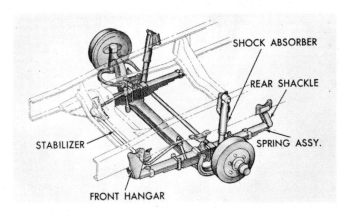

Fig. 38-2. A solid axle beam and leaf spring front suspension is generally used on medium and heavy-duty trucks.

bars and direct, double-acting shock absorbers. In solid axle construction, the axle beam and wheel assemblies are connected to the car by leaf springs and direct or indirect-acting shock absorbers.

With the solid axle setup, the steering knuckle and wheel spindle assemblies are connected to the axle beam by bronze-bushed kingpins, or spindle bolts, which provide pivot points for each front wheel. See Fig. 38-3. Modern independent from wheel suspension systems use ball joints, or spherical joints, to ac-

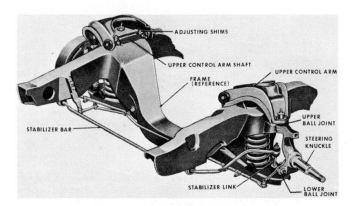

Fig. 38-1. Independent front suspension with coil springs and control arms are used on many passenger cars and light-duty trucks.

Front Suspension Types

There are two types of front suspension in general use: the independent system, Fig. 38-1, and the solid axle system, Fig. 38-2. Independent suspension usually operates through heavy-duty coil springs or torsion

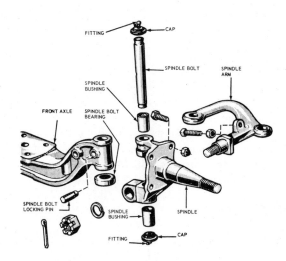

Fig. 38-3. In solid axle front suspension, axle beam is connected to front wheel spindle by means of king pins, or spindle bolts.

complish this purpose, Fig. 38-4. In operation, the swiveling action of the ball joints allows the wheel and spindle assemblies to be turned left or right and to move up and down with changes in road surface.

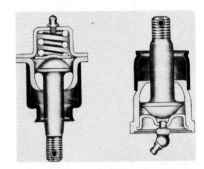

Fig. 38-4. Generally, upper ball joint (left) is spring-loaded in its socket; lower ball joint is firmly seated by weight of car.

Leaf Springs

Front leaf, or plate, springs are used in conjunction with solid axle beams in most truck applications. Rear leaf springs are used on trucks and some passenger cars. Single leaf or multi-leaf springs are usually mounted longitudinally over the front axle beam or under the rear axle housing. See Fig. 38-2. The spring center bolt fastens the leaves together and its head locates the spring in the axle beam or saddle on the rear axle housing. U-bolts clamp the spring firmly in place and keep it from shifting. Eyebolts, brackets and shackles attach it to the frame at each end.

In many cases, leaf springs are used at the rear of the vehicle in combination with another type of spring in front. Chrysler, for example, uses leaf springs at the rear, torsion bars in front, Fig. 38-5. Ford for many years used leaf springs at rear, coil springs in front, Fig. 38-6. Buick still uses coil springs all around. See Fig. 38-7. In some foreign cars, torsion bars are used front and rear; in others, leaf springs are mounted crosswise for use with independently suspended wheels.

However, when used in U.S. vehicles, rear leaf springs are generally placed parallel to the frame to absorb the torque of the driving wheels. The front half of each rear leaf spring acts like a radius rod or control arm to transmit the driving force from the rear wheels to the frame (Hotchkiss drive). With this suspension setup, the leaf springs also serve as stabilizers to control side sway of the chassis.

Coil Springs

Many independent front suspension systems incorporate compression-type coil springs mounted between the lower control arms and spring housing in the frame. See Figs. 38-1 and 38-8. Others have the

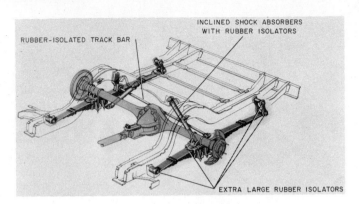

Fig. 38-5. Chrysler cars use leaf springs at rear, torsion bars in front. In this rear suspension setup, spring center bolt is offset toward front.

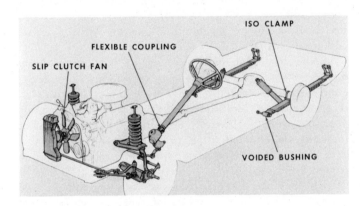

Fig. 38-6. Ford favored combination of coil springs at front and leaf springs at rear for many model years. Later models are equipped with coil springs all around.

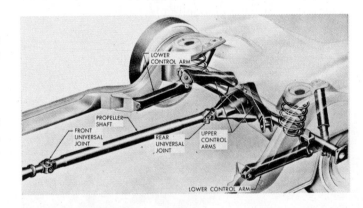

Fig. 38-7. Full-size Buicks have front springs mounted between lower control arms and frame (see Fig. 38-1), rear springs between axle housing and pockets in frame.

coil springs mounted above the upper control arms, compressed between a pivoting spring seat bolted to the control arm and a spring tower formed in the front end sheet metal, Fig. 38-9.

The upper control arm pivots on a bushing and shaft assembly which is bolted to the frame. The lower arm pivots on a bushing and shaft assembly or on a bolt in the frame cross member. When the lower control arm is not the A-frame type, it is supported by a strut which runs diagonally from the lower control arm to a bracket attached to the frame. On some models, this strut serves only as a support; on others, it also provides a means of adjusting caster, Fig. 38-9.

Stabilizers or sway bars are used on many cars to dampen road shocks and minimize road sway. These bars are bracketed to the frame front cross member and extend from one lower control arm to the other. See Fig. 38-1.

Actually, the S.L.A. (short-long arm) system of front suspension has been adopted almost universally for passenger cars. The proportionate lengths of the upper and lower control arms – and their engineered placement – are designed to keep the rise and fall of each front wheel in a vertical plane. See Fig. 38-10. With this arrangement, changes in wheel angularity, weight balance and tire-scuffing tendencies are negligible when compared with solid axle suspension.

When coil springs are used in both front and rear suspension, Figs. 38-1 and 38-7, three or four control arms are placed between the rear axle housing and the frame to carry driving and braking torque. The lower control arms pivot in the frame members and sometimes support the rear coil springs to provide for up and down movement of the axle and wheel assembly.

In addition a sway bar, or track bar, is usually attached from the upper control arm to the frame side rail to hold the rear axle housing in proper alignment with the frame and to prevent side sway of the body. However, if the rear coil springs are mounted between the frame and a swinging half axle, the independently suspended rear wheels have a sturdy axle housing attached to the differential housing which, in turn, is bolted to the frame.

Torsion Bars

Although torsion bars were and are used extensively on European cars, this type of suspension system received only token attention from the U.S. manufacturers until Chrysler developed their system in

Fig. 38-9. Smaller cars often have front coil springs installed above upper control arms. Shock absorbers mount inside between spring seats and brackets in engine compartment.

the early 1950s. Before that, only a few buses, trailers and race cars were equipped with torsion bar suspension.

Basically, torsion bar suspension is a method of utilizing the flexibility of a steel bar or tube twisting lengthwise to provide spring action. Instead of the flexing action of a leaf spring, or the compressing-and-extending action of a coil spring, the torsion bar twists to exert resistance against up-and-down movement. For example, an independently suspended front

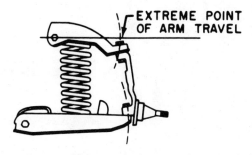

Fig. 38-10. Upper and lower control arms and steering knuckle are designed so that tire-to-road contact area will remain in a vertical line as front springs flex.

system with torsion bars mounted lengthwise would have one end of the bars anchored to the car frame and the other end attached to the lower control arms. With each rise and fall of a front wheel, the control arm pivots up and down, twisting the torsion bar along its length to absorb road shock and cushion the ride.

Chrysler cars are equipped with left and right, noninterchangeable, front torsion bars with hex-shaped ends, Fig. 38-11. In position, the bars extend from hex-shaped rear anchors in the frame cross member to hex-shaped holes in the front lower control arm. Adjusting bolts are provided at the front mounting to

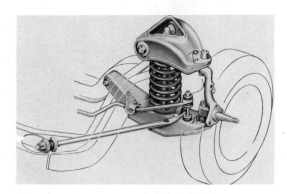

Fig. 38-8. Most front coil springs are located between seat formed in lower control arm and spring housing in frame. Shock absorbers mount inside springs.

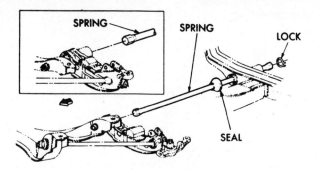

Fig. 38-11. Torsion bars on Chrysler cars are not interchangeable side for side. Bars are marked either right or left by an R or L stamped on end of bar.

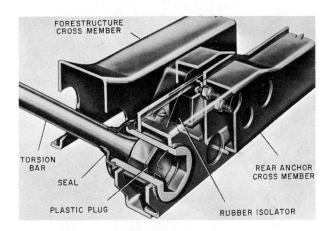

Fig. 38-12. Certain late model Chrysler Corporation cars are fitted with a removable cross member with rubber-isolated mounts at torsion bar rear anchors.

increase or decrease torsion bar twist and thereby control front suspension height. Over the years, Chrysler has made many improvements in the system, including: lengthening the torsion bars to lower the spring rate; adding a removable rear anchor cross member that is rubber-isolated from the frame; de-

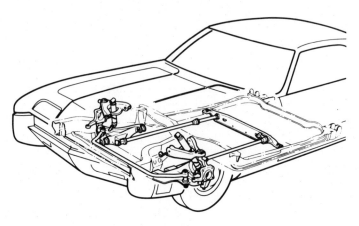

Fig. 38-13. Drawing of Oldsmobile Toronado highlights torsion bar front suspension. Cross member is cut away at right to reveal adjusting mechanism.

vising a plastic plug and a balloon seal for the rear anchor. See Fig. 38-12. Oldsmobile Toronado and Cadillac Eldorado front wheel drive cars also use lengthwise mounted torsion bars to support the front

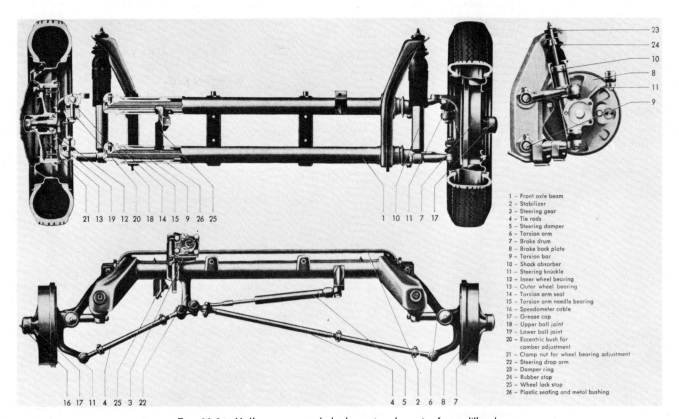

1 – Front axle beam
2 – Stabilizer
3 – Steering gear
4 – Tie rods
5 – Steering damper
6 – Torsion arm
7 – Brake drum
8 – Brake back plate
9 – Torsion bar
10 – Shock absorber
11 – Steering knuckle
12 – Inner wheel bearing
13 – Outer wheel bearing
14 – Torsion arm seal
15 – Torsion arm needle bearing
16 – Speedometer cable
17 – Grease cap
18 – Upper ball joint
19 – Lower ball joint
20 – Eccentric bush for camber adjustment
21 – Clamp nut for wheel bearing adjustment
22 – Steering drop arm
23 – Damper ring
24 – Rubber stop
25 – Wheel lock stop
26 – Plastic seating and metal bushing

Fig. 38-14. Volkswagen used dual torsion bars in front. Wheels are attached to swinging lever arms that trail behind torsion bars.

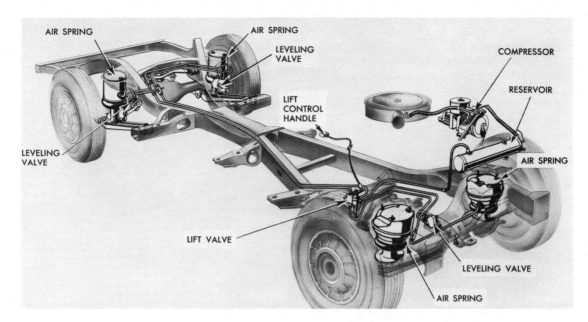

Fig. 38-15. This air suspension system was used by Cadillac in earlier models. After a relatively short trial in late 1950s, air springs were discontinued.

end and to provide for height adjustment, Fig. 38-13.

Torsion bars can also be used laterally to provide spring action for front and/or rear wheel independent suspension systems. Volkswagen cars offer a unique torsion bar arrangement with all four wheels independently suspended, but with two different torsion bar setups in use. At the front, two laminated square torsion bars housed in separate axle tubes are anchored at the center to counteract twisting and lateral movement, Fig. 38-14. Each bar has a lever or torsion arm attached to its outer end. Ball joints connect the torsion arms to the steering knuckle. Thus, the wheel spindle trails behind the axle and tends to swing in an arc when moved up and down by road irregularities.

At the rear, Volkswagen utilizes one short, round torsion bar on each side. These bars are splined at both ends and anchored in the center of the frame cross member. The outer ends of the torsion bars carry the spring plates to which the wheels are attached. Here, too, the wheels follow behind the torsion bars on "trailing arms."

Air Suspension

Air suspension systems are designed to cushion the ride and keep the car, bus or truck level fore and aft and at a constant height regardless of load. Air suspension was introduced on many luxury cars in the late 1950s, Fig. 38-15, but was dropped after one or two model years. Recently, however, new leveling systems have been researched and developed for passenger car use.

A typical air suspension system consists of an engine-driven air compressor, supply tank, filter or condenser, valves, piping, controls and air springs or bellows. In operation, the air compressor main-

tains a constant pressure in the supply tank, and air is piped to the control valves which feed it to each air spring as needed. Pressure is automatically increased on either side or at front or rear as required to keep the car level and at any desired height from the road (within limits of system).

Automatic Level Control

Air springs are not used in Cadillac's automatic level control system. Rather, the rear shock absorbers extend or compress to bring the rear of the car to the same level as the front. This automatic system utilizes an air compressor, reservoir, regulator, hoses, lines, height control valve and special shock absorbers. See Fig. 38-16.

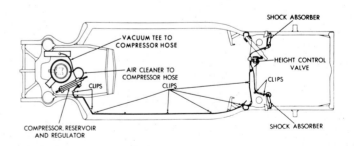

Fig. 38-16. Cadillac automatic level control arrangement utilizes air-adjustable rear shock absorbers to provide automatic leveling when needed.

Ford has two leveling systems which utilize air bags in conjunction with rear coil springs. The automatic system consists of air reservoir and pump, leveling valve, air bags, nylon tubing and metal fittings and connectors, Fig. 38-17. The manual system has similar air bags connected to lines leading to the trunk of the car where an air valve connection permits leveling by application of air under pressure from an outside compressed air source.

mount to a bracket on the frame. In the case of high-mounted coil springs, Fig. 38-9, the shock absorbers extend from the upper control arm to a platform mounted in the spring tower or to a bracket on the wheel housing in the engine compartment.

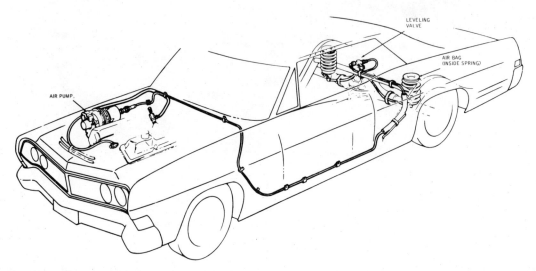

Fig. 38-17. Ford has air spring stabilizing system in which minimum clearance is maintained between body frame and rear axle under loaded conditions.

Shock Absorbers

A wide variety of shock absorbing devices have been used to control spring action, but direct, double-acting, "telescoping" hydraulic units now have almost universal application, Fig. 38-18.

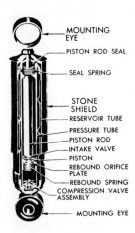

Fig. 38-18. Call-outs in cross-sectional view identify various components of typical, direct, double-acting shock absorber in assembled order.

At the front, the shock absorbers often extend through the coil spring from the lower control arm to a bracket attached to the frame, Fig. 38-8. On Chrysler cars with torsion bar suspension, the front shock absorbers attach to the lower control arm and

At the rear, one end of the shock absorbers is usually attached to a bracket welded to the axle housing; the other end is fastened to the frame or to the coil spring upper seat which is integral with frame or body. On cars with rear leaf springs, the shock absorbers generally extend from a stud attached to the spring U-bolt mounting bracket to the frame cross member. Quite often the rear units are mounted at an angle to assist in restricting lateral movement as well as vertical movement. Oldsmobile Toronado and Cadillac Eldorado cars use four rear shock absorbers to give better ride control, Fig. 38-19. For this

Fig. 38-19. Oldsmobile Toronado features four rear shock absorbers, two on either side, for smoother ride, less rear spring "wind-up" and controlled braking.

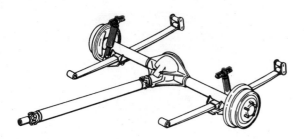

Fig. 38-20. Certain late model Chevrolet cars are equipped with "bias-mounted" rear shock absorbers. Curb-side units are mounted in front of axle housing, street-side units in back.

valves, Fig. 38-18. The hydraulic shock absorber automatically adapts itself to the severity of the shock. If the axle moves slowly, resistance to the flow of fluid will be light. If axle movement is rapid or forceful, the resistance is much stronger because more time is required to force the fluid through the orifices.

Thus the shock absorbers permit a soft ride over small bumps and provide firm control over spring action for large bumps. The double-acting unit operates in both directions since spring rebound can be almost as violent as the original action.

Steering Systems

In a broad sense, there are two general types of steering systems: manual and power. In the manual system, the driver's effort to turn the steering wheel is the primary force that causes the front wheels to swivel to left or right on the steering knuckles. With power steering, the driver's turning efforts are multiplied by a hydraulic assist.

The manual system incorporates a steering wheel and shaft, manual gearbox, linkage, steering knuckles and wheel spindle assemblies, Fig. 38-21. Power

same reason, some late model Chevrolet cars have "bias-mounted" rear shock absorbers. The curb-side unit is mounted in front of the axle housing; the street-side unit is mounted in back of the housing. See Fig. 38-20.

The operating principle of direct-acting hydraulic shock absorbers consists of forcing fluid through restricting orifices in the valves to slow down and control the rapid movement of the car springs as they react to road irregularities. Generally, the flow of fluid through the piston is controlled by spring-loaded

Left. Dodge Colt has unique front suspension. Strut-type design has shock absorber made integral with wheel spindle and mounted with a coil spring. Right. Ford rear suspension employs coil springs, diagonally mounted shock absorbers and upper and lower control arms.

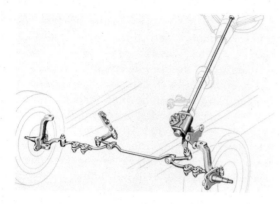

Fig. 38-21. Drawing of Ford manual steering system details shaft, gearbox, pitman and idler arms, intermediate arm, tie rods and steering knuckle assemblies.

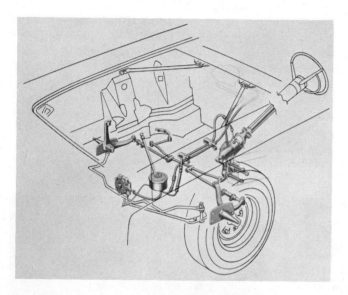

Fig. 38-22. Typical power steering system involves use of an integral steering gear mounted in line with steering column, an engine-driven pump and connecting lines and hoses.

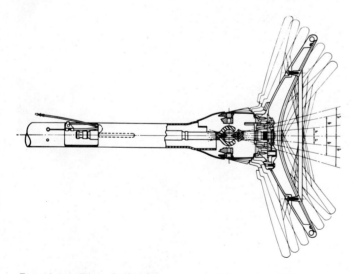

Fig. 38-23. Typical tilting steering wheel has seven different driving positions. Wheel position is selected by lifting a lever on left side of column.

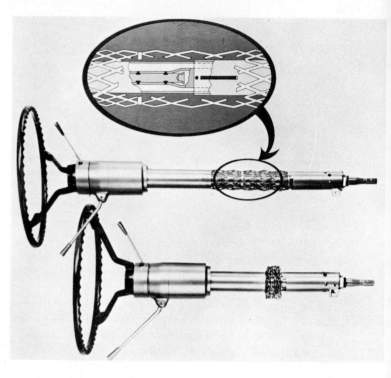

Fig. 38-24. Energy-absorbing steering column reduces chance of serious injury in a collision. Upon impact, mesh jacket compresses, steering shaft and shift tube telescope.

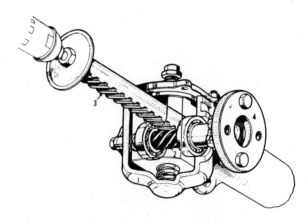

Fig. 38-25. Rack and pinion type of manual steering gear shown was used on earlier Renault cars.

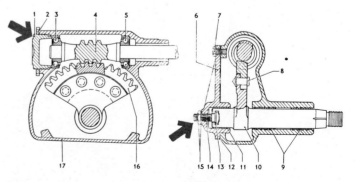

Fig. 38-26. Worm and sector type of steering gear used on English Bedford cars featured: 1-worm bearings adjuster; 14-gear mesh adjuster screw.

steering adds a hydraulic pump, fluid reservoir, hoses, lines and either a steering assist unit mounted on the linkage or a power steering gear assembly. See Fig. 38-22.

Generally, round steering wheels are splined to the top end of the steering shaft. Tilting steering wheel assemblies, Fig. 38-23, offer the advantage of angular adjustment to suit the individual driver and the particular situation. Collapsible steering columns, Fig. 38-24, are used in late model cars as a safety item. Looking ahead, lever-type steering arrangements are being researched and developed.

Manual Steering Gears and Linkage

There are several different manual steering gears in current use. The rack and pinion type, Fig. 38-25, is featured on various foreign cars, including the Renault. Worm and sector gears, Fig. 38-26, are popular in England and on some smaller U.S. makes. But most U.S. cars with manual steering are fitted with worm and recirculating ball systems, Fig. 38-27.

The worm and recirculating ball steering gear works on the principle of having turning forces transmitted through ball bearings from a worm gear on the steering shaft to a sector gear on the pitman arm shaft. In operation, a ball nut assembly is filled with ball bearings which "roll" along grooves between the worm teeth and grooves inside the ball nut. Thus, when the steering wheel is turned, the worm gear on the end of the steering shaft rotates and the movement of the recirculating balls causes the ball nut to move up and down along the worm. Movement of the ball nut is carried to the sector gear by teeth on the side of ball nut. The sector gear, in turn, moves with the ball nut to rotate the pitman arm shaft and activate the steering linkage. The balls recirculate from one end of the ball nut to the other through a pair of ball return guides, Fig. 38-27.

A steering gearbox houses the manual steering gear assembly. It is securely attached to the frame side rail and is filled with a water-resistant, extreme pressure lubricant. The pitman arm shaft projects downward from the gearbox and is splined to the pitman arm, which converts rotary motion of the shaft to lateral movement of the arm.

The pitman arm, generally, is connected to a relay rod which reaches across to an idler arm attached to the frame side rail on the opposite side. The relay rod is connected to two adjustable tie rods that transmit the lateral movement of the relay rod to the steering arms at each steering knuckle, Fig. 38-28.

Manual steering is considered to be entirely adequate for smaller cars and for cars with the engine in the rear. It is light, fast and accurate in maintaining steering control. However, larger and heavier engines, greater front overhang on U.S. cars, and the trend toward wide tread tires have increased the steering effort required. Gearboxes with higher gear

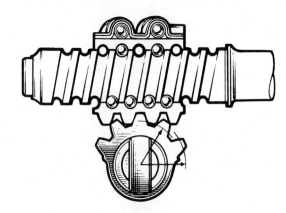

Fig. 38-27. Steering gear on Dodge Colt utilizes a 5-tooth sector and ball nut that travels on a worm shaft, while riding on recirculating ball bearings.

ratios were tried, but these were slower acting so engineering was accelerated to develop efficient and dependable power steering systems.

Power Steering

Advanced power steering got its start during World War II in military vehicles of all kinds. With the development of heavier and faster cars in the early 1950s, modified versions of the wartime gears were installed by the car manufacturers. As popularity increased, new power steering setups were devised until a lightweight, compact, self-lubricating, in-line power steering gear was developed in the late 1950s.

More recently, an integral-type rotary valve system was designed and produced. This system is now used on most factory-installed, power steering equipped cars. Other systems include the linkage-booster type which is "applied" to the steering linkage and the semi-integral system which combines features of the

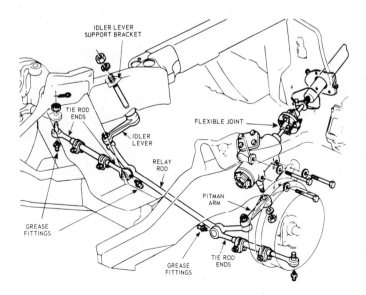

Fig. 38-28. Chevrolet manual steering linkage is parallel relay type located back of frame front cross member. Major parts and assemblies are called out.

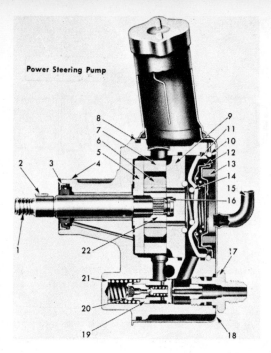

Power Steering Pump

8
7
6
5
4
2
3
1
9
11
10
12
13
14
15
16
22
21
20
19
17
18

1. Shaft
2. Woodruff Key
3. Shaft Seal
4. Pump Housing
5. Thrust Plate
6. Vanes
7. Pump Ring
8. Reservoir "O" Ring Seal
9. Pressure Plate
10. End Plate Retaining Ring
11. End Plate
12. Filter Cage Assembly
13. Filter Element
14. Pressure Plate Spring
15. Pump Inlet Tube
16. Rotor-to-Drive Shaft Retaining Ring
17. Pump Outlet Union
18. Reservoir
19. Flow Control Valve
20. Flow Control Valve Cap Screw
21. Flow Control Valve Spring
22. Rotor

Fig. 38-29. Vane-type power steering pump is encased in reservoir of fluid. Pressure relief valve limits pressures; flow control system allows external pump flow to drop off at higher speeds.

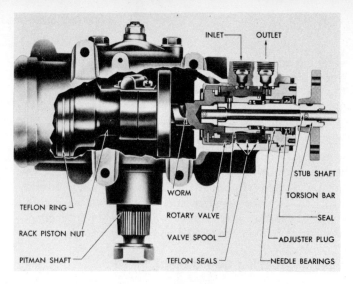

INLET   OUTLET

TEFLON RING
RACK PISTON NUT
PITMAN SHAFT
WORM
ROTARY VALVE
VALVE SPOOL
TEFLON SEALS
STUB SHAFT
TORSION BAR
SEAL
ADJUSTER PLUG
NEEDLE BEARINGS

Fig. 38-30. Rotary valve power steering gear displaces fluid to provide hydraulic fluid pressure assists when turning. Mechanical element of gear is a recirculating ball system.

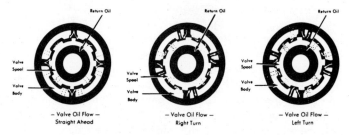

— Valve Oil Flow —
Straight Ahead

— Valve Oil Flow —
Right Turn

— Valve Oil Flow —
Left Turn

Fig. 38-31. Rotary valve operation in integral power steering gear is illustrated in straight ahead, right turn and left turn positions. Lower gear assembly is always full of oil.

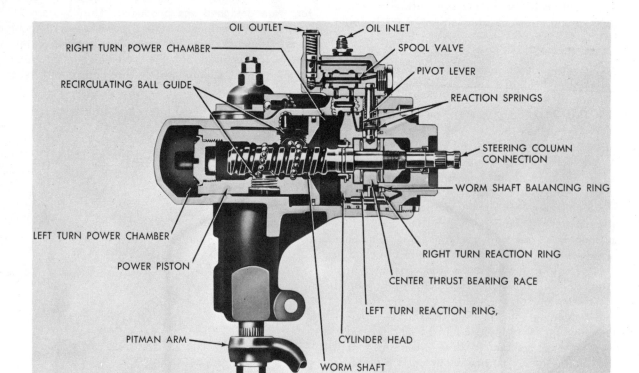

OIL OUTLET   OIL INLET
RIGHT TURN POWER CHAMBER   SPOOL VALVE
RECIRCULATING BALL GUIDE   PIVOT LEVER
REACTION SPRINGS
STEERING COLUMN CONNECTION
WORM SHAFT BALANCING RING
LEFT TURN POWER CHAMBER
POWER PISTON
RIGHT TURN REACTION RING
CENTER THRUST BEARING RACE
LEFT TURN REACTION RING,
PITMAN ARM
CYLINDER HEAD
WORM SHAFT

Fig. 38-32. Chrysler's integral power steering gear has gear teeth broached in side of power piston, which is geared to worm shaft through recirculating balls. Steering valve is mounted on top.

other two systems. The power steering pump is belted, geared or otherwise attached to the engine or some driven accessory. (Some earlier units were mounted on generator armature shaft.) The pump is connected to the power unit by lines and hoses, and it incorporates a control valve somewhere in the hydraulic circuit. See Fig. 38-29.

Automobile power steering is actually "power assisted steering." All automotive systems are constructed so that the car can be steered manually when the engine is not running or if any failure occurs at the power source.

Integral Type

The integral type of power steering gear is constructed with the power cylinder and control valve built into the steering gear unit. Using one model of Saginaw gear as an example of system operation, Fig. 38-30, it may be seen that in the straight-ahead position, the hydraulic fluid is circulating through the "open" position of the valve assembly and back into the pump reservoir without circulating in the power cylinder in which the rack piston is located. See Fig. 38-31.

When the steering wheel is turned to the right, resistance between the front tires and road causes the torsion bar to be deflected. This changes the register of the valve grooves and valve body grooves, Fig. 38-31. The right turn grooves are closed off from the return grooves and opened to the pressure grooves. The left turn grooves are closed off from the pressure grooves and opened to the return grooves. This causes the oil to flow under pressure into one half of the power cylinder, moving the rack piston and pitman shaft gear to overcome tire friction in that direction. Fluid in the other end of the power cylinder is forced out through the valve and back to the pump reservoir.

When the driver stops turning the steering wheel, the valve returns to its neutral position, and pressures on both sides of the power piston are equalized. The steering geometry of the front wheels causes them to return to the straight-ahead position.

When the steering wheel is turned to the left, an exact reverse operation occurs. That is, the valve grooves register for left turn operation and the rack piston moves in the opposite direction, Fig. 38-31.

Chrysler's integral power steering gear is illustrated and described in Fig. 38-32.

Linkage-Booster Type

The linkage-booster type of power steering system consists of a power cylinder and control valve mounted on the steering linkage and a pulley-driven pump, Fig. 38-33. The control valve is mounted between the pitman arm and the relay rod. Two flexible hoses connect the control valve to the booster cylinder, which is also attached to the relay rod.

The power cylinder is double acting. By proper routing of fluid under pressure, the booster can be made to apply force to the steering linkage in either direction. When the steering wheel is turned, movement of the pitman arm actuates a valve, and fluid is directed to one side of the booster cylinder. This hy-

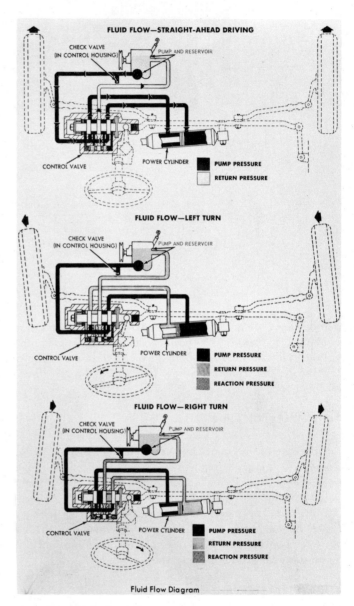

Fig. 38-33. With this linkage-booster type of power steering system, control valve directs fluid under pressure to proper section of power cylinder to provide power assist.

draulic action moves the valve in one direction or the other and thereby provides power assistance directly to the relay rod. The control valve also directs fluid being forced out of the other side of the cylinder back to the pump.

In the straight-ahead position, fluid passes through the open center of the valve and is routed back to the

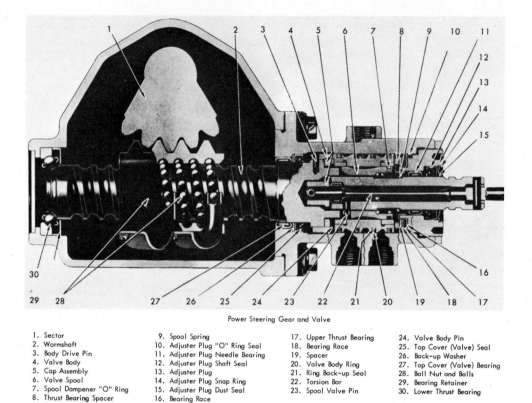

Power Steering Gear and Valve

1. Sector	9. Spool Spring
2. Wormshaft	10. Adjuster Plug "O" Ring Seal
3. Body Drive Pin	11. Adjuster Plug Needle Bearing
4. Valve Body	12. Adjuster Plug Shaft Seal
5. Cap Assembly	13. Adjuster Plug
6. Valve Spool	14. Adjuster Plug Snap Ring
7. Spool Dampener "O" Ring	15. Adjuster Plug Dust Seal
8. Thrust Bearing Spacer	16. Bearing Race

17. Upper Thrust Bearing	24. Valve Body Pin
18. Bearing Race	25. Top Cover (Valve) Seal
19. Spacer	26. Back-up Washer
20. Valve Body Ring	27. Top Cover (Valve) Bearing
21. Ring Back-up Seal	28. Ball Nut and Balls
22. Torsion Bar	29. Bearing Retainer
23. Spool Valve Pin	30. Lower Thrust Bearing

Fig. 38-34. Semi-integral type of power steering system combines in-line gear and valve assembly with linkage-mounted power cylinder.

pump reservoir. A small piston in the control valve provides hydraulic "reaction" to movement of the valve spool in the valve body. This resistance opposes turning of the steering wheel to give the driver "feel-of-the-road."

Semi-Integral Type

The semi-integral power steering system, Fig. 38-34, is designed for use on trucks and other heavy equipment. One unit, for example, features a rotary valve mechanism at the end of the steering column and a power cylinder mounted on the steering linkage. Fixed hoses carry the fluid under pressure from the pulley-mounted pump to the power steering unit to avoid damage by flexing and stretching.

Pumps and Hoses

Several types of power steering pumps are in use. The vane-type hydraulic pump, Fig. 38-29, incorporates a rotor with six to ten vanes which rotate in an elliptical housing. Fluid trapped between the vanes is forced out under pressure as the vanes move from the long diameter of the housing to the short diameter. Some vane-type pumps are capable of 1450 psi output.

A roll-type pump operates much like the vane-type. Instead of vanes, six rollers on a toothed carrier unit rotate inside of a cam insert to build up fluid pressure. A slipper-type pump, Fig. 38-35, produces pres-

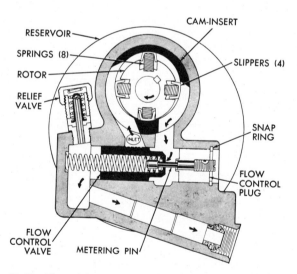

Fig. 38-35. This slipper-type power steering pump is belt-driven. As rotor revolves, spring-loaded slippers force fluid from inlet side of pump to flow control valve.

sure by rotating four to eight spring-loaded slippers around a cam insert within the pump body. The internal gear pump has a six-tooth gear mounted eccentrically with the internal gear which rotates within the pump housing. As the gear turns, fluid is trapped between the teeth and is emitted under pressure.

Most modern power steering pumps contain a flow control valve, which limits fluid flow to the power cylinder to about two gallons per minute, and a relief valve which limits pressure according to system demands.

The power steering hoses serve as a means of transmitting the fluid under pressure from the pump to the power cylinder and return. In addition, the hoses must provide the proper amount of expansion to absorb any shock surge and offer enough restriction to the fluid flow to keep the pump cavity full of fluid at all times.

Variable Ratio Steering

A major step forward in steering gear design was accomplished with the introduction of variable ratio steering. In conventional, or constant ratio, steering the degree of turn of the front wheels is always in direct proportion to the degree of turn of the steering wheel. In variable ratio steering, the ratio remains constant for approximately the first 40 deg. of steering wheel movement. Then the ratio decreases and the response of the front wheels quickens for every degree of turn of the steering wheel, Fig. 38-36.

The "variable" effect is made possible by the design of the steering gear. With constant ratio gears of the sector and rack type, the teeth of the sector are all the same length. This causes the sector to swing the pitman arm the same number of degrees with each tooth of the sector. With variable ratio gears, the center tooth of the sector is longer than the other teeth, which produces a slower response of the pitman arm in shallow turn situations and faster response near the extremes of steering wheel

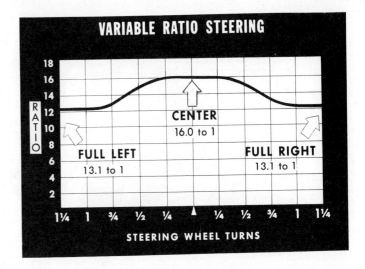

Fig. 38-36. *Advantage of variable ratio steering is that front wheels respond more quickly to steering wheel movement as the degree of turn increases.*

travel for sharp turns. In some applications, Fig. 38-27, a specially contoured worm gear alters the ratio.

Typically, a variable ratio steering gear will provide a ratio of about 16:1 for straight ahead driving, and about a 13:1 ratio in full turns. In relation to steering wheel movement with variable ratio steering, the first quarter-turn in either direction will produce a relatively "slow" response from the front wheels. Then the response "speeds up" as the steering wheel is turned from one-half to a full turn. After that, the lowest ratio comes into effect when it is needed for parking or backing up.

Quiz - Spring Suspension and Steering

1. What are the two basic types of front suspension?
2. What is "unsprung" weight?
3. What type of spring is used in conjunction with solid axle beams?
   a. Coil springs.
   b. Leaf springs.
   c. Torsion bars.
4. Are front coil springs always placed between the lower control arm and the frame?
5. What keeps the rise and fall of the front wheels in a vertical plane in independent suspension systems?
   a. Proportionate lengths of control arms.
   b. Front suspension height specification.
   c. Correct caster setting.
6. When coil springs are used at the rear, what carries driving and braking torque?
   a. Control arms.
   b. Shock absorbers.
   c. Torsion bars.
7. Are torsion bars usually adjustable?
8. How is tension increased on a torsion bar?
   a. By flexing.
   b. By compressing.
   c. By twisting.
9. Does a Volkswagen use torsion bars front and rear?
10. Can air springs be automatically controlled?
11. What is the main purpose of a shock absorber?
12. Are cars always equipped with four shock absorbers, two in front and two at rear?
13. What is the operating principle of a shock absorber?
14. What are the two general types of steering systems?
15. Which manual steering gear type is most popular on late model cars?
16. Name three components of manual steering linkage.
17. What are the three basic power steering systems?
18. Give two types of power steering pumps.

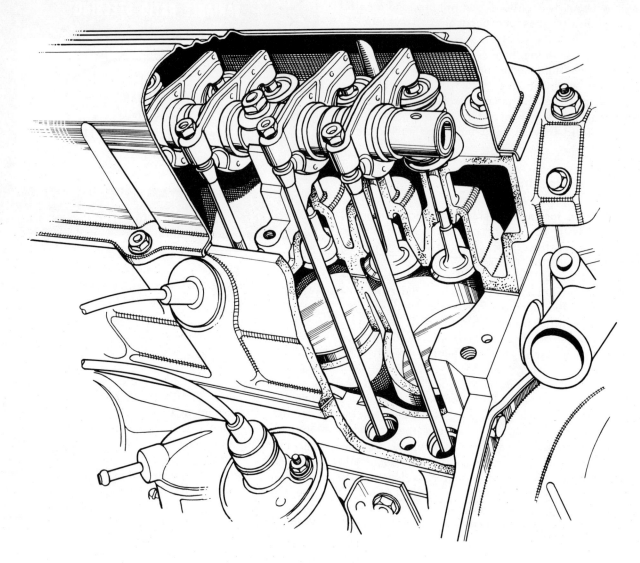

Dodge Dart engine, valve train.

WHEEL ALIGNMENT

Front wheel alignment (variously known as front end alignment, steering alignment or steering balance) involves many factors that must be correct and co-ordinated before a car will steer, track and hold the road properly. Wheel alignment is balancing the steering angles (caster, camber, toe-in, steering axis inclination and toe-out on turns) with the physical forces being exerted (gravity, momentum, friction and centrifugal force).

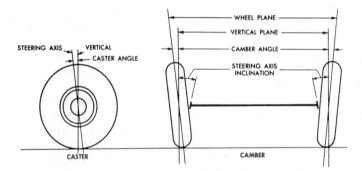

Fig. 39-1. Alignment angles are exaggerated to show various settings of front wheels which work together to provide smooth rolling and easy steering that extends tire life.

Steering Balance

The entire matter of steering control relies on whether or not the tires maintain close contact with the road surface. Tire-to-road contact, of course, is influenced by the tire tread, tire inflation, wheel balance, weight on the wheel, shock absorber action, spring action and wheel angularity. A balanced condition between these elements will establish a perfect pivot point from which the wheels can rotate with the least friction. And this definite point on the tread of each front tire is the target of all steering angle adjustments. See Fig. 39-1.

The area of contact varies with tire inflation pressure and load, Fig. 39-2. Under or over-inflation affects the rolling characteristics of the wheels by changing the degree of friction between the tires and the road surface. If one tire is under-inflated, or has a worn tread, it will have a tendency to hold back - and the car will steer toward the side holding back. Any-

thing that tends to increase the area of tire tread contact with the road will increase the rolling resistance on that side - resulting in the car steering to one side.

For satisfactory alignment, both front tires should be of the same size, make and type, and have a similar amount of tread wear. Under ideal conditions - if both front wheels are carrying the same weight, are equipped with tires having approximately the same degree of tread wear and inflated to the same pressure, and are properly and equally adjusted for angularity - the tires would maintain the same contact on a smooth road surface.

Obviously, though, it is impossible to maintain this constant contact. The wheels bounce up and down at different times, at different rates of speed and to differing heights. Here, the effects of momentum and inertia change the area of tread contact. The deflection of the car springs constantly changes the angles at which the steering system operates. Centrifugal force on the wheels emphasizes any lack of balance. And the extremely flexible characteristics of the tires defeats the possibility of true and uniform steering geometry.

It follows that a tire must be almost perfectly round if it is to maintain constant contact with the road (or as constant contact as road conditions will allow). Also in this connection, each of the four wheels acts as a flywheel, storing energy as it acquires momentum. The tire, wheel and brake drum rotate as a unit. Anything added to this rotating mass - such as tires with excessively heavy treads - will increase the flywheel effect.

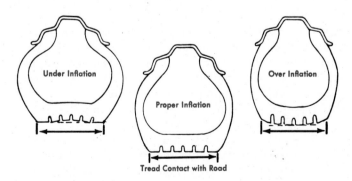

Fig. 39-2. Tire wear is governed by tread contact with road surface. Note area of contact under conditions of under-inflation, proper inflation and over-inflation.

Wheel Balance and Unbalance

Another important matter to be considered before alignment angles are set is the possibility that the wheels and tires are unbalanced. The tires may be round and true when rotated slowly, yet give trouble on the road when they turn fast enough to get into the realm of centrifugal force. This unbalance can exist in the tire, wheel, brake drum or hub – or in any combination of the four.

When an unbalanced wheel revolves, centrifugal force acts on the heaviest portion and tends to lift the wheel off the road, then slam it down during each revolution. This results in flat spots on the tire tread and worn out ball joints, tie rod ends, steering gears and shock absorbers.

Centrifugal force is exerted away from the center of rotation – and it increases as the square of the speed of rotation. For example: a weight of one ounce on the tread of a tire 30 in. in diameter will exert a force of about 3 lb. at 30 mph. If the speed is doubled (60 mph), the force becomes four times as great, or about 12 lb. If the speed is tripled (90 mph), the force becomes nine times as great, or about 27 lb.

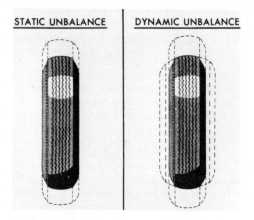

Fig. 39-3. Static unbalance is uneven distribution of weight in tire assembly in plane of rotation. Dynamic unbalance is uneven distribution of weight to right and left of plane of rotation.

If the unbalance lies in the plane of the rotation, it is known as static unbalance, Fig. 39-3. If it lies on either or both sides of the plane of wheel rotation, it is known as dynamic unbalance. Either condition will cause the wheels to bounce. Dynamic unbalance in the front wheels will cause them to wobble as well. Rear wheels should be kept in balance to avoid a bouncing action which will set up a heavy vibration in the chassis and affect steering balance.

Unbalance can be detected with the aid of special equipment which also indicates the proper location for weights to restore balance. In spite of regular maintenance, however, uneven tire wear can result from drivers' habits as their modern automobiles accelerate faster, take curves at a higher rate of speed and

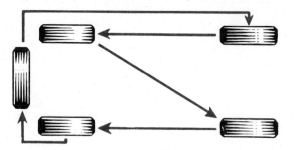

Fig. 39-4. Planned tire rotation extends tire life since each tire is used four-fifths of time. In addition, tires get varied wear conditions operating in left and right, front and rear locations.

stop more quickly. To counteract uneven wear that leads to unbalance, most manufacturers recommend that tires should be rotated every five thousand miles. See Fig. 39-4.

Car Weight Balance

The next step in balancing steering alignment is to check the accuracy of attachment of the wheels to the load being carried. The frame must be checked to see that it is square and level. Also, the axles and wheels must be located properly in relation to the frame. This involves making a series of measurements to establish the parallel and right angle relationships between the frame and wheels before attempting to make any angular adjustments of the front wheels.

The essential part of this relationship is a straight, undistorted frame, Fig. 39-5. In the process of alignment, an accurate center line must first be established. Then, if straight lines are drawn through the centers of both rear and both front spindle locations, they must be parallel to each other and form right angles with the center line of the frame, Fig. 39-6.

Thus, when the wheels are attached to the front spindles and rear axles, the rear wheels should be parallel to the center line of the frame. Likewise, the front wheels in their straight ahead position should be parallel to this line (except for slight toe-in or toe-out). This is necessary so that each wheel will tend to roll straight and true in relation to this frame center line.

Wheelbase - Tread Width

Another point of importance when locating axles and spindles is the wheelbase measurement. Wheelbase is the distance between the center of the front wheel and the center of the rear wheel, Fig. 39-7. This distance (left front to left rear, right front to right rear) with the front wheels in the "straight ahead" position, must be exactly the same on each side for proper weight balance and the ability of the car's wheels to track correctly.

Tread width is also a key measurement in this respect. Tread width is the distance between the center points of the left tire tread and the right tire tread as they come in contact with the road. See Fig. 39-8. While the front and rear wheels may have different tread widths, each front wheel must be the same distance from the center line of the frame, and each rear

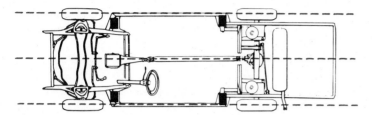

Fig. 39-5. Before making alignment checks, see that the frame is straight, square and level. Side rails must be parallel to center line.

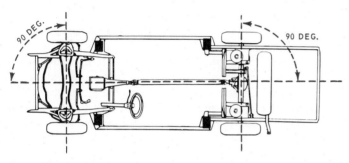

Fig. 39-6. Straight lines drawn through centers of both rear axle and front spindle locations must be parallel and form right angles with center line of frame.

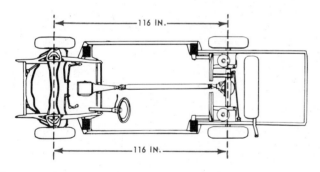

Fig. 39-7. Wheelbase — or distance between centers of front and rear wheels — must measure as specified and be exactly equal on each side.

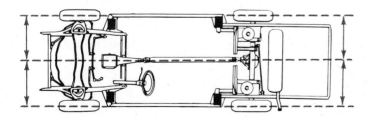

Fig. 39-8. Tread width is distance between center points of left tire tread and right tire tread. Measurements are taken from frame center line to center of tire in each case to establish correct frame-to-wheels relationship.

wheel must be the same distance from this center line.

This parallel relationship between the frame center line and wheels establishes a balance between front and rear — and between right and left. While this balance may not mean equal weight at these points, it does mean that a balanced distribution of weight and stress has been acquired for the proper setting of front wheel angles.

However, if the car has been damaged in an accident, the impact may have shifted the frame side rails, forcing the frame into a diamond shape and changing the relationship between the axle and spindle locations and the frame center line.

Rear Wheel Track

An out-of-line condition, not caused by an accident, can usually be traced to a mechanical defect or sag due to stress in the middle, or at one corner, of the frame. In any case, a frame that is out of line must be straightened before it is possible to obtain correct steering alignment. The frame rails must be the same height from the floor on each side at the spring seats, along with the essential parallel and right angle relationships.

Also vital in this matter of weight balance is the condition of the car springs. They control the up-and-down motion of the car and, therefore, the height of the car above the road. If one or more of the springs is collapsed or broken, it causes an unbalanced distribution of weight. This unbalance creates a lopsided appearance and not only puts an added strain on related parts but also changes the angularity of the front wheels.

This condition also may occur when the load is distributed unequally; that is, greater weight on the springs on one side than on the other. In fact, anything that changes the ratio of weight on the springs will have a definite bearing on the alignment angles and also on the area of tire tread contact that is so important in balancing steering alignment.

Suspension Height

The height of the car above the road must be checked — front and rear, right and left — before any of the steering angles are adjusted, Fig. 39-9. Although the method of checking varies with type of suspension, the measurements should be made with the car parked on a level floor or on an alignment machine with the tires equally inflated, fuel tank full, no passenger load and no excess weight on either side.

Shock Absorber Action

Still another factor involved in controlling the up-and-down motion of a moving vehicle is efficient shock absorbing action. The shock absorbers serve as an aid to steering balance by furnishing a dampening effect that protects the springs from sudden overloading or unloading action while holding wheel bounce to a minimum. Obviously, if the shock absorbers are not operating properly, the car will bounce excessively, causing steering angles to change oftener and to a greater extent.

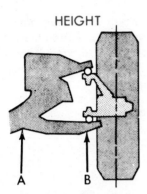

HEIGHT

Fig. 39-9. Front suspension height must be correct if wheel alignment angles are to be maintained. Proper height – left and right, front and rear – helps provide trim appearance and satisfactory ride.

In this connection, there is a possibility that the steering angles will check out correctly on the alignment equipment, yet the car will not handle satisfactorily on the road. This situation could be caused by defective springs or shock absorbers, worn parts in the steering gear or front system, driving conditions, or habits of the driver.

One other chassis control feature that merits consideration is the use of stabilizers or "sway bars." Some cars require these bars to steady the chassis – particularly front end roll and sway on turns. Stabilizers are designed to control this centrifugal tendency which forces a rising action on the side toward the inside of the turn.

With all of these weight balance factors to be checked out and corrected, it is apparent that steering alignment is more than just an adjustment of the steering angles. It involves many essential preliminary steps ranging from tire inflation to weight on the wheels and concerns everything from habits of the driver to the wide range of physical forces exerted.

This whole theory of steering alignment revolves around balanced weight distribution on the wheels and proper tire tread contact with the road surface while the vehicle is in motion.

Front Wheel Angularity

The angles involved in front wheel alignment are caster, camber, toe-in, steering axis inclination and toe-out on turns. These angles refer to the tilt of the wheels and steering axis, and they govern the way the front wheels behave while the vehicle is in motion.

Actually, the alignment angles are so closely related that changing one will often change the others.

In order to check and adjust them properly, it is necessary to use special equipment capable of a high degree of accuracy. In many cases, caster and camber specifications are given in minutes (fractions of a degree).

Here again balance enters the picture as the adjustment goal becomes a balanced relationship of these steering angles – with due regard for road and load factors involved in each individual case.

Caster

Caster is the steering angle that utilizes the weight and momentum of the car's chassis to lead the front wheels in a straight path. See Fig. 39-1. Caster is the backward or forward tilt of the steering axis that tends to stabilize steering in a straight direction by placing the weight of the vehicle either ahead or behind the area of tire-to-road contact.

It would be easier to visualize the effect of the caster angle by projecting an imaginary line lengthwise through the center of the ball joints and downward to the road surface. This line, called the "steering axis," would be found to intersect the road at a point ahead of or in back of the center point of the tire tread contact. Obviously then, if the front wheels were given a generous amount of caster, they would be subjected to a leading or trailing action much like an ordinary furniture caster that tends to line up and drag its wheel in the direction of movement.

"Positive" caster is the angular amount that the upper ball joint is farther back than the lower joint. "Negative" caster is the condition when the upper ball joint is farther ahead than the lower one. See Fig. 39-10. The caster angle, then, is the number of degrees – or fraction of one degree – that the steering axis is tilted backward or forward from the vertical axis of the front wheels.

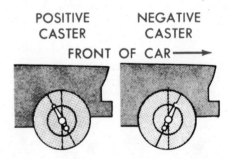

POSITIVE CASTER　　NEGATIVE CASTER

FRONT OF CAR ➝

Fig. 39-10. Caster is degree of tilt of steering axis forward or backward from vertical center line of wheel.

Specifications for solid front axle systems call for as much as 8 or 9 degrees of positive caster as compared with the fractional-degree requirements of independent suspension. This reduction was possible because of the relatively smaller changes in the caster angle during the up-and-down movement of the inde-

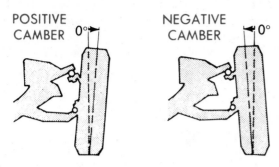

Fig. 39-11. Camber is amount wheel tilts in or out at top from its vertical center line.

pendently suspended wheels in relation to the frame.

This up-and-down movement will affect the other steering angles to a great extent regardless of the type of suspension involved. Camber and steering axis inclination, for example, vary considerably during fast stop and extreme bounce conditions.

Camber - Steering Axis Inclination

Camber is the outward tilt of the wheels at the top, Fig. 39-11. It is built into the wheel spindle by forming the spindle with a downward tilt to provide positive camber. Steering axis inclination is the inward tilt of the steering knuckle, Fig. 39-12. It is so interrelated with camber that they share a common side (vertical axis of wheel). The combination of these two angles forms what is known as the included angle.

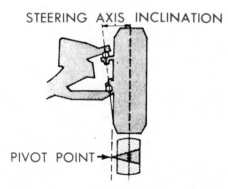

Fig. 39-12. Steering axis inclination is inward tilt of steering knuckle from vertical center line of wheel.

The purpose of this two-angle team is to place the turning point of the wheel at the center of the tire tread contact area. To clarify this, it must be remembered that, originally, the front wheels were pivoted to swing in a vertical position. This created a difference between the pivoting center line and the wheel center line which caused the wheels to pull or scuff on rough roads.

The car manufacturers recognized this fact and went about solving it by tilting the pivoting center line in at the top (steering axis inclination) and tilting the wheel out at the top (camber). This created an included

angle that intersected close to the center of tire tread contact and reduced the scuff area to a minimum. See Fig. 39-1.

When camber and steering axis inclination are correct, they contribute to steering ease and tire life. Also, by placing the tread contact area more nearly under the point of load, a "straightening up" tendency is provided which serves to minimize the need for a large caster angle.

To illustrate this, consider the movement of front wheel spindle with the weight off the wheels. First, the downward tilt of the spindle provides camber. Then, with a vertical steering axis, the spindle would pivot at right angles and its tip would move in a horizontal plane when turning from one extreme to the other.

However, with the steering axis tilted inward (steering axis inclination), the end of the spindle will describe an arc that is noticeably lower in the extreme turn position than in the center or straight ahead position. In normal operation then, as the weight of the car prevents the spindle from moving up and down, the car itself is forced upward when the front wheels are turned and the force of gravity tends to straighten the wheels.

Thus the weight of the car helps to provide a kind of automatic steering effect that is brought about by the accurate adjustment of the steering angles. Additional alignment benefits become apparent when some of the troubles caused by misalignment are noted. These include hard steering, wander and unequal or excessive tire wear.

Toe-In

Equally important in this respect is the relationship of toe-in to steering balance. Toe-in is the term used to specify the amount in fractions of an inch that the front wheels are closer together in front than at the rear, when measured at hub height, Fig. 39-13. Present specifications, for example, generally call for a toe-in setting of 1/16 in. to 3/16 in. Here again precision testing equipment and careful measurement and correction will prevent any slipping or scuffing action between the tires and road.

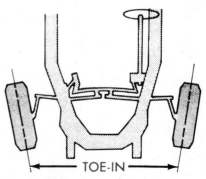

Fig. 39-13. Toe-in is amount front wheels are closer together in front than at rear at hub height.

Actually, the slight amount of toe-in that is specified serves to keep the front wheels running parallel on the road by offsetting other forces which tend to spread the wheels apart. The major force is the backward thrust of the road against the tire tread while the car is moving forward. Other factors include compensation for unavoidable play in the tie rod assembly and allowance for angular changes caused by wheel bounce or variations in road conditions.

If toe-in is incorrect, the tires will be dragged along the road, scuffing and featheredging the tread ribs. Unusual tread wear patterns result from a combination of causes. Changes in road or load conditions will affect more than one steering angle and, also in this respect, the toe-in reading will change when other angular adjustments are made. For this reason, toe-in should be measured first and corrected last on all front end alignment jobs.

From the mechanical standpoint, the parallel relationship between the front wheels is controlled by the tie rod and the angularity of the steering arms, Fig. 39-14. Since these connecting links are relatively

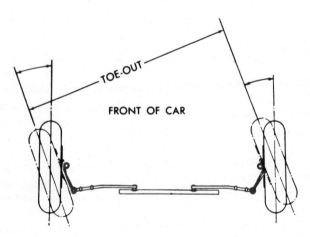

Fig. 39-14. *Tie rods and steering arms control parallel relationship between front wheels both in straight-ahead driving and on turns.*

rigid, it might be assumed that toe-in would remain constant. This could be the case when a single tie rod is used, but when a car is equipped with independent suspension and has more than one tie rod, toe-in will vary under excessive load or bounce conditions.

Toe-Out on Turns

It is obvious that driving conditions make it impossible to keep the front wheels parallel at all times. Regardless of how accurately the front wheels are positioned for straight ahead driving, they could be out of their correct relative position on turns. Considering that the outside wheel is approximately five feet farther away from the point about which the car is turning, it must turn at a lesser angle and travel in a greater circle than the inside wheel. This condition

is called "toe-out on turns," which simply means that each front wheel requires a separate turning radius to keep the inside tire from slipping and scuffing on turns, Fig. 39-15.

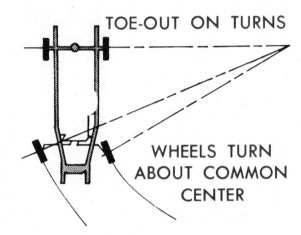

Fig. 39-15. *Toe-out on turns is angular relationship between front wheels when turned to right or left.*

Toe-out on turns, then, is the relationship between the front wheels which allows them to turn about a common center. To accomplish this, the steering arms are designed to angle several degrees inside of the parallel position, Fig. 39-16. The exact amount depends on the tread and wheelbase of the car and on the arrangement of the steering control linkage.

The theory of this design is that an imaginary line drawn through each steering arm will intersect near the differential. In practice, this serves to speed the action of steering arm on the inside of the turn as it moves toward center line of the wheel spindle. The effect on outside steering arm is to slow it down as it moves away from center of wheel spindle. Therefore, the outside wheel turns at a lesser angle - its turning circle is greater - and true rolling contact is obtained.

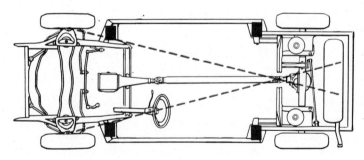

Fig. 39-16. *Steering arms are angled inward to provide a separate turning radius for each front wheel.*

Consider that, in turning, a car must pivot about some theoretical point along the extended center line of the rear axle. Then recall that the front wheels must turn about a common center. Put them together and it becomes clear that the turning radius lines for both front wheels must intersect at some point along the rear axle center line regardless of degree of turn. The sharper the turn, of course, the nearer this point is to the car itself.

A typical specification for toe-out on turns calls for 23 deg. angularity on the inside wheel while the outside one is turning 20 deg. If a bent steering arm is indicated, it must be replaced. However, all other possibilties should be eliminated:

1. All other steering angles must be correct.
2. Steering control linkage must be aligned properly.

Quiz - Wheel Alignment

1. Name five things that influence tire tread contact with the road surface.
2. Name the five steering angles.
3. Does dynamic unbalance lie in the plane of wheel rotation?
4. What is the correct terminology for the distance between the center points of the left tire tread and the right tire tread as they come in contact with the road?
   a. Wheelbase.   b. Tread width.   c. Toe-in.
5. Name three things beside improperly adjusted steering angles that could cause car handling complaints.
6. If the upper ball joint is farther back than the lower ball joint, what angularity is the wheel said to have?
   a. Positive caster.
   b. Positive camber.
   c. Positive steering axis inclination.
7. Which two steering angles make up the included angle?
8. What is the purpose of the included angle?
9. When a car is turning, should the front wheels toe-in or toe-out?
10. Why are the steering arms angled several degrees inside the parallel position?

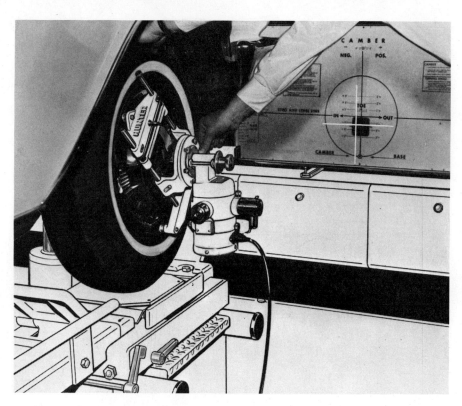

Alignment equipment comes in many forms. This setup incorporates an alignment rack of specified height, turntables, light beam projectors that mount on front wheels and a calibrated alignment screen.

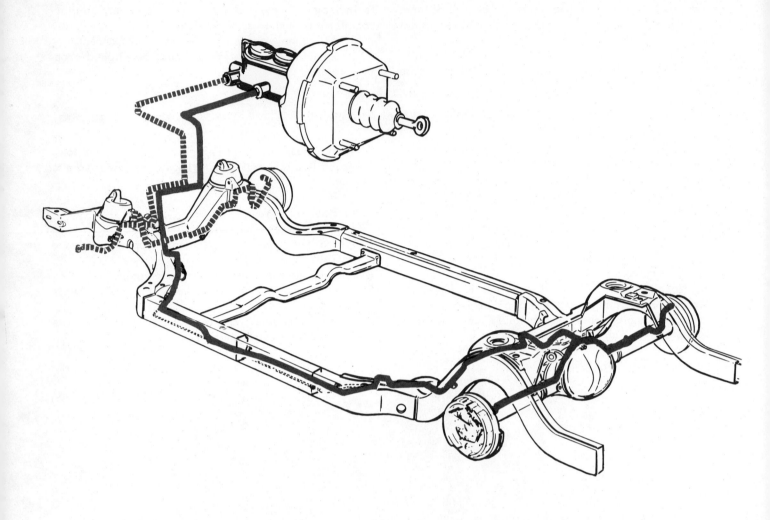

*Dual hydraulic brake systems on all late model U.S. cars eliminate possibility of total brake failure if a fluid leak occurs.
Note that dual master cylinder feeds fluid to two separate systems via front lines (dashed) and rear lines (solid).*

WHEEL ALIGNMENT CORRECTION

Wheel alignment correction calls for a careful determination of whether or not the problem lies in misalignment, steering, suspension or in the wheel and tire assemblies. A good alignment specialist must be able to visualize the behavior of a loaded vehicle going 70 mph on a superhighway, and make corrective adjustments on an empty car standing on an alignment rack.

A thorough understanding of the principles involved and enough imagination to picture actual operating conditions are absolutely essential in this specialized field. And, in addition, the serviceman must have and know how to use equipment of outstanding accuracy.

As for the vehicles themselves, the need for frequent and regular wheel alignment checks has increased with technological advances. Power steering, softer springing, rubber-bushed suspension parts, improved soundproofing and the use of wide tread tires allow constant abuse of car suspension without forewarning the driver. Add to this: more moving parts in modern suspension systems; more miles driven at superhighway speeds; more miles driven per car per year. With this in mind, most manufacturers recommend wheel alignment checks at least once a year. Another rule-of-thumb is the need for an alignment check at the first sign of uneven tread wear.

Consider Interrelated Angles

Remember that alignment correction includes adjustment of all interrelated factors affecting the running and steering of the front wheels of the vehicle. See Fig. 40-1. Changing one angle will often change others, so it is necessary to recheck all angles when one is changed. The method of inspection and detection varies with type of equipment, but generally, the angles should be checked in the following order:

1. Front suspension height.
2. Caster.
3. Camber.
4. Toe-in.
5. Steering axis inclination.
6. Toe-out on turns.

However, certain preliminary checks should be made to eliminate obvious problems and to set up the vehicle for the alignment tests.

Preliminary Checks

Generally, cars should be checked for alignment at "curb height" and "curb weight." (Certain car manufacturers specify use of alignment spacers to insure proper suspension heights.) "Curb weight" means the

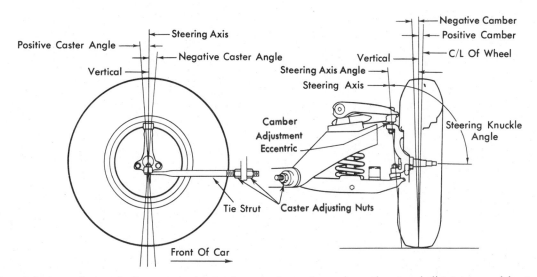

Fig. 40-1. Interrelation of alignment angles is shown in these views of a coil-spring, ball-joint type of front suspension system. Note typical points of adjustment for caster and camber.

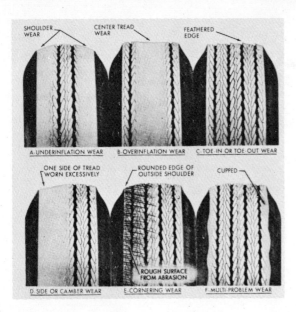

Fig. 40-2. Comparison of worn tire treads depicts pattern of wear and what caused it. If alignment is correct, life of tires depends on car operating conditions and driving habits.

basic automobile, less passengers, with a full fuel tank and proper amounts of coolant and lubricants. The spare tire and wheel, jack and jack handle must be in design position, and the front seats should be in their rear-most position.

Then proceed as follows:

Check front tires to see that tread wear is approximately the same and not abnormal, Fig. 40-2. Test for recommended air pressure in all four tires and remove stones and caked mud from wheels and tires.

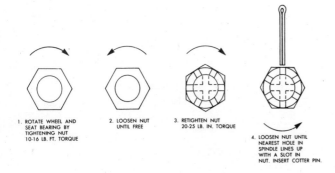

Fig. 40-3. Front wheel tapered roller bearings should have slightly loose "feel." Using a dial indicator, end play should be from 0 to .005 in. on most cars.

Check wheel lugs for looseness and/or improper installation. Test action and rebound of all shock absorbers by jouncing all four corners of car. Car should rebound slowly, not bounce.

Test steering effort and steering wheel return from both directions. Check for inconsistent effort, harshness, noise, binding or excessive free play. Check steering gear for excessive backlash and for "high

point" with reference to steering wheel position and straight ahead position of front wheels. Adjust steering gear as required.

Raise the vehicle and test front wheel bearings for looseness. Grasp tire at top and bottom and try to rock assembly on its spindle. Adjust bearings if necessary, Fig. 40-3. Use a dial indicator to check each front wheel and tire assembly for runout, making sure that wheel is not damaged and tire is seated in rim of wheel. Mark point of maximum runout on tire sidewall, Fig. 40-4, then spin each front wheel and balance as required.

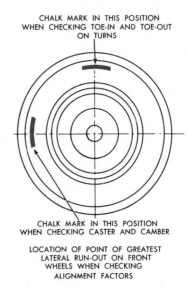

Fig. 40-4. Point of maximum lateral runout should be marked on front tire sidewall. Place mark to front or rear for caster/camber checks, at top for toe-in.

Manually check front end for looseness or wear at control arm pivot shafts or bolts, suspension ball joints, struts, stabilizer and all mounting bolts and nuts. Visually check condition of suspension ball joints and seals. Inspect all springs for sagging or breakage. Check for looseness of brake caliper attaching bolts on vehicles so equipped.

Test for looseness of steering gear mounting bolts at frame. Manually check for looseness or wear at all steering pivot points: pitman arm, relay rod, tie rod ends and idler arm, Fig. 40-5. Inspect for bent steering arms.

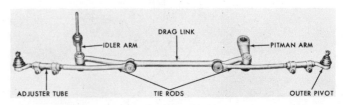

Fig. 40-5. Typical steering linkage arrangement as viewed from above. Points of greatest wear include tie rod ends, idler arm bushings and relay rod-to-tie rod connections.

Setting Up the Car

Lower the car and drive it far enough in a straight line to establish the straight ahead position of the front wheels. Then mark the steering wheel hub and steering column collar for use as a reference point during the alignment procedure, Fig. 40-6. At this time, rear

Fig. 40-7. Suspension height is measured, left and right, to help guarantee accuracy of angular checks which follow.

Fig. 40-6. Mark straight ahead position of front wheels on steering wheel hub and steering column collar for future reference in making alignment checks.

wheel track can be checked by running the car in and out of a wet area and examining the tread marks left by the front and rear tires. Since front and rear tread widths are seldom the same, the marks may not coincide. However, there should be equal spacing between marks left by the left front tire and left rear, and also between the right front tire and right rear. If the accuracy of the car's tracking ability is questionable, make more precise measurements of the frame-to-wheels relationship. See Figs. 39-5 to 39-8.

Measuring Suspension Height

To prepare the car for a suspension height check, jounce it lightly, front and rear, until suspension parts equalize. If excessive friction in the suspension system is suspected, make two quick checks of bumper height and compare the difference. First lift the car manually by the bumper and let it settle slowly to normal standing height. Measure from the center of the bumper to the floor. Then push down on the bumper and release it slowly. Take this measurement and compare it with the first. If the two height measurements are not within approximately one inch of each other, excessive suspension friction exists.

If the above checks are within the limit, jounce the car lightly, measure front suspension height at the points specified by the car manufacturer, and compare the measurements with specifications. See Fig. 40-7. If the suspension height is below minimum requirements on cars with coil springs, replace both springs. If one side is within specifications and the other side

is not, replace the weak spring. In cars equipped with torsion bars, make the necessary adjustments to obtain correct front suspension height. See Figs. 40-8 and 40-9.

If alignment spacers are required for making certain angular checks: place car on floating turntables; raise car body and install spacers front and rear;

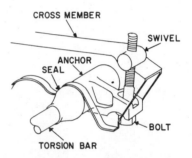

Fig. 40-8. Older Chrysler Corporation cars with torsion bars have adjusting device located at rear anchors in frame center cross member.

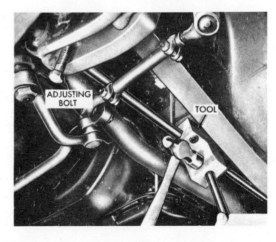

Fig. 40-9. Later Chrysler cars utilize torsion bar adjustment at front suspension lower control arm. A special torsion bar removing tool is shown.

lower car body. Generally, spacers in front are placed between suspension lower control arms and frame spring pockets. See Fig. 40-10. At the rear, spacers are installed between rear axle housing and frame, Fig. 40-11.

Checking and Setting Caster

Caster is the angle measured between a true vertical line through the center of the wheel and the center line through the upper and lower ball joints or kingpin. See Fig. 40-1. On cars with ball joints, increase positive caster by moving the upper ball joint

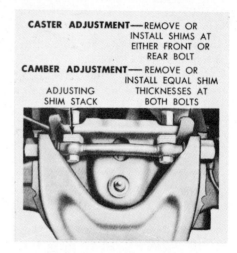

Fig. 40-12. *Shim adjustment of caster and camber provides simple expedient for positioning suspension control arms at precise angles called for.*

Fig. 40-10. *Correct suspension height is such a critical preliminary alignment step that some manufacturers recommend using alignment spacers.*

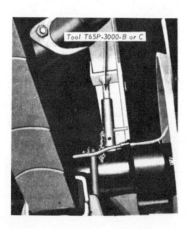

Fig. 40-11. *Alignment spacers, front or rear, serve to support car body at correct height above wheels, so alignment checks are valid.*

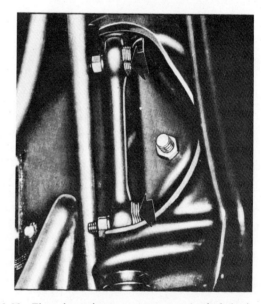

Fig. 40-13. *This shim adjustment moves pivot shaft farther inboard when shims are added in contrast to outboard movement in Fig. 40-12.*

to the rear or the lower ball joint to the front. Many cars are provided with shims under the upper control arm mounting bolts, Fig. 40-12, so transferring shims from under the rear bolt to the front bolt increases caster. Reversing this transfer of shims decreases caster. However, if the control arm pivot shaft is located inboard of the frame bracket, then the entire shimming procedure is reversed. See Fig. 40-13. Either of these caster adjustments affect camber, so caster and camber adjustments should be made simultaneously.

Another popular caster adjustment design is the strut rod type. With this arrangement, adjustable strut rods run diagonally from the lower control arms to the frame front cross member, Fig. 40-14. To make an adjustment, loosen the lock nuts at the forward end of

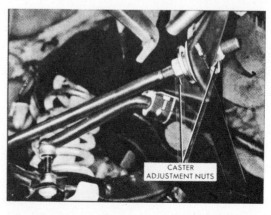

Fig. 40-14. *Some late model cars use diagonal strut rods, or tie-struts, as a means of caster adjustment. Struts also lend support to lower control arms.*

the struts, then shorten the rod to increase caster (this moves lower ball joint forward). Lengthening the rod by lock nut adjustment decreases caster.

Ford cars have used still another means of caster adjustment, Fig. 40-15. Elongated bolt holes are provided in the chassis frame where the upper control arm pivot shaft attaches. To make an adjustment,

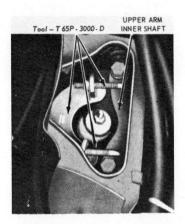

Fig. 40-15. Caster and camber is adjusted on Ford cars by moving pivot shaft of upper control arm in or out by means of elongated bolt holes. Special tools aid in moving and holding pivot shaft.

loosen the attaching bolts and slide the shaft in or out at the front or rear to tilt the steering axis forward or backward as required by the prescribed caster setting. Here again the same adjustment point is used for obtaining correct camber, so both angular adjustments should be made simultaneously.

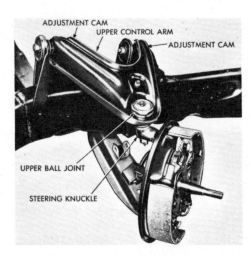

Fig. 40-16. Cam-bolt adjustment at inner ends of upper control arm on Chrysler cars, offers convenient way of positioning arm and setting correct camber.

Some late model cars have cam-bolt adjustments located at the inner ends of the upper control arms, Fig. 40-16, or at the lower control arms, Fig. 40-17. After loosening the lock nut, turn each cam bolt to re-

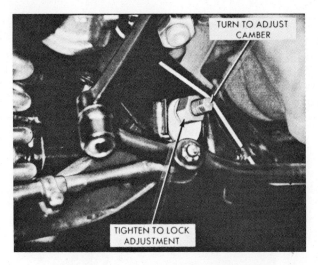

Fig. 40-17. Cam-bolt adjustment on lower control arm of Chevrolet cars, is easily accessible and close to strut bar adjustment of caster when balancing angles.

position the control arm and obtain correct caster and camber settings. For least effect on camber, the correct caster setting can be obtained by turning the cams an equal amount in opposite directions.

Some older models with kingpins incorporate caster-camber adjusting pins at the outboard end of the upper control arms. To make an adjustment, remove the grease fitting and loosen the clamp bolt. Then turn the adjusting pin to tilt the kingpin fore and aft to get the correct caster setting.

Adjusting Camber

Camber is the angle formed by the true vertical center line and the vertical center line of the tire. See Fig. 40-1. In cars with ball joints, increase positive camber by moving the upper ball joint outward or lower ball joint inward. On cars with shims under the upper control arm pivot shaft bolts, add an equal number of shims under front and rear bolts to increase positive camber, remove an equal number of shims to decrease camber, Fig. 40-12. This must be done in conjunction with the caster adjustment to relate the angles to each other. If the control arm pivot shaft is located inboard of the frame bracket, reverse this shimming procedure. Naturally, if the shims are located under the lower control arm pivot shaft, the opposite effects are obtained, so opposite shimming procedures must be followed.

Other types of camber adjustments that are integrated with caster settings (elongated bolt holes in chassis frame, cam bolts, and upper control arm adjusting pins) must be adjusted with both caster and camber settings in mind. This means many trial-and-error settings are necessary, although several car manufacturers and equipment manufacturers provide guidelines for the number of shims or amount of cam-bolt rotation necessary to obtain a given degree of correction.

The other relatively new camber adjustment design has a camber eccentric located in the steering knuckle upper support, Fig. 40-18. To make an adjustment, loosen lock nut one turn, tap bottom of stud with a soft mallet to free the eccentric in the knuckle. Turn the eccentric to obtain the specified camber angle, then tighten the lock nut and recheck camber. This type of camber adjustment is usually used in conjunction with strut rods for caster adjustment.

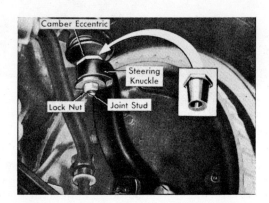

Fig. 40-18. Many Cadillac cars are fitted with camber eccentrics at base of upper ball joints. This setup is used in conjunction with strut-rod type caster adjustment.

Correcting Toe-In

Toe-in is the difference in measurement of the distance between the extreme front of both front wheels and the extreme rear. It is measured at hub height with the wheels in the straight ahead position. Most cars utilize two adjustable tie rods to facilitate the adjustment, Fig. 40-5.

To make the toe-in adjustment, loosen the clamp bolts on the tie rod sleeves and turn the sleeves to adjust tie rod length, Fig. 40-19. A tie rod behind the

Fig. 40-19. Tie rod sleeves permit adjustment of toe-in. When tightening clamp, open side should be down and within 45 deg. of vertical to avoid interference with frame.

front wheels must be lengthened to increase toe-in; a tie rod ahead of the front wheels must be shortened. However, tie rod adjustment also controls position of the steering wheel, so this "centering" adjustment should be made after correct toe-in has been established. Each tie rod adjusting sleeve is turned to shorten or lengthen each tie rod an equal amount to center the steering wheel but not disturb the toe-in adjustment.

Fig. 40-20. Toe-out on turns is checked with weight of car on wheels on floating turntables so that turning angles of each front wheel can be compared.

In some cases, alignment spacers are specified to be in place during the toe-in adjustment. In others, the spacers are removed and the car must be correct curb weight.

Checking Steering Axis Inclination

Steering axis inclination is the angle formed by the true vertical center line and the center line of the upper and lower ball joints. See Fig. 40-1. It is created by the inward tilt of the steering knuckle and is not adjustable. If steering axis inclination is out of specifications, replace the steering knuckle and check all alignment factors.

Toe-Out on Turns

Toe-out on turns is the variation in turning angle of each front wheel to avoid side slip on turns. It is built into the steering arms and is not adjustable. To get comparative readings, place the car on floating turntables, Fig. 40-20, set the inside wheel to a 20 deg. turn, then check the reading of the outside wheel against specifications. Repeat this check with the wheels turned in the opposite direction. If all other angles are correct and toe-out on turns is not, replace the steering arm on the side that is out of specifications.

Straightening or welding of parts should not be attempted. Bending of parts when cold may cause stresses and cracks. Straightening by heat will destroy the original heat treatment. Welding will change the grain structure of the metal.

Alignment Trouble Shooting

Proper steering control depends on more than just the steering system. Suspension and wheel alignment contribute so much to steering that all three must be considered when trouble shooting car handling complaints. See Figs. 40-21 to 40-25. Bear in mind that

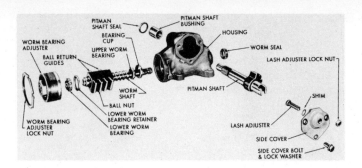

Fig. 40-21. *Exploded view of popular recirculating ball and worm manual steering gear reveals construction and sequence of assembly of parts.*

the car, load and passengers must be balanced above the tires and springs while being subjected to many and varied driving conditions. This weight on the wheels moves up and down with road irregularities, tends to go sideways from the action of centrifugal

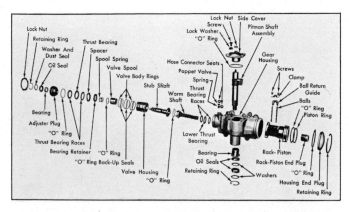

Fig. 40-22. *Increased number of parts used in power steering integral unit complicates service procedures, although control valve adjustment is common correction.*

force and wind pressures, and alternately shifts forward and backward under acceleration and braking. There may be an unequal distribution of load because of engine torque reaction on the frame or uneven passenger or cargo loading.

Usually, there is no quick and easy remedy for a given handling problem. A series of causes and effects

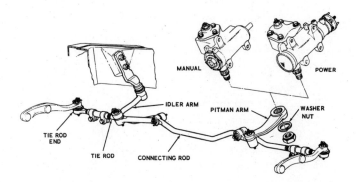

Fig. 40-23. *Exploded view shows how manual and power steering gears use basically same steering linkage to turn front wheels.*

must be analyzed with due regard for the alignment theories involved. Often a combination of minor defects add up to more serious trouble.

The following alignment trouble shooting check list gives some of the more common causes of car handling problems:

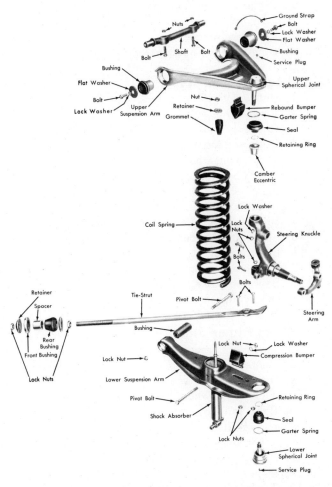

Fig. 40-24. *This coil spring front suspension system features upper and lower control arms, shock absorbers, ball joints, camber eccentric and tie-struts for adjusting caster.*

Shimmy or Wheel Tramp

1. Incorrect or unequal tire pressures.
2. Cupped, eccentric or bulged tires.
3. Unbalanced wheels.
4. Out-of-round wheel or brake drum.
5. Weak or inoperative shock absorbers.
6. Loose wheel bearing adjustment.
7. Incorrect front wheel alignment, particularly caster.
8. Loose or worn control arm bushings.
9. Loose or worn suspension ball joints.
10. Loose or worn steering linkage.
11. Loose steering gear on frame.
12. Loose steering gear adjustment.
13. Inoperative stabilizer.
14. Loose or worn strut bushings.

Hard or Rough Ride

1. High air pressure in tires.
2. Wrong type or size of tire.
3. Tight steering gear adjustment.
4. Incorrect wheel alignment, particularly caster.
5. Inoperative shock absorbers.
6. Overloaded or unevenly loaded vehicle.
7. Sagging or broken spring.
8. Lack of lubrication of front suspension and steering linkage.
9. Binding front suspension parts.

Car Leads to One Side

1. Unequal tire pressures.
2. Varied tire sizes.
3. Unevenly loaded vehicle.
4. Dragging front brakes.
5. Tight front wheel bearings.
6. Bent spindle, spindle arm or steering knuckle.
7. Incorrect or uneven front wheel alignment.
8. Loose strut bushings.
9. Sagging or broken front spring.
10. Inoperative shock absorber.
11. Broken rear spring center bolt.
12. Off-center rear spring center bolt.
13. Bent rear axle housing.
14. Out-of-line frame or underbody.

Wander to Either Side

1. Incorrect or unequal tire pressures.
2. Varied tire sizes.
3. Overloaded or unevenly loaded vehicle.
4. Tight front wheel bearing adjustment.
5. Bent spindle, spindle arm or steering knuckle.
6. Incorrect front wheel alignment.
7. Tight suspension ball joints.
8. Binding control arm shafts.
9. Inoperative shock absorbers.
10. Tight idler arm bushing.
11. Loose, worn or damaged steering linkage.
12. Loose steering gear on frame.
13. Incorrect steering gear adjustment.
14. Inoperative shock absorbers.
15. Broken rear spring center bolt.

Rear Suspension Out of Line

1. Broken rear spring center bolt.
2. Off-center rear spring center bolt.
3. Broken rear spring main leaf.
4. Mislocated rear spring front hanger.
5. Bent rear axle housing.
6. Out-of-line frame or underbody.

Uneven Tire Tread Wear

1. Incorrect tire pressures.
2. Failure to rotate tires.
3. Incorrect front wheel alignment, particularly camber and toe-in.
4. Excessive wheel runout.

5. Bent spindle, spindle arm or steering knuckle.
6. Grabbing brakes.
7. Loose, worn or damaged suspension parts.
8. Excessive speed on turns.

Tire Squeal on Turns

1. Low air pressure in tires.
2. Varied tire sizes.
3. Bent spindle, spindle arm or steering knuckle.
4. Incorrect front wheel alignment, particularly toe-in.
5. Loose or weak shock absorbers.

Noise in System

1. Loose front wheel bearing adjustment.
2. Loose shock absorber mountings.
3. Loose steering gear adjustment.

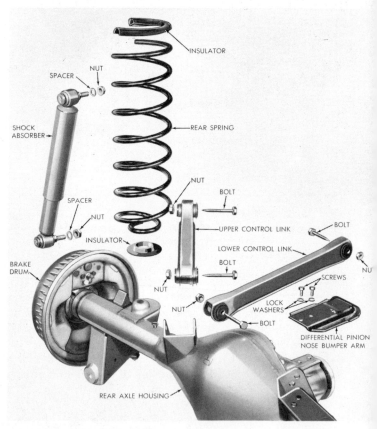

Fig. 40-25. *Typical rear suspension system utilizes coil springs, shock absorbers and three or four control arms, or links, to connect rear axle housing to frame.*

4. Loose steering gear on frame.
5. Worn steering linkage.
6. Worn control arm bushings.
7. Loose suspension strut bushings.
8. Insufficient suspension ball joint lubrication.
9. Worn idler arm bushings.
10. Loose or worn spring shackles.
11. Loose or worn stabilizer bushings.

Power Steering Trouble Shooting

When a car is equipped with power steering, it is important to make sure that the wheels are in correct alignment, that tires are properly inflated, and all parts of the steering linkage are adequately lubricated and in good operating condition. Power steering may prevent the driver from realizing that binding or looseness exists, so he may ignore it until serious damage is done.

Use a suitably calibrated pressure gauge to check hydraulic pressures in the system, which may approach 1450 psi, Fig. 40-26. Pressure lines are usually marked for high or low pressure. In any case, different fittings are used for attachment to the pump and steering gear power cylinder. When checking fluid pressure, the engine and power steering fluid should be at operating temperatures. Maximum pressure will be generated with the steering wheel held in the extreme turn position. NOTE: Do not hold wheel in extreme turn position for more than a few seconds or it may cause undue wear or damage to pump parts.

Check the Alignment Trouble Shooting check list for causes common to both manual and power systems and follow this check list to pinpoint the cause of problems in the power steering system:

Hard Steering
1. Loose pump V-belt.
2. Low fluid level.
3. Insufficient pump pressure.
4. Tight or frozen steering shaft bushings.
5. Binding steering wheel.
6. Low front suspension height.
7. Incorrect steering gear adjustment.
8. Sticking pressure control valve.
9. External oil leaks.
10. Internal oil leaks.
11. Air in fluid.

Excessive Steering Looseness
1. Incorrect steering gear adjustment.
2. Maladjusted pressure control valve.
3. Air in fluid.

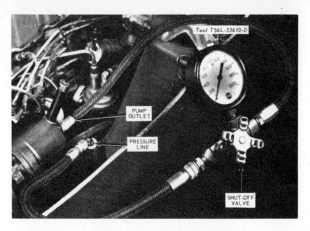

Fig. 40-26. Pressure gauge for testing power steering system is connected in series between pump outlet and pressure line hose. Test setup calls for shutoff valve so that tests can be made with unrestricted flow or under load.

Poor Return From Turns
1. Tight steering shaft bushings.
2. Misaligned steering gear.
3. Binding steering wheel.
4. Sticking pressure control valve.
5. Internal fluid leakage.
6. Air in fluid.

Temporary Loss of Power Assist
1. Loose pump V-belt.
2. Low fluid level.
3. Internal fluid leakage.
4. Too slow engine idle speed.
5. Air in fluid.

Noise in System
1. Sticking pressure control valve.
2. Loose pump V-belt.
3. Low fluid level.
4. Air in fluid.
5. Scored pump vanes or body.
6. Improperly routed pressure hoses.

NOTE: A hissing or squealing sound may occur in any power steering system when steering wheel is held in extreme turn position. This is normal, unless it is especially loud.

Quiz - Wheel Alignment Correction

1. Are alignment angles independent of each other or interrelated?
2. Generally, does the adjustment of front wheel roller bearings call for end play or preload?
3. Should each front wheel and tire assembly be checked for runout and balance before checking alignment angles?
4. Can front suspension height be adjusted on Chrysler cars with torsion bars?
5. How are alignment spacers used?
   a. As a means of adjusting position of control arms to set caster and camber.
   b. As a means of supporting car body above wheels for alignment checks.
   c. As a means of adjusting steering axis inclination.
6. Name two common caster adjusting points.
7. How is toe-in adjusted?
   a. Shortening or lengthening tie rods.
   b. Shortening or lengthening relay rod.
   c. Shimming control arms.

8. Where is toe-in reading taken?
    a. At vertical center lines of front tires at top.
    b. At point of tread-to-road contact of left and right front tires.
    c. At hub height of left and right front wheels.
9. Why is correct toe-out on turns important?
10. How is toe-out on turns checked?
    a. With weight of car on wheels.
    b. With alignment spacers in place.
    c. With front wheels in straight ahead position.

11. If toe-out on turns is out of specification, what correction is usually required?
12. If steering axis inclination is out of specification, what correction is usually required?
13. Which steering angle, if incorrect, causes shimmy or wheel tramp?
14. Which steering angles, if incorrect, cause uneven tire wear?
15. What type of tester is used to check power steering system operation?

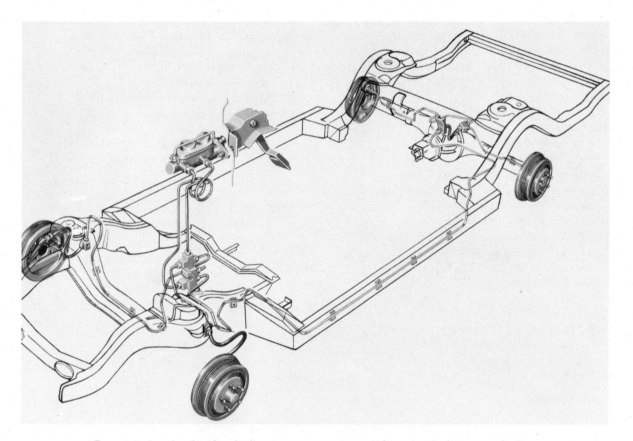

Fig. 41-1. Layout of modern braking system, incorporating late type dual master cylinder.

AUTOMOTIVE BRAKES

An automotive brake, Fig. 41-1, is a friction device which changes power into heat. Brakes may also be described as mechanical devices for retarding the motion of the vehicle by means of friction. The engine converts the heat of combustion, resulting from the burning of fuel, into useful power which is used to propel the vehicle. The brakes convert the power of momentum (kinetic energy) of the moving vehicle into heat by means of friction.

Friction is the resistance to relative motion between two bodies in contact. Friction varies not only with different materials, but also with the condition of the materials. In general, friction is less between polished surfaces than between rough; it is less be-

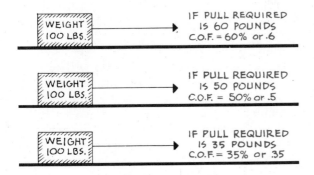

Fig. 41-2. *The coefficient of friction is equal to the force required to slide a body across a surface divided by the weight of the body.*

tween surfaces of different material than between those of the same material; also it is less when one surface rolls over the other than when it slides. Friction is caused by the interlocking of the projections and depressions of the two surfaces in contact. Rolling friction is supposed to be caused by the fact that the wheel indents more or less the surface over which it rolls so that in effect it is always climbing a little hill. If the surface is very hard, the indentation is less so that the friction will be less.

The amount of friction is proportional to the pressure between the two surfaces in contact, and is independent of the area of the surface in contact.

The amount of friction developed by any two bodies in contact is said to be their coefficient of friction. This is found by dividing the force required to slide

the weight over the surface, by the weight of the object. For example, Fig. 41-2, if to slide the 100 lb. weight requires a 60 lb. pull, then the coefficient of friction would be 60 divided by 100, or .60. If only 35 lb. is required to slide the 100 lb. weight, then the coefficient of friction would be .35.

The coefficient of friction will change with any variation of the condition of the surfaces. Any lubricant will of course greatly reduce the coefficient of friction. That is why it is so important to keep any oil or grease from brake lining. Even an extremely damp day will cause some variation in the coefficient of friction.

Braking Forces

Tremendous forces are involved when braking a vehicle. This arises from the fact that the vehicle must be brought to a stop in a much shorter time than is required to bring it up to speed. A simple method of explaining this is to make a comparison between the horsepower required to accelerate a vehicle, and the horsepower required to stop it.

A vehicle with a 100 hp engine requires about 60 seconds to accelerate to 60 mph. However, the same vehicle is expected to be able to stop from 60 mph in not more than 6 seconds. In other words, the brakes must do the same amount of work as the engine but in one-tenth the time. This means they must develop approximately 1,000 hp to stop the vehicle.

Effect Of Weight And Speed

The effect of weight and speed of the vehicle on braking is important for both passenger cars and trucks. If the weight of the vehicle is doubled, the energy of motion to be changed into heat energy is also doubled. In other words, if the weight is doubled, the amount of heat to be dissipated and absorbed is also doubled. For that reason it is important that vehicles not be overloaded.

The effect of higher speeds is much more serious. If the speed is doubled, four times as much stopping power must be developed, and the brakes must absorb or dissipate four times as much heat.

It naturally follows that if both weight and speed of a vehicle are doubled, the stopping power must be increased eight times and the brakes must absorb or dissipate eight times as much heat, Fig. 41-3.

Fig. 41-3. Effect of weight and speed on braking.

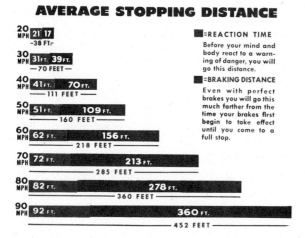

Fig. 41-4. Average stopping distances when traveling at various speeds.

Stopping Distance

As shown in Fig. 41-4, a vehicle which will just stop in 38 ft. from 20 mph will require 111 ft. to stop from 40 mph and 218 ft. from 60 mph.

When calculating the distance required to stop a vehicle, it is necessary to consider the time required for the driver to note the need for applying the brakes, and the time needed to move his foot and apply the brakes. That time is known as the reaction time. As will be noted in Fig. 41-4, the car will travel 21 ft. before the brakes are actually applied when travelling at 20 mph. When travelling at 90 mph, the car will travel 92 ft., before the brakes are applied, and the total distance needed to bring the vehicle to a stop would be 452 ft.

Brake Temperatures

As previously pointed out, brakes are devices which convert the energy of the moving vehicle into heat whenever the brakes are applied. This heat must be absorbed and dissipated by the brake parts. Unless the heat is carried away as fast as it is produced, the brake parts increase in temperature. The heat gener-

ated by brake applications is usually many times the rate of heat dissipation which results in high brake temperatures. These temperatures may become so high as to damage the brake lining, the brake drums, the brake fluid and in extreme cases the tires have been set on fire.

The factors that tend to increase brake temperatures include:
1. Load on vehicle.
2. Driver abuse.
3. Speed of vehicle.
4. Adjustment of brakes.
5. Care in installation of brake parts.
6. Balance of braking at each wheel.

The amount of heat developed in stopping a vehicle is easily calculated. Assuming a car weighing 4,000 lb. and travelling at a speed of 60 mph (or 88 ft. per second), the heat developed in stopping this car from that speed is found as follows:

$$\text{Kinetic energy in ft. lb.} = \frac{W\,V^2}{64.4}, \text{ in which } W$$

is the weight of the car in pounds and V the velocity in feet per second.

$$\text{Kinetic energy} = \frac{4000 \times 88^2}{64.4} = 480,994 \text{ ft. lb.}$$

Heat energy is measured in British thermal units (Btu's) and one Btu = 778 ft. lb. Therefore the heat energy of the car is:

$$\text{Btu} = \frac{480,994}{778} = 618 \text{ Btu}$$

If the car is stopped, the 618 Btu will go into the braking system. If we assume that all of this heat goes into the brake drums (usually about 90%) and also assuming that each brake drum weighs 10 lb. or a total of 40 lb. and the specific heat of the brake drum is .110 then the drum temperature rise would be:

$$\frac{618}{40 \times .110} = 140 \text{ deg. F.}$$

and assuming that the atmospheric temperature was 80 degrees, then the final drum temperature would be:
$$80 + 140 = 220 \text{ deg. F.}$$

If several stops are made in rapid succession, so that the brakes will not have time to cool, much higher temperatures will be reached. Also if speeds are increased, or the weight of the vehicle is increased, temperatures will soar still higher. In fact, under extreme conditions of unbalanced brakes on a heavy truck having an emergency stop from high speed, enough heat will be generated to melt a cube of iron weighing 11.2 lb. It must be remembered that if the brake lining surface does not conform to the surface of the brake drum all the work of stopping will be done by a small area of brake lining. The same amount of work will be done, but being concentrated on a small area, the temperature will be a great deal higher. If the area of braking is one fourth the normal area, the temperature will be four times higher than it should be. If the full area of contact is 40 sq. in and the normal braking temperature 150 deg., the temperatures will then soar to 600 deg., if only one fourth of the braking area is used.

Brake And Tire Friction

When brakes are applied on a vehicle, the brake shoes are forced into contact with the brake drums, thereby slowing the rotation of the wheel. Then, the friction between the tires and the road surface slows the speed of the vehicle. However, the friction be-

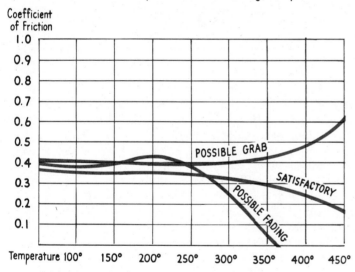

EFFECT OF TEMPERATURE ON COEFFICIENT OF FRICTION OF BRAKE LININGS

Three types of linings on cast iron drums
Same friction at low temperatures. Different at higher temperatures.

Fig. 41-5. Note how temperature effected the coefficient of friction of three different brake linings.

tween the brake shoe and the brake drum does not remain constant, but tends to increase with the temperature. From tests, the coefficient of friction of brake lining has been found to range from 0.35 to 0.50. Another variable is the materials of which the brake lining is made, and also the material of the brake drum. The friction of the tire on the road is approximately .02, but this also varies with the road surface.

The fastest stops are obtained with the wheels rotating. As soon as the wheels become locked, there is less friction and the car will not be stopped so quickly.

While the coefficient of friction of many linings

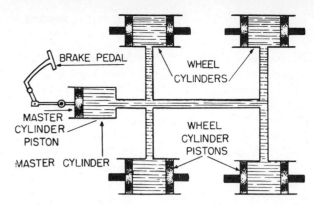

Fig. 41-6. Schematic drawing of hydraulic brake system.

tends to increase with higher temperatures, such is not always the case. This is brought out in Fig. 41-5, which shows how the coefficient of friction of one lining increased with higher temperatures, resulting in grabbing brakes. Another remained practically constant, while on a third lining, the coefficient dropped rapidly and fading brakes resulted.

Hydraulic Brakes

As was pointed out in the chapter on hydraulics, liquids are virtually incompressible, and pressure throughout a closed system will be the same. This principle is used to operate the service brakes on most passenger cars. A schematic drawing of a hydraulic brake system is shown in Fig. 41-6. In such a system, the foot pedal is attached to a master cylinder. As the pedal is depressed, it moves a piston within the master cylinder. The movement of this piston forces the hydraulic fluid throughout the system and into cylinders at each wheel. Here it causes the wheel cylinder pistons to move, which in turn forces the brake shoes against the brake drums.

Fig. 41-7 shows how the force applied to the brake

The automobile Hydraulic System
TRANSMITS MOTION AND FORCE
and
CHANGES THE AMOUNT OF FORCE

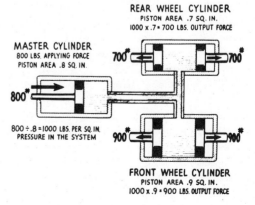

Fig. 41-7. Showing how the force applied to the brake pedal is multiplied hydraulically.

pedal is multiplied. In this instance, 800 lb. is applied to a piston area of 0.8 sq. in., resulting in a pressure in the system of 1,000 psi. At the rear wheel cylinders which have an area of 0.7 sq. in., a force of 700 psi is produced for each piston making a total of 1400 psi. The front wheel cylinders being larger, a combined force of 1,800 psi is produced.

Weight Transfer

In Fig. 41-7, the wheel cylinders on the front wheels are larger than those on the rear wheels. The reason for this is to compensate for weight transfer to the front of the vehicle when the brakes are applied for a rapid stop. As a result of this weight transfer, the front brakes are required to do more work than the rear brakes.

This weight transfer effect comes about because the center of gravity of the automobile is located above the center of the car wheels as illustrated in Fig. 41-8. The result of this action is noticeable by a sinking of the front of the car, and simultaneous rising of the rear of the car whenever a severe brake application is made.

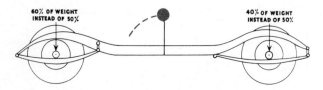

Fig. 41-8. Center of gravity being above wheel centers, a sudden stop will remove some weight from rear wheels and place it on front wheels.

Brake Effectiveness

There are several factors that contribute to the effectiveness of brakes. These include:
1. The area of the brake lining.
2. The amount of pressure applied to the brake shoes.
3. The radius of the brake drum.
4. The radius of the car wheel.
5. The coefficient of friction of the braking surfaces.
6. The coefficient of friction between the tire and the road surface.

Points 3 and 4 are simply a matter of leverage. It is obvious that a brake drum of small diameter applied to a wheel of large diameter, will require more frictional surface or higher pressures on the surface, than a large brake drum on a small wheel.

If the road surface is covered with ice, or is in such condition that there is little friction between the tires and the road surface, braking effectiveness will be greatly reduced. Also, a worn tread on one tire and a new tread on another tire will provide unequal brak-

ing. As pointed out previously, maximum braking effort is obtained as long as the wheel is rotating. But once the brake has become locked and the wheel does not rotate, braking effectiveness is reduced.

Point 2 is among the more important points to be considered in the effectiveness of brakes. The pressure of the brake shoes against the brake drums starts with the force applied to the brake pedal. There it is multiplied by leverage and frequently further assisted by a power brake unit. This is further increased hydraulically, by the size of the master cylinder, and the size of the wheel cylinders. In addition, there are the important factors of self-energization and the servo action which greatly multiply the force pressing the shoes against the brake drums.

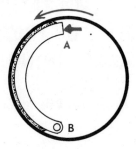

Fig. 41-9. The shoe is pivoted at (B) and the force applied at (A).

This servo action and self-energization, is obtained by the location of the brake anchor pin and is caused by the tendency of the rotating drum to drag the lining along with it. Fig. 41-9 shows that one end of the shoe is anchored at point "B." When the drum is rotating in the direction shown, the frictional force between the brake drum and lining tries to turn the shoe around the anchor pin. Since the drum itself prevents this, the shoe is forced even more strongly against the drum than the applying force is pushing it. This is known as self-energization.

The nearer the center of rotation the anchor pin is located, the more powerful will be the wedging action. This wedging action starts at the toe of the

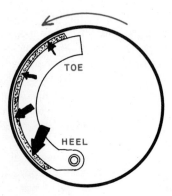

Fig. 41-10. The relative size of the arrows indicates the increase of pressure from the toe to the heel with the pivot set toward the center.

shoe, and keeps increasing as it nears the anchor pin, Fig. 41-10. If the drum is revolved in the opposite direction, there will be no self-energization. However, as there are two shoes, one or the other is effective either way the drum turns.

This self-energization can be amplified to include both shoes by letting one shoe push the other shoe, Fig. 41-11. When such is the case, the amplification of forces is known as servo-action. To accomplish this, the shoes are linked together at the bottom and clearance is provided between the ends of the shoes and the anchor pin, so the shoes can be rotated slightly in relation to the axle shaft or wheel spindle. Then, as the brakes are applied, both the shoes will move with the rotation of the drum, until the rearward shoe is stopped by the anchor pin and the forward shoe is also stopped, as it is linked to the rearward shoe through the connecting link or adjusting screw.

The shoe that starts or generates the servo-action is known as the primary shoe, and the other shoe is the secondary.

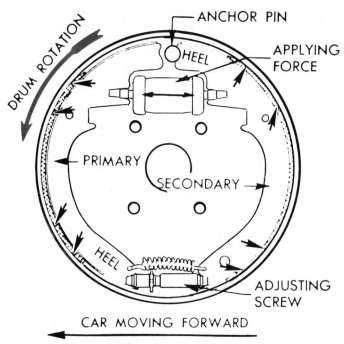

Fig. 41-11. Showing how thrust of brake shoes against brake drum is multiplied by servo-action.

Brake Lining Materials

There are two main types of brake linings:
1. Organic.
2. Metallic.

Organic lining consists basically of a gray-white compound of asbestos, filler materials and powdered resins which are thoroughly mixed, formed into shape and placed under heat and pressure until a hard slate-like board is formed. The material is cut and bent into individual segments and attached to brake shoes. This

is known as molded lining. Some organic lining is woven from strands of asbestos and threads of other materials and impregnated with a rubber compound. In some instances, organic brake lining will also have fine metal wires included.

Metallic brake lining is made of sintered metal, and is composed of finely powdered iron or copper, graphite and lesser amounts of inorganic fillers and friction modifiers. After thorough mixing, a lubricating oil is added to prevent segregation of the different materials. The mixture is then put through a briquetting process and compressed into the desired form.

The organic type brake lining is used almost exclusively for ordinary brake service. Under extreme braking conditions as encountered in service such as police cars, ambulance and sports car service, the metallic type lining is being used extensively. Under such extreme service, the frictional characteristics of the metallic lining are more constant than that of the organic lining. However, metallic brake lining has low initial friction and resultant hard pedal.

Brake Drum Materials

The use of cast iron for the braking surface of brake drums is practically universal. In the past some steel brake drums were used, however, the coefficient of friction is less than cast iron, and there is a greater tendency for such material to gall.

While cast iron has proved to be ideal material for the braking surface, it conducts heat more slowly than aluminum and as a result some drums are now made of aluminum with a cast iron liner for the braking surface. Because of its higher conductivity of heat a brake drum of such construction will operate at much lower temperatures. In some tests made with 50 mph fade stops at 0.2 mile intervals, it was found that the

Fig. 41-12. More fins are used on brake drums to increase dissipation of heat and thereby improve braking characteristics.

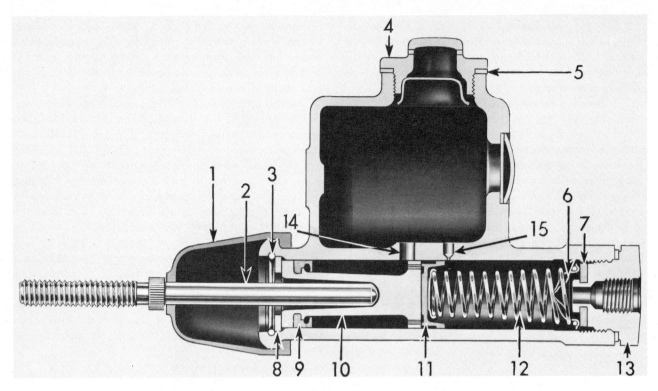

Fig. 41-13. Typical master cylinder. 1—Rubber boot. 2—Push rod. 3—Lock ring. 4—Filler plug. 5—Filler plug gasket. 6—Valve assembly. 7—Valve seat. 8—Flat washer. 9—Secondary cup. 10—Piston. 11—Primary cup. 12—Spring. 13—Outlet fitting. 14—Breather port. 15—Compensating port.

conventional cast iron drum reached a temperature of 700 deg., while the temperature of the aluminum drum with cast iron liner was slightly less than 500 deg. Obviously brake lining life is greatly improved under such conditions, and safer conditions are established.

Many brake drums are made of steel with inner linings of cast iron. In this way, the assembly has the strength of steel, and the frictional properties of cast iron. In addition, there is no difficulty in getting the cast iron to bind with the steel, which is the case when aluminum is used.

To aid in the dissipation of heat, brake drums, regardless of the material of which they are made, are usually provided with some form of cooling fin, Fig. 41-12.

Operation of Hydraulic Brakes

The conventional hydraulic brake system is pedal operated, and applies the brakes at all four wheels with equalized pressure.

A hydraulic system consists of one master cylinder, Fig. 41-13, connected by pipes and flexible tubing, Fig. 41-1, to a wheel cylinder, Fig. 41-14, or wheel cylinders, Fig. 41-15, which control the movement of the brake shoes at each wheel.

The master cylinder, connecting lines and wheel cylinders, are filled with special hydraulic fluid which is forced through the system by the movement of the master cylinder piston.

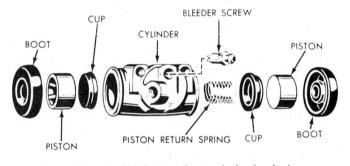

Fig. 41-14. Exploded view of typical wheel cylinder.

Fig. 41-15. Separate wheel cylinders are used for each brake shoe of this Lockheed hydraulic brake.

When the brakes are fully released, the master cylinder piston, Fig. 41-13 and Fig. 41-16, view A, is held against the stop plate, and the primary cup is held just clear of the compensating port by the master cylinder spring, which also holds the check valve against its seat on the head nut. The pressure chamber is filled with fluid at atmospheric pressure due to the open compensating port and reservoir vent. All lines and cylinders are filled with fluid under a static pressure of 8 - 16 lb., which helps to hold the

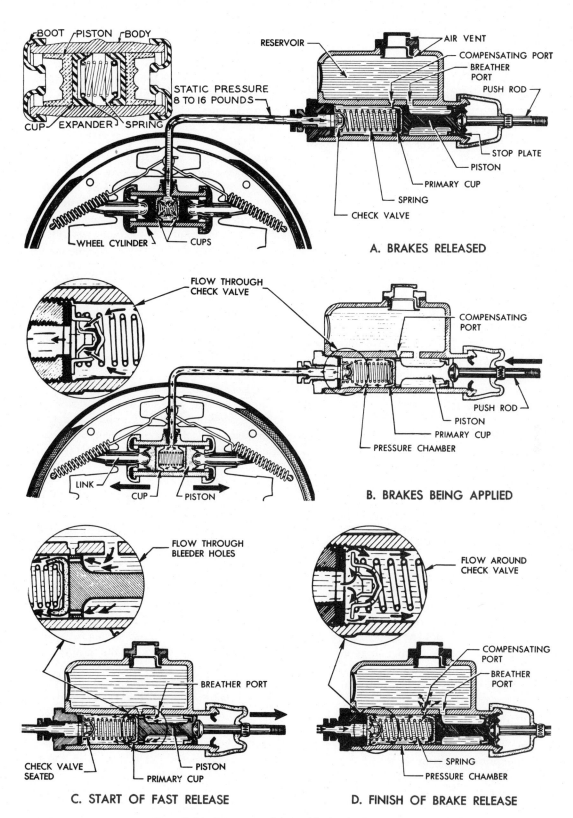

Fig. 41-16. Operation of typical hydraulic brake system.

lips of the wheel cylinder cups in firm contact with the cylinder walls to prevent loss of fluid or the entrance of air into the system.

When the brake pedal is applied, the push rod forces the master cylinder piston and primary cup forward, Fig. 41-16, view B. As this movement starts, the lip of the primary cup covers the compensating port to prevent escape of the fluid back to the reservoir. Continued movement of the piston builds pressure in the pressure chamber, and fluid is then forced through holes in the check valve and out into the lines leading to each of the wheel cylinders. Fluid forced into the wheel cylinders between the pistons and cups, Fig. 41-16, view B, causes pistons and connecting links to move outward, forcing the brake shoes into contact with the brake drums.

When the brake pedal is released, the master cylinder spring forces the pedal back until the push rod contacts the stop plate in the master cylinder. This spring also forces the piston and primary cup to follow the push rod, and pushes the check valve firmly against its seat.

At the start of a fast release, the piston moves faster than the fluid can follow it in returning from the wheel cylinders and lines, and a partial vacuum is momentarily created in the pressure chamber. Fluid supplied through the breather port is then drawn through the bleeder holes in the piston head, and past the primary cup, to keep the pressure chamber filled, Fig. 41-16, view C. As pressure drops in the master cylinder, the shoe return springs retract all brake shoes, and the connecting links push the wheel cylinder pistons inward, forcing the fluid back to the master cylinder. Pressure of returning fluid causes a rubber disk to close holes in the check valve, and forces the check valve off its seat against the tension of the master cylinder spring, view D, Fig. 41-16. Fluid then flows around the check valve into the pressure chamber. With the piston bearing against the stop plate, and the lip of the primary cup just clear of the compensating port, excess fluid which entered through the bleeder holes, or was created by expansion due to increased temperature, now returns to reservoir through uncovered compensating port. When pressure in wheel cylinders and lines becomes slightly less than the tension of master cylinder spring, the check valve returns to its seat on head nut to hold the 8 to 16 lb. static pressure in the lines and cylinders.

SPLIT-SYSTEM MASTER CYLINDER: The split-system cylinder, also known as the dual or tandem master cylinder, Fig. 41-16a, is designed so the front and rear brakes have separate hydraulic systems. Should a leak occur in one system, the other system will still be in operation, making it possible to stop the car.

As shown in schematic, Fig. 41-16a, the dual system master cylinder is provided with two separate reservoirs and also one primary piston and one secondary piston. Note that the reservoirs are completely separate. An older type had the reservoirs joined at the top. When bleeding the types illustrated, a special bleeder adapter cover should be used, making it possible to bleed both primary and secondary systems at one operation.

Hydraulic Brake Fluid

To provide positive brake action under all conditions, brake fluid must meet a lot of requirements. First of all, hyrdraulic brake fluid must not swell or soften the rubber parts used throughout the system. Failure to meet that requirement results in brakes locking up, leaks or short life of rubber parts. It must also be compatible with the different metals used in the hydraulic system. If any rusting or corrosion is caused, the result will be frozen brakes, pulling brakes or loss of brakes due to leaks.

Hydraulic brake fluid must not vaporize at the highest temperature encountered in actual service. Failure to meet that requirement, results in complete loss of brakes without warning. It must remain fluid at low temperatures, and must remain in a fluid state even when a small amount of water is added. Hydraulic fluid must also act as a lubricant to the moving parts of the system. It must retain all its characteristics over a long period of time. It must also mix satisfactorily with other makes of hydraulic brake fluid.

As previously pointed out, stopping a 4,000 lb. car from 60 mph will result in raising the temperature of the brakes to 250 deg., and 700 deg. will be reached if repeated stops are made every 0.2 miles from 50 mph. With such temperatures, it is easily understood that care must be exercised in selecting brake fluid. Only hydraulic fluid meeting the Society of Automotive Engineers specification 70 R 1, or better, should be used.

When the brake fluid in the system becomes hot enough to vaporize (SAE specification is 295 deg.) gas pockets or bubbles are formed in the tops of the cylinders. When the fluid starts to vaporize, it emits gas and a drop of fluid changed into vapor forms a gas bubble many times the volume of the liquid drop. This gas formation forces some of the brake fluid back through the lines, through the master cylinder check valve, and through the small by-pass hole into the reservoir.

The check valve holds a static pressure in the line which tends to keep the fluid from boiling. Once the brake fluid reaches the boiling point, it may continue to change into gas until a large bubble is formed. If this bubble has pushed more brake fluid back into the reservoir than one stroke of the pedal can pump back into the system, complete loss of brakes will occur. Such gas is easily compressible, and small quantities produce what is known as a "spongy pedal" with partial loss of braking.

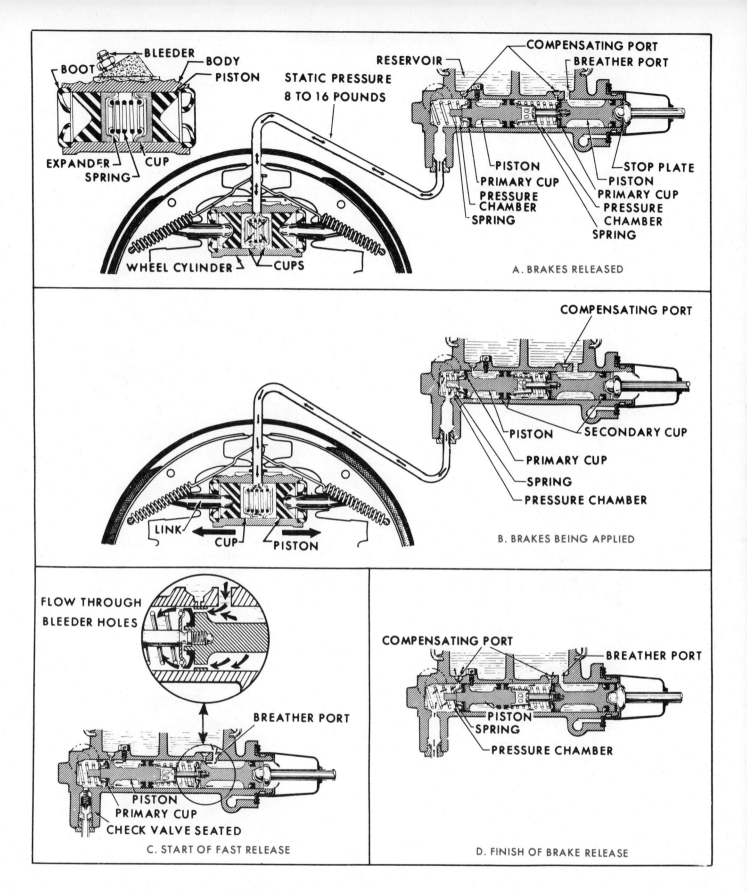

Fig. 41-16a. *In a typical dual hydraulic system: When fully released (A), pistons are held against retaining ring and primary cups clear compensating port. Fluid in pressure chambers is under atmospheric pressure. In applied position (B), pistons move forward and primary cups cover bypass holes, causing hydraulic pressure to be transmitted to front and rear wheel cylinders. On fast release (C), pistons move faster than returning fluid and a partial vacuum is created. Fluid enters pressure chamber via breather and bleeder holes in piston heads to keep chamber filled. At finish of release (D), piston returns against retaining ring and fluid returns to reservoirs by way of compensating ports.*

In addition to vapor lock occurring in the wheel cylinders, it may also occur in the master cylinder. In such cases brakes will fail without warning. Pumping the pedal will not remove the vapor lock.

Mountain driving puts increased duty on brakes and brake fluid. With every 2,000 ft. increase in altitude, the atmospheric pressure drops approximately one pound and the boiling point of the brake fluid drops 2 deg. to 3 deg. This naturally increases the tendency toward vapor lock.

Brake Types

Bendix Single Anchor

A typical Bendix brake of the single anchor type is shown in Fig. 41-17. In some installations the anchor is fixed, and in other designs, it is adjustable. There are two types of adjustable anchors. In one design the anchor is eccentric, which can be turned to move the anchor pin. In the other design, the anchor pin is mounted in an elongated hole so the pin can be moved up or down, as desired.

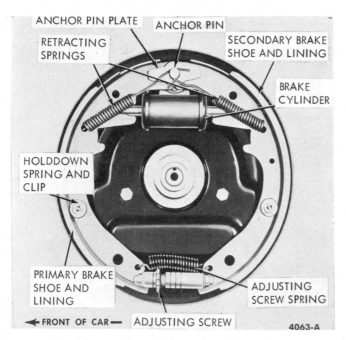

Fig. 41-17. Details of Bendix duo-servo, single anchor pin brake.

Only a single wheel cylinder is used in this Bendix brake, and the shoes are held in the released position by means of individual springs from the anchor pin to each shoe. Each shoe is also provided with a hold down spring and clip to keep the shoes snugly against the backing plate.

A single adjustment is provided, which is reached through a port in the backing plate, Fig. 41-18. Raising the handle of the tool upward will expand the shoes aginst the brake drums.

Bendix Self-Adjusting Brake

This brake, which closely resembles the Bendix single anchor brake, is illustrated in Fig. 41-19. The two brake shoes rest on the single anchor pin, until the wheel cylinder expands the upper ends of the shoes against the brake drums. As the drum rotates, one shoe is pulled away from the anchor pin by this

Fig. 41-18. Method of making the adjustment on the Bendix duo-servo brake.

rotation, and the shoe is moved slightly in the direction of drum rotation. The floating link connecting the two shoes at the bottom forces the second shoe to contact the drum at the bottom, and thus both shoes are energized. The action of the brake is similar to that of the conventional single anchor brake. When applying the brakes in reverse, the opposite shoe becomes the lead shoe, and as it pulls away from the

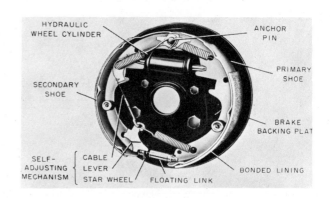

Fig. 41-19. Bendix self-adjusting brake.

anchor pin, it pulls on the cable of the self-adjusting mechanism, Fig. 41-19, which raises the adjusting lever. When sufficient lining wear has occurred and not before, the lever can engage the next notch in the star adjusting wheel. A spring on the lever pulls it down and this increases the length of the floating link 0.0005 in. to expand the shoes. This self-adjusting feature operates only when the car is moving backward and the brakes are applied.

Bendix Hydraulic

In this type brake, Fig. 41-20, the ends of the brake shoes bear directly on the pistons in the wheel cylinder. Only a single shoe retracting spring is used, but separate adjustments are provided for the shoes. These shoes are of the eccentric or cam type.

Lockheed Hydraulic

The front brakes of a Lockheed hydraulic brake system provide individual wheel cylinders for each brake shoe, Fig. 41-15, while the rear brakes use a single wheel cylinder for the operation of both shoes, Fig. 41-21. In the case of the front brakes, two adjustments are provided for each shoe, a cam shoe stop, and an eccentric anchor. Similarly, the rear brake shoes also have two adjustments. The illustration shows a brake gauge which is used when making adjustment.

Chrysler Center-Plane Brake

This brake, also known as the total contact brake, is illustrated in Fig. 41-22 and Fig. 41-23. The braking action is centralized between two support plates, which align the shoes and hold the anchors and wheel cylinders. The applying force from the piston and the shoe return springs, are all in a center plane. As a result, the shoes do not tend to twist, which would

result in uneven contact. Side movement of the shoes is controlled by guides which maintain constant pressure against the webs of the shoes. The wheel cylinders operate in the conventional manner, and are

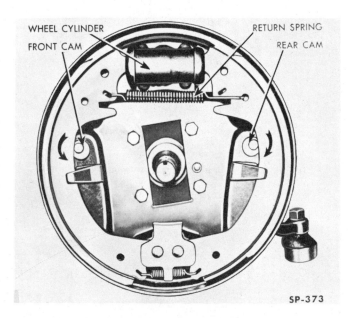

Fig. 41-20. *Bendix hydraulic brake as used on Rambler and others. Note shoe adjusting cams.*

mounted on the brake support plate. Self-energizing action is effective on all front brake shoes, and the rear brake front shoe when the car is moving forward, and self-energizing action on the rear shoe of the rear brakes when the car is backing.

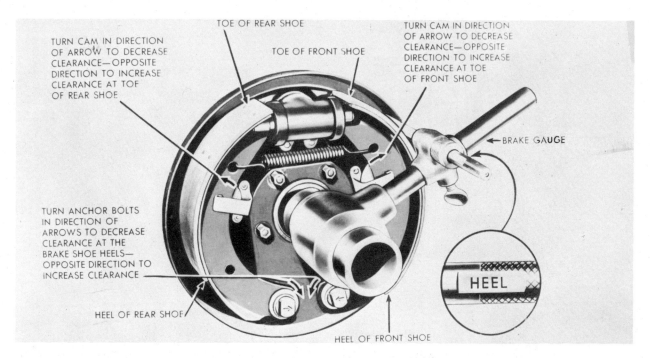

Fig. 41-21. *Rear shoe construction of Lockheed hydraulic brake. Note gauge for adjusting clearance of shoes.*

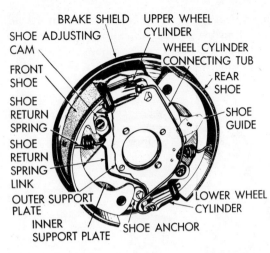

Fig. 41-22. Construction of center plane brake.

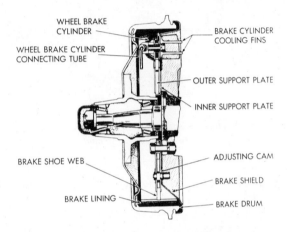

Fig. 41-23. End view of center plane brake.

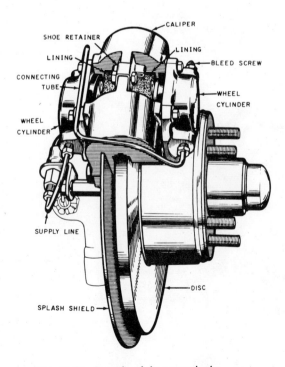

Fig. 41-24. Details of disc type brake.

Disc Brakes

With the demands for increased safety in the operation of automotive vehicles, many cars are now equipped with disc type brakes, either as standard equipment or as special equipment. The major advantage of the disc type brake is a great reduction in tendency toward brake fade and consequent marked reduction in the distance required to stop the vehicle.

Braking with disc type brakes is accomplished by forcing friction pads (linings) against both sides of a rotating metal disc. This disc or rotor, turns with the wheel of the vehicle and within a stationary housing called the caliper assembly, Fig. 41-24. The caliper contains the pistons, similar to those used in conventional drum type hydraulic brakes. When the brakes are applied, the hydraulic fluid forces the pistons and the friction pads (lining) against the rotating disc thereby retarding the movement of the vehicle.

As disc brakes do not have servo or multiplying action, the applying force on the brake pedal must be very great in order to obtain a brake force comparable to that obtained with the conventional drum type brake. Consequently, disc type brakes are always provided with a power or booster unit which incorporates the conventional master hydraulic cylinder.

In many installations, disc type brakes are used only on the front wheel, while the familiar drum type brake is continued on the rear.

Ford, Lincoln, Mustang Brakes

The disc brake design, Fig. 41-25, used on Lincoln, Thunderbird, Mustang and other makes is described as a fixed caliper, opposed piston, nonenergized, ventilated disc type unit, energized by the hydraulic system.

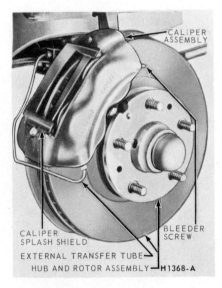

Fig. 41-25. Details of disc brake as installed on 1965–1967 Ford cars.

There is no lateral movement of the disc. The caliper assembly consists of two caliper housings, Fig. 41-26, bolted together, with each half containing two cylinders and each cylinder contains a piston with attached molded rubber dust boot to seal the

sure from the master cylinder, forces the pistons out of the caliper bores against their respective shoe and lining assemblies. The force of the pistons against the shoes moves the linings against both sides of the revolving rotor to effect braking action.

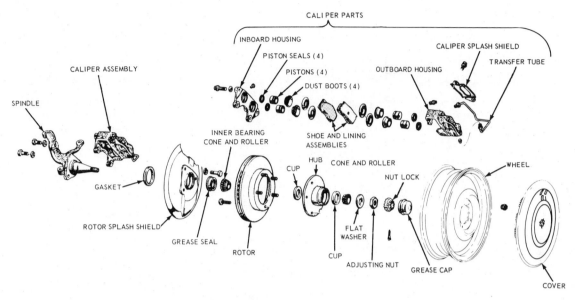

Fig. 41-26. Exploded view of Ford disc brake.

cylinder bore from contamination. Square-sectioned rubber piston seals are positioned in the grooves in the cylinder bores, Fig. 41-27. The piston seals perform three important tasks:

1. They provide sealing between the cylinders and pistons.
2. They return the pistons to the released position when the hydraulic pressure is released.
3. They maintain the friction pads in correct alignment at all times; their action being comparable to automatic adjusters on drum type brakes.

The cylinders are connected hydraulically by means of internal passages in the caliper housings and an external transfer tube between the two halves of the caliper assembly. One bleeder screw and fluid inlet fitting is provided on each caliper assembly.

The shoe and lining assemblies are located between parallel machined abutments within the caliper, and are supported radially by tabs on the outer ends of the shoe assemblies, Fig. 41-26. The shoes slide axially in the caliper abutments by means of tabs which ride on the machined ledges (bridges) when hydraulic pressure is applied to the piston, Fig. 41-27.

A shoe and lining assembly consists of friction material riveted to a metal plate called the shoe or pad. It is replaced as a unit.

The rotor or disc is ventilated and permits circulation of air through the rotor, resulting in more rapid cooling and reduction in brake fade.

As the brake pedal is depressed, hydraulic pres-

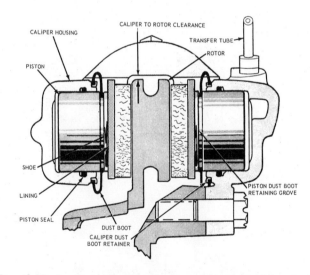

Fig. 41-27. Sectional view of caliper assembly on Ford disc brake.

During braking application, the rubber seal on each piston stretches as the piston moves against the shoe, Fig. 41-27. When the hydraulic pressure is released, the seal is relaxed and returns to its normal position and pulls the piston away from the shoe approximately .005 in. In that way the force of the lining against the rotor is relieved and permits the needed running clearance.

A proportioning valve, Fig. 41-27a, located between the master cylinder and the rear brake wheel cylinders, provides balanced braking action between the

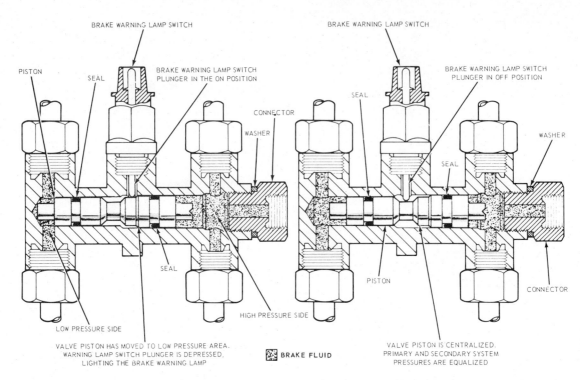

Fig. 41-27a. Pressure differential valve and brake warning light switch.

front and the rear brakes under a wide range of braking conditions. In addition the unit includes a warning light system which indicates when one portion of the brake system fails.

1968 Ford Disc Brake

The disc brakes installed on some Ford cars in 1968 are similar to those used in the preceding year, but the caliper is a one-piece housing, instead of two, Fig. 41-27b. In addition, it is not held in a fixed posi-

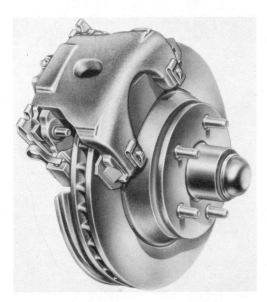

Fig. 41-27b. Caliper on 1968 Ford disc brake has a one-piece housing and moves inward and outward as brakes are applied.

tion and is free to move inboard and outboard as the brakes are applied and released. Only one piston is used in each caliper. This double acting piston applies braking pressure directly to the outboard shoe through the movable caliper.

The caliper over the anchor plate is bolted to the wheel spindle. On brake application, braking thrust is transferred from the caliper and brake shoes to the anchor plate, preventing rotation of the entire assembly. The caliper is held on the anchor plate by flexible steel stabilizers.

When brakes are applied, hydraulic pressure moves the piston outward, bringing the lining of the inboard brake shoe against the inner face of the rotor. However, no appreciable braking takes place until more fluid enters the brake cylinder and slides the entire caliper inward. This movement brings the lining of the outboard shoe (which is attached to the caliper) into contact with the outer face of the caliper. Then, any further increase in hydraulic pressure is transmitted equally to both shoes and faces of the rotor. Brake shoes are retracted by the action of the square cross section of the piston seal.

The caliper is easily removed by removing the two attaching bolts. However, care must be taken on reassembling so as to obtain correct alignment of the anchor plate. Reassembling procedure is as follows:

After setting the caliper and anchor plate in position on the rotor and spindle, Fig. 41-27c, install the lower bolt that holds the anchor plate to the spindle, and run it up only finger tight. Then install the upper bolt and torque it to specifications. Then torque the lower bolt. When wiring the bolts, be sure to twist the ends of the wire at least five times. Then position the ends of the wires away from the brake hose.

Unlike previous disc brakes, shoes with worn linings can be replaced only by removing the caliper and anchor plate from the spindle. Inboard and outboard shoe and lining assemblies are not interchangeable.

Corvette Disc Brake

In the Corvette disc brake system Fig. 41-28, the caliper assembly has no external transfer tube to conduct the fluid from one side of the caliper to the other. Fluid delivered to one piston area is routed to the piston area on the opposite side of the caliper by a drilled internal passage which is sealed by an "O" ring where the two castings join. Each half of the caliper assembly contains two pistons, making four pistons per wheel.

A deep groove in the center of the pads indicates when pad replacement is necessary. When the groove is worn to the point where it is almost unnoticeable, new pads should be installed. An arrow printed on the back of all new shoes indicates the direction of forward wheel and disc rotation. The shoes, Fig. 41-29, and Fig. 41-30, are held in position in the caliper by a clevis type shoe guide pin, retained by a simple spring clip. Removing the wheel and guide pin permits the pads to be lifted out of the caliper. However, a special set of thin spring steel clamps are required to hold the pistons in the bores when the pads are being removed and replaced.

On the Corvette, disc brakes are installed on the rear as well as the front wheels.

An opening on the upper surface of the caliper is provided which permits checking the thickness of the lining. When groove across the center is gone, or when the bonded lining is within .063 in. of the shoe, the lining should be replaced. If riveted lining is used, the lining should be replaced when total shoe and lining is .250 in. or less.

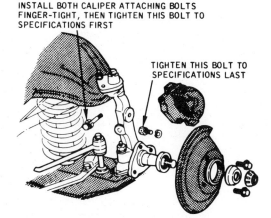

INSTALL BOTH CALIPER ATTACHING BOLTS FINGER-TIGHT, THEN TIGHTEN THIS BOLT TO SPECIFICATIONS FIRST

TIGHTEN THIS BOLT TO SPECIFICATIONS LAST

Fig. 41-27c. Showing installation procedure on Ford 1968 disc brake.

Fig. 41-28. Disc brake used on Corvette. Illustration shows method of adjusting rear shoes on brake drum.

Fig. 41-29. Exploded view of brake caliper on Corvette disc brake. 1—Caliper bolts. 2—Bleeder valve. 3—Caliper half. 4—Piston spring. 5—Seal. 6—Piston assembly. 7—Piston boot. 8—Brake shoes. 9—"O" rings. 10—Caliper half. 11—Retaining pin. 12—Cotter pin.

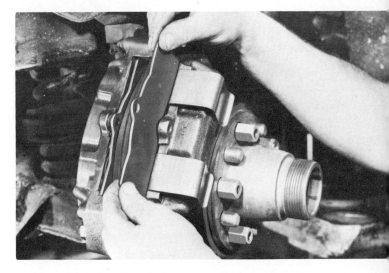

Fig. 41-30. Installing brake shoes on Corvette disc brake.

Plymouth, Dodge, Chrysler Disc Brakes

Disc brakes such as are found on Plymouth Fury, Dodge Polara and Monaco, and Chrysler cars consists of a fixed caliper, two friction pads bonded to steel shoes, four pistons, piston return springs, piston seals, dust boots and retainers.

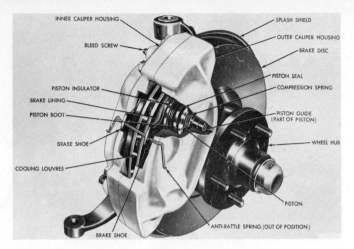

Fig. 41-31. Disc brake installation on some Plymouth, Dodge, and Chrysler cars.

The brake disc is mounted on the front wheel hub and is straddled by the caliper, Fig. 41-31, which is attached to the steering knuckle and steering knuckle arm. The caliper assembly is composed of two housings. In each housing there are two cylinder bores

return springs position the brake shoes lightly against the disc ready for the next application. As a result the design automatically compensates for lining wear. Shoes and lining should be replaced when the groove is no longer visible on the lining pad.

To replace the brake lining and shoe assembly, raise the car and remove wheel and tire assembly. Remove the anti-rattle spring. Remove the bolts that attach the caliper assembly to the steering knuckle and steering arm. Remove caliper from disc by sliding caliper assembly up and away from the brake disc. Brake shoe and lining assembly can then be removed, one at a time through the top opening. A piston compressing tool should then be inserted between piston insulator pads to keep the pistons compressed.

The disc brakes used on Dodge Coronet and Charger, and on Plymouth Belvedere and Satellite cars is somewhat similar to that installed on Rambler cars. A major difference is that the Dodge and Plymouth models use a ventilated disc .870 in. thick and a pro-

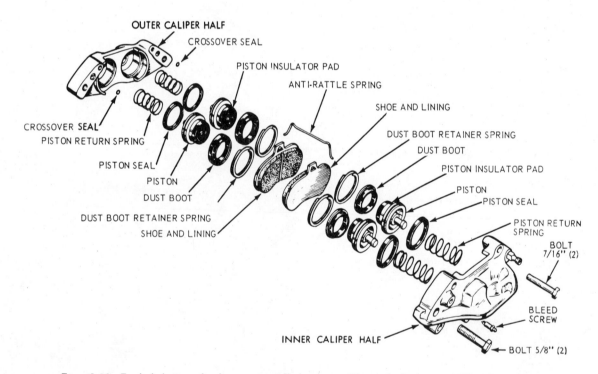

Fig. 41-32. Exploded view of caliper as installed on some Plymouth, Dodge, and Chrysler cars.

each containing a piston, piston seal, piston return spring; protected by a dust boot and retainer. Attached to the outer end of the piston is a heat-resistant pad which contacts the shoe and acts as a heat insulator. Inserted between the pistons and the disc is the segmented lining and shoe assembly which are held in position by the shoe anti-rattle spring, Fig. 41-32.

As the brake pedal is depressed, the hydraulic pressure forces the pistons against the brake shoe pads and when the pedal is released, the piston

portioning valve. In addition, these cars do not use shims and the linings are a different shape. The complete disc is shown in Fig. 41-33 and an exploded view of the caliper in Fig. 41-34.

To check the lining thickness through the two inspection holes on top of the caliper, it is first necessary to remove a wheel. If the linings are worn within .060 in. of the shoe, the shoe and lining should be replaced. If total thickness of shoe and lining, as measured at six points around outer edge of shoe is

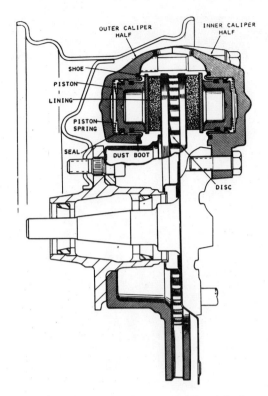

Fig. 41-33. Caliper mounting on some models of Dodge and Plymouth cars.

Remove two caliper mounting bolts. Hold lower edge of caliper with one hand and grasp tabs of shims (if so installed), slide shims off bolt and store shims with bolt. Repeat and remove upper bolt and shims.

With the bolts removed, lift caliper off disc and lay caliper on the tie rod. After removing brake fluid from master cylinder, use two screwdrivers between the linings to press all four pistons slowly into their cylinders until the pistons bottom firmly. Press gradually since fluid return to reservoir is restricted by the master cylinder compensating port.

Lift worn shoes and linings from caliper. Discard old shoes and old brake fluid. Clean all parts and caliper inner surface with alcohol. Use reduced air pressure to blow dry. Replace any worn or defective parts.

Insert new shoe and lining assembly in caliper curved edge first with shoes against open end of pistons. Spread shoes apart and attach caliper to mounting bracket with caliper mounting bolts. If shims were used, be sure they are replaced in original positions. Tighten bolts to 75-80 ft. lb. torque.

Secure hydraulic tube-to-tube mounting bracket with tube clip. After replacing shoes and lining on other brakes, depress brake pedal several times to seat linings. Refill master cylinder. Check caliper alignment.

Caliper Alignment

The caliper alignment surfaces and flat friction surfaces of the disc must have the same clearance on both sides of the disc – within .010 in. Both ends of the caliper must be checked to be sure clearance is the same. In other words disc and caliper must be parallel.

less than .195 in. new shoes and linings should be installed.

To replace shoe and lining, first remove sufficient brake fluid from master cylinder to prevent overflow from the reservoir when fluid is returned from the caliper cylinders.

Then remove one wheel. Work one wheel at a time to avoid "popping" wheel cylinder pistons when working on another caliper.

Remove the tube clip and hydraulic tube from the mounting tube bracket. Do not loosen any hydraulic fittings.

Clearance and alignment of disc and caliper are of great importance. On models with shims, be sure shims are replaced exactly as originally installed.

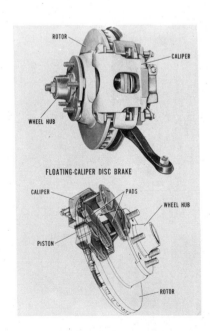

Fig. 41-35. Chrysler's floating caliper brake.

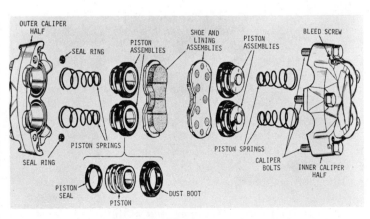

Fig. 41-34. Exploded view of caliper.

Pontiac, Oldsmobile, Cadillac Disc Brakes

The disc type brake as installed on Pontiac, Oldsmobile and Cadillac Eldorado is illustrated in Figs. 41-36 and 41-37. In this system, when hydraulic pressure is applied to the pistons they force the lining against the brake disc, clamping the disc between the lining with equal and opposite force. When the brake pedal is released, the pressure decreases and the compressed piston springs in the cylinder bores position the linings lightly against the disc, ready for the next brake application.

Since the brake linings brush lightly against the disc when the brakes are not applied, disc brakes automatically compensate for lining wear, therefore no adjustment is required. As lining wears, the pis-

Fig. 41-36. Details of caliper as installed on 1967 Oldsmobile.

Fig. 41-37. Oldsmobile and most GM cars in 1967–68 used 4-piston, fixed caliper disc brake.

Fig. 41-38. Beginning in 1969, most GM cars featured single-piston, floating caliper disc brake.

tons move further out of the caliper cylinder bores. The large diameter of the cylinder bores requires considerable volume of brake fluid and consequently the master cylinder fluid level should be checked frequently.

Shoe and lining should be changed if the lining is approximately .020 in. or less in thickness over the rivet heads.

Brake Shoe Installation

When replacing brake shoes, first attach a drain hose to caliper bleed screw and submerge the other end in a container partly filled with clean brake fluid. Then bottoming pistons, open the bleed screw to allow excess fluid to drain. After pistons are bottomed, tighten bleed screw before relieving pressure on pistons. This is necessary since insertion of full thickness lining will force pistons back into caliper, displacing brake fluid.

After bleeding the brakes as indicated, remove and discard cotter pin from inboard end of shoe retaining pin and slide out retaining pin.

Starting with the shoe closest to the car, push back as far as it will go from the disc. Use special tool or screwdriver and press pistons to bottom of cylinder bores. Piston springs will not permit pistons to remain completely bottomed. Worn shoes can then be removed. Insert new replacements by rotating either end out of caliper and pulling shoe from caliper. Shoes must be replaced in axle sets only.

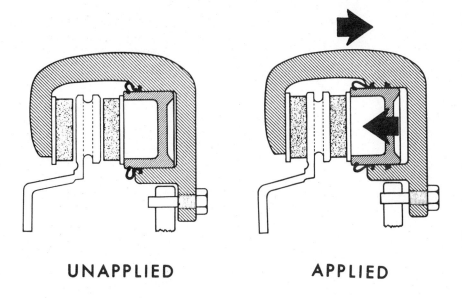

UNAPPLIED   APPLIED

Fig. 41-39. Key to floating caliper operation is when hydraulic pressure on bottom of cylinder bore causes caliper to float sideways and apply brake shoes to rotor surfaces.

Floating Caliper Disc Brake

The 4-piston, fixed caliper type disc brake was dropped from most U. S. passenger car lines in 1968 or 1969 in favor of the single-piston, floating caliper assembly. Cadillac, for example, adopted the single-piston set-up in 1968, then modified it still further in 1972 with the introduction of an integral front wheel hub and disc brake rotor as well as the front wheel spindle, Fig. 41-38.

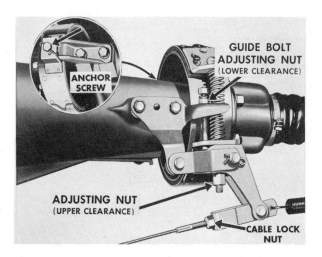

Fig. 41-40. External contracting type of parking or hand brake.

The principle of operation of floating caliper disc brake is to allow the fluid pressure to build up between bottom of the piston and bottom of the cylinder bore. Pressure on piston forces the inboard shoe and lining against the inboard rotor surface. Pressure

against bottom of the bore causes the caliper to float or slide on mounting bolts or sleeves, Fig. 41-39, forcing outboard shoe and lining against outboard rotor surface. As line pressure continues to build up, the clamping action of the friction surfaces stops the car.

Parking Brakes

When the parking brake is mounted on the drive shaft, it is usually operated by a cable within a conduit leading to a hand lever. Multiplication of the leverage at the brake band cam or lever is obtained by a considerable leverage at the brake hand lever or parking brake pedal lever, Fig. 41-40.

An external type of parking brake is shown in Fig. 41-40, and an internal expanding type brake is shown in Fig. 41-41. On the external band type construction,

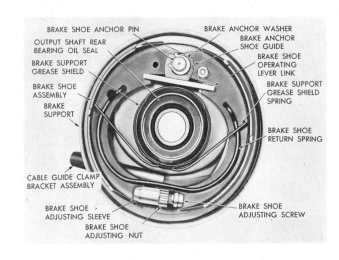

Fig. 41-41. Internal expanding type parking brake. (Chrysler)

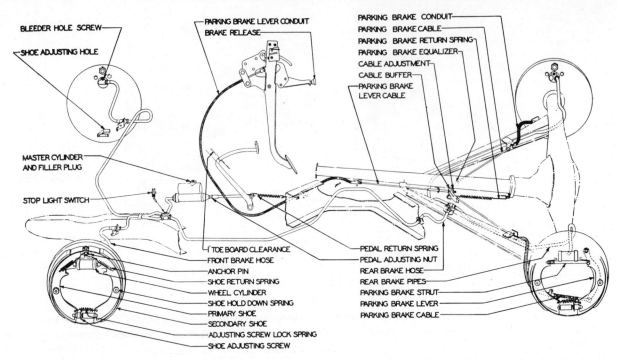

Fig. 41-42. *One method of hooking mechanical leverage to the hydraulic shoes for a pedal operated parking brake.*

the band is anchored at the center, and the two ends of the band are tightened around the drum by means of levers.

The external type parking brake mounted on the propeller shaft, has the shoes anchored at the top with the adjustment for shoe clearance at the bottom.

Instead of having the parking brake on the propeller shaft, many cars use the rear wheel brakes for both service and parking. To do this, mechanical linkage is provided as shown in Fig. 41-42.

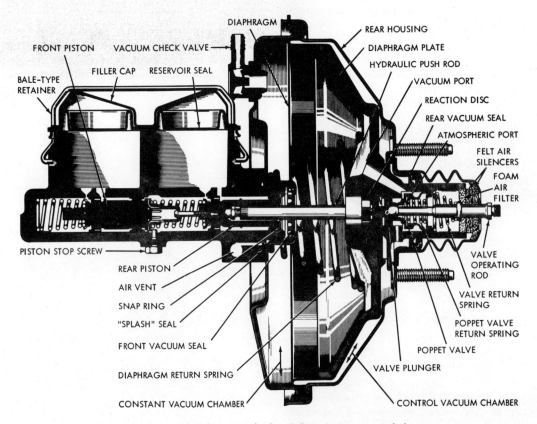

Fig. 41-43. *Bendix power brake of the vacuum suspended type.*

Power Brakes

The power brake unit as used on passenger cars is of two general types: The air suspended type and the vacuum suspended type. The latter is now used almost exclusively.

In the released position, the power piston of the atmosphere suspended type, Fig. 41-48, has atmospheric pressure on both sides of the piston. Then as the brake pedal is depressed, manifold vacuum is admitted through the control valve to one side of the piston. Atmospheric pressure on the other side then causes the piston to move and apply the brakes through suitable linkage.

The operation of the vacuum suspended type, Fig. 41-16a is similar. In this case, when the brakes are in the released position, both sides of the piston are open to manifold vacuum. As the brakes are applied, air is admitted through the control valve to one side of the diaphragm, causing it to move and in turn move the hydraulic piston in the master cylinder which in turn applies the brakes.

Operation of one type of the Bendix vacuum suspended type, Fig. 41-43 is as follows: When the engine is still running and the brake is released, engine vacuum removes the air from the power brake chamber. Also the valve operating rod and valve plunger are held to the right (as illustrated), thereby closing the atmospheric port, Fig. 41-44. With the vacuum port open, the diaphragm is balanced as there is vacuum on both sides.

As the brakes are applied, the operating valve moves forward to compress the valve return spring and bring the poppet valve into contact with the vacuum port seat to close the vacuum port. Any additional movement of the valve operating rod in the applied direction, moves the valve plunger away from the poppet valve to open the atmosphere port and admit atmospheric pressure through the air filter to the control vacuum chamber. With vacuum to the left of the piston and diaphragm, the atmospheric pressure on the other side exerts force to move the power piston and diaphragm which in turn operate the push rod in the master cylinder.

The Delco Moraine power brake, Fig. 41-45, is also of the vacuum suspended type. The line from the intake manifold is connected to the vacuum check valve in the front housing of the power brake. In the released position, the air valve is seated on the floating control valve. The air at atmospheric pressure, enters through the air filter, is shut off at the floating control valve. The vacuum is at both sides of the power piston and any air at the right side of the piston is drawn off by the vacuum over the floating control valve seat and through two small holes in the power piston.

As the brake pedal is depressed, the valve operating rod carries the air valve away from the floating control valve which will follow it until it is in

contact with the raised seat in the power piston. This shuts off the vacuum to the right of the piston and air at atmospheric pressure travels past the air valve and through two passages into the housing on

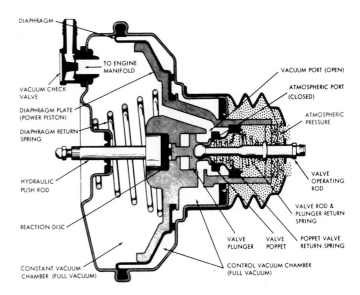

Fig. 41-44. With the engine running and the brake in the release position, the atmospheric port is closed.

the right side of the power piston. This causes the power piston to move to the left, carrying with it the master cylinder push rod to operate the master cylinder in the usual manner.

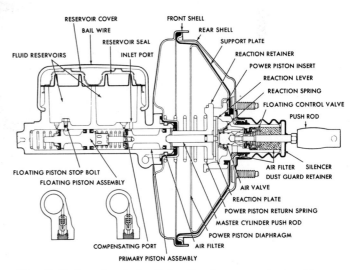

Fig. 41-45. Details of the Delco Moraine power brake. (Vacuum suspended type.)

When the desired pedal pressure is reached, the power piston moves to the left until the floating control valve, which is still seated on the power piston, again seats on the air valve. The power brake will now remain stationary until pressure on the brake pedal is altered.

When pedal pressure is released, the air valve spring forces the air valve back until its snap ring rests against the power piston. As it returns, the air valve pushes the floating control valve off its seat on the power piston. This opens the space to the right of the power piston to vacuum. Both sides of the piston are now under vacuum, the power piston return spring will return the piston to the released position.

except for the hydraulic push rod which has a self-locking adjustment screw at one end with a piston head at the other.

With the brakes in the released position, Fig. 41-46 and the engine running, vacuum from the intake manifold is admitted through the vacuum check valve to the front (left) vacuum chamber and to the vacuum chamber to the front (left) of the rear diaphragm,

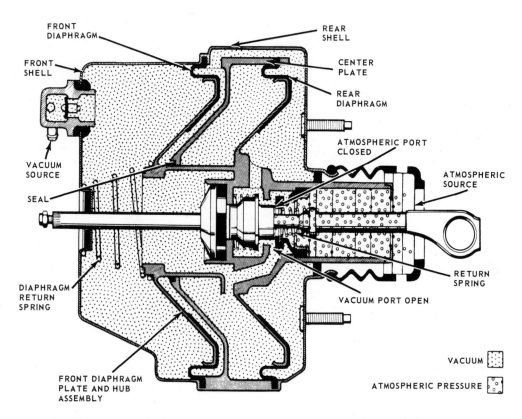

Fig. 41-46. Bendix tandem diaphragm power brake. Shown in the released position.

Another vacuum suspended type is the Bendix tandem diaphragm power brake. This unit, Fig. 41-46, has three basic elements:

1. A vacuum power chamber which consists of a front and a rear shell, a center plate, a front and a rear diaphragm, a hydraulic push rod and a vacuum diaphragm return spring.

2. A mechanically actuated control valve, integral with the vacuum power diaphragms that control the degree of power brake application or release in accordance with the foot pressure applied to the valve operating rod through the brake pedal linkage. The control valve consists of a single poppet with an atmospheric port. The vacuum port seat is a part of the valve body attached to the diaphragm assembly. The atmospheric port seat is a part of the valve plunger which moves within the valve housing and vacuum power diaphragm assembly.

3. A hydraulic cylinder which contains all the elements of the conventional master cylinder,

Fig. 41-46. The valve operating rod and valve plunger are held to the right in the valve housing by the valve return spring to close the atmospheric port and open the vacuum port. With the valve in that position, the chambers to the rear of both the front and the rear diaphragms are open to vacuum through the portings around the edge of the center plate and through the hub of the valve housing. The vacuum power diaphragms are now balanced since the same degree of vacuum is on each side. The vacuum power return spring is then free to return the diaphragm assembly with the hydraulic push rod to the released position.

As the brakes are applied, the valve operating rod and valve plunger move to the left in the power diaphragm assembly to compress the valve return spring and bring the poppet valve into contact with the vacuum valve seat in the valve housing to close the vacuum port, Fig. 41-47. Any additional movement of the valve operating rod in the applied direction moves the valve plunger away from the poppet valve to open the atmospheric port and admit atmosphere through the filter to

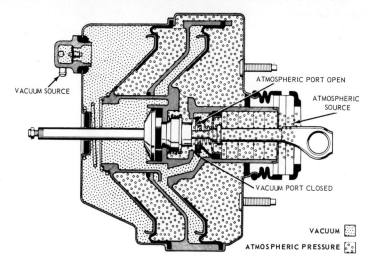

Fig. 41-47. Tandem diaphragm power brake in the applied position.

the chambers at the right sides of both the front and the rear vacuum power diaphragms. With vacuum on the left side of the front and rear diaphragms and atmospheric pressure on the right side of the front and rear diaphragms, a force is developed to move the vacuum power diaphragm assembly and hydraulic push rod to operate the master cylinder in the usual manner.

Operation Of Air-Suspended Type

In the released position, Fig. 41-48, the air valve return spring holds the air valve, push rod, and brake pedal rearward so the air valve is clear of the floating control valve. Although vacuum is present at the floating control valve through the flexible hose, the

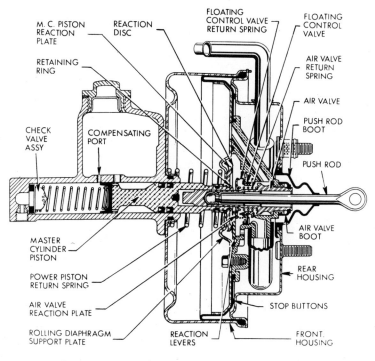

Fig. 41-48. Air suspended type of power cylinder in the released position.

control valve return spring holds the rubber face of the valve against its annular seat in the power piston, thereby closing off manifold vacuum.

Atmospheric air enters through the air filter into the air chamber, and flows through holes in the power piston into the reaction lever area. From here it flows past the open annular seat on the air valve, through a passage in the power piston into the vacuum chamber. With the vacuum passage closed and the vacuum chamber open to outside air, the power piston is balanced by atmospheric pressure on both sides, and is held against the rear housing by the return spring.

The air valve return spring and the floating control valve return spring, are holding the air valve reaction plate against the inner ends of the reaction levers. Since the outer ends of these levers are against their pivot points in the power piston, the

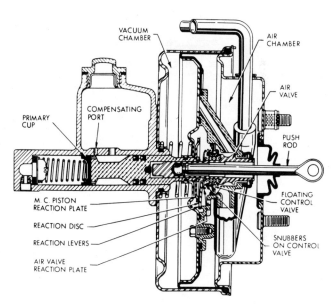

Fig. 41-49. Applying position of power brake unit. (Air suspended type.)

levers are pushing forward against the reaction discs. This disc in turn, is holding the master cylinder piston and reaction plate assembly forward so that the reaction plate is against its stop. In the released position of the power cylinder, the reaction mechanism is fully forward, and the two valves are fully rearward.

As the brake pedal is depressed, the push rod moves the air valve forward until its annular seat contacts the floating control valve, at which point atmospheric pressure is sealed off from the vacuum chamber. Further movement of the air valve pushes the floating control valve away from its annular seat in the power piston, thus connecting the vacuum chamber to the vacuum source. As air is exhausted out of the vacuum chamber, atmospheric pressure in the air chamber starts moving the power piston forward, Fig. 41-49.

As the power piston moves forward, it carries the master cylinder piston into the master cylinder, building up pressure in the hydraulic system to apply the brake shoes. At the same time, a reaction pressure is transmitted back to the brake pedal to give the driver an indication of the power being applied to the brakes. As soon as pressure starts to build up in the hydraulic system, the pressure on the end of the master cylinder piston causes the master cylinder reaction plate to move away from its stop, and press against

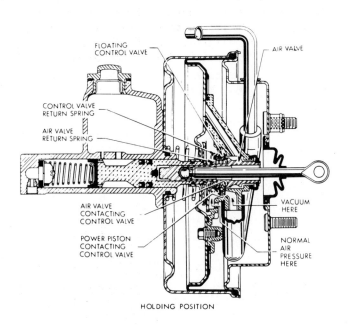

FIG. 41-50. Holding position of power brake unit. (Air suspended type.)

the reaction discs and the reaction levers. The levers in turn swing around their pivots in the power piston, and push the air valve reaction plate back against the floating control valve snubbers, Fig. 41-49.

In this manner, approximately 40 percent of the load on the master cylinder piston is transferred through the air valve and push rod to the brake pedal, to oppose the foot pressure applied by the driver.

When the desired brake pedal apply pressure is reached and the brake pedal is held still, the air valve and floating control valve are also held motionless. The power piston, however, continues forward momentarily until its annular seat contacts the floating control valve, Fig. 41-50. At this point, both the air valve and power piston are seated on the floating control valve, so the passage to the vacuum chamber is closed to atmospheric pressure as well as vacuum. As a result, the power piston is held stationary until the brake pedal is moved.

When the brake pedal is released, the air valve return spring forces the air valve away from the floating control valve. This allows the floating control valve return spring to seat the control valve against the power piston, closing the vacuum passage. Since both sides of the power are now open to atmospheric pressure, the piston return spring forces the power piston and related parts rearward to the unapplied position.

Electric Brakes

Several electrically operated braking systems have been developed. To date they have not been used as extensively as vacuum and air operation. There are

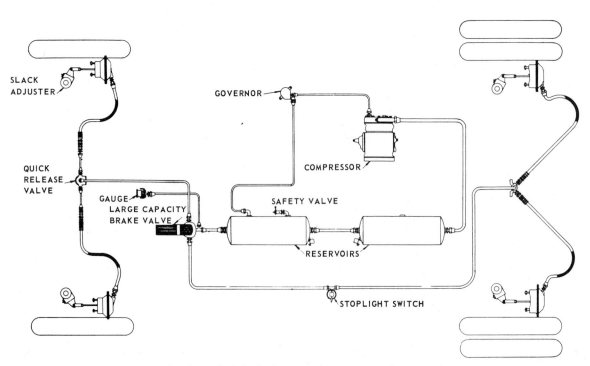

Fig. 41-51. Typical air brake layout and units required on a truck.

several different ways of using electrical energy to operate brakes. It is customary to control the severity of the brake operation, by the amount of current flowing through a magnet.

In one popular electric brake, the armature is attached to the wheel and the magnet attached to the axle. The magnet has a lug and cam levers on it which press the brake shoe lining against the drum when current flows in the magnet. The amount of pressure applied to the lining is regulated by a foot pedal or hand lever which operates a rheostat connected to the battery.

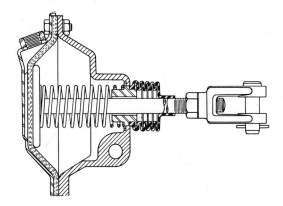

Fig. 41-53. This cross section shows the construction of a typical power brake application cylinder.

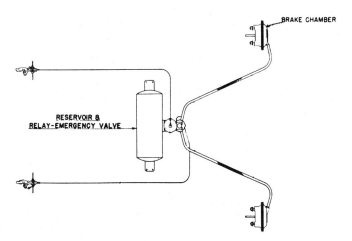

Fig. 41-52. As used on a two wheel trailer this air brake is connected to the truck-tractor system.

Air Brakes

Air operated brakes should not be confused with vacuum boosters. Air brakes are used on trucks and heavy duty vehicles but are not necessary on ordinary passenger automobiles. An air braking system is expensive and complicated but it does prove effective for heavy duty.

The system consists of an air compressor attached to the engine, storage tanks to hold the compressed air, a governor, pressure cylinders or diaphragm chambers at each wheel, suitable control valves and the necessary piping and connections. The air may also be piped to a trailer equipped with air brakes and therefore the truck driver can control the trailer as well as the truck-tractor. A typical system is illustrated in Figs. 41-51 and 41-52. Fig. 41-53 shows the construction of a typical power cylinder.

Combination Of Units

It now becomes apparent that we can have various combinations of units to fit different conditions.

We have passenger cars with either mechanical or hydraulic brakes and with or without vacuum boosters.

We have trucks with electric brakes or with either mechanical or hydraulic brakes that use vacuum boosters, vacuum power operation or air power operation.

We have trailers with electric brakes or with mechanical or hydraulic brakes operated by either air power or vacuum power.

Also all sorts of combinations of these different units. For example, a diesel truck which has no intake manifold vacuum may be equipped with air operated mechanical or hydraulic brakes. Perhaps it is desired to pull a trailer that is equipped with vacuum operated mechanical or hydraulic brakes. In this case we will have to provide the truck with a vacuum pump in order to operate the trailer brakes.

There are dozens of combinations of different units in this fashion. Furthermore air cylinders or diaphragms are combined with hydraulic cylinders in one unit, etc., etc. For these reasons the brake serviceman must understand all of the different units and know how each should function separately and in combination with the other units.

Brake Accessories

For additional convenience to drivers, several automatic accessories are added to the hydraulic system and become a part of it.

For example, the stoplight switch is often hydraulically operated and mounted on the master cylinder. If the diaphragm in this switch should leak or rupture the hydraulic fluid will escape through the switch and the brakes will fail to operate.

NoRol Hill Holder

As the name indicates, NoRol is an automatic device to prevent the car rolling backward when it is stopped on an upgrade. It consists of a valve that is controlled by the angle of the car and the clutch pedal to which it is connected. The valve sets at an angle and when the clutch pedal is depressed with the car on an upgrade a ball rolls by gravity and seals the pressure in the brake system after the brakes are applied and until the clutch is released.

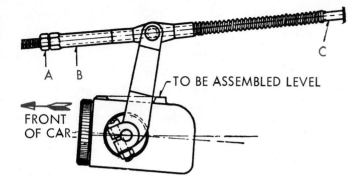

Fig. 41-54. The NoRol unit is mounted on the car at a slight angle as gauged by the bosses on top of the housing.

If the car is level or on a downgrade the device does not operate. The device is illustrated in Fig. 41-54. Adjustments are covered in the trouble shooting section of this book.

Brake Service

Attaching Brake Lining

There are two general methods of attaching brake lining to brake bands or brake shoes; by using rivets, and by bonding. With riveting it is considered there is less possibility of the lining coming loose, while with the bonding method the full surface of the lining is used as none is sacrificed for the rivet holes.

On external bands, such as used for parking brakes on many cars, it is common practice to rivet both ends of the woven lining in place leaving a slight hump in the middle as shown in Fig. 41-55. The lining is then forced down in place so it fits snugly against the metal brake band.

Fig. 41-55. One method of insuring a tight fit of the lining inside an external brake band.

On internal expanding brake shoes, where molded lining is used, it is advisable to use a special brake lining clamp to force the lining down tightly against the brake shoe at all points. If such a clamp is not available, the next best method is to rivet in the middle, and work out to the ends, as shown in Fig. 41-56.

Rivets used in fastening brake lining to brake shoes are usually of brass, copper or aluminum.

If the head of the rivet should touch the brake drum, scoring will result. The rivets are therefore countersunk below the surface of the lining as shown in Fig. 41-57. It is customary to countersink the rivet hole about two thirds the way through the lining. The countersunk holes should be exactly the same size as the rivet head for greatest strength, and the rivet hole in the lining should be the same size as the hole in the brake shoe. It is, of course essential that the rivet fit snugly in the rivet hole and be of the right

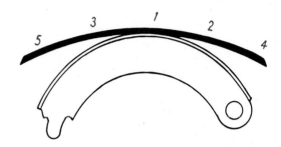

Fig. 41-56. The rivets should be placed first in the middle, then at 2, 3, 4 and 5 when riveting lining to a shoe unless a suitable clamp is available.

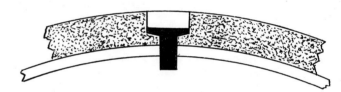

Fig. 41-57. Countersink hole in lining should be accurate to the size and shape of the rivet.

length to "upset" smoothly and easily. A good rule for rivet length is to have the rivet extend through the hole about two thirds of the rivet diameter. For example, a 3/16 in. rivet should have a 1/8 in. shank sticking out for riveting over, Fig. 41-58.

In bonding brake lining to the shoes, a cement is used between the shoes and the lining. The lining is then clamped tightly and placed in a special oven for curing. The cement can be applied to the lining in the form of a paste, or in the form of a tape interposed between the lining and the shoe.

Before applying new lining to a shoe, it is essential that the surface of the shoe be perfectly clean. This

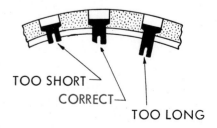

TOO SHORT

CORRECT

TOO LONG

Fig. 41-58. Rivets should be set with a roll punch instead of a star punch.

Fig. 41-59. *Checking a brake drum with a special gauge, for diameter, bell-mouth condition and out-of-round.*

is essential, whether the new lining is to be riveted in place or bonded. Special sanders are available for cleaning the shoes so the new lining will adhere tightly to the shoe, and there will be a minimum of resistance to the transmission of the heat of braking.

Preparation Of Shoes

Before relining brakes it is important to make sure that the diameter of the brake drum is standard, Fig. 41-59. If the brake drum has been reconditioned, it will be larger in diameter. If the diameter has been increased more than .030 in., lining of oversize thickness should be installed.

The surface of the brake lining of newly relined shoes does not conform accurately to the surface of the brake drum. New lining has slight high and low spots. In addition, the brake shoes may be bent or warped, Fig. 41-60. Or if the drum has been reconditioned, it will be slightly larger in diameter and will not conform to the arc of the brake shoes.

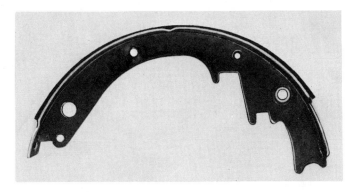

Fig. 41-60. *Note that most of the wear is at the center of the brake shoe and very little at the ends, indicating shoe was used in oversize drums, or possibly the brake shoe was warped.*

Brake shoes should therefore be sanded with special brake shoe sanding equipment, Fig. 41-61, not only to smooth the surface, but so it will conform to the curvature of the brake drum.

Such sanding equipment will provide a smooth even surface. If the shoes are used without such sanding, the high spots of the lining will do all the braking, and much higher temperature than normal will result. Such high temperatures will quickly ruin the new lining and in addition, the brakes may become heat checked.

Care must always be exercised that no grease or oil reaches the brake lining, as that will affect the coefficient of friction and grabbing brakes will result. In that connection, it is always good policy to install new grease seals whenever new brake lining is installed. Also wheel cylinders should be examined to make sure they are not leaking. When handling brake shoes, care must be taken that the hands are not greasy.

Fig. 41-61. *Sanding the surface of a brake shoe.*

When lubricating the front wheel bearings, only grease specified for that purpose should be used, and only enough applied to lubricate the bearing. Excess lubricant may get on the brake lining and ruin it.

Servicing The Drums

The surface of the brake drum must be smooth and free from galling, ridges and heat checks, Fig. 41-62. In addition, the drum must not be bell-mouthed or out-of-round. The ridges, galling and check marks are easily visible, but a drum gauge should be used to check for the other conditions. Fig. 41-59 shows a modern brake drum gauge. The manner in which the brake lining is worn on the shoe will also indicate the condition of the drum, as a drum that is bell-mouthed will cause the lining to wear more on one side of the shoe than on the other.

An important reason for checking the diameter of the drum, is to note whether there is enough metal to permit reconditioning. Passenger car brake drums should not be reconditioned to more than 0.060 in. oversize. More than that amount will severely weaken

Fig. 41-62. Badly scored brake drum.

the drum. Not only will the drum become oval when the brakes are applied, but because of less metal, the drum will operate at much higher temperatures, with attendant brake fade and short lining life.

Brake drums can be reconditioned either by turning on a lathe, Fig. 41-63, or by grinding, Fig. 41-64. Both methods are used extensively. The regrinding method is used particularly in cases where the drum has hard spots.

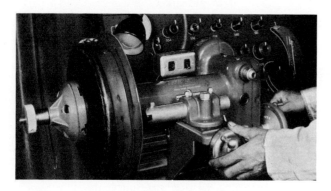

Fig. 41-63. Reconditioning a brake drum by turning on a brake drum lathe.

When turning a drum on a lathe, care must be exercised that the lathe tool is sharpened correctly, and the tool feed is not too fast, as that would result in a "screw thread" type of surface which would cause rapid wear of the brake lining.

Anchor Pins

Centralization of the brake shoes within the drum, is largely dependent on the position of the anchor pin. If the anchor pin is not correctly placed, the effectiveness of the brakes will be greatly reduced. Fig. 41-65, shows how the effective force is reduced when the anchor pin is too low and Fig. 41-66, shows the results of having it too high, with the strong possibility of grabbing condition. Fig. 41-67, shows how the servo action of the brake is built up smoothly and

rapidly, when the anchor pin is correctly located. On those brakes which have adjustable anchor pins, care should therefore be taken to adjust the anchor pin correctly.

Hydraulic Service

No hydraulic brake system can operate satisfactorily unless the various parts are in good mechanical condition and the system full of CLEAN fluid of the proper type. Lubricating oil or mineral hydraulic oil is not the proper type. Mineral oil of any kind will swell and ruin the rubber cups and other parts of the system. Furthermore, it does not have the proper viscosity characteristics for use in an automobile.

The fluid MUST be CLEAN. Any dirt is liable to get in the valves and cause them to leak. Furthermore, adding clean fluid to dirty fluid means dirty

Fig. 41-64. Grinding a brake drum.

Brake shoes low on anchor
(Arrow shows effective force)

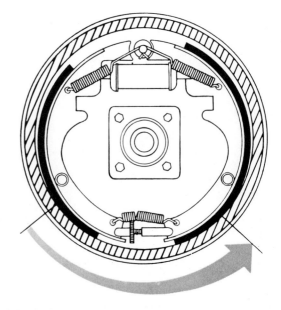

Fig. 41-65. Unless anchor pins are correctly located, full braking will not be attained. Here the anchor pin is too low.

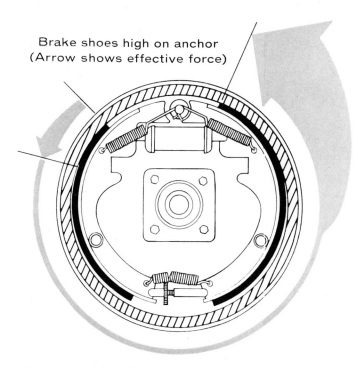

Brake shoes high on anchor
(Arrow shows effective force)

Fig. 41-66. Grabbing brakes result when anchor pins are too high.

fluid. Therefore if there is any doubt about dirt being in the system, it should be drained out and flushed. Equipment and material are available for flushing out hydraulic systems and their use will avoid clogging of ports, sticking valves, leaking and scored cylinders and erratic brake action. In addition, periodic flushing will remove any gum from the old fluid, condensed moisture, bits of scale and rubber, etc.

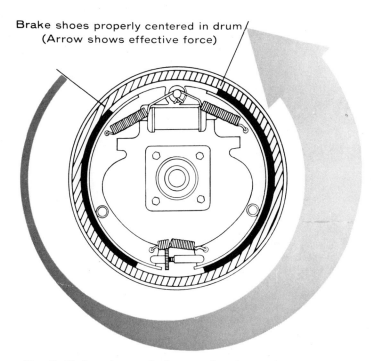

Brake shoes properly centered in drum
(Arrow shows effective force)

Fig. 41-67. Smooth, even braking results when anchor pins are set correctly.

Before adding new fluid, if the car is old, it is well to inspect the flexible lines or hose to make sure that they are not weakened, frayed or swollen inside. All connections and fittings should be checked for leaks and to make sure that the pipe lines are securely fastened to the frame to avoid vibration and eventual breakage. Sometimes lines will also get kinked or dented or worn thin from some other part rubbing on them. If defective in any way they should be replaced.

If the master cylinder and wheel cylinders are known to be in good condition, the fresh fluid can then be added and the system "bled" to remove all air. If there is any air in the system, the pedal will have a "spongy" feel as the hydraulic pressure is compressing the air in the system. When the brakes are applied the pedal should be solid as the hydraulic fluid does not compress.

Bleeding Brakes

There are two general methods in use for bleeding hydraulic brake systems. The manual method requires two men and is slower than pressure bleeding. Pressure bleeding has other advantages but involves the use of special equipment. This equipment consists of a closed, airtight container which contains brake fluid to which air pressure is applied. See Fig. 41-68. The container is then connected to the master

Fig. 41-68. One type of pressure flushing and bleeding equipment complete with necessary fittings.

cylinder fill opening by suitable fittings and flexible hose. The air pressure forces the fluid to each wheel cylinder and each one is bled in turn by opening the bleeder valve and closing it when the fluid is clear and bubbles no longer appear.

This equipment can also be used for flushing out the system when desired by using a flushing fluid instead of brake fluid. In addition to one man operation and faster operation, there is no loss of fluid from spillage and no air can get in the system. Furthermore if the fill plug opening and the area around it is thoroughly cleaned before the plug is removed and the hose connected, no dirt can fall into the master cylinder.

When the manual method is employed, one man "pumps" the pedal to force the fluid through the lines and the other man bleeds the brakes. The first one bled is the farthest from the master cylinder, in most cases the right rear. Next the left rear, then the right front and lastly the left front. With either power or manual bleeding, a hose is attached to the bleeder valve and the other end immersed in a glass jar containing brake fluid. This enables bubbles to be seen and also avoids waste of fluid, Fig. 41-69.

Fig. 41-69. A glass jar permits observation of the bubbles in the brake fluid during the bleeding process.

When bleeding brakes by the manual method it is necessary to watch the level of the fluid in the master cylinder because if it gets low enough, air will be drawn into the master cylinder. Other ways in which air may get into the system include being drawn in around a master cylinder secondary cup, any repair to a master cylinder, wheel cylinder, hose or tubing. Sometimes brake fluid may boil and gas in the lines in hot weather if the master cylinder or brake lines are located too near the muffler or exhaust line. Also if one brake were to drag long enough to overheat the wheel cylinder the result might be air in the line.

After bleeding, the reservoir should be checked and the fluid at a level one-half inch from the top of the reservoir. Also it is wise to check the breather ports in the filler plug to make sure they are not plugged.

BLEEDING SPLIT-SYSTEM MASTER CYLINDER:

When pressure bleeding a tandem piston (split system) master cylinder with a rectangular cover, Fig. 41-16a, the procedure is to fill both reservoirs

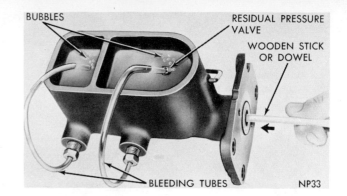

Fig. 41-69a. Bench bleeding a dual master cylinder.

and attach a special pressure bleeder cover to the master cylinder in place of the regular cover. Then as fluid under pressure is applied to the system, bleed rear and then front brakes in the usual manner.

In the tandem piston master cylinder which has two filler caps a different procedure is necessary. The procedure is to attach the pressure bleeding hose to the front filler opening and as pressure is applied, bleed the rear wheel cylinders in the usual manner. Then attach the pressure bleeding hose to the rear opening of the master cylinder and repeat bleeding operation on front wheel cylinders. In the case of the Corvette, however, the front reservoir is connected to the front wheels and the rear reservoir to the rear wheels.

Due to the extra components inside the dual master cylinder, it is more difficult to remove the air bubbles than on previous models. It is therefore advisable to purge the master cylinder of air before connecting the brake lines. This can be done in the car or on the workbench. The best method is to connect short lengths of brake tube to the outlet port of the master cylinder and immerse the other ends in the master cylinder reservoirs, Fig. 41-69a. Then apply the master cylinder push rod a full stroke and repeat until all air bubbles have been eliminated. Then connect the brake lines to the master cylinder and bleed each of the wheel cylinders in turn.

Checking Hydraulic Cylinders

When any work is needed on either the master cylinder or wheel cylinders, it must be done with a high degree of accuracy and absolute cleanliness is of utmost importance. Of course solvents or gasoline should not be used to clean the boots, cups, check valve assembly or any rubber parts. Alcohol is the proper cleaning fluid. The metal parts may be cleaned in solvent if they are then rinsed in alcohol.

The compensating port in the master cylinder must be open and this can be checked by pushing a very small gauge wire through it. The cylinders must be free of scratches, grooves or pits and should be measured to make sure that they have not been honed oversize. If it is oversize it will be necessary to replace it, install a sleeve in it or use an oversize piston.

If the cylinder is not oversize but is rough, it can be polished with a special hone made for the purpose. After honing, the by-pass port should be reamed with a special burr removing tool to make sure there will be no sharp edge around the hole which might scratch the primary cup as it moves back and forth within the cylinder.

Before reassembling, all parts should be washed in clean alcohol and dipped in brake fluid. Ordinary gasoline, kerosene, solvents and cleaning fluids should never be used.

When installing the master cylinder, it is important that the piston rod be adjusted properly so that the edge of the piston cup does not cover the compensating port. If there is any doubt, a small wire can be inserted into the compensating port through the fill cap opening with the brake pedal in the released position when the adjustment is correct.

If this port is covered with the pedal in the released position, the fluid cannot return from the lines to the reservoir. This will cause the brakes to drag as previously explained.

The rubber boot that fits around the push rods should be firm and fit snugly at both ends to prevent the entry of dust or dirt which would score the piston.

The wheel cylinders also have rubber boots on

Fig. 41-70. If clamps are not installed on wheel cylinders during disassembly, brake fluid may leak from cylinder. In any case, fluid leak signals trouble.

them to keep dirt out of the wheel cylinders. These too must be in good condition and fit snugly. If these boots should leak, brake fluid might get on the brake lining and cause the brakes to grab, Fig. 41-70. Put clamps on the wheel cylinders before removing the retractor springs from the shoes; otherwise the wheel cylinder cups may move outward and cause air to enter the system. This would necessitate bleeding the brakes and possible relining.

Brake Trouble Shooting

Symptom Or Probable Cause	Probable Remedy
Pedal Spongy	
1. Air in brake lines.	1. Bleed brakes.
All Brakes Drag	
1. Mineral oil in system.	1. Flush entire system and replace all rubber parts.
2. Improper push rod to main cylinder piston clearance.	2. Overhaul master cylinder.
One Brake Drags	
1. Loose or damaged wheel bearing.	1. Adjust or replace wheel bearings.
2. Weak, broken or unhooked brake shoe return spring.	2. Replace retractor spring.
3. Incorrect parking brake adjustment.	3. Readjust parking brake at equalizer.
4. Damaged or frozen parking brake cable.	4. Free-up or replace parking brake assembly.
Excessive Pedal Travel	
1. Normal lining wear or improper shoe adjustment.	1. Adjust brakes.
2. Fluid low in master cylinder.	2. Fill master cylinder to correct level.
Pedal Gradually Goes To Floor When Brakes Are Applied	
1. External fluid leaks.	1. Check master cylinder and wheel cylinder for leaks. Check brake lines for leaks.
2. Master cylinder leaks past primary cup.	2. Overhaul master cylinder.

Brakes Uneven

1. Grease on lining.

2. Tires improperly inflated.
3. Front suspension faulty.
4. Rough turned brake drum.

1. Replace lining and correct cause of grease getting on lining.
2. Inflate tires.
3. Correct alignment.
4. Have drum finish turned.

Excessive Pedal Pressure

1. Grease or water on lining.
2. Full area of lining not contacting drums.
3. Scored brake drums.

1. Clean or replace lining.
2. Adjust anchor pin. Replace shoes.
3. Turn drums and install new shoes.

Pedal Hop

1. Drums out-of-round.

1. Replace drums.

Brake Fade

1. Defective master cylinder.
2. External fluid leaks.
3. Vapor lock.
4. Thin brake drums.

1. Overhaul master cylinder.
2. Locate and repair.
3. Flush and refill hydraulic system with quality fluid.
4. Install new brake drums.

Diving

1. Shoes not centered.
2. Primary and secondary shoes reversed.

1. Adjust anchor pins.
2. Install shoes correctly.

Brake Chatter

1. Loose brake lining.
2. Shoes not centered.
3. Rough turned brake drum.

1. Install new lining.
2. Adjust anchor pins.
3. Finish turn brake drum.

Trouble Shooting Power Brakes

1. Test for power brake operation as follows: With the engine stopped, depress brake pedal several times to eliminate all vacuum from the system. Apply the brakes and while holding foot pressure on the brake pedal, start the engine. If power cylinder is operating, the pedal will move slightly forward when vacuum power reaches the system.

2. If test shows power system is not working, check the following items: Check all vacuum lines (including those to other vacuum operated units) to be sure there is no leakage at any point; check condition of air cleaner; check for badly dented vacuum cylinder; and check for defects within power brake unit, requiring removal and overhaul.

Quiz - Brakes

1. What is friction?
2. Friction is the same for all materials.
   a. True.   b. False.
3. If the area between two contacting surfaces is increased, what happens to the friction?
   a. It increases.
   b. It decreases.
   c. Remains the same.

4. How is the coefficient of friction calculated?
5. If the weight of a vehicle is doubled, will the amount of heat developed in braking be twice as much, or four times as much?
6. If the speed of a car is increased from 30 mph to 60 mph, will the heat developed in stopping, be twice as much or four times as much?
7. Define reaction time as applied to applying brakes.

8. Give the formula used in calculating the kinetic energy developed in stopping a car.

9. List five factors that tend to increase brake temperatures.

10. When will the fastest stops be made? With the wheels rotating or with the wheels locked.

11. Is the hydraulic pressure in a brake system the same through the entire system or does it vary?

12. How is the force in a hydraulic brake system multiplied?

13. If the pressure provided by master cylinder is 500 psi, what is the total pressure at a wheel cylinder of 2 sq. in. area?
    a. 500 lb.
    b. 1000 lb.
    c. 2000 lb.

14. What is meant by the term weight transfer?

15. List five factors that contribute to the effectiveness of brakes.

16. Describe self-energization.

17. Which brake will have the greater self-energization? One with the anchor pin nearer the center of rotation or one with the anchor pin far from the center of rotation.

18. List the two main types of brake lining materials.

19. What material is used mostly for the braking surface of brake drums?
    a. Cast iron.
    b. Wrought iron.
    c. Steel.

20. What is the advantage of using aluminum in a brake drum?

21. Describe the operation of a hydraulic brake system.

22. What is meant by the term split system master cylinder?

23. List five qualities that a good hydraulic brake fluid must meet.

24. What is the purpose of the check valve in the master cylinder?

25. Under extreme conditions, what temperature may be expected in the brakes?
    a. 700 deg.
    b. 100 deg.
    c. 2000 deg.
    d. 950 deg.

26. What causes vapor lock in a brake system?

27. Where is there the greater tendency toward vapor lock?
    a. On top of a mountain.
    b. At sea level.

28. On a conventional Bendix single anchor brake where it is desired to expand the shoes in the drums, how should the handle of the adjusting tool be moved?
    a. Upward.
    b. Downward.

29. How many wheel cylinders are used on the front brakes of the Lockheed hydraulic brakes?
    a. One.
    b. Two.

30. Are the operating temperatures of the disc or caliper type brake as used on many European cars, higher or lower than on brakes of the conventional drum type?
    a. Higher.   b. Lower.

31. What is meant by the vacuum suspended type of power brake unit?

32. What is meant by the air suspended type of power brake unit?

33. When riveting brake lining to a brake shoe, how far should the hole be countersunk into the lining?
    a. 1/3.
    b. 1/2.
    c. 2/3.

34. Give one advantage of bonded lining over riveted lining.

35. When should oversize lining be installed on brake shoes?

36. What is the limit in oversize when reconditioning brake drums?
    a. .060 in.
    b. .125 in.
    c. .030 in.
    d. .006 in.

37. Why must care be exercised when setting the adjustable type of anchor pin?

38. What results will happen if mineral oil is used in an hydraulic brake system?

39. Describe the procedure for bleeding brakes.

40. When cleaning hydraulic brake parts, what type cleaning fluid should be used?
    a. Alcohol.
    b. Good grade of cleaning solvent.
    c. Kerosene.

41. What is the basic major advantage of a split, or dual, hydraulic brake system?

42. In disc brake design, how many pistons are incorporated in a fixed caliper?
    a. One.
    b. Two.
    c. Four.

43. How many pistons in a floating caliper?
    a. One.
    b. Two.
    c. Four.

44. How does a floating caliper work?

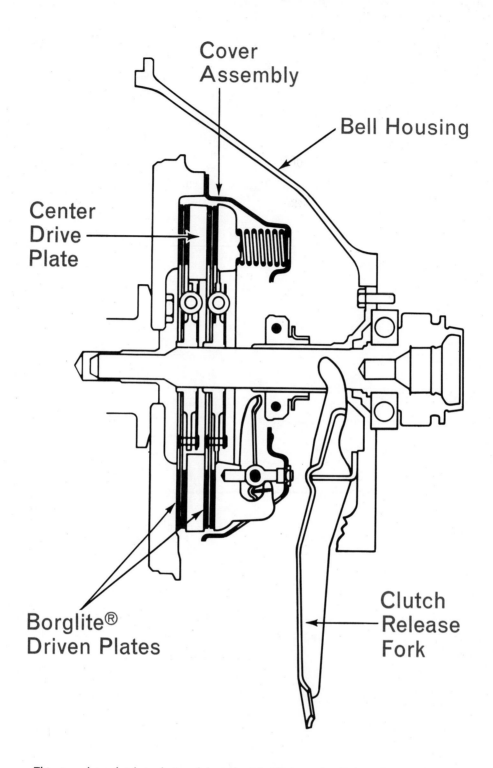

Cover
Assembly

Bell Housing

Center
Drive
Plate

Borglite® Driven Plates

Clutch
Release
Fork

This two-plate clutch is designed for use with 400 in. – plus high performance passenger and sports car engines. Advantages claimed include longer facing life and smooth operation with reduced pedal effort.

CLUTCHES

Clutches are friction devices used to connect and disconnect a driving force from a driven member. A clutch used in conjunction with an engine flywheel serves to accomplish smooth engagement and disengagement of the engine and the input shaft of a manual transmission.

Since an internal combustion engine develops little power or torque at low rpm, it must gain speed before it is required to put the vehicle in motion. Obviously then, if a rapidly rotating engine is suddenly connected to the drive line of a stationary vehicle, a violent shock will result.

So gradual application of load, along with some slowing of engine speed, is needed to provide reasonable and comfortable starts. This is accomplished by various mechanical, electrical and hydraulic means of connecting the engine to the driving wheels. The electrical, hydraulic and some mechanical devices are described in the transmission section of this text. In this chapter, we are concerned with mechanical clutches.

Design and Construction

Most cars with manual transmissions use a single plate, dry disc clutch. The disc has friction material facing on each side and is operated by a pressure plate and release bearing, Fig. 42-1. Some heavy-duty trucks use two discs in conjunction with a pressure plate and an intermediate pressure plate, Fig. 42-2. In either case, the disc or discs are positioned between the engine flywheel and the pressure plate.

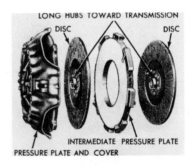

Fig. 42-2. Trucks often use two-plate clutches in which front and rear discs and an intermediate pressure plate are sandwiched between the pressure plate and flywheel.

Engagement and disengagement of the clutch assembly is controlled by a foot pedal and linkage that must be properly adjusted and relatively easy to apply. The machined surfaces of the flywheel and pressure plate against which the clutch facings bear must be flat, true and free from cracks or score marks. The transmission, pressure plate, flywheel housing, clutch disc, flywheel and crankshaft must be properly aligned to prevent slippage, vibration and noise.

Operation

When the clutch pedal is depressed, this movement is transmitted to the clutch fork by way of rods or a cable, a cross shaft and fork push rod, Fig. 42-3. The fork, in turn, moves the clutch release bearing (throwout bearing) against the release levers of the pressure plate, relieving the spring pressure on the plate and releasing the clutch disc from the engine flywheel, Fig. 42-4.

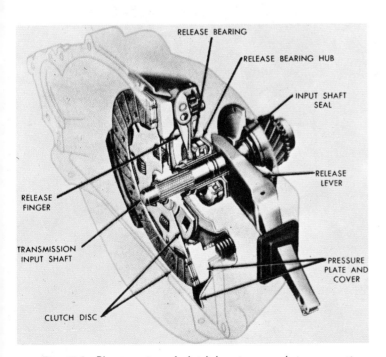

Fig. 42-1. Phantom view of clutch housing reveals cross section of typical clutch assembly, including transmission input shaft and bearing retainer.

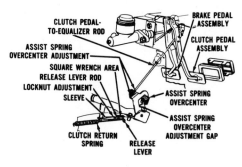

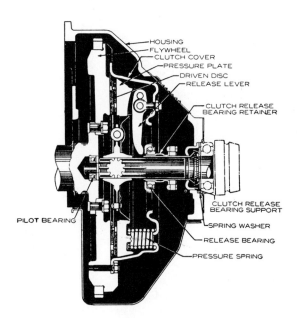

Fig. 42-3. Clutch linkage arrangement on typical suspended pedal setup features pedal and rod and over-center bracket. Locknut adjustment is incorporated in release lever rod.

When the driver takes his foot from the clutch pedal, a return spring pulls the linkage into driving position and returns the pedal against a pedal stop. This also lets the clutch fork and release bearing back away from the pressure plate release levers, permitting the pressure plate springs to compress the clutch disc between the plate and engine flywheel.

Fig. 42-4. Call outs in sectional view of single disc clutch assembly highlight major parts involved in engagement and disengagement of clutch.

Clutch Discs and Facings

The clutch disc is made up of a circular metal plate attached to a reinforced, splined hub. Often, the disc hub is mounted on coil springs to provide cushioned engagement. The outer half of the disc is covered over with friction facings on both sides. Generally, the clutch facings are made of molded or woven asbestos riveted or bonded to the clutch disc, Fig. 42-5. The thickness of the disc assembly must be uniform and its friction facings must be smooth, although not necessarily flat and true. In some cases the facing

or disc, or both, are purposely warped to encourage "soft" engagement. When the clutch is fully engaged, the pressure plate springs press the disc and facings flat between the flywheel and pressure plate. At this point, the slight warpage is not a factor.

Fig. 42-5. Basic components of clutch assembly are shown: multi-spring pressure plate; clutch disc; flywheel. Punch marks noted by arrows aid in reassembly and reinstallation.

When two clutch discs are used, they are located on either side of the intermediate pressure plate, Fig. 42-6. The flywheel, intermediate plate and pressure plate are made to rotate together, but are mounted so that the pressure plate and intermediate plate can move in or out of engagement.

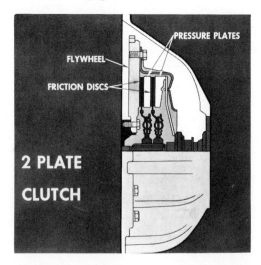

Fig. 42-6. Two-plate clutch used on 1971 Oldsmobile manual transmission equipped cars has front disc, intermediate pressure plate, rear disc and pressure plate.

Pressure Plates

The pressure plate assembly basically consists of the heavy plate, coil springs or a diaphragm, release levers or fingers and a cover, Fig. 42-5. The cover is bolted to the engine flywheel, and spring pressure is exerted between the pressure plate and cover. Most

Fig. 42-7. A diaphragm or dished-type spring is used in this design of pressure plate to compress clutch disc between plate and engine flywheel.

give it an over-center action in applying and releasing pressure on the pressure plate and clutch disc, Fig. 42-8.

To disengage the clutch, the spring pressure must be released. In the diaphragm spring type of pressure plate, this is accomplished when the clutch release bearing bears against and compresses the spring, Fig. 42-9. In the multiple spring type, spring pressure is released by three levers, or fingers, spaced at equal intervals around the clutch cover and activated by a clutch release bearing. In most cases a ball bearing assembly is used, although some clutch

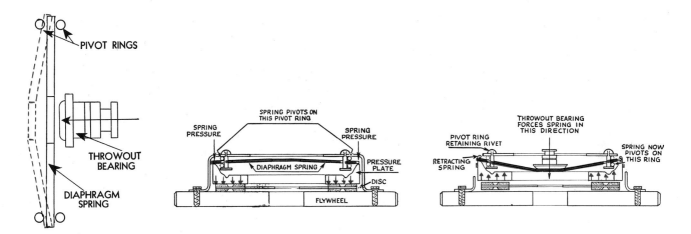

Fig. 42-8. Three diagrammatic views illustrate how pivot rings give diaphragm spring an over-center action when clutch release bearing forces spring toward engine flywheel.

clutches use many small coil springs for this purpose, although diaphragm springs are still in use. See Figs. 42-7 and 42-8.

In multiple spring pressure plates, the springs are spaced around the pressure plate inside the cover so that uniform pressure will be placed on the clutch disc when it is engaged. The diaphragm spring is shaped like a dished plate. It utilizes pivot rings to

arrangements use a bearing made of a composition such as carbon or graphite.

The clutch cover serves to contain the pressure plate assembly. Most covers are vented to allow heat to escape and cooling air to enter. Some are designed

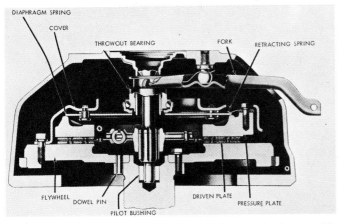

Fig. 42-9. Cross section of clutch housing and clutch assembly provides excellent operational view of diaphragm spring, pivot rings and clutch release bearing.

Fig. 42-10. Clutch covers are often designed with built-in cooling feature that provides circulation of air while clutch assembly rotates.

to provide a fan action for forced circulation of air to help cool them, Fig. 42-10. Even proper use of a clutch generates some heat because of normal slippage while it is being engaged.

Semi-Centrifugal Clutch

A more-or-less unusual clutch pressure plate set-up is used on late model Chrysler cars. Called a semi-centrifugal clutch, the pressure plate has six cylindrical rollers which move outward under centrifugal force until they contact the cover, Fig. 42-11.

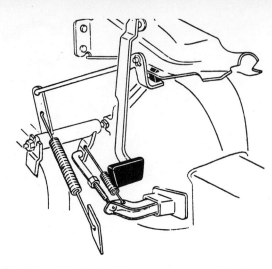

Fig. 42-12. Chevrolet clutch linkage arrangement affords positive transfer of pedal movement by way of pedal rod, cross shaft and clutch fork push rod.

As engine speed increases, the rollers wedge themselves between the pressure plate and cover so that the faster the clutch rotates, the greater the pressure exerted on the pressure plate and clutch disc.

Clutch Linkage

Clutch linkage connects the clutch pedal to the fork mounted in the clutch housing at the rear of the engine, Fig. 42-12. The linkage usually consists of a

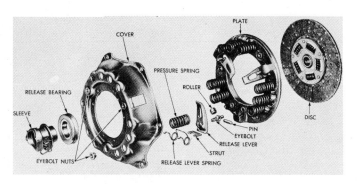

Fig. 42-11. Semi-centrifugal clutch in Chrysler cars has cylindrical rollers which are forced outward by centrifugal action to apply extra pressure on pressure plate.

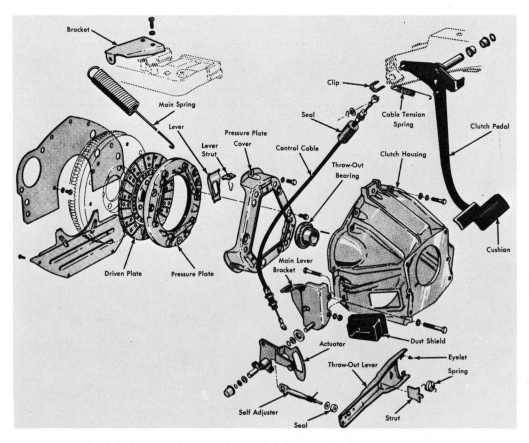

Fig. 42-13. Clutch linkage is shown in this exploded view of components that include: control cable; main lever bracket; pin; actuator and self-adjuster.

pedal rod or cable, a cross shaft assembly to provide the necessary pivoting action, an adjustable fork push rod and a return spring, Fig. 42-13. Linkage varies on practically every make and model, but its basic goal is to relay clutch pedal movement to the clutch fork and afford a means of adjustment to compensate for normal clutch facing wear. At the same time, correct adjustment of clutch pedal free play, positions the clutch release bearing far enough from the release levers of the pressure plate to prevent the bearing from running continually until failure.

Frame design and location of clutch units in several European cars sometimes cause complications in the clutch linkage. In these cases, hydraulic operation of the clutch is utilized. A master cylinder, very similar to a brake master cylinder, is attached to the clutch pedal. A slave cylinder, somewhat similar to a brake wheel cylinder, is attached to the clutch release shaft. The arrangement is used on the English Jaguar.

Fig. 42-14. Heart of American Motors "E-Stick" clutch system is control unit mounted at right rear of engine. Servo piston rod actuates lever that engages clutch.

Automatic Clutches

Automatic clutches are used in certain U.S. and European cars. American Motors Corporation introduced the "E-Stick" clutch which eliminated the need for physical operation of the clutch pedal. Daimler-Benz of Germany engineered an automatic clutch system called "Hydrak," which consisted of a fluid flywheel connected to a single, dry disc clutch.

The "E-Stick" setup differs from a conventional clutch in several ways:

1. The pressure plate levers "engage" the clutch disc rather than "release" them.
2. The clutch remains disengaged until the servo unit, Fig. 42-14, is applied by oil pressure when the shift lever is placed "in gear" with the engine running.
3. The release bearing operates constantly while the car is moving in gear.

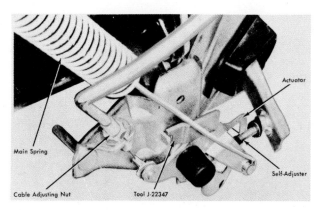

Fig. 42-15. Automatic adjustment of clutch is provided through operation of clutch pedal. Pedal movement causes wire extension to extend threaded portion of self-adjuster.

The "Hydrak" unit also begins operation when the gear shift lever is put "in gear." This releases an electric contact which opens a valve in the vacuum-operated booster unit. Thus activated, the booster unit then disengages the clutch disc. The driving and driven parts of the hydraulic clutch are bridged over by a free-wheel unit which goes into action when the speed of the rear wheels is higher than the speed of the engine. A special device controls engagement of the mechanical clutch, depending on whether the rear axle is in traction or is pushed by car momentum.

Automatic adjustment is another American Motor's innovation. As the clutch disc facings wear, the stroke of the clutch pedal actuates the spring steel wire extension on the self-adjuster and automatically extends the threaded portion, Fig. 42-15.

Fluid Flywheels

Fluid flywheels, or couplings, were widely used with early automatic and semiautomatic transmissions.

In operation, a fluid flywheel acts like an automatic clutch: it slips at idling speed; holds to transmit power as engine speed increases. With this system, power is transmitted through oil. There is no mechanical connection between the engine and drive shaft.

One side of the unit is attached to the engine, the other side to the drive shaft. Each side is made up of vaned sections facing each other. A fluid flywheel used with a sliding gear transmission is partially filled with oil and is a sealed unit. In automatic transmissions, the oil is circulated by pump pressure to the fluid flywheel as well as to other parts of the transmission. When the engine operates fast enough, oil is thrown from the "impeller" side to the "runner" side, causing it to turn in the same direction. See Fig. 42-16.

The fluid flywheel is not a hydraulic torque converter (which will be covered later in this text). The fluid flywheel transmits little power at slow speed; but when the "impeller" speeds up, it forces oil against the vanes of the "runner" with increasing force and vehicle movement results.

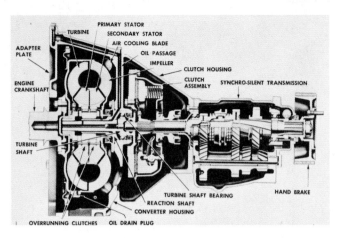

Fig. 42-16. A fluid flywheel used in connection with a dry-disc clutch reduces slippage of clutch disc and eases gear shifting in sliding gear transmissions.

Clutch Service

Perhaps the most common cause of clutch trouble is misalignment. The transmission input shaft upon which the clutch disc is mounted should be in perfect alignment with the engine crankshaft and at right angles to the flywheel face.

Imperfect alignment can be caused in many ways: bent crankshaft flange; bent flywheel web; burr on a bolt or a chip between the crankshaft flange and flywheel web; warped clutch housing; warped transmission housing; incorrectly centered transmission housing; chips between the clutch housing and transmission housing.

In addition to misalignment of the housings, there is always a possibility of misalignment of the transmission input shaft. A worn front bearing in the trans-

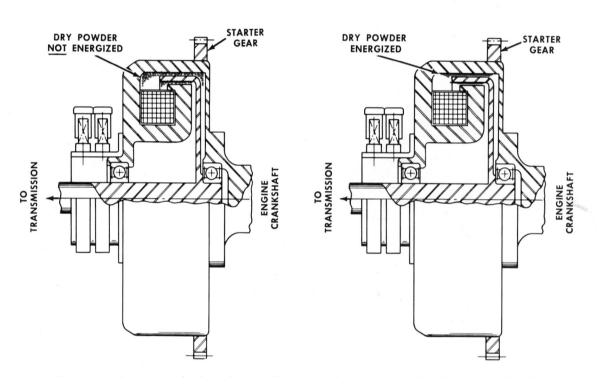

Fig. 42-17. Action of magnetic clutch is shown in demagnetized and magnetized condition. At right, dry powder particles are drawn together to form solid drive unit.

Magnetic Clutches

A different type of clutch is used on air conditioning compressors, fans, etc. Known as a magnetic clutch, the structure comprises a coil completely enclosed by a magnetic circuit. A mixture of magnetizable metal and dry lubricant is used as the clutching medium.

When the coil is energized, the fine metal and lubricant particles are drawn together in a strong load-transmitting bond, Fig. 42-17. The mixture is literally "frozen" and "unfrozen" in direct proportion to the amount of current applied. Therefore, any desired amount of slippage or solid drive may be had.

mission or excessive wear in the pilot bearing or bushing will permit the input shaft to run untrue. Another frequent cause of misalignment is a sprung input shaft.

A bent or sprung input shaft or clutch disc is usually caused by carelessness in removing or replacing the transmission. If the transmission is unsupported while being removed or installed, the weight of the unit is liable to spring the shaft or disc. For this reason, a transmission lift or hoist should always be used to aid in moving the transmission in or out of place.

To check clutch housing alignment, use a dial indicator attached to a special tool installed in the pilot bearing or bushing, Figs. 42-18 and 42-19. Then check the flywheel for proper alignment by mounting the dial indicator on the clutch housing.

Distortion of the clutch cover will also cause misalignment. Such distortion or warpage is caused by carelessness in removing or replacing the cover. The retaining bolts must be loosened and tightened evenly or the cover may be sprung or distorted by spring pressure. The safest method is to insert wood blocks between the release levers and the cover before the

bolts are loosened. These blocks keep the spring tension off of the bolts and facilitate removal and replacement of the bolts. After reinstallation, remove the wedges.

Another thing to be kept in mind is that the engine is usually balanced with the clutch assembly installed. Before removing the clutch cover, mark the cover and flywheel and reinstall the cover in the same relative position, Fig. 42-20. Otherwise, the rotating balance of the engine assembly may be disturbed, thus creating vibration.

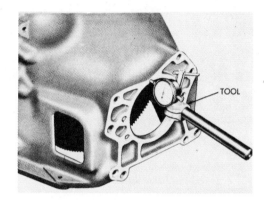

Fig. 42-18. To check clutch housing face alignment, dial indicator is mounted as shown, and flywheel is turned one revolution.

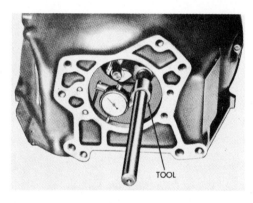

Fig. 42-19. To check clutch housing bore for runout, dial indicator is installed and flywheel is rotated.

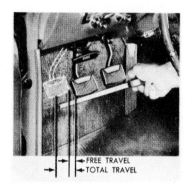

Fig. 42-21. In most applications, correct clutch pedal free play is 1 in. This insures adequate clearance between clutch release bearing and pressure plate release levers.

Clutch Adjustment

The principle cause of a damaged clutch release bearing is neglect of clutch adjustment to compensate for wear. As the lining is gradually worn from the disc in normal use, the pressure plate moves closer to the flywheel and the release levers move outward. This forces the release bearing backward and the clutch pedal with it. If the pedal is forced against the pedal stop, the bearing will contact the release levers and turn at all times. This continuous pressure on the clutch release bearing will tend to partially disengage the clutch, causing the clutch disc friction facings to slip and wear rapidly.

Therefore, check clutch pedal free play occasionally and adjust when necessary to restore proper clearance. Clearance should be about 1 in. of free play, Fig. 42-21. Usually, this adjustment can be made at the clutch fork push rod, Fig. 42-22. In most cases, the adjustment is located at the outer end of the clutch pedal rod.

Clutch Trouble Shooting

Clutch troubles can be broken down as follows:

Chattering
    1. Oil or grease on clutch disc facing.
    2. Glazed or worn facing.
    3. Warped clutch disc.

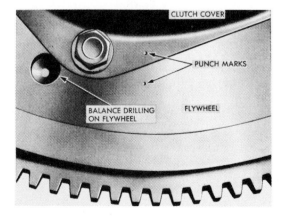

Fig. 42-20. Flywheel and clutch cover should be punch marked to maintain balance if original pressure plate is reinstalled.

4. Worn or loose splines in hub or on transmission input shaft.
5. Splined hub sticking on splined shaft.
6. Warped pressure plate.
7. Cracked or scored pressure plate or flywheel face.
8. Sticking or binding release levers.
9. Unequally adjusted release levers.
10. Unequal length or strength of clutch springs.
11. Bent transmission input shaft.
12. Worn, loose or spongy engine mounts.
13. Worn or loose universal joint, differential, drive axle, torque tube or torque rod mounting.
14. Misalignment of clutch housing, clutch assembly, etc.

Dragging

1. Oil or grease on clutch disc facing.
2. Warped clutch disc.
3. Broken disc facing.
4. Splined hub sticking on splined shaft.
5. Accumulation of dust in clutch.
6. Warped pressure plate or clutch cover.
7. Excessive clutch pedal free play.
8. Sticking pilot bearing or bushing.
9. Sticking release bearing retainer.
10. Engine idling too fast.
11. Misalignment of clutch housing, clutch assembly, etc.

Squeaks

1. Clutch release bearing needs lubrication.
2. Pilot bearing needs lubrication.
3. Release bearing retainer needs lubrication.
4. Pressure plate release lever driving lugs and pins need lubrication.
5. Misalignment of clutch housing, clutch assembly, etc.

Rattles

1. Loose hub in clutch disc.
2. Broken or loose coil springs in clutch disc.
3. Worn splines in hub or on shaft.
4. Worn driving lugs or pins in pressure plate.
5. Unequal adjustment of release levers.
6. Worn release bearing.
7. Worn release parts.
8. Worn pilot bearing or bushing.
9. Bent transmission input shaft.
10. Worn transmission bearings.
11. Wear in transmission or drive line.
12. Misalignment of clutch housing, clutch assembly, etc.

Grabbing

1. Oil or grease on clutch disc facing.
2. Glazed or worn facing.
3. Splined hub sticking or binding on splined shaft.
4. Sticking driving lugs or pins in pressure plate.

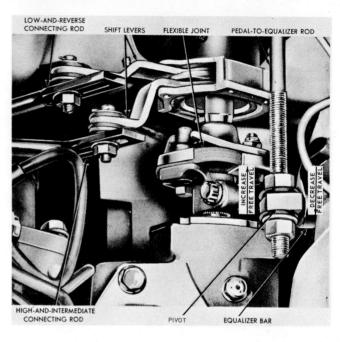

Fig. 42-22. Clutch adjustment is usually located at clutch fork push rod, which is threaded and fitted with an adjusting nut and locknut.

5. Sticking or binding release levers.
6. Sticking or binding clutch pedal or linkage.
7. Misalignment of clutch housing, clutch assembly, etc.

Slipping

1. Worn clutch disc facing.
2. Oil or grease on disc facing.
3. Warped disc.
4. Weak or broken pressure plate springs.
5. Warped pressure plate.
6. Sticking release levers.
7. Pressure plate sticking or binding at driving lugs and pins.
8. Insufficient clutch pedal free play.
9. Misalignment of clutch housing, clutch assembly, etc.

Failure

1. Disc hub torn out.
2. Friction facing torn off or worn off.
3. Splined hub stuck on splined shaft.
4. Broken springs in pressure plate.
5. Incorrect adjustment of pressure plate.
6. Insufficient clutch pedal free play.

Vibration

1. Defective clutch disc.
2. Dust in clutch.
3. Use of rigid disc instead of flexible type.
4. Improper installation of clutch on flywheel.
5. Bent transmission input shaft.
6. Unmatched pressure plate springs.
7. Misalignment of clutch housing, clutch assembly, etc.

Clutch Overhaul

Corrective service usually consists of repair, adjustment or replacement of the faulty part or assembly. To inspect and correct major troubles in clutch operation, proceed as follows:

1. Remove drive shaft and transmission, Fig. 42-23.
2. Remove flywheel cover or clutch bell housing, if so equipped.
3. Locate X marks on flywheel and clutch cover, or prick-punch these units to insure proper installation if old clutch is used.
4. Unhook clutch return spring, back off clutch adjustment if necessary and remove release bearing assembly.

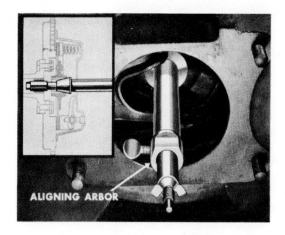

Fig. 42-24. Aligning arbor inserted through hub of clutch disc and into pilot bushing centers disc on flywheel while pressure plate is bolted in place.

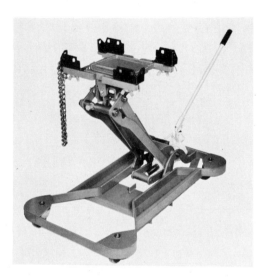

Fig. 42-23. With misalignment considered to be major cause of clutch trouble, a transmission jack provides best means of moving transmission in and out of place.

5. Install wooden wedges between release levers and cover, then loosen clutch-to-flywheel bolts evenly, one turn at a time, until spring pressure is released.
6. Remove bolts and clutch assembly.
7. Clean flywheel and inspect pilot bearing or bushing for wear or score marks. Replace if necessary, using a special installing tool.
8. Pack bearing with lubricant, or wipe lubricant on bushing and install small quantity of lubricant in crankshaft depression in front of bushing.
9. Check clutch housing alignment, Figs. 42-18 and 42-19. Correct as required by shimming or dowel replacement.
10. Check flywheel alignment. Correct as required.
11. Check fit of new clutch disc on transmission input shaft spline.
12. Lubricate pressure plate between driving lugs and edge of plate openings.

13. Install clutch disc and pressure plate, using an aligning tool or old transmission input shaft, Fig. 42-24.
14. Tighten clutch-to-flywheel bolts evenly, then remove aligning tool or input shaft.
15. Install new clutch release bearing on bearing retainer, using care to insure proper seating and to avoid damage to bearing. Then check free sliding fit of bearing assembly on transmission input shaft bearing retainer.
16. Wipe light coating of lubricant on face of release bearing, using care to avoid getting lubricant on clutch disc. Also wipe film of lubricant on arms of clutch fork and lubricate fork ball and socket.
17. Place release bearing assembly on arms of clutch fork and center assembly over wheel hub hole in clutch disc.
18. Install clutch bell housing, if so equipped.
19. Apply light coat of lubricant on transmission input shaft bearing retainer, then install transmission and drive shaft, torquing attaching bolts to specified values.
20. Adjust fork push rod to obtain specified amount of free play at clutch pedal, Fig. 42-22. If equipped with over-center assist spring, make this adjustment first.
21. Install flywheel cover, if so equipped.
22. Test clutch operation.

Quiz - Clutches

1. What is the function of a clutch mounted on the engine flywheel?
2. Do the clutch springs, or diaphragm spring, hold the clutch disc against the flywheel or the pressure plate?
   a. Flywheel.
   b. Pressure plate.
   c. Both.

3. Describe the action of a diaphragm spring in a clutch cover.
4. Should all clutch springs in a multi-spring clutch be of the same length and strength?
5. How many clutch release levers are customarily used on a clutch having six springs?
   a. One.
   b. Three.
   c. Six.
6. What is the most common application of a single magnetic clutch in an automobile?
7. What added components afford centrifugal action to a semi-centrifugal clutch?
   a. Cylindrical rollers.
   b. Heavier driving lugs.
   c. Stronger pressure plate springs.

8. What is the function of the clutch release bearing?
9. Where is the clutch adjustment usually located?
   a. At clutch cross shaft.
   b. At clutch pedal stop.
   c. At clutch fork push rod.
10. Is a fluid flywheel the same as a torque converter?
11. Name two advantages of a fluid flywheel.
12. Where should dial indicator be mounted to check runout of flywheel?
13. Where should dial indicator be mounted to check alignment of clutch housing?
14. Rule-of-thumb figure for clutch pedal free play is:
    a. 1/2 in.
    b. 1 in.
    c. 1 1/2 in.
15. Name six causes of misalignment of a clutch.

TRANSMISSION
FUNDAMENTALS

Transmissions are speed and power changing devices installed at some point between the engine and driving wheels of a vehicle. These units are geared to a power ratio that puts the car in motion and to one or more speed ratios that keep it rolling.

An automobile without a transmission could be started on a level road by accelerating the engine then engaging the clutch. However, a start under these conditions would be slow, noisy and uncomfortable and would place a tremendous strain on the engine and driving parts of the automobile. In addition, cars often are required to travel uphill and must have some means of multiplying the torque or turning effort of the engine. This is the task of the transmission.

Application of Torque

Power and torque are not the same thing. Torque is derived from power, but the operating characteristics of a gasoline engine are such that the maximum torque, or turning effort, is not necessarily attained at the peak of power output. The engine section of this text makes it clear that the amount of torque obtainable from a source of power is proportional to the distance from the center of rotation at which it is applied.

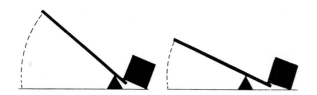

Fig. 43-1. Distance between fulcrum and object is comparable to distance between center and rim of a pulley or gear. Thus a small gear will drive a large gear more slowly but with greater power.

Obviously, therefore, if we have a shaft - such as an engine crankshaft - rotating at any given speed, we can put gears or pulleys of different sizes on the shaft and obtain different results. If we put a large gear or pulley on the shaft, we will get more speed and less power at the rim than with a small pulley.

If we have another shaft parallel to our driving shaft and place gears or pulleys on it in line with those on the driving shaft, we can obtain almost any desired combination of speed or power within the limits of the engine's ability. That is exactly what an automobile transmission does by means of gears or other methods.

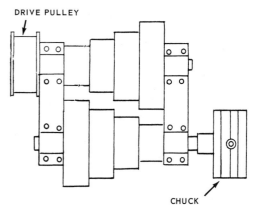

Fig. 43-2. Stepped pulleys on parallel shafts provide a means of trading speed for power, or vice-versa, by shifting belt from one set of pulleys to another. Various size gears would produce same effect.

Gear Usage

Gears are simply a means of applying leverage to rotating parts. An ordinary lever, for example, has more power as the fulcrum gets closer to the object of power application. The closer the fulcrum approaches the object, the longer the distance the lever end has to be moved. See Fig. 43-1. The same principle applies to gears and pulleys.

A good example of this is a machinist's lathe with stepped pulleys for the drive belt. When the machinist wants to make a light cut, he gets speed by putting the belt on the end of the drive shaft having the larger pulley in line with the small pulley on the lathe spindle shaft. If he needs more power for a heavier cut, he trades speed for power and puts the belt at the other end. See Fig. 43-2.

A modern transmission provides both speed and power. The engineer who designed it, selected the gear sizes that would give the best all around performance.

Transmission Development

A Frenchman named Levassor is generally credited with developing the first sliding gear transmission. It consisted of two shafts mounted parallel to each other with slideable spur gears of different sizes arranged to mesh with each other to provide a change in the relative speed of the driving and driven shafts. See Fig. 43-3. It had a low, intermediate and high gear as well as reverse. The high gear was not a direct drive, but was geared up. The modern helical gear, synchromesh, ball and roller bearing transmission is far removed from that plain bearing, spur gear contraption which was an ingenious "first."

Gear Ratios

A certain amount of gear noise was expected and accepted as inevitable in cars for many years. This was especially true of geared up overdrives which were expected to whine...and did. Changes in gear cases, gear design and gear ratio* have all contributed to quieter operation. Gear ratios in transmissions are not standardized, but are engineered to fit changes in the engine, car weight, etc., in order to obtain maximum performance.

A typical automobile sliding gear transmission has ratios as follows:

Reverse gear . . . . 3.8 to 1
Low gear . . . . 2.8 to 1
Second gear . . . . 1.7 to 1
High gear . . . . 1.0 to 1
Overdrive . . . . 0.7 to 1

*Gear ratios can be determined by counting the teeth on a pair of gears. If the driving gear has 20 teeth and the driven gear 40 teeth, the ratio would be 2 to 1. If the driving gear had 40 teeth and the driven gear 20 teeth, the ratio would be 1 to 2. The transmission gear ratios should not be confused with the final drive ratio or car gear ratio which refers to the overall ratio between the engine revolutions and the rear axle shaft revolutions. This, of course, includes the gear reduction in the rear axle or differential.

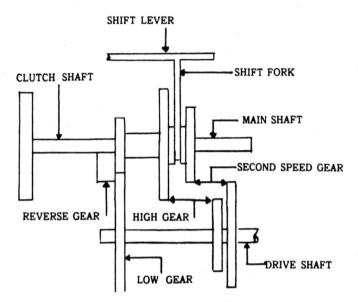

Fig. 43-3. In diagrammatic form: A small gear on main shaft is meshed with a large low gear for maximum power. Second speed gears are nearly same size for more speed on drive shaft. In this application, high speed gear on main shaft is larger than high gear on drive shaft, so higher speed on driven shaft would result.

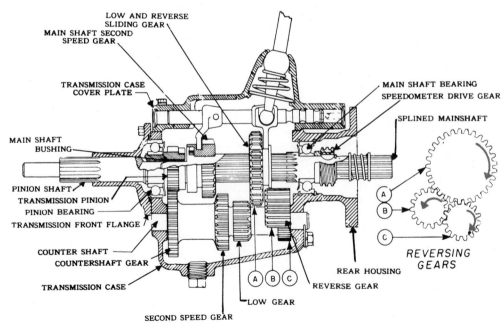

Fig. 43-4. Typical spur gear three-speed transmission is shown with reverse gearing inset at right:
A—Low and reverse sliding gear. B—Reverse idler gear. C—Countershaft gear.

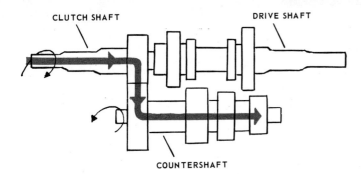

Fig. 43-5. With engine running and three-speed manual transmission in neutral position, countershaft turns but no power is applied to drive shaft.

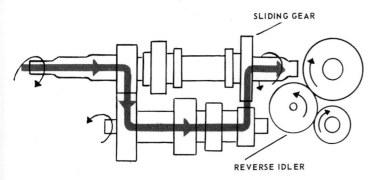

Fig. 43-6. When shift lever is moved to reverse, an idler gear is interposed between main shaft and countershaft to reverse direction of rotation of drive shaft.

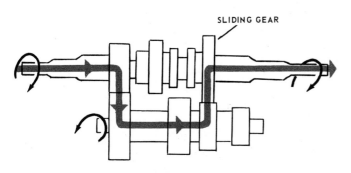

Fig. 43-7. When shift lever is placed in low gear, power is transmitted through countershaft to low and reverse sliding gear to main shaft.

In high hear, or 1 to 1 ratio, the output shaft of the transmission turns at the same speed as the engine crankshaft. In overdrive, the output shaft turns faster; in all other gear combinations, it turns more slowly but provides greater power.

To illustrate the gear arrangment, a conventional spur gear three-speed transmission is shown in Fig. 43-4. The housing is split in two in a vertical plane and an end view of the reverse gearing appears at the right. The clutch attaches to the pinion shaft at the left; the drive shaft attaches to the splined main shaft at the right. The forward end of the main shaft runs in the main shaft bushing within the pinion gear. As illustrated in Fig. 43-4, the transmission gears are in the neutral position.

Neutral Position

In the neutral position, the clutch turns the pinion shaft which rotates the countershaft gear, the second speed gear, the low gear and the reverse gear. The main shaft does not revolve. See Fig. 43-5.

Reverse Gear

In order to engage reverse gear, Fig. 43-4, the low and reverse sliding gear A on the main shaft is moved backward to engage reverse gear B which is driven by gear C on the countershaft. Interposing idler gear B between gears A and C reverses the rotation of the main shaft. See Fig. 43-6.

Low Gear

To engage low gear, the low and reverse sliding gear on the main shaft is moved forward into mesh with the low gear. Thus the pinion shaft turns the countershaft gear (attached to low gear) which turns the low and reverse gear. The low gear on the counter-shaft, being smaller than the mating gear on the main shaft, provides a gear reduction and turns the main shaft at slower speed with greater power. See Fig. 43-7.

Second Gear

To shift into second gear, the low and reverse sliding gear is returned to neutral, Fig. 43-5, and the main shaft second speed gear is moved backward into mesh with the second speed gear on the countershaft. Since there is less difference in the size of these gears, the main shaft will turn at a higher rate of speed than in low gear. The principal gear reduction is now between the pinion shaft gear and the counter-shaft gear. See Fig. 43-8.

High Gear

For high gear, the main shaft second speed gear is disengaged from the second speed gear on the countershaft and moved forward until projections on the

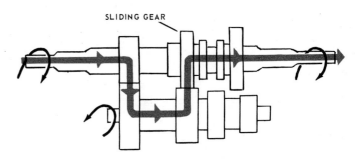

Fig. 43-8. With shift lever in second gear, power flow is through countershaft to second speed sliding gear to main shaft.

rear face of the pinion shaft gear engage with matching indentations or notches in the forward face of the main shaft second speed gear. This locks the pinion shaft and main shaft together and they turn at the same speed. The gears on the countershaft continue to rotate, but do not carry any power since they are not coupled to any gears on the main shaft. See Fig. 43-9.

All shift operations on the main shaft are controlled by collars or forks. The forks are attached to two parallel shafts, and the gear shift lever can be moved to the side, forward or backward to engage either shifting shaft as desired. An interlocking device is placed between the shafts so that only one shaft can be moved at a time to avoid engaging more than one pair of gears at a time.

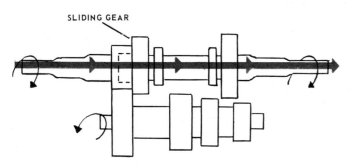

Fig. 43-9. In high gear position, power does not go through gears but is transmitted directly from input shaft to main shaft.

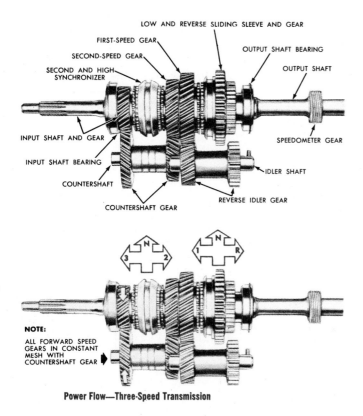

Power Flow—Three-Speed Transmission

Fig. 43-10. Gear arrangement in a typical helical gear synchromesh three-speed transmission, features constant mesh gears with synchronized shifts.

Helical Gears

Helical gear synchromesh transmissions, Fig. 43-10, are somewhat similar to the spur gear type. The principal differences are in the shape of the gear teeth; the additon of synchronizing clutches to the second and high speed gears (first gear too, in many cases); and the fact that some of the main shaft gears are free to turn on bearings until engaged. The low and reverse sliding gear does not ordinarily need a synchronizing clutch because the car is usually standing still when either is shifted into engagement.

Synchronizing Clutch

The synchronizing clutch is a drum or sleeve that slides to and fro on the splined main shaft by means of the shifting fork. Generally, it has a bronze cone on each side that engages with a tapered mating cone on the second and high speed gears. When this drum is moved along the main shaft, the cones act as a clutch. Upon touching the gear which is to be engaged, the main shaft is speeded up or slowed down as required until the speeds of the main shaft and gear are synchronized.

This action occurs during partial movement of the shift lever. Completion of lever movement then slides the drum and gear into complete engagement. This action can be readily grasped by remembering that the hub of the drum slides on the splines of the main shaft to engage the cones and then the drum slides on the hub to engage the gears. See Fig. 43-11. Fig. 43-10 shows the synchronizers and all other parts in their assembled positions.

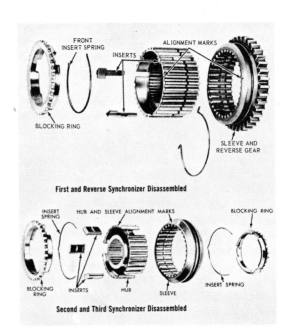

Fig. 43-11. Exploded view of synchronizer assemblies show relative positions of internal and external splined hub, sleeve inserts and blocking rings.

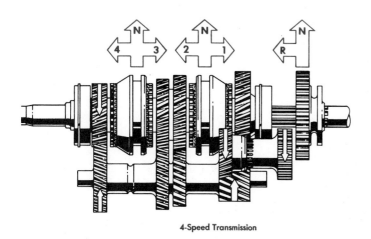

4-Speed Transmission

Fig. 43-12. Four-speed transmission is a favorite of sports car enthusiasts. Fully synchronized, all upshifts and downshifts can be made while car is in motion

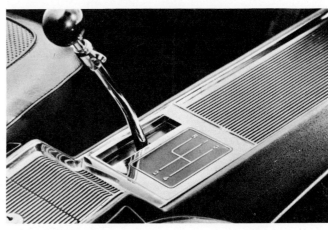

Fig. 43-13. Short-shanked gearshift lever mounted on a console gives four-speed stick-shift transmission sporty terminology, "four-on-the-floor."

POWER FLOW

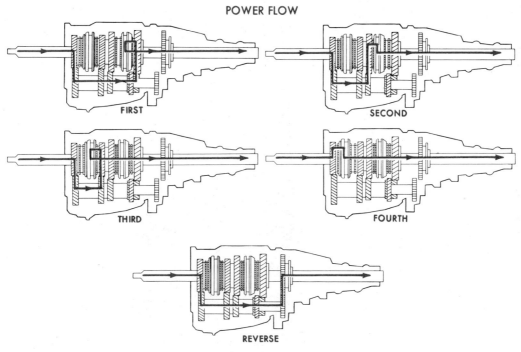

Fig. 43-14. Power flow of four-speed transmission is illustrated in each drive position forward and also in reverse.

Four-On-The-Floor

Four-speed manual transmissions are popular combinations with high performance engines. Generally, all four forward speeds are synchronized and engineered with closely spaced gear ratios to provide minimum loss of engine speed at shift points. All gears are in constant mesh with the exception of the reverse sliding gear, Fig. 43-12. With four-speed transmissions, manual gear shifting is usually accomplished with a floor-type shift lever mounted on a console, Fig. 43-13.

In neutral, with clutch engaged, the input shaft drives the countershaft. However, with all synchronizers neutrally positioned and the reverse sliding gear out of mesh, power does not flow to the main shaft. See Fig. 43-14.

In all forward speeds, power is transmitted from the input shaft to the countershaft gear and to first, second, third or fourth speed gears, in turn, each of which is locked with a synchronizer assembly to drive the main shaft.

In reverse, the reverse sliding gear is moved into mesh with the reverse rear idler gear. Power is transmitted from the input shaft to the countershaft gear, then to the constant mesh reverse front idler gear and through splines and reverse gearing to the main shaft.

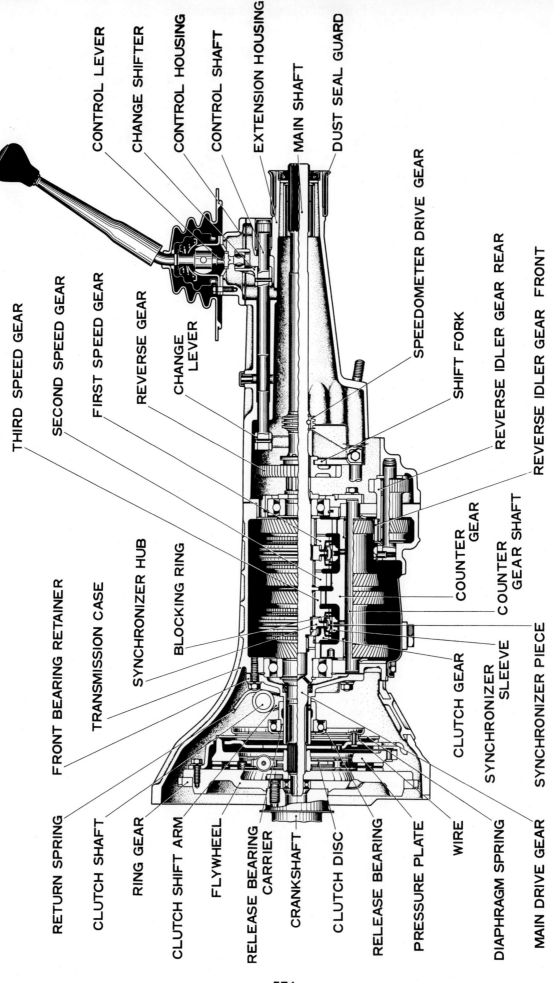

THIRD SPEED GEAR

SECOND SPEED GEAR

FIRST SPEED GEAR

REVERSE GEAR

CHANGE LEVER

CONTROL LEVER

CHANGE SHIFTER

CONTROL HOUSING

CONTROL SHAFT

EXTENSION HOUSING

MAIN SHAFT

DUST SEAL GUARD

SPEEDOMETER DRIVE GEAR

SHIFT FORK

REVERSE IDLER GEAR REAR

REVERSE IDLER GEAR FRONT

RETURN SPRING

CLUTCH SHAFT

RING GEAR

CLUTCH SHIFT ARM

FLYWHEEL

RELEASE BEARING CARRIER

CRANKSHAFT

CLUTCH DISC

RELEASE BEARING

PRESSURE PLATE

WIRE

DIAPHRAGM SPRING

MAIN DRIVE GEAR

FRONT BEARING RETAINER

TRANSMISSION CASE

SYNCHRONIZER HUB

BLOCKING RING

COUNTER GEAR

COUNTER GEAR SHAFT

CLUTCH GEAR

SYNCHRONIZER SLEEVE

SYNCHRONIZER PIECE

Dodge Colt has 3-speed, fully synchronized manual transmission available, in addition to 4-speed manual and 3-speed automatic transmissions. The floor-mounted 3-speed unit is shown in cutaway and sectional view.

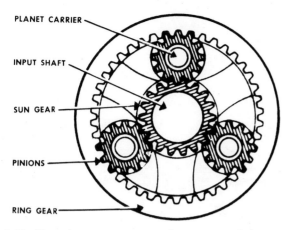

PLANET CARRIER

INPUT SHAFT

SUN GEAR

PINIONS

RING GEAR

Fig. 43-15. This planetary gear set utilizes a typical three-pinion arrangement. Two and four-pinion types also have been used.

Planetary Gear Systems

Planetary gears are used in one form or another to a great extent in automatic transmissions and overdrives. The name is derived from their similarity to our solar system. The pinions or planet gears each turn on their own axis while rotating at the same time around the central or sun gear in a manner similar to the earth and other planets rotating around the sun. These gears are surrounded by a ring gear, Fig. 43-15.

Planetary gears are used in one form as a reduction gear and in another form as an overgear. They are used for reverse and are used in multiples sets where more than two forward speeds are wanted. Earlier designs were operated by levers or pedals. Now they are usually controlled by hydraulic pressure in combination with automatic mechanical governors, electrical solenoids and vacuum diaphragms.

Methods of Connecting Parts

In a planetary gear set, the gears are in mesh at all times and are never shifted in and out of engagement. The gears are attached to different drums which, in turn, are attached to other operating parts of the system. This enables the gears to function in different ways as the various drums are held from rotation by brake bands.

A simple form of planetary gearset, Fig. 43-15, has three pinions mounted between and meshed with both the sun gear and ring gear at all times. The pinions revolve on pins or axles which are a part of the planet carrier drum. The pinions are held in spaced relation with one another yet can turn freely on their own pins and can also rotate around the sun gear and within the ring gear.

Therefore, we have three units:
1. The sun gear.
2. The planet carrier, drum and pinions.
3. The ring gear and drum.

The gears can be arranged so that they will function as driving elements or driven elements to provide different results by connecting them in different ways.

For example, if the engine is connected to the sun gear and the planet or pinion carrier to the drive shaft, the entire assembly will rotate as a unit (pinions do not turn on their pins). In this case, there will be no gear reduction and the drive shaft (driven shaft in this case) will rotate at the same speed as the driving or engine shaft.

If, however, a brake band is placed around the ring gear to hold it from turning, the pinions will be forced to travel around inside the ring gear carrying the pinion carrier along at reduced speed. In this case, the pinion gears turn on their pins in the opposite direction of rotation of the sun gear, while the pinion carrier turns in the same direction as the sun gear but at reduced speed.

With these few gears and a band to hold the drum, we have a basic transmission of the planetary type with a gear reduction for low gear and a direct drive for high gear. In addition, a clutch is needed between the engine and transmission to allow the car to stand still while the engine runs. Also required is some means of reversing the transmission. These additions to the basic planetary gear setup are shown in Fig. 43-16.

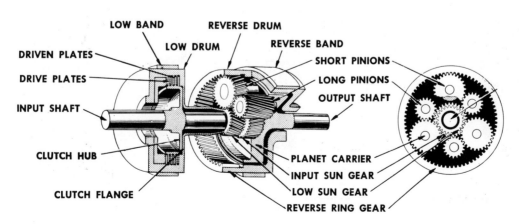

LOW BAND   REVERSE DRUM

DRIVEN PLATES   LOW DRUM   REVERSE BAND

DRIVE PLATES   SHORT PINIONS

INPUT SHAFT   LONG PINIONS

OUTPUT SHAFT

CLUTCH HUB

PLANET CARRIER

INPUT SUN GEAR

CLUTCH FLANGE   LOW SUN GEAR

REVERSE RING GEAR

Fig. 43-16. Addition of three more pinions and a clutch to basic three-pinion planetary gear setup provides transmission with neutral and reverse.

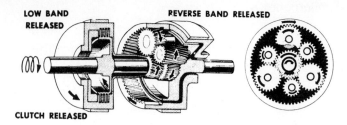

Fig. 43-17. *In neutral, planet carrier which is attached to drive shaft is standing still while all gears rotate around it.*

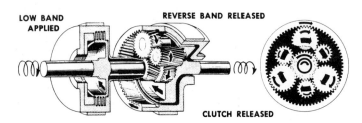

Fig. 43-18. *In low speed position, planet carrier and gears are all revolving but at different relative speeds.*

Method of Operation

The operation of a two forward speed and reverse planetary transmission is shown in Figs. 43-17 to 43-20, inclusive. In each case, the rotation of each gear is shown by light arrows, while the rotation of the gear assembly is shown by heavy arrows. A thorough understanding of all these gear actions is absolutely necessary in order to be able to understand the operation of the more complicated automatic transmissions.

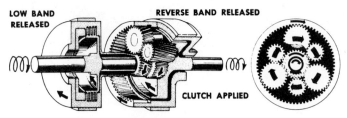

Fig. 43-19. *In high gear (direct drive), everything turns and speed of rotation of output shaft is same as speed of input shaft.*

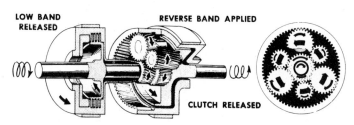

Fig. 43-20. *In reverse position, ring gear stands still and planet carrier rotates in opposite direction.*

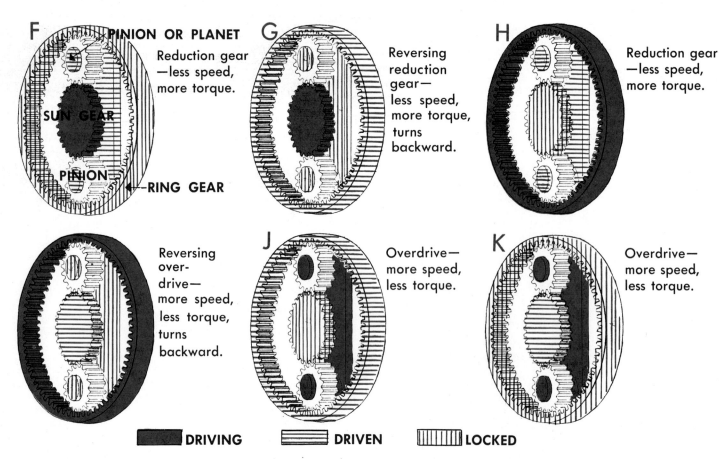

Fig. 43-21. *Any one of three units in a planetary gear set — sun gear, ring gear or planet carrier — can be held from rotating to obtain different results.*

Transmission Overdrives

Utilizing the same fundamental gears used in planetary transmissions, we can change the hookup to get an overdrive. If we attached the engine to the planet carrier instead of the sun gear and the drive shaft (or driven shaft) to the ring gear instead of the planet carrier, we would change the entire operation. By holding the sun gear from rotating, we can reverse the action of the gearing and get an increase in gear ratio instead of a reduction. See Fig. 43-21. That is, the drive shaft will turn faster than the engine shaft with a consequent improvement in gasoline mileage.

Of course, the gear ratio could be changed either in the transmission or the rear axle. The two-speed rear axle was used for a time in certain passenger cars, then someone worked out the answer to the over-drive problem. It was the combination of planetary gears with a free-wheel unit (overrunning clutch). This combination was light in weight, not too expensive to build and could be attached to the transmission where it would be carried by the car springs as part of the sprung weight. Furthermore, it could be controlled by the driver and could be made automatic in operation.

Arranging Overdrive

There are several ways of hooking up planetary gearing to accomplish different results. One method is to increase gear ratio by attaching the driven shaft to the ring gear and holding the sun gear from rotating. But when the sun gear is released, the pinions will simply chase around between the sun gear and ring gear in the opposite direction and no power will be transmitted.

This was solved by installing a free-wheel unit on the transmission main shaft. Then when drive shaft speed exceeds engine speed (coasting), the rollers release. When accelerating the engine, the rollers are wedged on the cam and power is transmitted, Fig. 43-22. A cutaway view of this type of installation is shown in Fig. 43-23, which also shows the method of control.

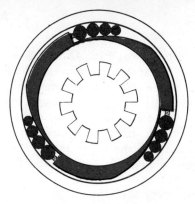

Fig. 43-22. On overrunning clutch: if outer rim turns clockwise, rollers will roll up on cams and hub will turn at same speed as rim. If rim turns counterclockwise, rollers roll down cams against springs and hub will "free wheel" (cease to rotate).

Methods of Control

Control must be in the hands of the driver. Free-wheeling can be dangerous unless it is locked out when braking effect of the engine is needed. With the control handle pushed in, a solenoid switch is energized at speeds above 25-30 mph. Then if the accelerator pedal is momentarily released, a locking pawl engages the sun gear hub and balk ring assembly. When the accelerator is again depressed, overdrive is in operation and free-wheeling becomes inoperative. See Figs. 43-24 and 43-25.

With the control handle pulled out, overdrive is locked out. A cable from the handle is connected to a transmission lever that operates a shifting fork. The fork mates with a shifting collar on the sun gear which is shifted into engagement with lock-up teeth on the planet carrier. The entire overdrive and free-wheel unit is locked together and the car will operate as if it is equipped with a three-speed manual transmission.

Solenoid Magnet Operation

Solenoids are used extensively as control devices for vacuum and power units which do the actual shifting. The solenoid, in an overdrive transmission, consists of an iron plunger within coils of wire through

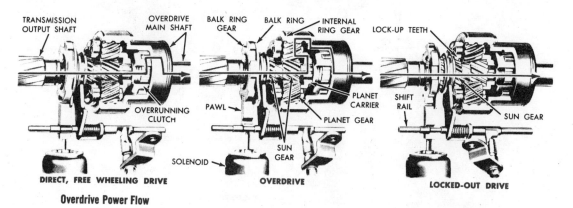

Overdrive Power Flow

DIRECT, FREE WHEELING DRIVE — OVERDRIVE — LOCKED-OUT DRIVE

Fig. 43-23. Power flow in overdrive transmission is shown in three different situations. Note that locking pawl is engaged with slot in balk ring gear in overdrive; disengaged otherwise.

which electricity flows, Fig. 43-26. When the current is turned on, the iron core moves into the magnetic field and pushes the pawl into engagement. In this case, there are two coils of wire: a heavy winding to move the plunger; and a lighter winding to hold it in place after it is moved. Both coils are used to move the plunger which opens the contacts for the closing coil and leaves the holding coil in operation. See Fig. 43-27.

Mechanical Governor Operation

Since it is desirable to have the overdrive function above a car speed of about 25 mph and undesirable to have it in use below that speed, some automatic device is needed to connect it and disconnect it. This is accomplished by a mechanical centrifugal governor which operates an electrical switch to control the flow of electricity to the solenoid.

This overdrive governor is geared to and driven by the drive shaft, Fig. 43-28. Centrifugal force causes the weights to fly outward and raise a floating shaft which closes the contact points in the cover. The governor is designed and adjusted to close at a somewhat higher speed than it opens.

Kickdown Switch Needed

It is desirable to be able to change from overdrive to direct drive when climbing a hill or accelerating to pass another car. For this purpose, an electrical switch is located under the accelerator pedal or in a position where it can be operated by the accelerator linkage. Pushing the pedal down will close contacts in the switch and cut out the overdrive. This action momentarily "shorts out" the ignition distributor to permit the locking pawl to be released. As soon as it releases (one or two turns of the crankshaft), ignition is restored.

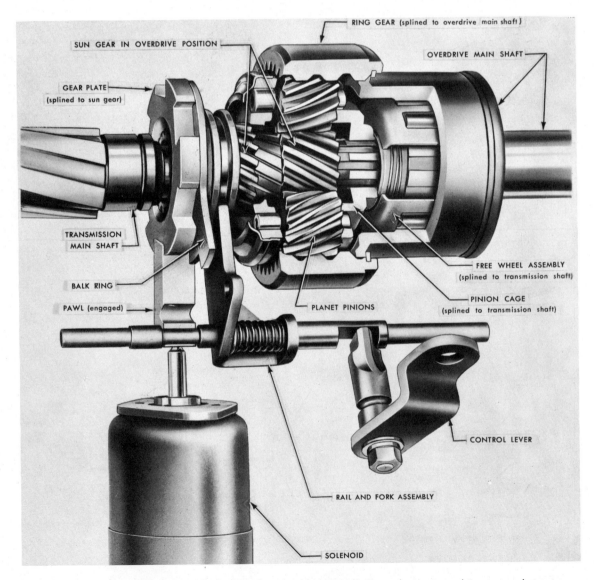

Fig. 43-24. In overdrive: sun gear is locked in place by pawl in balk ring; planet gears drive internal ring gear; ring gear drives overdrive main shaft.

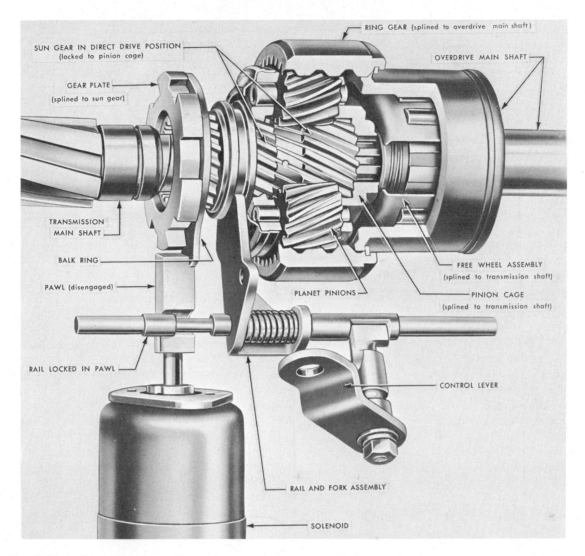

Fig. 43-25. In direct drive: power flow is from transmission output shaft to overdrive main shaft. Free wheel assembly permits engine to drive rear wheels, but rear wheels cannot drive engine.

Use of Balk Ring

The balk ring is intended to avoid harsh and sudden locking of the sun gear. Under kickdown conditions, the car will stay in direct drive until the accelerator is eased up again. If engine speed is above cut-in speed (25-30 mph), the solenoid is energized, allowing the locking pawl to engage the sun gear hub and balk ring assembly. See Figs. 43-24 and 43-25.

Operation of Vacuum Cylinders

Since an internal combustion engine is also a vacuum pump, there is always vacuum power available while the engine is running. Designers have taken advantage of this fact to build a multitude of vacuum operated accessories such as windshield wipers, brake boosters, gear shifters, etc. A small pipe connection is made to the intake manifold and vacuum is piped to wherever it is needed.

However, suction derived from the engine through a small pipe is not powerful enough to apply brakes and shift gears. Instead, it is used to create air power which does the actual work. The amount of power created in this fashion is directly dependent upon the size of the diaphragm in the vacuum cylinder upon which the air pressure acts.

Automatic Transmission

Obviously, then, a vacuum cylinder can be attached to the brake pedal to operate the brakes, or to the clutch pedal to operate the clutch, or to the gear shift lever to shift the gears.

Hydraulic pressure also can be utilized for shifting gears and in the control of automatic transmissions. By using an oil pump driven by the engine, we can obtain almost any amount of hydraulic pressure or power we need. This power can be piped or channeled to any point where required. The amount of pressure can be controlled by spring-loaded valves. Since a fluid under pressure expands equally in all di-

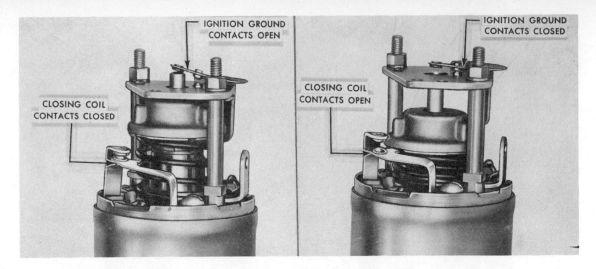

Fig. 43-26. Opposite end of solenoid, shown in Figs. 43-24 and 43-25, incorporates closing coil contacts and ignition ground contacts which control movement of plunger.

rections, engineers can control the power exerted by changing the size of the passages and the pressure on the fluid.

It is clear, then, that there are several ways to approach automatic transmission operation:

A. Use electricity, air pressure or hydraulic pressure for either or both clutch and transmission. We can also combine each of three sources of power with others.
   1. To shift a sliding gear transmission.
   2. To operate the clutch.
   3. To operate a planetary transmission.
B. Use a fluid coupling instead of a power-operated clutch.
C. Combine various elements to obtain automatic operation.
D. Use a hydraulic torque converter instead of some gearing, or in combination with gearing, and with or without a clutch.

Transmission Lubrication

Lubrication is required for the gear teeth, the bearings upon which the shafts turn, the splines upon which the gears slide and the other parts. Therefore, the gear case is made oil tight by placing gaskets between the case and cover and any other parts that are bolted to the case. Oil seals are also placed at each of the bearings on the main shaft.

The oil used in manual transmissions is heavier than engine oil in most cases and is known as SAE 80 or 90 Gear Oil. The case is filled to the level of the fill plug opening, which is usually slightly below the countershaft.

In automatic transmissions, light oil is a satisfactory lubricant for the gears, bearings and bands of the planetary set. When planetary gears are used in an overdrive, no bands are required and the gear oil used in the transmission housing is satisfactory in

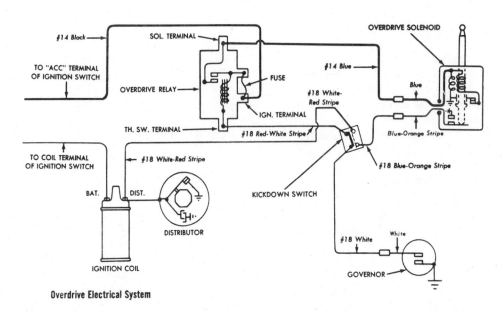

Overdrive Electrical System

Fig. 43-27. Overdrive electrical system consists of: governor circuit which opens and closes relay; solenoid circuit which supplies current to energize solenoid; and ignition interrupter circuit.

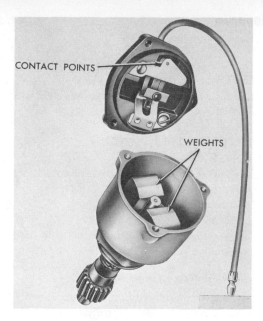

Fig. 43-28. At approximately 25-30 mph, governor weights raise floating shaft to close contact points and permit current to flow from battery through relay to solenoid.

most cases. The tooth pressures in planetary gearing are low and an extreme pressure lubricant is not required. Engine oil SAE 60 or transmission oil SAE 80 are ideal lubricants for overdrives.

Transmission Trouble Shooting Spur and Helical Gears

Transmission Noisy in Neutral:

This may be a growl or hum that can be stopped by depressing clutch pedal. In some cases a bump or thud also will be present, indicating a broken gear or bearing. Defects in main shaft, other than pilot bearing, are not included in this group because main shaft does not rotate when transmission is in neutral.
1. Insufficient lubricant in transmission.
2. Abnormal end play in countershaft gears, reverse idler gear or pinion shaft.
3. Pinion gear badly worn or broken.
4. Pinion shaft bearing badly worn or broken.
5. Misalignment between engine and transmission.
6. Wear in countershaft drive gear.
7. Wear in reverse and/or reverse idler gear.
8. Countershaft bearings badly worn.
9. Reverse idler shaft bearings badly worn.
10. Countershaft sprung or bent.
11. Pilot shaft bearing worn or broken.
NOTE: If replacement of a gear is required, mating gear should be replaced too.

Transmission Noisy in Gear:

Most causes of noises in neutral will also appear when transmission is in gear. Same parts are still in operation, plus main shaft which adds following:
1. Main shaft rear bearing worn or broken.
2. Sliding gears badly worn or broken.
3. Excessive end play of main shaft.
4. Badly worn speedometer gears.

Transmission Slips Out of High Gear:

Principal cause is misalignment between transmission and engine. Front end of pinion shaft runs in a bearing in crankshaft, and rear end in transmission case. If this shaft is not in a straight line with engine crankshaft and transmission main shaft, it will create an angular contact. Other less frequent causes are:
1. Pinion gear teeth worn or tapered.
2. Pinion gear bearing badly worn.
3. Improper adjustment of shift linkage.
4. Worn shift detent parts.

Transmission Slips Out of Second Gear:
1. Badly worn or broken gear.
2. Badly worn transmission bearings.
3. Improper adjustment of shift linkage.
4. Worn shift detent parts.
5. Excessive end play of main or countershaft.

Transmission Slips Out of First or Reverse Gear:
1. Badly worn or broken gears.
2. Badly worn transmission bearings.
3. Main shaft splines worn or distorted.
4. Excessive end play of main, countershaft or reverse idler shaft.
5. Worn shift detent parts.
6. Improper adjustment of shift linkage.

Transmission Difficult to Shift:
1. Engine clutch not releasing.
2. Distorted or burred main shaft splines.
3. Improper adjustment of shift linkage.

Transmission Oil Leaks:
1. Damaged oil seals.
2. Damaged oil throw rings.
3. Damaged or missing gaskets.
4. Case or cover bolts loose or missing.
5. Case plugs loose or threads stripped.
6. Oil level too high.
7. Vent stopped up.
8. Use of a lubricant that foams excessively.

Planetary Trouble Shooting

Growling or Humming Noises:
1. Insufficient lubricant in housing.
2. Dragging bands.
3. Excessive wear in gear teeth.
4. Excessive wear in gear bushings or shafts.

Rough or Harsh Engagement:
1. Glazed or burned band linings.
2. Lubricant excessively thin.
3. Scored drums.
4. Improper adjustment of band operating device.
5. Burned or gummed clutch plates.

Grinding or Clicking Noises:

1. Excessive wear in gears.
2. Damaged gear teeth.
3. Worn bushings or broken needle bearings.
4. Insufficient lubricant.
5. Excessive wear in clutch hub or drum driving pins or slots.

Slipping or Slow Engagement:

1. Bands too loose.
2. Improper adjustment of band operating device.
3. Scored or burned drums.
4. Scored or burned band linings.
5. Warped, scored or burned clutch plates.
6. Clutch plates sticking on hub or in drum.

Overdrive Trouble Shooting

When attempting to diagnose trouble with an overdrive, bear in mind that trouble can be caused by electrical defects, mechanical defects or a combination of both. Since electrical troubles are more likely to occur, check electrical system first and eliminate any defects before going on to mechanical difficulties. Electrical troubles can occur in relay, solenoid, governor, kickdown switch or in any wires connecting these units. Most common trouble is loose or dirty connections on wiring terminals. Any wire or connection can be tested with electrical meters or by temporary substitution of a "jumper" or test wire.

Overdrive Does Not Engage:

1. Fuse blown on relay.
2. Defective connecting wires, loose or corroded terminals.
3. Defective relay unit.
4. Defective solenoid.
5. Defective governor contacts.
6. Defective kickdown switch.

7. Dash control improperly adjusted.
8. Governor gear drive pin sheared.
9. Damaged gears, bearings or shifting parts within overdrive unit.

Overdrive Does Not Release:

1. Defective relay unit.
2. Defective connecting wires, loose or corroded terminals.
3. Sticking, bent or damaged pawl.
4. Defective kickdown switch.
5. Damaged gears, shafts or shifting parts within the overdrive unit.

Kickdown Does Not Operate:

1. Kickdown switch improperly adjusted.
2. Loose or corroded terminals or defective connecting wires.
3. Defective operation of contacts in solenoids.
4. Defective kickdown switch.

Engine Stops When Kickdown Is Used:

1. Defective kickdown switch.
2. Ground in wiring or solenoid.

Car Will Not Reverse:

1. Shift rail operation defective.

Harsh Overdrive Engagement:

1. Defective balk ring action.

All splines, shafts and bushings should operate smoothly and be free from nicks or excessive wear. All gear teeth should be smooth, free from nicks and excessive wear. Free-wheel rollers, cam and shell surfaces should be smooth and free from nicks or pronounced indentations. All ball, roller and needle bearings should be free and smooth in operation and have no perceptible wear or noise. Balk ring friction fit should be checked with a spring scale and replaced if not within friction limits specified by manufacturer.

Quiz - Transmission Fundamentals

1. What function does a transmission perform?
2. Are power and torque the same?
3. Will a larger gear on the driving shaft increase the speed of rotation of the driven shaft?
4. How can the ratio of mating gears be determined?
5. What is the gear ratio of a setup where the driving gear has 20 teeth and the driven gear has 50?
   a. 2.5 to 1.
   b. 1 to 2.5.
   c. 5 to 2.0.
6. Which two manual transmission shafts turn in neutral?
   a. Input shaft and main shaft.
   b. Input shaft and countershaft.
   c. Main shaft and countershaft.

7. When a manual transmission is shifted into reverse, what extra gear is interposed to reverse the direction of the main shaft?
   a. Low and reverse sliding gear.
   b. Reverse idler gear.
   c. Reverse synchromesh ring.
8. Name the three major units in a planetary gearset.
9. In a planetary transmission, if the sun gear is held and the ring gear is driven, will this increase or decrease the speed of the drive shaft?
10. What is the function of an overrunning clutch in an overdrive transmission?
    a. Eliminates the clutch.
    b. Disengages the overdrive unit.
    c. Restricts drive to one direction only.

11. Which control device on an overdrive transmission operates the locking pawl?
   a. Solenoid.
   b. Governor.
   c. Relay.
12. Which control device connects and disconnects the overdrive unit?
   a. Solenoid.
   b. Governor.
   c. Relay.
13. What is the purpose of the balk ring in an overdrive?
14. Generally, what grade or weight of oil is used in a manual transmission?
15. Name three possible causes for a manual transmission slipping out of high gear.
16. Name three possible causes for slippage in a planetary transmission.
17. Name four possible causes for a transmission overdrive not engaging.

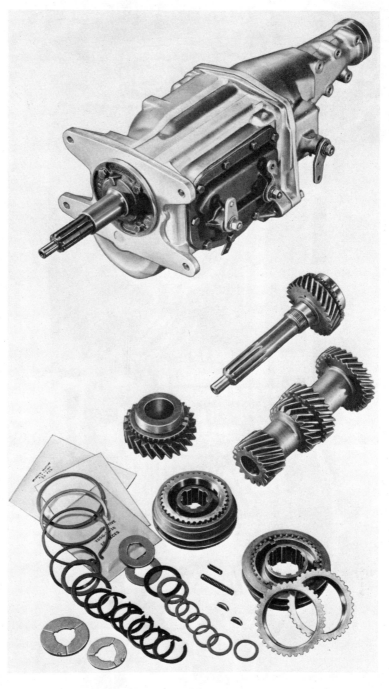

Manual transmission manufacturer provides replacement gearsets for installation in 4-speed transmission during rebuilding operation. Set includes main drive gear, cluster gear, synchronized gears, synchronizing rings and varied width spacers and snap rings to provide correct end play in assemblies.

Volkswagen "automatic stick shift" transmission couples 3-speed fully synchronized gearbox with vacuum-operated clutch and torque converter, which permits car to be brought to a stop in any gear range without shifting.

FLUID COUPLING
AUTOMATIC TRANSMISSIONS

Automatic transmissions are installed in most new cars coming off the assembly lines. Car buyers want the comfort and convenience afforded by these labor-saving, automatically controlled, power transfer devices.

Design and construction differs between makes, but all modern automatic transmissions incorporate the following elements:

1. One or more fluid couplings or a torque converter.
2. One or more planetary gearsets.
3. Suitable valves to direct the flow of automatic transmission fluid (ATF).
4. Various valve controls or combinations of valve controls.

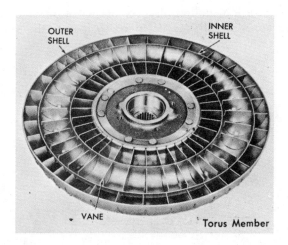

Fig. 44-2. Each torus member of fluid coupling is divided into many sections by designed arrangement of inner and outer shells and vanes.

addition, steps up or multiplies engine torque when operating conditions demand it.

Planetary gearsets, Fig. 44-3, provide suitable gear ratios for all driving conditions by means of pinion gears turning on their own axis while rotating around a sun gear and within a ring gear having internal teeth. When used with a combination of clutches,

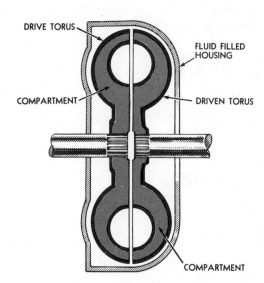

Fig. 44-1. Typical fluid coupling has two facing halves called "torus members" which are splined to separate shafts and operate in a fluid-filled housing.

Automatic Transmission Operation

When used in conjunction with an automatic transmission, a fluid coupling, Figs. 44-1 and 44-2, serves as a hydraulic clutch used to transmit engine torque to the transmission and to "cushion" the flow of power. A torque converter performs similar duties but, in

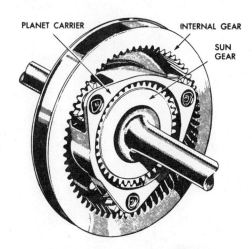

Fig. 44-3. In operation, planetary gearsets provide automatic transmission with various gear ratios as one element is "held" while power is applied to another.

brake bands and valves, a number of planetary gear-sets will automatically provide all of the foward and reverse gear ratios needed for efficient operation under normal operating conditions.

Valves and Valve Controls

One means of mechanical control of an automatic transmission is by connecting a valve to a hand lever operated by the driver. Another is by connecting a valve to the accelerator pedal so that driver demands (pressure on pedal) will automatically operate the valve, Fig. 44-4.

In addition, action of a control valve may be regulated automatically as required by load on the engine.

This is done by connecting the valve to the intake manifold (vacuum in manifold decreases as load increases). Also, a valve may be operated hydraulically by oil pressure generated in the transmission by an oil pump or pumps.

Engine speed may be used to operate control valves by connecting them to speed-sensitive governors mounted on the engine. In like manner, car speed will control a valve if the governor is attached to the drive shaft of the automobile.

Any of these valves may be opened or closed entirely or partially, slowly or rapidly. Along with mechanical, hydraulic and vacuum operation, almost any type of electrically operated device can be incorporated in the control system of an automatic transmission. Several of these devices can be combined to provide almost any kind of automatic control _ or degree of control _ desired.

For example, it is possible to attach more than one control to a single valve in order to balance the action. One control might be connected to the accelerator pedal and another to the intake manifold. In this case, the system could be set up so that pressure on the accelerator pedal would open the valve under light load conditions (high vacuum). But if the engine is put under heavy load, valve action is delayed by the interconnected vacuum control until engine load decreases.

In any case, by connecting different controls to the valves in the transmission, adjustment to speed, load, and the demands of the driver are automatically made in the transmission ratios.

To provide specific examples of how an automatic transmission operates and how it is controlled, various typical units will be described and illustrated in this chapter and the next. However, the extreme variety of makes and models precludes the possibility of giving detailed and explicit repair and trouble shooting pro-

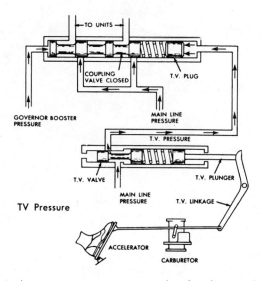

Fig. 44-4. Automatic transmissions are fitted with many different types of valves and valve controls that provide means for application and release of various clutches and bands.

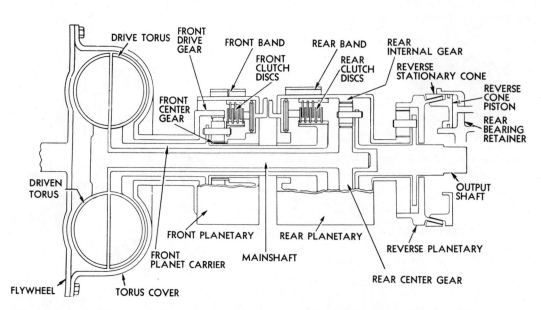

Fig. 44-5. Hydra-Matic is fluid coupling automatic transmission first introduced in 1939 Oldsmobile, redesigned several times through 1963.

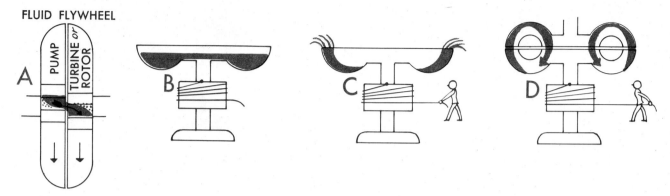

Fig. 44-6. A—In theory, fluid from pump half of fluid coupling crosses over to make turbine or rotor rotate in same direction. This principle of centrifugal force is shown in B, C and D as lower bowl revolves rapidly, causing fluid to climb into upper bowl, then drop back again.

cedures in this text. Complete repair manuals are available from the car manufacturers and gear manufacturers if a transmission overhaul or extensive repairs are contemplated.

Hydra-Matic Transmissions

The Hydra-Matic transmission is an outstanding example of an automatic transmission. Used for many years on a number of different makes of automobiles, early Hydra-Matics employ a fluid coupling to connect the engine to the transmission. Inside the case, front

This action can be compared to a shallow, round bowl placed on a spinning turntable, Fig. 44-6. If water is poured into the center of the bowl, it will fly up and out due to the action of centrifugal force. If an identical bowl is inverted over the first one, the water will enter the upper bowl, be guided toward the center and drop back in the lower bowl. Thus, a system of circulation of the fluid is established, and this is the action that takes place in the Hydra-Matic fluid coupling, Fig. 44-7.

At high speed, the fluid coupling is very effective as loss of speed between the two torus members is

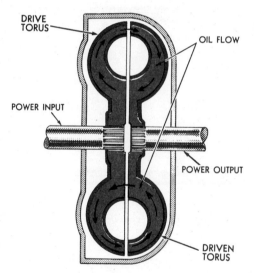

Fig. 44-7. In actual operation, driving torus of fluid coupling causes oil within it to be forced radially outward against vanes of driven member.

Fig. 44-8. A servo is a hydraulically operated piston and cylinder assembly used to control brake bands in automatic transmissions.

and rear planetary gearsets, one behind the other, are connected in series, Fig. 44-5. A reverse planetary set is used in conjunction with a reverse "cone" clutch.

The fluid coupling operates full of fluid which circulates through it from the transmission. An inner shell and outer vanes are incorporated in the driving torus and driven torus (oil-filled members) to better control the action of centrifugal force on the oil.

probably not over one or two percent. At low speeds, there is considerable slippage; at idling speed, almost 100 percent slippage. However, some energy is transmitted and the car may have a tendency to creep. To overcome this tendency, Hydra-Matic transmissions utilize gear reduction of the front planetary unit to turn the driving torus slower than the idle speed of the engine.

Planetary Gear Controls

The planetary gear bands operate hydraulically, so an oil pump is required to furnish the pressure. Earlier Hydra-Matics have two pumps: one driven by the engine and another driven by the vehicle drive shaft, Fig. 44-4. These pumps circulate oil under pressure through the fluid coupling and to the hydraulic operating pistons known as "servos." See Fig. 44-8. Control valves are needed to direct the flow of oil, to turn the flow off and on, to regulate pressure, etc. This built-in control system is a combination of balanced pressures depending on car speed, engine speed and the demands of the driver.

Driver Control

Obviously, the matter of gear selection and shifting cannot remain entirely automatic, but must be under the control of the driver, Fig. 44-9. Because of varied traffic conditions, car speed is not always the most desirable method of choosing gear reduction. The driver expresses his desires through the accelerator pedal, which is linked to a throttle valve in the transmission, Fig. 44-4. This valve is regulated so that throttle valve pressure varies with throttle opening.

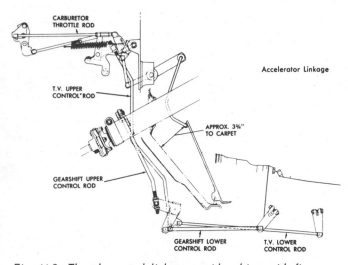

Fig. 44-9. Throttle control linkage provides driver with firm control over automatic action of transmission through degree of pressure exerted on accelerator pedal.

If the throttle is opened slightly, oil pressure on the shift valves will be low, oil pressure from the governor will open the shift valves and the shift will occur at low speed. If the throttle is opened wide, greater car speed will be required to build up governor pressure and the transmission will shift at higher car speed.

An automatic transmission control system operates on a balanced pressure plan. Spring action and varying pressures and speeds are balanced one against the other until sensitive and responsive control is obtained

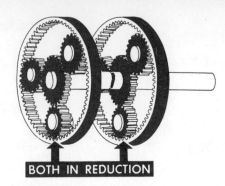

Fig. 44-10. Hydra-Matic utilizes two planetary gearsets in series to obtain four forward speeds. In first speed, both planetary units are in reduction.

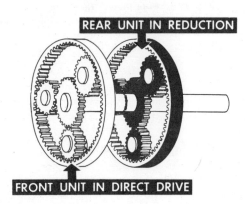

Fig. 44-11. In second speed, front planetary unit is in direct drive and rear unit is in reduction.

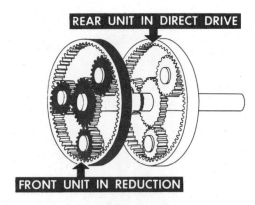

Fig. 44-12. In third speed, front planetary unit is in reduction and rear unit is in direct drive.

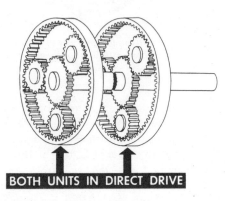

Fig. 44-13. In fourth speed, both planetary units are in direct drive.

over the transmission mechanism. These varying pressures are obtained with springs of different size, length and strength and can be further varied by screw adjustments.

Balancing the Forces

Different amounts of power can be obtained from a hydraulic cylinder by altering the size of the cylinder or by varying the amount of pressure. For example, if a spring is placed on one end of a piston in a hydraulic cylinder, pressure can be regulated by means of a screw adjustment. Then if oil under pressure is placed on the other side of the piston, at less

In first speed, the front unit supplies 40 percent gear reduction and the rear unit 60 percent, Fig. 44-14. In second speed, only the rear unit is in reduction (60 percent). In third speed, only the front unit is in reduction (40 percent). In fourth speed, neither unit is in reduction (direct drive).

Later Hydra-Matic Transmissions

Certain changes were made in Hydra-Matic transmissions in order to provide a dual range in the drive position, but necessary alterations did not change the transmission. The selector dial was changed to provide "Dual Range" markings. New parts included an

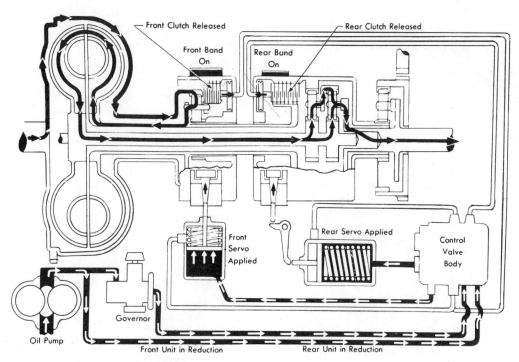

Fig. 44-14. Flow of power from engine through transmission in first gear is traced by black arrows. Oil flow under pressure is shown in white arrows.

than spring pressure, the piston will go in one direction. However, if the speed of the pump is increased, higher oil pressure starts the piston moving the other way. See Fig. 44-4. Since spring pressure increases with the amount the spring is compressed, and hydraulic pressure varies with the speed of the oil pump, almost any series of control variations can be obtained.

Hydra-Matic Gear Shifting

A planetary gearset provides only one reduction and one direct drive in the same direction of rotation, so it is necessary to use two planetary units connected together in series to obtain four forward speeds, Figs. 44-10 to 44-13. Front and rear planetary units in the Hydra-Matic are similar, but the rear unit is larger and provides a greater gear reduction.

improved front pump of the vane type with a moving slide that determined pump output. Minor changes were made in hydraulic valves and controls to adapt them to the needs of the dual range construction.

The next new Hydra-Matic to be offered was a complete redesign, Fig. 44-15. This Controlled Coupling Hydra-Matic became the first to offer a positive-shift automatic transmission with no band adjustments, greater manual control and smoother operation. Principal changes in this second generation Hydra-Matic include:

1. Multiple disc type front clutch eliminated and replaced by a controlled coupling (fluid clutch).
2. Front band eliminated and replaced by a sprag type clutch.
3. Rear band eliminated and replaced by a sprag clutch.

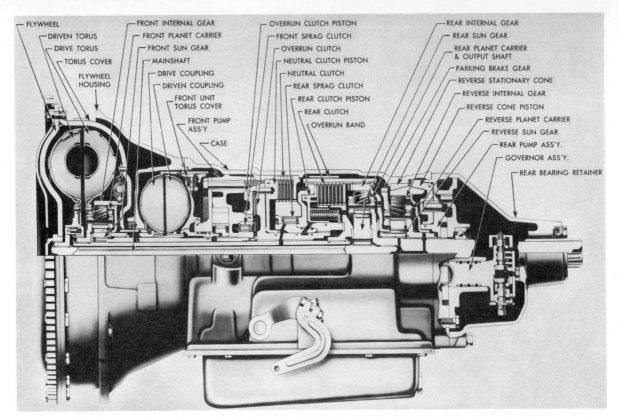

FLYWHEEL · DRIVEN TORUS · DRIVE TORUS · TORUS COVER · FLYWHEEL HOUSING · FRONT INTERNAL GEAR · FRONT PLANET CARRIER · FRONT SUN GEAR · MAINSHAFT · DRIVE COUPLING · DRIVEN COUPLING · FRONT UNIT TORUS COVER · FRONT PUMP ASS'Y · CASE · OVERRUN CLUTCH PISTON · FRONT SPRAG CLUTCH · OVERRUN CLUTCH · NEUTRAL CLUTCH PISTON · NEUTRAL CLUTCH · REAR SPRAG CLUTCH · REAR CLUTCH PISTON · REAR CLUTCH · OVERRUN BAND · REAR INTERNAL GEAR · REAR SUN GEAR · REAR PLANET CARRIER & OUTPUT SHAFT · PARKING BRAKE GEAR · REVERSE STATIONARY CONE · REVERSE INTERNAL GEAR · REVERSE CONE PISTON · REVERSE PLANET CARRIER · REVERSE SUN GEAR · REAR PUMP ASS'Y. · GOVERNOR ASS'Y. · REAR BEARING RETAINER

Fig. 44-15. Construction details of Controlled Coupling Hydra-Matic transmission are called out. Note smaller controlled coupling in back of familiar fluid coupling.

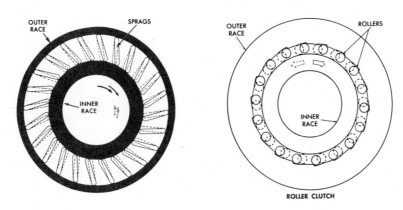

Fig. 44-16. Principle of sprag clutch is illustrated by operation of individual sprag segment. Action allows rotation in one direction but not in other.

The controlled coupling is located to the rear of the larger fluid coupling, Fig. 44-15. By providing a rapid method of filling and emptying this controlled coupling, it is possible to have a complete release of power application or a positive connection. The sprag clutch, Fig. 44-16, operates in much the same manner as the roller and ramp type of free-wheel device, but uses special-shape sprag segments instead of rollers.

To better visualize how the Controlled Coupling Hydra-Matic operates, consider that it is divided into four sections:

1. The front section includes the fluid coupling, front planetary gearset, controlled coupling, front sprag clutch and the overrun clutch.

2. The rear section includes the neutral clutch,

rear sprag clutch, low band, rear multiple disc clutch and rear planetary gearset.

3. The reverse section includes the reverse stationary cone, reverse piston and the reverse planetary gearset.

4. The hydraulic control section includes the front and rear pumps, the valve body assembly, accumulator and governor, Fig. 44-15.

For normal driving, the selector of the Controlled Coupling Hydra-Matic is placed in the left position of the Drive Range. The power flow through the transmission in the left position is shown in Figs. 44-17 to 44-22.

The right position of the Drive Range is used in congested traffic and when descending long mountain grades. The overrun clutch is applied in this position and the transmission actually operates in third speed. When applied, the overrun clutch holds the sun gear, preventing it from rotating in a clockwise direction and keeping the front unit in reduction. In this manner, the overrun clutch application produces engine braking to prevent the rear wheels of the car from driving the transmission and overrunning the front sprag clutch which will free-wheel in third speed.

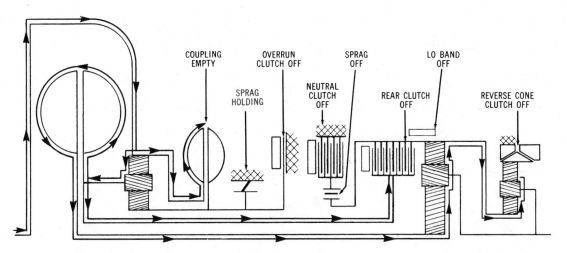

Fig. 44-17. Diagram shows power flow in Controlled Coupling Hydra-Matic in neutral with engine running.

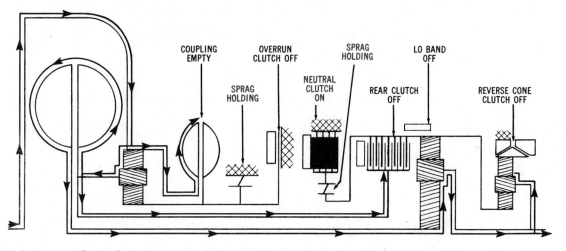

Fig. 44-18. Power flow is diagrammed in first speed with selector placed in left position of DR range.

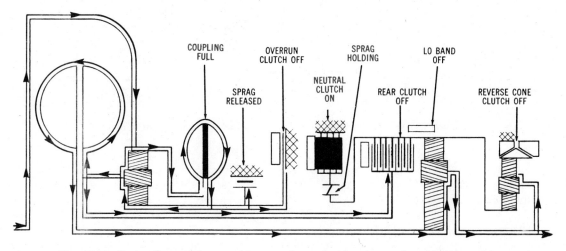

Fig. 44-19. Power flow can be traced in second speed with selector placed in left position.

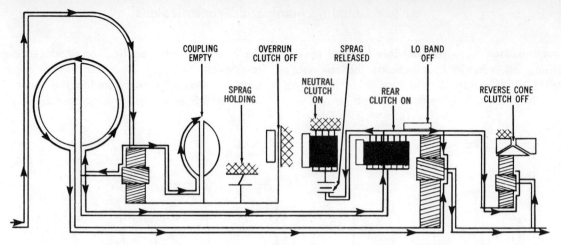

Fig. 44-20. Power flow is shown in third speed with selector in left position.

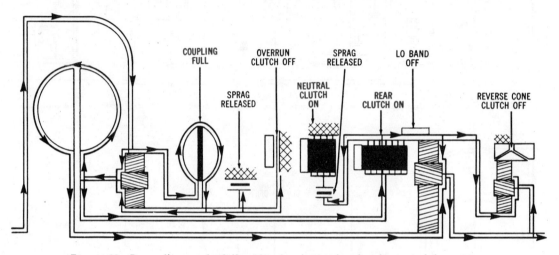

Fig. 44-21. Power flow can be followed in fourth speed with selector in left position.

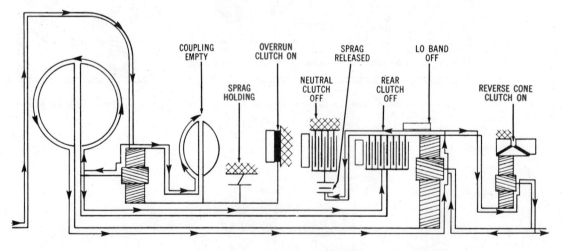

Fig. 44-22. Power flow in Controlled Coupling Hydra-Matic is shown in reverse.

Because the Controlled Coupling Hydra-Matic is so radically different, you should consider the following basic principles of operation:

1. Proper shift action is controlled by hydraulic pressure directed to proper places by control valve body and governor.

2. Forward movement requires application of at least one control unit in both front and rear sections of transmission.

3. Neutral clutch is applied in forward speeds only.

4. Front section is in reduction when controlled coupling is empty, and in direct drive when coupling is full.

5. Rear section is in reduction when rear clutch is released, and in direct drive when rear clutch is applied.
6. Overrun clutch and low overrun band are used for engine braking only. They do not drive or transmit power to drive line.
7. Only purpose of accumulator is to cushion rear clutch application.

Roto Hydra-Matic

The third generation Hydra-Matic transmission is known as Roto Hydra-Matic or Accel-A-Rotor Hydra-Matic, Fig. 44-23. This transmission is unusual in that it does not have the conventional fluid coupling between the engine and the transmission case. However, it does use a small "fill and dump" coupling similar to the one

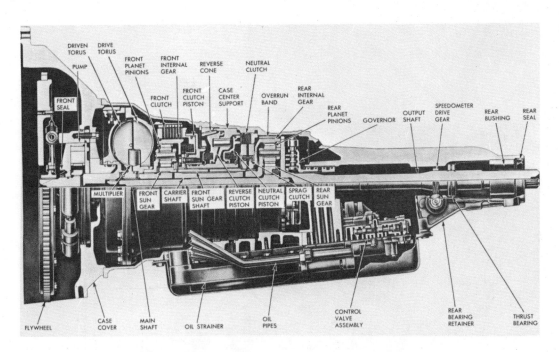

Fig. 44-23. Major components of Roto Hydra-Matic transmission are called out in this sectional view of last of Hydra-Matic transmissions using a fluid coupling.

used in the Controlled Coupling unit, but with the addition of fixed stator blades between the two coupling halves. In effect, it is a small torque converter, although, Oldsmobile and Pontiac prefer to call it a "torque multiplier." See Fig. 44-24.

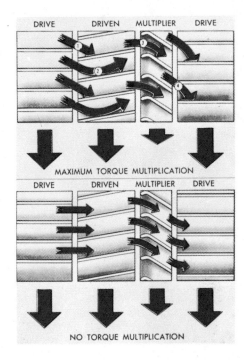

Fig. 44-24. Torque multiplier featured in Roto Hydra-Matic transmission operates on principle shown. Multiplier directs fluid to back side of drive member vanes.

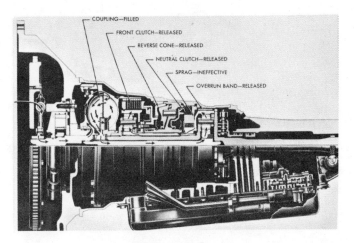

Fig. 44-25. When Roto Hydra-Matic is in neutral, both front and rear unit internal gears spin freely, so no torque is transferred to carriers or output shaft.

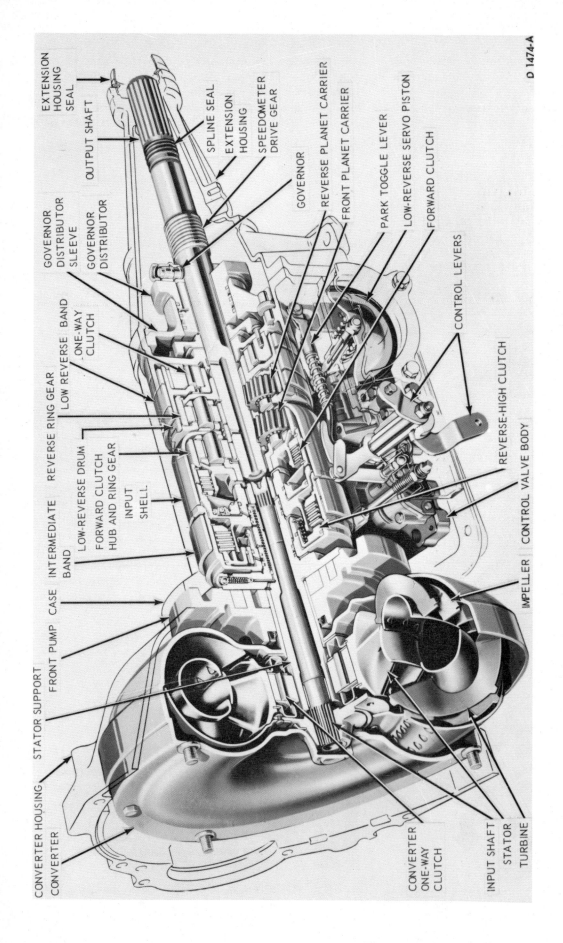

CONVERTER HOUSING
CONVERTER

STATOR SUPPORT

FRONT PUMP

CASE

INTERMEDIATE BAND

REVERSE RING GEAR

LOW-REVERSE DRUM

FORWARD CLUTCH HUB AND RING GEAR

INPUT SHELL

GOVERNOR DISTRIBUTOR SLEEVE

GOVERNOR DISTRIBUTOR

LOW REVERSE BAND

ONE-WAY CLUTCH

OUTPUT SHAFT

EXTENSION HOUSING SEAL

SPLINE SEAL

EXTENSION HOUSING

SPEEDOMETER DRIVE GEAR

GOVERNOR

REVERSE PLANET CARRIER

FRONT PLANET CARRIER

PARK TOGGLE LEVER

LOW-REVERSE SERVO PISTON

FORWARD CLUTCH

CONTROL LEVERS

REVERSE-HIGH CLUTCH

CONTROL VALVE BODY

IMPELLER

CONVERTER ONE-WAY CLUTCH

INPUT SHAFT

STATOR

TURBINE

D 1474-A

Ford C-4 automatic dual range transmission, section view.

594

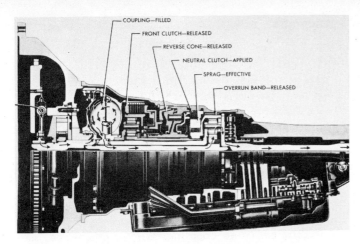

Fig. 44-26. Power flow in first and second drive range is through rear planetary unit gear reduction. Different ratios are accomplished because multiplier is no longer effective in second.

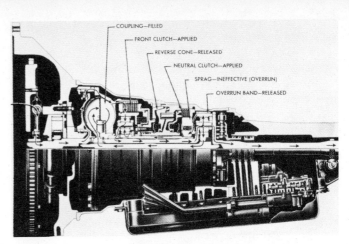

Fig. 44-28. In fourth drive range, power flow is from front sun gear to rear internal gear to front internal gear to rear sun gear. Entire train revolves as one common unit in direct drive.

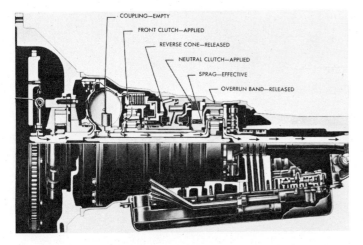

Fig. 44-27. In third drive range, coupling is empty so engine torque is mechanically applied to front planetary unit internal gear. Torque multiplication is due to front unit gear ratio.

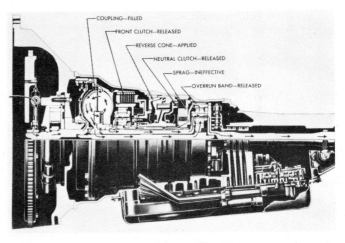

Fig. 44-29. In reverse, Roto Hydra-Matic reverse cone holds front planetary unit internal gear stationary. Both front and rear unit carriers turn output shaft in reverse in reduction.

This four-speed transmission retains the cone clutch for reverse operation, the overrun band, the two multiple disc clutch packs, but eliminates one of the sprag clutches and one planetary gearset, Fig. 44-23. The most interesting feature of this unit is that in third speed range, the multiplier "empties" and power flow between the engine and output shaft becomes a pure mechanical lockup. See Figs. 44-25 to 44-29.

From this point, the fourth generation Turbo Hydra-Matic became a torque converter automatic transmission.

Quiz - Fluid Coupling
Automatic Transmissions

1. Name the four elements generally found in automatic transmissions.
2. What purpose does a fluid coupling accomplish in an automatic transmission?
   a. Serves as hydraulic clutch.
   b. Multiplies engine torque.
   c. Builds up hydraulic pressure to operate valves.

3. What is the primary function of a planetary gearset in an automatic transmission?
   a. Connects engine to fluid coupling.
   b. Cushions effect of gear changes in transmission.
   c. Provides suitable gear ratios.
4. Which of these three factors is used to control automatic transmission operation?
   a. Engine speed.
   b. Engine weight.
   c. Engine compression.
5. Which of these three factors is NOT used to control automatic transmission operation?
   a. Hand levers.
   b. Foot pedals.
   c. Car weight.
6. Is the hydraulic fluid sealed in the fluid coupling of a Hydra-Matic transmission?
7. When is a fluid coupling most effective?
   a. High speed.
   b. Low speed.
   c. Idling speed.

8. Can hydraulic pressure and spring action be combined on a single valve to provide a balance of forces?
9. When a Hydra-Matic is in fourth speed, which planetary units are in reduction?
   a. Front unit.
   b. Rear unit.
   c. Neither unit.
10. Can more than one fluid coupling be used in an automatic transmission?
11. Can more than one free-wheel clutch be used in an automatic transmission?
12. Does a sprag clutch and a free-wheel clutch operate in the same manner?
13. What replaced bands in Controlled Coupling Hydra-Matic transmissions?
    a. Servo units.
    b. Sprag clutches.
    c. Overrun clutches.
14. When is the right position of the Drive Range of a Controlled Coupling Hydra-Matic used?
    a. Turnpike driving.
    b. Congested traffic.
    c. Normal driving.
15. What is the purpose of the accumulator in a Controlled Coupling Hydra-Matic?
    a. Builds hydraulic pressure.
    b. Cushions rear clutch application.
    c. Connects front and rear planetary gearsets.
16. The Roto Hydra-Matic transmission uses a "torque multiplier" fluid coupling. What element provides torque multiplication?
    a. Drive torus.
    b. Driven torus.
    c. Fixed stator blades.
17. In which speed is the torque multiplier effective?
    a. First   c. Third
    b. Second

TORQUE CONVERTER AUTOMATIC TRANSMISSIONS

Automatic transmissions are powered by the engine through one or more fluid couplings or a torque converter. As established in the chapter on Fluid Coupling Automatic Transmissions, a fluid coupling merely transmits engine torque applied to it while a torque converter multiplies it.

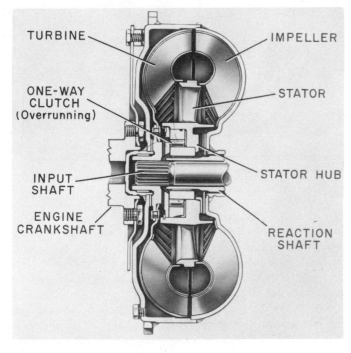

Fig. 45-1. Cross-sectional view of typical torque converter shows attachment to engine crankshaft and relationship of three major elements: impeller, turbine and stator.

Modern torque converters, Fig. 45-1, utilize three major rotating elements to multiply engine torque:
1. An engine-driven pump or impeller.
2. A fluid-driven turbine.
3. A stator.
Some older automatic transmissions, Buick Dynaflow, for example, have four or five-element torque converters (which include first turbine and second turbine, primary and secondary stators, etc.). However, the three-element unit has proved to be efficient and remarkably trouble-free.

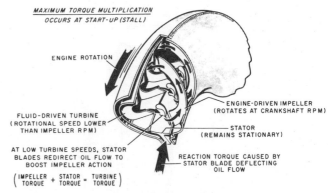

Fig. 45-2. Three elements are pictured in operation at point of start-up stall with stator stationary and torque multiplication at maximum.

Method of Operation

All hydraulic-type torque converters are based on the same principle of operation, Fig. 45-2. All use the engine to drive the impeller which, in turn, impels fluid against the vanes of a turbine connected through transmission gears to the drive shaft of the automobile. The third element, the stator, is the middle ele-

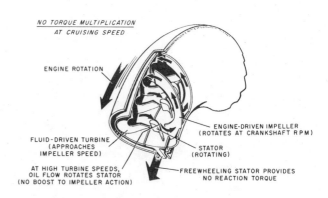

Fig. 45-3. In this position, car is at cruising speed and one-way clutch permits stator to free-wheel and rotate with impeller and turbine.

ment and serves to redirect oil flow from the turbine to boost impeller action and multiply engine torque.

These three elements work together in a fluid-filled housing to provide the desired torque multiplication at low speed and perform as an efficient fluid coupling at high speed, Fig. 45-3.

When the engine is running, the fluid in the torque converter is pumped from the impeller vanes across to the turbine vanes, then back to the impeller through the stator, Fig. 45-4. The action of centrifugal force

stead, it is directed against the curved face of the stator blades. See Fig. 45-2. This impact creates reaction torque since the stator is held stationary by a one-way or overrunning clutch, and engine torque is multiplied at variable ratios up to at least 2:1 when the turbine is in start-up stall.

When enough torque is developed by the impeller, the turbine begins to rotate along with the transmission input shaft. As turbine speed approaches impeller speed, torque multiplication lessens, since the angle

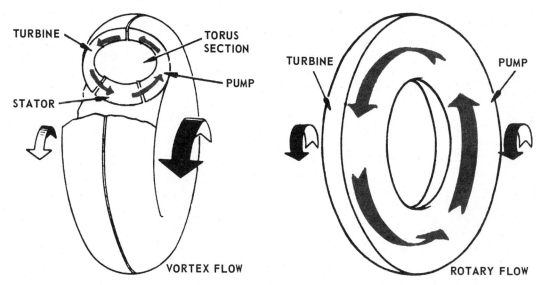

Fig. 45-4. When torque converter is in operation, there are two types of oil circulation within unit: vortex and rotary flow.

sets up a vortex flow of oil within the torque converter, while the angle of the vanes tends to set up a rotary flow. This results in a corkscrew action as the combined flow sets up a pattern something like a coil spring with the ends connected, Fig. 45-5.

This whirling ring of oil emerges from the twisting passages of the turbine, in a direction opposite to pump rotation. If the oil flow was directed into the pump at this time, it would cause a loss of power. In-

of fluid flow against the face of the stator blades becomes less efficient. Then, just before turbine speed equals impeller speed, the fluid strikes the back face of the stator blades, releasing the overrunning clutch and permitting the three elements to rotate together as a fluid coupling. See Fig. 45-3.

In most cases, as with the Chrysler TorqueFlite torque converter illustrated, the stator blades are "fixed" at a predetermined angle. In other cases, Oldsmobile Jetaway and Buick Super Turbine 300, for example, a variable pitch stator assembly is used, Fig. 45-6. For normal operation in drive range, the stator blades are automatically set at a low angle. For increased acceleration and performance, greater torque is obtained by setting the stator blades at a high angle.

Turbo Hydra-Matic

The Turbo Hydra-Matic is a torque converter automatic transmission used in broad application in late model General Motors cars. This aluminum case, three-speed transmission incorporates a torque converter (with either fixed or variable stator), a compound planetary gearset, three multiple disc clutch

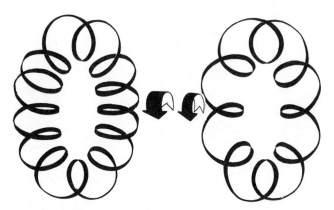

Fig. 45-5. Two types of oil flow in torque converter combine to produce a spiral action or coil spring effect.

packs, two bands and two sprags. Minor modifications in this arrangement occur across the various General Motors lines but, basically, these are the major elements, Fig. 45-7.

The torque converter is a three-element unit consisting of impeller, turbine and stator assembly. The stator is mounted on an overrunning clutch and provides torque multiplication on acceleration. Some Turbo Hydra-Matic torque converters are equipped with variable pitch stator blades, Fig. 45-6. The high stator blade angle means increased engine speed and torque multiplication. The low angle results in more efficient converter operation as a fluid coupling at cruising speed and above.

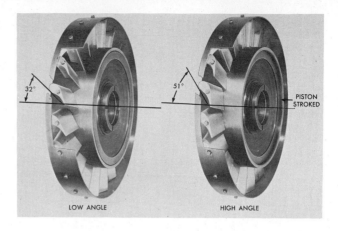

Fig. 45-6. Variable pitch stator affords automatic adjustment of stator blade angle to provide greater torque when needed.

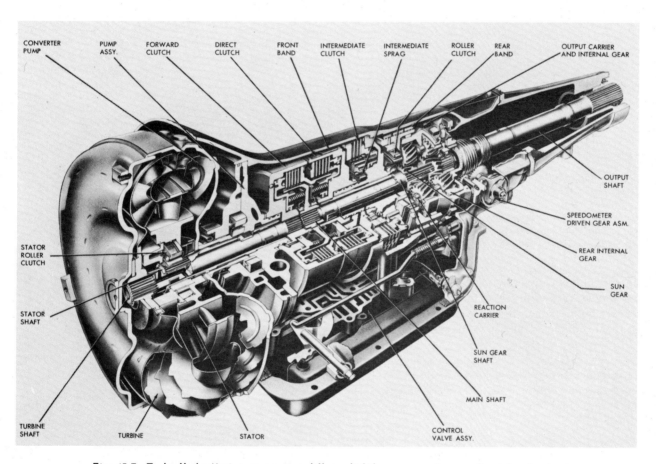

Fig. 45-7. Turbo Hydra-Matic construction differs slightly among various applications, but basic assemblies indicated are used in all automatic transmissions of this type.

Variable Pitch Stator

The angle of the stator blades is usually controlled by a switch mounted on the throttle linkage, a stator solenoid and a stator valve, Fig. 45-8. At engine idle speed, the switch activates the solenoid which exhausts line pressure and the stator valve shifts the blade angle from low to high. At light or medium throttle, the solenoid is not activated and line pressure on the stator valve puts the blades at a low angle. At about 3/4 throttle opening, or under heavy acceler-

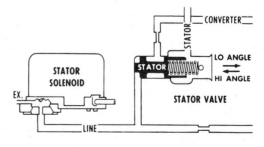

Fig. 45-8. Stator valve piston shifts in its housing according to throttle position to change angle of stator blades to high or low pitch.

ation, the solenoid again exhausts line pressure, and the stator valve moves the stator blades to the high angle for maximum performance.

Cadillac uses a speedometer-activated switch located in back of the speedometer head to signal for changes in stator blade angle.

Transmission Controls

The transmission fluid is pressurized by a gear-type pump which provides working oil pressure needed to operate valve controls and friction elements. A pressure regulator valve in the pump controls main line pressure, as directed by the modulator valve, Fig. 45-9, and it also controls the flow of oil that charges the torque converter.

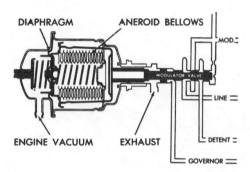

Fig. 45-9. Vacuum modulator operates in conjunction with modulator valve, to control line pressure to various units according to engine vacuum.

The modulator valve, in turn, is controlled by the vacuum modulator, which is attached to the outside of the transmission case. It is connected to the engine intake manifold and basically changes line oil pressure in the transmission to meet engine needs. For example, the vacuum modulator increases line pressure at full throttle, or under heavy load (low vacuum), to provide more "holding" power for the clutches. Under light load (high vacuum), it reduces line pressure to promote smooth shifts.

Other controls include: a governor which increases or decreases oil pressure according to car speed; a manual valve which establishes the particular range of transmission operation selected by the driver; a shift valve which permits 1-2 or 2-1 shifts; a detent valve which provides a downshift when the throttle is opened wide; an accumulator which permits smooth clutch and band engagements; and servos which apply and release front and rear bands.

Turbo Hydra-Matic Operation

The selector quadrant for a Turbo Hydra-Matic has six positions: P, R, N, D, L2, L1, or P, R, N, D, S, L.

Park position locks the transmission output shaft to the case to prevent the car from moving forward or backward.

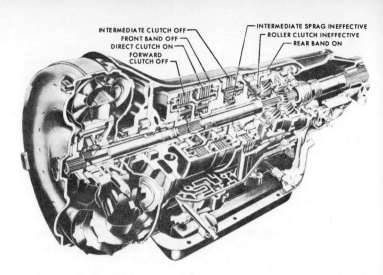

Fig. 45-10. In reverse, power flow is through turbine sun gear shaft, sun gear, front planetary pinions, front internal gear to output shaft.

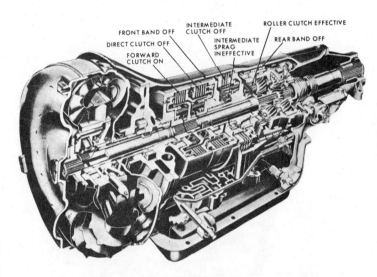

Fig. 45-11. In first gear, power flow is through turbine main shaft, rear planetary internal gear, rear pinions, sun gear, front planetary pinions, front internal gear, output carrier to output shaft.

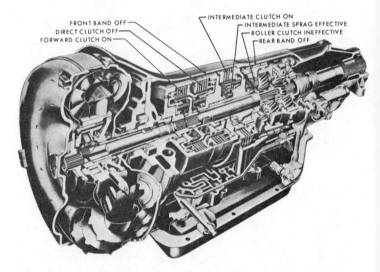

Fig. 45-12. In second gear, power flow is through turbine, forward clutch, main shaft, rear planetary internal gear, rear pinions, output carrier to output shaft.

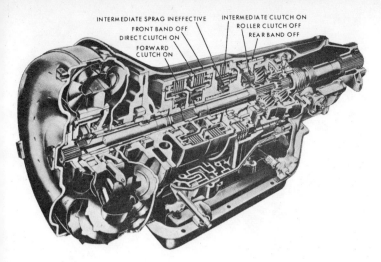

Fig. 45-13. *In third gear (direct drive), power flow is through turbine, forward clutch, main shaft, rear planetary internal gear, sun gear shaft to sun gear. Planetary gearset turns as a unit to drive output shaft.*

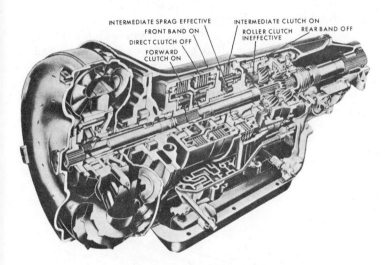

Fig. 45-14. *In L2 or S position, power flow is through turbine, forward clutch, main shaft, rear planetary internal gear, rear pinions, output carrier and output shaft.*

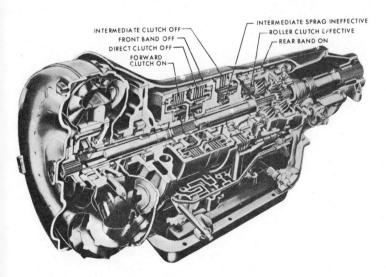

Fig. 45-15. *In L1 or L position, power flow is through turbine, forward clutch, main shaft, rear planetary internal gear, rear pinions, front internal gear, output carrier and output shaft.*

In Neutral, all clutches and bands are released, permitting the engine to run but not drive the vehicle.

In Reverse, the direct clutch is engaged and rear band is applied, permitting the car to move backwards, Fig. 45-10.

In Drive range, the forward clutch is engaged when the transmission is in first gear; forward and intermediate clutches are engaged in second gear; forward, intermediate and direct clutches are engaged in third gear (direct drive). See Figs. 45-11 to 45-13.

In L2 or S position, forward and intermediate clutches and front band are engaged, Fig. 45-14.

In L1 or L position, forward clutch is engaged and rear band is applied. The transmission cannot upshift regardless of car speed or engine speed, Fig. 45-15.

Jetaway or Super Turbine 300

The Oldsmobile Jetaway, Buick Super Turbine 300 and Pontiac Automatic are similar torque converter transmissions having only minor differences in internal construction. This basic two-speed automatic transmission has a three-element torque converter, compound planetary gearset, two multiple disc clutches and a low band, Fig. 45-16.

The torque converter consists of a pump, turbine and either fixed or variable-pitch stator assembly in which the stator blades operate at high angle or low angle, much like the Turbo Hydra-Matic converter of this type.

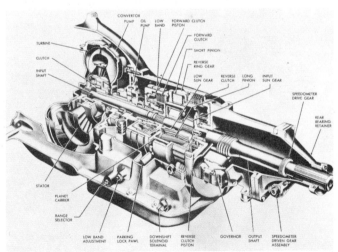

Fig. 45-16. *Two-speed automatic transmission in Oldsmobile, Buick and Pontiac smaller cars, utilizes either fixed or variable-pitch stator design.*

A positive-displacement, gear-type pump is used to supply oil to the converter and provide oil under pressure for the engagement of forward and reverse clutches and for the application and release of the low band. It also circulates oil for lubrication and heat transfer.

The planetary gearset consists of input sun gear, low sun gear, short and long pinions, a reverse ring gear and planet carrier. See Fig. 45-17. The input sun gear is splined to the input shaft and is in mesh with the three long pinions. These long pinions are in mesh

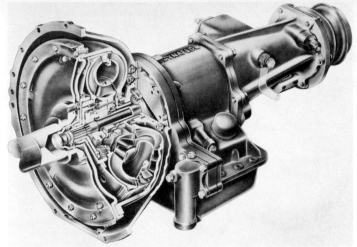

Fig. 45-18. Buick Dynaflow units feature four or five-element torque converters and, in later applications, variable-pitch stator blades.

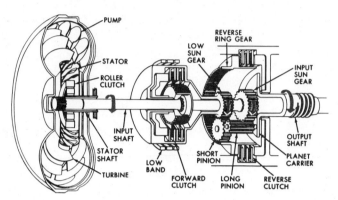

Fig. 45-17. In direct drive, power flow is through turbine, forward clutch, low sun gear, short pinions, long pinions, input sun gear to output shaft.

with the three short pinions which, in turn, are in mesh with the low sun gear and reverse ring gear.

The forward clutch assembly consists of a drum, piston, springs, seals and a clutch pack. See Fig. 45-16. When oil pressure is applied to the piston, the clutch plates are pressed together, connecting the clutch drum to the input shaft in direct drive.

The low band surrounds the forward clutch drum. It is hydraulically applied by the low servo piston and released by spring pressure. When the low band is applied, the transmission operates in low range.

The reverse clutch consists of a piston, seals, springs, clutch pack and reaction plate. When oil pressure is applied to the piston, the clutch plates are pressed together, "holding" the reverse ring gear and causing reverse rotation of the output shaft.

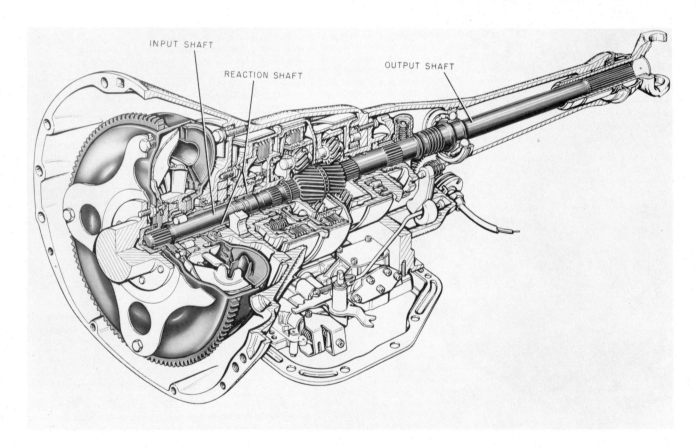

Fig. 45-19. TorqueFlite transmission shafts are darkened in this illustration to show power flow from turbine to output shaft.

Dynaflow

The Dynaflow transmission, in various forms, was used in Buick cars for many years. Earlier versions consist of a five-element torque converter: primary pump; secondary pump; turbine; primary stator; secondary stator.

In operation, this Dynaflow converter utilizes the basic principles of the three-element unit. However, the additional pump and stator elements serve to increase torque multiplication.

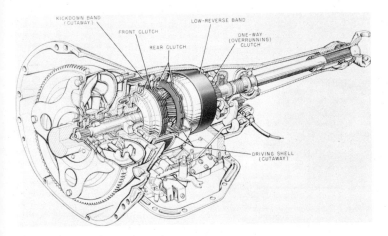

Fig. 45-20. Clutches and bands applied by hydraulic controls called servos, transmit engine torque through planetary gearsets.

Later Dynaflow units incorporate a four-element converter with geared turbines, Fig. 45-18. A built-in planetary gearset connects the first and second turbines to further multiply torque. In another engineering advance, variable pitch stator blades which shift automatically were adopted. Then another stator was added to the torque converter and, finally, the bands used on planetary gearsets were discarded in favor of multiple disc clutches. Also, a grade retarder was added in the form of paddles or fins on a rotating plate. When applied, these fins agitate the fluid in the transmission housing to create resistance to rotation.

TorqueFlite

The Chrysler Corporation's TorqueFlite automatic transmission evolved from the three-speed torque converter-type unit introduced on some 1956 Imperials. Over the years, many of the basic concepts of this introductory model have been retained and improved upon, Fig. 45-19.

Some of these improvements include: a one-piece aluminum housing; higher capacity elements developed to transmit the higher torque of larger V-8 engines; internal oil filters; harder clutch discs, reaction shaft and impeller hubs; larger input shaft; sliding-spline output shaft; higher helix angle on planetary gear teeth; internally actuated parking sprag; high accuracy speed-ometer pinion; new clutch disc lining materials; higher stall speed torque converter; also, elimination of the parking brake assembly from the drive shaft, the rear oil pump and the drain plug.

Torque Converter Construction

The modern TorqueFlite has a three-element torque converter that transmits power from the engine through the transmission shafts to the drive shaft, Fig. 45-19. The converter utilizes an impeller, turbine and fixed-blade stator to more than double engine torque at start-up stall. See Fig. 45-2. Cooling of the converter is accomplished by circulating the transmission fluid through an oil-to-water type cooler built into the lower radiator tank.

Hydraulic System Makeup

The hydraulic system involves four basic control groups:
1. The pressure supply system which consists of the single front oil pump which furnishes oil under pressure for all hydraulic and lubrication requirements.
2. The pressure regulating valves which include the regulator valve, torque converter control valve, governor valve and throttle valve.
3. The flow control valves which consist of the manual valve, 1-2 shift valve, 2-3 shift valve, kickdown valve and shuttle valve.
4. The clutch and band servos and accumulator. See. Fig. 45-20.

The TorqueFlite gear selection is controlled by a push-button system on older models, by a lever-type gearshift on the steering column, or in a floor console on later models. The control has six positions: P, R, N, D, 2, 1.

Planetary System Operation

The planetary gear system consists of two planetary gearsets which operate individually or together to produce three forward ratios and one reverse ratio,

Fig. 45-21. Planetary gear train provides various gear ratios, including three in forward speeds and one in reverse.

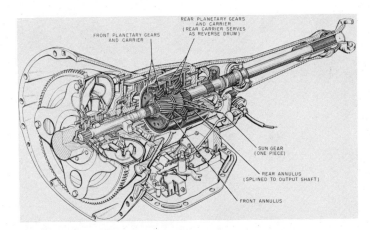

Fig. 45-21. In second speed, for example, the front (kickdown) band is applied and the rear clutch is engaged. Power flow is from the engine and torque converter, through the input shaft to the rear clutch and front annulus gear, Fig. 45-22. This internal gear of the front planetary gearset drives the planet pinions and planetary carrier around the sun gear, which is held stationary, and transmits driving torque to the output shaft.

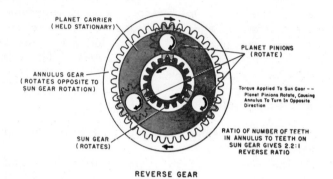

REVERSE GEAR

Fig. 45-22. Principles of operation of planetary gearset are based on driving one or more elements and holding another to obtain various ratios.

In operation, then the four principle elements of each planetary gearset are driven or held as directed by the hydraulic control system, Fig. 45-23, to produce the ratios built into the TorqueFlite transmission.

PowerFlite

Chrysler's PowerFlite transmission was a running mate of the TorqueFlite for about ten years. The major difference between the two is in the number of forward speeds: PowerFlite, two; TorqueFlite, three.

Early PowerFlites used a four-element torque converter. Later, the three-element converter was adopted to drive two planetary gearsets controlled by two bands and a multiple disc clutch.

With the selector placed in neutral position, no units are applied. In low gear, only the kickdown band is applied. In high — or direct drive — the kickdown band is released and the multiple disc clutch is en-

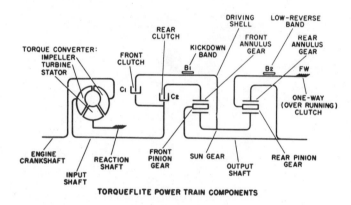

TORQUEFLITE POWER TRAIN COMPONENTS

Fig. 45-23. Schematic of TorqueFlite power train components spells out basic assemblies and shows their relationship to each other.

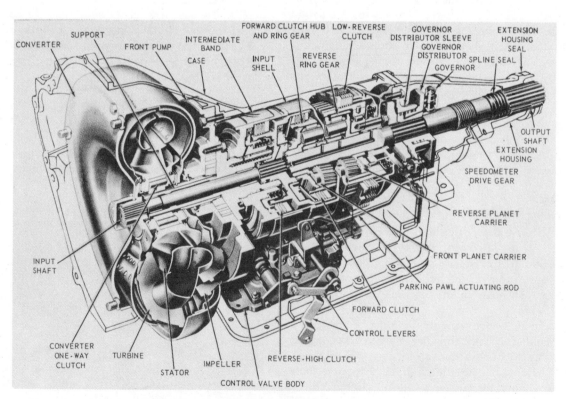

Fig. 45-24. Ford Select Shift Cruise-O-Matic transmissions incorporate select shift feature, permitting driver option of selecting gears manually.

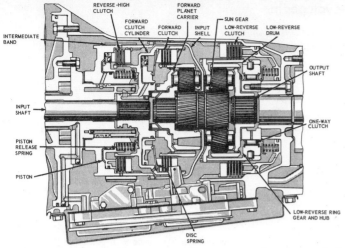

Fig. 45-25. Cruise-O-Matic planetary gear train has input shaft splined to turbine of torque converter and forward clutch cylinder.

gaged. In reverse, both the kickdown band and the clutch are released and the reverse band is applied. The bands and clutch are automatically controlled by the hydraulic system which consists of two oil pumps, several regulating valves and a valve body.

Select Shift Cruise-O-Matic

The Ford Select Shift Cruise-O-Matic transmissions (labeled C6 in earlier models) are built in three versions, each tailored to a particular engine, axle ratio and load capacity, Fig. 45-24. Variations in construction exist, but all incorporate the "Select Shift" feature, which provides either automatic upshifts and downshifts or manual selection of first and second gears. Major assemblies consist of a three-element torque converter, planetary gear train, forward clutch, low-reverse clutch, reverse-high clutch, intermediate servo and band.

Hydraulic system components include: gear-type pump, main oil pressure regulator valves; manual valves; primary throttle valve and altitude compensating diaphragm assembly; main oil pressure booster; governor and various other valves.

The planetary gear train consists of an input shaft splined to the turbine of the converter and to the forward clutch cylinder, Fig. 45-25.

When the reverse-high clutch is engaged, its hub drives the input shell and rotates the sun gear. When the forward clutch is engaged, its hub and ring gear drives the forward planet gears. When the intermediate band is applied, it "holds" the reverse-high clutch drum, input shell and sun gear from rotating.

The sun gear, driven by the input shell, is meshed with the forward and reverse planet gears. The reverse planet carrier is splined to the low-reverse clutch hub which can be held from rotating by a one-way clutch. The forward planet carrier, reverse ring gear hub, park gear and governor distributor are all splined to the output shaft, Fig. 45-25.

In neutral, no clutches or bands are applied, Fig. 45-26.

In low gear, Fig. 45-27, the forward clutch is engaged and the planet one-way clutch or low-reverse clutch is holding the low-reverse clutch hub and reverse planet carrier from rotating.

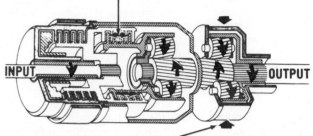

CLUTCHES AND THE BAND ARE RELEASED

NEUTRAL

Fig. 45-26. In neutral, input shaft turns with torque converter turbine; output shaft remains stationary.

THE FORWARD CLUTCH IS APPLIED. THE FRONT PLANETARY UNIT RING GEAR IS LOCKED TO THE INPUT SHAFT.

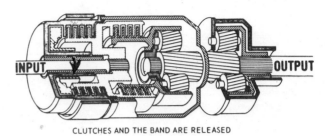

THE LOW AND REVERSE CLUTCH (LOW RANGE) OR THE ONE-WAY CLUTCH (D1 RANGE) IS HOLDING THE REVERSE UNIT PLANET CARRIER STATIONARY.

FIRST GEAR

Fig. 45-27. In first gear, power flow is through: input shaft, forward clutch, clutch cylinder and hub and ring gear, reverse planet gears, reverse ring gear and hub to output shaft.

In intermediate gear, the forward clutch is engaged and the intermediate band is holding the reverse-high clutch drum, input shell and sun gear from turning, Fig. 45-28.

THE INTERMEDIATE BAND IS APPLIED. THE REVERSE AND HIGH CLUTCH DRUM, THE INPUT SHELL AND THE SUN GEAR ARE HELD STATIONARY.

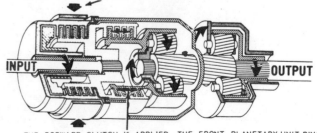

THE FORWARD CLUTCH IS APPLIED. THE FRONT PLANETARY UNIT RING GEAR IS LOCKED TO THE INPUT SHAFT.

SECOND GEAR

Fig. 45-28. In second gear, power flow is through: input shaft; forward clutch; forward planet assembly ring gear and pinions, forward planet carrier to output shaft.

In high gear, Fig. 45-29, the forward and reverse-high clutches are engaged.

In reverse gear, the reverse-high clutch and low-reverse clutch are engaged, Fig. 45-30.

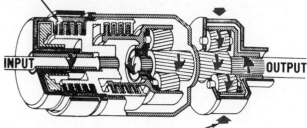

THE REVERSE AND HIGH CLUTCH IS APPLIED. THE INPUT SHAFT IS LOCKED TO THE REVERSE AND HIGH CLUTCH DRUM, THE INPUT SHELL AND THE SUN GEAR.

THE LOW AND REVERSE CLUTCH IS APPLIED. THE REVERSE UNIT PLANET CARRIER IS HELD STATIONARY.

REVERSE

Fig. 45-30. In reverse, power flow is through input shaft; reverse-high clutch; input shell; sun gear; reverse planet gears to output shaft.

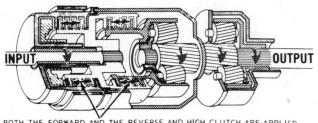

BOTH THE FORWARD AND THE REVERSE AND HIGH CLUTCH ARE APPLIED. ALL PLANETARY GEAR MEMBERS ARE LOCKED TO EACH OTHER AND ARE LOCKED TO THE OUTPUT SHAFT.

HIGH GEAR

Fig. 45-29. In third gear, power flow is through: input shaft, forward clutch; hub and ring gear; forward planet carrier. Reverse-high clutch directs power flow through: input shell through sun gear; front planet assembly to output shaft.

Ford C4 Automatic Transmission

Major components of the C4 transmission include: a three-element torque converter; planetary gear train; forward clutch; reverse-high clutch; intermediate servo and bands; low-reverse servo and band, Fig. 45-31. The torque converter is the fixed-stator type. Front and reverse planetary gearsets provide the ratios needed for the three speeds forward and one in reverse.

A gear-type pump supplies fluid for the operation of the hydraulic control systems. A constant flow of fluid to the converter is maintained. Fluid from the converter is forced through a cooler located in the radiator tank.

Pressure to the various valves is controlled by the main pressure regulator valve. The manual valve is positioned by the manual linkage according to the desires of the driver. Positions are P, R, N, D1, D2, L.

In Neutral, the clutches and bands are not applied. In Low gear (L and D1), the forward clutch is engaged and the one-way clutch or low-reverse band is "holding" the low-reverse drum and reverse planet carrier from rotating. In Intermediate gear (D1 and D2), the

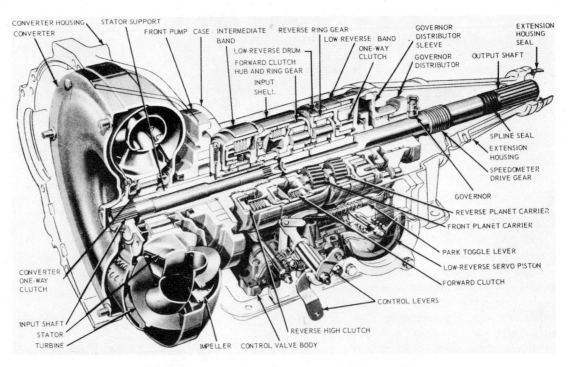

Fig. 45-31. Major assemblies that make up Ford C4 automatic transmission. In unusual arrangement, when reverse-high clutch is engaged, clutch drives input shell to rotate sun gear.

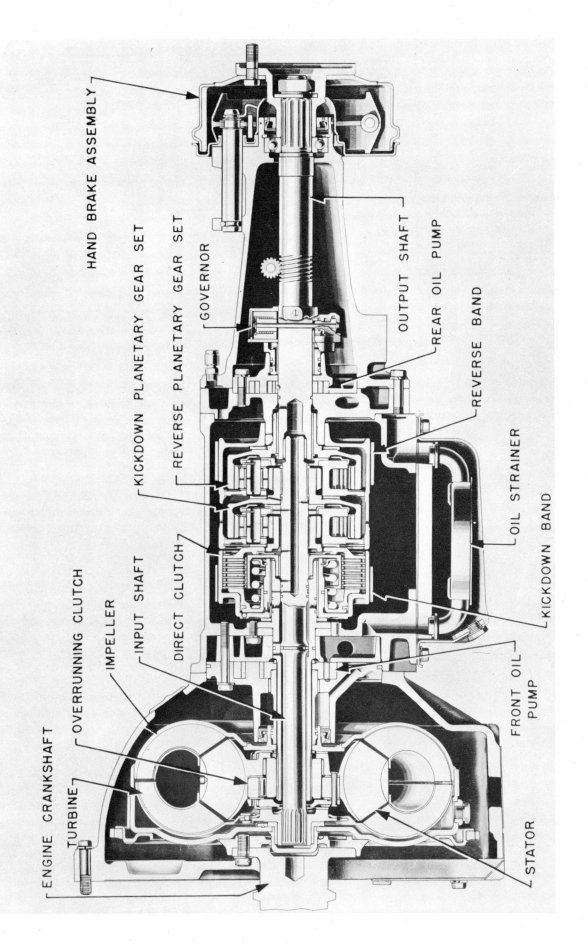

HAND BRAKE ASSEMBLY

KICKDOWN PLANETARY GEAR SET

REVERSE PLANETARY GEAR SET

GOVERNOR

OUTPUT SHAFT

REAR OIL PUMP

REVERSE BAND

OIL STRAINER

KICKDOWN BAND

FRONT OIL PUMP

STATOR

ENGINE CRANKSHAFT

TURBINE

OVERRUNNING CLUTCH

IMPELLER

INPUT SHAFT

DIRECT CLUTCH

Plymouth PowerFlite transmission, section view.

forward clutch is engaged and the intermediate band is "holding" the reverse-high clutch drum, input shell and sun gear. In High gear (D1 and D2), the forward and reverse-high clutches are engaged. In Reverse, the reverse-high clutch is engaged and the low-reverse band is applied.

Fordomatic

The Fordomatic transmission is a torque converter type using three elements: the usual impeller, turbine and stator units connected to a planetary gear transmission. Ford terms the torque converter a combination hydraulic torque multiplier and fluid coupling. The planetary gear system is a compound gearset. On later models, one multiple disc clutch and two bands provide two forward speeds and one speed in reverse.

Two pumps are used to supply oil under pressure to operate the control band and clutch, lubricate the entire transmission and keep the converter filled. One pump is driven by the converter impeller, the other by the transmission output shaft.

The selector lever has five positions: P (Park), R (Reverse), N (Neutral), D (Drive) and L (Low).

In Neutral and Park positions, the clutch and both bands are released by spring pressure, and drive through the transmission is impossible. In Drive position - first gear - in Low position and also in kickdown, the low band is applied. In Drive position - high gear - the low band is released and the high clutch is engaged. In Reverse position, the reverse band is applied.

Fig. 45-32. Flash-O-Matic features three-element torque converter and dual driving range transmission that may be manually controlled.

Flash-O-Matic

The Flash-O-Matic consists of a torque converter coupled to a three-speed dual driving range automatic transmission, Fig. 45-32. The converter incorporates an impeller connected to the engine crankshaft, a turbine splined to the transmission input shaft, and a stator connected to and controlled by a free-wheel unit.

Front and rear oil pumps, Fig. 45-33, are used to supply fluid to the converter, lubricate the parts and

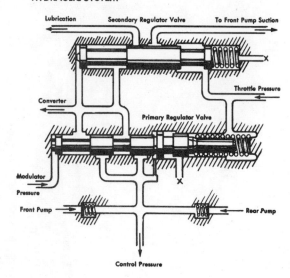

HYDRAULIC SYSTEM

Fig. 45-33. Hydraulic system utilizes two oil pumps which provide working oil pressure needed to operate various control units and valves.

build pressure in the various oil circuits. A primary regulator valve regulates control pressure to meet all driving requirements. A manual valve, controlled by the transmission selector lever, opens combinations of oil passages to the valve and units which are required for the drive range selected.

A compound planetary gear train supplies the necessary gear combinations to provide neutral, low, intermediate, high and reverse gear ratios. Major elements include a primary sun gear, secondary sun gear, primary and secondary pinions held in a common pinion carrier, and an internal gear attached to the transmission output shaft, Fig. 45-32. The selector lever has six positions: P, R, N, D2, D1 and L. In D2, the transmission starts in intermediate and automatically upshifts to direct drive. In D1, it starts in low and automatically upshifts to intermediate, then direct. In L, the transmission stays in low gear. The selector lever may be moved from D2 to D1 to L or from L to D1 to D2 at any car speed.

The various gear ratios are dependent on which gears are being held and which are driving. This phase of automatic transmission control is accomplished by clutches, bands and servos. Front and rear multiple disc clutches are used. Actuation of the front servo applies the front band to the rear clutch drum and locks the secondary sun gear to the transmission case. Actuation of the rear servo applies the rear band to the pinion carrier, locking it to the transmission case.

In Neutral position, none of the gear train members are held or driving, so there is no transfer of power. In Park, the parking pawl is engaged with external teeth on the output shaft internal gear, locking the output shaft to the transmission case.

In Drive range, D1, the front clutch couples the primary sun gear to the input shaft, Fig. 45-34. The

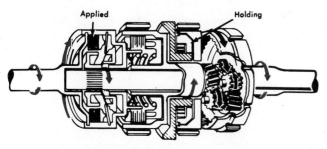

Power Flow in Low (First Gear Range Shown)

Fig. 45-34. In first gear, front clutch is engaged.

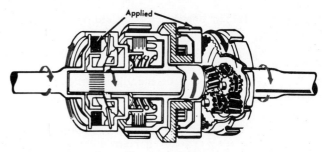

Power Flow in Low (L-Range)

Fig. 45-37. In low range (L), front clutch is engaged and rear band is applied.

sprag clutch is engaged and holds the planetary pinion carrier. The primary sun gear drives the planetary pinion which, in turn, drives the internal gear and output shaft.

In Intermediate position (second speed), the front clutch connects the primary sun gear to the input shaft,

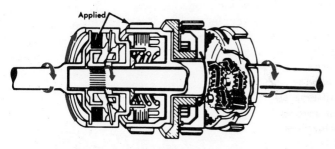

Power Flow in Intermediate (Second Gear)

Fig. 45-35. In second gear, front clutch is engaged and front band is applied.

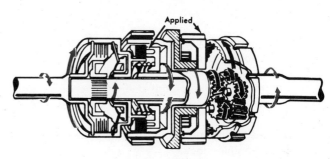

Power Flow in Reverse

Fig. 45-38. In reverse, rear clutch is engaged and rear bands applied.

while the front band "holds" the secondary sun gear stationary. Power flow is through the primary sun gear, planet pinions and carrier to the internal gear and output shaft, Fig. 45-35.

In High position (direct drive), the front clutch connects the primary sun gear to the input shaft, while the rear clutch connects the secondary sun gear to the input shaft. This locks the pinions together and all units turned in direct ratio to the input shaft, Fig. 45-36.

In Low range (L), Fig. 45-37, the front clutch connects the primary sun gear to the input shaft, while the rear band "holds" the pinion carrier stationary.

In Reverse, Fig. 45-38, the rear clutch connects the secondary sun gear to the input shaft, while the rear band "holds" the pinion carrier stationary. Power flow is through the secondary sun gear, secondary pinions to the internal gear and output shaft.

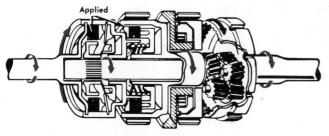

Power Flow in High (Direct)

Fig. 45-36. In high, front and rear clutches are engaged.

Quiz - Torque Converter Automatic Transmissions

1. What is the difference between a fluid coupling and a torque converter?
2. What are the three major rotating elements in most torque converters?
3. Which element creates reaction torque in a torque converter? a. Impeller. b. Turbine. c. Stator.
4. Torque multiplication in a torque converter is greater at what speed?
   a. Low speed.
   b. Cruising speed.
   c. High speed.
5. Are stator blades always "fixed?"

6. Can more than one turbine or stator assembly be used in a torque converter?

7. What are the main advantages of a variable pitched stator?

8. What is the purpose of the vacuum modulator and modulator valve in a Turbo Hydra-Matic transmission?
   a. Permits smooth clutch and band engagements.
   b. Establishes range of transmission selected by driver.
   c. Changes line oil pressure in transmission to meet engine needs.

9. What is the purpose of a manual valve?
   a. Permits smooth clutch and band engagements.
   b. Establishes range of transmission selected by driver.
   c. Changes line oil pressure in transmission to meet engine needs.

10. What is the purpose of an accumulator?
    a. Permits smooth clutch and band engagements.
    b. Establishes range of transmission selected by driver.
    c. Changes line oil pressure in transmission to meet engine needs.

11. What is the primary function of TorqueFlite automatic transmission clutches and bands?
    a. Smooth transmission shifts.
    b. Transmit engine torque through planetary gearsets.
    c. Provide various gear ratios selected by driver.

12. What are the four principle elements of a planetary gearset?

13. What is the purpose of a planetary gear train in an automatic transmission?

14. What is "Select Shift" feature of Ford Cruise-O-Matic transmission?
    a. Permits driver to shift gears manually.
    b. Provides extra forward speed range.
    c. Gives driver option of "kickdown" from high to second gear.

15. Do Fordomatic and Flash-O-Matic transmissions use two oil pumps?

16. What happens to Flash-O-Matic planetary gear train in direct drive?
    a. All units lock together.
    b. Pinion carrier is "held" stationary.
    c. None of the gear train members are "held" stationary.

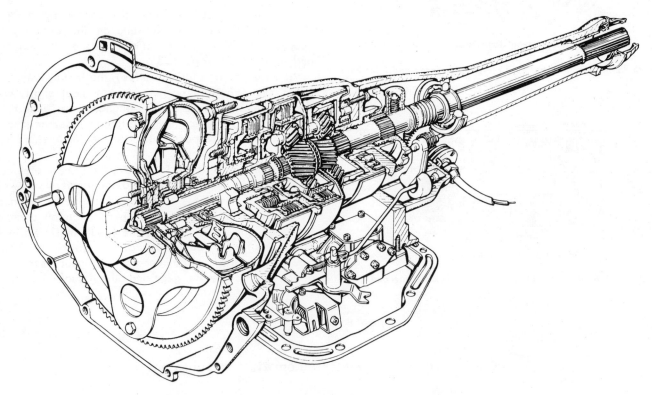

American Motors Torque-Command automatic transmission basically is a 3-speed, hydraulically controlled gearbox with 500 parts housed in an aluminum casting. It does not require band adjustment and, under normal conditions, oil changes are not required.

DRIVE LINE, UNIVERSAL JOINTS, DIFFERENTIALS

In basic passenger car design, the drive line connects the transmission with the driving axles. In effect, it transmits engine power to the driving wheels.

Ordinarily, the engine is mounted on the frame, and the driving wheels are free to move up and down in relation to the frame. In between, the line of drive is constantly changing. This means flexibility is needed in the drive system and, usually, it is provided by universal joints. See Figs. 46-1 and 46-2.

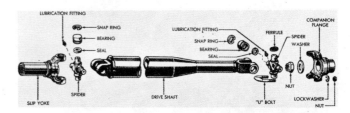

Fig. 46-3. Major components of typical one-piece drive shaft with exploded views of front and rear universal joint assemblies.

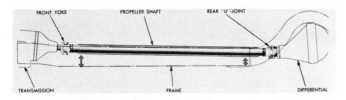

Fig. 46-1. Typical angularity of drive line is illustrated. Note relationship of drive shaft to transmission, differential and wheels.

Universal Joints

Although it would be desirable to have the drive shaft in line with the engine crankshaft, this design is not practical. In the first place, the wheels move up and down because of road irregularities. Second, the frame moves up and down in relation to the wheels. How much it moves depends on the amount of weight

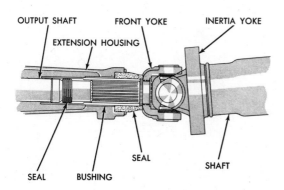

Fig. 46-2. A cross and roller universal joint with sliding spline is front joint arrangement on late model Chrysler-built cars with TorqueFlite transmission.

in the automobile body and the limits of the suspension springs and linkage. So a compromise is made, and the "workable" design is intended to provide as nearly a straight line as possible under average conditions.

The universal joints, Fig. 46-2, serve to compensate for changes in the line of drive by transmitting power from a driving shaft through an angle to a driven shaft. Most cars use two or three universal joints in the drive line between the transmission and differential, Fig. 46-3.

Differentials

The differential is a gear system that transfers power from the drive shaft to the driving axles, Fig. 46-4. It also permits one driving wheel to turn faster than the other to prevent skidding and scuffing of tires on turns.

In tracing the drive train to this point, power is relayed:

1. From drive shaft to pinion gear.
2. From pinion gear to ring gear.
3. From ring gear to attached differential case, pinion gears and side gears.
4. From side gears to driving axles.

Torque Changes

However, when engine power is applied to the drive train, torque is developed in the driving wheels. This action creates further changes in the angularity of the drive line, Fig. 46-5.

When power is transmitted by the drive shaft, the pinion gear tries to turn the ring gear. Since the ring gear must turn the axle shafts (and the wheels, indirectly), it resists being moved. The pinion gear attempts to "roll around" the ring gear. Since it cannot, the pinion instead transfers the turning effort, or torque, to the axle housing. The magnitude of this torque is indicated by the tendency of the back end of the car to dip when power is suddenly applied to the driving wheels.

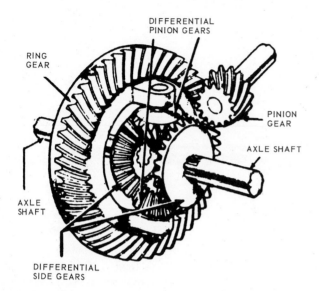

Fig. 46-4. *Typical differential gear makeup consists of drive pinion, ring gear, differential case, differential pinions and differential side gears.*

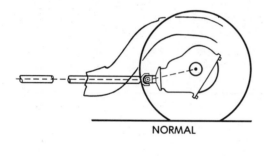

Fig. 46-5. *Differential housing will tilt upward when engine torque is relayed from drive shaft to drive pinion to rear axle housing.*

Torque Transfer

This powerful torque force is transferred from the pinion shaft to the axle housing and from the axle housing to the springs, torque tube or control arms. In the Hotchkiss type of drive, it results in flexing and

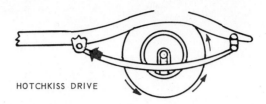

Fig. 46-6. *In Hotchkiss drive setup, driving force is transmitted from rear wheels to front of rear springs.*

distortion of the spring, Fig. 46-6. This distortion or "wind-up" of the springs will raise the pinion shaft at the front end, thereby decreasing the angle between the pinion shaft and the drive shaft.

Hotchkiss Drive

Two universal joints are used in the Hotchkiss type of drive to compensate for variations in road surfaces, load conditions and power application which cause changes in alignment between the transmission output shaft and drive pinion shaft. When the Hotchkiss type of drive is used, the vehicle is moved forward by the front end of the rear springs pushing against the frame, Fig. 46-6.

Torque Tube Drive

In cars equipped with torque tube drive, the pushing action is at the front end of the torque tube, Fig. 46-7. Only one universal joint is used in the drive line, at the front end of the drive shaft. In this case, the drive shaft is within a stout tube which is anchored to the

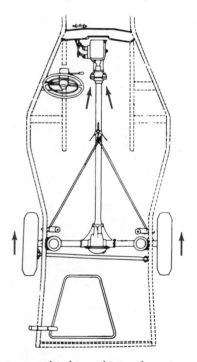

Fig. 46-7. *In torque tube drive, driving force is transmitted from rear wheels to front of torque tube.*

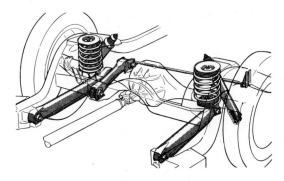

Fig. 46-8. Ford-Mercury rear suspension features control arm drive. Two parallel lower arms extend forward to rubber-bushed anchors for transfer of driving force.

axle housing. This torque tube does not permit the axle housing to twist when engine power is applied. The springs do not absorb any torque and are required only to cushion the ride.

With torque tube drive, the engine is usually mounted as low as possible in the frame or at an angle with the rear end lower than the front. The object is to obtain as nearly as possible a straight line for power transmission, because power is always lost by any angularity in the drive line.

An unusual development in torque tube drive is found in early Pontiac Tempest cars. A comparatively slender drive shaft is used within a torque tube which is fastened rigidly to the engine at one end and to a transaxle (combination transmission and axle) at the other end. The drive shaft bends or flexes as required to compensate for relative movement between engine and axle. Vibration and whipping is minimized by a rubber mounted ball bearing near the middle of the shaft.

Control Arm Drive

In control arm drive, driving and braking forces are transferred to the front end of heavy-duty control arms, Fig. 46-8. The torque transfer effect is similar to Hotchkiss drive, but coil springs are used at the rear rather than leaf type springs. Some cars use three control arms, most use four.

Drive Shaft Length

In addition to line of drive problems caused by angularity of the drive shaft, the distance between the transmission output shaft and the drive pinion shaft is subject to change. This creates the need for some flexibility in the length of the drive shaft.

In referring to the Hotchkiss drive in Fig. 46-9, the front end of the drive shaft is attached to the transmission shaft (B). The rear end is attached to the drive pinion shaft (C). As the wheels move up and down, the drive shaft swings up and down in the arc (A-A) around pivot (B). At the same time, the pinion shaft (C) - being attached to the rear axle - swings in

an arc (D-D) around the pivot where the spring is anchored to the frame at (E). Therefore, as the arcs (A-A) and (D-D) do not coincide, it will be necessary for the drive shaft to alternately lengthen and shorten as the wheels move up and down in relation to the frame.

Slip Joints

One method of lengthening or shortening the drive shaft is by means of a splined shaft coupling or "slip joint" as shown in Fig. 46-10. Another method is shown in Fig. 46-11. This movement is less pronounced on a torque tube drive, but a slip joint is used at the one universal joint.

When the type of slip joint shown in Fig. 46-10 is used, it is possible to assemble it incorrectly. This results in annoying vibration. Such joints are usually marked for correct assembly. If they are not marked, make sure both yokes are in the same plane, or "in phase."

Fig. 46-9. In Hotchkiss drive, length of drive shaft varies because of changes in wheelbase as rear wheels move up and down with road surface irregularities.

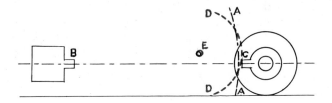

Fig. 46-10. Arrows must align when splined end of drive shaft is installed in universal joint yoke. On unmarked shafts, front and rear yokes must be "in phase."

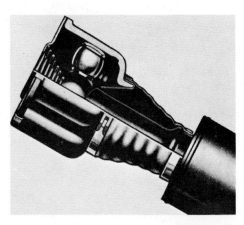

Fig. 46-11. Chrysler Corporation ball and trunnion universal joints utilize balls that travel in raceways of housing to permit variation in drive shaft length.

Effect of Varying Shaft Speeds

When the two yokes of the drive shaft are "in phase," the speed of the transmission output shaft and the pinion shaft will be constant and the same if the line of drive of both shafts is uniform. The velocity of the drive shaft will not be constant, but this is unimportant as long as the velocity of the driving and driven shafts is uniform.

housing and is engineered to an exact length so that the weight oscillates at the natural frequency of the drive line.

More recently, Chrysler took a different design approach, building into the drive shaft an "internal vibration absorber," Fig. 46-13. This unit obtains the same basic effect as the Ford "absorber." It absorbs the natural vibrations created by the fluctuation in speed of the drive shaft.

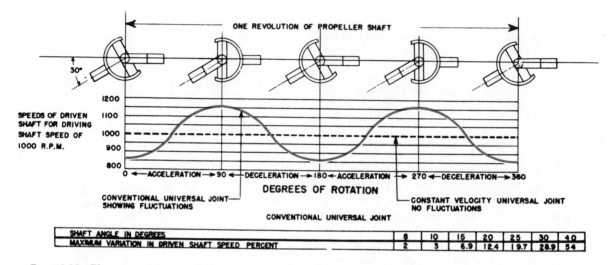

SHAFT ANGLE IN DEGREES							8	10	15	20	25	30	40
MAXIMUM VARIATION IN DRIVEN SHAFT SPEED PERCENT							2	3	6.9	12.4	19.7	28.9	54

Fig. 46-12. Fluctuations in speed of a conventional universal joint operating at a 30 deg. angle, are compared with smooth operation of a constant velocity joint.

When the two yokes are "out of phase," the rotational speed of the shafts will be uniform only if the shafts are operated in a straight line. When operating at an angle with the yokes "out of phase," a conventional universal joint will cause the driven shaft to speed up and slow down each revolution, Fig. 46-12. The number of turns per shaft will be the same, but the velocity of the driven shaft will fluctuate.

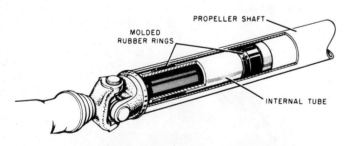

Fig. 46-13. Drive shaft on late model Chrysler-built cars, has an internal vibration absorber designed to absorb vibrations created by normal fluctuating speeds of universal joints.

In an attempt to absorb some of the natural vibration created by the drive line, Ford introduced a "tuned dynamic absorber" for use on lighter vehicles. This absorber consists of a 7 lb. weight suspended by a beam below the front universal joint. The beam is attached to the rear of the transmission extension

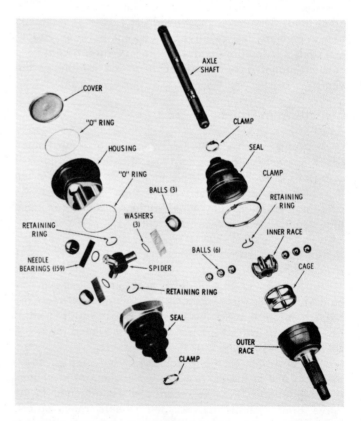

Fig. 46-14. Exploded view details left drive axle assembly used on Oldsmobile Toronado front wheel drive cars. Cadillac Eldorado setup is similar.

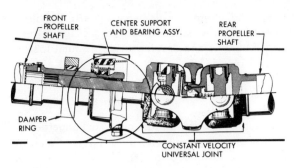

Fig. 46-15. *This constant velocity universal joint consists of two single joints connected by a link yoke and maintained in relative position by a center ball and socket.*

This fluctuation of speed is further emphasized in the design of driving axles. In the case of front wheel drive vehicles, the universal joint, or joints, used in the driving axle assemblies must transfer driving power to the front wheels and, at the same time, compensate for steering action on turns.

Constant Velocity Joints

To solve this problem, special universal joints known as "constant velocity" types were developed, Fig. 46-14. In the example shown, rolling balls in curved grooves are utilized to obtain uniform motion. The balls, which are the driving contact, move laterally as the joint rotates. This permits the point of driving contact between the two halves of the coupling to remain in a plane which bisects the angle between the two shafts. By this means, the fluctuation in speed is avoided.

In a later development, Fig. 46-15, two yoke and cross universal joints are placed adjacent and connected to achieve the desired results.

Transfer Cases

When a vehicle is driven by both front and rear wheels, it is necessary to provide a sort of power takeoff to drive both axles. This auxiliary device is known as a transfer case, Fig. 46-16. It is customary

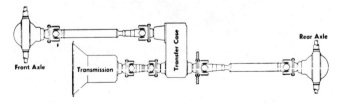

Fig. 46-16. *Engine torque goes from transmission to transfer case where it is applied to drive shafts extending to each driving axle.*

to provide a shifting device on such units so that the front drive can be disconnected if desired.

As the angularity of the drive shafts between front and rear wheels changes constantly, the transfer case

is positioned in the best possible compromise to serve both axles. Each drive shaft is fitted with a slip joint to accommodate changes in distance between axles and transfer case as the wheels move up and down. See Fig. 46-16.

Center Bearings

In the case of long trucks and some passenger automobiles, the drive shaft is divided into two lengths and a supporting "center bearing" is utilized, Figs. 46-17 and 46-18.

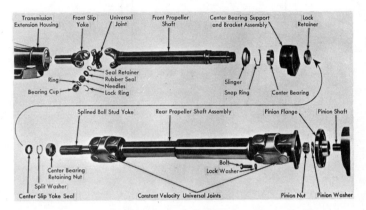

Fig. 46-17. *On applications having two drive shafts, a center bearing usually supports front drive shaft. Bearing is mounted in rubber to insulate it from frame.*

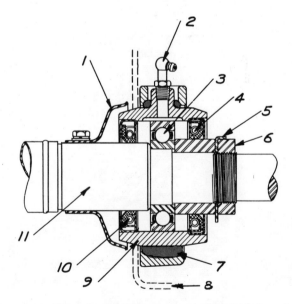

Fig. 46-18. *Typical center bearing assembly includes: 1—Dust shield. 2—Lubricator. 3—Bearing. 4—Rear oil seal. 5—Lock washer. 6—Retaining nut. 7—Insulator. 8—Cross frame. 9—Housing. 10—Front oil seal. 11—Forward drive shaft.*

This type of bearing is used to stabilize the shaft and reduce vibration and "whip." The whip comes from centrifugal force aided by any unbalance that may exist in the shaft. For this reason, drive shafts are carefully balanced.

Differentials and Axles

Early automobiles were driven by means of belts or ropes around pulleys mounted on the driving wheels and engine shaft or transmission shaft. Because there always was some slippage of the belts, one wheel could rotate faster than the other when turning a corner.

When belts proved unsatisfactory, the builders borrowed an idea from bicycle design and applied

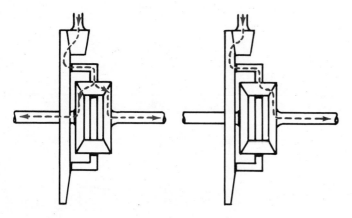

Fig. 46-19. Differential gearing shown in diagrammatical view indicates flow of power: (left) straight ahead; (right) during left turn.

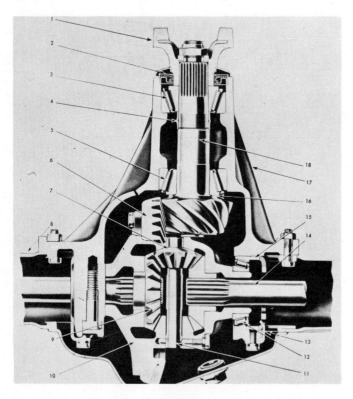

Fig. 46-20. Typical rear axle-differential setup consists of: 1—Pinion drive flange. 2—Oil seal. 3—Front pinion bearing. 4—Pinion bearing spacer. 5—Rear pinion bearing. 6—Ring gear. 7—Differential pinion. 8—Axle housing. 9—Differential side gear. 10—Case. 11—Differential pinion shaft. 12—Differential side bearing. 13—Adjusting sleeve lock. 14—Axle shaft. 15—Adjusting sleeve. 16—Pinion shim. 17—Carrier. 18—Drive pinion.

sprockets and chains. This was a positive driving arrangement, so it was necessary to provide differential gearing to permit one driving wheel to turn faster than the other, Fig. 46-19.

Differential Gears

In a typical differential gear arrangement, Fig. 46-20, the pinion gear turns the ring gear and the differential case attached to it. The differential pinion gears mounted in the case, mesh with the differential side gears that are splined to the rear axles shafts.

In straight ahead operation, the ring gear and differential case (with enclosed differential pinion gears and side gears) rotate as a unit. The differential pinion gears do not turn about their own axis, but apply equal effort to each of the differential side gears and axle shafts.

On turns, the resistance against the rotation of one axle increases as the wheels turn at different speeds. This causes the differential pinion gears to turn on their own axis and roll around the differential side gear on the reluctant one of the two axles.

This action allows the reluctant axle to slow down or stand still, causing a corresponding increase in the speed of rotation of the other axle. If one axle does not turn at all, the other axle will turn at almost twice the normal speed. Thus, it is possible for the drive wheels to turn at unequal speeds while the same amount of power is applied to both of them.

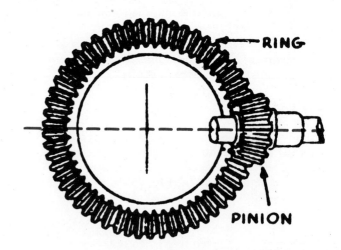

Fig. 46-21. Straight bevel ring gear and pinion design features bevel-shaped teeth with drive pinion positioned in line with center of ring gear.

Bevel Gears

Pinion and ring gears have different tooth designs. The original type was known as a "straight bevel." The teeth were straight like a spur gear, Fig. 46-21.

Another type is known as a "spiral bevel." In this case, the teeth are curved, Fig. 46-22, and operate

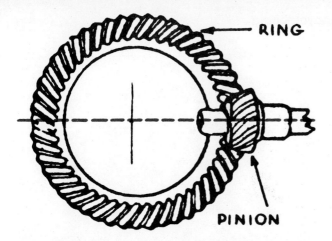

Fig. 46-22. Spiral bevel ring gear and pinion design incorporates curved teeth which provide greater surface contact. Pinion shaft bisects ring gear.

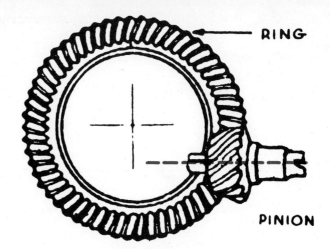

Fig. 46-23. Hypoid type ring gear and pinion also has curved teeth, but drive pinion shaft is located below center of ring gear.

more quietly than the straight bevel because the teeth make a sliding contact. The spiral bevel ring gear and pinion setup is stronger because more than one tooth is in contact at all times.

The differential assembly is mounted either on a differential carrier, Fig. 46-24, or directly in the rear axle housing, Fig. 46-25. In all cases, there is a bearing on each side of the assembly which provides a

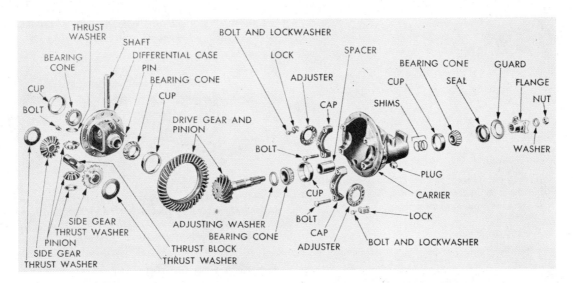

Fig. 46-24. Exploded view of hypoid type differential assembly shows "carrier" arrangement in which differential is assembled and adjusted, then installed in axle housing.

Hypoid Gears

Note that the pinion shaft in both Figs. 46-21 and 46-22 is in line with the center of the ring gear. Fig. 46-23 shows a hypoid gear with the pinion shaft below the center of the ring gear. The advantage of this design is that it allows the drive shaft to be placed lower to permit lowering the floor of the automobile body.

Differential Mounting

Passenger car differentials ordinarily use two differential pinions on a straight shaft. The exploded illustration, Fig. 46-24, shows the differential case and gears. Heavy-duty differentials used on trucks often have a four pinion differential gearing.

means of adjustment to move the ring gear toward or away from the pinion gear. See Fig. 46-26.

When the setting is completed, the bearings are locked in place by means of heavy saddles, Figs. 46-26 and 46-27. The retaining bolts or screws are secured by lock washers or wiring.

Pinion Mounting

The drive pinion which meshes with the ring gear is also mounted on bearings in the pinion carrier or axle housing, Fig. 46-28. If the torque tube type of drive is used, the mounting is quite similar. Or, instead of using a pair of opposed tapered roller bearings, some constructions consist of a roller bearing and a ball bearing.

Thrust Loads

Whatever the construction, the bearings must prevent any endwise motion of the pinion shaft. In the case of the opposed angular roller bearings, the bearings themselves handle both radial and thrust loads. In the case of the ball bearing-roller bearing setup, the ball bearing is a combination radial and thrust design.

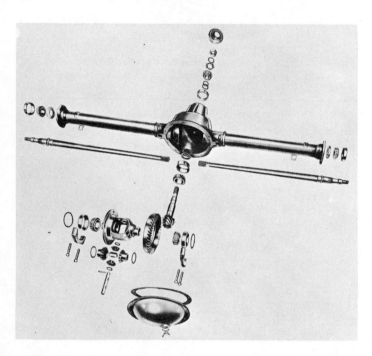

Fig. 46-25. In this rear axle setup, the parts and subassemblies must be installed in the axle housing. They are then adjusted and torqued to specifications.

Fig. 46-26. Rigid bearings and large diameter adjusters are provided on each side to permit adjustment of ring gear-to-pinion tooth contact.

Fig. 46-27. Bearing adjusters are secured by heavy saddles which are tightened in place after adjustment is completed. Special locks keep adjusters from turning.

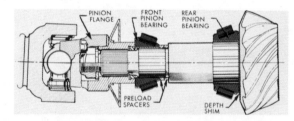

Fig. 46-28. Most drive pinion assemblies have two opposed tapered roller bearings which are preloaded by applying light torque to pinion nut.

Bearing Preloading

Many car manufacturers specify "preloading" of drive pinion bearings. In some cases, this is done by slight overtightening of the bearing adjustments. In other cases, it is accomplished by the use of a special bearing spacer or sleeve, Fig. 46-29. The sleeve between the two bearings is made with a weakened section. After installation, the bearings are pulled together until the sleeve distorts, Fig. 46-30.

Equally important, there should be no radial movement of the pinion. In heavy-duty units, the pinion is often "straddle mounted." That is, there is a bearing on each side of the pinion, Fig. 46-31.

Limited Slip Differentials

Limited slip differentials are a popular option on a number of different makes of automobiles under a number of different names. Some use cone clutches, and others use disc clutches to direct power flow to the axle of the wheel having the best traction. At the same time, less power is applied to the wheel that tends to slip so better traction is obtained for both driving wheels.

Fig. 46-29. Pinion shaft and bearing assembly is shown in proper sequence of assembly. Note special preload bushing at center.

Fig. 46-30. A new bearing spacer sleeve is compared with a distorted one. Obviously, a new sleeve must be installed each time assembly is taken apart and reassembled.

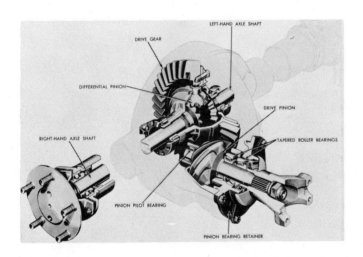

Fig. 46-31. Drive pinion on heavy-duty applications is straddle-mounted, that is: supported by bearings on both sides of pinion gear.

One commonly used limited slip design has beveled ends on the differential pinion shafts and corresponding "ramps" cut in the shaft openings of the differential case, Figs. 46-32 and 46-33. With this construction, the differential pinions and pinion shafts float between the differential side gears and the case. When power is applied, the ramps tend to force the side gears apart and apply pressure to the clutch assembly having the best traction.

Another popular limited slip differential utilizes cone clutches that are preloaded with six springs. The

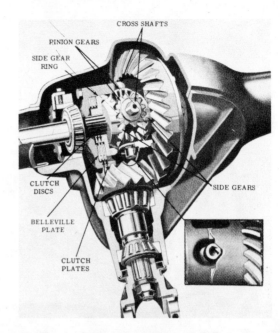

Fig. 46-32. Typical limited slip differential, utilizes disc clutches and notched case for differential pinion shaft which is shaped to fit notches.

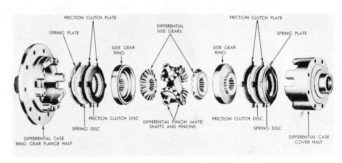

Fig. 46-33. Exploded view of limited slip differential illustrates location and arrangement of friction clutch plates.

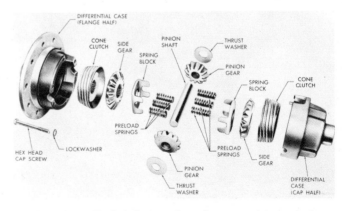

Fig. 46-34. Exploded view of another type of limited slip unit shows cone clutches and preload spring construction.

frictional surface of the cones contain a coarse spiral thread that provides passages for the flow of lubricant, Fig. 46-34. In straight ahead operation, the pressure of the springs and separating force created between

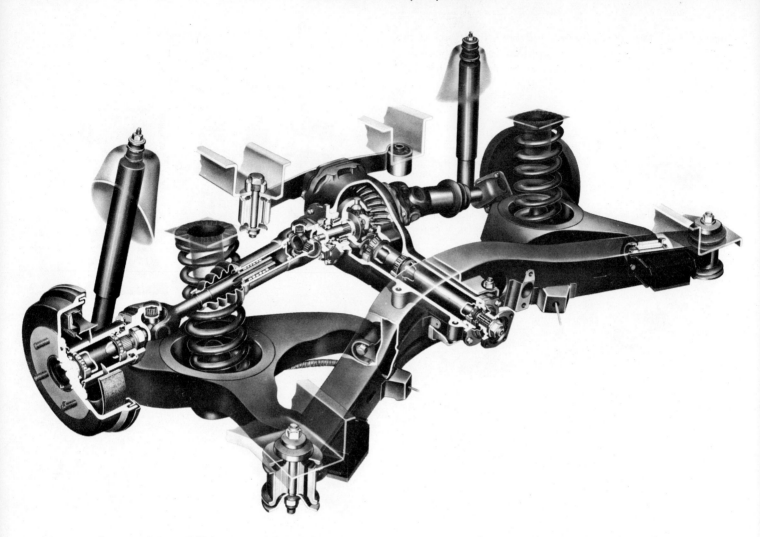

Japanese Datsun 1800 has semi-trailing type rear suspension. Differential is fixed to underside of body to minimize vertical motion of propeller shaft. Rear wheel drive shafts are spline type; drum brakes and ball bearings are used.

the pinion gears and side gears forces the clutch cones against the case. On turns, the axles are automatically unlocked by differential action, overcoming the spring load on the clutch cones and permitting them to over-run.

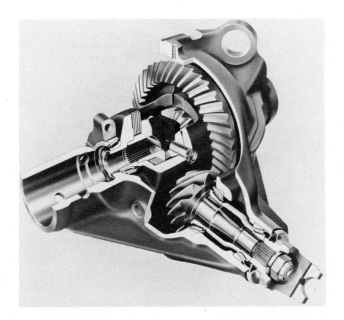

Fig. 46-35. Latest developments in limited slip differentials permit use of fewer parts. In this unit, S-shaped spring preloads disc clutches.

Another disc clutch type of limited slip differential is shown in Fig. 46-35. In this unit, an S-shaped spring is used to preload the differential side gears.

Planetary Differentials

A planetary differential is used on certain front wheel drive cars to provide an axle gear package of minimum width alongside the engine. The Oldsmobile Toronado, for example, couples a spiral bevel ring gear with a spiral bevel drive pinion gear that is straddle mounted by two tapered roller bearings, Fig. 46-36. Note that during straight ahead driving, the ring gear, planet pinions and sun gear rotate as a unit, Fig. 46-37. On turns, the planet gears and sun gear rotate within the ring gear and allow the drive axles to rotate at different speeds.

Two-Speed, Double Reduction Axles

Other variations in differential design include "two-speed" and "double reduction." These units have been made in various arrangements and types.

A double reduction differential which uses a hypoid pinion meshed with a comparatively small gear for primary reduction is shown in Fig. 46-38. The ring gear shaft is fitted with two helical gears which mesh with a like pair attached to the axle shafts to accomplish the secondary reduction.

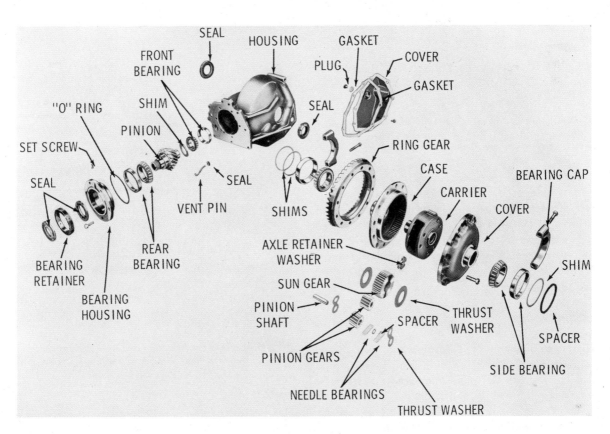

Fig. 46-36. Oldsmobile Toronado front wheel drive cars have a specially designed planetary differential mounted along left side of engine.

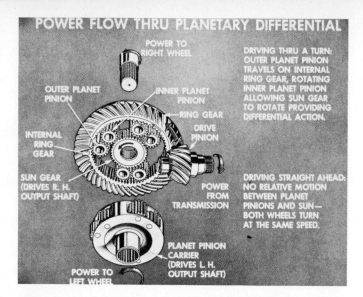

POWER TO RIGHT WHEEL

DRIVING THRU A TURN: OUTER PLANET PINION TRAVELS ON INTERNAL RING GEAR, ROTATING INNER PLANET PINION ALLOWING SUN GEAR TO ROTATE PROVIDING DIFFERENTIAL ACTION.

OUTER PLANET PINION

INNER PLANET PINION

RING GEAR

INTERNAL RING GEAR

DRIVE PINION

SUN GEAR (DRIVES R. H. OUTPUT SHAFT)

POWER FROM TRANSMISSION

POWER TO LEFT WHEEL

DRIVING STRAIGHT AHEAD: NO RELATIVE MOTION BETWEEN PLANET PINIONS AND SUN— BOTH WHEELS TURN AT THE SAME SPEED.

PLANET PINION CARRIER (DRIVES L. H. OUTPUT SHAFT)

Fig. 46-37. Power flow is shown in planetary differential used on Oldsmobile Toronado. Note that sun gear drives right output shaft; planet pinion carrier drives left output shaft.

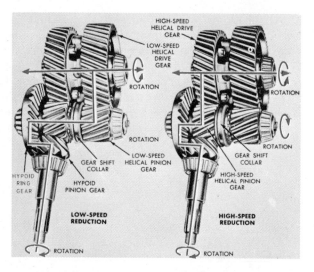

HIGH-SPEED HELICAL DRIVE GEAR

LOW-SPEED HELICAL DRIVE GEAR

ROTATION

ROTATION

ROTATION

ROTATION

HYPOID RING GEAR

GEAR SHIFT COLLAR

HYPOID PINION GEAR

LOW-SPEED HELICAL PINION GEAR

GEAR SHIFT COLLAR

HIGH-SPEED HELICAL PINION GEAR

LOW-SPEED REDUCTION

HIGH-SPEED REDUCTION

ROTATION

ROTATION

Fig. 46-38. Power flow is traced in a two-speed, double-reduction rear axle, first in low-speed then in high.

Fig. 46-39 illustrates one type of two-speed design in which planetary gearing is used. (For a full explanation of planetary gearing, see the transmission section of this text.) A means of shifting these axles is usually provided by an electrically operated shift unit which is controlled by the operator of the vehicle. In some cases, both types are combined and called "two-speed, double-reduction" axles.

Full-Floating Axles

In addition to different types of gearing, axles used for driving vehicles are known as "full-floating," and "semi-floating." These designations have to do with the duties imposed on the axle shaft. In the full-floating type, the axle shaft does not carry any of the car weight. Its sole duty is to propel the vehicle.

A typical full-floating axle construction is shown in Fig. 46-40. Note that the axle housing is fitted with

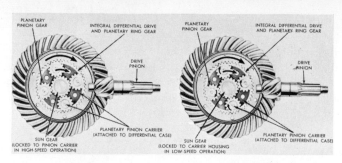

PLANETARY PINION GEAR

INTEGRAL DIFFERENTIAL DRIVE AND PLANETARY RING GEAR

DRIVE PINION

PLANETARY PINION GEAR

INTEGRAL DIFFERENTIAL DRIVE AND PLANETARY RING GEAR

DRIVE PINION

SUN GEAR (LOCKED TO PINION CARRIER IN HIGH-SPEED OPERATION)

PLANETARY PINION CARRIER (ATTACHED TO DIFFERENTIAL CASE)

SUN GEAR (LOCKED TO CARRIER HOUSING IN LOW-SPEED OPERATION)

PLANETARY PINION CARRIER (ATTACHED TO DIFFERENTIAL CASE)

Fig. 46-39. Power flow is indicated in a planetary two-speed rear axle: (left) planetary unit in high; (right) planetary unit in low.

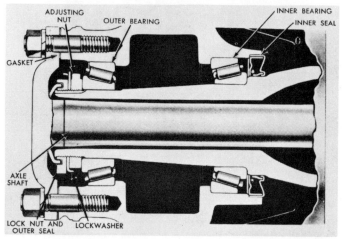

ADJUSTING NUT

OUTER BEARING

INNER BEARING

INNER SEAL

GASKET

AXLE SHAFT

LOCK NUT AND OUTER SEAL

LOCKWASHER

Fig. 46-40. Full-floating rear axle and hub is used in truck applications. Weight of vehicle rests on roller bearings mounted in axle housing.

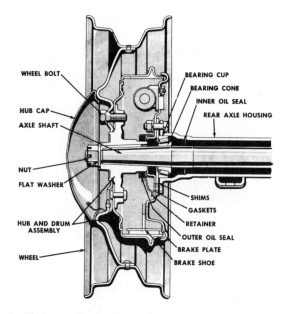

WHEEL BOLT

HUB CAP

AXLE SHAFT

NUT

FLAT WASHER

HUB AND DRUM ASSEMBLY

WHEEL

BEARING CUP

BEARING CONE

INNER OIL SEAL

REAR AXLE HOUSING

SHIMS

GASKETS

RETAINER

OUTER OIL SEAL

BRAKE PLATE

BRAKE SHOE

Fig. 46-41. This semi-floating rear axle design is used on Chrysler-built cars earlier than 1965. Weight of car rests on axle shafts and wheel bearings.

two roller bearings which carry the weight of the vehicle. The axle shaft is upset or flanged on the outer end and bolted to the hub. A full-floating axle can be removed without disturbing the wheel.

Semi-Floating Axles

In a semi-floating axle, a bearing is placed between the axle shaft and axle housing, Fig. 46-41. Thus, the axle supports the weight of the vehicle in addition to being the means of propulsion. In some cases, a semi-floating axle shaft is tapered at the outer end to fit into a tapered hub. It is also keyed in place and held by a nut on the threaded end of the axle shaft. To remove the hub from this type of axle, it is usually necessary to use a wheel puller.

Semi-floating designs are also shown in Figs. 46-42 and 46-43. In these cars, the hub is bolted to the flanged end of the axle shaft instead of being keyed. A straight, tapered roller or ball bearing is used on this axle shaft within the axle housing.

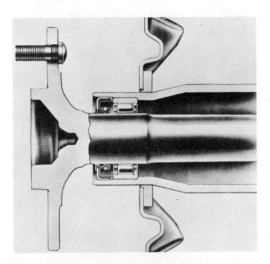

Fig. 46-42. Another semi-floating axle design, featured on most General Motors cars, has flanged outer end to which wheel hub is attached by lug nuts or bolts.

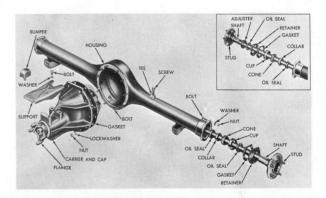

Fig. 46-43. Flanged-type semi-floating rear axle is used on late model Chrysler-built cars. Some are equipped with ball bearings, others with tapered roller bearings.

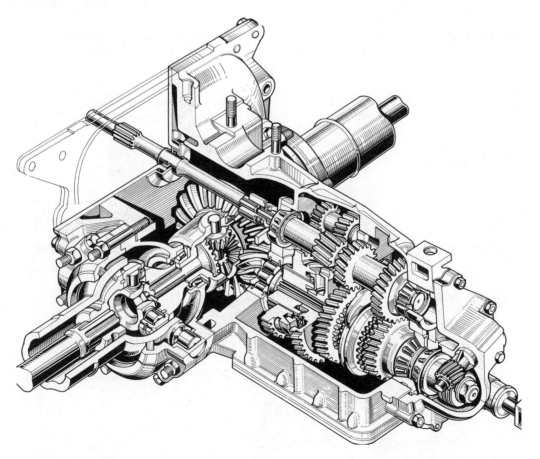

Fig. 46-44. Swing-type rear axles are used on Renault cars. In this design, inner end of each drive axle is fitted with a universal joint, outer end is not.

Independently Suspended Wheels

Independently suspended rear wheels may be hung on swing axles, Fig. 46-44, or on axle shafts using two universal joints (De Dion system), Fig. 46-45. One advantage of De Dion construction is that the weight of the differential is carried on the springs. On cars with swing axles _ unlike De Dion suspension _ the tread of the rear wheels varies as the wheels rise

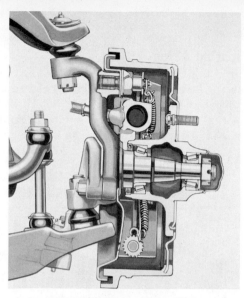

Fig. 46-46. Generally, passenger car front wheels have tapered roller bearings mated to races installed in both sides of hub and adjusted by a spindle nut.

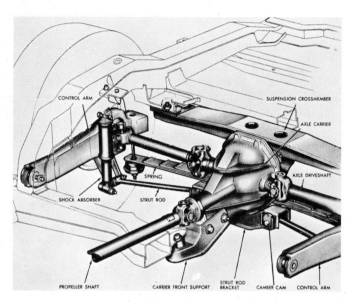

Fig. 46-45. Corvette rear suspension and drive line components illustrate De Dion drive axle setup. In this concept, two universal joints are used on each drive axle.

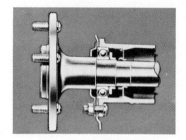

Fig. 46-47. Lighter vehicles sometimes have ball bearing assemblies installed on rear axle shafts and seated against a shoulder in axle housing.

Fig. 46-48. This cutaway view of Ford tractor differential and rear axle arrangement, illustrates similarity of construction between tractor and automobile drive line components.

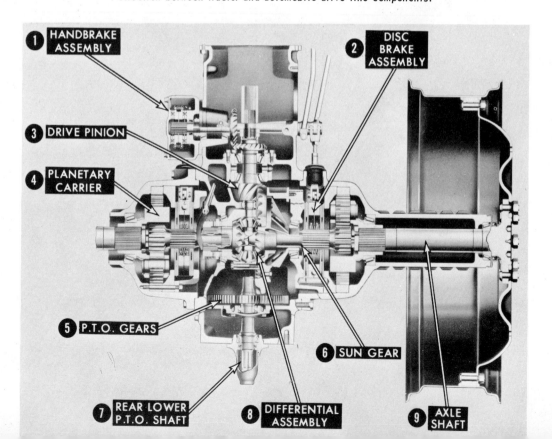

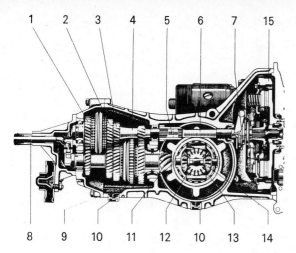

Fig. 46-49. Volkswagen transaxle features; 1—4th speed gears; 2—3rd speed gears; 3—2nd speed gears; 4—main drive shaft, front; 5—reverse gear; 6—main drive shaft rear; 7—clutch release bearing; 8—transmission shift lever; 9—1st speed gears; 10—oil drain plugs; 11—drive pinion; 12—differential side gear; 13—differential housing; 14—differential pinion; 15—flywheel.

and fall. In some cases, the rear wheels may be toed-in or toed-out slightly, depending upon the angles of the axle supporting members.

Independent rear wheel suspension is popular in European-built automobiles, notably Volkswagen and Renault. U. S.-built automobiles having independent rear wheel suspension include Corvair, Corvette and early Pontiac Tempests.

The Oldsmobile Toronado and Cadillac Eldorado front wheel drive cars suspend the front wheels on drive shafts utilizing inner and outer universal joints on each side. See Fig. 46-14.

Wheel Bearings

Each front wheel hub ordinarily uses a pair of roller bearings, Fig. 46-46. The front wheels on some older cars, Chevrolet and Buick for example, are fitted with ball bearings. Straight and tapered roller bearings are used in the rear wheel assemblies of medium weight and heavier passenger cars, Figs. 46-42 and 46-43. Ball bearings are used in the rear wheels of lighter vehicles, Fig. 46-47.

The wheel bearings, axle assemblies, differentials and gearing of wheel type farm and industrial tractors are quite similar to those used in automobiles and trucks. This similarity of design and construction is shown in Fig. 46-48. Service procedures and lubrication are also quite similar.

Fig. 46-50. Corvair transaxle arrangement is another example of how transmission and differential are coupled to form compact rear engine drive setup.

625

Transaxles

When the transmission and rear axle differential are combined in one unit, it is called a "transaxle." Examples of this gear arrangement are shown in Figs. 46-49 and 46-50. In rear engine cars, it is customary to bolt the transaxle directly to the engine.

This method of construction has the advantage of providing an extremely rigid unit of engine and drive components. Misalignment is generally avoided and compactness is achieved. By mounting the differential to the frame in this manner, the weight of the differential assembly is above and supported by the car springs, and better riding qualities are obtained.

Quiz - Drive Line, Universal Joints, Differential

1. On acceleration, engine torque will cause the drive pinion shaft to:
   a. Dip.　　　b. Raise.
   c. Remain in the same plane.
2. Driving force is transmitted to the front of the rear springs on cars equipped with:
   a. Hotchkiss drive.
   b. Torque tube drive.
   c. Control arm drive.
3. Does the length of the drive shaft change while the car is being driven?
4. What is the purpose of a slip joint in the drive line?
5. Why are center bearings used on two-piece drive shafts?
   a. To support the front shaft.
   b. To support the rear shaft.
   c. To support the drive pinion.
6. With a conventional differential, does the wheel having better traction tend to turn faster than the wheel having poor traction?
7. Does a spiral bevel gear or a hypoid gear have the drive pinion shaft below the center of the ring gear?
8. Can the differential ring gear be moved toward and away from the drive pinion gear?
9. Can the drive pinion gear be raised or lowered vertically with regard to the ring gear?
10. What is meant by the term "preloading" a bearing?
11. With a limited slip differential, does the wheel having better traction turn faster than the wheel having poor traction?
12. With full-floating rear axles, the weight of the car is carried by:
    a. Axles.
    b. Control arms.
    c. Bearings and axle housing.
13. With semi-floating rear axles, the weight of the car is carried by:
    a. Axles and bearings.
    b. Control arms.
    c. Axle housing.
14. What is a "swing axle?"
15. How does a De Dion axle differ from a swing axle?
    a. Has no universal joints.
    b. Has one universal joint.
    c. Has two universal joints.
16. Are rear wheels ever toed-in or toed-out?
17. What is meant by "straddle mounting?"
18. Why are constant velocity joints necessary?
19. Describe the difference between a two-speed differential and a double-reduction differential?
20. Does rear wheel tread ever vary on an automobile?

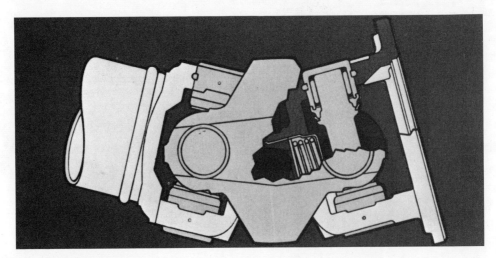

Oldsmobile rear joints for 1971-72 are constant velocity type. When disassembling joint, nylon retainer is sheared and metal retaining rings must be installed.

DRIVE LINE
SERVICE

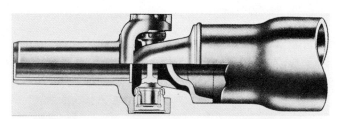

Fig. 47-1.Cross section of cross and roller universal joint, shows precise positioning of cross in bearing cups to maintain balance.

It readily can be seen that the constantly fluctuating speed of the drive shaft will cause vibration. Add to this any lack of rotating balance, and the result is serious vibration; serious enough in some cases to shake the entire automobile and cause discomfort to the passengers.

For example, a one-ounce weight placed on the drive shaft two inches from the center of rotation will exert a force of 50 lbs. at 3750 rpm. At that speed, this force would be exerted in opposite directions 62 1/2 times per second, causing a heavy vibration.

Even when the drive shaft is balanced, it must be mounted properly to run true on the vehicle. The flanges to which the universal joints are bolted must be machined true, and the spline machining must be accurate. From this example, it is easy to see why all drive shafts must be balanced, properly mounted assemblies with all working parts lubricated by a special universal joint lubricant. On cross and roller joints, the cross, or spider, must be centered within the bearing cups, Fig. 47-1. On ball and trunnion joints, it is necessary to measure carefully when replacing the cross pin, Fig. 47-2. This pin must be centered within .006 in. in the shaft end. In addition, all bolts, washers, nuts, etc., used to assemble the joints and flanges must be the same weight.

Drive Shaft Requirements

Drive shafts, therefore, must be:
1. Carefully and accurately manufactured.
2. Correctly assembled.
3. Straight.
4. Balanced.
5. Properly mounted in the automobile.
6. Frequently checked.

Even when all these things are done, the shaft still can get out of balance when in use. Journal cross bearings can wear. Splines wear. Bolts and keys get loose. The drive shaft can become bent. Balance weights can fall off. Lubricant becomes misplaced or leaks out. Sometimes a drive shaft is thrown out of balance by careless spraying of undercoating.

Fig. 47-2. Special driving tool and pedestal (1), are used to center pin in drive shaft to avoid vibration.

New developments in universal joint design and the use of constant velocity joints have eliminated the need for regular maintenance service, Fig. 47-3. The joints are prelubricated and sealed at the time of manufacture. However, the manufacturer does specify frequent inspections for universal joint wear or lubricant leakage.

Universal Joint Service

If a universal joint becomes worn or noisy, service the drive shaft. Mark the yokes and universal joints to aid in reassembly, then remove the drive shaft. If a double drive shaft is used, handle it with care to avoid jamming the joints, and keep it in a relatively straight line. Clamp the drive shaft in a vise by the universal joint yoke. Disassemble and inspect the joints for roughness, ripples or pitting. Constant

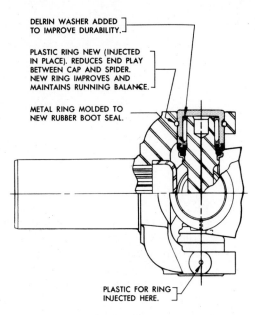

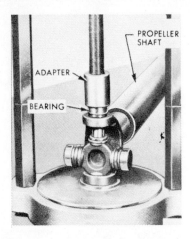

Fig. 47-3. Improvements in universal joint design include tapered needle bearings for better load distribution.

Fig. 47-5. A bench vise or press can be used to install kit parts in drive shaft. Bearing cups must be locked in place on cross.

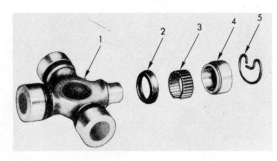

Fig. 47-4. Repair kit for typical cross and roller universal joint includes: 1—Cross. 2—Seal. 3—Bearing rollers. 4—Bearing cup. 5—Locking clip.

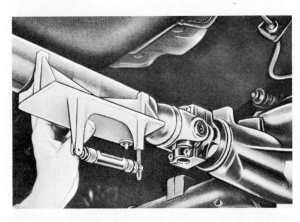

Fig. 47-6. A protractor will reveal rear universal joint angle, which is difference between drive shaft angle and tilt of differential housing.

Fig. 47-7. If an adjustment of rear universal joint angle is necessary, add wedges or shims to rear spring to tilt differential housing.

velocity joints, in particular, require special service equipment to do the job right. If wear or damage is evident, install a complete service kit, Fig. 47-4.

Reassemble drive shaft carefully, Fig. 47-5, to maintain balance, and see that the newly installed joints operate freely in all directions. Tighten the attaching bolts to the proper torque. Check the angularity of the drive shaft against the manufacturer's specifications, Fig. 47-6.

Angularity can be checked with a protractor or cable-and-bracket setup. With this gauge, a spring-loaded steel cable is stretched between the front of the chassis and the differential carrier. If the angle is correct, this cable will clear the underside of the pinion flange by a given amount. If not, shims or wedges must be added to the rear springs, Fig. 47-7.

Center Bearing Service

The center bearing is usually attached to a cross member mounted between the left and right side rails of the frame. Center bearings on older models are equipped with lubrication fittings. Most late models have plugs or access points to provide for special lubrication attachments to lubricate the bearing. If service is required, the center support and bearing can be disassembled by use of a special puller, Fig. 47-8.

Differential Requirements

Differentials are heavy-duty, precision-produced, mated-gear assemblies that generally do not require maintenance other than occasional lubricant changes. Because of the tremendous power transmitted through the differential assembly, the pressures involved are

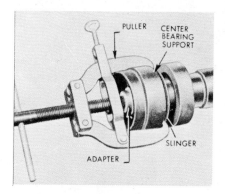

Fig. 47-8. With drive shaft held in vise, remove retaining nut and pull bearing from machined surface of shaft.

exceptionally high. The pressures are so high that considerable distortion of the heavy and, in most cases, hardened parts is bound to occur, Fig. 47-9. Because of the high standards of quietness demanded, adjustments must be made to extremely close dimensions and distortion under stress held to a minimum.

The differential housing, or case, is attached to the ring gear, and the entire propelling force is transmitted through this attachment. This calls for a tight union of parts, and several methods of assembly are used: cold riveting, hot riveting, bolts or cap screws. In any case, it is essential that the size of the holes is accurate, and that the rivet or bolts are a tight fit in the holes.

Fig. 47-9. Differential drive pinion and ring gear are mated to each other by lapping process to obtain proper contact of gear teeth.

Bolt Attachment

If the ring gear is bolted to the case, the bolts are machined to an accurate diameter and the holes are drilled and reamed to correct size for a tight fit. The nuts on the bolts are then drawn up tightly and securely locked, Fig. 47-10.

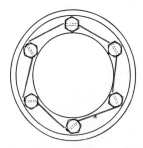

Fig. 47-10. Note that ring of cap screws is wired so that tension of lock wire is exerted in direction of tightening.

If cap screws are used, the holes in the ring gear are threaded before the gear is hardened. The threads on the cap screw do not extend into the holes in the differential case, and the cap screw often has a shoulder between the threads and the head. This shoulder is finished to a size that fits tightly in the holes in the differential case.

Troubles and Remedies

Service problems are usually limited to lubricant leakage at the drive pinion oil seal or noisy operation of the differential.

To replace the drive pinion oil seal:
1. Disconnect rear universal joint.
2. Remove drive pinion flange nut, washer and flange.
3. Use a special seal puller to remove pinion oil seal.

Reassemble in reverse order, but observe the following precautions:
1. Install oil seal with sealing lip facing lubricant.
2. Coat OD of seal body with nonhardening sealing compound.
3. Use correct driving tool to bottom seal against shoulder in rear axle housing.
4. Make sure machined bearing surface of pinion flange is not worn, scored or nicked in area where it rotates against seal.
5. Tighten drive pinion nut to original position, plus 1/8 turn to preload pinion bearings.
6. Refill rear axle housing to correct level with recommended lubricant, Fig. 47-11.

Noisy operation of a differential unit is usually caused by worn or damaged gears or bearings. However, a thorough test should be made to pinpoint where the noise is coming from: rear axle assembly; rough road surface; under-inflated tires, or tires with un-evenly worn tread; front or rear bearings; engine or transmission. Noises telegraph to other parts of the car, so establishing the source of the noise is of first importance.

If the differential assembly is noisy, check for: low level of lubricant in rear axle housing; excessive backlash between teeth of the drive pinion gear and ring gear; looseness of pinion bearings. Removal and complete disassembly of the differential unit is probably called for.

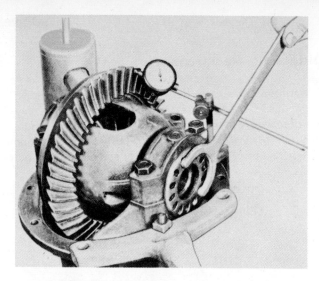

Fig. 47-12. Special adjusting tools are provided to set correct position of ring gear and preload of differential side bearings.

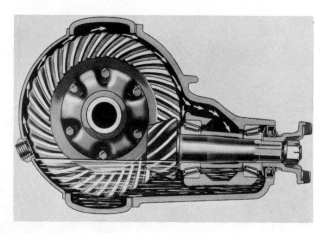

Fig. 47-11. Rotation of ring gear distributes lubricant to all gears and bearings, if lubricant level is maintained at lower edge of filler hole.

Inspection

When disassembling the differential, be sure to mark mating parts so that they can be reassembled on the correct side and in the proper position. For example, mark the two halves of the differential case, the two bearing adjusters, etc. Since the gears and bearings are a press fit, in many cases, avoid the use of hammers and drifts. Use a suitable press or puller to prevent chipping of hardened parts and distortion of other parts.

After the parts have been disassembled and thoroughly cleaned, carefully inspect them for scuffed surfaces, cracks, warpage or any other visible defects. If the surfaces of the gear teeth are scratched or scuffed, the gears must be replaced. If there are any cracks visible in the differential case, it should be replaced. If the differential pinion bushings or shaft are worn or loose, new parts are required.

Pay particular attention to the pinion shaft and differential side bearings and the shaft or housings on which, and in which, the bearings seat. The inside cone of the bearings must be a tight fit on the shaft or housing upon which they are mounted. The outer race or cone must be a snug fit in the housing in which it seats. No looseness can be tolerated. The bearings must not show any indication of wear. The races and rollers or balls and cups must be absolutely smooth and polished on the contact surfaces.

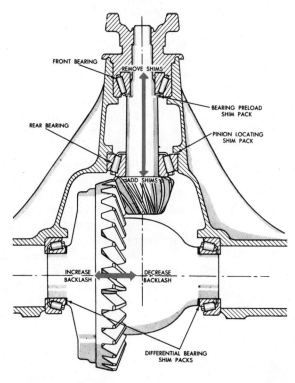

Fig. 47-13. Other differential designs demand placement of shims under side bearings, to position ring gear for correct tooth contact.

Hardened antifriction bearings are used. No other type of bearing could stand the speeds and pressures and continue to maintain correct alignment of the gears. Such high standards of manufacture deserve equally high standards of careful work and adjustment when repairs are made.

Reassembly and Adjustment

When reassembling, use new shims, spacers, washers, gaskets and oil seals. Lock all cap screws in place, either by locking strips or soft steel wire, Fig. 47-10. Thoroughly clean the inside of the housing of all grease and oil to make sure that no metal chips or abrasive material is left inside to be circulated by the lubricant.

The manufacturer's instructions concerning whether or not the bearings are to be preloaded, and how much, are needed for proper assembly. Also required is the method of adjusting gear contact by measurement with special gauges or micrometers. Necessary, too, are specifications on the amount of torque to be applied to all the bolts and nuts. When ball bearings are used, make sure that the thrust side of the bearing is correctly placed to handle endwise thrust in the proper direction.

Two adjustments can be made which will affect tooth contact pattern: backlash and the position of the drive pinion in relation to the ring gear.

Backlash is adjusted by means of side bearing ad-

justers, Fig. 47-12, or bearing adjusting shims, Fig. 47-13, which move the entire case and ring gear assembly closer to, or farther from, the drive pinion. To increase backlash, remove shims from ring gear side and install them on pinion side. To reduce backlash, reverse this procedure.

The position of the drive pinion is adjusted by increasing or decreasing the shim thickness between the pinion head and the inner face of the rear pinion bearing, Fig. 47-13. Adding shims will move it closer to the center line of the ring gear; removing shims will move the pinion farther away, Fig. 47-14.

While specifications for these adjustments are usually available, in an emergency adjust the bearings so that there is no perceptible movement of the shaft, yet no bind in the bearing. Check the tooth contact with red lead and oil, and move the pinion gear and

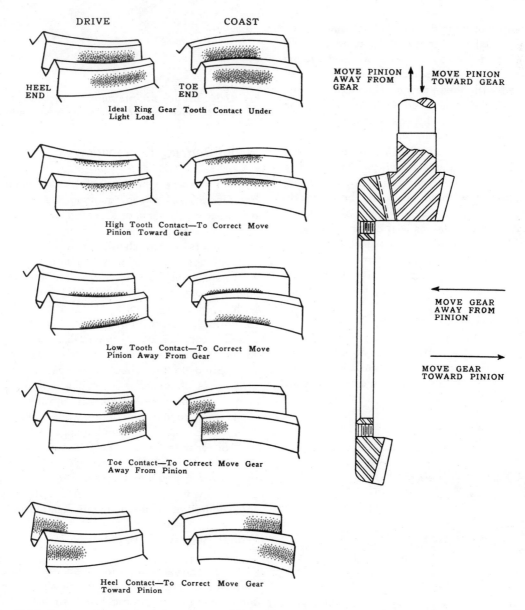

Fig. 47-14. Pattern of ring gear tooth contact is shown along with corrective steps required to provide ideal contact.

ring gear experimentally until the proper contact is obtained, Fig. 47-14. Tighten all bolts and nuts gradually and equally to reasonable tightness if torque specifications are not available.

Correct adjustment of hypoid gears is of paramount importance because they will often wear excessively without making any noise. There is such a pronounced wiping action between the gear teeth, they can overheat and gall very quickly unless correctly adjusted and lubricated by a special hypoid lubricant.

Gear Lubrication

Proper lubrication is of utmost importance. The straight, bevel, and spur gears were successfully lubricated with a heavy mineral gear oil. When spiral bevel gears were adopted, it was found necessary to add some ingredients to the oil to enable it to withstand the high pressure sliding or wiping action of the gear teeth.

With the adoption of hypoid gears, the sliding action was greatly increased, and previously used straight gear oils and extreme pressure gear oils were found inadequate. Special hypoid lubricants were developed and must be used with these gears. The vehicle manufacturer furnishes specific recommendations for type of lubricant, proper level and frequency of change.

As may be seen from Fig. 47-11, the ring gear acts as a circulating pump to distribute the lubricant over the gear teeth and to the bearings. As the oil is in constant circulation when the vehicle is in motion, any abrasive material or metal chips will be promptly carried to the working surfaces. If abrasive, undue wear of gear teeth and bearings will occur. If a metal chip goes through the gears, it will probably break gear teeth, spring parts out of alignment, or both. Care must be exercised to keep the oil clean before and during refilling.

Transaxle Lubrication

In transaxles, the differential unit is combined with either a manual or automatic transmission. While some types of gearing require an extreme pressure

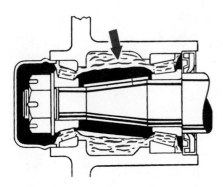

Fig. 47-15. Front wheel bearings should be packed with special short fiber lubricant. Note small reserve supply packed in hub.

type of lubricant, this lubricant is unsuited to other types of gears. Whether or not the transmission and differential are interconnected, there is always the possibility that lubricant will seep or leak from one unit to the other.

For these reasons, it is absolutely essential to follow the manufacturer's instructions when adding to or replacing lubricant in a transaxle.

Fig. 47-16. Bearing packers do a thorough job of forcing grease under pressure through and around rollers.

Wheel Bearing Lubrication

While some wheel bearings are automatically lubricated by oil creeping along the axle shaft from the differential, others are sealed off and require separate lubrication. The manufacturer supplies lubrication charts which should be followed both as to type of lubricant and frequency of lubrication.

Front wheel bearings call for the use of a special wheel bearing grease. This is a short fiber grease with a high melting point. The high melting point is essential because the brake drums surrounding the wheel bearings often get hot. Brake drum temperatures at times approach 700 deg. F. Not all this heat is applied to the wheel bearings, but a considerable amount is absorbed by the hubs. If the grease melts, it may get by the oil seal and ruin the brake linings.

In this connection, front wheel bearings are often overfilled. The hubs and hubcaps should not be packed full of grease. Fig. 47-15 shows a properly packed front wheel hub. The bearings are packed by hand or by use of a bearing packer, Fig. 47-16. A reserve is placed in the hub. When the proper grease is used, this method provides adequate lubrication.

Wheel Bearing Service

A defective rear wheel bearing can be replaced by removal of the rear axle on the side affected. Pull the old bearing from the machined surface of the axle shaft and press on the replacement bearing until it bottoms against a shoulder on the shaft, Fig. 47-17. Always install a new oil seal when an axle shaft is removed.

Front wheel bearings require occasional repacking with grease. Remove the old bearings from the hub and

inspect them carefully for wear, score marks, pits, nicks and discoloration from overheating. Replace a faulty bearing and race as an assembly: press old race from hub; clean hub and spindle thoroughly (never add grease - some wheel bearing greases are not com-

Fig. 47-17. A press must be used to force old bearing from rear axle shaft. New bearing should be "bottomed" against shoulder on shaft.

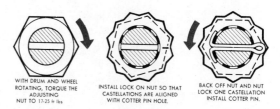

WITH DRUM AND WHEEL ROTATING, TORQUE THE ADJUSTING NUT TO 17-25 ft lbs

INSTALL LOCK ON NUT SO THAT CASTELLATIONS ARE ALIGNED WITH COTTER PIN HOLE.

BACK OFF NUT AND NUT LOCK ONE CASTELLATION INSTALL COTTER PIN.

Fig. 47-18. Spindle nut torque seats wheel bearings, then nut is backed off to hole in spindle. Ford specifications are shown.

patible); install a new race; apply a light coating of wheel bearing grease to wheel spindle and inside of wheel hub, Fig. 47-15. Make certain bearing assemblies are free to creep on spindle of steering knuckle. Pack roller bearings with wheel bearing grease, by hand or by special packer, Fig. 47-16. Install a new oil seal and place wheel on spindle. Adjust spindle nut to provide zero preload or end play according to manufacturer's specifications, Fig. 47-18.

Quiz - Drive Line Service

1. The cross pin in ball and trunnion universal joints used on Chrysler cars should be centered in the end of the drive shaft within:
   a. .006 in.
   b. .012 in.
   c. .06 in.
2. Angularity of the drive shaft is usually checked with a:
   a. Pinion setting gauge.
   b. Universal joint tester.
   c. Protractor.
3. What is the best way to "hold" a drive shaft for servicing?
   a. Clamp drive shaft tube in vise.
   b. Clamp universal joint yoke in vise.
   c. Clamp end of drive shaft in vise.
4. Give three noises that could be incorrectly diagnosed as differential noise.

5. Noisy operation of a differential is usually caused by:
   a. Worn or loose drive pinion bearings.
   b. Rough or maladjusted differential side bearings.
   c. Damaged differential pinion gears.
6. What is the correct level of lubricant in a differential housing?
7. Why do hypoid gears require a special type of lubricant?
8. How can the ring gear and pinion be checked for proper tooth contact?
9. What two methods are used to adjust backlash between the ring gear and pinion?
10. What type of grease is used to lubricate most front wheel bearings:?
    a. Long fiber.
    b. Short fiber.
    c. Extreme pressure.

Paxton Turbocar, entered in Indianapolis 500-mile race, stripped to chassis. Note that the driver and the Pratt and Whitney turbine aircraft engine sit side-by-side.

AUTOMOBILE AIR CONDITIONING

The history of automotive air conditioning, in terms of cooling by refrigeration, dates back to a few buses in the late 1930s and a few thousand Packards in the early 1940s. After World War II, car manufacturers again offered an air conditioning option, but real strides forward in research, development, production and demand came in the late 1950s.

Today, well over 30 percent of the new cars are ordered with factory-installed air conditioning, plus over a half-million "hang-on" units per year. Luxury cars, in particular, are getting a big play with nearly 100 percent application in Cadillac, Lincoln Continental and Chrysler Imperial.

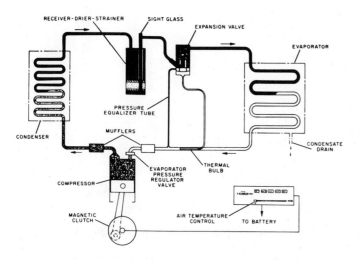

Fig. 48-1. Schematic depicts typical refrigerant circuit in automobile air conditioning system: refrigerant is a liquid in darker high-pressure area; gas in lighter low pressure area.

Principles of Operation

Modern automobile air conditioners are heat transfer units. Their operation is based on the thermal law that fluids absorb heat while changing from a liquid to a gas and give up heat in changing from a gas to a liquid. See Fig. 48-1.

Changes from a liquid to a gas are often accomplished by means of heat. For example, heat causes water to boil and sends a gas or vapor into the air.

This same vapor can be returned to liquid form – water – by cooling and condensation. If a glass of cold water is placed in a warm room, the warm air collects on the outside of the glass, becomes cooler and condenses into water.

This transformation of liquid into gas and gas into liquid occurs at atmospheric pressure. Higher pressures can also be used to reduce a gas to liquid form. "Bottled gas" for the home and liquified petroleum gas (LPG) for engines are examples of the use of pressure for this purpose.

Application of Refrigeration

To apply this thermal law to the process of cooling an automobile, Fig. 48-2, the liquid refrigerant changes into a gas in an evaporator unit where it absorbs heat from the passenger compartment. The heat-laden gas is then drawn into the compressor and discharged under pressure into the condenser where it cools and returns to liquid form as fresh air passes

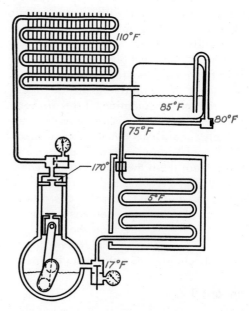

Fig. 48-2. Refrigeration process is based on thermal law that fluids absorb heat while changing from a liquid to a gas, and give up heat in changing from a gas to a liquid. Temperature and pressure are controlling factors.

over the coils carrying the refrigerant. The amount of heat removed in the process can be measured in British thermal units (Btu). One Btu is the amount of heat required to raise the temperature of one pound of water one degree Fahrenheit.

Heat Flow

Heat flow, another consideration in automobile air conditioning, is always from a warmer body to a cooler one. The heat may flow by one or more of three methods: conduction, convection or radiation. For example: Conduction is the effect when one end of an iron rod is in the fire and heat travels along the rod to the other end. Convection is what happens when warm air circulates heat from a furnace to rooms in a house. Radiation is the transfer of heat by heat rays, such as heat from the sun.

Relating this to the automobile, the passenger compartment is subjected to conduction of some heat from the engine, convection of some heat from air circulation, and radiation of heat from the sun. Of the three, radiation is the predominant factor.

It is possible to insulate the body from engine heat. If the windows are closed, the circulation of hot air can be avoided. If the car windows are fitted with special heat filtering glass, radiation from the sun will be reduced. A visor over the windshield also shields out radiation as will paint of a light color, particularly on the roof section. Insulation under the roof and inside the body panels also helps keep the passenger compartment cool and reduces the work load of the air conditioning system.

Comfort Considerations

However, in dealing with human comfort, other things beside actual temperature must be considered:
A. Humidity control.
B. Air movement and circulation.
C. Air filtering, cleaning and purification.
The amount of humidity in the air affects the rate of evaporation of perspiration. If the air contains much moisture, one may feel uncomfortable even if the air is relatively cool. Air circulation is also important because if cool, dry air is moved past a warm body, radiation of heat from the body will increase.

Air filtering, cleaning and purification is also necessary to keep out dust, eliminate smoke and odors, and add to comfort. For these reasons, it is necessary to consider factors other than the actual temperature attained if an air conditioning system can be expected to operate efficiently and satisfactorily.

Refrigerant Types

Further consideration of the refrigerating cycle described earlier will indicate that it is desirable to use a refrigerant that will change easily from a liquid to a gas and back to a liquid. Refrigerant-12, R-12, or Freon-12 (F-12) is used in automobile air conditioning because it is clean, dry and free from contamination as received in factory-filled containers.

R-12, which is actually Dichlorodifluoromethane or CCl_2F_2, is nontoxic, noncorrosive, noninflammable, nonexplosive and odorless under ordinary usage. However, certain safety precautions must be observed, and these will be covered later under service hints.

Another advantage in using only one type of refrigerant in the automobile field is that each refrigerant has its own pressure-temperature relationship. Since the boiling point of any liquid will increase when pressure is exerted on it, a pressure-temperature relationship can be established for R-12 that will aid in making a diagnosis when trouble-shooting the system. See Fig. 48-3.

TEMPERATURE-PRESSURE CHART

* F.	** PSIG	* F.	** PSIG
-21	0	84	90
- 9	5	90	100
1	10	96	110
11	15	102	120
19	20	107	130
25	25	112	140
32	30	117	150
38	35	121	160
44	40	125	170
49	45	129	180
54	50	133	190
59	55	138	200
62	60	141	210
66	65	144	220
70	70	148	230
74	75	152	240
76	80	155	250

* Degrees Fahrenheit.
** Pounds per square inch at gauge, which reads 0 at atmospheric pressure.

Fig. 48-3. Temperature-pressure relationship of Refrigerant-12 is charted to provide key to checking pressure test results. For example: if refrigerant in the evaporator coils is under 30 lbs. pressure, its evaporating temperature is 32 deg. F.; which is effectively low enough to absorb heat from a 72 deg. F. passenger compartment.

Automotive Air Conditioning

All automotive air conditioning systems operate on the same general principles, but differ considerably in detail, design and installation, Fig. 48-1. This diagram symbolizes the various units, shows how they are connected in a typical automotive installation, and indicates the state of the refrigerant (liquid, gas, etc.).

Regardless of type, all automotive air conditioning systems consist of four basic elements: a compressor, a condenser, an expansion valve and an evaporator,

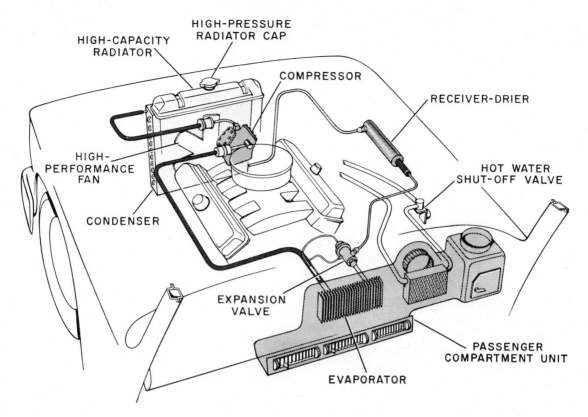

Fig. 48-4. Basic units contained in typical automobile air conditioning system are shown in relative locations. In this installation, car heater is "packaged" with condenser and one blower assembly is used.

Fig. 48-4. Each is equally important to the system. A malfunction of any one of these units will interrupt the heat exchange cycle and disrupt operation of the whole system.

denser where the vapor cools and returns to a liquid state.

All compressors are belt-driven and are of varying capacities to suit each particular engine application. To control the amount of cooling the system will produce, the compressor is fitted with a magnetic

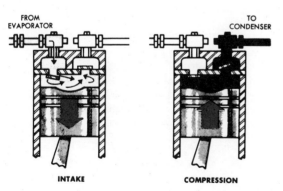

Fig. 48-5. Engine-driven compressor draws in low-pressure refrigerant gas on downstroke of piston, compresses it on upstroke to increase its temperature and pressurize the system.

Compressor

The compressor is needed to compress and concentrate heat molecules in the refrigerant vapor and to circulate the refrigerant through the sealed system, Fig. 48-5. This pumping action places hot refrigerant gas under high pressure and circulates it to the con-

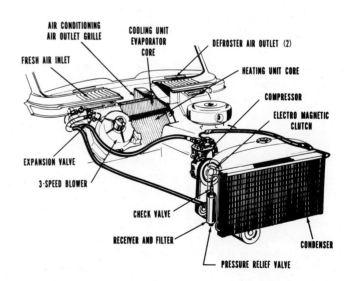

Fig. 48-6. Condenser used in air conditioning systems is a heat exchanger. Hot refrigerant vapor enters top of condenser, cools as it passes through coils and gives up heat to surrounding air, and condenses back to a liquid.

clutch pulley that cuts the compressor in and out of operation. The magnetic clutch is controlled by a thermostatic switch which, generally, has its temperature-sensing bulb inserted in the fins of the evaporator core.

Condenser

The condenser is similar in appearance and function to the radiator in an engine cooling system, Fig. 48-6. In fact, the condenser is placed in front of the radiator where intake air passing through the condenser core removes heat given off by the refrigerant vapor. The vapor cools, condenses and returns to liquid form. This condensing action is the change of state of the refrigerant from a vapor to a liquid, and it is controlled by the combination of pressure on the refrigerant and airflow over the condenser.

The liquid refrigerant then passes through a receiver-dehydrator (also called receiver-drier) before it reaches the thermostatic expansion valve. The receiver-dehydrator filters and stores the refrigerant and absorbs small traces of moisture, Fig. 48-7.

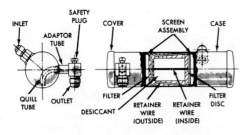

Fig. 48-7. Receiver-dehydrator stores liquid refrigerant and removes moisture that could cause freezing in system. Most units incorporate filters, screens and a drying agent; some mount horizontally, others vertically.

Expansion Valve

The expansion valve removes pressure from the liquid refrigerant to allow expansion or change from a liquid to a vapor in the evaporator, Fig. 48-8. This is the point where the "high" side of the air conditioning system ends. It begins at the compressor valve plate where the "low" side of the system ends.

The expansion valve is designed to reduce pressure (liquids evaporate more rapidly under low pressure). As the compressor draws refrigerant vapor out of the evaporator, liquid tends to flow in and take its place. The expansion valve restricts this flow until pressure decreases in the evaporator side of the valve and pressure builds up on the high pressure side.

The expansion valve incorporates a temperature-sensing bulb which is attached to the outlet pipe of the evaporator. This thermal bulb controls expansion valve operation according to the temperature of the refrigerant at the evaporator outlet. Therefore, as the temperature rises, the expansion valve increases the flow of refrigerant into the evaporator. The increased flow causes faster cooling in the evaporator core, thereby reducing the temperature at the evaporator outlet and, of course, reducing the flow of fluid. This metering process is continuous and automatic.

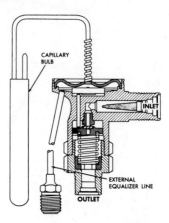

Fig. 48-8. Expansion valve meters liquid refrigerant under high-pressure into low-pressure area of evaporator, as directed by a temperature sensing bulb located at evaporator outlet.

Evaporator

Refrigerant in the liquid state enters the evaporator, which is a radiator-like container, Fig. 48-9. Here it is subjected to decreased pressure and exposed to increased area so it will evaporate (boil and turn to a vapor) and absorb heat from the passenger compartment of the automobile. The heat-laden refrigerant is then drawn into the compressor to complete the cycle.

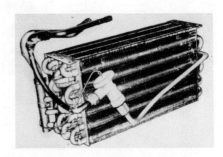

Fig. 48-9. Evaporator has coil and fins like condenser but functions in reverse. It allows refrigerant vapor to expand into gas and absorb heat from surrounding area (passenger compartment of automobile).

Another expansion valve is placed in the bypass line to balance or regulate pressure in some systems to help prevent a freeze-up. It serves to bypass vapor when the system is not cooling. On a cold day, the system will bypass almost continuously. As the temperature rises, the bypass will work less and less. In hot weather, it may not bypass at all.

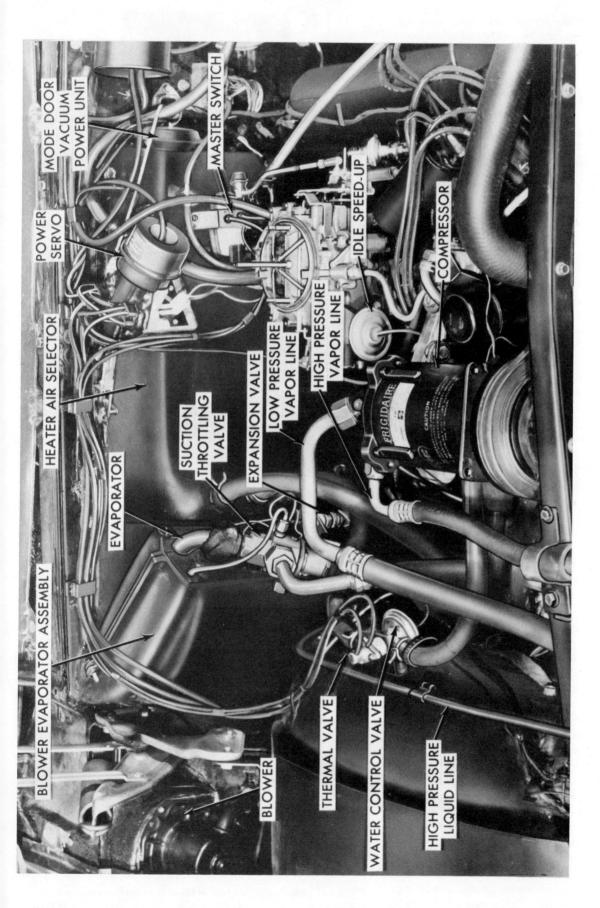

MODE DOOR
VACUUM
POWER UNIT

MASTER SWITCH

POWER
SERVO

IDLE SPEED-UP

COMPRESSOR

HEATER AIR SELECTOR

FRIGIDAIRE

SUCTION
THROTTLING
VALVE

EXPANSION VALVE

LOW PRESSURE
VAPOR LINE

HIGH PRESSURE
VAPOR LINE

EVAPORATOR

BLOWER EVAPORATOR ASSEMBLY

THERMAL VALVE

WATER CONTROL VALVE

HIGH PRESSURE
LIQUID LINE

BLOWER

Air conditioning system components. (Cadillac)

In addition to these four major elements, a variety of other accessory items are installed in the connecting lines to control or regulate the flow of refrigerant. These include a sight glass inserted in the line connecting the condenser to the expansion valve; evaporator pressure regulating valves, suction throttling valves; high and low pressure bypass valves. Electrical controls are used to regulate the passenger compartment temperature: switches, rheostats, blower motors, clutch and dampers. Belts, hoses, brackets, special mounts and fittings make up the complete working system.

Sight Glass

The sight glass, Fig. 48-10, is used to check whether there is enough refrigerant in the system. It is located anywhere in the high pressure line between the condenser and evaporator. In some installations it is incorporated in the expansion valve, in others it is part of the receiver-dehydrator unit.

If foam or bubbles are apparent in the sight glass while the compressor is operating, a loss of refrigerant is indicated. Make the test at 1500 rpm and with the controls set for maximum cooling. Bubbles will appear at start-up under normal circumstances, then disappear as the system begins cycling. If the refrigerant is low, the system must be checked for leaks, then repaired as required and charged with the proper amount of Refrigerant-12.

No bubbles in the sight glass indicates either a full charge or a complete loss of refrigerant. Since R-12 is clear, it is impossible to tell which situation exists. To determine this, watch the sight glass while cycling the magnetic clutch off and on while the engine is running at 1500 rpm. If bubbles appear when the clutch is off, then disappear when the clutch is on, the system is full of refrigerant.

Service Valves and Connectors

Compressor service valves are built into some systems. They serve as a point of attachment for test gauges or servicing hoses. The service valves are three-position controls: front-seated, mid-position, and back-seated, Fig. 48-11.

Position of this double-faced valve is controlled by rotating the valve stem with a service valve wrench. Clockwise rotation will seat the front face of the valve and shut off all refrigerant flow in the system. Counterclockwise rotation will unseat the valve and open the system to refrigerant flow (mid-position). Systematic checks are performed with a manifold gauge set, Fig. 48-12, with the service valves in mid-position. Further counterclockwise rotation of the valve stem will seat the rear face of the valve. This position opens the system to the flow of refrigerant but shuts off refrigerant to the test connector. The service valves are used for testing pressure; for isolating the compres-

SIGHT GLASS

Fig. 48-10. Sight glass in system provides means of checking refrigerant level. When normalized and operating under heavy load, no bubbles or foam should appear in sight glass if system is charged.

sor for repair or replacement; and for discharging, evacuating, and charging the system.

Instead of service valves, some late model compressors have "Schrader" or "Dill" service connectors or gauge port fittings. Special test hoses are

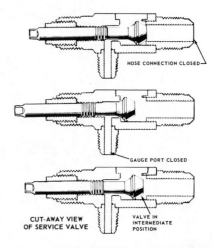

HOSE CONNECTION CLOSED

GAUGE PORT CLOSED

CUT-AWAY VIEW OF SERVICE VALVE — VALVE IN INTERMEDIATE POSITION

Fig. 48-11. Service valves incorporated in some compressors provide a means of access to refrigerant circuit. Valve can be front-seated (top), back-seated (middle), or set in intermediate position (bottom).

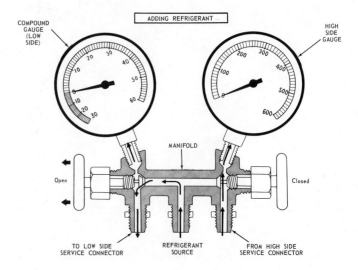

COMPOUND GAUGE (LOW SIDE) — ADDING REFRIGERANT — HIGH SIDE GAUGE

MANIFOLD

Open — Closed

TO LOW SIDE SERVICE CONNECTOR — REFRIGERANT SOURCE — FROM HIGH SIDE SERVICE CONNECTOR

Fig. 48-12. Manifold gauge set, with either two or three test gauges, can be attached to compressor service valves or connectors to test system.

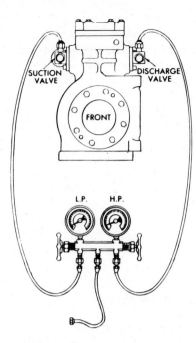

Fig. 48-13. In attaching manifold gauge set for testing pressure in the system; low pressure gauge is connected to suction service valve; high pressure gauge is connected to discharge service valve.

available to fit these connectors, or adapters can be used with standard test hoses. The refrigerant is sealed in the system until the special hose or adapter is attached. Removal of the hose or adapter closes the system.

Service Tools and Equipment

Mechanic's hand and specialty tools are needed to install and service automobile air conditioners. In addition, a manifold gauge set, refrigerant leak detector, vacuum pump, thermometer, tachometer and goggles are needed to test and service the system.

The manifold gauge set, Fig. 48-13, is used to test pressure developed on the high and low pressure sides of the compressor. There are usually two gauges in the set (later model Chrysler cars require three gauges), mounted on a manifold assembly complete with shutoff valves. Connections to the compressor are made at the suction and discharge service valves or connectors fitted with "Schrader" or "Dill" valves. The suction (low pressure) side of the compressor is where the hose from the evaporator attaches. The discharge (high pressure) side is where the hose to the condenser attaches. The manifold gauge set also has a center port to which a hose can be attached to bleed excess refrigerant from the system. In addition, it can be used to purge, or discharge, refrigerant from the system, evacuate air and moisture, and charge the system with Refrigerant-12. See Fig. 48-14.

The leak detector may be anything from a colored dye additive for the refrigerant to a sophisticated electronic unit that provides maximum sensitivity and accuracy when used according to the manufacturer's operating instructions.

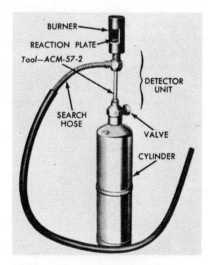

Fig. 48-15. Torch-type leak detector utilizes small flame and search hose to "sniff" for refrigerant leaks. Flame changes color if leak is detected.

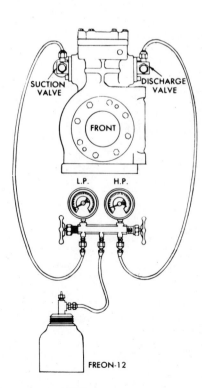

Fig. 48-14. In using manifold gauge set to charge system with refrigerant, hose is connected to center port of manifold and to refrigerant supply.

The colored dye added to the refrigerant will show discoloration at the point of leakage while the system is in operation. The Halide detector, or propane torch, is the most commonly used refrigerant leak detector, Fig. 48-15. In operation, the unit's sampling hose is moved under all parts and connections of the air conditioning system and the color of the flame is ob-

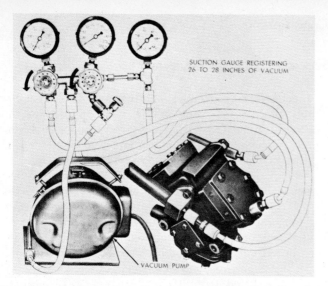

Fig. 48-16. *Vacuum pump is used to evacuate air and moisture from system before charging. Moisture causes rust, ice crystals at expansion valve, and sludge that clogs strainers, valves and capillary tubes.*

SUCTION GAUGE REGISTERING 26 TO 28 INCHES OF VACUUM

VACUUM PUMP

Safety Precautions

Refrigerant-12 is generally considered safe to work with, but certain precautions must be observed. Always wear goggles to protect the eyes while working on any part of the system containing refrigerant. Remember, the system is always under pressure – high or low. Keep your face away from any fitting when it is disconnected. Place a clean cloth over any valve or connection when it is opened. Be sure to close the shutoff valves provided before disconnecting the lines or fittings.

Because the system is sealed, heat applied to any part will cause an immediate rise in pressure. To avoid an explosion, never weld, solder, use a blow torch or steam-clean around or near any part of the air conditioning system.

Do not leave refrigerant cans or drums exposed to direct sunlight or carry them in the passenger compartment of the car. When heat is required to prepare refrigerant for charging a system, never use water above 125 deg. F. and never use a torch, stove or radiator as a source of heat.

All connecting pipes should be free of dents and kinks. Even a slight kink will sharply reduce the ca-

served. A blue flame is normal; yellow indicates a slight leak; purple signals a high-quantity leak of R-12 gas. This test should be made in a well-ventilated area because R-12 passing over an open flame will give off a toxic phosgene gas.

Fig. 48-17. *Cadillac's integral heating and air conditioning system is good example of modern trend toward automatic temperature and humidity conditioning according to desire of driver and passengers.*

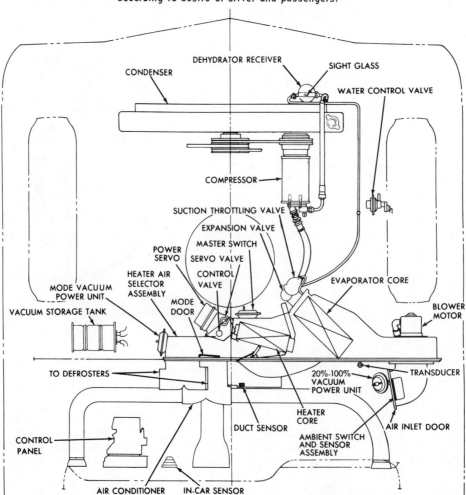

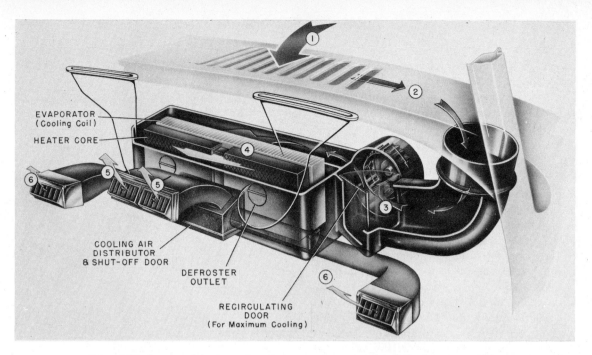

Fig. 48-18. Late model air conditioners, in some cases, employ reheat principle for controlling air temperature and humidity. Flow is from (1) grille to (2) plenum chamber to (3) blower to (4) cooling coil of evaporator and heater core to (5 and 6) discharge outlets.

In the figure: EVAPORATOR (Cooling Coil); HEATER CORE; COOLING AIR DISTRIBUTOR & SHUT-OFF DOOR; DEFROSTER OUTLET; RECIRCULATING DOOR (For Maximum Cooling)

pacity of the entire system. All flares on tubing ends and on fittings must be smooth and unmarked. When a joint is disconnected, cap the pipe and fitting immediately to prevent the entry of air and moisture.

Discharging System

To prepare to discharge refrigerant from the system, connect the manifold gauge set to the compressor service valves or connectors, Fig. 48-13. Attach the test hoses to the center connection of the manifold assembly and place the open end of the hoses in an exhaust gas removal hose, in an open container, or in a large rag.

Open the high pressure service valve, then crack open the manifold high pressure valve to allow the refrigerant to slowly discharge from the system. Do not discharge rapidly or the compressor lubricant will be forced out with the refrigerant gas.

Open the low pressure service valve, followed by the manifold low pressure valve to complete the discharge operation. When the refrigerant stops bleeding from the hose, close both service valves and both manifold gauge valves. And remember, adequate ventilation is required.

Evacuating System

Install a manifold gauge set to evacuate the system. A can of Refrigerant-12 and a vacuum pump are also required. See Fig. 48-16. (Three-gauge set used on Chrysler cars is shown.)

First make certain that the Refrigerant-12 tank valve is tightly closed. Set both service valves in the mid-position. Open both manifold valves to release

pressure in the system. Open the vacuum pump valve and run the pump until the low pressure gauge reads at least 25-30 in. of vacuum.

Continue vacuum pump operation for at least 30 minutes to remove moisture from the system. Then close the pump valve and turn off the pump.

Charging the System

With the manifold gauge set connected to the compressor ports, install a hose from the center port of the manifold to a refrigerant can or tank, Fig. 48-14. Loosen the charging hose at the center connector of the manifold and crack the refrigerant can or tank shutoff valve to purge air from the hose. Tighten the charging hose connection at the manifold and close the shutoff valve.

Open the manifold low pressure valve, close the manifold high pressure valve, and set all controls to maximum cold position. Then open the refrigerant can or tank shutoff valve, run the engine at 1500 rpm, and allow refrigerant to be drawn into the system until the weight of the refrigerant is to proper specification. Watch the sight glass until bubbles disappear. Close the shutoff valve.

Adding Compressor Oil

Oil level in the compressor can be checked with a dipstick. If oil needs to be added, connect the manifold gauge set to the compressor ports and place the open end of the hose from the center of the manifold into a container of clean compressor oil.

Discharge the system slightly, then allow oil to enter the compressor. (On "Schrader" and "Dill" valve systems, complete refrigerant charge must be discharged, then recharged after adding oil.) Generally, there is no oil reservoir, the oil is carried along in the refrigerant. A typical charge of oil is approximately 10 ounces.

Operational Test

Make an operational test with the engine running at 1500 rpm. Test with the hood down and doors closed, (some manufacturers specify "doors open," check requirements). Adjust system controls for maximum efficiency. The system should be operated for approximately 15 minutes for all parts to become stabilized. Satisfactory indications are a clear sight glass; high side reading of 180-200 psi, low side reading of 15-30 psi, depending on ambient (surrounding) temperature.

If the operational test is unsatisfactory (little or no cooling effect), further diagnosis of the symptoms is required. Here the temperature-pressure relationship is especially important since the boiling point (evaporating temperature of the refrigerant) varies with the pressure exerted on it.

For example, a pressure reading at the evaporator coils will indicate what the evaporating temperature of the refrigerant is at that point in the system. Since R-12 boils (evaporates) at -21.6 deg. F. at atmospheric pressure, the evaporating pressure based on amount of pressure exerted can be precisely charted. See Fig. 48-3.

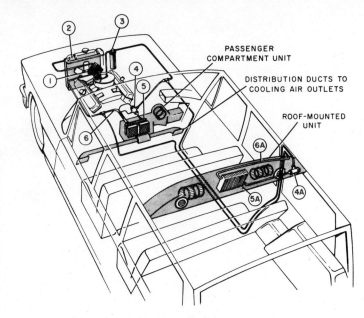

Fig. 48-19. Roof-mounted rear air conditioners are used in some station wagons and taxi cabs. Refrigerant flows from (1) compressor to (2) condenser to (3) receiver-dehydrator to (4 and 4A) expansion valves to (5 and 5A) evaporators and through (6 and 6A) return lines.

If air conditioning system troubles are definitely indicated, they can usually be pinpointed to the source by checking a schematic of the system, Figs. 48-17 to 48-19, and by using a trouble shooting chart as follows:

AIR CONDITIONING TROUBLE SHOOTING CHART

COMPLAINT	CAUSE	CORRECTION
System does not produce cool air; no refrigeration action at all.	1. Drive belt loose or broken.	1. Replace belt or tighten to correct tension.
	2. Compressor inoperative. Belt slips on pulley or pulley will not turn when clutch is engaged.	2. Remove compressor for service or replacement.
	3. Compressor valves inoperative. High and low gauge readings show only slight variation at different engine speeds.	3. Service or replace compressor valves.
	4. Expansion valve stuck open. Low gauge reading "high," evaporator flooding.	4. Replace expansion valve.
	5. Fuse blown; wire disconnected or broken; switch or blower motor inoperative.	5. Replace fuse; repair or replace wire, switch or blower motor.
	6. Refrigerant line broken or leak in system. High or low gauges read zero.	6. Replace line; leak-test system and repair as required. Replace dehydrator.
	7. Clogged screen in receiver-dehydrator or expansion valve plugged hose on coil. Low gauge shows vacuum. Frosting usually occurs at point of restriction.	7. Repair as required. Replace dehydrator.

AIR CONDITIONING TROUBLE SHOOTING CHART
(continued)

COMPLAINT	CAUSE	CORRECTION
System does not produce sufficient amount of cool air at discharge side of blower.	1. Compressor clutch slipping.	1. Remove clutch assembly for service or replacement.
	2. Insufficient air comes from discharge passage.	2. Clean or replace air filter; remove obstruction from passage or kinks from flexible ducts.
	3. Blower motor sluggish.	3. Replace motor.
	4. Outside air vents open.	4. Close vents.
	5. Insufficient air circulation over condenser coils. High gauge reading excessively high.	5. Clean engine radiator and condenser. Install heavy-duty fan, fan shroud or reposition radiator and condenser.
	6. Evaporator clogged with lint, dust or residue.	6. Clean evaporator coils and fins.
	7. Evaporator control valves defective or improperly adjusted. Low gauge usually reads high.	7. Replace or adjust valves as required.
	8. Insufficient refrigerant. Bubbles appear in sight glass; high gauge reads low.	8. Recharge system until bubbles disappear and gauge readings stabilize.
	9. Expansive valve not operating properly. High and low gauge readings excessively high or low.	9. Purge system; clean screen or replace expansion valve.
	10. Receiver screen clogged. High and low gauges higher or lower than normal.	10. Purge system; replace receiver.
	11. Moisture in system. Excessive "high" side gauge reading.	11. Purge system; replace dehydrator.
	12. Air in system. High gauge reads excessively high; sight glass is cloudy or shows bubbles.	12. Purge, evacuate and charge system.
	13. Service valves improperly set.	13. Turn valves to maximum counterclockwise position.
System runs too cool.	1. Faulty thermostatic control.	1. Replace control.
	2. Poor air distribution.	2. Adjust linkage to control panel switch.
System cools intermittently.	1. Compressor clutch slipping; high gauge reading builds up.	1. Remove compressor for service or replacement.
	2. Defective circuit breaker, blower motor or blower motor switch.	2. Replace defective part.
	3. Compressor clutch coil or solenoid has loose connection or poor ground.	3. Remove clutch coil or solenoid for service or replacement.
	4. Moisture in system, causing unit to ice up intermittently.	4. Replace expansion valve and dehydrator.
	5. Thermostatic control defective. Low gauge reads low or excessively high.	5. Replace control.
	6. Evaporator control valve stuck.	6. Purge and evacuate system; replace dehydrator and free or replace stuck valves. Charge system.

AIR CONDITIONING TROUBLE SHOOTING CHART
(continued)

COMPLAINT	CAUSE	CORRECTION
Noise in system.	1. Drive belt loose or excessively worn.	1. Replace belt or tighten to correct tension.
	2. Compressor parts worn or mounting bracket loose.	2. Remove compressor for service or replacement; tighten bracket.
	3. Compressor oil level low.	3. Fill to correct level.
	4. Clutch slips or makes noise.	4. Remove clutch for service or replacement.
	5. Blower motor loose or worn.	5. Tighten motor mounting or remove motor for service or replacement.
	6. Excessive charge in system, causing rumbling or thumping noise, excessive high and low gauge readings, bubbles in sight glass.	6. Discharge excess refrigerant until pressure gauge readings drop to specifications and bubbles disappear from sight glass.
	7. Low charge in system, causing hissing at expansion valve; bubbles and cloudiness in sight glass; low gauge reading excessively low.	7. Locate leak in system, purge system and repair. Evacuate system and replace dehydrator; charge system.
	8. Moisture in system, causing noise at expansion valve.	8. Purge and evacuate system; replace dehydrator; charge system.
	9. High pressure service valve closed, causing compressor to knock and high gauge to read excessively high.	9. Open valve immediately.

Quiz - Automobile Air Conditioning

1. Do fluids give up heat when changing from a liquid to a gas?
2. Can pressure be used to reduce a gas to a liquid?
3. What is a Btu?
4. Is heat flow always from a warmer body to a cooler one?
5. What refrigerant is used in automobile air conditioning systems?
6. What is the state of the refrigerant when it is pumped by the compressor to the condenser?
   a. Liquid.   b. Gas.   c. Liquid and gas.
7. Does the expansion valve raise the pressure in the refrigerant in the system?
8. What is the function of the evaporator?
   a. Removes heat from refrigerant.
   b. Absorbs heat from passenger compartment.
   c. Absorbs moisture from refrigerant.
9. What is indicated if bubbles appear in sight glass?
   a. System is fully charged with refrigerant.
   b. System is low on refrigerant.
   c. Refrigerant is fully discharged from system.
10. What is the primary usage of a manifold gauge set?
11. Give five safety precautions to observe when working on an air conditioning system.
12. How can the need for recharging be determined: Visually? By test?

TIRES,
TIRE SERVICE

Without the pneumatic tire, the modern automobile would be an impossibility. In addition to comfort, the tire also contributes to speed and safety. It is designed to provide traction for the vehicle, and at the same time, absorb irregularities of the road surface so that they are not transmitted to the vehicle.

Tire Types

At present there are two main types of tires; the tubeless and those requiring inner tubes.

The tubeless tire is so designed that the air is sealed within the rim and the tire casing, Fig. 49-1. When an inner tube is used, the air is contained within the tube, while the outer casing serves only to protect the tube and absorb the road shocks.

Tubeless tires are now used on passenger cars and small trucks, while tires requiring tubes are used primarily on larger trucks.

Tires may also be classified as to the type of tread. Different types of treads are available for different types of service, including:
1. Highway tread for improved highways.
2. Off the road tread for off the road work such as farm tractors, etc.
3. Snow tread for use on snow and ice.
4. Two-way tread for use on and off the highway.
5. Super Traction tread for use on vehicles working on soft earth.

In addition there are special treads for vehicles operating primarily on sandy terrain, and a rock tread for mine and quarry work. There are also special treads for racing.

Passenger cars are fitted with tires having a highway type of tread, or a two-way tread.

With the introduction of two-ply tires, tread width has been increased, resulting in greater area in contact with the road.

Tire Materials

A cross section of a typical tire casing is shown in Fig. 49-1. Tread material consists of varying proportions of natural and artificial rubber, and cords which are usually of rayon or nylon. Other cord materials such as aluminum and steel are also used in some tires. Cotton is no longer used for the cords in tires. Bead wires when used are of steel.

There is a controversy among authorities regarding the relative merits of rayon and nylon for tire cords.

Wire cord tires are noted for their strength and are used primarily for off the road use. On buses they are used primarily on the front wheels because of greater safety.

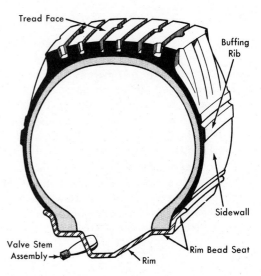

Fig. 49-1. Cross section of modern tubeless tire.

Tire Inflation

When inflating a pneumatic tire, consideration must be given to its temperature, as the pressure in a warm tire is higher than in a cold tire. Pressures as specified by the car and tire manufacturer apply to tires that have not been driven for at least three hours, or driven less than a mile at moderate speed. Also if air temperatures are below freezing, tires should be inflated two pounds higher. If the car has been driven three or more miles at speeds below 40 miles per hour, the pressure in the tires should read two pounds higher than normal. Pressure four pounds higher than normal is considered correct on tires which have been driven at least three miles at speeds in excess of 40 mph.

Manufacturers emphasize that it is impossible to inflate tires correctly when they are hot. Pressures normally increase as tires get warm as the result of road friction and friction within the tire due to flexing. Tires should not be deflated to offset this increase in pressure.

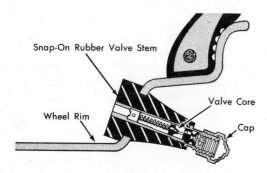

Fig. 49-2. Showing location and details of tire valve in rim of tubeless tire.

Tire Valves

Basically tire valves have changed very little since they were first introduced. Details of a tire valve such as used in a tubeless tire are shown in Fig. 49-2. The inner valve or core acts as a check valve for the air, but positive sealing is provided by the valve cap which contains a soft rubber washer or gasket. It is this gasket, pressed against the end of the valve stem which seals the air in the tire. The careless practice of operating tires without the valve cap should therefore not be followed. Without the valve cap in place, there is usually a slow seepage of air from the tire with the result that the tire will be operated in an under inflated condition.

Tire Wear

Under inflation, rapid stops, fast acceleration, misalignment, and unbalanced conditions, will seriously reduce the life of a tire. Road surface will also affect tire life. Sand and gravel roads will wear tires quickly, whereas concrete and asphalt surfaces aid in promoting maximum tire life.

In addition to normal wear in which the tire tread is worn evenly and smoothly, other types of tire wear include:

1. Spotty wear.
2. Over inflation wear.
3. Under inflation wear.
4. Toe-in wear.
5. Toe-out wear.
6. Camber wear.
7. Cornering wear.

Fig. 49-3. Spotty type wear which results from a combination of causes including under inflation and misalignment.

Fig. 49-3, shows a condition of spotty wear. This condition results usually from a combination of conditions to which the design of the particular tire tread contributes. Under inflation and incorrect camber are the main factors, along with excessive toe-in or toe-out.

Over inflation causes tires to wear excessively at the center of the tread surface as illustrated in Fig. 49-4. In addition, there is usually a little wear on the outer edges of the tire. This causes early failure at the center ribs and also breaks in the tire wall.

Fig. 49-4. Over inflation caused this type of wear.

Wear due to under inflation is shown in Figs. 49-5 and 49-9. This is characterized by excessive wear on the two tread ribs adjacent to the inner and outer shoulder ribs. In many cases, under inflation also causes spotty wear shown in Fig. 49-3.

The amount of toe-in or toe-out is one of the most important factors governing tire wear. Unless the toe-

Fig. 49-5. This type wear results from under inflation.

in is correct, the tires will have a scrubbing action on the road surface, and excessive wear will result. Fig. 49-6 shows the wear due to excessive toe-in, and Fig. 49-7 shows wear due to toe-out condition. Toe-in wear produces a feather-like edge on the

Fig. 49-6. Excessive toe-in caused this type of wear.

inner edges of the tread ribs, and can usually be felt by rubbing the hand over the face of the tire. The wear resulting from toe-out is of the reverse type, with the feather edge being produced on the outer edges of the tread ribs.

Fig. 49-7. Excessive toe-out caused this type of wear.

Excessive camber will produce wear such as is illustrated in Fig. 49-8. If there is too much camber, the wear will be on the outer ribs, and if the camber is negative, the wear will occur on the inner side of the tire tread. If there is excessive wear on both the inner and outer areas of the tread, it is probably caused by excessive skidding on turns.

Fig. 49-8. This type of wear results from incorrect camber.

It should be pointed out when considering tire wear that the wear usually results from a combination of conditions.

Tires wear at a different rate on all four wheels

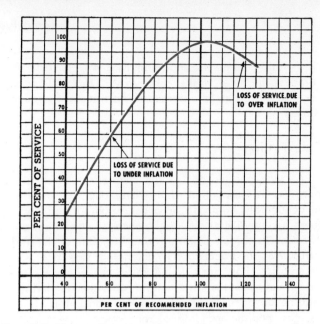

Fig. 49-9. Showing how tire wear is affected by under inflation.

due to driving conditions, the weight of the vehicle, the power on the driving wheels, the crown of the road, the alignment of the wheels, overloading the vehicle, Fig. 49-10, tire inflation, and probably most important of all, the driving habits of the driver.

Fast starts, quick stops, high speeds, and taking turns at high speeds, all take their toll of tire life. Conservative driving habits promote maximum tire life and economy.

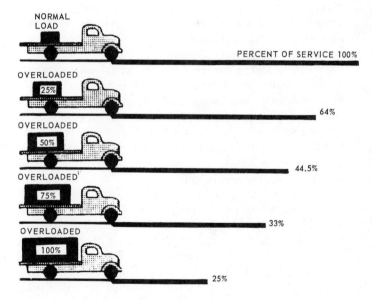

Fig. 49-10. Overloading a vehicle reduces tire life.

Tire Rotation

In order to evenly distribute the wear of tires and help to obtain the maximum tire life, manufacturers recommend that tires be rotated from one wheel to another every 5,000 miles. The generally accepted plan for rotating tires is shown in Fig. 49-11. This plan includes the use of the spare tire. Up to 20 percent more tire life can be obtained if the tires are properly rotated.

Tire Truing

As was pointed out in the chapter on wheel alignment, it is important that wheel and tire assembly be accurately balanced, in order to obtain satisfactory steering conditions. Such balance is also necessary in order to obtain maximum tire life. One of the major difficulties in accurately balancing tire and wheel assemblies has been found to be the eccentricity of the wheel and the tire. High road speeds definitely require an accurately balanced and concentric assembly for radial and lateral movement. However, that practice will not disclose whether error is in the wheel, or in the tire. The correct procedure is to check the wheel and make sure it is true. When measurements indicate that the radial runout of the wheel and tire assembly exceeds .090 in., or approximately 3/32 in., or, if the lateral (or wobble) runout exceeds .100 in., the tire should be removed from the wheel and the wheel checked separately.

Referring to Fig. 49-12, the radial runout at each point indicated by "A" and "C" should not exceed .035 in., and the lateral runout when checked at points "B," should not exceed .045 in.

When checking a wheel for runout, it should be mounted on a hub that is free to rotate, but tight enough to prevent wobble. An accurate dial indicator should be used, and attached to a firm surface to insure accuracy of measurement.

When studying the problem of wheel and tire balance, it must be remembered that unbalance and out-of-round are two separate conditions. An out-of-round assembly can be balanced, but tire thump on a smooth road will be evident. The reverse is also true. A perfectly round tire and wheel assembly can be out of balance, and an annoying thump will be evident when the car is driven.

In order to provide smooth riding, and obtain full mileage from the tires, it is essential that wheel and tire assembly be concentric and balanced. If the wheel has been checked and found to be true and the tire is correctly mounted on the wheel and the assembly is still found to be eccentric, then authorities advise buffing the tire tread so that it will be concentric with the center of rotation.

At first, it would seem that buffing rubber from the tread of the tire would shorten its life. Actually its life is extended as it will roll smoothly on the road without thumping. The amount of runout is usually less than .125 in. Buffing is not recommended, if the high spots exceed 7/32 in.

The increase in tire life results from the fact that the tire being a true circle and concentric with the wheel spindle will roll smoothly along the road.

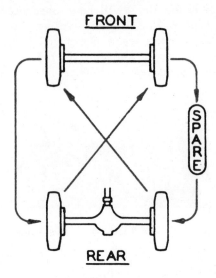

Fig. 49-11. To insure maximum tire life, the position of the tires on the vehicle should be rotated every 5,000 miles.

Consequently, there will be no bouncing and flexing as would be the case with an out-of-round assembly. Flexing increases tire temperature, which is one of the greatest enemies of tire life.

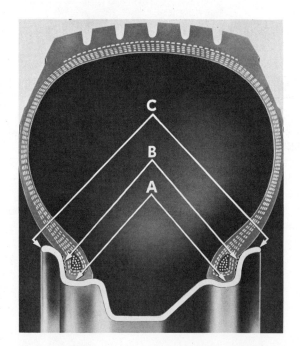

Fig. 49-12. To insure true running, rims should be checked for lateral and diametral runout.

Mounting Tires

The general procedure for mounting tubeless tires is to place the casing on the rim so the beads are resting uniformly on the bead ledge and quickly apply a large volume of air. This forces the bead over the bead seat and against the flanges, where the air seal for the tire is obtained. Some authorities advise using a lubricant on the tire bead which aids in slipping the tire onto the wheel and also helps insure a leak proof seal between the tire and the rim. The detailed procedure for mounting the tire is as follows:

1. Mount the tire on the wheel. This operation is greatly simplified by using some of the equipment that has been designed for that purpose. If such equipment is not available, the tire bead can be levered over the wheel rim by means of tire irons of the lever type.

2. Remove the valve core from the tire and inflate the tire. The sudden rush of air (unrestricted by the valve core) should force the tire beads against the bead seats on the wheel rim. If the beads do not contact both bead seats, then the beads must be spread by means of equipment such as shown in Fig. 49-13. If such equipment is not available, a simple rope tourniquet passed around the circumference of the tire can be used.

3. When the beads have been forced out to contact the seats, again apply air pressure, but only enough to seat the tire beads. Remove constricting equipment, and install valve core and inflate tire to 10 to 15 lb. pressure. Check position of tire in relation to rim, making sure that it is concentric. To assist in this check, tires have a ring molded on the tire side wall. This should be concentric with the edge of the wheel rim. If it is not concentric, the tire and wheel assembly can be jounced on the floor until the tire is correctly mounted. Then inflate the tire to the recommended pressure.

When mounting or removing tubeless tires, it is important that the tire irons and other tools that are used are smooth and free from burrs and other roughness. Such defects will score the tire bead and cause leaks to occur. Similarly, before mounting the tire, the rim should be carefully checked to make sure it is smooth. Any dirt or rust should be removed from the bead seats.

When using tire irons to lever the tire over the wheel rim, take small "bites" with the tire iron to avoid damaging the rim seal ledges, and pry the bead over the rim flange so that the section nearest the valve stem will be applied last. To break the tire bead loose from the rim, manual or power bead-breaking equipment should be employed, Fig. 49-14.

Tire Repairs

In case of a puncture or other leakage, the first step is to remove the nail or other cause and then make the necessary repairs to make the tire air tight. The repairs can be made by cementing a patch to the inside of the tire or by inserting a plug from the outside. In the latter case it is not necessary to remove the tire from the wheel.

Fig. 49-13. *To spread the bead against the tire rim, special equipment is available.*

If the tire is flat, reinflate and listen for a fast leak. If the leak is too slow to be found by sound, remove the wheel and tire assembly and submerge

Fig. 49-14. *Method of breaking loose tire bead from wheel rim.*

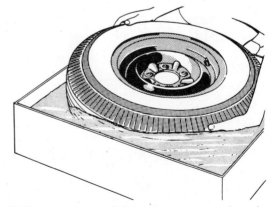

Fig. 49-15. *Immersing a tubeless tire in a test tank to check it for leaks.*

it in a water test tank, Fig. 49-15. If a test tank is not available, apply a coating of soap solution, making sure to cover the entire surface of the tire, valve stem and juncture of the tire and rim flange. Any leak will appear in the form of soapy bubbles.

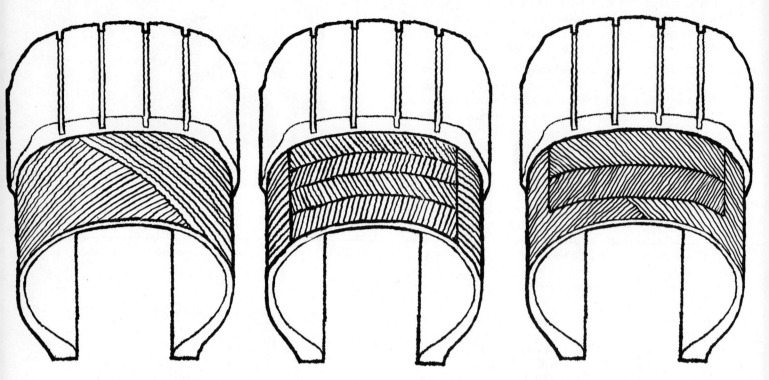

Left. In conventional bias-ply tire cords cross tire at an angle. Center. In radial-ply tire cords run straight across, and an additional layered belt of fabric is placed between plies and tread. Right. Belted bias-ply tire combines these designs, with cords crossing at an angle and a belt situated between plies and tread.

There have been cases of rim leakage through cracks or rivets in the rim. If the leak is not located in the tire, check the rim for defects.

One way of repairing punctures in tubeless tires is known as the plug method, Figs. 49-16 to 49-19 incl. A kit provides an assortment of plugs of different sizes, together with a needle inserting tool and repair cement.

Fig. 49-16. Forcing cement in tire hole, before installing repair plug.

After removing the puncturing nail or other object from the hole, dip the needle in repair cement, and probe into the puncture to locate its direction, Fig. 49-16. Repeat until the hole is well covered with cement. Do not force the needle into the hole if it seems blocked as that may enlarge it, making it more difficult to seal. Select a plug that is approximately twice the diameter of the hole. Dip the plug and needle end in cement and immediately insert in hole in tire with a firm and steady motion, Fig. 49-17. Push the

Fig. 49-17. Starting the repair plug through the hole in tire.

needle and plug in, until the short end of the plug snaps through the tire, as shown in Fig. 49-18. Remove the needle by pulling straight out. The plug will unhook automatically. Trim the outer end of the plug approximately 1/8 in. above the tread surface, Fig. 49-19.

For larger holes, and those which cannot be repaired by the plug method, it will be necessary to repair the tire casing from the inside. After removing the tire from the wheel and the damaged area is located, spread the tire apart using special spreaders, one type of which is shown in Fig. 49-20. This will

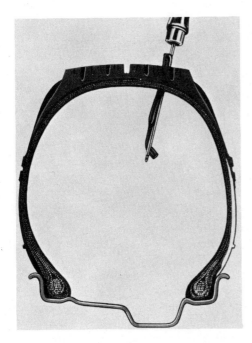

Fig. 49-18. Repair plug after being forced through hole in tire.

provide easy access to the damaged area. Clean the area surrounding the injury with a rasp. Fill the hole with cement or tire compound. Again clean the inside area with a hand buffer or wire brush. Apply cement

Fig. 49-19. Repair plug cut off close to surface of tire tread.

Fig. 49-20. Tire spread apart for inspection and repair.

around the area and allow to dry. Apply a cold patch to the cemented area, pressing it down firmly using toothed wheel provided with the patching kit.

Punctures can also be repaired from the inside of the tire using a hot patch method. The procedure is the same as described for a cold patch, except cement is not applied to the buffed area. Instead the hot patch is clamped in position and the patch is ignited. After the patch is cool, the tire is mounted and inflated. See Fig. 49-20.

Plugs can also be applied from the inside of the tire. In such cases the plug has a large flat head covering an area of an inch or two.

Valve Replacement

Should air leaks occur around the valve stem, it is necessary to install a new valve stem assembly, Fig. 49-2. This is easily accomplished by means of a special lever type tool as shown in Fig. 49-21.

Fig. 49-21. Installing a new tire valve in rim of tubeless tire.

Retreading And Recapping

The life of a tire can be materially extended by either recapping or retreading the tire. Recapping means adding a top strip (called camelback) of synthetic or reclaimed rubber to the buffed and roughened surface of a worn tire. Retreading means adding full width new rubber to the worn tire. The terms are used rather loosely and interchangeably in the tire industry; but a retread is ordinarily a better and more thorough job since new rubber is bonded shoulder to shoulder of the tire.

In general, tires are ready for retreading after about 23,000 miles, depending on the type of service.

The experience of truck fleet operators show that by retreading tire life is increased about 75 percent. Tires that have weak spots should not be retreaded. Most operators will have the tires retreaded when there is still some of the old tread design still visible.

Improvements In Tire Design

Conventional tires, as used on the average car, have been made in what is described as four-ply construction. That is there were four plies of cords running diagonally across the tire, Fig. 49-22, each

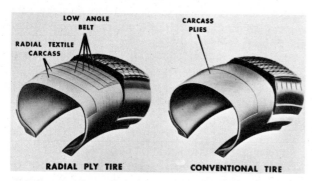

Fig. 49-22. Comparing the construction of the conventional tire and the new radial tire.

ply being separated by a layer of rubber. More recently the design was changed to two-ply construction. While only two plies were used, the construction was as strong or stronger than the four ply because the cord break strength was approximately 72 lb. each for a total of 142 lb. for the two plies as compared to the four ply of 26 lb. each for a total of 104 lb., according to one manufacturer.

Advantages claimed for the two-ply construction include: Equal or better strength with no unnecessary bulk, less heat buildup and less rolling resistance.

More recently, the radial tire construction has been introduced. In previous designs the cords run diagonally through the tread of the tire. In the case of the radial design the cords run from bead to bead, at right angles to the center line of the tire tread, Fig. 49-22. In most makes there is also a girdle or belt of two or more plies of cord running around the circumference of the tire between the radial plies and the tread.

In most cases the cords are of nylon or rayon, but steel cords are used in at least one manufacturer's design. As the result of the materials and also the construction, the radial tire (also known as the belted tire) is stronger than comparable tires of the conventional two or four-ply construction.

The radial casing of the belted tires combined with the stiffness of the belt, distributes the distortion around the tire and relieves the tread contact area from unwanted "squirms." In that way less heat is developed and tire life promoted. Skidding tendencies are also reduced as the tread is harder to deform because its stiff belt keeps it flat on the road surface and the side walls are more flexible.

Improved fuel economy is also claimed for the radial tire because the reduced scuffing and heat buildup reduces rolling resistance.

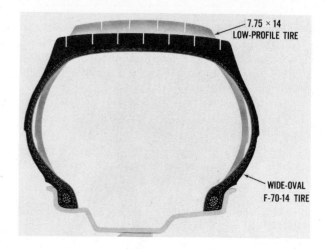

Fig. 49-23. Comparison of the low-profile tire with the wide oval tire.

Further, in connection with heat buildup, the radial design permits deflection of the cords without internal friction as is the case with the diagonal cord tires.

Wide-Oval: Another advance in tire construction is known as the wide-oval tire, Fig. 49-23. It will be noted that with this design the diameter of the tire is reduced and in addition there is a greater area in contact with the ground. This provides better traction and reduced tendency toward skidding.

Another new development is the use of fiberglass cord as a reinforcing material for tires, particularly as applied to radial tires.

Tire Tread Wear Indicator

On some makes of tires, a tire tread wear indicator is now being built into the tire to serve as a visual indicator that the tire tread has approached a worn-out condition. The indicator is located in several positions around the tread circumference and will appear as a solid strip in the tread, Fig. 49-24. This strip interrupts tread continuity so that it is clearly visible on inspection.

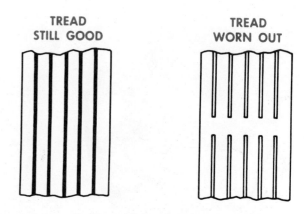

Fig. 49-24. Tire tread wear indicator appears as solid strip in the tread. Serves as a visual indicator.

Quiz - Tires, Tire Service

1. What are the advantages of the pneumatic tire?
2. List five different types of tire treads.
3. Only natural rubber is used in the manufacture of tires. True or False.
4. Wire cord tires are used primarily on bus
   Rear wheels ---
   Front wheels ---
   All four wheels ---
5. Does tire pressure increase or decrease as its temperature increases?
6. After driving more than three miles at 40 mph, the temperature of a tire will increase
   4 degrees   6 degrees   12 degrees
7. Which provides positive sealing for a tire?
   a. the valve cap.
   b. the valve core.
8. Taking turns too fast (cornering) will wear tires at
   a. the center of the tread.
   b. on the outer edges of the tread.
9. Describe the wear on tires resulting from excessive toe-in.
10. Draw a diagram showing a plan for rotating tires, using the spare tire.
11. How much radial runout is permitted on a wheel rim?
12. What is the purpose of the ring molded in the side wall of the tire?
13. If a test tank is not available, how would you test a tire for leaks?
14. Which is considered better, retreading or recapping?

New diagnostic analyzer pinpoints "problem tires" which can cause erratic vibrations in wheel assemblies. Tire uniformity indicator measures both positive and negative distortion in tires while rotating at 5 mph under load. Distortion is recorded on wheel-mounted graph, and compared with reference line made without any load on tires.

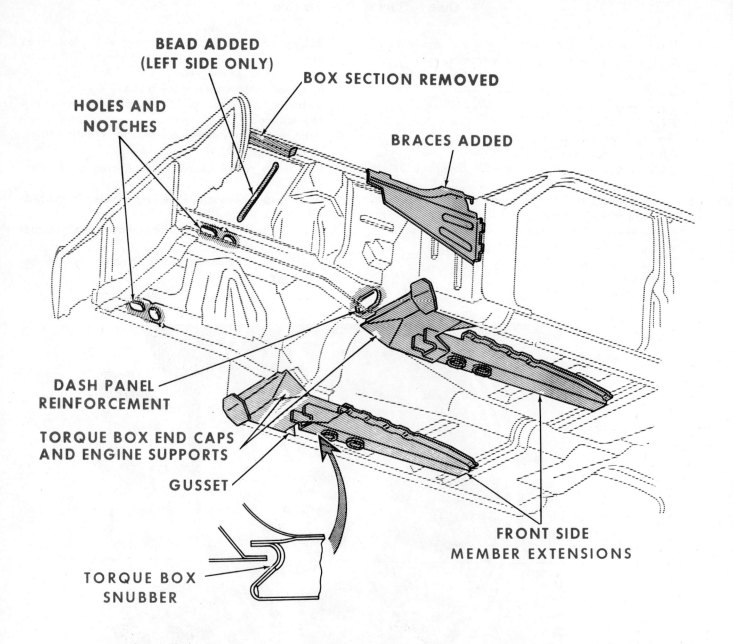

BEAD ADDED
(LEFT SIDE ONLY)

BOX SECTION REMOVED

HOLES AND
NOTCHES

BRACES ADDED

DASH PANEL
REINFORCEMENT

TORQUE BOX END CAPS
AND ENGINE SUPPORTS

GUSSET

FRONT SIDE
MEMBER EXTENSIONS

TORQUE BOX
SNUBBER

In keeping with rigid safety standards, Ford engineered changes (as noted on illustration) in understructure of cars to provide "controlled crush" under severe crash conditions. With this design, impact is absorbed as far forward of passenger compartment as possible.

BODY REPAIRING, REFINISHING

Regardless of how badly a body panel or fender has been damaged, it can be straightened. All that is required is the necessary tools and equipment, plus the required skill on the mechanic's part. However, in cases of severe damage, it may be quicker and more economical to replace the part than to repair it.

Straightening sheet metal is much easier than it appears to be. With modern equipment and tools the work proceeds rapidly. The necessary skill can be attained in a relatively short time by practicing on junked fenders, doors or panels.

The ease and speed with which sheet metal is straightened is largely dependent on starting the repair work in the right way. When done correctly, not only is the amount of dinging, as the process is called, reduced, but also, stretching of the sheet metal will be kept to a minimum, and the amount of hand filing and sanding will be materially reduced.

When straightening a wrinkled panel, the damage should be removed in the reverse order in which it was made. When a collision occurs, there will be a major depression in the panel, followed by a buckled area and then by a series of ridges.

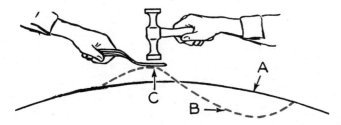

Fig. 50-1. To remove a dent, pressure is first applied at the ridge farthest from where the panel was struck.

Without proper instruction, a mechanic will usually apply pressure at the spot where the panel was struck first and where it is depressed the most. The correct method is to apply pressure at the ridge furthermost from the point where the body was struck first. It is not unusual when this is done that the entire damage will spring back into its original position.

To make this procedure clear, assume that the original form of the panel is shown at (A) in Fig. 50-1. The point (B) is where it was struck and (C) is a ridge

formed last and consequently should be treated first. Place a spoon, Fig. 50-2, on top of the ridge and strike it with a mallet or hammer. Follow the ridge with the spoon and mallet and it will be found that as the ridge

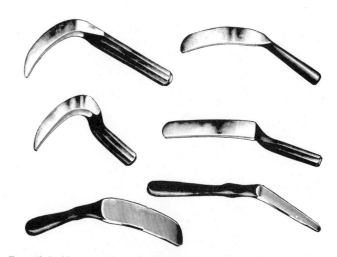

Fig. 50-2. Various types of spoons. Upper: Short elbow and curved spoons. Center: Offset straight and long elbow spoons. Lower: Curved flat and flat long spoons. (Duro Metal Products)

is removed, the major depression at (A) will also spring back so that it conforms very closely with the original contour of the panel.

The few remaining dents are then removed with a dolly block, Fig. 50-3, and hammer. Select a dolly block with a face of the same general curvature as the

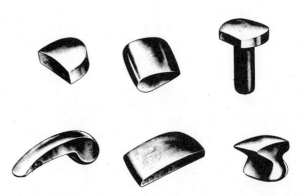

Fig. 50-3. Assortment of dolly blocks. Upper: Heel, utility and mushroom dollies. Lower: Wedge, toe and general purpose dollies.

panel. Hold it under the panel and strike the high point of the dents with a dinging hammer. In this way the dolly block acts as an anvil. The blows will tend to stretch the metal by making it thinner. All that is re-

Fig. 50-4, different weights, different size faces (square faces, round faces, serrated faces), varying length shanks (pointed shanks, roughing hammers, etc.); each designed for a specific type of work. For

Tools Required in Body Repair Work

Hand fender-straightening tools	Stepladder
Bench for straightening panels and doors	Tap-and-die sets
Bolt cutters	Headlight testers
Car horses or trestles	Radiator repair equipment
C-clamps	Thread chasers
Center punches and drifts	Tire repair equipment
Cold chisels	Towing and wrecking equipment
Air compressor	Complete wrench sets
Creepers	Electric drills (1/4, 1/2, & 3/4)
Drill sets	Trouble light
Bolt extractors	Paint sprayer
Fender covers	Welding outfit
Fire extinguishers	Sander and polisher
Bench grinder	Glass cutting and grinding equipment
Hammers	Arbor press
Chain hoist	Frame straightener
Garage jack	Wheel-aligning gauges
Hand jacks	Wheel pullers
Lift	Bench vise
Metal shears	Workbench
Pliers	Wheel balancer
Pry bars	Wheel straightener
Hacksaws	Striping brushes
Hole saws	Drying lamps
Power saws	Spray booth
Screwdrivers	Ventilating fan
Power sheet metal saw	Power fender straightener
Seat covers	Body straightening jacks
Soldering iron	Panel clamping-repair units
Steel rule	Pull rods

quired of the hammer is to press the sheet metal back into position. Therefore, a lot of light hammer blows should be used rather than attempting to use a few heavy ones. If the metal is stretched, a large bulge will result which will require shrinking. Furthermore, the hammer blows should be at the rate of approximately 60 per minute, and the mechanic should "pull" the hammer as it strikes the surface of the sheet metal. In other words, the hammer is used so as to give a sliding or glancing type blow.

It is also important to note that when the dent raises above the surface of the dolly block, the hammer should strike the center of the dent. But if the dent is below the surface of the metal and toward the dolly, the dolly should be placed against the head of the dent and the hammer blows should be directed against the edge of the dent.

The hammer should be held loosely with the thumb along the top of the handle for better control of the bounce. There are many different designs of hammers,

example, the short shank is needed where there is limited space to swing the hammer. The long shank type is needed when working in a deep contour, the serrated face for shrinking metal, the tapered shank for working on molding, etc. All are important and should be in every bodyman's kit.

Similarly, there are a large variety of spoons, Fig. 50-2, and dolly blocks, Fig. 50-3, each designed to make certain tough jobs easy. The spoons primarily are designed for use on polished surfaces; that is, the spoon is placed against the finished surface of panel and is struck with the hammer. They are occasionally used as a dolly, where space limitations prevent a mechanic from using a regular dolly. They are also used for prying a bulge in a door or trunk lid back into place.

Dollies vary in weight, shape, and contour so that they will conform to the curve of the panel and can be used in cramped quarters. Some provide grooves for working beads and molding. Skill in using these tools

Using Pull Rods

When removing dents and creases from auto body panels, considerable time is often required to first remove interior trim. Also, the work is complicated when the damage is located in certain areas such as doors and rear trunk lids, because of metal braces and other structural members which make it difficult to use the conventional dolly and hammer method.

Fig. 50-6. Flexible milled tooth body file for use in holder shown in Fig. 50-5.

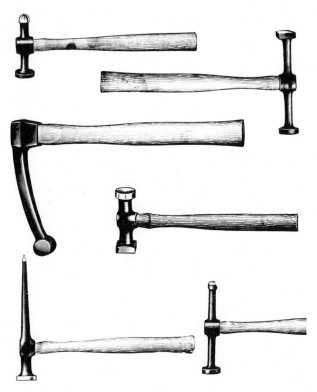

Fig. 50-4. Two types of dinging hammers are shown in the top row. Two roughing hammers are shown in the center. On bottom row at left is a pick hammer and on right another dinging hammer.

On many such jobs, the use of pull rods makes it unnecessary to remove upholstery or interior trim, as the work is done entirely from the outside of the damaged panel.

The procedure is to drill a series of 9/64 in. holes in deepest part of the creases. These holes should be about 1/4 in. apart, Fig. 50-6a. The crease is then

can be quickly attained by working on junk panels and fenders. The important point is to have a wide selection of spoons, dollies and hammers, so that all types of body work can be handled.

As the dents in the body panel are gradually removed, the mechanic should occasionally rub his hand over the surface. This will help determine those spots which require further straightening. Then when that method fails to show any high or low spots, the body file, Figs. 50-5 and 50-6, should be used. Only light cuts should be made, and the mechanic should remember that the purpose is not to remove metal, but to show the areas that require further attention with the dolly and hammer.

Finally a sander, Fig. 50-7, is used, first to locate the few remaining irregularities, and last to remove any slight roughness that cannot be removed with the dolly.

Fig. 50-6a. A series of 9/64 in. holes are drilled in the deepest part of the crease.

worked up gradually by inserting the hooked ends of the pull rods in the holes and pulling on the handles, Fig. 50-6b. Two in each hand may be used. The repair is started, in this case, Fig. 50-6a, at the front edge of the door. Work to the rear, then start at the front again. Pull on the rods should be at right angle to the surface of the panel. Be sure to pull and not pry. In this method, light reflection is a big help in locating high and low spots.

After the dents have been removed, the holes are filled with solder, Fig. 50-6c.

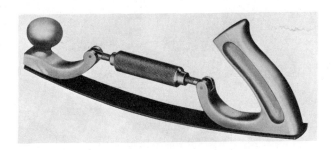

Fig. 50-5. Flexible type body file holder.

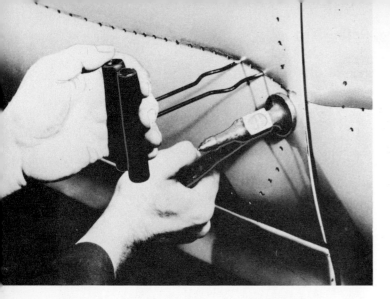

Fig. 50-6b. By means of the pull rods, the metal is pulled out until it coincides with the original contour.

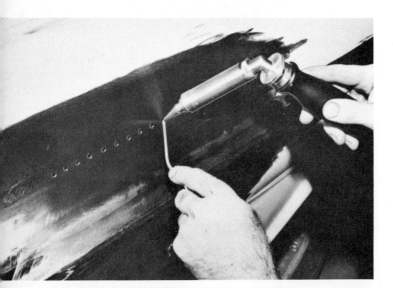

Fig. 50-6c. After straightening the metal, the holes are filled with solder.

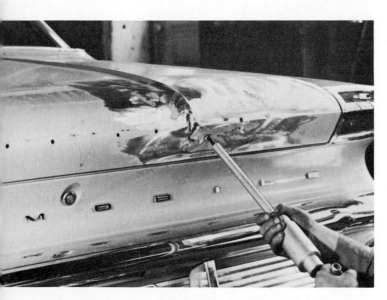

Fig. 50-6d. In case of heavy damage, a slide hammer can be used.

In cases of severe damage, a slide hammer can be used in a similar manner to pull out the dents, Fig. 50-6d. If necessary, a reenforcing plate can be placed on the inside of the panel to prevent the slide hammer from pulling through the sheet metal of the panel.

Fig. 50-7. Using a disk sander.

Power Straightening

While the hand dolly and dinging hammer are used extensively, there is a growing trend toward the use of power dinging equipment, Fig. 50-8. These tools are available from a number of different manufacturers. Both electric and pneumatic types are available. On

Fig. 50-8. Using a pneumatic power fender straightener.

panels where they can be used, considerable time can be saved. In addition to the advantage of speed, such tools will not stretch the metal as much as conventional dolly and hammer work. The amount of filing

Fig. 50-9. *Specialized jacks aid in straightening car bodies. Here one is being used to push out a front fender.* (Hein-Werner)

Fig. 50-11. *Using hydraulic power equipment to pull the sides of a trunk opening into alignment.*

or sanding required to finish the fender or panel is usually less than required with hand methods.

There is occasional trouble in using power operated dinging hammers on car tops and other large areas where damage is more than 18 or 20 in. from edge of panel. However, on areas where damage is close to edge, damage is quickly removed.

Another important piece of equipment for straightening bodies is the specialized hydraulic jack, Fig. 50-9, with fittings and accessories designed to remove dents and to push or pull badly damaged panels and other car parts back into position. In addition to rough

Fig. 50-12. *Using a mechanical body jack to aid in removing a dent from the top.*

Fig. 50-10. *Straightening windshield opening.*

straightening of panels, this equipment has many other uses, such as straightening diamond-shaped door and window frames, squaring bodies, correcting door curvature and frame and bumper work, Figs. 50-10, 50-11, 50-12 and 50-13.

When using such hydraulic equipment to take a dent out of a panel, the same principle as is used with hand dollies should be followed. In other words, pressure is first applied at the outer edge of the dent. Then pro-

Fig. 50-13. *Straightening a door with special power equipment.* (Blackhawk)

ceed and work around the dent, gradually approaching the center, Fig. 50-14. The work is then completed with a hand dolly or a power straightener.

Before starting to straighten a panel, it is important to clean all the dirt from both sides. This can be done by scraping or by heating it lightly with a torch. Similarly, it is important to remove any undercoating

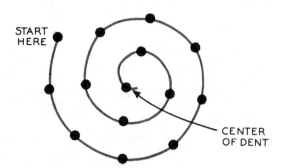

Fig. 50-16. Using a Pulldozer to pull crumpled panels into alignment.

Fig. 50-14. When using the hydraulic jack type of straightening equipment on a dent, start at the outer edge and work in a spiral toward the center.

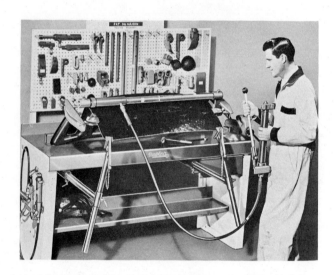

Fig. 50-15. Special bench for holding tools and equipment. Damaged panel can be secured to bench while being straightened.

or sound deadening material from the fenders and panels. Mud and grit adhering to panels will mar the surface of the straightening tools, and undercoating will, of course, make straightening difficult.

Another important piece of equipment that is of value in straightening doors and other panels is the straightening bench or table, Fig. 50-15. The damaged door or panel is attached to the bench with suitable clamps. In this way, the part is held rigidly and in such a position that it can be easily straightened with hand or power tools.

Another type of power straightening equipment, which is available under various trade names such as "Pulldozer," Fig. 50-16, is designed to pull the crumpled metal back into its original position. As shown in

the illustration, one end of the equipment is anchored to the chassis of the vehicle, while the other is attached to the damaged area. Operation of the jack will then pull the damaged area forward into alignment. The job is completed with the usual ding work. When pulling the damaged area forward, heat is often used in cases of severe damage.

Power Straightening Methods

Modern power straightening equipment not only speeds body repairing but also does many jobs which are otherwise virtually impossible. There are an infinite number of different body repair jobs which such equipment can do. A few of them are shown in Figs. 50-17 to 50-22 incl. It is, of course, difficult to make comparative time studies on bodywork, but as nearly as can be ascertained, savings of 50 percent are not unusual when special equipment is used.

In addition to bodywork, straightening equipment can also be used for other shopwork, such as straightening, pulling, and pushing. By cutting time and saving labor, it brings added profits to the shop.

Body Files

After the sheet metal has been made as smooth as possible by means of a hammer and dolly, the next step is to sand or file the surface to remove any tool marks or other dents that are too small to remove by the hammer and dolly. In addition, it is necessary to sand back (feather) the paint, Fig. 50-23, surrounding the edges of the straightened area of sheet metal. This is important, as a smooth surface must be provided for the filler, primer and other coats of refinishing material.

Special files, sanding materials and equipment are, of course, used and are designed especially for automotive bodywork.

Fig. 50-17. Straightening a radiator support with hydraulic straightening equipment. (Hein-Werner)

Fig. 50-18. Direct push with special equipment to align radiator core support. (Hein-Werner)

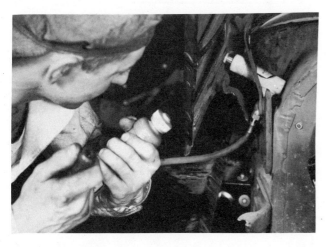

Fig. 50-19. Pressing out a dent in the side of a hood with special type body jack.

Fig. 50-20. Reshaping car top with Porto-Power equipment. Two setups exert pressure on left side and rear top body section, while third setup pushes out dents in center of car top.

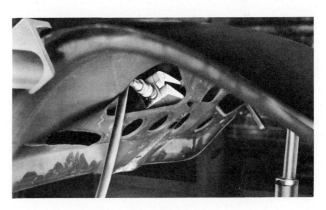

Fig. 50-21. Popping out dent in deck lid with hydraulic spreader. (Blackhawk)

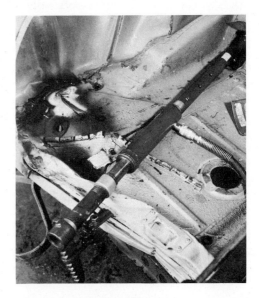

Fig. 50-22. Using hydraulic straightening equipment to straighten damaged floor of car.

Fig. 50-23. Featheredging with a block-type sander. Disk-type sanders are also used for that purpose.

In the case of the files, these are flexible, so that when used in a special holder they can be arched to conform to the curvature of the body panel. The teeth are curved and are designed especially for bodywork. These files cut fast and will not load up when used on the sheet iron of the body or a solder-filled dent.

Conventional machinist files cannot be used for bodywork. As previously pointed out, some mechanics prefer body files, particularly for use in locating the high and low spots while proceeding with the dinging. Whether used for that purpose or for the final smoothing, the surface is filed first in one direction and then in the other, at approximate right angles. On the return stroke, the file should be lifted from the surface being filed. This will not only produce a smoother surface but will also prolong the life of the files, as dragging the file along the surface of the metal on the return stroke will tend to dull the file teeth. It is important to note that special body files can be resharpened.

Power Sanding

Because a sanding disk is flexible, it will follow the larger indentations in a body and for that reason is used to locate the high and low spots only when the straightening process has been nearly completed. Of course, for the final finishing of the metal surface, it does an excellent and fast job. In addition to being used for sanding the metal surface, it is used to remove the paint or other refinishing material surrounding the damaged area. This is known as featheredging.

Before sanding a panel, it is important to select the disk having the correct abrasive for that particular surface. In this connection, many shops use three different grits to prepare the surface for repainting. They first use a 16 grit disk to remove rust and loose paint and for cutting down solder spots. This is followed with a 24 grit disk for surfacing the metal, restoring contours, and for cutting down welds. Then for final finish, a 50 grit disk is used.

Instead of three different grits, some shops prefer to use a 24 grit disk as an all-purpose sander. However, a manufacturer of sanding disks claims that for comparable jobs the three-disk method will require 11.7 minutes to complete the work while 15 to 18 min-

utes will be required for the single abrasive method.

For sharply curved surfaces which cannot be reached by conventional sanders, special cone-type sanders are available. These sanders will reach such curved surfaces as are found around headlights, fender joints, back deck panels, etc.

After the surface of the panel has been thoroughly sanded, it is necessary to sand the edges of the paint surrounding the area of the panel that has been straightened. Some body mechanics use a disk-type sander, others prefer an oscillating or block-type sander, while some still use hand sanding.

In disk featheredging, a 100 grit disk is usually recommended; 80 is used in the oscillating sander and for hand sanding too, with 220 grit being used for finished featheredging.

When disk sanding, it is important to hold the disk grinding machine at an angle of approximately 20 degrees to work, Fig. 50-24. Sufficient pressure is applied so that about 1 inch of the disk is bent and is in contact with the surface being sanded. The disk sander should never be operated so the entire area of the disk is flat against the surface of the work, nor at an extreme angle. The disk grinder should not be swung in an arc, but should always be moved so that it is perpendicular to the scratch lines. This is important, as less conditioning is required to prepare the metal for priming.

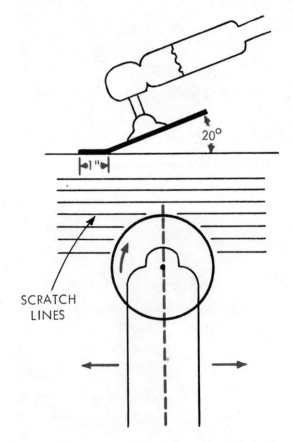

Fig. 50-24. When using a disk sander, it should be held at approximately 20 deg. to the surface of the panel.

Similarly, an oscillating sander should be operated so that the scratch lines will be approximately parallel. Hand sanding should produce the same effect.

There are many different types and grits of sanding disks available, and the manufacturers' instructions should be followed as to their use. However, open grain disks are designed for paint removal where other disks would tend to load up. Closed grain disks are for use on base metal. The latter are available in grits from 16 (very coarse) to 180 (extremely fine), whereas, the open grain disks are available only up to 120 grit.

Patching Rusted Areas

When body panels have become rusted through or dented in such a way that it is difficult to remove dents, many mechanics repair the damage by one of the commercial methods that have been developed for the purpose. One of the popular methods consists essentially of using sheets of special fabric such as fiber glass. This method is used extensively on doors and other panels where heat and solder cannot be used without first removing the interior upholstery and trim. For example, the dent shown in the door, Fig. 50-25, could not be filled with solder as the heat would destroy the interior trim, unless the trim was first removed. With the fabric plastic method, such additional work is not necessary.

Fig. 50-25. Dents such as this can be filled with special body compounds or with fiber glass, without the need of removing the interior trim.

The first step is to thoroughly sand the surface of the dent to remove all traces of rust, paint and other foreign material. The dent is then filled with resin-soaked fiber glass patches, the final patch being cut large enough to lap over the surrounding undamaged surfaces, Fig. 50-26. Epoxy metal solder is then applied, Fig. 50-27, over the last patch with a putty knife to build patch to final contour and to fill pits and indentations. After this has become thoroughly dry, the surface of the epoxy solder is sanded, Fig. 50-28, and the job is ready for painting.

Another method is to use a body cement or plastic

Fig. 50-26. After sanding the surface, sheet of fiber glass soaked in special solutions is used to fill the dent.

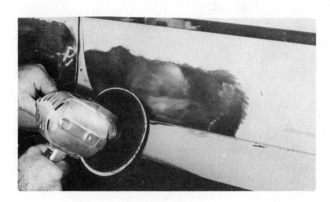

Fig. 50-27. Epoxy metal solder is then applied with a putty knife.

Fig. 50-28. After thorough drying the surface is sanded and made ready for painting.

solder, Fig. 50-29. The material is first mixed according to the manufacturer's directions, and then applied as shown in the illustration. It is then sanded in the usual manner.

Naturally, details of making such repairs as have been described will differ somewhat with the various manufacturers' products. However, it is essential that the surface of the metal be thoroughly cleaned and sanded before making the repair. This is necessary in order to obtain proper adherence between the repair material and the sheet metal of the body.

This type of repair material sands well, is readily featheredged, and the sanded surface is well adapted for all forms and types of paint. When properly applied and prepared, the final finish cannot be distinguished from the original body finish.

If the area to be repaired is small, the special body metal is all that is needed. In such cases, it is usually applied with a putty knife or spatula. If the dents are deep, allow ample time for drying.

Body Solder

An early but still popular method of filling dents in automobile bodies is by means of solder. This in an effective and satisfactory method. Solder is used extensively for filling small dents and smoothing rough surfaces, which are difficult to straighten completely with dolly block and hammer. Another use for solder is to form crushed drip moldings and other contours which are difficult to restore to their normal shape. While solder can be used for filling large dents, most mechanics prefer to at least "rough out" the damaged surface. In that way, the amount of solder used is materially reduced.

Manufacturers provide solder of special formulas designed especially for automotive body repairing. This solder is correctly proportioned so that it is easily applied on vertical surfaces, can be sanded, and refinishing materials will adhere to it.

Before attempting to fill a dent with body solder, the surface should be thoroughly cleaned to remove all paint, rust and grease. This is important, as it is impossible to tin a dirty surface. To remove rust and paint, most mechanics use a No. 16 grit open coat paper and follow that up with a No. 24 grit closed coat. When the surface is clean, it is given a coat of flux and then tinned.

Since the body metal is sheet steel, a flux designed for use on that metal should be used. Always follow the manufacturer's instructions if a commercial flux is used. However, many shops use a solution made from zinc dissolved in hydrochloric acid. The body panel surface is heated slightly and is then given a coating of the flux.

There are several different methods used by mechanics in tinning. Some use a conventional soldering iron. The solder is pressed against the body panel with the hot iron or torch, until it melts, after which the solder is distributed over the desired area by means of the soldering iron. Naturally, on large areas it will be necessary to apply additional quantities of solder until the entire surface is tinned.

Another method is to use steel wool or a piece of cloth to distribute the solder over the surface of the panel, Fig. 50-30. Here a few drops of solder have been melted by the torch so that they adhere to the panel. Then as more heat is applied, the solder becomes liquified so it can be spread over the surface by using the steel wool. The steel wool method has the advantage that the solder can be brushed down into crevices, cracks and depressions.

Once the surface has been tinned, the body metal can be applied. As heat is applied to the body solder, it becomes plastic but not liquid, so that it can be spread with a paddle, Fig. 50-31. After some lead has been applied to the panel, the mechanic keeps the torch in motion over the area being worked. The distance of the torch from the panel varies with the size of the flame. A little experimenting will enable the

Fig. 50-29. Applying a special body cement or plastic solder to fill dents in a fender.

Fig. 50-30. Melting solder on the surface with a torch, preparatory to tinning the surface.

Fig. 50-31. While keeping the solder soft with the torch, it is spread with a wooden paddle.

mechanic to judge the distance the flame must be held from the work, and the speed at which it should be moved back and forth.

After the dent has been filled and the surface made as smooth as possible with the paddle, it should be further dressed with a body file, Fig. 50-32, and then sanded with a power sander. Painting is done in the usual manner.

Lead solder is also used to cover welds, Fig. 50-33. In such cases, the welded seam is first driven below the surface of the surrounding metal. This is done with

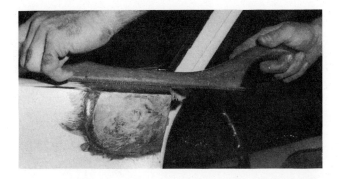

Fig. 50-32. Smoothing the solder-covered surface with a body file.

a blunt edged dolly and a hammer or power tool. A groove a little wider than the weld, and about 3/16 in. deep will be produced. The groove is sanded, tinned and filled with solder. A body file should then be used to rough down the surface of the solder and a power sander used for final finishing.

Rain gutters and beading are difficult to straighten, and a lot of time can be saved by forming them with body solder. After tinning, the solder is applied in the

it becomes necessary to cut out the damaged area and weld in a section of a new panel. Replacement panels are available and either the entire panel is replaced or only a portion can be used depending on the size of the damaged area.

In replacing the panel, the procedure is as follows:

Rough out and shape the damaged area, making sure that the undamaged portion is in correct contour, and is not sprung out of alignment. Carefully measure the piece of metal to be replaced, Fig. 50-34. These measurements should be taken from the edge of the panel, the molding or beading. This is important, as these points are to be transferred to the replacement panel. Scribe a line around the area to be cut from the service panel, and cut along the scribed line. The method of cutting will, of course, vary with the type of equipment available. Electric arc, gas or mechanical cutters can be used.

The edges of this portion of new panel are carefully straightened, the new section is positioned over the damaged area, and a line scribed around its outer edge. This line is now used as a guide in cutting out the damaged area, Fig. 50-35.

After straightening the cut edge of the fender on the car, fit the new section in position and hold it by means of C-clamps, Fig. 50-36. Tack weld the section in place, starting the welds at the top center and work out to the sides and then down the sides. Then make a continuous weld, doing a length about six inches long at a time. To reduce distortion, the welds should be staggered.

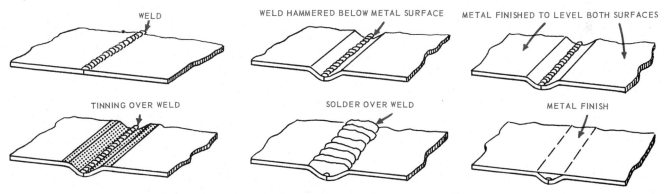

Fig. 50-33. Steps in covering welded joint with solder.

usual manner and rough formed with the paddle while still soft. Files, scrapers and sanders are then used to finish form the gutter or beading to the desired shape.

Replacing Panels

In cases where body damage is extensive, instead of straightening the damaged area, time can be saved by installing a new panel or part such as a complete door or trunk lid. In the case of a damaged body panel,

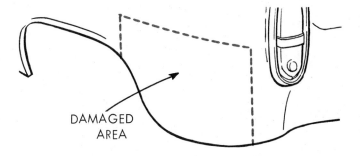

Fig. 50-34. Outline the damaged area of the fender as shown.

Fig. 50-35. *Cutting damaged area from fender with electric torch.*

be of strong texture so that it will not tear readily as it is being applied. Tape must also retain its adhering qualities when it is drenched during wet sanding operations. Flexibility or stretch is another desirable characteristic of masking tape. This is important when applying the tape to the rounded corners of window frames, etc.

One of the new timesaving methods automatically applies the tape along the edge of the masking paper so that half of the width of tape extends beyond the edge of the paper. The paper is then placed in the desired position on the car, and the exposed area of the

Fig. 50-37. *Dispenser for masking paper and tape.*

tape when pressed against the panel or trim will hold the masking paper in place. This method is faster than the former method when the paper was held against the car and the tape applied to the paper and car at the same time.

To mask a headlight, use 6 in. wide paper and cut a piece that will go approximately three-fourths the distance around the light. Place the tape along one edge of the paper, so that one-half of the tape is exposed. Place the paper and tape at the desired point along the edge of the lamp rim, Fig. 50-38, leading with the right hand and adjusting the position of the tape with the left. Then apply a second piece of paper in a similar manner to close the exposed gap.

With a grooved dolly, hammer the weld so it is about 1/16 in. below the surface of the surrounding panel, Fig. 50-33. This area around the weld is then sanded with a power sander or filed to produce the correct contour. Next, fill the groove with hot or cold solder and then sand the surface to prepare it for painting.

If the damaged area to be replaced is at a pillar post or at a spot-welded seam, the seam can be split by driving a thin sharp chisel between the two pieces.

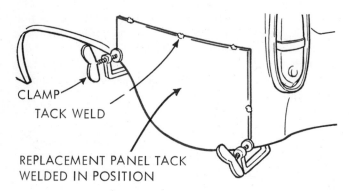

CLAMP

TACK WELD

REPLACEMENT PANEL TACK
WELDED IN POSITION

Fig. 50-36. *Secure the section of new fender in place with C-clamps and then weld in place.*

Masking

In order to protect surfaces and panels, while adjacent areas are being painted, the car is covered with paper which is secured in position with tape. The paper is called masking paper and the tape is known as masking tape.

Manufacturers of masking tape and paper have devoted much time and expense to improving their products, and their research in this field has produced special tape and paper dispensers, Fig. 50-37, as well as shortcut methods of doing the actual masking.

Good quality masking paper will not permit any paint to penetrate or seep through to the panel it is protecting. It should be of tough texture, but flexible, and at the same time there should be no possibility of it scratching the painted surface.

Tape, of course, must adhere easily to painted and unpainted surfaces, chrome and other materials and

Fig. 50-38. *First step in masking a headlight.*

When the paper and tape have been applied all around the lamp rim, the masking paper will be cone-shaped, Fig. 50-39. Twist and fold the cone against the front of the lamp.

Take two short pieces of tape and place them so that the paper will be held flat against the lamp, Fig. 50-40.

There are many different methods of masking a window. One method is shown in Figs. 50-41, 50-42

Fig. 50-39. Placing second piece of masking paper on rim of headlight.

Fig. 50-40. The cone-shaped masking paper covering the headlight is folded back and then taped down with strips of masking tape.

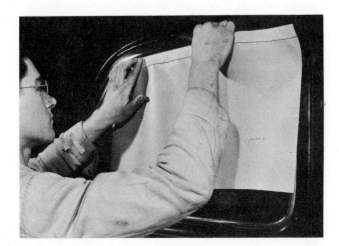

Fig. 50-41. When masking a window, the first piece of paper is placed along the upper edge.

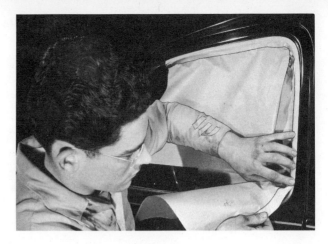

Fig. 50-42. The next step is to place masking paper along the right side of the window.

and 50-43. The first piece is applied along the upper edge. The second, along the right side and portion of the bottom edge, while the third covers the wind deflector and remaining portion of the lower edge. Use short pieces of tape to hold the folds down. Be sure that the lower sheets are underneath the upper sheet. This will prevent water from wet sanding running underneath the paper.

Fig. 50-43. Use a third piece of masking paper to cover the forward portion of the window, with short pieces of tape to hold the edges down.

When you have to apply a masking apron around an inside curved surface, first pleat the apron, Fig. 50-44. This will make it easier to follow the curved contour, and will prevent the apron from bunching and wrinkling. Here's how it is done:

1. Cut a piece of masking paper the desired length.
2. Make a pleat about 1/4 in. deep by crimping both edges. The pleat should extend the full width of the apron.
3. Continue pleating the full length of the apron, making a pleat every two to four inches.
4. Apply the apron to the surface. Then, after pleated apron is securely in place, fold the untaped edge so that it will catch the overspray.

This "pleating" method can be used to good advantage on wheels, Fig. 50-45, and also on the curved edge of doors as shown in Fig. 50-46.

669

Fig. 50-44. When applying masking paper to a curved edge, the first step is to pleat the paper.

Fig. 50-45. Applying masking paper, which has been pleated, to a wheel.

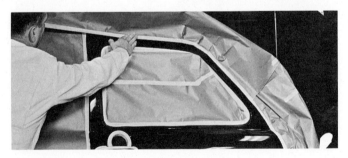

Fig. 50-46. Applying masking paper to the curved edge of a door. Note the pleats in the paper.

When using this method to mask a wheel, it saves the time of removing the wheel and tire. The procedure is to simply apply a pleated six inch wide mask around the entire circumference of the rim, securing the tape to the surface of the tire. Then, after removing the hubcap, the wheel and hub can be sprayed.

When masking a windshield, one method is to use 3/4 in. tape on 12 in. wide masking paper for the initial step, Fig. 50-47. Next, lay the paper on the windshield from bottom to top – securing the tape to the window's bottom edge. The overlapping ends of the mask should then be curved up the two side edges. After the 12 in. mask is in place, lay a 6 in. mask along the windshield's top edge – allowing the paper to overlap the surface of the first covering, Fig. 50-48. When both the 6 in. and 12 in. masks are in place, finish the job by applying a 3/4 in. strip of tape over the seam formed by the overhanging mask. For very large windshields, however, it may be necessary to use both a 12 in. mask on the lower portion of the window, as well as on the top.

Before masking a front door, first mask off all chrome fittings and moldings. Secondly, apply a 12 in. wide length of masking paper over the lower portion of the window, and a 6 in. wide mask over the upper portion. For the third step, apply a 12 in. wide mask from the door's rear edge, back over the rear window and side panel area. A similar 6 in. wide mask is applied from the front fender to the rear fender along the door's bottom edge. Finish the job by running a partially pleated 12 in. mask along the door's forward and top edges to protect the fender and roof from overspray while painting. (Pleating the paper permits it to conform to the door's curved edges.)

Some manufacturers emphasize that masking tape should never be pulled or stretched during application; that the proper method is to lay it down easily as it comes from the roll. In this way, the possibility of it pulling back during the painting operation is eliminated. By not stretching the tape's crepe backing, it is permitted to expand and contract without pulling away when the solvents are applied.

For inside curves, narrow moldings and tabbing, 1/4 in. or 1/2 in. width tapes are usually used. For wider moldings, 3/4 in. and 1 in. widths are more satisfactory.

Fig. 50-47. One method of masking a windshield is to use 3/4 in. tape on 12 in. masking paper, covering the lower section of the windshield first as shown.

Fig. 50-48. The next step is to apply masking paper to the top of the windshield and cover the overlapping edge with a strip of tape.

When masking fender emblems, Fig. 50-49, 3/4 in. tape will do an excellent job. First apply the tape along the edges of the emblem to form a sharp separation line. At sharp outside curves, lay the tape over the sharpest point of the curve and draw the loose ends back along the edge of the emblem. After all the edges have been masked, finish by filling the open areas with short strips.

Welding Body Panels

The importance of welding in a shop can best be appreciated from the fact that over 85 percent of the shops have such equipment. Skill in using the equipment is not difficult to develop. Practice and a thorough understanding of the adjustment of the flame and the selection of the correct tips for the different types of work are the main requisites in the case of gas welding, and the correct current when welding or cutting with electricity.

Before starting any gas welding or cutting job, it is important that the oxygen and acetylene cylinders be either chained to a post or placed in a special cylinder truck, Fig. 50-50. This prevents them from being tipped over. Before attaching the regulators, Fig. 50-51, to the cylinders, each valve should be opened slightly to blow any dirt from the valve seat. To avoid danger of fire, be sure there is no flame or sparks close to the acetylene cylinder and always be certain that fire extinguishers are nearby. Remember that the acetylene connections have left-hand threads. Acetylene connections can also be recognized, as they are painted red, while oxygen connections are green.

After installing the oxygen regulator, open the regulator handwheel. The lower gauge will register the pressure in the tank. After attaching the acetylene regulator, open the acetylene valve about 1 1/2 turns.

After connecting the welding hoses to their respective regulators, the welding head (tip) and blow-

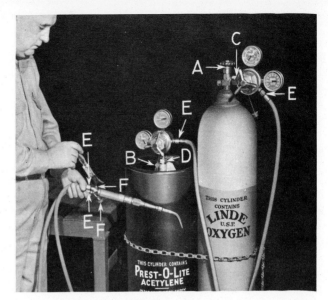

Fig. 50-50. Oxygen and acetylene cylinders should be mounted in a truck or chained to a post or workbench.

Fig. 50-51. An acetylene regulator is shown at the left and an oxygen regulator at the right.

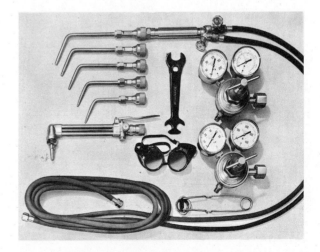

Fig. 50-52. Welding and cutting torch, together with gauges, wrench and igniter. Note assorted tips for welding.

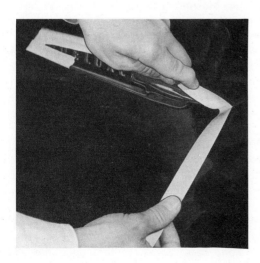

Fig. 50-49. Masking emblems can be quickly done with wide tape as shown.

pipe, Fig. 50-52, is connected to the other end of the hoses. The size tip selected will depend on the type of welding or cutting that is to be done. The size des-

671

ignation varies with different manufacturers. However, when welding body sheet metal, the smallest tip is usually used. Similarly, if body sheet metal is to be cut, a small tip is preferred. Larger size tips are needed if heavy sections, such as frames, are to be welded or cut, and still larger tips are used when heating axles preparatory to straightening, etc.

Different pressures are needed for welding and cutting different thicknesses of metal. For welding sheet metal, the acetylene pressure should be 5 psi, while the oxygen pressure should be 10 psi. For cutting sheet metal, the pressure of the oxygen should be 10-15 psi, and acetylene 3-5 psi.

To light the flame, first open the oxygen valve 1/4 turn. Then open the acetylene valve one full turn, and light the gas at the tip with a friction-type lighter. Never use matches. When lighting the gas, have the tip of the torch turned down and away from any person standing nearby.

Adjusting the flame is accomplished by opening the oxygen valve slowly. The flame will change from a yellow acetylene flame to a blue flame which is called a reducing flame. Starting with an excess acetylene flame, a neutral flame is obtained by closing the acetylene valve until the acetylene "feather" at the inner cone of the flame disappears, Fig. 50-53.

To obtain an oxidizing flame, either increase the

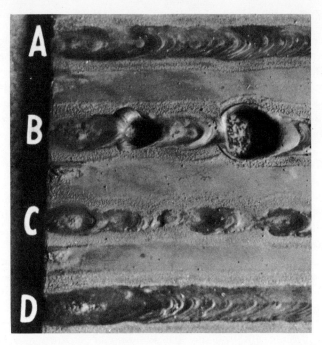

Fig. 50-54. A practice piece with good results at (A) and (D). Excess heat caused holes to be burned as shown at (B), while too little heat was used at (C). No welding rod was used when making this practice piece. (Linde Air Products Co.)

oxygen or decrease the acetylene until the inner cone of the flame is about 2/10 shorter.

If the flame is yellow or backfires, readjust the acetylene to 10 psi, and open the torch needle valve more. If this does not correct the condition, the torch probably requires cleaning.

To weld sheet metal, a neutral flame should be used, and skill can be attained by practicing on strips of sheet metal. At first, do not attempt to weld two pieces of sheet steel together, but move the flame across the surface of the sheet metal, carrying the "puddle" along the surface, Fig. 50-54. Do not use any welding rod. The purpose of this exercise is to obtain skill in carrying a puddle across the surface of the sheet. The blowpipe or torch should be held so that the flame points in the same direction that the weld will be made, and at an angle of about 45 deg. The inner cone of the flame should be about 1/8 in. away from the surface of the sheet. Hold the torch in this position until a pool of molten metal about 3/16 in. to 1/4 in. in diameter is formed. Then move the torch slowly to move the puddle in the desired direction to obtain an even ripple effect. To do this, the torch should be swung from side to side in a small arc. If the torch is moved too slowly, holes may be burned through the sheet metal. If the torch is moved too quickly, the desired degree of melting and overlapping of the puddles will not be obtained.

After the desired skill is attained without using a welding rod, repeat the preceding exercise, using a welding rod, Fig. 50-55. In this case the addition of the welding rod will produce a slight ridge of metal above the surface of the sheet.

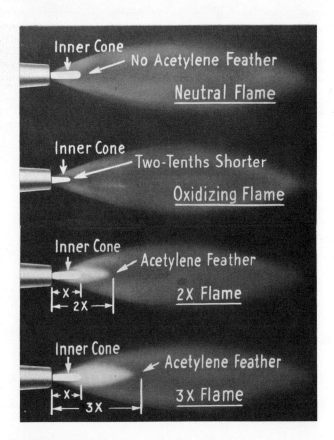

Fig. 50-53. Illustrating the method for indicating the amount of excess acetylene to be used. After the flame has been adjusted to neutral, the blowpipe acetylene valve should be opened, or the oxygen valve closed until the desired acetylene feather is obtained.

Fig. 50-55. Example of good and poor welds. Those at (A) and (D) are satisfactory, while the weld at (B) shows the effects of too much heat. Insufficient heat, little fusion and improper melting of the welding rod produced the weld shown at (C).
(Linde Air Products Co.)

Body Panel Cutting Methods

With the car body construction as used today, many shops have adopted the policy of replacing sections of panels rather than attempting any straightening operations. In cases of severe damage, such procedure saves a great deal of time and not only enables the shop to turn out more jobs per day, thereby increasing profits, but also often results in lower prices to the customer. Replacement panels are available from car dealers and independent parts jobbers.

Cutting out such panels is relatively simple with the equipment that is available. There are three basic types of such equipment; the oxy-acetylene cutting torch, Figs. 50-56, 50-57 and 50-58; the electric torch and various types of power driven cutters. All are

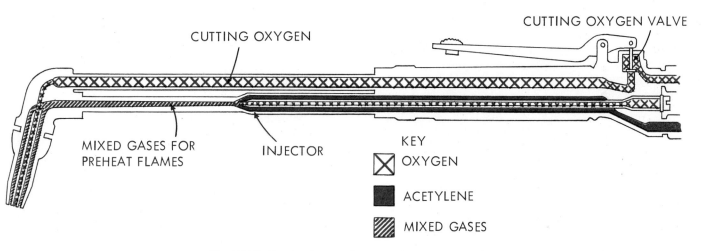

Fig. 50-56. Sectional view of oxyacetylene cutting torch.

The position of the welding rod should be similar to the welding torch, except that it is held in the left hand and at an angle of slightly more than 45 deg. The spot on the sheet and the tip of the welding rod should be brought to the melting temperature at the same time. It will be found that the best position for the end of the welding rod is just inside the outer end of the flame while the flame is being concentrated on the spot at the start of the weld.

After having practiced the use of the welding rod, place the edges of two pieces of sheet metal 1/16 in. apart and weld them together. In this case, it is important that the welding action penetrate completely through to the underside of the sheet so that the weld will have sufficient strength.

During the welding action, the welding puddle must be controlled so it will not fall through the gap. However, the metal added from the rod must be thoroughly fused with the base metal on both sides of the joint for the entire thickness of the sheet.

After sufficient skill has been attained on welding small sheets of metal together, work on an actual fender or body panel can be attempted.

good, and all have their adherents among body shops.

To cut sheet metal with oxy-acetylene, a special torch, Fig. 50-56, is needed which differs materially from the one used for welding. A cutting torch provides a stream of pure oxygen which does the actual cutting after the starting point of the cut has been heated to a red temperature by small oxy-acetylene flames. In the cutting torch, the oxy-acetylene flames are produced at a series of openings in the tip. These openings surround the central opening or jet from

Fig. 50-57. Electric equipment for welding and cutting.

which the oxygen passes. Details of construction vary with different manufacturers.

Cutting is accomplished when the sheet metal is heated red hot and exposed to the oxygen. An intense reaction then takes place, and so much heat is then liberated that not only is the oxide that is formed melted, but some of the unoxidized steel or iron is heated sufficiently so that it, too, is melted. So that the direction of the cut can be changed, cutting nozzles are made with a ring of openings, usually four or more, which surround the oxygen orifice. In this way, several smaller flames of oxy-acetylene are supplied so that the direction of the cut can be changed.

The cutting torch has two valves to regulate the quantities of oxygen and acetylene that are mixed, for the preheat flame, and a third valve usually operated by a lever, controls the stream of oxygen.

Fig. 50-58. One type of mechanical cutter for use on body panels.

When using a cutting torch, the same safety precautions specified for welding should be followed. Fire extinguishers should be readily available, and it must be remembered that it is unsafe to feed oxygen into a confined space, as it will cause oil, wood, clothing, or sound deadening material, if ignited, to burn with great intensity.

When cutting out a body panel, the line along which the cut is to be made should first be marked with chalk. It is important that allowance be made for the width of the metal that will be melted. The chalk mark should, therefore, be made approximately 1/2 in. from the desired line. Any upholstery or other material should be removed from the opposite side of the panel. Most mechanics use both hands when cutting metal with a torch, one to control the flow of oxygen and the other to steady the torch. The torch nozzle is held perpendicular to the surface of the work and kept in the same spot until the metal is bright red. The oxygen valve is then opened and as soon as the flame starts cutting, there will be a shower of sparks from the opposite side of the metal. The torch is then moved slowly, but steadily, in the desired directions.

If the torch is moved too slowly, the heat from the preheating flames will tend to melt the edges of the cut and produce a ragged appearance. If it is moved too fast, the cutting jet will fail to go through the metal. Should this occur, close the oxygen valve and re-

heat the point where the cut stopped, and then reopen the oxygen valve to start the cut again.

Cutting is also done with an electric arc, Fig. 50-57. While any electric arc welder can be used for cutting, the use of large high-capacity units results in too wide a cut and considerable wastage of metal. The smaller, low-amperage units are, therefore, preferred for cutting and also welding body sheet metal.

Hand shears can also be used, but body men prefer special cutters which are driven by electric or pneumatic drills, Fig. 50-58. Such cutters can cut curves with radii as small as 1 in. and are used to cut sheet metal up to .040 in. They have the advantage of not bending or stretching the metal and no burrs are produced.

Preparing the Surface for Painting

Before actual painting begins, it is essential that the surface be prepared for the paint by removing all traces of wax, grease, oil, and dirt. If the paint on the car or truck is of poor quality or seriously deteriorated, it should be removed.

In this final preparation of the body before applying paint, the body man has several methods to choose from. The method selected is dependent on the condition of the existing paint, the equipment available and quality of the finished job desired.

If the paint on the car is in good condition; that is, it has good adherence and is without surface defects, most shops prefer to go over the surface with a disk sander. An open coated disk of No. 16 to 24 grit is used. The disk is held at a slight angle to the surface and worked forward and backward. This will remove most of the old finish down to the metal. This is then followed with a No. 50 close coated disk to remove scratches. If the paint is being removed from only a portion of the panel, the sanded area should taper back into the old paint to produce a featheredge, Fig. 50-23. This is then followed with a 150 grit paper in a block sander, and the final featheredge is obtained by water sanding with wet or dry paper of 280 or 320 grit. Some manufacturers of abrasive paper will advise different grits with variations of the above procedure. Body mechanics should then follow the instructions of the manufacturer.

The foregoing is a popular method for preparing the surface for touching-up and refinishing individual panels and is also used for the entire vehicle if the original paint is in poor condition.

For removing paint from the entire vehicle, many shops prefer sandblasting, hot caustic strippers or paint removers.

When using paint removers, the manufacturer's instructions should be closely followed. The usual method is to apply the remover to the surface with either a paintbrush or sponge. Then, after the proper time interval, the paint is scraped from the surface with a putty knife, or in some instances, it can be flushed from the surface with a strong stream of water or steam. Because of fumes, paint remover should only be used in well ventilated rooms.

The use of sandblasting for removing paint is favored by many shops. In metropolitan areas, there are specialists who limit their work to removing paint by this method and who are patronized by car dealers, independent repair shops and paint shops. Among the

Primer coats should be applied as soon as possible after the paint is removed. This is particularly important when the surface has been sandblasted, because the metal surface is practically in the raw state and will quickly start rusting.

Steam cleaning of a chassis and engine forms part of any good paint job, and in itself is a profitable shop operation.

AIR OPERATED EQUIPMENT	ESTIMATED AVERAGE C.F.M. Air Consumption	A No. of Units of Each Type	B C.F.M. Per Unit	C Total C.F.M.	D Total C.F.M. Times Factor 100	E Total C.F.M. Times Factor 300	F Total C.F.M. Times Factor 500
Air filter cleaner							
Dusting gun							
Car lift							
Drill							
Engine cleaner							
Fender hammer							
Garage door opener							
Grease gun							
Spray gun (touch-up)							
Spray gun (production)							
Sander							
Spark plug cleaner							
Tire inflator							
Tire changer							
Undercoat gun							
Vacuum cleaner							
Wrench							

Total D   Total E   Total F

1. Add D, E, F together. Place a decimal point before the last three figures. This will give the minimum C.F.M. required of the compressor.
2. Add on 1/4 of the above as a safety factor.
3. Add the above two for recommended minimum rating of the compressor required.

Transfer total here →

Transfer above total here →

Fig. 50-59. Estimating compressed air requirements of the shop.

advantages claimed for the sandblast method are: speed, low cost and the surface resulting in good paint adherence.

After removing paint, the surface should be further cleaned with special cleaners to remove any rust, wax, or oil film. This is necessary to obtain good paint adherence.

Air Requirements for Painting

Too often when a shop owner decides to start a paint department, he simply runs an air line to the compressor, connects a spray gun and thinks he is ready for business. True, the setup will spray paint, but it will also spray a lot of oil, dust and condensed moisture from the compressor. In addition, because of pressure variation, the resulting spray pattern will vary considerably. The net result is poor paint jobs.

Among the first steps in setting up a paint department, is to make sure there is adequate air to handle the spray guns and other air operated equipment that is connected to the compressor. In addition, it must be ascertained that the shop air compressor is in good mechanical condition and is delivering its rated capacity. In this connection, many shops find it advisable to install a separate compressor for paint work. This not only avoids overloading the shop air compressor, but also the additional equipment can be cut into the shop line in case of emergency.

To estimate the compressed air requirements of the shop and the load on the compressor, it is necessary to know the amount of air used by the pneumatic equipment in the shop. The method of calculating the total requirements is given in Fig. 50-59.

Referring to Fig. 50-59, you will note columns designated A, B, C, D, E and F. Column D is for equipment in average intermittent repair shop use; column E is for use where specialized departments are maintained, as, for example, a paint department where several different air operated tools may be used by possibly only one man; column F is for the use of large shops where there may be several hammers, paint guns or other equipment requiring a relatively steady supply of air.

In using this form, you should obtain the actual consumption of the tools in your shop. When column C is completely filled out, then multiply each figure in the column by the factor given in column D, E, or F, whichever applies to your shop conditions, and place the answer in that column.

When these figures have all been totaled up, as indicated on the chart, you will notice that you have the minimum cfm required of the compressor. As it is desirable to have a safe working margin for unusually busy periods and to handle future additional tools or equipment, it is recommended that 25 percent be added to the total.

Simply totaling the cfm demands of the various pieces of equipment in the shop does not furnish the capacity of the air compressor required, the reason being that some tools and equipment are used for only a short period and at irregular intervals, while others are used almost constantly. To obtain the capacity of the compressor required to operate the shop's equipment, simply follow the instructions in the table.

To get the best performance and long life from any air compressor, it must be serviced and inspected at regular intervals. A compressor and its separator or transformer used for paint spraying require more special care if clean air is to be supplied.

The manufacturer's service instructions should be carefully followed. If these are not available, the oil in the compressor should be changed every 60 to 90 days. The air filter should be cleaned each month,

and the air tank or receiver should be drained every morning. Another daily job is draining the air transformer. In fact, in extremely humid weather, this should be done several times each day.

If the equipment is provided with a separate receiver with a pop valve, it should be checked occasionally to make sure that it is operating correctly. Otherwise, check the pressure gauges and switches, noting the time required to cut-in and cut-out. This time interval compared to the specified time will serve as a warning for many air supply system troubles.

Of course, all lines should be checked for leaks. When installing a new system, it is important to select pipe of sufficient size to carry the necessary amount of air. Also, when installing the piping it should always drain back to the receiver, rather than forward to the air hose.

Air hose must also be of adequate size to keep air pressure drop at a minimum, Fig. 50-60. Common sizes of spray gun air hose are 1/4 in., 5/16 in., and 3/8 in. Naturally, the smaller the diameter, the greater loss in pressure. The 3/8 in. diameter hose is the preferred size.

Size of Air Hose	AIR PRESSURE DROP AT SPRAY GUN				
	5 ft. length	10 ft. length	15 ft. length	20 ft. length	25 ft. length
1/4 in.					
at 40 lbs. pres.	6.0 lbs.	8.0 lbs.	9.5 lbs.	11.0 lbs.	12.7 lbs.
at 50 lbs. pres.	7.5 lbs.	10.0 lbs.	12.0 lbs.	14.0 lbs.	16.0 lbs.
at 60 lbs. pres.	9.0 lbs.	12.5 lbs.	14.5 lbs.	16.7 lbs.	19.0 lbs.
5/16 in.					
at 40 lbs. pres.	2.2 lbs.	2.7 lbs.	3.2 lbs.	3.5 lbs.	4.0 lbs.
at 50 lbs. pres.	3.0 lbs.	3.5 lbs.	4.0 lbs.	4.5 lbs.	5.0 lbs.
at 60 lbs. pres.	3.7 lbs.	4.5 lbs.	5.0 lbs.	5.5 lbs.	6.0 lbs.

Fig. 50-60. Air pressure drop at spray gun.

Care of a Spray Gun

There are a lot of factors which determine the quality of a paint job, and one of the most important is the condition of the spray gun and the way in which it is used.

It is impossible to do a good job of spray painting with a gun that has not been cleaned or is otherwise defective. Furthermore, the compressed air used for spraying must be free of moisture, oil, and dirt, and pressures must be accurately regulated. In other words, the compressor must be equipped with an extractor or transformer, Fig. 50-61, which not only regulates the pressure but also provides clean, filtered air for painting.

The manufacturer's instructions should be carefully followed when taking care of a spray gun. In gen-

Fig. 50-61. Air transformer with regulator provides clean air and regulates air pressure. (DeVilbiss)

eral, such instructions emphasize thorough cleaning each time the gun is used, and lubricating of the bearing surfaces and packing at regular intervals. A typical spray gun is shown in Fig. 50-62.

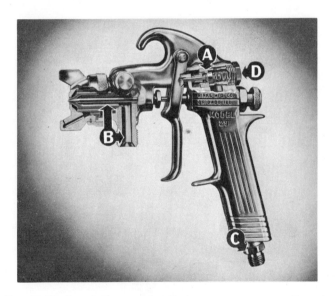

Fig. 50-62. Sectional view of a Binks paint spray gun. Note the cartridge type air valve (A). Passage for paint, lacquer or enamel, (B). Air entrance at (C) or if desired at (D).

Thinner is used to clean the gun, but it should never be immersed in the solution, as it will destroy the lubricant in the packing. A knife, wire or other metal implement should never be used to clean out the air passages. Caustic and acid solutions should never be used for cleaning, as they will corrode the aluminum alloy of which portions of the gun are usually made.

As soon as the spraying is completed, the gun and cup should be cleaned immediately. The first step in cleaning a gun is to empty all the remaining lacquer or enamel from the cup. Then rinse the cup thoroughly with some thinner and then put a small quantity of

thinner in the cup and spray through the gun in the usual manner. This will clean all the passages in the gun. Then dry the parts with air, and the gun and cup will be ready for the next job.

The air valve stem should be lubricated daily with a few drops of light oil, and all packing should be kept soft and pliant by occasional oiling.

As pointed out before, the compressed air used for spray painting must be clean and free from oil or moisture. The air compressor must, therefore, be provided with an air transformer or oil and water extractor, as they are also called. Such units are designed to not only trap oil and water vapor and prevent them from reaching the gun, but also supply air at specified pressures suitable for different types of spray painting.

Transformers or extractors, Fig. 50-61, are available in different sizes so that one or more spray guns can be operated from a single unit. For large departments, pressure feed paint tanks are available. These are designed for conveyance of large quantities of finishing material to the spray guns, under constant and accurate control.

When setting up a paint spray department, it is important that sufficient air be available. Many shops, therefore, find it advisable to use a separate compressor, Fig. 50-63, for such work. The size required will depend on the type and quantity of paint spray guns, and the refinishing material to be sprayed. Compressor units capable of handling any number of guns, from one up, are available.

Fig. 50-63. Air compressor designed specifically for spray painting.

Spray guns are provided with two adjustments: one controlling the amount of fluid being sprayed, and the other governing its shape so that either a round or fan shaped spray can be obtained. The various patterns obtained from a spray gun are shown in Figs. 50-64 to 50-68 incl.

Tips on Spraying

Anyone can spray paint, but to do a job that does not sag or ripple, and will dry smooth with maximum lustre, takes some know-how which can be acquired with a little practice.

Fig. 50-64. A correctly adjusted and clean spray gun, held at the correct distance from the work, should give a symmetrical pattern as shown.

The gun used for refinishing cars is usually of the syphon cup gun type, Fig. 50-69. On this gun, the trigger controls both the air and the paint. All spray guns suitable for first-class work have an assortment of tips, needles and spray cups which will adapt them for use with any type material and any size job. Most shops find it advisable to have several guns, one for

Fig. 50-66. If the spray pattern is light in the center and heavy at each end it indicates that the atomizing air pressure is too high. This can be corrected by increasing the width of the spray pattern or reducing the fluid pressure.

each type of material sprayed: primer, lacquer, synthetic enamel and acrylic enamel. In that way there will be no danger of mixing different types of paints which results in poor paint jobs.

Fig. 50-67. Dried fluid around the outside of the fluid nozzle tip, restricting the atomizing air will cause the pattern to be heavy and wider at either top or bottom.

Fig. 50-65. Insufficient atomizing pressure will give a pattern heavy in the center or heavy at one end and light at the other.

One of the "musts" in spraying is that the paint be at the correct viscosity. This can be best determined by following the instructions on the paint can. Too many painters determine the viscosity by the rate at which the paint runs from the stirring rod. This can lead to plenty of trouble, as only a slight change in viscosity can spoil an otherwise good job. The reason for this is that the amount of thinner not only determines the thickness of the coat, but also influences the evaporation rate between the time the material leaves the gun and the time it arrives at the body panel.

Fig. 50-68. A crescent-shaped pattern is caused by a wing port being clogged by dry material.

High viscosities usually result in sag and orange peel, while low viscosities produce improper flow-out and waste of thinner. It is, therefore, important to measure the proportions of thinner and lacquer or enamel accurately in a graduated measuring cup.

The temperature at which the spraying is done is also an important factor in turning out a good job. This applies not only to the temperature of the shop, but the temperature of the car or truck as well. Shop temperatures should be maintained at 70 deg. F. and the vehicle should be brought into the shop well in advance of spraying time so that it is the same temperature as the shop. Spraying lacquer on a surface that is too cold or too hot from being in the sun will upset the flowing time of the material and will cause orange peel and poor adherence to the surface.

Another important factor in doing a good paint job is the thickness of the paint film on the surface. Obviously, a thick film takes longer to dry than a thin one, and, as a result, the paint will sag, ripple or orange peel. In the case of enamels, blistering may result.

The painter should, therefore, produce a coat that will remain wet long enough for proper flow-out, but no longer. The amount of material sprayed on a surface with one stroke of a gun will depend on the width of the fan, the distance of the gun from the sprayed surface, the air pressure, and the amount of thinner used. In addition, the speed of the spray stroke will also affect the thickness of the coat. The best pro-

cedure is to adjust the gun to obtain a wet film which will remain wet only long enough for good flow-out, and to get the final finish thickness by spraying an additional coat after the first has dried.

Nearly all standard spray guns are designed to give best performance when held at a distance of 8 to 12 in. from the surface to be sprayed. When the gun is held too close, the air pressure tends to ripple the wet film, especially if it is too thick. On the other hand, if the distance is too great, a greater percentage of the thinner will be evaporated in the spraying operation, and orange peel or a dry film will result, because the spray droplets will not have an opportunity to flow together.

It is, therefore, imperative that the gun be held at the specified distance from the work. In addition, it must not be tilted or held at an angle. Care must also be taken that the gun is not swung in an arc, but is

Fig. 50-69. For refinishing automobiles, spray guns of the syphon cup gun type are used.

moved parallel to the work. The only occasion where it is permissible to fan the gun is on a small spot where it is desired to have the paint thin out over the edges of the area.

The effects of incorrect handling of the spray gun are shown in Fig. 50-70.

For most painting, the conventional spray gun with attached cup is satisfactory, but on many modern bodies which have undercut surfaces it is necessary to hold the gun at such an angle that such a gun cannot be used. For jobs of this nature, a gun with a remote or separate cup is necessary.

Clean Surface Required

The life and appearance of a repaint job is largely dependent on the condition of the surface to which the finish coats are applied. That is why it is so important to do a good job of straightening the sheet metal, and also to make sure that the rest of the surface of the vehicle is in good condition. The surface must be clean, free from rust, dirt, wax, oil, or other foreign matter; and, in addition, the old paint must have good adherence to the base metal.

wax that may be present. This should be done before and after the final sanding. The directions accompanying the cleaner should be carefully followed. When wiping the surface, do not use the ordinary shop cloths,

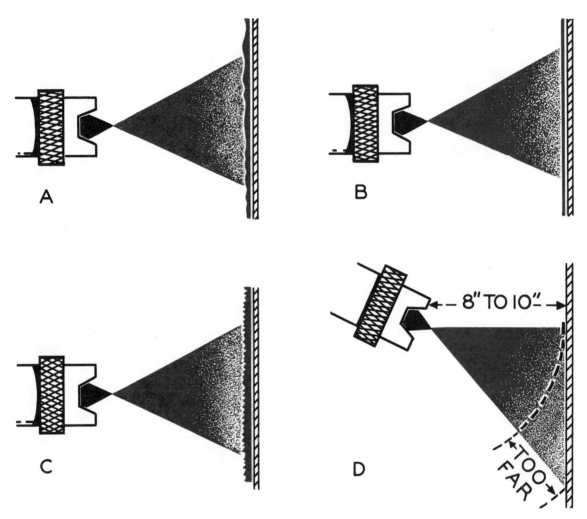

Fig. 50-70. A—Heavy coats with sags, ripples, or orange peel may be caused by a dirty air nozzle, gun too close to work, paint too thin, low air pressure, gun movement too slow, or too much overlap. B—Correct paint application with good flow-out and no orange peel can only be obtained with a clean, properly adjusted gun held at the correct distance from the work. In addition the paint must be correctly thinned, the air pressure must be right and the gun must be stroked at the correct speed and with 50 percent overlap. C—Thin coats which are rough, dry and without lustre are caused by using the wrong type air nozzle, spray gun being too far from work, incorrect air adjustment, too fast gun-stroke or insufficient overlap. D—When guns are fanned or held at an angle to the work, thickness of coat will taper as shown.

So, before starting a refinish job, there are two points which have to be checked before any spraying is done. First, that any original paint has good adhesion and second, that the surface is clean. To check for adhesion, sand a small spot through to the base metal and feather the edges. If the thin edge does not break or crumble, it is safe to assume that there is good adhesion. The other point is that the surface must be clean. Old wax, rust, oil film and other foreign material must be removed, and the best method is to use one of the special cleaners that are available. Gasoline is not satisfactory, as it will not dissolve any

as these usually retain a certain amount of grease or other chemicals as received from the laundry. If air is used to blow off dust, the compressor supplying the air must be fitted with a transformer so the air is free of oil and moisture.

Another important point is that the surface should not be touched by the hands, as the natural oil from the skin will cause poor adhesion and the finish will tend to peel. Examples of paint that has been applied to various types of poorly prepared surfaces are shown in Figs. 50-71 to 50-84 incl.

It is also necessary to determine whether the

Fig. 50-71. Lifting—A puckering and wrinkled effect usually resulting from the application of material carrying strong solvents over a partially oxidized surface. It may also be caused by lack of cleanliness, wax, etc. REMEDY: Sand and refinish.

original finish is lacquer or enamel. A quick check for this is to moisten a finger with lacquer thinner and rub a small area. If the surface is lacquer, it will be dissolved.

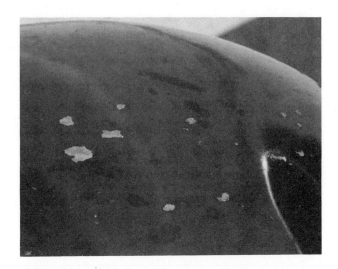

Fig. 50-72. Bruises and Chipping—Caused by stones, etc., striking the surface and is not due to the finish. REMEDY: Sand out and refinish.

Fig. 50-73. Peeling Over Solder Spot—Usually noticeable a few weeks after refinishing. Typlified by loss of luster and gets progressively worse until paint peels from surface. REMEDY: After soldering, surface should be washed with a solution of equal parts of ammonia, alcohol, and water. Be sure surface is thoroughly dry before refinishing.

On lacquer jobs which are to be refinished with lacquer, it is important to prevent swelling of the old coat. Swelling usually occurs when sanding has been done, and unless the new solvents are prevented from reaching the old finish, no amount of care will prevent the old scratches from showing.

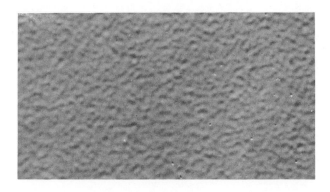

Fig. 50-74. Orange Peel—This condition may result from a number of causes: Improper air pressure at the gun, insufficient reduction and selection of solvent. A thinner that dries too quickly will produce orange peel as will lacquer sprayed on a hot surface. REMEDY: Check thinner, air pressure, and make sure surface temperature is 70 deg.

This swelling does not occur on the unmarred or scratched surface of the lacquer which is covered with an insoluble outer layer, but it does occur when the new lacquer contacts the freshly exposed surfaces in the scratches. After all the solvents have evaporated, and the new finish shrinks, small furrows following the scratches will result.

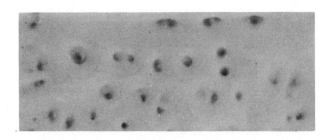

Fig. 50-75. Fish-eyes—This is usually caused by failure to remove silicone polish. REMEDY: Sand, thoroughly clean surface and then refinish.

It is, therefore, necessary on lacquer repaint jobs where much of the old refinishing material is not removed, to use a "sealer." This is applied after the necessary sanding and proper treatment of the bare metal. Sealer has good adhesion to the old finish and will prevent penetration of the new lacquer and swelling is prevented. If it is necessary to use any primer surfacer for filling rough spots, this should be applied first and then, after sanding, the sealer is applied.

It is necessary to sand enamel finishes carefully, making sure that the abrasive is not too coarse, and

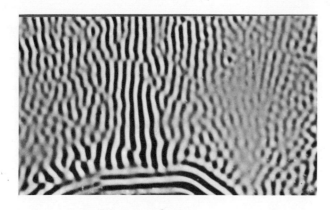

Fig. 50-76. Wrinkling—Usually found only in synthetic enamel finish. Results from the application of a heavy coat. Aggravated by high temperatures. REMEDY: Apply thinner coats.

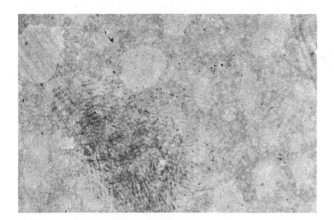

Fig. 50-77. Water Spotting—Caused by washing car in bright sunlight. REMEDY: Use paste cleaner and refinish.

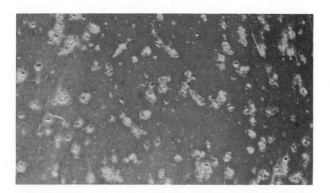

Fig. 50-78. Rust under the finish usually appears as a raised section of the finish, or blistering, and is caused by poor penetration and cleaning of the surface. REMEDY: Sand off surface, treat surface with rust remover and refinish.

that the old finish has been sanded to produce a good surface for the new finish. It is not necessary to use a surfacer if the enamel is in good condition. However, if the old enamel is badly worn and pitted, it is much better to use a surfacer or primer, as much better adhesion and better appearance will be obtained.

Modern primers, glazing putties, fabric patches,

cold solder and hot solder will fill almost any rough surface. However, the surface should be as smooth as possible before any of these materials are applied. After the primer and/or other surfacing material is applied, thorough sanding is essential. Many painters recommend three or four grades of paper, ranging from coarse to fine. In other words, a No. 16 open

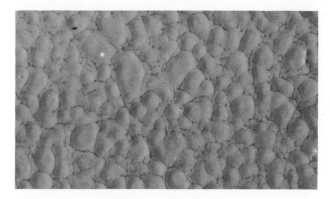

Fig. 50-79. Pitting—Usually caused by oil or moisture escaping through the air line. REMEDY: Sand down to smooth surface and refinish. Also overhaul compressor and separator.

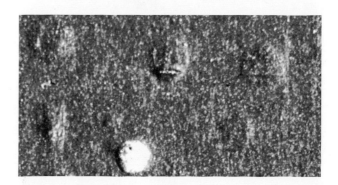

Fig. 50-80. Blistering is caused by rust, moisture, oil, grease or other foreign materials working in between coats and causing them to separate. Oil or water in air lines will cause blistering as will high temperatures and high humidity. REMEDY: Remove finish to the metal and refinish.

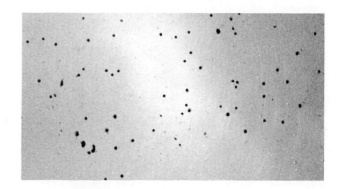

Fig. 50-81. Pin Point Blistering—This type of blistering is often confused with pitting because small broken blisters have the appearance of pits. These pinpoint blisters range in size from a pinhead to a point. REMEDY: Sand down to metal and refinish.

Fig. 50-82. Paint will have a mottled appearance if applied on surface which had been polished with silicone type polish. It is therefore imperative that all traces of such polish be removed from the surface before refinishing. Another example of paint applied to a surface from which the silicone polish was not carefully removed is shown in another illustration.

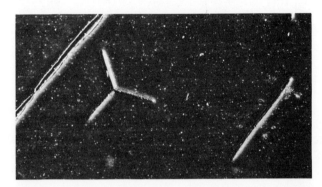

Fig. 50-83. Cracking and checking may extend to the metal. Or, it may go only as far as the undercoating. Depressions in film caused by cracks in the undercoat also are typical. Simple line cracks are caused by temperature stresses, flexing of body panels, second-coat application before first is dry, and poor paint mixing. REMEDY: Remove finish to bare metal and refinish.

Fig. 50-84. Chalking is surface disintegration. It is primarily due to weathering and sunlight and is characterized by dulling and powdering of the surface. REMEDY: Apply paste cleaner followed by polish. In extreme cases, refinishing is necessary.

coated paper may be used first. This is followed with No. 50 close coated and final sanding is done with No. 150 paper.

Modern surfacing and refinishing materials have greatly simplified automobile painting, but good appearance and long life of the finish is still dependent on the care taken in preparing the surface for the final finish coats.

STEPS IN REFINISHING

Lacquer Over Old Finishes

1. Water sand old finish, using No. 320 paper. Remove old wax or silicone polish with special remover before sanding.
2. Using clean air, blow out all cracks.
3. Clean surface with special grease, rust and wax remover.
4. Spray surfacer on bare metal spots. If necessary, use spot putty or equivalent.
5. Water sand undercoats with No. 320 paper. If any spots are sanded through to base metal, spray again with surfacer and water sand.
6. Seal scratches with special sealer if car was previously finished with lacquer.
7. Blow out cracks with clean air.
8. Again clean surface with special cleaner.
9. Apply lacquer color coats. Three double coats are recommended.
10. Water sand with No. 400 paper.
11. Polish.

Enamel Over Old Finishes

1. Remove all wax and silicone polish with special cleaner.
2. Wet sand old finish with No. 320 paper.
3. Clean surface with a special wax, grease and rust remover.
4. Spray on undercoats.
5. Sand undercoats with No. 280 paper.
6. Respray undercoats if sanding has gone through to base metal.
7. Resand undercoat.
8. Blow out all cracks with clean air.
9. Clean surface with special cleaner to remove hand marks.
10. Wipe surface with tack rag to remove lint and dust.
11. Spray a light coat of enamel over all cracks.
12. Apply a tack coat and follow immediately with a full coat of enamel. If drying lights or oven are not available, allow to dry at least 12 hours in dust-free room.

Removing Sand Scratches

Sand scratches have spoiled many jobs which otherwise would have been perfect, and unfortunately the scratches do not show up until after the finish coat has been sprayed.

Of course, the basis of any good paint job is smooth metal, and unless the man finishing the metal does a good job, it will be virtually impossible for the painter to fill the scratches so that they will not show. Careless filing or bearing too hard on a coarse disk leaves scratches, gouges, and furrows that are hard to fill.

Many experienced body men will, therefore, use a coarse disk for roughing and cutting down weld spots and high areas only. Then the major part of the sanding is done with a 24 disk and final finishing of the metal with a disk of No. 50 or 80 grit. Even with such care some sand scratches may be made, as there are often small burrs or fins of torn metal along the edges of the sand scratches. Many mechanics have found that it pays to follow up the heavy power sanding with a little hand sanding, using No. 150 paper.

Fig. 50-85. One type of equipment designed to prepare a desired shade of color.

While primers have been vastly improved in their ability to fill and cover a surface, they cannot be depended on to do a job with a single coat. Several coats should be applied and ample time should be allowed for the individual coats to dry. This is much better practice than applying a single heavy coat, as it is difficult to tell when such an application has dried all the way through.

Fine paper should be used when sanding priming coats. Paper such as No. 220 or 240 will produce scratches that usually show through the first coats. In some instances, such paper can be used for the initial sanding of primers but experienced body men advise the use of No. 320 or 360 with final finish sanding with No. 400 paper.

When lacquer is used to finish the car, the lacquer thinner penetrates the undercoat. Where the undercoat is heaviest, the swelling will be the greatest. The swelling will be still greater if the lacquer is sanded and polished before all the thinner has evaporated. A good practice is to first spray a light fog coat of lacquer as this will reduce the possibility of sand scratch swelling and spoiling the appearance of the finished job.

Scratches can also be caused in the final polishing of the finish coat if care is not exercised in the selection of the rubbing compound. The finer the abrasive in the rubbing coat, the less chance there is of producing any scratches.

When doing spot painting, it is important that the spot be carefully featheredged. It is important to give the area and edge a careful final sanding with No. 360 or 400 paper to eliminate any scratches. If any rubbing compound is used, the area should be cleaned with a good wax and grease remover, as many rubbing compounds contain a lubricant.

Old lacquer surfaces should not be sanded with any paper coarser than No. 360. The reason for this is that when new lacquer is sprayed on the old finish, the lacquer solvents will penetrate any scratches and cause swelling of the original lacquer.

In general, the same care must be used with synthetic enamel. While there are no strong solvents to cause difficulty, as in the case of lacquer, the high lustre of the enamel will tend to magnify any scratches that may be present.

Matching Colors

Even though paint manufacturers have made ready-mixed paints for standard production colors of automobiles available, the number is so great that virtually no jobber carries the complete line. Consequently, the painter is often faced with the problem of mixing his own colors.

Matching colors is not easy. Since automobiles are being turned out with ever increasing varieties of shades and tones, paint men are finding their work becoming more difficult. The problem of fading further complicates the situation.

Greatly aiding the paint man in meeting the problem of color matching is the work of various paint manufacturers in providing instructions, specialized equipment and basic colors. One type of equipment designed to prepare paint of a desired color is shown in Fig. 50-85.

Probably the most important point in color mixing is that painters have good color perception. Many color mixing aids are available. These include besides thirty basic colors, mixing containers, stirring paddles, test panels, and color mixing equipment which is being used by an increasing number of shops.

The important thing for the beginner to know is that every color has what is known as a "mass-tone" and a "tint-tone." The mass-tone can be judged from the color as it appears on the painted panel or in the can. The tint-tone of a color is the shade resulting from mixing a small quantity of the color with a large quantity of white. For example, a dark green mass-tone will usually have a blue tint-tone and most maroons have a violet or purple tint-tone. Usually it is impossible to add white to a dark green to get a light green, or white to a maroon to get a light red. Small additions of color will tint according to its tint-tone, and large amounts will influence others according to mass-tone.

Black, of course, darkens a color and white lightens it. Black tends to dull a shade. Addition of white dilutes the tint.

Clean equipment is, of course, a must when matching colors. Dust, old paint or other material will spoil the desired effect. Before being applied, each basic color or paint must be stirred thoroughly. Mixtures must also be stirred thoroughly. When not in use, cans of paint must be tightly closed to reduce evaporation of the solvents and because of the effect of light. It is also important that matching should be done in sunlight or northern exposure, as artificial light changes tints and tones.

As almost all shades darken on drying, wait until the color is dry before making comparisons. When matching a color on a car, it is important that all waxes and polish have been removed, as they tend to change the color. Also, when making comparisons, it must be remembered that the larger the surface, the lighter the color will appear. This is caused by light reflection. Therefore, comparisons of areas of equal size should be made.

A lot of material can be saved if small amounts are first mixed and predominating colors used first. If a formula is being followed, start with the major shade, adding the minor quantities according to volume.

Usually the larger proportion of the formula will provide the desired depth of color, but further toning will be needed to produce the particular shade being matched. Only a very small amount of color is ordinarily required for toning. For example, a touch of red may mean a small quantity on the tip of a spatula added to a quart batch. This touch should be added last.

Colors should always be mixed full strength for matching and then diluted to spraying consistency.

White or opalescent is generally the base of almost all colors. Exceptions are reds, maroons, dark greens, dark browns, and dark blues. Red, blue, yellow and green will impart brightness to a mixture.

Touch-Up Jobs on Enamel

There are several different ways of doing spot touch-up jobs on enamel surfaces. Some, of course, are better than others. Time is undoubtedly the determining factor in deciding which one should be used.

First of all, if small nicks and scratches on the edges of doors and fenders are to be touched up, many shops use lacquer. It is applied by means of striping or other small brushes. As the area to be worked over is small, no sanding or undercoating is necessary because the lacquer adheres to the surrounding enamel. Naturally, a better job would result if the surface were sanded and the painter followed through with undercoat and lacquer. However, that would require considerably more time.

On large areas (especially if the customer is in a hurry for his car), it is permissible to use lacquer on enamel provided certain precautions are taken. As standard lacquers and enamels do not chalk at the same rate, painters advise using a lacquer containing a high percentage of synthetic enamels. In fact, several manufacturers have developed lacquers which are recommended for use over enamel. In addition, a thinner of high solvent power is used.

Maximum gloss will result from this mixture and the overspray will blend into the enameled areas beyond the repainted spot. Some painters advise spraying a final coat of lacquer, thinned twice as much as usual, as a mist coat for the entire area.

After repairing a baked enamel finish with lacquer, compounding may be necessary in some cases. However, it is important to avoid harsh, scratchy abrasives. A mild compound will help to "blend in" the spot and the possibility of "graying" the enamel will be avoided.

The best repair medium for a baked enamel finish is, of course, enamel. This is particularly true where large areas are involved and when some metalwork and sanding is necessary. Naturally, the use of enamel will require more time but this can be reduced if infrared drying lights are used. When enamel is used, the area to be painted is prepared in the usual way and the undercoat sanded down to the level of the surrounding enamel finish. A lacquer primer surfacer may be used as undercoat. Many painters, though, prefer a synthetic resin base primer.

Hot Lacquer

Cars have also been refinished by spraying with hot lacquer. While use of lacquer is being to a degree superceded by acrylic for refinishing, use of hot lac-

Fig. 50-86. *With this type of special equipment, the lacquer is first heated and then sprayed with a conventional spray gun.*

quer has certain advantages over spraying at room temperature and these advantages are said to outweigh cost of additional equipment and special care that is required.

First of all, hot spraying differs from the normal application of lacquer and synthetic enamel in that the paint is heated before spraying. This is accomplished by means of special heating units, Figs. 50-86 and 50-87, designed to maintain the temperature of the paint at 160 deg. In addition, a special air cap and nozzle for the spray gun should be used to obtain the best results.

By heating the lacquer or synthetic enamel to 160 deg., its viscosity is reduced from a third to a fourth of its value at 70 deg. Since this temperature is maintained at all times during the operation, the viscosity will be constant, regardless of the temperature of the shop. This is an important advantage, as every refinisher knows the difficulties encountered when shop temperatures vary.

In conventional spraying, lacquer strikes the car surface at from 20 to 25 deg. below shop temperature, and when the shop is cold or damp, blushing results.

When paint is sprayed at 70 deg., nearly 50 percent of it is lost, but when spraying hot lacquer at 25 to 35 lb. pressure, or hot enamel at 35 to 45 lb. pressure, virtually all of it gets to the surface being sprayed and and stays there.

Shops that have used hot spraying have found it saves both time and money. As less thinner is required, more lacquer or enamel reaches the surface being painted. In normal cold spraying, lacquer is reduced from 100 to 150 percent with thinner so that the solids comprise only about 16 to 20 percent. In hot lacquer work, the material is reduced with thinners to about 50 percent. The addition of heat results in 25 to 30 percent solid matter at the spray nozzle. In other words, with hot spraying, about one and a half times more solid matter reaches the surface than with cold spraying.

As a result, refinishers have found that a lacquer job can be done on a medium size car with two coats, cross sprayed, and use only 2 to 2 1/2 qts. of material. An enamel job on the same size car requires only 2 qts. In other words, one double or cross coat of hot lacquer is equivalent to four or five coats of lacquer sprayed in the conventional manner.

In addition to the fact that about one-half the number of coats of lacquer are required, hot spraying has the advantage of quicker drying time. Lacquer applied by hot spray is out of dust in about 15 to 20 minutes, and out of tack in from 30 to 45 minutes. Hardness of film is obtained in about 8 to 10 hours.

Additional toughness is obtained which is not apparent in cold application. After 8 to 10 hours drying, the lacquer can be compounded for added beauty and depth of color. In fact, sanding and rubbing of lacquer is reduced to a minimum, and polishing and compounding of enamel is eliminated.

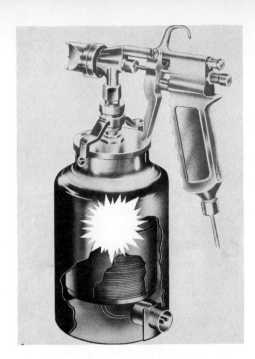

Fig. 50-87. A heating element is built into this gun to maintain the temperature of the lacquer or synthetic enamel at 160 deg.

There are many other advantages of hot spraying. The elimination of blushing has already been mentioned. The quicker drying time results in less dirt in the final finish. Material costs are about 13 1/2 percent lower, and the reduced time per job permits more jobs per week. Orange peel and overspray are also avoided, and the tendency to sag is reduced. If orange peel occurs, it can be compounded.

Hot lacquer dries with a higher gloss, often equal to synthetic enamel. If compounding is necessary, less time and effort is required. In many cases, polishing or dry buffing is all that is necessary. Similarly, when hot enamel is used, a more uniform and brilliant gloss is obtained.

In regards to the amount of thinner required, this varies with climatic conditions and the characteristics of the thinner. For normal conditions, some manufacturers recommend three parts of thinner to one part of lacquer. As shop temperatures increase, less thinner is required.

Spray gun manufacturers have special air caps and nozzles for their spray guns which are used for hot spraying, and several companies have developed heating units. For spotting, electrically heated cups which can be attached directly to the spray gun are available. For complete paint jobs, other units are available which rapidly heat the lacquer to the desired temperature and maintain it at that point, Fig. 50-87. The hot lacquer can then be poured into the regular spray cup as needed, Fig. 50-86.

Refinishing With Acrylic

Currently all passenger cars are being painted at the factory with either acrylic lacquer or acrylic enamel. The General Motors vehicles are being fin-

686

ished in acrylic lacquer, and the other manufacturers are using acrylic enamel. According to the manufacturers, acrylic lacquers and acrylic enamels withstand sun and extreme weather conditions much better than conventional lacquers and enamels. In addition, they have a high lustre which requires no polishing.

When using acrylic refinishing materials, certain precautions should be followed in order to maintain the high lustre and also to obtain maximum life of the material.

Cars finished with acrylic materials should not be polished or waxed for at least 60 days after delivery. In fact, polishing is usually not needed for at least 18 months. Furthermore, because acrylic is so extremely hard, it is nearly impervious to staining from oil and gasoline. Another point emphasized by the manufacturers is that conventional washing is all that is necessary to remove road film and maintain the original high gloss.

Particular care must be exercised when removing road tar from a car finished with acrylic, as many of the tar removers while highly satisfactory on ordinary lacquer and enamel, will cause spotting and dissolve the acrylic finish.

Acrylic should not be used to repair cars finished with conventional lacquer. Even with a sealer between the lacquer color and the acrylic, cracking failures will occur in a short time.

On vehicles originally finished with acrylic lacquer, the same material may be used when doing a refinishing job. Also, most makes of acrylic lacquer may be used when refinishing a car originally painted with acrylic enamel.

Synthetic enamel should never be sprayed directly over acrylic because of early failure. If desired, a sealer should be first sprayed over the acrylic, and then the enamel applied over the sealer. However, enamel should not be used for spot repair over acrylic.

If acrylic is not available for spot repairs, conventional lacquer may be used, but the durability is not equal to that of acrylic. If lacquer is used to repair acrylic, the acrylic should be sanded lightly and the conventional lacquer applied to complete panels.

If it is desired to completely refinish or two-tone a car previously finished with acrylic, standard lacquer may be used provided the original acrylic is sanded to almost complete removal, or to a point where the undercoat is showing over at least 90 percent of the area. If this is not done, objectionable softening may occur. Note that it is not necessary to sand the surface to the bare metal.

When repairing the finish of cars finished with acrylic, the temperature of the refinishing room should not be less than 65 deg. If refinishing is attempted at a lower temperature, a cracked condition will result.

Special spray gun heads have been developed to properly atomize acrylic and a pressure of 40 to 45 lbs. is usually adequate to produce the desired shade, maximum amount of leveling and high gloss. High pressure promotes orange peel and a lighter grayer shade with iridescent colors.

Before spraying the surface, all traces of wax, polish and grease must be removed. This should be done with a cleaner designed for the purpose. The next step is to wipe the surface dry with a clean cloth.

The edges of the area to be refinished should then be cut with coarse abrasive paper. Then feather the edges with No. 400 abrasive paper. On new metal, a metal conditioner should be used. Then wash with water and dry.

The surface is now ready to be sprayed with primer surfacer and the instructions for thinning given by the manufacturer should be followed. Heavy coats should not be applied. Instead, use two or three medium coats, allowing each coat to become dull and dry for at least 30 minutes, before applying the next coat.

The next step is sanding. If dry sanded, use No. 360 paper, or if wet sanding is preferred, use No. 400 paper. Any imperfections in the surface should be filled with putty. After two hours drying time, the surface is again sanded, and then sealed with a light coat of primer surfacer.

In spot area repairs, the edge of the area should be rubbed with rubbing compound to remove overspray.

The acrylic finish is then sprayed, and three or four wet double coats should be applied. Allow each coat to "flash" before applying the next coat. In spot repair, extend each color coat a little beyond the previous coat to blend into surrounding finish. Some factories then advise a spray mist coat of thinner to improve leveling and gloss.

If possible, allow the surface to dry for at least 10 hours. However, in an emergency, four hours should be enough. If infrared lights or oven are available, it can be force dried for at least 10 minutes at 180 deg. F. Process the surface with either hand or machine rubbing, followed by a dry buffing with a lamb's wool bonnet. A light sprinkle of a few drops of water will improve the lustre. However, to avoid loss of lustre, it is not advisable to buff until two weeks after spraying.

Water and Dust Leaks

The location and repair of water and dust leaks in automobile bodies is an important part of the duties of every body repairman.

In many cases, such leaks result from the dislocation of weather stripping and are easily located and repaired. In other cases, special effort and procedures are needed to locate, and then repair the difficulty.

If the exact location of the source of a leak is not known, the first step is to inspect the general area of the leak for watermarks, rust or dust trails, and trace these back to the source or beginning. If there are no such indications, a mechanic can sit in the car, while water is sprayed over the outside of the suspected leak point area. The mechanic, inside the car, can then see where the water is entering. In some cases, it may be necessary to remove head lining or other trim to locate the source of the leak.

Another method of locating leaks is to fill a syringe with powdered chalk, water, or a mixture of the two. Such syringes can be purchased at any drugstore and the powdered chalk at most hardware stores. The suspected leaky seam is then sprayed with the contents of the syringe, and the dust trail formed by this operation will quickly show the actual point of entry of the rain and dust.

A variety of materials are used for correcting water and dust leaks. Such materials include:

Black caulk and sealer.
Gray caulking cord.
Auto body sealer.
Rubber cement.
Metallic caulk and sealer.
Pressure gun for applying caulk.
Sponge rubber stripping.

Before attempting to repair any leaks around doors or deck lids, it is important to make sure that the doors and lids are correctly fitted, as poor fits invariably result in water and dust leaks. The easiest method of checking the fit of doors and deck lids is to note that the edges of the door or lid are the same distance from the surrounding body panel. When that has been corrected, slide a feeler gauge (approximately .005 in.) along the weather strip with the door or deck lid closed. If no resistance is noticed to the passage of the feeler gauge blade, leakage will occur at that point. Such leaks can be repaired by the installation of new weather stripping which is cemented in place with the appropriate sealer.

Leaks around the windshield can usually be repaired by means of the pressure gun filled with black caulk and sealer. The procedure is to slide the nozzle of the pressure gun between the rubber and the glass and force the compound as indicated in Fig. 50-88. The same illustration shows the area to apply the sealer when leaks occur between the windshield weather strip and the body flange.

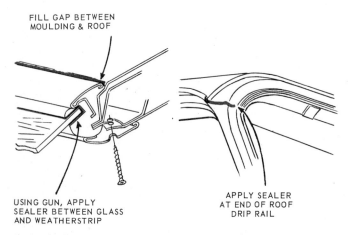

FILL GAP BETWEEN MOULDING & ROOF

USING GUN, APPLY SEALER BETWEEN GLASS AND WEATHERSTRIP

APPLY SEALER AT END OF ROOF DRIP RAIL

Fig. 50-88. Areas around windshield where leaks may occur.

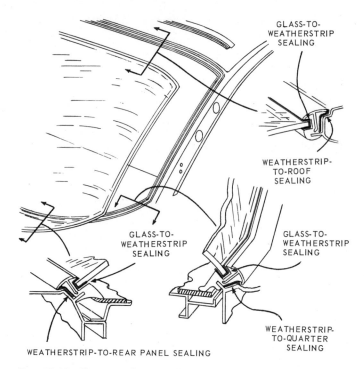

GLASS-TO-WEATHERSTRIP SEALING

WEATHERSTRIP-TO-ROOF SEALING

GLASS-TO-WEATHERSTRIP SEALING

GLASS-TO-WEATHERSTRIP SEALING

WEATHERSTRIP-TO-QUARTER SEALING

WEATHERSTRIP-TO-REAR PANEL SEALING

Fig. 50-89. Showing where caulking may be needed around rear window to overcome leaks.

It should be emphasized that in some cases of leaks around the windshield or rear window, that the difficulty be overcome only be removing the glass and then replacing it, using ample sealing compound. Areas where leaks may occur are indicated in Fig. 50-89.

Leaks may also occur through bolt and nut holes used to attach chrome trim to the body panels. In such cases, the difficulty can be overcome by applying special sealer to each of the clips and nut ends.

Fig. 50-90 shows the location of the weather stripping of a deck lid. In some instances it will be necessary to build up the existing weather stripping by means of 1/8 in. thick weather strip rubber. Leakage may also occur around deck lid locks. In such cases, install a small rubber washer on the lock cover shaft, between the lock housing and the spring.

When water leaks into the passenger compartment around the doors and cowl hinge pillar, it is important to make sure that all the drain holes on the bottom of each door are open. Also remove the door trim panel, and inspect the bottom edge of the water shield for proper sealing to the door. A good seal must be maintained completely around the water shield. Check by pouring water into the door at the belt line, to make sure that none of it will splash past the water shield. Leaks at the cowl hinge pillar may be corrected by installing a drain tube inside each hinge pillar.

Body Water Drain Locations

Automobile bodies are designed with provisions for draining water that normally enters certain areas of the body. The locations of the drain holes on a typical Fisher body as used on General Motors cars is shown in Fig. 50-91. It is important that these drain holes be cleaned periodically to insure proper drainage.

Each door is provided with two drain holes, A, Fig. 50-91, which are located along the bottom of the door. Each hole is covered by a sealing strip which prevents dust entry into the body. The shaded surface of the sealing strip should be lubricated periodically to prevent the strip from sticking to the metal.

A drain hole, B, is located in the rocker inner panel beneath the rear quarter window area, and is covered by a sealing strip to prevent entrance of dust. The shaded surface of this strip should be lubricated to prevent the strip from sticking to the metal.

Another drain hole, C, is located behind the rear wheel housing panel, and is formed in the rear quarter outer and rear compartment filler panel pinchweld flange.

Each deck lid is provided with two holes, D, and provide drainage for any moisture that may collect in the lid inner construction. Convertible models are provided with a drain hole at E. This is provided with a short drain hose to prevent the entrance of dust. A drain hose, F, is located at each outer corner of the back window drain gutter. The lower end of the hose is installed through the underbody adjacent to the wheel house panel.

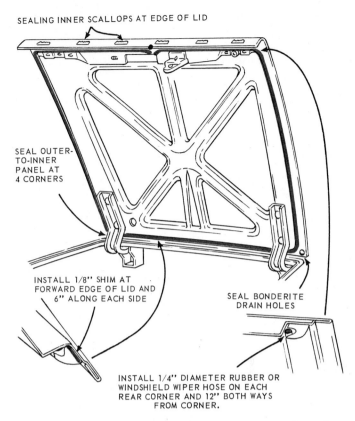

Fig. 50-90. Rear deck lids may leak at the points indicated.

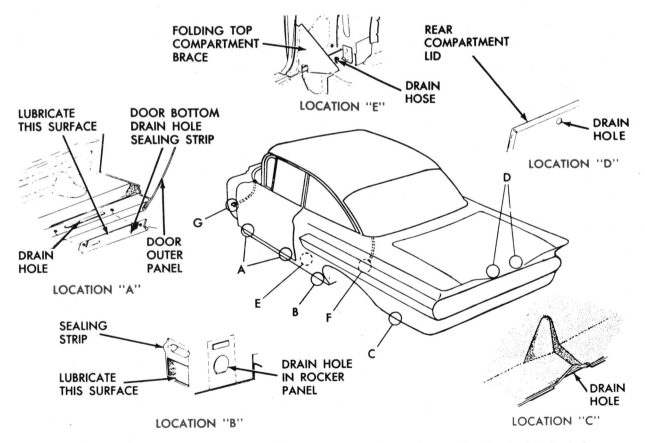

Fig. 50-91. It is important to keep body drain holes open to prevent bodies from rusting. A typical Fisher body as used on General Motors cars is illustrated.

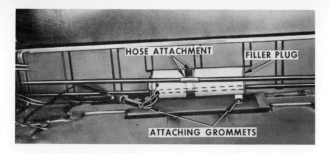

Fig. 50-92. Motor and pump assembly for power operated folding tops.

A drain hose, G, is located at each outer corner of the windshield drain gutter. The lower end of the hose is installed through the front body hinge pillar outer panel. The lower ends of these hoses are located behind the front fenders, and cannot be readily cleaned. In cases where cleaning is required, a flexible wire can be inserted into the hose at the top end.

Power Operated Convertible Tops

To raise and lower the tops of convertible cars, a high pressure hydroelectric system is used by some manufacturers. By means of such a system, the top (after being unlatched and raised above the windshield by hand) can be lowered and raised by actuating a con-

enters the bottom of the hydraulic cylinders, forcing the pistons upward, thus raising the top.

The hydroelectric unit consists of a 12V reversible type motor, a rotor type pump, two hydraulic lift cylinders, and an upper and lower hydraulic hose assembly. One type motor and pump assembly is shown in Fig. 50-92.

THE HYDRAULIC SYSTEM: To fill the hydraulic system, heavy-duty brake fluid is used. The top must be in the raised position. A filler plug adapter, as shown in Fig. 50-93, is installed in place of the filler plug at the end of the unit. The filler plug adapter is then connected to the container of hydraulic fluid by means of rubber tubing. The container must be placed in the rear compartment area of the body, and below the level of the motor pump assembly.

Then operate the top to the down position and continue to operate for 10 to 15 seconds after the top is fully lowered, or until the noise level of the pump is noticeably reduced. Reduction in pump noise indicates that the hydraulic system is being filled with fluid.

Operate the top several times, or until the operation of the top is consistently smooth in both up and down cycles. When that has been attained, remove the adapter and replace filler plug. Fluid level should be 1/4 in. below lower edge of filler plug opening.

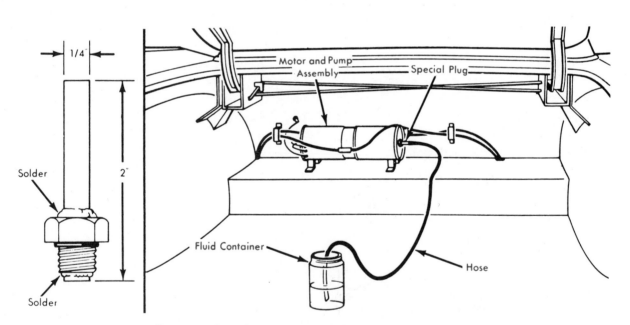

Fig. 50-93. Procedure for filling and bleeding hydraulic system.

trol switch on the instrument panel. Hydraulic fluid from an electrically driven pump (usually located behind the back of the back seat backrest) is forced through tubing to the double-acting piston type cylinders located at each rear quarter section of the car. Pressurized fluid entering the top of the lift cylinders forces the pistons down, thus lowering the top.

When the control on the instrument panel is operated in the reverse manner, the pressurized fluid

The above procedure is also used to bleed the system of air. At all times, care must be exercised that the hose is always below the surface of the fluid in the container.

ELECTRICAL CHECKS: A failure in the electrical system may be caused by a low battery, break in the wiring, faulty connections, short circuits, etc.

Checks for current, shorts and opens are made in the usual manner by means of a 12V test lamp or a voltmeter as explained in the electrical section of this Encyclopedia. Fig. 50-94 shows the motor leads being checked with a light tester.

LIFT CYLINDERS: To check the operation of the lift cylinders, operate the folding top switch and observe the lift cylinders during "up" and "down" cycles. If the movement of the cylinder is not coordinated, or

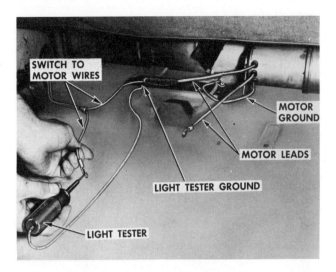

Fig. 50-94. Checking motor wiring.

sluggish when motor is actuated, check the hydraulic hoses from motor and pump to cylinder for kinks or other defects. If one cylinder rod moves slower than the other, the cylinder having the slower moving rod is defective and should be replaced. If both cylinder rods move slowly, or not at all, replace both cylinders.

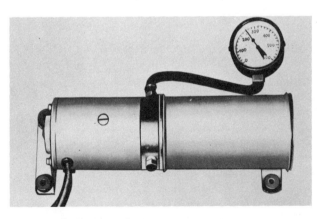

Fig. 50-95. Checking pressure of pump.

PUMP PRESSURE: To check pump pressure, remove motor and pump assembly from rear compartment and install a plug in one port and a pressure gauge in the other port, Fig. 50-95. Operate motor by connecting to 12V battery, and pressure gauge should indicate 340 to 380 psi. Then check pressure in other port. Reading for both ports must be within specified values.

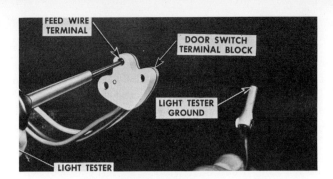

Fig. 50-96. Checking for current at door window switch.

Power Windows

Power operated windows are operated from 12V motors, one motor being used for each window. Failures in a circuit are usually caused by short circuits or open circuits. Open circuits are usually caused by breaks in the wiring, faulty connections or mechanical failure in a component, such as a switch or circuit breaker. Short circuits are usually caused by wires from different components of the circuit contacting each other, or by a wire or component grounding on the metal of the body due to a screw being driven through the wire, insulation cut through by a sharp metal edge, etc.

CIRCUIT BREAKER FEED CIRCUIT: To check the feed circuit continuity at the circuit breaker, connect one test light lead to battery circuit of circuit breaker and ground the other lead. Circuit breaker is located at fuse block. If tester does not light, there is an open circuit in feed circuit to breaker. To check circuit breaker, disconnect output feed wire from breaker and check terminal from which wire was disconnected with test light. If tester does not light, circuit breaker is defective.

WINDOW CONTROL SWITCH CIRCUIT: To check feed circuit continuity at window control switch, connect one test light lead to feed terminal of switch block and ground other lead of tester to body metal, Fig. 50-96. If tester does not light, there is an open or short circuit between switch and power source.

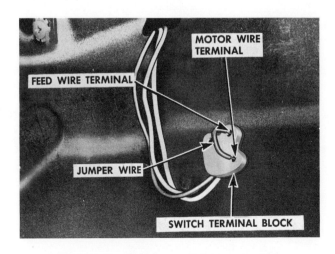

Fig. 50-97. Checking window control switch.

691

WINDOW CONTROL SWITCH: To check the condition of the window control switch, insert one end of a 12 ga. jumper wire to switch feed terminal, and other end to one of the motor lead terminals in the switch block. Repeat this check on the remaining motor terminal, Fig. 50-97.

DOOR WINDOW SWITCH AND MOTOR: To check the wires between door window switch and door window motor, disengage harness connector from window motor connector. Thumb release on harness connector must be depressed before it can be disengaged from motor. Insert one end of a 12 ga. jumper wire to switch feed terminal and other end to one of the motor lead terminals in switch block, Fig. 50-97. With a test light, check for current at motor connector terminal being checked, Fig. 50-98. If tester does not light, there is an open circuit or short circuit in wiring harness between control switch and motor connector.

on many Fisher body cars is shown in Fig. 50-99. In this type of construction, the seat can be moved forward or to the rear after depressing a knob at the left of the seat which locks the adjustment.

One type of electrically operated front seat provides fore and aft movement of the seat, Fig. 50-100, while another type, known as the six-way seat, Fig. 50-101, provides forward, rearward, upward, downward or tilting of the seat.

On the two-way seat, Fig. 50-100, difficulties may be encountered as the result of misalignment, or wear of the various parts. Such troubles are easily located by observing the operation of the seat. Electrical troubles may also be experienced. These can be traced by means of the familiar test light or voltmeter. If current is found to be reaching the electric motor, but the seat still does not operate, the motor is defective and should be replaced.

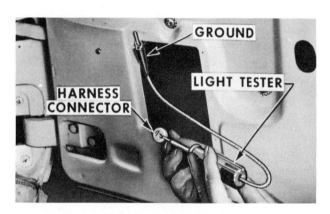

Fig. 50-98. Checking circuit between switch and motor.

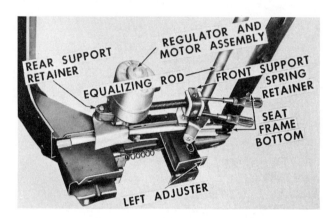

Fig. 50-100. Details of two-way electric seat adjuster, showing screwdrivers being used to pry open seat adjuster regulator front support spring retainer to disengage jack screw nut from support.

Manually and Electrically Operated Seats

For greater comfort of passengers, the front seats of passenger cars are made adjustable. Some are adjusted manually; others are adjusted electrically.

Details of a manually adjustable front seat as used

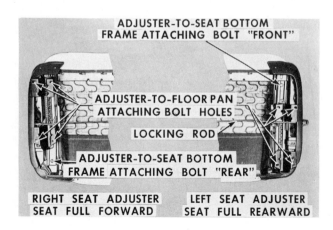

Fig. 50-99. Showing construction of manually adjustable front seat.

Similar troubles may be experienced in the six-way seat, Fig. 50-101. In this design, the seat adjuster operating mechanism incorporates a transmission assembly which includes three solenoids and six drive cables leading to the seat adjuster. Solenoid No. 1, Fig. 50-101, controls the vertical movement of the rear edge of the seat. Solenoid No. 2 controls the horizontal movement of the rear edge of the seat. Solenoid No. 3 controls the vertical movement of the front edge of the seat. In addition to the six seat adjuster drive cables at the transmission assembly, a motor drive cable is installed from the motor to the transmission assembly.

When one of the control switch buttons is actuated, the motor and one of the solenoids are energized simultaneously. The solenoid plunger engages the large gears with a driving gear. The driving gear rotates the large gears which rotate the drive cables and operate both adjusters. When the switch contacts are opened, a spring returns the solenoid plunger to its original position, disengaging the large gears from the driving gears.

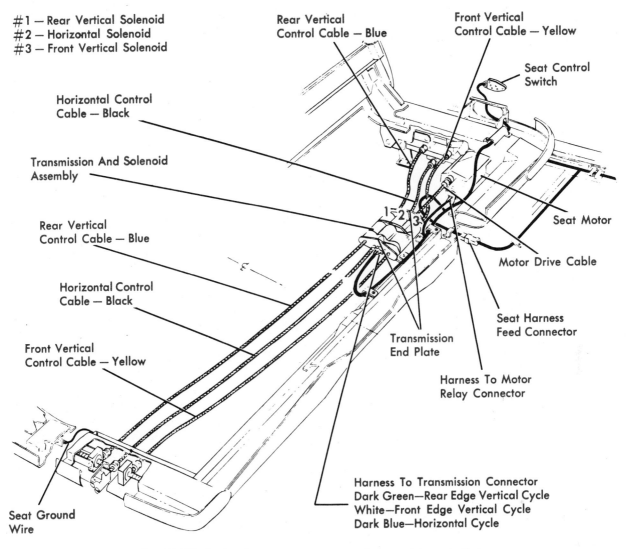

#1 — Rear Vertical Solenoid
#2 — Horizontal Solenoid
#3 — Front Vertical Solenoid

Rear Vertical Control Cable — Blue

Front Vertical Control Cable — Yellow

Seat Control Switch

Horizontal Control Cable — Black

Transmission And Solenoid Assembly

Rear Vertical Control Cable — Blue

Seat Motor

Motor Drive Cable

Horizontal Control Cable — Black

Front Vertical Control Cable — Yellow

Transmission End Plate

Seat Harness Feed Connector

Harness To Motor Relay Connector

Seat Ground Wire

Harness To Transmission Connector
Dark Green—Rear Edge Vertical Cycle
White—Front Edge Vertical Cycle
Dark Blue—Horizontal Cycle

Fig. 50-101. In the six-way seat, movement of the seat is controlled by means of the electric motor, solenoids, gearing and drive cables.

Quiz - Body Repairing, Refinishing

1. When straightening a wrinkled panel, the damage should be removed:
   a. In the same manner as it was made.
   b. In the reverse manner in which it was made.
2. If a dent rises above the surface of a dolly block, the hammer should strike:
   a. The center of the dent.
   b. The edge of the dent.
3. The primary purpose of a body file is to remove metal or to locate high spots on the surface. True or False?
4. Describe what is meant by the term featheredging.
5. For what purpose is body solder used?
6. Describe the procedure for replacing a portion of a body panel.
7. What is the primary purpose of masking?

8. Describe the procedure for masking a head lamp.
9. The main reason for chaining oxygen and acetylene tanks to a post is:
   a. To prevent their theft.
   b. To prevent their tipping over.
   c. So that they will be out of the way.
10. Before attaching a regulator to the oxygen and acetylene tanks, why should the valve first be opened for an instant?
11. The connections of acetylene tanks have:
    a. Right-hand threads.
    b. Left-hand threads.
12. Oxygen connections are painted:
    a. Red.   c. Blue.
    b. White.   d. Green.

13. If the flame at the torch is yellow or backfires, what should be done to correct the condition?

14. Before applying any paint, what should be done to the surface of the panel?

15. Why should primer coats be applied immediately after paint has been removed?

16. Describe the best procedure for taking care of a paint spray gun.

17. What is indicated if the spray pattern of a spray gun is heavy at the ends and light at the center?

18. At what distance should a spray gun be held from the surface of the work?

19. What is the best material to be used when repairing the surface of a body painted with acrylic lacquer?

20. Describe a method of locating the source of a water leak in an automobile body.

21. Why is it important to keep the drain holes in an automobile body open?

Unibody corrosion protection as offered by Chrysler Corp.

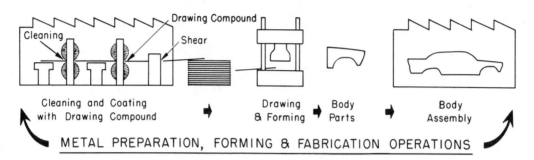

METAL PREPARATION, FORMING & FABRICATION OPERATIONS

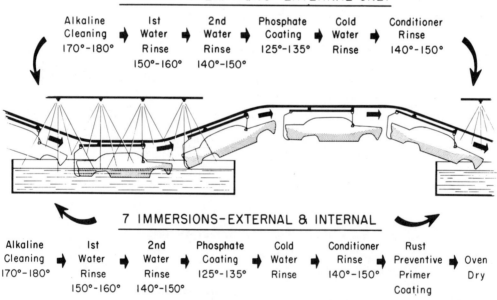

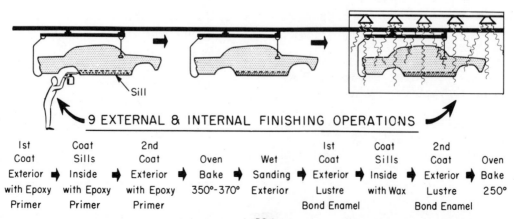

HYDRAULICS
AND PNEUMATICS

Hydraulics

The study of hydraulics is important and necessary to the automotive mechanic because so many parts of the automotive vehicle and servicing equipment are dependent for their operation on liquids under pressure, and in motion. For example, the conventional braking system used on passenger cars is of the hydraulic type and the modern automatic transmission depends on hydraulics for its operation. In the service field, jacks, lifts and presses are operated hydraulically.

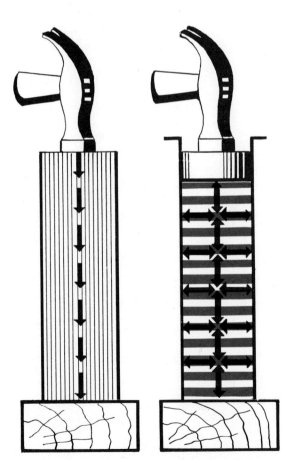

Fig. 51-1. Illustrating the difference in the action of forces when a solid bar is struck, and when a force is applied to the end of a confined liquid.

Technically, liquids and gases are considered as fluids, and while they have many characteristics in common, they differ mainly in that liquids change but slightly when they are compressed. In addition, they have a free surface. Gases, however, are compressible and will fill all parts of the containing vessel.

The complete science of hydraulics includes the manner in which liquids act in tanks and pipes. It includes the laws of floating bodies and the behavior of liquids on submerged surfaces. The subject also treats the flow of liquids under various conditions and methods of directing this flow to accomplish useful work.

In this text, however, the study will be limited primarily to hydraulics as it is applied in the automotive field.

Advantages of Hydraulic Systems

Among the advantages of hydraulic systems are:
a. The elimination of complicated systems of gears, cams and rods.
b. Motion can be transmitted without slack or lost motion.
c. Liquids are not subjected to wear or breakage as in the case with mechanical parts.
d. Hydraulic systems require no lubrication.
e. Applied force can be greatly multiplied and transmitted considerable distances with negligible loss.

Physical Properties of Liquids

Liquids differ from solids in that they do not have a definite form of their own, but conform to the shape of the vessel in which they are contained. Because of the shapelessness of liquids, they can be carried in tubing by gravity or by applying force to them.

In general, liquids may be considered as being incompressible. In fact, a force of 15 lbs. on a cubic inch of water will compress it only 1/20,000 and it would take a force of 32 tons to reduce it 10 percent. When pressure is removed, the liquid being elastic, immediately returns to its original volume.

Transmission of Forces

One of the most important characteristics of liquids is that when force is applied to a confined liquid, it will be transmitted in ALL directions. This is known as Pascal's principle.

To make this clear, consider a metal bar. Striking it on the end, the force will be transmitted the length of the bar, Fig. 51-1. The more rigid the bar, the less force is lost inside the bar, or will be transmitted at right angles to the direction of the blow.

However, when a force is applied to the end of a confined liquid, also shown in Fig. 51-1, it is transmitted straight through to the other end (the same as in the case of the metal bar) but in addition, the force is transmitted equally and undiminished in every direction – forwards, backwards, sidewards – so that the containing vessel is literally filled with pressure.

Furthermore, this pressure is at right angles to the containing surfaces. Pressure of a liquid standing in an open vessel is dependent on the depth of the liquid. This is known as the hydraulic head. Pressure due to the hydraulic head is also dependent on the weight of the liquid. This is known as the density of the liquid, which is the weight in pounds of a cubic inch or cubic foot of the liquid. Water weighs 62.357 lbs. per cu. ft. or .03612 lb. per cu. in. Heavy petroleum oil weighs .0317 and light oil .0287 lb. per cu. in.

In the example illustrated in Fig. 51-2, the water would have to be 222 in. deep to exert a pressure of 8 psi. In the case of heavy oil, it would have to be 252 in.

Specific Gravity

One method of comparing liquids is by their specific gravity, which is the ratio of the weight of a unit volume of that substance (its density) to the weight of 1 cu. in. of water. Since the weight may vary as temperature changes, the measurement is always made at 39.1 deg. F. or 4 deg. C.

The weight of a cubic inch of water is .036 lb., while the weight of a typical hydraulic fluid such as is used in an automotive brake system, is .0357 lb. per cu. in. The specific gravity of the fluid is then obtained by dividing .0357 by .036 which equals 0.99 sp. gr.

In automotive service work, specific gravity is used particularly in the measurement of antifreeze solutions to determine at what temperature the solution in the system will freeze. It is also used in measuring the state of charge in a starting battery.

Hydrometers

To measure the specific gravity of a solution, an instrument known as a hydrometer is used. As shown in Fig. 51-3, the hydrometer consists of a glass tube, containing a calibrated float. The fluid to be measured

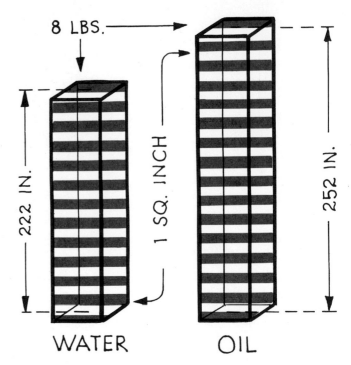

Fig. 51-2. *Illustrating the effect of density on pressure. The 222 in. column of water and the 252 column of oil produce the same pressure.*

is drawn into the glass tube by means of a rubber suction bulb at one end. Then, the height of the float above the surface of the liquid is a measurement of its specific gravity.

Pressure and Force in Hydraulic Systems

According to Pascal's law, any force applied to a confined liquid is transmitted equally in all directions through the liquid regardless of the shape of the container. In Fig. 51-4, when a force is applied to piston No. 1, a pressure will be created throughout the entire system which will act at right angles to all surfaces with equal strength. Pressure is defined as the force divided by the area over which it is distributed. In the

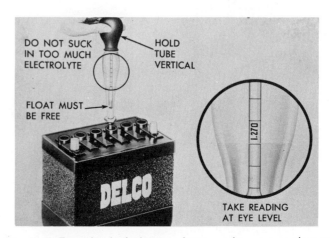

Fig. 51-3. *Example of a hydrometer being used to measure the specific gravity of the acid solution in a storage battery.*

case illustrated in Fig. 51-4, the force applied at piston No. 1 is 100 lbs. as the area of the piston is 10 sq. in., then the pressure is 100 divided by 10 or 10 lbs. psi.

This pressure of 10 psi is exerted over the entire system, the sides of the system as well as piston No. 2, which is at the greatest distance from piston No. 1, where the force is applied. As the vessel containing the fluid is of uniform cross section, and both pistons are the same area, the upward force on piston No. 2, is the same as the force applied to piston No. 1. What has been done is to change the direction of the force from downward at piston No. 1, to upward at piston No. 2.

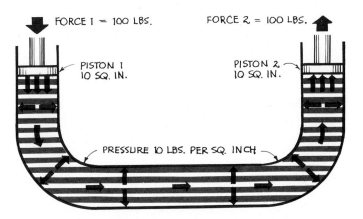

Fig. 51-4. Force applied to a fluid in a confined system is transmitted equally in all directions throughout the system, regardless of the shape of the system.

While the system shown in Fig. 51-4 is of uniform cross section, this is not necessary in order that the same force is available at the output side as is applied at the input side. This is true because of Pascal's law. In other words, the connection between piston No. 1 and piston No. 2 can be any shape or size. This is made clear in Fig. 51-5, where the connection between the two pistons is a tube of smaller diameter than the pistons.

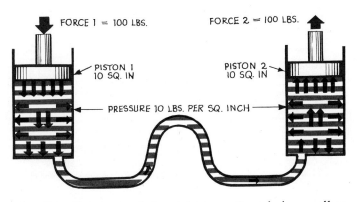

Fig. 51-5. The shape and size of the connecting tube has no effect on the pressure in the cylinders.

Multiplying the Force

In the cases considered so far, there has been no increase in the force as the input piston has been the same size as the output piston. However, if the output piston is made larger in diameter than the input piston, the force will be increased in the same proportions as the areas of the two pistons. For example, in Fig. 51-6, piston No. 1 (the input piston) has an area of 2 sq. in., while the area of the output piston No. 2, is 20 sq. in. If a force of 20 lbs. is applied to piston No. 1, the pressure on the liquid will be 10 psi (20 lbs. divided by 2 sq. in. equals 10 psi).

As this pressure acts equally throughout the system, there will be 10 psi acting on the piston No. 2, but as its area is 20 sq. in., the total force on that piston will be 200 lbs. (20 sq. in. times 10 psi equals 200 lbs.).

A system shown in Fig. 51-6 could also be used in a reverse manner. In other words, it could be used to reduce forces rather than increase them.

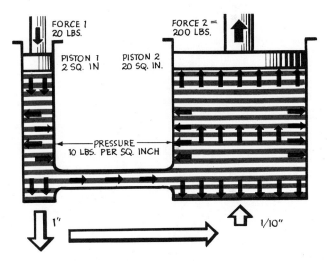

Fig. 51-6. Forces can be multiplied by making the output piston larger than the input piston.

Movement of Liquid

In the examples given in Figs. 51-4 and 51-5, the areas of the pistons were equal. Therefore, if one piston is moved down 1 in., the other piston will be moved upward a corresponding amount. The reason for that is that as the liquid is virtually incompressible, the liquid displaced by the first piston must have some place to go, and it can only move by displacing the second piston an equal amount.

Applying this to the system shown in Fig. 51-6, pushing piston No. 1 down 1 in., will displace 2 cu. in. of liquid. To accommodate that volume of liquid, piston No. 2 will have to move 0.10 in. (the volume of fluid 2 cu. in. divided by the area of the piston 20 sq. in. equals 0.10 in. movement of the piston).

Application of Hydraulic Principles

The principles which have been discussed have wide application in the automotive industry. Hydraulic brakes and jacks utilize these principles. By proper application of these principles, hydraulic jacks are designed so that a small child can raise a heavy truck, and heavy vehicles can be stopped with ease. The special application of hydraulics to automatic transmissions is discussed in the transmission section of this text.

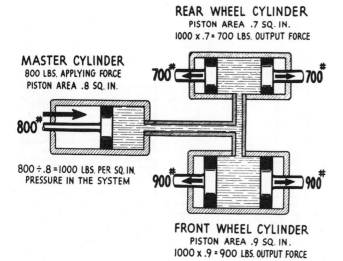

The automobile Hydraulic System
TRANSMITS MOTION AND FORCE
and
CHANGES THE AMOUNT OF FORCE

REAR WHEEL CYLINDER
PISTON AREA .7 SQ. IN.
1000 x .7 = 700 LBS. OUTPUT FORCE

MASTER CYLINDER
800 LBS. APPLYING FORCE
PISTON AREA .8 SQ. IN.

700#   700#

800#

800 ÷ .8 = 1000 LBS. PER SQ. IN.
PRESSURE IN THE SYSTEM

900#   900#

FRONT WHEEL CYLINDER
PISTON AREA .9 SQ. IN.
1000 x .9 = 900 LBS. OUTPUT FORCE

Fig. 51-7. Illustrating the principle of the hydraulic brake.

Hydraulic Brakes

The modern hydraulic brake is an application of multiple outlet pistons (the wheel cylinders) to distribute forces applied at the foot pedal which operates the master input cylinder.

The cylinder in which the master input piston moves is connected by tubing to a cylinder at each wheel, Fig. 51-7. Each of these cylinders contains two opposed pistons, and each piston operates a brake shoe. When force is applied at the brake pedal, pressure is transmitted equally throughout the fluid to each of the wheel cylinders. As a result, all of the wheel cylinders are forced outward, forcing the brake shoes against the brake drums.

When the pressure is removed from the brake pedal, springs on the brake shoes force the shoes back to their normal released position. This movement of the shoes, in turn, forces the pistons inward, return-

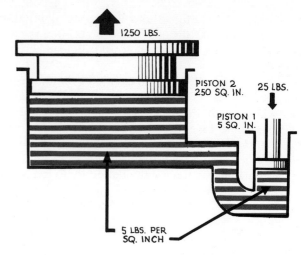

Fig. 51-8. Illustrating the principle of the hydraulic jack.

ing the fluid back to the master cylinder and its reservoir.

This description covers the operation of a simple hydraulic brake with all wheel cylinders of the same diameter. In actual practice, smaller pistons are often used to operate the rear wheel brakes. Some designs provide individual cylinders for each shoe and in some instances, the wheel cylinders are designed with a large diameter cylinder for operating forward shoes and smaller piston for operating the rear shoes of a single brake. Such construction is discussed in the chapter on brakes.

Hydraulic Jacks

A schematic drawing of the principle used in the operation of hydraulic jacks is shown in Fig. 51-8. In the illustration, the small piston, where the force is applied, has an area of 5 sq. in. Its cylinder is directly connected to a large cylinder with a piston which has an area of 250 sq. in. This large piston forms the platform which is used to raise the load.

If a force of 25 lbs. is applied to the small piston, a pressure of 5 lbs. psi will be produced in the hy-

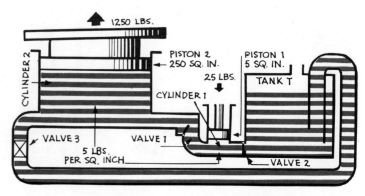

Fig. 51-9. Schematic drawing of hydraulic jack showing the valving necessary to maintain the load at the desired height, and also to lower the load when desired.

draulic fluid. This 5 psi will act over the entire area of the large piston with its 250 sq. in. surface. The resulting force will be 250 x 5 = 1250 lifting force. In other words, an initial force of only 25 lbs. has been transformed into a force capable of lifting more than one half ton.

It must be remembered, however, that while the original force has been multiplied 50 times, the distance traveled is just the opposite. If the small piston is moved 5 in., then 25 cu. in. of liquid will be displaced. Distributing this over 250 sq. in. of the larger piston, the piston will be raised 25 divided by 250 or 0.1 in.

To prevent the weight of the load on the platform from forcing the fluid back through the system, and also to provide ways and means of lowering the load, it is necessary to include various valves in the system, Fig. 51-9.

Quiz - Hydraulics

1. Give three examples of the use of hydraulics in the automotive field.
2. Define hydraulics.
3. Name four major advantages of the hydraulic system.
4. State Pascal's law.
5. What is meant by hydraulic head?
6. On what two factors does hydraulic head depend?
7. a. What is the weight of a cu. in. of water?
   b. What is the weight of a cu. in. of hydraulic fluid?
8. Define density of a fluid.
9. Define specific gravity.
10. What piece of automotive equipment depends on specific gravity for its operation?
11. Define pressure as applied to a hydraulic system.
12. If a force of 50 lbs. is applied to a piston of 2 sq. in. in area on a hydraulic cylinder, what is the pressure?
13. In a hydraulic jack, the input piston has an area of 3 sq. in. and the output piston an area of 300 sq. in. If 30 lbs. is applied at the input piston, what is the lifting force at the output piston?

Pneumatics

Pneumatics is the study of the mechanical properties of air and other gases, and has many applications in the automotive field. It is particularly important in the study of carburetion and pneumatic or air brakes.

Technically, air and other gases are considered fluids and have many of the same characteristics as liquids. Gases differ from liquids mainly in that they are highly compressible and completely fill any containing vessel. But gases are the same as liquids, in that they conform to the shape of their containers, and pressure in a gas acts equally in all directions.

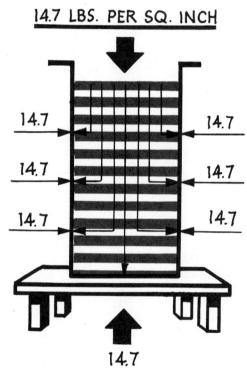

Fig. 51-10. *Atmospheric pressure acting on the surface of gas or liquid is transmitted equally throughout.*

Air and any gas has weight, and therefore exerts pressure by virtue of its head; that is, its depth from the upper surface to the lower surface of the gas. Although any small volume of any gas weighs very little, the pressure of air at sea level under standard conditions amounts to 14.7 psi. The pressure or the head is the weight of the air from the surface of the earth extending many miles upward into space.

Since air is compressed by its own weight, the same volume of air at sea level will weigh considerably more than on a mountain top. In other words, air becomes less dense as altitude or distance from the earth increases. This is particularly important because of its effect on carburetion. As altitude increases, less air enters the carburetor, consequently the mixture of fuel and air becomes richer. Instruments designed to measure the pressure of the atmosphere are known as barometers. They are used largely in forecasting weather, and in measuring altitudes.

As has been pointed out, gases are compressed by their own weight, and therefore the same volume of air at sea level will weigh considerably more than on top of a mountain. In addition, gases expand as their temperature is increased, so that a volume of gas at high temperature will weigh less than the same volume of gas at low temperature. That is why the efficiency of an automobile decreases as the temperature of the air entering the carburetor increases.

Atmospheric pressures obey Pascal's law in the same manner as liquids. This condition is shown in Fig. 51-10, where atmospheric pressure, acting on the surface of the gas or liquid, is transmitted equally throughout the gas or liquid to the walls of the container, but it is balanced by the pressure on the outer walls of the container. The thinnest of paper, when suspended in the atmosphere will not be torn in spite of the fact that air pressure of 14.7 psi is pressing on it, Fig. 51-11. The reason the paper is not torn is that the pressure is exerted on both sides of the sheet and the pressures are therefore balanced.

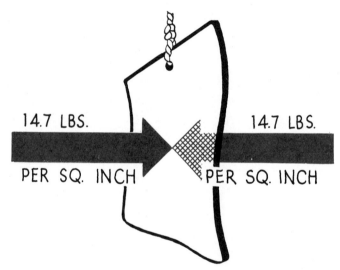

Fig. 51-11. *Thin paper will not be torn in spite of the fact that air pressure of 14.7 psi is pressing on it.*

In Fig. 51-12, atmospheric pressure acting on one piston is balanced by the same pressure acting on the surface of the other piston. The fact that the two pistons are of different areas makes no difference as the unit pressure, that is the pressure per square inch, is the same on both pistons.

Effect of Vacuum

As pointed out in the preceding paragraph, with equal atmospheric pressure acting on the two surfaces, Fig. 51-12, the liquid will be at the same height in both sides of the U-shape tube. If the pressure on

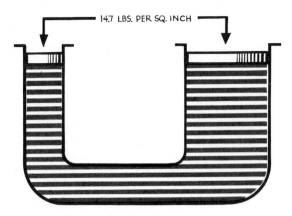

Fig. 51-12. *Atmospheric pressure acting on one piston is balanced by the same pressure acting on the other piston.*

one side of the tube is reduced, there will be a movement of liquid to the side of the reduced pressure.

This can be illustrated by the familiar situation of drinking soda through a straw, Fig. 51-13. When soda is sucked through a straw, the balance of pressures acting on the liquid is disturbed. The pressure within the straw is reduced as the result of suction, and as a result the air pressure (14.7 psi) acting on the surface of the liquid in the glass, forces the liquid into the straw.

The liquid can be held at any desired level in the straw. This level will always be where the pressure of the head of the liquid, Fig. 51-13, equals the difference between the pressure in the straw, and that on the surface of the liquid.

Sucking on the straw has produced a partial vacuum on the surface of the liquid within the straw. A partial vacuum is actually a pressure that is less than the prevailing atmospheric pressure. Theoretically, the limit of this process would be a condition of zero

pressure − a complete vacuum. In actual practice this has never been attained.

This simple principle, illustrated by sucking soda through a straw is identical with that which is used in the operation of a conventional power brake with which

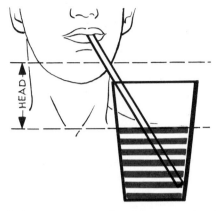

Fig. 51-13. *With air pressure within the straw reduced below that of the atmosphere, air pressure forces the liquid into the straw.*

many passenger cars are equipped, Fig. 51-14. Vacuum from the intake manifold is connected to one side of a cylinder. Atmospheric pressure on the other side causes a piston to move toward the vacuum side and this motion is used to apply the brake.

Compressed Air

Compressed air is air which has been forced into a smaller space than which it would ordinarily occupy in its free or atmospheric state. In the automotive field, compressed air has many uses. In addition to inflating tires, it is used for such purposes as spray-

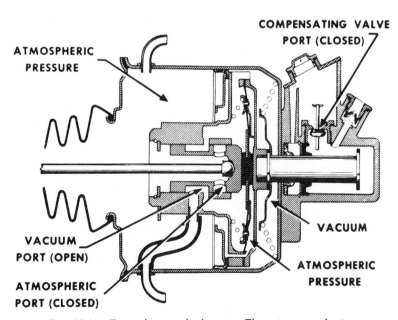

Fig. 51-14. *Typical power brake unit. There is atmospheric pressure on one side of the piston and vacuum on the other.*

ing paint, blowing dirt and other foreign matter from parts, operating brakes on heavy trucks, and to operate impact wrenches.

As pointed out previously, normal air (due to the weight of air above it) has a pressure of 14.7 psi. However, when speaking of compressed air, its initial pressure of 14.7 psi is ignored, and the pressure of the compressed air is given as the amount of pressure above atmospheric. In other words, a gauge for measuring the pressure of compressed air registers zero when connected only to the atmosphere.

By providing suitable piping, compressed air will "flow" in much the same manner as liquids flow along connecting pipes. For example, if two reservoirs are connected, one containing air under pressure, and the other, air at atmospheric pressure, air will flow from the reservoir of higher pressure to that of lower pressure. This flow will continue until both reservoirs are at the same pressure.

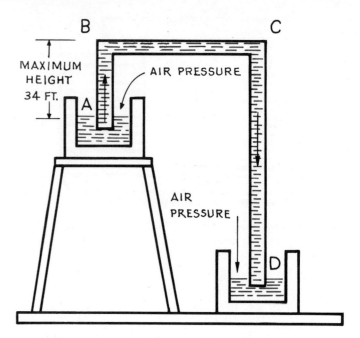

Fig. 51-16. Atmospheric pressure causes the liquid in a syphon to flow from the upper tank to the lower tank.

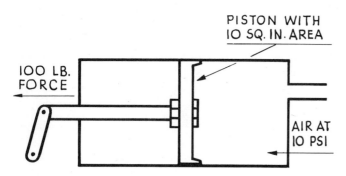

Fig. 51-15. Illustrating the principle of a simple air brake.

Air Brakes

The application of compressed air in the operation of automotive air brakes is relatively simple. In Fig. 51-15, compressed air is admitted into a cylinder which encloses a piston. The force of the compressed air will cause the piston to move until it encounters a resistance equal to the force developed by the compressed air. As the piston in Fig. 51-15 has an area of 10 sq. in., and the compressed air a pressure of 10 psi, the total force developed will be 10 x 10 or 100 lbs. This is similar to the effect of hydraulic power illustrated in Figs. 51-4 and 51-6.

It must be remembered that the quantity of air acting on the piston does not affect the force developed. The only factors involved are the air pressure, and the area of the piston on which the air pressure is acting.

Principle of the Syphon

Normal air pressure (or the pressure of the atmosphere) is used to do many kinds of work. For example, the syphon drains tanks by means of atmospheric pressure. In a syphon, a tube or pipe is con-

nected to two tanks, one higher than the other, as shown in Fig. 51-16. Once the connecting tube has been filled with liquid, it will continue to flow to the lower tank until the level of the liquid is the same in both tanks or until the upper tank is empty. The force that causes the liquid to flow is the pressure of the atmosphere. This pressure forces the liquid up the short arm of the syphon (AB). Theoretically, the liquid can be raised a height of 34 ft. if the liquid is water. Denser liquids cannot be raised as far. However, at high altitudes, where air pressure is less than at sea level, the liquid could be raised a shorter distance.

The action of the syphon is of interest. The force of the atmosphere tending to push the liquid up the short arm of the syphon is opposed by the downward pressure due to the weight of the liquid, as in AB, Fig. 51-16. Similarly, the atmospheric pressure tends to drive the liquid up the long arm, CD, but is resisted by the weight of the liquid. As the weight of the liquid in CD is greater than that in AB, the atmospheric pressure meets greater resistance in pushing the liquid up CD than it meets in pushing it in the opposite direction. The liquid will therefore flow up the arm, AB, and continue until it reaches the lower reservoir.

Venturi Tube

Because of its importance in carburetion, it is necessary to study the action of the venturi tube. A venturi tube is a tube with a restricted section, Fig. 51-17. When a liquid or air is passed through such a tube, the speed of flow is increased at the area of restriction, and the fluid pressure is decreased. Since the same amount or volume of air flows through all sections of the carburetor throat, obviously if the area decreases, the velocity must increase in order to maintain the same rate of flow. Then when the area increases, the velocity will decrease.

This is clearly illustrated in Fig. 51-17. This shows the variation in vacuum in different sections of the carburetor. Vacuum is measured in inches of mercury and is designated as inches Hg, (the initials used in the chemical symbol representing mercury). Note at the point of maximum restriction that the vacuum and the velocity of airflow is at a maximum. Also at the air inlet to the carburetor where the air pressure is normal, the vacuum is zero.

The operation of the venturi is used in carburetors to maintain the correct air-fuel ratio throughout the range of speeds and loads of the engine.

Boyle's Law

An important characteristic of air and other gases is that if the pressure on a gas in a confined space is doubled, the gas will be compressed to half its origi-

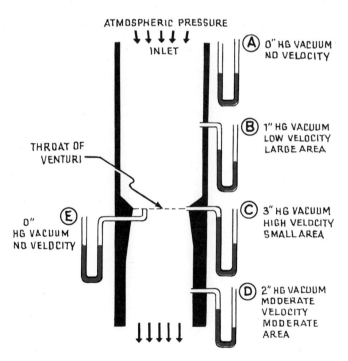

Fig. 51-17. In the throat of the venturi, moving air will have the greatest velocity and maximum vacuum will exist, as shown at C. However, if airflow is stopped, the vacuum becomes zero.

nal volume, provided the temperature remains the same. This is known as Boyle's law after its discoverer. The law is normally given as follows: If the temperature of a confined gas is kept constant, its volume will vary inversely with its pressure.

This may be expressed as follows:

$$P'V' = PV$$

where P and V represent the pressure and volume of a gas before compression, and P' and V' the pressure and volume after compression. For example, if the pressure of a quantity of gas is 50 psi, and it occupies 10 cu. ft., this air is then compressed until it exerts a pressure of 75 psi. Temperature remains constant. What is the volume of the gas after compression?

$$\frac{V}{V'} = \frac{P'}{P}$$

$$\frac{75}{50} = \frac{10}{P}$$

$$75P = 500$$

$$P = 6.66 \text{ cu. ft.}$$

Charles' Law

Another important law relating to the behavior of gases under different conditions is known as Charles' law which states that under constant pressure, volume of a gas varies directly with the absolute temperature of the gas. The absolute temperature is the temperature in C. degrees plus 273. This law is expressed as follows:

$$\frac{V'}{V_2} = \frac{T'}{T_2}$$

where V' is the volume of a gas when its absolute temperature is T' and V_2 is the volume of the same gas when its absolute temperature is T_2.

Example: To what volume will 110 cu. ft. of gas at 15 deg. C. expand if heated at a constant pressure to 55 deg. C.?

$$T' = 15° + 273 = 288° \text{ absolute}$$
$$T_2 = 55° + 273 = 328° \text{ absolute}$$

$$\frac{110}{V_2} = \frac{288}{328}$$

$$36080 = 288V_2$$

$$V_2 = 125.3 \text{ cu. ft.}$$

Quiz - Pneumatics

1. What is the normal pressure of the atmosphere?
2. What is the major difference between a liquid and a gas?
3. What causes the liquid to rise in a soda straw?

4. In the conventional power or booster brake used on a passenger car, what power is used to assist the driver to apply the brakes?
5. In a conventional gauge such as is used to mea-

sure the pressure in a tank of compressed air, what will the gauge register when the tank is open to the atmosphere?

6. Draw an illustration and explain the principle of a syphon.

7. What is a venturi tube?

8. At what point in a carburetor is the airflow the fastest?

9. For what purpose is the venturi used in a carburetor?

10. State Boyle's Law.

11. State Charles' Law.

JOB
OPPORTUNITIES

For the young man with ability, educational background, and practical training, the automotive field offers a wide range of job opportunities.

It sometimes happens when choosing a vocation, that only a limited area of the field is observed. This is a mistake, because the first job should be considered as a stepping stone to a higher and better paying job.

Let us take a quick look at some of the job possibilities the automotive field offers:

Auto Mechanic

Were you to get a job in a retail automotive business, the first important job you are likely to get after you have had some training and experience as a helper, is Auto Mechanic.

The days of the "greaseball" mechanic are over. Most shops today are clean, well lighted and ventilated, and are equipped with laborsaving tools and testing devices, which make the jobs easier and more interesting. Modern mechanics wear neat working clothes.

An auto mechanic's job calls for a broad range of both light and heavy repair work. It requires the ability to diagnose and locate trouble, and to make the right adjustment or replacement. A good auto mechanic is well paid, and his work is always in demand.

Specialty Mechanic

A Specialty Mechanic is a serviceman who has become a specialist in some one phase of repair work. You can specialize in diagnosis and tune-up, electrical repair, body work, automatic transmissions, front end and steering or any of a number of other kinds of service.

Shop Foreman

A Shop Foreman is the man in charge of mechanics in an automotive dealership, independent service garage, or private garage of a transportation company. He is usually an expert mechanic who has been promoted to foreman. His job involves scheduling and routing repair work as it comes into the shop - supervising and instructing mechanics - inspecting finished repairs - and being responsible generally for quality work and satisfactory shop operation.

Service Manager

A Service Manager is the department head, supervising all service employes and responsible for customer satisfaction. He should be a good manager and should have the ability to get along well with both employes and customers. In addition to department supervision, he must try to build up business for the shop with advertising and sales promotion activities.

Motor Vehicle Salesman

Motor Vehicle Salesman is the job for you if you have a special liking for selling. Experience in the service department gives you an excellent background for sales work because, if you know the mechanics of a vehicle you can do a much better job of talking about the car or truck, demonstrating it and comparing it with other competing makes.

Sales Manager

A Sales Manager has charge of the entire selling activity of a dealership, including service. This is one of the best positions in the retail automotive business usually held by a man who has made a success of selling and who has managerial ability.

Parts Manager

A Parts Manager for a car or truck dealer has an important job ordering, stocking and selling replacement parts and accessories. He supplies the shop in his dealership and sells parts and accessories at wholesale to the independent repair garages in his community. Training in service work and parts sales are valuable experience for this job.

Jobber Salesman

Jobber Salesman is an interesting occupation in the parts field, a job that should appeal to a sales-minded young man with automotive service training. A jobber salesman, representing a wholesale house, travels over a certain territory selling the products of several manufacturers to all kinds of automotive repair and supply shops.

Employment with Manufacturers of Motor Vehicles

Employment with Manufacturers of Motor Vehicles is sometimes open to men with automotive mechanics training and other qualifications. This applies to such positions as: Factory District Manager, Factory Service Manager, Factory Service Representative, Factory Parts Manager and Factory Service Instructor.

Employment in Automotive Factories

Employment in Automotive Factories can make use of training in automotive mechanics in such jobs as: Final Assembly Car Inspector, Final Assembly Repairman, Dynamometer Tester, Experimental Driver, Driver Mechanic, and Engineering Garage Mechanic and Repairman.

Technical Teacher

Technical Teacher, either in a public school or as a factory service instructor, is an interesting career. You might be employed by the factory to train service personnel in new developments, or you might teach automotive mechanics in schools.

Driver of a Truck or Bus

Driver of a Truck or Bus is a job employing over 6 million persons, the second largest occupational group in America. Many operators of large fleets of trucks or buses prefer that their drivers have automotive mechanics training. Such drivers take better care of their vehicles; they can make emergency repairs if necessary; and in general they are more reliable.

Insurance Adjuster and Claim Examiner

Insurance Adjuster and Claim Examiner are jobs that insurance companies like to fill with young men who, in addition to other qualifications, have automotive service training.

Representatives

Representatives of many companies which supply the automotive industry are frequently bright, high-caliber young men who began their careers with training in automotive mechanics.

Owners of Service Stations or Specialty Repair Shops

Owners of Service Stations or Specialty Repair Shops can certainly use automotive service training to advantage. If you have any ambition to become this kind of independent business man, training in automotive mechanics can help you achieve your goal.

Automotive Dealers

Automotive Dealers, men who operate their own businesses and are frequently leaders in their communities, often get their start as automotive mechanics.

You can see from the foregoing that training in automotive mechanics could be your key to any one of a number of interesting careers. You can see that automotive service is a big, broad, many-sided business with enough opportunities to interest almost anyone who has the desire and determination to make good in a worthwhile job.

Remember, your most valuable asset is the ambition and determination to succeed. By alertness, application and perseverance, you can gain knowledge and skill for which there is an eager market offering many satisfying rewards.

GLOSSARY OF AUTOMOTIVE TERMS

AAA: American Automobile Association.

AABM: Association of American Battery Manufacturers, Inc.

ABRASION: Wearing or rubbing away. Example: action of sandpaper on wood.

A/C: Air conditioning.

AC: Alternating current.

ACCELERATOR: A foot-operated pedal for regulating speed of an engine.

ACCUMULATOR: English term for a storage battery.

ACETYLENE OR OXY-ACETYLENE WELDING: Utilization of an acetylene flame to heat metal to fusion or melting point when uniting it.

ACKERMAN PRINCIPLE: Design having wheel spindles mounted on axle ends to permit spindles to be turned at an angle to axle for steering purposes.

ACRYLIC: A surface finish made from synthetic polymers. Like lacquer, acrylic dries by solvent evaporation.

ACTIVE MATERIAL: In a storage battery: peroxide of lead (brown) in positive plates and metallic lead (gray) in negative plates upon which sulphuric acid acts.

ADAPTOR CARBURETOR: A device attached to a gasoline carburetor which permits an internal combustion engine to run either on gasoline or liquefied petroleum gas.

ADDITIVE: In automotive oils: material added to oil to give it certain properties. Example: material added to engine oil to lessen its tendency to thicken at low temperature.

AEA: Automotive Electric Association.

AERA: Automotive Engine Rebuilders Association.

AIR: A gas containing approximately 4/5 nitrogen, 1/5 oxygen and some carbonic gas.

AIR CLEANER: A device for filtering, cleaning, and removing dust from intake air to a unit, such as an engine or air compressor.

AIR-FUEL RATIO: Ratio by weight of the fuel as compared to air in carburetor mixture.

AIR GAP: Space between spark plug electrodes, motor and generator armatures, field shoes, etc.

AIR HORN: Air inlet of carburetor to which air cleaner is ordinarily attached.

AIR-LOCK: A bubble of air trapped in a fluid circuit which interferes with normal circulation of fluid.

AIR SPRING: An air-filled bag or device that is pressurized to provide spring action.

ALIGNMENT: An adjustment to bring related components into a line.

ALLEN WRENCH: A hexagonal wrench which fits into a recessed hexagonal hole.

ALLOY: A mixture of different metals. Example: solder is an alloy of lead and tin.

ALTERNATING CURRENT: An electric current alternating back and forth in direction of flow.

ALTERNATOR: Generator in which alternating current is changed to direct current by means of a rectifier.

ALUMINUM: A metal noted for its lightness and often alloyed with small quantities of other metals for automotive use.

AMA: Automobile Manufacturers Association.

AMBIENT: Surrounding on all sides.

AMMETER: An instrument for measuring flow of electric current.

AMPERE: Unit of measurement for flow of electric current.

AMPERE-HOUR CAPACITY: A term used to indicate capacity of a storage battery. Example: delivery of a certain number of amperes for a certain number of hours.

ANNEALING: A process of softening metal. Example: heating and slow cooling of a piece of iron.

ANNULAR BALL BEARING: A ball bearing with a nonadjustable inner and outer race or races.

ANNULUS: In planetary gear system: an internal ring gear that operates in conjunction with a sun gear, pinion gears and pinion carrier. See RING GEAR.

ANODE: A positive pole of an electric current.

ANTIFREEZE: A material such as ethylene glycol added to water to lower its freezing point.

ANTIFRICTION BEARING: A bearing constructed with balls or rollers between journal and bearing surface to provide rolling instead of sliding friction.

ANTISMOG DEVICE: A special part or system designed to reduce or eliminate emission of noxious gases from exhaust of engine. See EXHAUST EMISSIONS.

APERTURE: An opening, hole or port.

API: American Petroleum Institute.

ARC WELDING: A method of utilizing an electric current jumping an air gap to provide heat for welding metal.

ARMATURE: Part of an electrical device which includes main current-carrying winding. In a generator, it is usually core which rotates within pole shoes which are surrounded by field coils.

ARTICULATED MOUNTING: A term used where parts are connected by links and links are anchored to provide a double hinging action.

ASBESTOS: A natural fibrous mineral with great heat resisting ability.

ASME: American Society of Mechanical Engineers.

ATA: American Trucking Association.

ATMOSPHERIC PRESSURE: Weight of air at sea level: about 14.7 lbs. per square inch; less at higher altitudes.

ATOM: Smallest distinct chemical unit of a substance, composed of electrons, neutrons and protons.

AUTOMATIC STEERING EFFECT: Built-in tendency of an automobile to resume travel in a straight line when released from a turn.

AXLE: Shaft or shafts of a vehicle upon which wheels are mounted.

B & S GAUGE: Brown and Sharpe gauge which is a standard measure of wire size. Smaller the number: larger the wire.

BACKFIRE: Ignition of mixture in intake manifold by flame from a cylinder, possibly from a leaking inlet valve.

BACKLASH: Clearance or "play" between two parts, such as meshed gears.

BACK-PRESSURE: A resistance to free flow, such as a restriction in exhaust line.

BAFFLE OR BAFFLE PLATE: An obstruction for checking or deflecting flow of gases or sound.

BALK RING: A friction-regulated pawl or plunger used to facilitate engagement of gears.

BALL BEARING: An antifriction bearing consisting of a hardened inner and outer race with hardened steel balls interposed between two races. Called ball runners in England.

BATTERY: Any number of complete electrical cells assembled in one housing or case.

B.D.C.: Bottom dead center.

BEARING: A part in which a journal, shaft, or pivot turns or moves.

BELL HOUSING: Covering around flywheel and clutch or torque converter.

BENDIX GEAR OR BENDIX DRIVE: A gear mounted on a screw shaft attached to starting motor armature which automatically engages and disengages electric starting motor.

BENZOL: A by-product of manufacture of coke, sometimes used as an engine fuel.

BEZEL: A grooved ring or rim in which a transparent instrument cover is placed.

BHP: Brake horsepower. A measurement of power developed by an engine in actual operation.

BLOW-BY: A leakage or loss of pressure, often used with reference to leakage of compression past piston ring between piston and cylinder.

BOILING POINT: Temperature at atmospheric pressure at which bubbles or vapors rise to surface and escape.

BONDED LINING: Brake lining cemented to shoes or bands which eliminates need for rivets.

BONNET: English name for hood.

BOOSTER: A mechanical or hydraulic device attached to brake or steering systems to add to manual power applied by operator.

BORE: Diameter of a hole, such as a cylinder; also to enlarge a hole as distinguished from making a hole with a drill.

BORING BAR: A stiff bar equipped with multiple cutting bits which is used to bore a series of bearings or journals in proper alignment with each other.

BOSS: An extension or strengthened section, such as projections within a piston which support piston pin or piston pin bushings.

BOTTLED GAS: Liquefied petroleum gas compressed and contained in portable cylinders.

BOUNCE: Applied to engine valves: a condition where valve is not held tightly to its seat when cam is not lifting it. In ignition distributor: a condition where breaker points make and break contact when they should remain closed.

BRAKE ANCHOR: Pivot pin on brake backing plate against which shoe bears.

BRAKE BAND: A band, surrounding a brake drum, to which lining is attached.

BRAKE BLEEDING: Procedure for removing air from lines of a hydraulic system.

BRAKE CYLINDER: A cylinder containing a movable piston which is actuated by hydraulic pressure to move brake shoes against braking surface of drum or disc.

BRAKE DISC: A circular plate against which brake lining is forced to retard vehicle.

BRAKE DRUM: A metal cylinder attached to wheel and surrounding shoe and lining.

BRAKE "FADE": A condition where repeated severe applications of brakes cause expansion of brake drum or loss of frictional ability or both, which results in impaired braking ability.

BRAKE FLUID: A compounded liquid for use in hydraulic brake systems which must meet exacting conditions (impervious to heat, freezing, thickening, bubbling, etc.).

BRAKE FLUSHING: A procedure for removing fluid from a brake system and washing out any sediment it contains.

BRAKE LINING: A material having a suitable coefficient of friction which is attached to brake shoe and which contacts brake drum to retard vehicle.

BRAKE SHOE: Carrier to which brake lining is attached, and which is used to force lining in contact with brake drum.

BRAKE SHOE HEEL: Generally, end of brake shoe nearest anchor pin.

BRAKE SHOE TOE: Generally, end of brake shoe opposite anchor pin.

BRAZE: To join two pieces of metal with use of a comparatively high melting point material. Example: join two pieces of steel by using brass or bronze as a solder.

BREAKER ARM: Movable part of a pair of contact points in an ignition distributor or magneto.

BREAKER POINTS: Two separable points usually faced with silver, platinum or tungsten which interrupt primary circuit in distributor or magneto for purpose of inducing a high tension current in ignition system.

BREAK-IN: Process of wearing into a desirable fit between surfaces of two new or reconditioned parts.

BRINELL HARDNESS: A scale for designating degree of hardness possessed by a substance.

BROACH: To finish surface of metal by pushing or pulling a multiple edge cutting tool over or through it.

BRUSHES: Bars of carbon or other conducting material which contact commutator of an electric motor or generator.

BTU (British Thermal Unit): A measurement of amount of heat required to raise temperature of 1 lb. of water, 1 degree, Fahrenheit.

BUCKLED PLATES: Battery plates that have been bent or warped out of a flat plane.

BURNISH: To smooth or polish by use of a sliding tool under pressure.

BUSHING: A removable liner for a bearing. Called a bush in England.

BUTANE: A petroleum hydrocarbon compound which has a boiling point of about 32 deg. F. which is used as engine fuel. Loosely referred to as Liquefied Petroleum Gas and often combined with Propane.

BYPASS: An alternate path for a flowing substance.

CALIBRATE: To determine or adjust graduation or scale of any instrument giving quantitative measurements.

CALIPER: Applied to disc brakes: that part which straddles disc and contains hydraulic components.

CALIPERS: An adjustable tool for determining inside or outside diameter by contact and retaining dimension for measurement or comparison.

CALORIFIC VALUE: A measure of heating value of fuel.

CALORIMETER: An instrument to measure amount of heat given off by a substance when burned.

CALORY: Metric measurement of amount of heat required to raise 1 gram of water from zero degree to 1 degree Centigrade.

CAM OR BREAKER CAM: Multilobed cam rotating in ignition distributor which serves to interrupt primary circuit to induce a high tension spark for ignition.

CAM ANGLE: Applied to an ignition distributor: number of degrees of rotation of distributor shaft during which contact points are closed.

CAMBER: In wheel alignment: outward or inward tilt of wheel at top.

CAM GROUND PISTON: A piston ground to a slightly oval shape which under heat of operation becomes round.

CAMSHAFT: Shaft containing lobes or cams which operate engine valves.

CAPE CHISEL: A metal cutting chisel shaped to cut or work in channels or grooves.

CARBON: A common nonmetallic element which is an excellent conductor of electricity. It also forms in combustion chamber of an engine during burning of fuel and lubricating oil.

CARBON DIOXIDE: Compressed into solid form, this material is known as "dry ice" and remains at a temperature of -109 degrees, F. It goes directly from a solid to a vapor state.

CARBON MONOXIDE: Gas formed by incomplete combustion. Colorless, odorless, very poisonous.

CARBONIZE: Process of carbon formation within an engine. Examples: deposits on spark plugs and within combustion chamber.

CARBURETOR: A device for automatically mixing fuel in proper proportion with air to produce a combustible gas.

CARBURETOR "ICING": A term used to describe formation of ice on a carburetor throttle plate during certain atmospheric conditions.

CARDAN JOINT: A universal joint with corresponding yokes at a right angle with each other.

CASE-HARDEN: To harden surface of steel.

CASING: English name for housing.

CASING HEAD GASOLINE: A term used to describe lighter parts of petroleum products which were obtained as a natural gasoline by condensing natural gas from an oil well.

CASTELLATE: Formed to resemble a castle battlement. Example: a castellated nut.

CASTER: In wheel alignment: backward or forward tilt of steering axis.

CATHODE: Negative pole of an electric current.

CELL: Unit of a battery containing a group of positive and negative plates along with electrolyte.

CELL CONNECTOR: Lead bar or link connecting pole of one cell to pole of another.

CENTER OF GRAVITY: Point of a body from which it could be suspended, or on which it could be supported, and be in balance. Example: center of gravity of a wheel is center of wheel hub.

CENTIGRADE: A measurement of temperature used principally in foreign countries. Zero on Centigrade scale is 32 deg. on Fahrenheit scale.

CENTRIFUGAL FORCE: A force which tends to move a body away from its center of rotation. Example: a whirling weight attached to a string.

CENTRIFUSE BRAKE DRUMS: In order to combine strength of a steel drum with desirable friction characteristics of cast iron, a lining of cast iron is sprayed on inside of a steel drum. Both metals are handled while hot to encourage fusing of two metals.

CHAMFER: A bevel or taper at edge of a hole.

CHARGE (or Recharge): Passing an electrical current through a battery to restore it to activity.

CHASE: To straighten up or repair damaged threads.

CHASSIS: A French word meaning framework of a vehicle without a body and fenders.

CHASSIS DYNAMOMETER: A machine for measuring amount of power delivered to drive wheels of a vehicle.

CHECK VALVE: A gate or valve which allows passage of gas or fluid in one direction only.

CHEMICAL COMPOUND: Combination of two or more chemical elements which can be a gas, a liquid or a solid.

CHEMICAL ELEMENT: Gaseous, liquid or solid matter which cannot be divided into simpler form.

CHILLED IRON: Cast iron with hardened surface.

CHIP: To cut with a chisel.

CHOKE: A reduced passage. Example: valve in carburetor air inlet to cut down volume of air admitted.

CHROMIUM STEEL: An alloy of steel with a small amount of chromium to produce a metal which is highly resistant to oxidation and corrosion.

CIRCUIT: Path of electric current, fluids or gases. Examples: for electricity, a wire; for fluids and gases, a pipe.

CIRCUIT BREAKER: A device for interrupting an electrical circuit; often automatic and also known as "contact breaker," "interrupter," "cut-out" or "relay."

CLEARANCE: Space allowed between two parts. Example: space between a journal and a bearing.

CLOCKWISE ROTATION: Rotation in same direction as hands of a clock.

CLUTCH: A device for connecting and disconnecting engine from transmission, or for a similar purpose in other units.

COEFFICIENT OF FRICTION: Amount of friction developed between two surfaces pressed together and moved one on the other.

"COLD" MANIFOLD: An intake manifold to which exhaust gas is not applied for heating purposes.

COMBUSTION: Process of burning.

COMBUSTION SPACE OR CHAMBER: Volume of cylinder above piston with piston on top center.

COMMUTATOR: A ring of adjacent copper bars insulated from each other to which wires of armature or winding are attached.

COMPENSATING PORT: An opening in a brake master cylinder to permit fluid return to reservoir.

COMPOUND: A mixture of two or more ingredients.

COMPOUND WINDING: Two electric windings: one in series, other in shunt or parallel with other electric units or equipment. Applied to electric motors or generators: one winding is shunted across armature; other is in series with armature.

COMPRESSION: Reduction in volume of a gas. Applied to coil spring: squeezing together, or opposite of tension.

COMPRESSION RATIO: Volume of combustion chamber at end of compression stroke as compared to volume of cylinder and chamber with piston on bottom center.

CONCENTRIC: Two circles having same center but different diameters.

CONDENSATION: Process of a vapor becoming a liquid. Reverse of evaporation.

CONDENSER: A device for turning vapor into liquid form. Applied to an electric circuit: a device for temporarily collecting and storing a surge of electrical current for later discharge.

CONDUCTOR: A material along or through which electricity will flow with slight resistance: silver, copper and carbon are good conductors.

CONNECTING ROD: Rod that connects piston to crankshaft.

CONSTANT MESH TRANSMISSION: An arrangement of gearing where gears remain in mesh instead of sliding in and out of engagement.

CONSTANT VELOCITY: Double universal joint that cancels out vibrations caused by driving power being transmitted through an angle.

CONTACT BREAKER: See CIRCUIT BREAKER.

CONTACT POINTS: See BREAKER POINTS.

CONTRACTION: A reduction in mass or dimension; opposite of expansion.

CONVECTION: A transfer of heat by circulating heated air.

CONVERTER: Applied to liquefied petroleum gas: a device which converts or changes L.P.G. from liquid to vapor for use in engine.

CORE HOLE PLUG: See FREEZE PLUG.

CORRODE: To eat away gradually as if by gnawing, especially by chemical action such as rust.

COUNTERBORE: To enlarge a hole to a given depth.

COUNTERCLOCKWISE ROTATION: Rotating opposite direction of hands on a clock.

COUNTERSINK: To cut or form a depression to allow head of a screw to go below surface.

COUPLING: A connecting means for transferring movement from one part to another; may be mechanical, hydraulic or electrical.

COWL: Portion of body between engine compartment and driver which ordinarily contains instruments used by operator.

CRANKCASE: Housing within which crankshaft operates.

CRANKCASE DILUTION: Under certain conditions of operation, unburned portions of fuel get past piston rings into crankcase where they "thin" engine lubricating oil.

CRANKSHAFT: Main shaft of an engine which in conjunction with connecting rods changes reciprocating motion of pistons into rotary motion.

CRANKSHAFT COUNTERBALANCE: Series of weights attached to or forged integrally with crankshaft and placed to offset reciprocating weight of each piston and rod assembly.

CRUDE OIL: Liquid oil as it comes from the ground.

CU. IN.: Cubic inch.

CURRENT: Flow of electricity.

CUT-OUT (Electric): See CIRCUIT BREAKER.

CUT-OUT (Muffler): A valve used to divert exhaust gases directly to atmosphere instead of through muffler.

CYCLE: A series of events which are repeated. Example: intake, compression, power and exhaust strokes of an internal combustion engine.

CYLINDER: A round hole having some depth bored to receive a piston. Also referred to as "bore" or "barrel."

CYLINDER BLOCK: Largest single part of an engine. Basic or main mass of metal in which cylinders are bored or placed.

CYLINDER HEAD: A detachable portion of an engine fastened securely to cylinder block which contains all or a portion of combustion chamber.

CYLINDER SLEEVE: A liner or tube interposed between piston and cylinder wall or cylinder block to provide a readily renewable wearing surface for cylinder.

DASH: Also known as fire wall. A partition between engine and operator.

DASHPOT: A device consisting of a piston and cylinder with a restricted opening used to slow down or delay operation of some moving part.

DC: Direct current.

DEAD CENTER: Extreme upper or lower position of crankshaft throw at which point piston is not moving in either direction.

DEAD REAR AXLE: A rear axle that does not turn. Example: rear axle of front wheel drive car.

DEBAR: English term for prevent.

DEGREE: Abbreviated deg. or indicated by a small ° placed alongside of a figure. May be used to designate temperature readings or angularity, one degree being 1/360 part of a circle.

DEMAGNETIZE: To remove magnetization of a pole which has previously been magnetized.

DEMOUNTABLE RIM: A rim for a tire that is readily removable from wheel.

DE-MISTER: English term for defroster.

DENATURED ALCOHOL: Ethyl alcohol to which a denaturant has been added.

DENSITY: Compactness: relative mass of matter in a given volume.

DEPOLARIZE: To remove polarity. Example: to demagnetize a permanent magnet.

DETERGENT: A compound of a soap-like nature used in engine oil to remove engine deposits and hold them in suspension in oil.

DETONATION: An engine sound that indicates a too rapid burning or explosion of air-fuel mixture in engine cylinders. It becomes audible through a vibration of combustion chamber walls.

DIAGNOSIS: Refers to use of instruments to determine cause of improper function of parts or systems of a vehicle.

DIAL GAUGE: A type of test instrument which indicates precise readings on a dial.

DIAPHRAGM: A flexible partition or wall separating two cavities.

DIE: One of a pair of hardened metal blocks for forming metal into a desired shape, or a device for cutting external threads.

DIE CASTING: An accurate and smooth casting made by pouring molten metal or composition into a metal mold or die under pressure.

DIESEL ENGINE: Named after its developer, Dr. Rudolph Diesel, engine ignites fuel in cylinder from heat generated by compression. Fuel is an oil rather than gasoline and no spark plug or carburetor is required.

DIFFERENTIAL GEAR: Gear system which permits one drive wheel to turn faster than other.

DILUTION: See CRANKCASE DILUTION.

DIODE: An electronic device that permits current to flow through it in one direction only.

DIRECT CURRENT: Electric current which flows continuously in one direction. Example: current from a storage battery.

DIRECT DRIVE: In automobile transmissions: refers to direct engagement between engine and drive shaft where engine crankshaft and drive shaft turn at same rpm.

DISC BRAKE: Brake system utilizing rotors that turn with vehicle wheels and to which pressure is applied to stop or retard motion of vehicle.

DISCHARGE: Applied to a battery: flow of electric current. Opposite of charge.

DISPLACEMENT: See PISTON DISPLACEMENT.

DISTORTION: A warpage or change in form from original shape.

DISTRIBUTORS: A valve, often rotary in design, which conducts a vapor or fluid to a number of outlets. Example: diesel engine oil distributors. See IGNITION DISTRIBUTORS.

DOG CLUTCH: Mating collars, flanges or lugs which can be moved as desired to engage or disengage similar collars, flanges or lugs in order to transmit rotary motion.

DOUBLE REDUCTION AXLE: A drive axle construction in which two sets of reduction gears are used for extreme reduction of gear ratio.

DOWEL PIN: A pin inserted in matching holes in two parts to maintain those parts in fixed relation to each other.

DOWN-DRAFT: Used to describe a carburetor in which mixture flows downward to engine.

DRAG LINK: Connecting rod or link between steering gear Pitman arm and steering control linkage.

DRAW: To form by a stretching process, or to soften hard metal.

DRAW-FILING: A method of filing where file is drawn across work at right angles.

DRILL: A tool for making a hole, or to sink a hole with a pointed cutting tool rotated under pressure.

DRIVE-FIT: Term used when shaft is slightly larger than hole and must be forced in place.

DRIVE LINE: Universal joints, drive shaft and other parts connecting transmission with driving axles.

DROP FORGING: A piece of steel shaped between dies while hot.

DRY BATTERIES: A complete battery unit which does not contain liquid electrolyte. Also called dry cell.

DUAL-FUEL ENGINE: An engine equipped to operate on two different fuels such as gasoline and L.P.G.

DUAL REDUCTION AXLE: A drive axle construction with two sets of pinions and gears, either of which can be used.

DWELL PERIOD: See CAM ANGLE.

DYNAMO: A generator of electricity.

DYNAMOMETER: A machine for measuring power produced by an internal combustion engine.

EARTH: English term for ground.

ECCENTRIC: One circle within another circle not having same center.

ECONOMIZER: A device installed in a carburetor to control amount of fuel used under certain conditions.

ELECTRODE: Refers to insulated center rod and rod attached to shell of spark plug.

ELECTROLYTE: A mixture of sulphuric acid and distilled water used in storage batteries of wet type.

ELECTROMAGNET: A coil of insulated wire wound around an iron rod (or series of rods) will magnetize it when an electric current is passed through wire. Example: a solenoid magnet.

ELECTRON: That portion of an atom which carries a negative charge of electricity.

ELEMENT: Applied to batteries: one set of positive plates and one set of negative plates complete with separators assembled together.

ELLIOTT STEERING KNUCKLE: Type of axle in which ends of axle beam straddle spindle.

EMF: Electromotive force, or voltage.

EMULSION: A milk-like viscous mixture of two liquids.

EMULSION BLOCK: English term for jet cluster.

ENAMEL: A combination of varnish and coloring pigment, sometimes heated during or after application to provide a hard surface.

EN-BLOC: Refers to cylinder block of an engine cast in one section.

ENERGY: Capacity for doing work.

ENGINE: Prime source of power generated to propel a vehicle.

ENGINE DISPLACEMENT: Sum of displacement of all engine cylinders.

ETHYL GASOLINE: Gasoline to which a compound of tetraethyl lead, ethylene dibromide and ethylene dichloride has been added. Material slows down and controls rate of burning of fuel in cylinder to produce an expansive force rather than an explosive force and thus reduce detonation or "knocking" in an engine.

EVAPORATION: Process of changing from a liquid to a vapor. Example: boiling water to produce steam. Evaporation is opposite of condensation.

EXHAUST EMISSIONS: Products of combustion that are discharged through exhaust system of vehicle.

EXHAUST GAS ANALYZER: An instrument for determining efficiency with which an engine is burning fuel. Also called combustion analyzer.

EXHAUST PIPE: Pipe connecting engine to muffler to conduct spent gases away from engine.

EXPANSION: An increase in size. Example: when a metal rod is heated, it increases in length and diameter. Expansion is opposite of contraction.

EXPANSION PLUG: See FREEZE PLUG.

EXTREME PRESSURE LUBRICANTS (E.P.): A lubricant to which an ingredient has been added to increase lubricant's ability to withstand high pressures between gear teeth, etc.

FAHRENHEIT (F.): A scale of temperature measurement ordinarily used in English speaking countries. Boiling point of water is 212 degrees, Fahrenheit, as compared to 100 degrees Centigrade.

FEELER GAUGE: A metal strip or blade, finished accurately with regard to thickness, used for measuring clearance between two parts. Blades are graduated in thickness by increments of .001 in.

FELLOWS: English term for adjoining parts.

FERROUS METAL: Metals which contain iron or steel, making them subject to rust.

F-HEAD ENGINE: An engine designed with one valve in cylinder block at side of piston and other valve in cylinder head above piston.

FIELD: Applied to generator or electric motor: area in which magnetic flow occurs.

FIELD COIL: A coil of insulated wire surrounding field pole.

FILE: To finish or trim with a hardened metal tool with cutting ridges.

FILLET: A rounded filling between two parts joined at an angle.

FILTER: A device designed to remove suspended impurities or particles of foreign matter from intake air, fuel system or lubricating system.

FIRE WALL: Insulated partition between engine and vehicle occupants.

FIT: Satisfactory contact between two machined surfaces.

FLANGE: A projecting rim or collar on an object for keeping it in place.

FLASH POINT: Temperature at which an oil will flash and burn.

FLOAT: A hollow part which is lighter than fuel or fluid in which it rests and which is ordinarily used to operate a valve controlling entrance of fuel or fluid.

FLOATING PISTON PIN: A piston pin which is not locked in connecting rod or piston, but is free to turn or oscillate in both connecting rod and piston.

FLOATING POWER: A system of mounting or supporting an engine with its center of gravity disposed on a line extending from one mounting to other, allowing engine to oscillate or float around its axis.

FLOAT LEVEL: Predetermined height of fuel in carburetor bowl, usually regulated by means of a suitable valve.

FLUID COUPLING: Applied to transmissions: a hydraulic clutch used to transmit engine torque to transmission gears. See FLUID DRIVE.

FLUID DRIVE: A pair of vaned rotating elements held close to each other without touching. Rotation is imparted to driven member by driving member through resistance of a body of oil.

"FLUTTER": See BOUNCE.

FLUX, ELECTRIC OR MAGNETIC: Lines of magnetic force passing or flowing in a magnetic field.

FLUX, SOLDERING, WELDING, BRAZING: Material used to cause joining metal to adhere to both parts to be joined.

FLYWHEEL: A heavy wheel in which energy is absorbed and stored by means of momentum.

FOOT POUND (or lbs. ft.): A measure of amount of energy or work required to lift 1 lb. 1 ft.

FORCE-FIT: See DRIVE FIT.

FORGE: To shape metal while hot and plastic by hammering.

FOUR CYCLE ENGINE: Engine in which an explosion occurs every other revolution of crankshaft. A cycle, also known as Otto cycle, is considered 1/2 revolution of crankshaft. Strokes are: (1) suction stroke; (2) compression stroke; (3) power stroke; (4) exhaust stroke.

FREE-WHEELING: A mechanical device in which driving member imparts motion to a driven member in one direction but not other.

FREEZE PLUG: A disc or cup-shaped metal device inserted in a hole in a casting through which core was removed when casting was formed. Also known as a core hole plug or expansion plug.

FRICTION DRIVE: A method of power transmission used on early automobiles where power is transmitted from a driving to a driven wheel by means of pressing one wheel against another at a right angle.

FUEL KNOCK: See DETONATION.

FULCRUM: A support, often wedge-shaped, on which a lever pivots when it lifts an object.

FULL-FLOATING AXLE: Drive axle construction where axle driving shaft does not carry car weight.

FUSE: A piece of wire which will carry a limited amount of current only, then melt and open electrical circuit as a safety measure to avoid damage from excessive current flow.

GAL.: Gallon.

GALVANIZE: To coat with a molten alloy of lead and tin to prevent rusting.

GALVANOMETER: An instrument used for location, measurement and direction of an electric current.

GAS: A substance which can be changed in volume and shape according to temperature and pressure applied to it. Example: air can be compressed into smaller volume or expanded by application of heat.

GASSING: Bubbling of battery electrolyte which occurs during process of charging a battery.

GASKET: Anything used as a packing, such as a non-metallic substance placed between two metal surfaces to act as a seal.

GEAR RATIO: Number of revolutions made by a driving gear as compared to number of revolutions made by a driven gear of different size. Example: if one gear makes three revolutions while other gear makes one revolution, gear ratio is 3 to 1.

GENERATOR: A device consisting of an armature, field coils and other parts which when rotated will generate electricity.

GLAZE: Applied to surface of engine cylinder: an extremely smooth or glossy surface polished over a long period of time by friction of piston rings.

GLAZE BREAKER: A tool for removing glossy surface finish in an engine cylinder.

GOVERNOR: A device to control and regulate speed. May be mechanical, hydraulic or electrical.

GRAM: A unit of measure of weight or mass equal to 0.03527 ounces.

GRID: Metal framework of an individual battery plate in which active material is placed.

GRIND: To finish or polish a surface by means of an abrasive wheel.

GROUND: Noninsulated terminal of battery. By connecting one terminal of each electrically operated unit to frame of vehicle, only one insulated wire is required to carry current to unit since frame serves as a return wire.

GROUP: Applied to a battery: a set of plates, either positive or negative, joined together but not assembled with separators.

GROWLER: An electrical device for testing electric motor or generator armatures.

GUDGEON PIN: See PISTON PIN.

GUM: In automotive fuels: oxidized petroleum products which accumulate in fuel system, carburetor or engine parts.

HARD PEDAL: A loss in braking efficiency so that an excessive amount of pressure is needed to actuate brakes.

HARD SOLDER: Uniting two pieces of metal with a material having a melting point higher than "soft" solder. Example: silver soldering.

HARMONIC BALANCER: A device designed to reduce torsional or twisting vibration which occurs along length of crankshaft used in multiple cylinder engines.

H.C.: High compression.

HEAT EXCHANGER: In general: a device which utilizes exhaust system heat to aid in fuel vaporization.

HEAT RISER: Passage between exhaust and intake manifolds.

HEAT SINK: Metal bracket in end frame of alternator that contains and absorbs heat from diodes.

HEAT TREATMENT: A combination of heating and cooling operations timed and applied to a metal in a solid state in a way that will produce desired properties.

HEEL: Outside or larger half of gear tooth.

HELICAL: Shaped like a coil of wire or a screw thread.

HELICAL GEAR: A gear design where gear teeth are cut at an angle to shaft.

HEMI: Hemispherical or dome-shaped combustion chamber in some engines.

HERRINGBONE GEAR: A pair of helical gears designed to operate together in which angle of pair of gears forms a V.

HIGH TENSION: In automotive electricity: secondary or induced high voltage electrical current. Includes wiring from ignition distributor cap to coil and to each spark plug.

HONE: An abrasive tool for correcting small irregularities or differences in diameter in an engine cylinder, brake cylinder, etc.

HOTCHKISS DRIVE: A driving axle design in which axle torque is absorbed by chassis springs.

HOT SPOT: Refers to a comparatively thin section of wall between intake and exhaust manifolds of an engine to allow hot exhaust gases to heat comparatively cool incoming mixture. Term is also used to designate local areas of cooling system which have attained above average temperatures.

HP: Horsepower. Energy required to lift 550 lbs. 1 ft. in 1 second.

HYDRAULIC: Pertains to fluids in motion, such as hydraulically operated brakes, hydraulic torque converters, power steering, etc.

HYDROCARBON: Any compound composed entirely of carbon and hydrogen. Example: petroleum products.

HYDROCARBON ENGINE: An engine using petroleum products, such as gas, liquefied gas, gasoline, kerosene or fuel oil as a fuel.

HYDROMETER: An instrument for determining state of charge in a battery by measuring specific gravity of electrolyte.

HYDROSTATIC GAUGE: Used in referring to gauges, such as a gasoline tank gauge, where depth of gasoline in tank controls air in connecting line to instrument which registers depth on a scale or dial.

HYPOID GEARS: A design of pinion and ring gear where center line of pinion is offset from center line of ring gear.

I.D.: Inside diameter.

IDLE: Refers to engine operating at its slowest speed with a vehicle not in motion.

IGNITION DISTRIBUTOR: An electrical device usually containing circuit breaker for primary circuit and providing a means for conveying secondary or high tension current to spark plug wires as required.

IGNITION SYSTEM: Means for igniting fuel in cylinders. Includes spark plugs, wiring, ignition distributor, ignition coil and source of electrical current supply.

I.H.P.: Indicated horsepower developed by an engine and a measure of pressure of explosion within cylinder expressed in pounds per square inch.

IN.: Inch.

INCLUDED ANGLE: In wheel alignment: combined angles of camber and kingpin or steering axis inclination.

INDEPENDENT SUSPENSION: A construction in which wheel on one side of vehicle may rise or fall independently of wheel on other side.

INDUCTION: Influence of magnetic fields of different strength not electrically connected to one another.

INDUCTION COIL: Essentially a transformer which through action of induction creates a high tension current by means of an increase in voltage.

INERTIA: A physical law which tends to keep a motionless body at rest or also tends to keep a moving body in motion. Effort is thus required to start a mass moving or to retard or stop it once it is in motion.

INHIBITOR: A material to restrain or hinder some unwanted action. Example: a rust inhibitor added to cooling systems to retard formation of rust.

INJECTOR: A pump which injects or inserts a fluid or gas, usually against pressure, into a cylinder or chamber.

INLET VALVE OR INTAKE VALVE: A valve which permits a fluid or gas to enter a chamber and seals against exit.

INPUT SHAFT: Applied to transmissions: shaft which receives power from engine and transmits it to transmission gears.

INSULATION: Any material which does not conduct electricity and is used to prevent leakage of current from a conductor. Term is also used to describe a material which does not conduct heat readily.

INSULATOR: A nonconducting material or shield covering an electrical conductor.

INTAKE MANIFOLD OR INLET PIPE: Tube or housing used to conduct air-fuel mixture from carburetor to engine cylinders.

INTEGRAL: The whole made up of parts.

INTENSIFY: To increase or concentrate. Example: increase voltage of an electrical current.

INTERMEDIATE GEAR: Applied to transmissions: gear or gears between low and high.

INTERMITTENT: Motion or action which occurs at intervals.

INTERNAL COMBUSTION: Burning of a fuel within an enclosed space.

INTERRUPTER: See CIRCUIT BREAKER.

JOURNAL: That part of a shaft or axle in actual contact with bearing.

JUMP SPARK: A high tension electrical current which jumps through the air from one terminal to another.

JUNK RING: A flexible ring used in cylinder head to provide a seal with inner sleeve of a sleeve valve engine.

KEY: A small block inserted between shaft and hub to prevent circumferential movement.

KEYWAY OR KEYSEAT: A groove or slot cut to permit insertion of a key.

KICK-DOWN SWITCH: An electrical switch used to cause a transmission to downshift from a higher to a lower gear ratio.

KILOMETER: A metric measurement of distance which is equivalent to 5/8 of a mile.

KILOWATT: A measure of electrical energy consisting of 1,000 watts. It is equal to 1 1/3 horsepower

KINGPIN: Shaft or journal upon which and around which steering spindle of an automobile front wheel turns.

KINGPIN INCLINATION: Angle at which kingpin is inclined inward from true vertical center line.

KNURL: To indent or roughen a finished surface.

KNOCK: A general term used to describe various noises occurring in an engine. Used to describe noises made by loose or worn mechanical parts, pre-ignition, detonation, etc.

LACQUER: Applied to automotive painting: a solution of solids in solvents which evaporate with great rapidity.

LAMINATE: To build up or construct out of a number of thin sheets. Example: laminated core in an electric motor or generator.

LAPPING: Process of fitting one surface to another by rubbing them together with an abrasive material between two surfaces.

LB.: Pound.

L.C.: Low compression.

LEAD BURNING: Joining two pieces of lead by melting or fusing the metal.

L-HEAD ENGINE: An engine design in which both valves are located on one side of engine cylinder.

LIMOUSINE: A type of automobile body where operator is separated from passengers by a partition.

LINER: Usually a thin section placed between two parts. Example: a replaceable cylinder liner in an engine.

LINKAGE: Any series of rods, yokes, and levers, etc., used to transmit motion from one unit to another.

LIQUID: Neither a gas nor a solid. Any substance which assumes shape of vessel in which it is placed without changing volume.

LIQUID WITHDRAWAL SYSTEM: A method of piping where liquid is taken from bottom of an L.P.G. tank and converted into gas by a vaporizer.

LITER: A measure of volume equal to 61.027 cu. in.

LIVE: Electrical parts connected to insulated side of electrical system. Example: an insulated wire connected to battery and often referred to as a "hot" wire.

LIVE AXLE: Shaft through which power travels from drive axle gears to driving wheels.

LOCK WASHER: A form of washer designed to prevent attaching nut from working loose.

LOST MOTION: Motion between a driving part and a driven part which does not cause actuation of driven part. See BACKLASH.

LOUVER OR LOUVRE: Openings or vents in hood or body of a vehicle, usually intended for ventilation.

LOW PEDAL: A condition wherein excessive clearance exists at some point in braking system so that excess pedal movement is required for application of brakes.

LOW SPEED: Gearing provided in an automobile which causes greatest number of revolutions of engine as compared to driving wheels.

L.P.G., LIQUEFIED PETROLEUM GAS: Made usable as a fuel for internal combustion engines by compressing volatile petroleum gases to liquid form. L.P.G. must be kept under pressure or at low temperature in order to remain in liquid form.

LUG: Applied to batteries: extension of plate grid for connecting plate to strap.

LUGGAGE BOOT: English name for trunk.

MAGNET (Permanent): A piece of hard steel often bent into a "U" shape to create and retain opposite poles when charged with magnetic power.

MAGNETIC FIELD: Flow of magnetic force or magnetism between opposite poles of a magnet.

MAGNETO: An electrical device which generates alternating current when rotated by an outside source of power. Device used to generate either low tension or high tension current.

MAKE-AND-BREAK IGNITION: A low tension ignition system used in early automobiles not equipped with spark plugs. Spark occurred within cylinder by mechanical closing and opening of circuit.

MALLEABLE CASTING: A casting which has been toughened by annealing.

MANIFOLD: A pipe with multiple openings used to connect various cylinders to one inlet or outlet.

MANGANESE BRONZE: An alloy of copper, zinc and manganese.

MANOMETER: A device for measuring a vacuum, consisting of a "U" shaped tube partially filled with fluid. One end of tube is open to air, other is connected to chamber in which vacuum is to be measured. A column of mercury 30 in. high equals 14.7 lbs. per sq. in., which is atmospheric pressure at sea level. Readings are given in inches of mercury.

MASTER CYLINDER: Single or dual hydraulic cylinder which is used to force the hydraulic fluid to individual wheel cylinders when brakes are applied.

MECHANICAL EFFICIENCY: Ratio between indicated horsepower and brake horsepower of an engine.

MELTING POINT: Temperature at which solid material becomes liquid.

MEMA: Motor and Equipment Manufacturers Association.

MERCURY COLUMN: A reference term used in connection with a manometer.

METER: A measure of length equal to 39.37 in.

METHANOL OR WOOD ALCOHOL: A poisonous alcohol made synthetically or from distillation of wood.

MEWA: Motor and Equipment Wholesalers Association.

MICROMETER: A measuring instrument for either external or internal measurement in thousandths and sometimes tenths of thousandths of inches.

MILL: To cut or machine with rotating tooth cutters.

MILLIMETER (mm.): One millimeter is metric equivalent of .039370 of an inch. One inch is equivalent to 25.4 mm.

MISFIRING: Failure of an explosion to occur in one or more cylinders while engine is running. This may be a continuous or intermittent failure.

MODULATOR: A pressure regulating device used in automatic transmissions.

MONO-BLOCK: All cylinders of an engine are contained in one casting. Same as en-bloc or in-block.

MOTOR: Principally, a machine which converts electrical energy to mechanical energy.

MPH: Miles per hour.

MUFFLER: A chamber attached to exhaust pipe which allows exhaust gases to expand and cool. It is usually fitted with baffles or porous plates and serves to reduce noise created by exhaust.

MULTIPLE DISC: A clutch having a number of driving and driven discs as compared to a single plate clutch.

NADA: National Automobile Dealers Association.

NAPA: National Automotive Parts Association.

NEEDLE BEARING: An antifriction bearing using a great number of rollers of small diameter in relation to their length.

NEGATIVE POLE: Point from which an electrical current flows as it passes through circuit. Designated by a minus sign (-).

NEON GAS: A rare element in air which has low electrical resistance and is therefore a good conductor for electricity. When placed in a closed glass tube and connected to a high tension electric current, neon gas gives off a bright glow.

NEUTRON: Portion of an atom which carries no electrical charge, and with protons form central core of atom about which electrons rotate in much the same manner earth rotates about sun.

NICKEL STEEL: Nickel is alloyed with steel to form a heat and corrosion resistant metal.

NIPPLE: English term for lubrication fitting.

NONFERROUS METALS: Metals which contain no iron or very little iron and are therefore not subject to rusting.

NORTH POLE: Pole of a magnet from which lines of force start. Opposite of south pole.

OCTANE NUMBER: A unit of measurement on a scale intended to indicate tendency of a fuel to detonate or knock.

OCTANE SELECTOR: A calibrated device for adjusting timing of ignition distributor in accordance with characteristics of fuel in use.

O.D.: Outside diameter.

ODOMETER: A device for measuring and registering number of miles traveled.

OHM: A measurement of resistance to flow of an electrical current through a conductor.

OIL PUMPING: A term used to describe an engine which is using an excessive amount of lubricating oil.

ONE-WAY CLUTCH: See FREE-WHEELING.

OPEN CIRCUIT: A break or opening in an electrical circuit which stops passage of current.

ORIFICE: Small opening in a tube, pipe or valve.

OSCILLATE: To swing back and forth like a pendulum.

OSCILLOSCOPE: An electrical testing device which shows a pattern wave form of spark ignition action on a viewing screen.

OTTO CYCLE: Four stroke cycle named after man who adopted principle of four stroke operation for each explosion in an engine cylinder. They are: (1) suction stroke; (2) compression stroke; (3) power stroke; (4) exhaust stroke.

OUTPUT SHAFT: Applied to transmissions: shaft which receives power from transmission and transmits it to vehicle drive shaft.

OVERDRIVE: Any arrangement of gearing which produces more revolutions of driven shaft than driving shaft.

OVERHEAD VALVE OR VALVE-IN-HEAD ENGINE: An engine design having valves located in cylinder head directly above pistons.

OVERRUNNING CLUTCH OR COUPLING: See FREE-WHEELING.

OXIDIZE: To combine an element with oxygen or convert into its oxide. Examples: when carbon burns, it combines with oxygen to form carbon dioxide or carbon monoxide; iron combines with oxygen in air to form an oxide of iron, or rust.

PCV: Positive crankcase ventilation.

"PANCAKE" ENGINE: A design where cylinders are laid horizontal to obtain a minimum of height.

PARAFFIN: English name for kerosene.

PARKING BRAKE: May be either a separate system or a separate application of service brake so that brake may be held in applied position indefinitely.

PAWL: A pivoted bar adapted to engage with teeth of a ratchet to prevent or impart motion.

PEEN: To stretch or clinch over by pounding with rounded end of a hammer.

PERIPHERY: Circumference of a circle. Example: tread of a tire.

PETCOCK: A small valve placed in a fluid circuit for draining purposes.

PETROL: European name for gasoline.

PETROLEUM: A group of liquid and gaseous compounds composed of carbon and hydrogen.

PHILLIPS SCREW OR SCREWDRIVER: A type of

screwhead having a cross instead of a slot for a corresponding type of screwdriver.

PHOSPHOR-BRONZE: An alloy consisting of copper, tin and lead, sometimes used in heavy-duty bearings.

PILOT VALVE: A small valve used to control action of a larger valve.

PINION: A small gear having teeth formed in hub.

PINION CARRIER: Mounting or bracket which retains bearings supporting a pinion shaft.

PINKING: English term for pinging.

PISTON: A cylindrical part closed at one end which is connected to the crankshaft by a connecting rod. Force of explosion in cylinder is exerted against closed end of piston causing connecting rod to move crankshaft.

PISTON COLLAPSE: A condition describing a reduction in diameter of piston skirt due to heat or stress.

PISTON DISPLACEMENT: Volume of air moved or displaced by moving piston from one end of its stroke to other.

PISTON HEAD: Part of piston above rings.

PISTON LANDS: Parts of piston between piston rings.

PISTON PIN: Journal for bearing in small end of an engine connecting rod which also passes through piston walls.

PISTON RING: An expanding ring placed in grooves of piston to provide a seal to prevent passage of fluid or gas past piston.

PISTON RING EXPANDER: A spring placed behind piston ring in groove to increase pressure of ring against cylinder wall.

PISTON RING GAP: Clearance between ends of piston ring.

PISTON RING GROOVE: Channel or slots in piston in which piston rings are placed.

PISTON SKIRT: Part of piston below rings.

PISTON SKIRT EXPANDER: A spring or other device inserted in piston skirt to compensate for collapse or decrease in diameter.

PITMAN ARM: Lever extending from steering gear to which steering linkage is attached.

PITOT TUBE: An instrument for measuring fluid velocity by means of difference in pressure between tip and side openings.

PIVOT: A pin or short shaft upon which another part rests or turns, or upon and about which another part rotates or oscillates.

PLANETARY GEARS: A system of gearing which is modeled after solar system. A pinion is surrounded by an internal ring gear with planet gears in mesh between ring gear and pinion.

PLANET CARRIER: Carrier or bracket in a planetary system which contains shafts upon which pinions or planet gears turn.

PLANET GEARS: Pinions of gears interposed between ring gear and sun gear and meshing with both in a planetary system.

PLATINUM: An expensive metal having an extremely high melting point and good electrical conductivity.

PNEUMATIC: Pertaining to air. Example: a device operated by air pressure is a pneumatic device.

POLARITY: Refers to positive or negative terminal of a battery or an electric circuit; also north or south pole of a magnet.

POPPET VALVE: A valve structure consisting of a circular head with an elongated stem attached in center. It is designed to open and close a circular hole or port.

PORCELAIN: General term applied to material or element used for insulating center electrode of a spark plug.

PORT: Applied to engines: openings in cylinder block for valves, exhaust and inlet pipes, or water connections. In two-cycle engines: openings for inlet and exhaust purposes.

"PORTING": Applied to racing engines: enlarging, matching, streamlining and polishing of inside of manifolds and valve ports to reduce friction of flow of gases.

POSITIVE POLE: Point to which current returns after passing through a circuit. Designated by plus sign (+).

POST: Applied to batteries: heavy circular part to which group of plates is attached and which extends through cell cover to provide a means of attachment to adjacent cell or battery cable.

POTENTIAL: An indication of amount of energy available.

POTENTIAL DIFFERENCE: A difference of electrical pressure which sets up a flow of electric current.

POTENTIAL DROP: A loss of electrical pressure due to resistance or leakage.

POWER STEERING: Application of hydrualic or mechanical power in addition to manual power in steering of an automobile.

PREFOCUSSED LAMP BULB: A bulb construction in which focus is not adjustable.

PREHEATING: Application of heat as a preliminary step to some further thermal or mechanical treatment.

PREIGNITION: Ignition occurring earlier than intended. Example: explosive mixture being fired in a cylinder by a flake of incandescent carbon before electric spark occurs.

PRELOADING: To adjust a small amount of pressure on an antifriction bearing to eliminate any looseness.

PRESS-FIT: See DRIVE FIT.

PRIMARY BRAKE SHOE: Brake shoe in a set which initiates self-energizing action.

PRIMARY WINDING: A wire which conducts low tension current to be transformed by induction into high tension current in secondary winding of ignition coil or magneto armature.

PRIMARY WIRES: Wiring circuit used for conducting low tension or primary current to points where it is used.

PROGRESSIVE TRANSMISSION: An early type of transmission in which it was necessary to go through all intermediate gears when shifting from lowest to highest gears and vice versa.

PROTON: Portion of an atom which carries a positive charge of electricity.

PRONY BRAKE: A machine for testing power of an engine while running against a friction brake.

PROPANE: A petroleum hydrocarbon compound which has a boiling point about -44 deg. F. It is used as an engine fuel, is loosely referred to as L.P.G. and is often combined with butane.

PROPELLER SHAFT: Drive shaft connecting transmission with rear axle.

PSI: Pounds per square inch; measure of pressure.

PUSH ROD: A connecting link in an operating mechanism. Example: rod interposed between valve lifter and rocker arm on an overhead valve engine.

QUADRANT: A term originally applied to section of a circle on steering post to which spark and throttle controls were connected. Now used to designate gearshift or transmission control lever selective mounting.

QUENCHING: A process of rapid cooling of hot metal by contact with liquids, gases or solids.

QUILL BEARING: See NEEDLE BEARING.

RACE: Applied to bearings: a finished inner and outer surface in which or on which balls or rollers operate.

"RACE-CAM": A type of camshaft for race cars which increases lift of valve, increases speed of valve opening and closing, increases length of time valve is held open, etc. Also known as "Full," "Three-quarter" or "Semi-race cams," depending upon design.

RADIAL ENGINE: An engine construction in which cylinders are mounted in a row or circle around crankcase.

RADIATION: Transfer of heat by rays. Example: heat from sun.

RADIUS RODS: Rods attached to axle and to frame to maintain correct horizontal position of axle, yet permit vertical motion.

RATIO: Relation or proportion that one number bears to another.

REAM: To finish a hole accurately with a rotating fluted tool.

RECIPROCATING: A back and forth movement. Example: action of a piston in a cylinder.

RECTIFIER: An electrical device for transforming or changing alternating current into direct current.

REFRIGERANT: A material used in an air conditioning system which absorbs and gives up heat as it changes from a liquid to a gas to a liquid.

REGULATOR: An automatic pressure reducing valve.

RELAY: See CIRCUIT BREAKER.

RELIEF: Amount one surface is set below or above another surface.

"RELIEVING": Applied to racing engines: removal of some metal from around valves and between cylinder and valves to facilitate flow of gases.

RESISTOR: A current-consuming piece of metal wire or carbon inserted into circuit to decrease flow of electricity.

RETARD: To cause spark to occur at a later time in cycle of engine operation. Opposite of spark advance.

REVERSE ELLIOT STEERING KNUCKLE: Type of axle construction in which steering spindle straddles ends of axle beam.

RIGHT HOME: English term for all the way in.

RING GEAR: Outer gear within which other gears revolve in a planetary system. Term also refers to driven gear which mates with drive pinion in a differential assembly.

RIVET: To attach with rivets or to batter or upset end of a pin.

RMA: The Rubber Manufacturers Association.

ROCKER ARM: Applied to engines: a lever located on a fulcrum or shaft; one end on valve stem, other on push rod.

ROCKWELL HARDNESS: A scale for designating degree of hardness possessed by a substance.

ROLLER BEARING: An inner and outer race upon which hardened steel rollers operate.

ROTARY ENGINE: Construction in which crankshaft remains stationary and cylinders spin around it.

ROTARY VALVE: A valve construction in which ported holes come into and out of register with each other to allow entrance and exit of fluids or gases.

ROTOR: Rotating valve or conductor for carrying fluid or electrical current from a central source to individual outlets as required.

RPM: Revolutions per minute.

RUBBER: An elastic vibration absorbing material of either natural or synthetic origin.

RUNNING-FIT: Where sufficient clearance has been allowed between shaft and journal to allow free running without overheating.

SAE: Society of Automotive Engineers.

SAE STEELS: A numerical index system used to identify composition of SAE steel. Basically first digit indicates type of steel: (1) carbon steel, (2) nickel steel, etc. Second digit generally indicates approximate percentage of predominant alloying element. Usually last two or three digits indicate approximate average carbon content in points or hundredths of 1 percent. Thus, SAE 2340 steel indicates a nickel steel of approximately 3 percent nickel and 0.40 percent carbon.

SAE THREAD: Refers to a table of threads set up by Society of Automotive Engineers and determines number of threads per inch. Example: a quarter inch diameter rod with an SAE thread would have 28 threads per inch.

SAFETY FACTOR: Degree of surplus strength over and above normal requirements which serves as insurance against failure.

SAFETY RELIEF VALVE: A spring-loaded valve designed to open and relieve excessive pressure in a device when it exceeds a predetermined safe point.

SANDBLAST: To clean a surface by means of sand propelled by compressed air.

SAYBOLT TEST: A method of measuring viscosity of oil with use of a viscosimeter.

SCALE: A flaky deposit occurring on steel or iron. Ordinarily used to describe accumulation of minerals and metals accumulating in an automobile cooling system.

SCORE: A scratch, ridge or groove marring a finished surface.

SCOTCHES: English term for blocks.

SCUTTLE: Air intake vent in England.

SEALED BEAM LAMPS: Lamp construction with reflector, lens and filament hermetically sealed in one unit.

SEALING COMPOUND: A readily melted, acid-proof, nonconducting material used in sealing battery cover in case.

SEAT: A surface, usually machined, upon which another part rests or seats. Example: surface upon which a valve face rests.

SECONDARY BRAKE SHOE: Brake shoe in a set which is energized by primary shoe and increases servo, or self-energization, action of brake.

SECONDARY WINDING: A wire in which a secondary or high tension current is created by induction due to interruption of current in adjacent primary winding of an ignition coil or magneto armature.

SEDIMENT: Applied to batteries: active material of plates which is gradually shed and accumulates in a space provided below plates.

SEIZE: When a surface moving upon another scratches, it is said to seize. Example: piston score or abrasion in a cylinder due to lack of lubrication or overexpansion.

SELECTIVE TRANSMISSION: Arrangement of gearing and shifting device in which it is possible to go directly from neutral position into any desired pair of gears.

SELF-ENERGIZATION: Applied to brakes: placing of shoes so that drum tends to drag lining along with it, resulting in a wedging action between anchor and drum.

SEMIDIESEL: A semidiesel engine operates on comparatively high compression and utilizes solid injection of fuel. However, it does use an electrical ignition system rather than depend solely upon heat generated by compression to furnish ignition.

SEMIFLOATING AXLE: A drive axle construction in which axle shafts support weight of car.

SEPARATORS: Applied to batteries: sheets of rubber or wood inserted between positive and negative plates of a cell to keep them out of contact with each other.

SERIES WINDING: An electric winding or coil of wire in series with other electrical equipment.

SERVO: In automatic transmissions: hydraulic piston and cylinder assembly used to control drum bands.

SERVO ACTION: A brake construction in which a primary shoe pushes a secondary shoe to generate self-energization.

SHACKLE BOLT: A link for connecting one end of a chassis spring to frame which allows spring end to oscillate laterally.

SHEAR: To cut between two blades.

SHIM: Thin sheets used as spacers between two parts. Example: alignment shims between control arm pivot shaft and frame serve to adjust caster and camber.

"SHIMMY": Applied to automobile steering: a wobbling or shaking of front wheels.

SHOCK ABSORBER: A device to provide mechanical or hydraulic friction to action of automobile springs to control excessive deflection.

SHORT CIRCUIT: To provide a shorter path. Often used to indicate an accidental ground in an electrical device or conductor.

SHRINK-FIT: An exceptionally tight fit. Example: if shaft or part is slightly larger than hole in which it is to be inserted, outer part is heated above its normal operating temperature or inner part chilled below its normal operating temperature, or both, and assembled in this condition. Upon cooling, a shrink fit is obtained.

SHUNT: To bypass around or turn aside. In electrical apparatus: an alternate path for current.

SHUNT WINDING: An electric winding or coil of wire which forms a bypass or alternate path for electric current. Applied to electric generators or motors: each end of field winding is connected to an armature brush.

SHUTTLE VALVE: A valve for diverting pressure from one channel to another.

SILENCER: See MUFFLERS.

SILICON STEEL: An alloy of silicon and chromium with steel. Since this alloy resists burning and oxidation and does not warp readily, it is often used for exhaust valves of internal combustion engines.

SILICONE: A special lubricant.

SILVER SOLDERING: See HARD SOLDER.

SLEEVE VALVE: A reciprocating sleeve or sleeves with ported openings placed between piston and cylinders of an engine to serve as valves.

SLIDING-FIT: Where sufficient clearance has been allowed between shaft and journal to allow free running without overheating.

SLIP-IN BEARING: A liner made to extremely accurate measurements which can be used for replacement purposes without additional fitting.

SLIP RINGS: Insulated metal rings mounted on alternator rotor shaft on which brushes make continuous sliding contact.

SLUDGE: Applied to engines: a composition of oxidized petroleum products along with an emulsion formed by mixture of oil and water, forming a pasty substance that clogs oil lines and passages and interferes with engine lubrication.

SOLDER: An alloy of lead and tin used to unite two metal parts.

SOLDERING: To unite two pieces of metal with a material having a comparatively low melting point.

SOLENOID: An iron core, surrounded by a coil of wire, which moves due to magnetic attraction when electric current is fed to coil. Often used to actuate mechanisms by electrical means.

SOLID INJECTION: System used in full diesel and semidiesel, where fuel in fluid state is injected into cylinder rather than a mixture of air and fuel drawn from a carburetor.

SOLVENT: A solution which dissolves some other material. Example: water is a solvent for sugar.

SOUTH POLE: Pole of a magnet to which lines of force flow. Opposite of north pole.

SPACER, SPACER WASHER: A sheet of metal or other material placed between two surfaces to reduce clearance or to provide a better thrust surface for fastener.

SPANNER: English name for wrench.

SPARK: An electic current possessing sufficient pressure to jump through air from one conductor to another.

SPARK ADVANCE: Applied to an ignition distributor: to cause spark to occur at an earlier time in cycle of engine operation. Opposite of retard.

SPARK GAP: Space between electrodes of a spark plug through which spark jumps. Term is also used for a safety device in a magneto to provide an alternate path for current when it exceeds a safe value.

SPARK KNOCK: See PREIGNITION.

SPARK PLUG: A device inserted into combustion chamber of an engine containing an insulated center electrode for conducting high tension current from ignition distributor or magneto. This insulated electrode is spaced a predetermined distance from side electrode to control dimensions of gap for spark to jump across.

SPECIFIC GRAVITY: Relative weight of a substance compared to water. Example: if a cubic inch of acid weighs twice as much as a cubic inch of water, specific gravity of substance is 2.

SPEEDOMETER: A device for measuring and indicating speed of a vehicle in miles per hour.

SPIN: Applied to metalwork: to shape sheet metal by forcing it against a form as it revolves.

SPIRAL BEVEL GEAR: A ring gear and pinion in which mating teeth are curved and placed at an angle with pinion shaft.

SPLAYED SPRING: A design in which leaf springs are placed at other than a 90 degree angle to axle.

SPLINE: A long keyway.

SPLINE JOINT: Two mating parts each with a series of splines around their circumference, one inner and one outer in order to provide a longitudinally movable joint without circumferential motion.

"SPONGY" BRAKE PEDAL: Air in hydraulic lines, distortion or stretching of connecting parts or swelling of hydraulic hose may allow pedal to be spongy or springy instead of solid.

SPOT WELD: To attach in spots by localized fusion of metal parts with aid of an electric current.

SPRUNG WEIGHT: A term used to describe all parts of an automobile that are supported by car springs. Example: frame, engine, body, etc.

SPUR GEAR: A gear in which teeth are cut parallel to shaft.

SPURT-HOLE: A hole drilled through a connecting rod and bearing which allows oil under pressure to be squirted out of bearing for additional lubrication of cylinder walls.

SQ. FT.: Square feet.

SQ. IN.: Square inch.

STAMPING: A piece of sheet metal cut and formed into a desired shape with use of dies.

STANDARD THREAD: Refers to U.S.S. table of number of threads per inch. Example: a quarter inch diameter standard thread would have 20 threads per inch.

STATIC ELECTRICITY: Atmospheric electricity as distinguished from electricity produced by a mechanical device.

STATOR: In torque converters: a wheel having curved blades interposed between pump and turbine elements. In electrical system: metal frame of alternator with three stationary windings which give overlapping pulses of alternating current.

STEEL CASTING: Cast iron to which varying amounts of scrap steel have been added.

STEERING AXIS INCLINATION: Angle formed by center line of kingpin or suspension ball joints and true vertical center line.

STEERING GEAR: Gears in steering unit. Also applied to assembly of parts and units required to control angularity of wheels to body of a vehicle.

STEERING GEOMETRY: See TOE-OUT ON TURNS.

STEERING KNUCKLE: Part about which front wheels pivot when turning.

STEERING POST OR COLUMN: Shaft connecting steering gear unit with steering wheel.

STEERING SPINDLE: A journal or shaft upon which steerable wheels of a vehicle are mounted.

STELLITE: An alloy of cobalt, chrome and tungsten which is often used for exhaust valve seat inserts. It has a high melting point, good corrosion resistance and unusual hardness when hot.

STRAP: Applied to batteries: a lead section to which plates of a group are joined.

STRESS: Force or strain to which a material is subjected.

STROBOSCOPE: A term applied to an ignition timing light, which by being connected to distributor points, gives effect of making a mark on a rapidly rotating pulley or harmonic balancer which appears to stand still for observation.

STROKE: Applied to engines: distance traveled by a piston.

"STROKING": Applied to racing engines: re-machining crankshaft throws "off center" to alter stroke.

STUDS: A rod with threads cut on both ends. It screws

into cylinder block on one end and has a nut placed on other end.

SUCTION: Suction exists in a vessel when pressure is lower than atmospheric pressure. See VACUUM.

SULPHATED: When a battery is improperly charged, or allowed to remain in a discharged condition for some length of time, plates will be coated with an abnormal amount of lead sulphate. Battery is then said to be "sulphated."

SUN GEAR: Central gear around which other gears revolve in a planetary gear system.

SUPERCHARGER: A blower or pump which forces air into cylinders at higher than atmospheric pressure. In an engine, increased pressure forces more air into cylinder, thus enabling more gasoline to be burned and more power to be produced.

SWEAT: To join metal pieces by clamping together with solder between them and applying heat.

SYNCHROMESH: A device used in transmission gearing to facilitate meshing of two gears by causing speed of both gears to coincide.

SYNCHRONIZE: To cause two events to occur in unison or at same time. Example: to time a mechanism so that two or more sparks will occur at same instant.

TACHOMETER: A device for measuring and indicating rotative speed of an engine.

TAP: To cut threads in a hole with a tapered, fluted, threaded tool. In England: term for drain cock.

TAPPET: Adjusting screw for varying clearance between valve stem and cam. May be built into valve lifter in an engine or may be installed in rocker arm on an overhead valve engine.

T.D.C.: Top dead center.

TEMPER: To change physical characteristics of metal by application of heat.

TENSION: Effort that is devoted towards elongation or "stretching" of a material.

TERMINAL: In automotive electrical work: a junction point where connections are made.

T-HEAD ENGINE: An engine design in which inlet valves are placed on one side of the cylinder and exhaust valves placed on other.

THERMAL EFFICIENCY: A gallon of fuel contains potential energy in form of heat when burned in combustion chamber. Some heat is lost and some is converted into power. Thermal efficiency is ratio of work accomplished compared to total quantity of heat contained in fuel.

THERMOSTAT: A heat-controlled valve used in cooling system of engine to regulate flow of water between cylinder block and radiator. A thermostat is also used in electrical circuit of car heating system to control amount of heat supplied to passengers.

THERMO-SYPHON: A method of cooling an engine which utilizes difference in specific gravity of hot and cold water. No pump is used, but water passages are larger than in pump circulation system.

THIRD BRUSH: Applied to generators: an auxiliary brush placed on commutator to control current output of generator.

THROW: Applied to engines: distance from center of crankshaft main bearing to center of connecting rod journal.

"TICK-OVER": English term for engine idle speed.

TIE ROD: Metal rod connecting steering spindle arms on opposite sides of vehicle.

TIMER: Ignition distributor which times or supplies a spark to spark plugs at proper instant.

TIMING CHAIN: Chain used to drive camshaft and accessory shafts of an engine.

TIMING GEARS: Any group of gears which are driven from engine crankshaft to cause valves, ignition and other engine driven apparatus to operate at desired time during engine cycle.

TOE: Inside or smaller half of a gear tooth.

TOE-OUT ON TURNS: Related angles assumed by front wheels of vehicle when turning.

TOLERANCE: A permissible variation between two extremes of a specification of dimensions.

TOMMY BAR: English term for "T" handle.

TOP UP: English term for fill up.

TORQUE: An effort devoted toward twisting or turning.

TORQUE CONVERTER: A turbine device utilizing a rotary pump, one or more reactors and a driven circular turbine. Power is transmitted from a driving to a driven member by hydraulic action.

TORQUE WRENCH: A special wrench with a built-in indicator to measure applied force.

TORSION BAR: Rod with built-in twist to provide spring action; usually adjustable.

TORUS: Applied to torque converters: an oil-filled member.

TRACTOR FUEL: A fuel similar to kerosene or like diesel oil and which is considerably less volatile than gasoline.

"TRAMP": A term used to describe an oscillating motion and heavy vibration when wheels are turning.

TRANSAXLE: Type of construction in which transmission and differential are combined in one unit.

TRANSFORMER: An electrical device, such as a high tension coil which transforms or changes characteristics of an electrical current.

TRANSISTOR: In electronics: a miniature amplifying device.

TRANSMISSION: A system of trading speed for power or vice versa, such as gearing or torque conversion. Includes various devices and combinations for changing ratio between engine revolutions and driving wheel revolutions.

TROUBLE SHOOTING: A process of diagnosing or deducing source of trouble by observation and testing.

TUNE-UP: A process of accurate and careful adjustments to obtain utmost in engine performance.

TURBINE: A series of blades located on a wheel at an angle with shaft against which fluids or gases are impelled to impart rotary motion to shaft.

TURBOCHARGER: A device which utilizes pressure

of exhaust gases to drive a supercharger which, in turn, forces more air into cylinders.

TURBULENCE: A disturbed, irregular motion of fluids or gases.

TURNING RADIUS: Diameter of a circle within which a vehicle can be turned around.

TWO-CYCLE ENGINE: An engine design permitting a power stroke once for each revolution of crankshaft.

UNDERCOATING: Spraying insulating material on exposed undersections of an automobile to retard corrosion and deaden noise.

UNIT POWER PLANT: An assembly in which engine, clutch and transmission are combined in one unit.

UNIVERSAL JOINT: A connection for transmitting power from a driving to a driven shaft through an angle.

UNSPRUNG WEIGHT: Weight that includes wheels, axles, etc., that are not supported by car springs.

UP-DRAFT: Used to describe a carburetor in which mixture flows upward to engine.

UPPER CYLINDER LUBRICATION: A method of introducing a lubricant into fuel or intake manifold in order to permit lubrication of upper cylinder, valve guides, etc.

UPSET: To compress at ends, causing an increase in diameter.

VACUUM: A pressure less than atmospheric pressure.

VACUUM CONTROL: Applied to ignition distributors: a diaphragm attached to spark advance which is controlled by changing of vacuum in intake manifold.

VACUUM GAUGE: An instrument designed to measure degree of vacuum existing in a chamber.

VALVE: A device for opening and sealing an aperture.

VALVE CLEARANCE: Air gap allowed between end of valve stem and valve lifter or rocker arm to compensate for expansion due to heat.

VALVE FACE: Part of a valve which mates with and rests upon a seating surface.

VALVE GRINDING: A process of mating valve seat and valve face.

VALVE HEAD: Portion of a valve upon which valve face is machined.

VALVE-IN-HEAD ENGINE: See OVERHEAD VALVE ENGINE.

VALVE KEY OR VALVE LOCK: Key, keeper, washer or other device which holds valve spring cup or washer in place on valve stem.

VALVE LIFTER: Solid part or hydraulic plunger placed between cam and valve on an engine.

VALVE MARGIN: Space or rim on a poppet valve between surface of head and surface of valve face.

VALVE OVERLAP: An interval expressed in degrees where both valves of an automobile engine cylinder are open at same time.

VALVE SEAT: Matched surface upon which valve face rests.

VALVE SPRING: A spring attached to a valve to return it to seat after lift is released.

VALVE STEM: Portion of a valve which rests within a guide.

VALVE STEM GUIDE: A bushing or hole for valve stem which allows lateral motion only.

VANES: Any plate or blade attached to an axis and moved by or in air or a liquid.

VAPORIZER: A device for transforming or helping to transform a liquid into a vapor.

VAPOR LOCK: A condition in which fuel boils in fuel system, forming bubbles which retard or stop flow of fuel to carburetor.

VAPOR PRESSURE: Pressure developed over a liquid in a closed vessel, depending upon liquid and temperature.

VAPOR WITHDRAWAL: A system of piping and connections to operate an engine directly on vapor taken from top of an L.P.G. tank.

VENTURI: Two tapering streamlined tubes joined at their small ends to reduce internal diameter.

VIBRATION DAMPER: See HARMONIC BALANCER.

VISCOSIMETER: An instrument for determining viscosity of an oil by passing a certain quantity at a definite temperature through a standard size orifice or port. Time required for oil to pass through, expressed in seconds, gives viscosity.

VISCOSITY: Resistance to flow or adhesiveness characteristics of an oil.

VOLATILITY: Tendency for a fluid to evaporate rapidly. Example: gasoline is more volatile than kerosene since it evaporates at a lower temperature.

VOLT: A unit of electrical force which will cause a current of one ampere to flow through a resistance of one ohm.

VOLTAGE REGULATOR: An electrical device for controlling or regulating voltage.

VOLTMETER: An instrument for measuring voltage in an electrical circuit.

VOLUME: Measure of space expressed as cubic inches, cubic feet, etc.

VOLUMETRIC EFFICIENCY: A combination between ideal and actual efficiency of an internal combustion engine. If engine completely filled each cylinder on each induction stroke, volumetric efficiency of engine would be 100 percent. In actual operation, however, volumetric efficiency is lowered by inertia of the gases, friction between gases and manifolds, temperature of gases and pressure of air entering carburetor. Volumetric efficiency is ordinarily increased by use of large valves, ports and manifolds and can be further increased with aid of a supercharger.

VORTEX: A whirling movement or mass of liquid or air.

"WANDERING": A condition in which steering wheels of an automobile tend to turn slowly in first one direction and other, thus interfering with directional control or stability.

WATER COLUMN: A reference term used in connection with a manometer.

WATT: A measuring unit of electrical power. It is obtained by multiplying amperes by volts.

WEDGE BLOCK: Combustion chamber design in which top of piston and surface of block form an angle.

WEIGHT TRANSFER EFFECT: Since center of gravity of vehicle is located above centers of wheel rotation, a sudden stoppage of vehicle tends to cause center of gravity to move forward, thus throwing more weight on front wheels and less on rear wheels.

WELDING: To join two pieces of metal by heating them to fusion or melting point.

WHEEL CYLINDERS: Hydraulic cylinders in a braking system which are actuated by hydraulic pressure to force brake lining into contact with braking drum or disc.

WHITE METAL: An alloy of tin, lead and antimony having a low melting point and a low coefficient of friction.

WINDSCREEN: English name for windshield.

WING: English name for fender.

WIRING DIAGRAM: A detailed drawing of all wiring, connections and units connected together in an electrical circuit.

WORM GEAR: A shaft having an extremely coarse thread which is designed to operate in engagement with a toothed wheel, as a pair of gears.

WRINGING-FIT: A fit with less clearance than for a running or sliding fit. Shaft will enter hole by means of twisting and pushing by hand.

WRIST PIN: Journal for bearing in small end of an engine connecting rod which also passes through piston walls. See PISTON PIN.

1958

MAKE AND MODEL	Wheelbase	Tire Size	No. of Cylinders Bore & Stroke	Displacement	Valve and Cylinder Arrangement	Compression Ratio	Maximum Brake Horsepower	Horsepower per Cu. In.	No. of Main Bearings	Operating Tappet Clearance Intake	Exhaust	Intake Tappet Clearance for Valve Timing	Intake Valve Opens - Deg.
Buick 40	122.0	7.10/15	V8-4.125 x 3.4	364.0	VO	9.5	250@4400	.687	5	hy	hy	hy	25
Buick 60	122.0	7.60/15	V8-4.125 x 3.4	364.0	VO	10.0	300@4600	.825	5	hy	hy	hy	34
Buick 50	127.5	7.60/15	V8-4.125 x 3.4	364.0	VO	10.0	300@4600	.825	5	hy	hy	hy	34
Buick 70	127.5	8.00/15	V8-4.125 x 3.4	364.0	VO	10.0	300@4600	.825	5	hy	hy	hy	34
Buick 700	127.5	8.00/15	V8-4.125 x 3.4	364.0	VO	10.0	300@4600	.825	5	hy	hy	hy	34
Cadillac 62	129.5	8.00/15	V8-4.00 x 3.62	365.0	VO	10.25	310@4800	.85	5	hy	hy	hy	39
Cadillac 60	133.0	8.00/15	V8-4.00 x 3.62	365.0	VO	10.25	310@4800	.85	5	hy	hy	hy	39
Cadillac 75	149.7	8.20/15	V8-4.00 x 3.62	365.0	VO	10.25	310@4800	.85	5	hy	hy	hy	39
Chevrolet Six	117.5	7.50/14	6-3.56 x 3.94	235.5	IO	8.25	145@4200	.62	4	hy	hy	hy	10-1/2
Chevrolet V-8	117.5	7.50/14	V8-3.875 x 3.00	283	VO	8.5	185@4600	.65	5	hy	hy	hy	12-1/2
Chevrolet V-8	117.5	7.50/14	V8-4.125 x 3.25	348	VO	9.5	250@4400	.72	5	hy	hy	hy	29-3/4
Chrysler Wind.	122	8.00/14	V8-3.94 x 3.63	354	VO	10.0	290@4600	.82	5	hy	hy	hy	13
Chrysler Sar.	126	8.50/14	V8-3.94 x 3.63	354	VO	10.0	310@4600	.87	5	hy	hy	hy	15
Chrysler 300D, N.Y.	126	9.00/14	V8-4.0 x 3.9	392	VO	10.0	345@4600	.88	5	hy	hy	hy	35
Continental	131	9.00/14	V8-4.3 x 3.7	430	VO	10.5	375@4800	.87	5	hy	hy	hy	27
Corvette	102	6.70/15	V8-3.875 x 3.0	283	VO	9.5	*250@5000	.87	5	hy	hy	hy	12-1/2
De Soto-Firesweep	122	8.00/14	V8-4.06 x 3.38	350	VO	10.0	280@4600	.80	5	hy	hy	hy	15
De Soto-Firedome	126	8.50/14	V8-4.12 x 3.38	361	VO	10.0	295@4600	.82	5	hy	hy	hy	15
De Soto-Fireflite	126	8.50/14	V8-4.12 x 3.38	361	VO	10.0	305@4600	.85	5	hy	hy	hy	15
De Soto-Adventurer	126	8.50/14	V8-4.12 x 3.38	361	VO	10.25	345@5000	.96	5	hy	hy	hy	15
Dodge Six	122	7.50/14	6-3.25 x 4.63	230	IL	8.0	138@4000	.60	4	.010H	.010H	.012	20
Dodge Coronet	122	7.50/14	V8-3.69 x 3.80	325	VO	8.5	252@4400	.78	5	hy	hy	hy	12
Dodge Royal	122	8.00/14	V8-3.69 x 3.80	325	VO	8.5	295@4600	.85	5	hy	hy	hy	10
Dodge Custom Royal	122	8.00/14	V8-4.06 x 3.38	350	VO	10.0	305@4600	.85	5	hy	hy	hy	15
Dodge Custom Sierra	122	8.00/14	V8-4.06 x 3.38	350	VO	10.0	305@4600	.85	5	hy	hy	hy	15
Dodge D500	122	8.00/14	V8-4.12 x 3.38	361	VO	10.0	305@4600	.85	5	hy	hy	hy	15
Edsel, Ranger	118	8.00/14	V8-4.05 x 3.50	361	VO	10.5	303@4600	.84	5	hy	hy	hy	15
Edsel, Pacer	118	8.00/14	V8-4.05 x 3.50	361	VO	10.5	303@4600	.84	5	hy	hy	hy	17
Edsel, Corsair	124	8.50/14	V8-4.20 x 3.70	410	VO	10.5	345@4600	.84	5	hy	hy	hy	17
Edsel, Citation	124	8.50/14	V8-4.20 x 3.70	410	VO	10.5	345@4600	.84	5	hy	hy	hy	27
Ford Six	116	7.50/14	I-6-3.6250x3.6093	223	IO	8.6	145@4200	.65	4	.019H	.019H	.019	17
Ford-300	116	7.50/14	V8-3.75 x 3.30	292	VO	9.1	205@4500	.70	5	.019H	.019H	18	17
Ford Fairlane	118	7.50/14	V8-4.00 x 3.30	332	VO	9.5	265@4600	.72	5	.019H	.019H	18	18
Ford - 500	118	7.50/14	V8-4.00 x 3.50	352	VO	10.2	300@4600	.85	5	.026H	.026H	21	18
Imperial	129	9.50/14	V8-4.00 x 3.90	392	VO	10.0	345@4600	.88	5	hy	hy	hy	21
Mercury, Mont. M.C.	122	8.00/14	V8-4.3 x 3.30	383	VO	10.5	330@4800	.81	5	hy	hy	hy	15
Mercury, Park La.	125	8.50/14	V8-4.3 x 3.70	430	VO	10.5	360@4600	.84	5	hy	hy	hy	34
Metropolitan	85	5.20/13	4-2 7/8 x 3.50	90.9	IO	7.20	52@4500	.57	3	.015C	.015C	.015C	-
Oldsmobile 88	122-1/2	8.50/14	V8-4 x 3.68	371	VO	10.1	265@4400	.72	5	hy	hy	hy	16
Oldsmobile, Sup. 88	122-1/2	8.50/14	V8-4 x 3.68	371	VO	10.1	305@4600	.82	5	hy	hy	hy	16
Oldsmobile 98	126-1/2	8.50/14	V8-4 x 3.68	371	VO	10.1	305@4600	.82	5	hy	hy	hy	16
Packard Hawk.	120-1/2	8.00/14	V8-3 9/16 x 3 5/8	289	VO	7.8	275@4800	.95	5	.024H	.024H	.026H	11
Plymouth Six	118	7.50/14	6-3.25 x 4.63	230	IL	8.0	132@3600	.57	4	.010H	.010H	.010	12
Plymouth Plaza	118	7.50/14	V8-3.91 x 3.31	318	VO	9.0	225@4400	.71	5	.012H	.018H	.010	8
Plymouth Sav., Bel.	122	7.50/14	V8-3.91 x 3.31	318	VO	9.0	225@4400	.71	5	.012H	.018H	.010	8
Plymouth Fury	118	7.50/14	V8-3.91 x 3.31	318	VO	9.25	290@5200	.91	5	.012H	.018H	.010	17
Plymouth Com.	122	7.50/14	V8-4.06 x 3.38	350	VO	10.0	305@5000	.87	5	hy	hy	hy	15
Pontiac Chief	122	8.00/14	V8-4.06 x 3.56	370	VO	8.6	240@4500	.65	5	hy	hy	hy	22d
Pontiac Sup. Chief	124	8.00/14	V8-4.06 x 3.56	370	VO	8.6	255@4500	.69	5	hy	hy	hy	22d
Rambler Six	108	6.40/15	6-3.125 x 4.25	195	IO	8.7	127@4200	.65	4	.012	.016	.012	12-1/2
Rambler Rebel	108	7.50/14	V8-3.5 x 3.25	250	VO	8.7	215@4900	.86	5	.012	.016	.012	12-1/2
Rambler Amb.	117	8.00/14	V8-4 x 3.25	327	VO	9.7	270@4700	.83	5	hy	hy	hy	12-1/2
Studebaker Champ. D1	116-1/2	6.40/15	6-3 x 4.37	185	IL	7.8	101@4000	.55	4	.016C	.016C	.016C	15
Studebaker Champ.	120-1/2	6.40/15	6-3 x 4.37	185	IL	7.8	101@4000	.55	4	.016C	.016C	.016C	15
Studebaker Comm.	116-1/2	7.50/14	V8-3 9/16 x 3 1/4	259	VO	8.3	180@4500	.70	5	.024H	.024H	.026C	11
Studebaker Pres.	120-1/2	8.00/14	V8-3 9/16 x 3 5/8	289	VO	8.3	225@4500	.78	5	.024H	.024H	.026C	11
Studebaker Gold. Hawk	120-1/2	8.00/14	V8-3 9/16 x 3 5/8	289	VO	7.8	275@4800	.95	5	.024H	.024H	.026C	11

*with fuel injection

ABBREVIATIONS

A - American Bosch	CS - Coil Spring	Ex - Exposed Propeller Shaft
AC - AC Spark Plug	CaS - Cantilever Spring	FO - Ford
AO - Automatic Optional	d - Applies to Manual Transmission cars,	FA - Ford or American Bosch
AL - Auto Lite	for Hydramatic cars, 30 deg. B.T.C.	FE - Full Elliptic Leaf Spring
Ac - Air-Cooled Engine	D - Dubonnet Front Suspension	FH - F-Head Engine
a - Others Also	DI - Diamond Ignition System	Fm - Fluidmatic Transmission
b - Left side + 3/8, Right side 0	DL - Detroit Lubricator Carburetor	H - With engine at operating Temp.
B - Before Top Center	DR - Delco Remy Ignition	HO - Holley
C - Carter Carburetor	DeJ - DeJon Ignition	HT - Hydraulically Operated Transmission
CB - Carter Ball & Ball Type	D.Tr - Double Transverse Springs	HV - Horizontal Valve Arrangement
CG - Chandler Grove	e - Fuel Injection Optional	Hy - Hydramatic Transmission
CH - Champion Spark Plug	E-V - Electric & Vacuum Operated	hy - Hydraulic Tappets

Tuneup Specifications

Carburetor Make	Make of Ignition System	Breaker Point Gap	Breaker Points Open - Deg.	Spark Plugs Make	Spark Plugs Model	Spark Plugs Gap	Automatic Transmission Type	Propeller Shaft	Front Suspension	Rear Suspension	Wheel Alignment Caster	Wheel Alignment Camber	Wheel Alignment Toe-In	King Pin Inclination	Cooling System Capacity -Qts. Without Heater	Crankcase Capacity Qts
C, S	DR	.015	5B	AC	44	.032	TQ	IC	CS	CS	-3/4	+22'	1/16	7@0°52'	16 1/2	5
C, R	DR	.015	5B	AC	44	.032	TQ	IC	CS	CS	-3/4	+22'	1/16	7@0°52'	16 1/2	5
C, R	DR	.015	5B	AC	44	.032	TQ	IC	CS	CS	-3/4	+22'	1/16	7@0°52'	16 1/2	5
C, R	DR	.015	5B	AC	44	.032	TQ	IC	CS	CS	-3/4	+22'	1/16	7@0°52'	16 1/2	5
C, R	DR	.015	5B	AC	44	.032	TQ	IC	CS	CS	-3/4	+22'	1/16	7°@0°52'	16 1/2	5
C, R	DR	.016	5B	AC	44	.035	HY	Ex	CS	CS	-1	+3/16	1/16	4	20.7	5
C, R	DR	.016	5B	AC	44	.035	HY	Ex	CS	CS	-1	+3/16	1/16	4	20.7	5
C, R	DR	.016	5B	AC	44	.035	HY	Ex	CS	CS	-1	+3/16	1/16	4	21.8	5
R	DR	.018	TC	AC	44	.035	TQ	Ex	CS	CS	+1	+1/2	1/8	4	16	5
R	DR	.018	4B	AC	44	.035	TQ	Ex	CS	CS	+1	+1/2	1/8	4	16	4
C, R	DR	.018	4B	AC	44	.035	TQ	Ex	CS	CS	+1	+1/2	1/8	4	22	4
C	AL	.015	8B	AL	AR42	.035	TQ	Ex	TB	Se	-3/4	+1/4	1/8	6 1/2°	22	4
C	AL	.015	6B	AL	AR42	.035	TQ	Ex	TB	Se	-3/4	+1/4	1/8	6 1/2°	22	4
C	AL	.015	6B	AL	AGR42	.035	TQ	Ex	TB	Se	-3/4	+1/4	1/8	6 1/2°	25	5
HO	F	.015	6B	CH	F-11-Y	.032	TQ	Ex	CS	CS	-1/2	+1/2	1/8	7 1/4	26	5
C	DR	.018	4B	AC	44	.035	TQ	Ex	CS	CS	+2 1/4	+1/2	1/16	4	16	5
C	AL	.015	6B	AL	AR42	.035	TQ	Ex	TB	Se	-3/4	+1/4	1/8	6 1/2°	16	4
C	AL	.015	6B	AL	AR42	.035	TQ	Ex	TB	Se	-3/4	+1/4	1/8	6 1/2°	16	4
C	AL	.015	6B	AL	AR42	.035	TQ	Ex	TB	Se	-3/4	+1/4	1/8	6 1/2°	16	4
C	AL	.015	8B	AL	AR32	.035	TQ	Ex	TB	Se	-3/4	+1/4	1/8	6 1/2°	16	4
S	AL	.022	2B	AL	AR51	.035	TQ	Ex	TB	Se	+1/4	+1/4	1/8	6 1/2°	13	5
S	AL	.015	6B	AL	AGR42	.035	TQ	Ex	TB	Se	+1/4	+1/4	1/8	6 1/2°	20	5
C	AL	.015	6B	AL	AR42	.035	TQ	Ex	TB	Se	+1/4	+1/4	1/8	6 1/2°	20	4
C	AL	.015	6B	AL	AR32	.035	TQ	Ex	TB	Se	+1/4	+1/4	1/8	6 1/2°	20	4
C	AL	.015	8B	AL	AR32	.035	TQ	Ex	TB	Se	+1/4	+1/4	1/8	6 1/2°	16	4
C	AL	.015-.022	8B	AL	AR32	.035	TQ	Ex	TB	Se	+1/4	+1/4	1/8	6 1/2°	16	4
FO or HO	FO	.015	7B	CH	F-11-Y	.035	TQ	Ex	CS	Se	30'to 1°30'	30'to 1°30'	.03	7°-0'	18.5	5
FO or HO	FO	.015	7B	CH	F-11-Y	.035	TQ	Ex	CS	Se	30'to1°30'	30'to 1°3'	.03	7°-0'	18.5	5
HO	FO	.015	7B	CH	F-11-Y	.035	TQ	Ex	CS	Se	0° to 1°	0° to 45'	.06	7°-0'	22	5
HO	FO	.015	7B	CH	F-11-Y	.035	TQ	Ex	CS	Se	0° to 1°	0° to 45'	.06	7°-0'	22	5
HO	HO-FO	.025	4B-6B	CH	870	.035	TQ	Ex	CS	Se	1/2°-1 1/2°	1/2°-1 1/2°	1/16	7°1'at 45	15	4
FO or HO	HO-FO	.015	6° B	CH	F-11-Y	.035	TQ	Ex	CS	Se	+30'	45'	+1°	7° 7'	19	5
HO	FO	.015	6° B	CH	F-11-Y	.035	TQ	Ex	CS	Se	+30'	45'	+1°	7° 7'	19	5
FO or C	FO	.015	6° B	CH	F-11-Y	.035	TQ	Ex	CS	Se	+30'	45'	+1°	7° 7'	19	5
C	AL	.015	6B	AL	AGR42	.035	TQ	Ex	CS	Se	0	0	1/16	6 1/2	25	5
HO	FO	.015	4B	AL	860	.035	TQ	Ex	CS	Se	-1 1/4	-20'	1/8	7	21.5	5
HO	FO	.015	7B	CH	860	.035	TQ	Ex	CS	Se	-1 1/4	-20'	1/8	7	2.5	5
Z	-	.015	11B	-	-	.024	TQ	Ex	CS	Se	+2 1/2	+1	1/16	6 1/2	8	4
R	DR	.015	2B	AC	44	.030	HY	Ex	CS	Se	-1/2	+1/4	1/16	7	21	4
R	DR	.015	2B	AC	44	.030	HY	Ex	CS	Se	-1/2	+1/4	1/16	7	21	4
R	DR	.016	2B	AC	44	.030	HY	Ex	CS	Se	-1/2	+1/4	1/16	7	21	4
S	DR	.015	4B	CH	H18Y	.035	TQ	Ex	CS	CS	-1 3/4	+1/2	3/16	6	18.5	5
C	AL	.020	2B	AL	AR51	.035	TQ	Ex	TB	Se	0	0	1/8	6 1/2	14	5
S	AL	.015	10B	AL	AR42	.035	TQ	Ex	TB	Se	0	0	1/8	6 1/2	21	5
S	AL	.015	10B	AL	AR42	.035	TQ	Ex	TB	Se	0	0	1/8	6 1/2	21	5
S	AL	.015	8B	AL	AR42	.035	TQ	Ex	TB	Se	0	0	1/8	6 1/2	21	5
-	AL	.015	8B	AL	AR32	.035	TQ	Ex	TB	Se	0	0	1/8	6 1/2	17	5
C(e)	DR	.016	6B	AC	45	.035	HY	Ex	CS	CS	-1/2	+1/2	1/32	4°-50'	22.3	5
C(e)	DR	.016	6B	AC	45	.035	HY	Ex	CS	CS	-1/2	+1/2	1/32	4°-50'	22.3	5
C	DR	.016	10	AL	7J	.035	TQ	IC	CS	CS	+1/4	0	1/8	6 1/6	11	4
HO	DR	.016	17-1/3	AL	7J	.035	TQ	IC	CS	CS	+1/4	0	1/8	6 1/6	21	4
HO	DR	.016	15-1/3	AL	7J	.035	TQ	IC	CS	CS	+1/4	0	1/8	6 1/6	20	4
C	AL	.020	5B	CH	7J	.030	TQ	Ex	CS	Se	-1 3/4	+1/2	3/16	6	12.5	5
C	AL	.020	5B	CH	7J	.030	TQ	Ex	CS	Se	-1 3/4	+1/2	3/16	6	12.5	5
S	DR	.015	4B	CH	H18Y	.035	TQ	Ex	CS	CS	-1 3/4	+1/2	3/16	6	18.5	5
C	DR	.015	4B	CH	H18Y	.035	TQ	Ex	CS	CS	-1 3/4	+1/2	3/16	6	18.5	5
S	DR	.015	4B	CH	H18Y	.035	TQ	Ex	CS	CS	-1 3/4	+1/2	3/16	6	18.5	5

IC - Independent Suspension W-Coil Spring
IL - In Line Engine with "L" Head
IO - In Line Engine with Overhead Valves
J - Johnson Carburetor
LU - Lucas
M - Marvel Carburetor
NE - Northeast Ignition
O - Optional
Oh - Overhead Valves & Cams
Op - Opposed Cylinders
R - Rochester Carburetor
S - Stromberg Carburetor

SV - Sliding Valves
Se - Semi-elliptic Springs
Sch - Schebler Carburetor
Ste - Stewart Carburetors
TA - Torque Arms
TB - Torsion Bar
TC - Top Center
TH - T-Head Engine
TQ - Torque Converter
TT - Torque Tube
Til - Tillotson Carburetor
Tr - Transverse Springs

VL - V-Engine with "L" Head
VO - V-engine with Overhead Valves
Vac - Vacuum Operated Shift
Var - Various
Z - Zenith Carburetor
1/4 - Quarter elliptic Springs
3/4 - Three-quarter elliptic Springs
3 - Three Speed Conventional Transmission
30 - Three Speed Transmission with Overdrive
4 - Four Speed Conventional Transmission

1959

MAKE AND MODEL	Wheelbase	Tire Size	No. of Cylinders Bore & Stroke	Displacement	Valve and Cylinder Arrangement	Compression Ratio	Maximum Brake Horsepower	Horsepower per Cu. In.	No. of Main Bearings	Operating Tappet Clearance Intake	Ex-haust
Buick LeSabre	123	7.60/15	V8-4.125 x 3.4	364	VO	10.5	250@4400	.687	5	hy	hy
Buick Invicta	123	8.00/15	V8-4.1875 x 3.64	401	VO	10.5	325@4400	.810	5	hy	hy
Buick Electra	126.3	8.00/15	V8-4.1875 x 3.64	401	VO	10.5	325@4400	.810	5	hy	hy
Cadillac 62	130	8.00/15	V8-4.0 x 3.875	390	VO	10.5	325@4800	.832	5	hy	hy
Cadillac 60	130	8.00/15	V8-4.0 x 3.875	390	VO	10.5	325@4800	.832	5	hy	hy
Cadillac 75	149.8	8.20/15	V8-4.0 x 3.875	390	VO	10.5	325@4800	.832	5	hy	hy
Cadillac El Dor.	130	8.00/15	V8-4.0 x 3.875	390	VO	10.5	345@4800	.885	5	hy	hy
Chevrolet Six	119	7.50/14	6-3.562 x 3.94	235	IO	8.25	135@4000	.573	4	hy	hy
Chevrolet 283	119	7.50/14	V8-3.875 x 3.00	283	VO	8.5	185@4600	.654	5	hy	hy
Chevrolet 348	119	7.50/14	V8-4.125 x 3.25	348	VO	9.5	250@4400	.719	5	hy	hy
Corvette 1 Carb.	102	6.70/15	V8-3.875 x 3.00	283	VO	9.5	230@4800	.813	5	hy	hy
Corvette, F. Inj.	102	6.70/15	V8-3.875 x 3.00	283	VO	9.5	250@5000	.884	5	hy	hy
Corvette 2 Carb.	102	6.70/15	V8-3.875 x 3.00	283	VO	9.5	245@5000	.868	5	hy	hy
Chrysler Wind.	126	8.00/14	V8-4.031 x 3.75	383	VO	10.0	305@4600	.796	5	hy	hy
Chrysler Sara.	126	8.50/14	V8-4.031 x 3.75	383	VO	10.0	325@4600	.849	5	hy	hy
Chrysler N. Y.	126	8.50/14	V8-4.188 x 3.75	413	VO	10.0	350@4600	.847	5	hy	hy
Chrysler 300	126	8.50/14	V8-4.188 x 3.75	413	VO	10.0	380@4600	.920	5	hy	hy
Chrysler Imp.	129	9.00/14	V8-4.188 x 3.75	413	VO	10.0	350@4600	.803	5	hy	hy
DeSoto F. Sweep	122	8.00/14	V8-4.125 x 3.38	361	VO	10.0	290@4600	.803	5	hy	hy
DeSoto F. Dome	126	8.50/14	V8-4.250 x 3.38	383	VO	10.0	305@4600	.796	5	hy	hy
DeSoto F. Flite	126	8.50/14	V8-4.250 x 3.38	383	VO	10.0	325@4600	.849	5	hy	hy
DeSoto Advent.	126	8.50/14	V8-4.250 x 3.38	383	VO	10.0	350@5000	.914	5	hy	hy
Dodge Six	122	7.50/14	6-3.25 x 4.625	230	IL	8.0	135@3600	.587	4	.011C	.014C
Dodge Coronet	122	8.00/14	V8-3.953 x 3.312	326	VO	10.1	255@4400	.782	5	hy	hy
Dodge Custom	122	8.00/14	V8-4.125 x 3.375	361	VO	10.1	305@4600	.845	5	hy	hy
Dodge Roy. Sier.	122	8.00/14	V8-4.125 x 3.375	361	VO	10.1	295@4600	.817	5	hy	hy
Dodge D500	122	8.00/14	V8-4.25 x 3.375	383	VO	10.0	320@4600	.835	5	hy	hy
Dodge D500 Super	122	8.00/14	V8-4.25 x 3.375	383	VO	10.0	345@500	.900	5	hy	hy
Edsel Six	120	7.50/14	6-3.625 x 3.593	223	VO	8.4	145@4000	.650	4	.019C	.019C
Edsel 292	120	8.00/14	V8-3.75 x 3.298	292	VO	8.8	200@4400	.685	5	.019C	.019C
Edsel 332	120	8.00/14	V8-4.00 x 3.296	332	VO	8.9	225@4000	.678	5	hy	hy
Edsel 361	120	8.00/14	V8-4.046 x 3.50	361	VO	9.6	303@4600	.837	5	hy	hy
Ford Six	118	7.50/14	6-3.625 x 3.593	223	VO	8.4	145@4000	.650	4	.019C	.019C
Ford 292	118	7.50/14	V8-3.75 x 3.296	292	VO	8.8	200@4400	.685	5	.018C	.018C
Ford 332	118	7.50/14	V8-4.00 x 3.296	332	VO	8.9	225@4000	.678	5	hy	hy
Ford 352	118	7.50/14	V8-4.00 x 3.50	352	VO	9.6	300@4600	.852	5	hy	hy
F. Thunderbird Std.	118	8.00/14	V8-4.00 x 3.50	352	VO	9.6	300@4600	.852	5	hy	hy
F. Thunderbird Opt.	118	8.00/14	V8-4.30 x 3.70	430	VO	10.1	350@4800	.814	5	hy	hy
Lincoln 1959	131	9.50/14	V8-4.30 x 3.70	430	VO	10.5	375@4800	.870	5	hy	hy
Mercury 312	126	8.00/14	V8-3.80 x 3.44	312	VO	9.6	210@4400	.673	5	.019H	.019H
Mercury 383	126	8.50/14	V8-4.30 x 3.30	383	VO	10.0	322@4600	.841	5	hy	hy
Mercury 430	126	8.50/14	V8-4.30 x 3.70	430	VO	10.0	345@4400	.802	5	hy	hy
Oldsmobile Dyn 88	123	8.50/14	V8-4 x 3.687	371	VO	9.75	270@4600	.728	5	hy	hy
Oldsmobile Sup 88	123	9.00/14	V8-4.125 x 3.687	394	VO	9.75	315@4600	.799	5	hy	hy
Oldsmobile 98	126.3	9.00/14	V8-4.125 x 3.687	394	VO	9.75	315@4600	.799	5	hy	hy
Plymouth Six	118	7.50/14	6-3 1/4 x 4.625	230	IL	8.0	132@3600	.574	4	.010H	.012H
Plymouth MP 2	118	7.50/14	V8-3.906 x 3.312	318	VO	9.0	230@4400	.723	5	.010H	.018H
Plymouth Sp. Fury	118	7.50/14	V8-3.906 x 3.312	318	VO	9.0	260@4400	.818	5	.010H	.018H
Pontiac 59-21	122	8.00/14	V8-3.062 x 3.75	389	VO	8.6	245@4200	.630	5	hy	hy
Pontiac 59-24	124	8.00/14	V8-3.062 x 3.75	389	VO	8.6	245@4200	.630	5	hy	hy
Pontiac 59-27, 28	122	8.00/14	V8-3.062 x 3.75	389	VO	8.6	260@4200	.668	5	hy	hy
Rambler Amer.	100	5.90/15	6-3.125 x 4.25	195.6	IL	8.0	90@3800	.460	4	.016C	.018C
Rambler Six	108	6.40/15	6-3.125 x 4.25	195.6	IO	8.7	127@4200	.649	4	.012H	.016H
Rambler Rebel	108	7.50/14	V8-3.50 x 3.25	250	VO	8.7	215@4900	.860	5	.012H	.014H
Rambler Amb.	117	8.00/14	V8-4.00 x 3.25	327	VO	9.7	270@4700	.826	5	hy	hy
Studebaker Lark VI	108 1/2	5.90/15	6-3.00 x 4.00	170	IL	8.3	90@4000	.531	4	.018C	.018C
Studebaker Lark VIII	108 1/2	6.40/15	V8-3.562 x 3.25	259	VO	8.8	180@4500	.694	5	.026C	.026C
Studebaker S.H. 6	120 1/2	6.40/15	6-3.00 x 4.00	170	IL	8.3	90@4000	.531	4	.018C	.018C
Studebaker S.H. V8	120 1/2	6.70/15	V8-3.562 x 3.25	259	VO	8.8	180@4500	.694	5	.026C	.026C
Willys Jeep CJ-5, CJ-3B	80	6.40/15	4-3.125 x 4.375	134	FH	6.9	72@4000	.538	3	.018C	M
Willys Jeep CJ-6	101	7.00/15	4-3.125 x 4.375	134	FH	6.9	72@4000	.538	3	.018C	M
Willys Station Wagon	104	7.00/15	6-3.3125 x4.375	226	IL	7.3	115@3650	.508	4	.014C	.014C
Willys Jeep DJ3A	80	6.40/15	4-3.3125 x4.375	134	IL	6.48	60@4000	.447	3	.016C	.016C
Willys Sta. Wagon 6-85	104	7.00/15	6-3.125 x 3.50	161	FH	6.90	75@4000	.466	4	.018C	.016C

ABBREVIATIONS:

AC	- AC Spark Plug
AO	- Automatic optional
AL	- Auto Lite
a	- others also
b	- left side 3/8, right side 0.
B	- Before top dead center
C	- Carter carburetor
CB	- Carter Ball and Ball type
CE	- Cross elliptic spring
CH	- Champion Spark Plug
CS	- Coil Spring
DR	- Delco Remy
EX	- Exposed propeller shaft
Exr	- Exposed on rear drive models
f	- Applies to engine with automatic transmission. On manual shift

transmission, intake valve opens 25 deg. BTDC.

FO	- Ford
FH	- Intake valves in head and exhaust valves in block
g	- at 5 deg. camber
h	- applies to manual steering
H	- with engine at operating temperature
HO	- Holley
Hy	- Hydramatic transmission
hy	- Hydraulic tappets
IC	- Inclosed propeller shaft
IL	- In-line engine with L-head
IO	- In-line engine with overhead valves
k	- Applies to left side. Right side is zero
m	- Eaton free spring is .012 in. Thompson

Tuneup Specifications

Intake Tappet Clearance for Valve Timing	Intake Valve Opens Degrees	Carburetor Make	Make of Ignition System	Breaker Point Gap	Breaker Points Open - Deg.	SPARK PLUGS Make	Model	Gap	Auto. Trans. Type	Propeller Shaft	Front Suspension	Rear Suspension	WHEEL ALIGNMENT Caster	Camber	Toe-In	King Pin Inclination	Cooling System Capacity, Qts. Without Heater	Crankcase Capacity, Qts.
hy	35f	S	DR	.015	4B	AC	44S	.032	TQ	IC	CS	CS	-1 1/2	+1/2	3/32	7 g	16 1/2	4
hy	33	C	DR	.015	4B	AC	44S	.032	TQ	IC	CS	CS	-1 1/2	+1/2	3/32	7 g	16 1/2	4
hy	33	C	DR	.015	4B	AC	44S	.032	TQ	IC	CS	CS	-1 1/2	+1/2	3/32	7 g	16 1/2	4
hy	27	C,R	DR	.016	5B	AC	44	.035	Hy	Ex	CS	CS	-1/2	0	3/16	4	18 1/2	5
hy	27	C,R	DR	.016	5B	AC	44	.035	Hy	Ex	CS	CS	-1/2	0	3/16	4	18 1/2	5
hy	27	C,R	DR	.016	5B	AC	44	.035	Hy	Ex	CS	CS	-1 1/4	0	3/16	4	18 1/2	5
hy	27	C,R	DR	.016	5B	AC	44	.035	Hy	Ex	CS	CS	-1/2	0	3/16	4	18 1/2	5
hy	16	R	DR	.016	5B	AC	44	.035	Fx	Ex	CS	CS	0	+1/2	1/16	7 1/6	17	5
hy	12 1/2	R	DR	.019	4B	AC	44	.035	TQ	Ex	CS	CS	0	+1/2	1/16	7 1/6	17 1/2	4
hy	18 1/2	R	DR	.019	4B	AC	44N	.035	TQ	Ex	CS	CS	0	+1/2	1/16	7 1/6	21	4
hy	12 1/2	C	DR	.018	4B	AC	46	.035	TQ	Ex	CS	Se	+2	0	1/16	4	17 1/2	4
hy	12 1/2	C	DR	.018	4B	AC	46	.035	TQ	Ex	CS	Se	+2	0	1/16	4	17 1/2	4
hy	12 1/2	C	DR	.018	4B	AC	46	.035	TQ	Ex	CS	Se	+2	0	1/16	4	17 1/2	4
hy	22	C	AL	.017	10B	AL	A42	.035	TQ	Ex	TB	Se	-3/4 h	+3/8 K	1/8	6 1/2	17	5
hy	22	C	AL	.017	10B	AL	A42	.035	TQ	Ex	TB	Se	-3/4 h	+3/8 K	1/8	6 1/2	16	5
hy	22	C	AL	.017	10B	AL	A42	.035	TQ	Ex	TB	Se	-3/4 h	+3/8 K	1/8	6 1/2	16	5
hy	20	C	AL	.017	10B	AL	A32	.035	TQ	Ex	TB	Se	-3/4 h	+3/8 K	1/8	6 1/2	16	5
hy	22	C	AL	.017	10B	AL	A42	.035	TQ	Ex	TB	Se	-3/4 h	+3/8 K	1/8	6 1/2	16	5
hy	15	C	AL	.017	10B	AL	A42	.035	TQ	Ex	TB	Se	-3/4 h	+3/8 K	1/8	6 1/2	15	5
hy	15	C	AL	.017	10B	AL	A42	.035	TQ	Ex	TB	Se	-3/4 h	+3/8 K	1/8	6 1/2	15	5
hy	20	C	AL	.017	10B	AL	A32	.035	TQ	Ex	TB	Se	-3/4 h	+3/8 K	1/8	6 1/2	15	5
.011	12	C	AL	.020	2 1/2B	AL	AR51	.035	TQ	Ex	TB	Se	-3/4 h	+3/8 K	1/8	6 1/2	13	5
hy	14	C	AL	.017	10B	AL	AR42	.035	TQ	Ex	TB	Se	-3/4 h	+3/8 K	1/8	6 1/2	20	5
hy	15	C	AL	.017	10B	AL	AR42	.035	TQ	Ex	TB	Se	-3/4 h	+3/8 K	1/8	6 1/2	16	5
hy	15	C	AL	.017	10B	AL	AR42	.035	TQ	Ex	TB	Se	-3/4 h	+3/8 K	1/8	6 1/2	16	5
hy	20	C	AL	.017	10B	AL	A32	.035	TQ	Ex	TB	Se	-3/4 h	+3/8 K	1/8	6 1/2	16	5
.019C	17	HO	HO	.025	4B	CH	870	.034	TQ	Ex	CS	Se	+1 1/2	+7/8	1/16	6 3/4	15	4
.019C	18	FO,HO	FO,HO	.015	3B	CH	F14Y	.034	TQ	Ex	CS	Se	+1 1/2	+7/8	1/16	6 3/4	19	5
hy	22	FO,HO	FO,HO	.015	3B	CH	F11Y	.034	TQ	Ex	CS	Se	+1 1/2	+7/8	1/16	6 3/4	19	5
hy	22	FO,HO	FO,HO	.015	3B	CH	F11Y	.034	TQ	Ex	CS	Se	+1 1/2	+7/8	1/16	6 3/4	19	5
.019C	17	HO	HO	.025	4B	CH	870	.034	TQ	Ex	CS	Se	+1/2	+1	1/16	6 3/4	15	4
.018C	12	FO,HO	FO,HO	.015	3B	CH	F14Y	.034	TQ	Ex	CS	Se	+1/2	+1	1/16	6 3/4	19	5
hy	22	FO,HO	FO,HO	.015	3B	CH	F11Y	.034	TQ	Ex	CS	Se	+1/2	+1	1/16	6 3/4	19	5
hy	22	FO,HO	FO,HO	.015	3B	CH	F11Y	.034	TQ	Ex	CS	Se	+1	+1	1/16	7 7"	19	5
hy	27	C	FO	.015	7B	CH	F11Y	.034	TQ	Ex	CS	Se	+1	+1	1/16	7 7"	20	5
hy	22	C	FO	.015	6B	CH	F11Y	.034	TQ	Ex	CS	Se	-3/4	+3/8	1/8	7 26"n	23	5
.019	18	HO	FO	.015	6B	CH	F14Y	.034	TQ	Ex	CS	Se	-3/4	+3/8	1/8	7 n	21	5
hy	22	FO	FO	.015	6B	CH	F11Y	.034	TQ	Ex	CS	Se	-3/4	+3/8	1/8	7 n	21	5
hy	22	C	FO	.015	6B	CH	F11Y	.034	TQ	Ex	CS	Se	-3/4	+3/8	1/8	7 n	21	5
hy	16	R	DR	.016	5B	AC	44	.030	Hy	Ex	CS	Se	+1/2	+1/8	1/32	10	20	4
hy	16	R	DR	.016	5B	AC	44	.030	Hy	Ex	CS	Se	+1/2	+1/8	1/32	10	20	4
hy	16	R	DR	.016	5B	AC	44	.030	Hy	Ex	CS	Se	+1/2	+1/8	1/32	10	20	4
.010	12	C	AL	.020	2 1/2B	AL	AR51	.035	TQ	Ex	TB	Se	-3/4 h	+3/8 K	1/8	6 1/2	13	5
.010	17	C	AL	.017	10B	AL	AR42	.035	TQ	Ex	TB	Se	-3/4 h	+3/8 K	1/8	6 1/2	20	5
.010	17	C	AL	.017	10B	AL	AR42	.035	TQ	Ex	TB	Se	-3/4 h	+3/8 K	1/8	6 1/2	20	5
hy	22	R	DR	.016	6B	AC	45	.035	Hy	Fx	CS	CS	-1 1/2	+1/4	1/32	4 1/2	21.4	5
hy	22	R	DR	.016	6B	AC	45	.035	Hy	Ex	CS	CS	-1 1/2	+1/4	1/32	4 1/2	21.4	5
hy	22	C	DR	.016	6B	AC	45	.035	Hy	Ex	CS	CS	-1 1/2	+1/4	1/32	4 1/2	21.4	5
.016	10	C	DR	.016	3B	CH	H10	.035	TQ	Ex	CS	Se	0	+1/4	1/8	6 11"	11	4
.012	12 1/2	HO	DR	.016	5B	AL	AL7	.035	TQ	IC	CS	CS	+1/2 h	0	1/8	6 11"	10	4
.012	12 1/2	HO	DR	.016	5B	AL	AL7	.035	TQ	IC	CS	CS	+1/2 h	0	1/8	6 11"	20	4
hy	12 1/2	HO	DR	.016	5B	AL	AL7	.035	TQ	IC	CS	CS	+1/2 h	0	1/8	6 11"	19	4
.018	15	C	AL	.020	0	CH	J7	.030	TQ	Ex	CS	Se	-1 3/4	+1/2	1/16	6	11	5
.026	11	S	DR	.016	0	CH	H18Y	.035	TQ	Ex	CS	Se	-1 3/4	+1/2	1/16	6	17	5
.018	15	C	AL	.020	0	CH	J7	.030	TQ	Ex	CS	Se	-1 3/4	+1/2	1/16	6	11	5
.026	11	S	DR	.016	0	CH	H18Y	.035	TQ	Ex	CS	Se	-1 3/4	+1/2	1/16	6	17	5
.018	9	C	AL	.020	5B	CH	J7	.030	N	Exr	Ser	Se	+3	+1 1/2	1/16	7 1/2	11	4
.018	9	C	AL	.020	5B	CH	J7	.030	N	Exr	Ser	Se	+3	+1 1/2	1/16	7 1/2	11	4
.014	10	C	AL	.020	4B	CH	J7	.030	TQ	CE	Ser	Se	+1	+1	3/32	5	13	4
.016C	9	C	AL	.020	5B	CH	J7	.030	N	Exr	Ser	Se	+3	+1	1/16	7 1/2	11	4
.018	9	C	AL	.020	5B	CH	J7	.030	TQ	Exr	Ser	Se	+1	+1	3/32	5	11	5

Roto-valve .016 in.
n   - at 3/4 deg. camber
O   - Optional
N   - None available
R   - Rochester carburetor
S   - Stromberg carburetor
Ser - Semi-elliptic springs with solid axle on rear drive models
Se - Semi-elliptic springs
TB - Torsion bar
TC - Top center
TQ - Torque converter
TT - Torque tube
Tr - Transverse springs
VO - V-engine with overhead valves

1960

MAKE AND MODEL	Wheelbase	Tire Size	No. of Cylinders Bore and Stroke	Displacement	Valve and Cylinder Arrangement	Compression Ratio	Maximum Brake Horse Power	H.P. per Cu. In.	No. of Main Bearings	Operating Tappet Clearance Intake	Operating Tappet Clearance Exhaust	Intake Tappet Clearance for Valve Timing
Buick LeSabre	123	7.60/15	V8-4.125x3.4	364	VO	10.25	250@4400	.696	5	hy	hy	hy
Buick Invicta	123	7.60/15	V8-4.1875x3.64	401	VO	10.25	325@4400	.810	5	hy	hy	hy
Buick Electra	126.3	8.00/15	V8-4.1875x3.64	401	VO	10.25	325@4400	.810	5	hy	hy	hy
Cadillac 60, 62, 63	130	8.00/15	V8-4.00x3.875	390	VO	10.5	325@4800	.833	5	hy	hy	hy
Cadillac 64	130	8.00/15	V8-4.00x3.875	390	VO	10.5	345@4800	.885	5	hy	hy	hy
Cadillac 67	149.8	8.20/15	V8-4.00x3.875	390	VO	10.5	325@4800	.833	5	hy	hy	hy
Chevrolet Six	119	7.50/14	6-3.56x3.94	235.5	IO	8.25	135@4000	.575	4	hy	hy	hy
Chevrolet 283	119	7.50/14	V8-3.875x3.00	283	VO	8.50	170@4200	.600	5	hy	hy	hy
Chevrolet 348	119	7.50/14	V8-4.125x3.25	348	VO	9.50	250@4400	.560	5	hy	hy	hy
Chevrolet Corvette	102	6.70/15	V8-3.875x3.00	283	VO	9.50	230@4800	.815	5	.012H	.018H	.012
Chevrolet Corvair	108	6.50/13	6-3.375x2.60	140	FA	8.00	80@4400	.571	4	hy	hy	hy
Chrysler Wind.	122	8.00/14	V8-4.03x3.75	383	VO	10.0	305@4600	.795	5	hy	hy	hy
Chrysler Sara	122	8.50/14	V8-4.03x3.75	383	VO	10.0	325@4600	.850	5	hy	hy	hy
Chrysler N. Y.	126	9.00/14	V8 4.18x3.75	413	VO	10.0	350@4600	.850	5	hy	hy	hy
Comet	114	6.00/13	6-3.50 x 2.50	144.3	VO	8.7	90@4200	.625	4	.016H	.016H	.016'
DeSoto PS1-L	122	8.00/14	V8-4.12x3.38	361	VO	10.0	295@4600	.818	5	hy	hy	hy
DeSoto PS3-M	122	8.00/14	V8-4.25x3.38	383	VO	10.0	305@4600	.795	5	hy	hy	hy
Dodge Matador	122	8.00/14	V8-4.12x3.38	361	VO	10.0	295@4600	.818	5	hy	hy	hy
Dodge Polara	122	8.00/14	V8-4.25x3.38	383	VO	10.0	325@4600	.849	5	hy	hy	hy
Dodge Dart PD3	118a	7.50/14	6-3.40x4.125	225	IO	8.5	145@4000	.645	4	.010H	.020H	.010
Dodge Dart PD4	118a	7.50/14	V8-3.91x3.31	318	VO	9.0	230@4400	.724	5	.010H	.018H	.010
Dodge Dart PD4-H	118	7.50/14	V8-4.12x3.38	361	VO	10.0	310@4800	.859	5	hy	hy	hy
Edsel Six	120	7.50/14	6-3.625x3.60	223	VO	8.4	145@4000	.650	4	.019H	.019H	.019H
Edsel 2V Eight	120	7.50/14	V8-3.75x3.30	292	VO	8.8	185@4200	.635	5	.019H	.019H	.019H
Edsel 4V Eight	120	8.00/14	V8-4.00x3.50	352	VO	9.6	300@4600	.851	5	hy	hy	hy
Falcon	109.5	6.00/13	6-3.50x2.50	144.3	IO	8.7	90@4200	.623	4	.016H	.016H	.016
Ford Six	119	7.50/14	6-3.62x3.60	223	VO	8.4	145@4000	.650	4	.019H	.019H	.019
Ford 292	119	7.50/14	V8-3.75x3.30	292	VO	8.8	185@4200	.635	5	.019H	.018H	.019
Ford 352	119	8.00/14	V8-4.00x3.50	352	VO	8.9	235@4400	.667	5	hy	hy	hy
Ford 430	119	8.00/14	V8-4.30x3.70	430	VO	10.0	350@4600	.814	5	hy	hy	hy
Ford Thunderbird 352	113	8.00/14	V8-4.00x3.50	352	VO	9.6	300@4600	.852	5	hy	hy	hy
Ford Thunderbird 430	113	8.50/14	V8-4.30x3.70	430	VO	10.0	350@4600	.814	5	hy	hy	hy
Lincoln & Continental	131	9.50/14	V8-4.30x3.70	430	VO	10.0	315@4100	.725	5	hy	hy	hy
Mercury Mtrey.	126	8.00/14	V8-3.80x3.44	312	VO	8.9	205@4400	.857	5	.019H	.019H	.019
Mercury Mtclar.	126	8.50/14	V8-4.30x3.70	430	VO	10.0	310@4100	.721	5	hy	hy	hy
Mercury P. Lane	126	8.50/14	V8-4.30x3.70	430	VO	10.0	310@4100	.721	5	hy	hy	hy
Oldsmobile Dyn. 88	123	8.50/14	V8-4x3.688	371	VO	8.75	240@4400	.648	5	hy	hy	hy
Oldsmobile Sup. 88	123	8.50/14	V8-4.125x3.688	394	VO	9.75	315@4600	.799	5	hy	hy	hy
Oldsmobile 98	126.3	9.00/14	V8-4.125x3.688	394	VO	9.75	315@4600	.799	5	hy	hy	hy
Plymouth Six	118	7.50/14	6-3.40x4.125	225	IO	8.50	145@4000	.645	4	.013c	.023c	.013
Plymouth Fury 318	118	7.50/14	V8-3.90x3.31	318	VO	9.0	230@4400	.724	5	.010H	.018H	.010
Plymouth 361	118	7.50/14	V8-4.12x3.38	361	VO	10.0	295@4600	.818	5	hy	hy	hy
Pontiac-Cata. Vent.	122	8.00/14	V8-4.06x3.75	389	VO	8.61	215@3600	.554	5	hy	hy	hy
Pontiac-S. Chief,Bonn.	124	8.00/14	V8-4.06x3.75	389	VO	8.61	281@4600	.722	5	hy	hy	hy
Pontiac Temp. 425A	124	8.00/14	V8-4.06x3.75	389	VO	10.75	348@ N	.895	5	hy	hy	hy
Rambler Amer.	100	5.90/15	6-3.125x4.25	195.6	IL	8.0	90@3800	.461	4	.016	.018	.016
Rambler 6010	108	6.40/15	6-3.125x4.25	195.6	IO	8.7	127@4200	.650	4	.012H	.016H	.012
Rambler 6020	108	7.50/14	V8-3.50x3.25	250.0	VO	8.7	200@4900	.800	5	.012H	.014H	.012
Rambler 6080	117	8.00/14	V8-4.0x3.25	327.0	VO	8.7	250@4700	.765	5	hy	hy	hy
Studebaker Lark VI	108.5a	5.90/15	6-3.0x4.0	169.6	IL	8.3	90@4000	.532	4	.018c	.018c	.018c
Studebaker Lark VIII	113a	6.40/15	V8-3.562x3.25	259.2	VO	8.8	180@4500	.695	5	.026c	.026c	.026c
Studebaker Hawk	120.5	6.70/15	V8-3.562x3.625	289	VO	8.8	210@4500	.726	5	.026c	.026c	.026c
Valiant	106.5	6.50/13	6-3.40x3.125	170	IO	8.5	N	N	4	.010H	.020H	.010

ABBREVIATIONS:

AC - AC Spark Plug
AL - AutoLite
AO - Automatic Optional
a - Others also
air - Air cooled engine
b - left side 3/8, right side 0
B - Before topdead center
c - with engine cold
C - Carter carburetor
CH - Champion Spark Plug
CS - Coil Spring
DR - Delco Remy
EX - Exposed propeller shaft
f - Applies to engine with automatic transmission. On manual shift transmissions, intake valve opens 25 deg.BTDC

FA - Horizontal opposed
FI - Fuel injection
FO - Ford
g - At 5 deg. camber
h - Applies to manual steering
H - With engine at operating temperature
HO - Holley
Hy - Hydramatic transmission
IC - Enclosed propeller shaft
IO - In-line engine with overhead valves
IL - In-line engine with valves in block. (L-head)
k - Applies to left side. Right side is zero
N - None available
n - At 3/4 deg. camber
O - Optional
p - With two barrel carburetor

Tuneup Specifications

Intake Valve Opens Deg. B.T.D.C.	Carburetor Make	Ignition System Make	Breaker Point Gap	Breaker Point Open Deg. B.T.D.C.	Spark Plugs Make	Model	Gap	Auto.Transmission Type	Propeller Shaft	Front Suspension	Rear Suspension	Caster	Camber	Toe-In	King Pin Inclination	Cooling System Capacity Without Heater	Crankcase Capacity Qts.
35j	C,S	DR	.015	5B	AC	44S	.032	TQ	TT	CS	CS	-2	+1/2	5/32	7	18.5	4
33	C,R	DR	..015	12B	AC	44S	.032	TQ	TT	CS	CS	-2	+1/2	5/32	7	18.5	4
33	C,R	DR	.015	12B	AC	44S	.032	TQ	TT	CS	CS	-2	+1/2	5/32	7	18.5	4
39	C,R	DR	.016	5B	AC	44	.035	Hy	EX	CS	CS	-1	0	1/4	4	19.25	5
39	C,R	DR	.016	5B	AC	44	.035	Hy	EX	CS	CS	-1	0	1/4	4	19.25	5
39	C,R	DR	.016	5B	AC	44	.035	Hy	EX	CS	CS	-1	0	1/4	4	19.25	5
16	R	DR	.019	5B	AC	44	.035	TQ	EX	CS	CS	0	+1/2	1/16	7°11"	18	4
18p	R,C	DR	.019	4B	AC	44	.035	TQ	EX	CS	CS	0	+1/2	1/16	7°11"	18 1/2	4
18 1/2	R,C	DR	.019	8q	AC	44N	.035	TQ	EX	CS	CS	0	+1/2	1/16	7°11"	22	4
12 1/2a	C,FI	DR	.019	4B	AC	44	.035	TQ	EX	CS	Se	+2	0	0	4	16 1/2	5
15	R	DR	.019	4B	AC	44FF	.035	TQ	RR	CS	CS	+4	+1/2	1/8	7	Air	4
15	C	AL	.016	10B	AL	A42	.035	TQ	EX	TB	Se	-3/4h	+3/8t	1/8	6 1/2	17	5
15	C	AL	.016	10B	AL	A42	.035	TQ	EX	TB	Se	-3/4h	+3/8t	1/8	6 1/2	17	5
15	C	AL	.016	10B	AL	A42	.035	TQ	EX	TB	Se	-3/4h	+3/8t	1/8	6 1/2	17	5
15	HO	FO	.025	TC	CH	F14Y	.034	TQ	EX	CS	Se	+1 1/2	+3/4	1/16	7	9.3	4.5
15	C	AL	.016	10B	AL	A42	.035	TQ	EX	TB	Se	-1/2h	+3/8t	1/8	6 1/2	17	5
15	C	AL	.016	10B	AL	A42	.035	TQ	EX	TB	Se	-1/2h	+3/8t	1/8	6 1/2	17	5
15	S	AL	.016	10B	AL	A42	.035	TQ	EX	TB	Se	-3/4h	+3/8t	1/8	6 1/2	17	5
15	HO	AL	.016	10B	AL	A42	.035	TQ	EX	TB	Se	-3/4h	+3/8t	1/8	6 1/2	17	5
TC	C	AL	.020	2 1/2B	AL	AG42	.035	TQ	EX	TB	Se	-3/4h	+3/8t	1/8	6 1/2	14	4
17	C	AL	.016	5B	AL	A42	.035	TQ	EX	TB	Se	-3/4h	+3/8t	1/8	6 1/2	21	5
20	C	AL	.016	10B	AL	A42	.035	TQ	EX	TB	Se	-3/4h	+3/8t	1/8	6 1/2	17	5
17	HO	HO	.025	4B	C	870	.034	TQ	EX	CS	Se	0	+1	1/8	6 3/4	16	4
12	HO,FO	HO	.015	3B	C	F14Y	.034	TQ	EX	CS	Se	0	+1	1/8	6 3/4	20	5
26	HO,FO	HO	.015	6B	C	F14Y	.034	TQ	EX	CS	Se	0	+1	1/8	6 3/4	20	5
15	HO	FO	.025	22Bv	CH	F14Y	.034	TQ	EX	CS	Se	+1 1/2	45'	3/32	7n	9.3	3 1/2
17	HO	HO	.025	4Bv	C	870	.034	TQ	EX	CS	Se	0	1	1/8	6 3/4	15	4
12	HO,FO	HO	.015	3Bv	C	F14Y	.034	TQ	EX	CS	Se	0	1	1/8	6 3/4	19	5
22	HO,FO	HO	.015	3Bv	C	F11Y	.034	TQ	EX	CS	Se	0	1	1/8	6 3/4	19	5
27	HO,FO	HO	.015	6Bv	C	F11Y	.034	TQ	EX	CS	Se	0	1	1/8	6 3/4	20	5
22	HO,FO	HO	.015	3Bv	C	F11Y	.034	TQ	EX	CS	Se	1	1	1/8	7°7'	20	5
27	HO,FO	HO	.015	6Bv	C	F11Y	.034	TQ	EX	CS	Se	1	1	1/8	7°7'	20	5
22	C	FO	.015	6B	C	F11Y	.034	TQ	EX	CS	Se	+3/4	+3/8	1/8	7°26"	26	5
12	HO	FO	.015	3B	C	F14Y	.034	TQ	EX	CS	Se	-3/4	+3/8	1/8	7	21	5
22	C	FO	.015	6B	C	F11Y	.034	TQ	EX	CS	Se	-3/4	+3/8	1/8	7	22	5
22	C	FO	.015	6B	C	F11Y	.034	TQ	EX	CS	Se	-3/4	+3/8	1/8	7	22	5
14	R	DR	.016	5B	AC	45	.030	Hy	EX	CS	Se	-1/2	-1/2	1/16	10	21	4
16	R	DR	.016	5B	AC	44	.030	Hy	EX	CS	Se	-1/2	-1/2	1/16	10	21	4
16	R	DR	.016	5B	AC	44	.030	Hy	EX	CS	Se	-1/2	-1/2	1/16	10	21	4
0	C	AL	.020	2 1/2B	AL	AG42	.035	TQ	EX	TB	Se	-3/4h	+3/8t	1/8	6 1/2	15	4
17	C	AL	.016	5B	AL	A42	.035	TQ	EX	TB	Se	-3/4h	+3/8t	1/8	6 1/2	21	5
15	C	AL	.016	10B	AL	A42	.035	TQ	EX	TB	Se	-3/4h	+3/8t	1/8	6 1/2	17	5
14	R	DR	.016	6B	AC	45S	.035	Hy	EX	CS	CS	-1 1/2	+1/4	1/16	4 1/2	22.2	5
14	C	DR	.016	6B	AC	45S	.035	Hy	EX	CS	CS	-1 1/2	+1/4	1/16	4 1/2	22.2	5
14	C	DR	.016	6B	AC	45S	.035	Hy	EX	CS	CS	-1 1/2	+1/4	1/16	4 1/2	22.2	5
10	C	AL	.019	3B	AL	AL-7	.035	TQ	EX	CS	Se	+1/2	0	3/32	8 1/2	12	4
12 1/2	HO	DR	.016	5B	C	H10	.035	TQ	TT	CS	CS	+1/2	0	5/32	6°41	11	4
12 1/2	HO	AL	.016	TC	C	H10	.035	TQ	TT	CS	CS	+1/2	0	3/16	6°41	21	4
12 1/2	HO	AL	.016	TC	C	H10	.035	TQ	TT	CS	CS	+1/2	0	3/16	6°41	20	4
15	C	AL	.020	2B	C	J-7	.030	TQ	EX	CS	Se	-1 3/4	+1/2	1/16	6	12	5
11	S	DR	.016	4B	C	H18Y	.035	TQ	EX	CS	Se	-1 3/4	+1/2	1/16	6	18	5
11	S	DR	.016	4B	C	H18Y	.035	TQ	EX	CS	Se	-1 3/4	+1/2	1/16	6	18	5
8	C	AL	.019	5B	AL	AG42	.035	TQ	EX	TB	Se	-3/4h	+3/8t	1/8	7 1/2	14	4

q - With regular cam
R - Rochester carburetor
RR - Rear engine rear drive
S - Stromberg carburetor
Se - Semi-elliptic springs
TB - Torsion bar
TC - Top center
TQ - Torque converter
TT - Torque tube
t - Applies to left side, right side 1/8 deg.
VO - V- engine with overhead valves
v - Applies to manual shift transmission

1961

MAKE AND MODEL	Wheelbase	No. of Cylinders Bore & Stroke	Displacement	Valves and Cylinder Arrangement	Compression Pressure	Maximum Brake Horsepower	Valve Tappet Clearance		Cylinder Bolt Torque	Connecting Rod Bolt Torque	Main Bearing Bolt Torque
							Intake	Exhaust			
Buick LaSabre	123	V8-4.125x3.40	364	VO	180	250@4400	hy	hy	70	42	105
Buick Invicta	123	V8-4.1875x3.64	401	VO	180	325@4400	hy	hy	70	42	105
Buick Electra	126	V8-4.1875x3.64	401	VO	180	325@4400	hy	hy	70	42	105
Buick Special	112	V8-3.50x2.80	215	VO	155	155@4400	hy	hy	52	32	55
Cadillac 62,60	129-1/2	V8-4.00x3.875	390	VO	175	325@4800	hy	hy	67	42	95
Cadillac 75	150	V8-4.00x3.875	390	VO	175	325@4800	hy	hy	67	42	95
Chevrolet Six	119	6-3.562x3.94	235	IO	130	135@4000	.008H	.015H	92	40	105
Chevrolet 283	119	V8-3.875x3.00	283	VO	140	170@4200	hy	hy	65	32	65
Chevrolet 348	119	V8-4.125x3.25	348	VO	150	250@4400	hy	hy	65	40	100
Chrysler Newpt.	122	V8-4.125x3.375	361	VO	150	265@4400	hy	hy	70	45	85
Chrysler Wind.	122	V8-4.25x3.375	383	VO	165	305@4600	hy	hy	70	45	85
Chrysler N.Y.	126	V8-4.1875x3.75	413	VO	165	350@4600	hy	hy	70	45	85
Comet 144	114	6-3.500x2.50	144	IO	170	90@4200	.016H	.016H	70	22	70
Comet 170	114	6-3.500x2.9375	170	IO	170	101@4200	.016H	.016H	70	22	70
Corvair	108	6-3.4375x2.60	145	HA	130	80@4400	hy	hy	30	23	---
Corvair Monza	108	6-3.4375x2.60	145	HA	130	98@4600	hy	hy	30	23	---
Corvette	102	V8-3.875x3.00	283	VO	150	230@4800	hy	hy	65	32	65
Desoto	122	V8-4.125x3.375	361	VO	150	265@4400	hy	hy	70	45	85
Dart Six	119	6-3.4062x4.125	225	IO	120	145@4000	.010H	.020H	65	45	85
Dart V8	118	V8-3.9062x3.312	318	VO	125	230@4400	.010H	.018H	85	45	85
Dodge V8 36	122	V8-4.125x3.375	361	VO	160	265@4400	hy	hy	70	45	85
Dodge V8 383	122	V8-4.250x3.375	383	VO	160	325@4600	hy	hy	70	45	85
Dodge Ram J.	122	V8-4.250x3.375	383	VO	160	330@4800	hy	hy	70	45	85
Falcon 144	109-1/2	6-3.50x2.50	144	IO	170	90@4200	.016H	.016H	70	22	70
Falcon 170	109-1/2	6-3.9062x3.312	170	IO	170	101@4200	.016H	.016H	70	22	70
Ford Six	119	6-3.625x3.60	223	IO	150	135@4000	.019H	.019H	110	42	100
Ford V8 292	119	V8-3.75x3.30	292	VO	160	175@4200	.019H	.019H	70	42	85
Ford V8 352	119	V8-4.00x3.50	352	VO	180	220@4400	hy	hy	85	42	100
Ford V8 390	119	V8-4.0468x3.781	390	VO	180	300@4600	hy	hy	85	42	100
Lancer	106-1/2	6-3.406x3.125	170	IO	130	101@4400	.010H	.020H	65	45	85
Lark Six	108-1/2	6-3.00x4.00	170	IO	140	112@4500	.026C	.026C	48	30	92
Lark Eight	108-1/2	V8-3.56x3.25	259	VO	140	180@4500	.026C	.026C	60	53	90
Lincoln	123	V8-4.30x3.70	430	VO	160	315@4100	hy	hy	95	47	100
Mercury Six	120	6-3.625x3.60	223	IO	150	135@4000	.019C	.019C	115	42	100
Mercury 292	120	V8-3.75x3.30	292	VO	160	175@4200	.019C	.019C	70	42	85
Mercury 352	120	V8-4.00x3.50	352	VO	180	220@4400	hy	hy	85	42	100
Mercury 390	120	V8-4.05x3.784	390	VO	180	300@4600	hy	hy	85	42	100
Oldsmobile 88	123	V8-4.125x3.688	394	VO	150	250@4200	hy	hy	70	45	120
Oldsmobile 98	126	V8-4.125x3.688	394	VO	160	325@4600	hy	hy	70	45	120
Plymouth Six	118	6-3.40x4.125	225	VO	145	145@4000	.010H	.020H	65	45	85
Plymouth STD8	118	V8-3.906x3.312	318	VO	150	230@4400	.010H	.020H	85	45	85
Plymouth G.C.	118	V8-4.125x3.375	361	VO	150	305@4800	hy	hy	70	45	85
Plymouth S.C.	118	V8-4.25x3.375	383	VO	165	330@4800	hy	hy	70	45	85
Pontiac Cat.,Vent.	119	V8-4.0625x3.75	389	VO	145	215@3600	hy	hy	95	45	95
Pontiac Bon., S.C.	123	V8-4.0625x3.75	389	VO	145	235@3600	hy	hy	95	45	95
Pontiac Tempest	112	4-4.0625x3.75	194.5	IO	140	110@3800	hy	hy	95	45	95
Pontiac Tempest	112	4-4.0625x3.75	194.5	IO	140	140@4400	hy	hy	95	45	95
Pontiac Tempest	112	V8-3.50x2.80	215.0	VO	140	155@4600	hy	hy	52	32	52
Rambler Amer.Del	100	6-3.125x4.25	196	IL	130	90@3800	.016C	.018C	60	30	65
Rambler Amer.Cust	100	6-3.125x4.25	196	IO	130	125@4200	.012H	.016H	60	30	65
Rambler Cl. Six	108	6-3.125x4.25	196	IO	130	127@4200	.012H	.016H	65	30	70
Rambler Cl. 8	108	V8-3.50x3.25	250	VO	130	200@4900	.014H	.016H	65	50	---
Rambler Amb.	117	V8-4.00x3.25	327	VO	150	250@4700	hy	hy	---	--	---
Studebaker Hawk	120-1/2	V8-3.563x3.625	289	VO	140	210@4500	.026C	.026C	60	53	90

Abbreviations:

hy	-	Hydraulic valve lifters	AL	-	Auto Lite
VD	-	Vibration damper	M	-	Manual steering
VO	-	Vee type engine with overhead valves	HA	-	Horizontal opposed
L	-	Left	P	-	Front pulley
H	-	Hot	CH	-	Champion Spark Plug
IO	-	In line engine with overhead valves	C	-	Cold
f	-	Flywheel	IL	-	In line L head

Tuneup Specifications

Firing Order	Timing Mark Location	Breaker Point Opens BTDC	Breaker Point Gap	Cam Angle	Spark Plug Make	Spark Plug Model	Spark Plug Gap	Caster	Camber	Toe-In	Steering Axis Inclination	Cooling System Capacity	Crankcase Capacity Qts.
12784563	VD	12	.015	30	AC	44S	.032	-1	+3/8	3/16	10	18-1/2	4
12784563	VD	12	.015	30	AC	44S	.032	-1	+3/8	3/16	10	18-1/2	4
12784563	VD	12	.015	30	AC	44S	.032	-1	+3/8	3/16	10	18-1/2	4
18436572	VD	5	.016	30	AC	45FFS	.035	-2	-5/8	1/16	7-1/2	13-1/2	4
18436572	VD	5	.016	30	AC	44	.035	-7/8	L+1/8	3/16	6	19-1/4	5
18436572	VD	5	.016	30	AC	44	.035	-7/8	R-1/8	3/16	6	20-3/4	5
153624	f	5	.016	32	AC	44	.035	0	+1/2	1/16	7-1/6	18	5
18436572	VD	4	.016	30	AC	44	.035	0	+1/2	1/16	7-1/6	18-1/2	4
18436572	VD	8	.019	30	AC	44N	.035	0	+1/2	1/16	7-1/6	22	4
18436572	VD	10	.017	30	AL	A42	.035	-1/2M	+1/2	1/8	6-1/2	17	5
18436572	VD	10	.017	30	AL	A42	.035	-1/2M	+1/2	1/8	6-1/2	17	5
18436572	VD	10	.017	30	AL	A42	.035	-1/2M	+1/2	1/8	6-1/2	17	5
153624	P	2	.025	36.5	CH	F14Y	.034	+1/2	+1/2	1/4	7	9.7	3-1/2
153624	P	2	.025	36.5	CH	F14Y	.034	+1/2	+1/2	1/4	7	9.7	3-1/2
145236	P	--	.016	33	AC	46FF	.035	+2-3/4	+1/2	1/8	7	AIR	4
145236	P	--	.016	33	AC	46FF	.035	+2-3/4	+1/2	1/8	7	AIR	4
18436572	VD	4	.016	30	AC	44	.035	+2	0	1/16	4	16-1/2	5
18436572	VD	10	.017	30	AL	42	.035	+3/4	+1/2	1/8	6-1/2	17	5
153624	VD	2-1/2	.020	42	AL	AG52	.035	-1/2M	+1/2	1/8	6-1/2	14	4
18436572	P	5	.017	30	AL	A42	.035	-1/2M	+1/2	1/8	6-1/2	21	5
18436572	VD	10	.017	30	AL	A42	.035	-1/2M	+1/2	1/8	6-1/2	17	5
18436572	VD	10	.017	30	AL	A42	.035	-1/2M	+1/2	1/8	6-1/2	17	5
153624	P	2	.025	36.5	CH	F14Y	.034	+1/2	+1/2	1/4	7	9.7	3-1/2
153624	P	2	.025	36.5	CH	F14Y	.034	+1/2	+1/2	1/4	7	9.7	3-1/2
153624	VD	3	.025	36.5	CH	870	.034	0	+3/8	3/16	6-3/4	16	4
15486372	VD	4	.015	27	CH	F14Y	.034	0	+3/8	3/16	6-3/4	20	5
15486372	VD	3	.015	27	CH	F11Y	.034	0	+3/8	3/16	6-3/4	20	5
15486372	VD	3	.015	27	CH	F11Y	.034	0	+3/8	3/16	6-3/4	20	5
153624	P	2-1/2	.020	42	AL	AG52	.035	+3/4	+1/8	1/8	7-1/2	14	4
153624	VD	2	.020	39	CH	H14Y	.035	-1/2	+1/2	1/16	6	12	5
18436572	VD	4	.016	30	CH	H14Y	.035	-1/2	+1/2	1/16	6	18	5
15426378	VD	6	.015	27	CH	F11Y	.035	-3/4	+3/8	1/8	7	25	5
153624	VD	4	.025	36.5	CH	870	.034	0	+5/8	3/16	---	16	4
15486372	VD	3	.015	27	CH	F14Y	.034	0	+5/8	3/16	---	20	5
15426378	VD	3	.015	27	CH	F11Y	.034	0	+5/8	3/16	---	20	5
15426378	VD	3	.015	27	CH	F11Y	.034	0	+5/8	3/16	---	20	5
18736542	VD	5	.016	30	AC	45	.030	-1/2	+1/4	1/16	10	20-1/4	4
18736542	VD	7-1/2	.016	30	AC	44	.030	-1/2	+1/4	1/16	10	20-1/4	4
153624	VD	2-1/2	.020	39	AL	AG52	.035	-1/2M	+1/2	1/8	6	14	4
18436572	VD	5	.017	30	AL	AG42	.035	-1/2M	+1/2	1/8	6	21	5
18436572	VD	10	.017	30	AL	AG32	.035	-1/2M	+1/2	1/8	6	17	5
18436572	VD	7-1/2	.017	30	AL	AG32	.035	-1/2M	+1/2	1/8	6	17	5
18436572	P	6	.016	30	AC	45S	.035	-1-1/2	+1/4	1/16	4-5/6	19-1/2	4
18436572	P	6	.016	30	AC	45S	.035	-1-1/2	+1/4	1/16	4-5/6	19-1/2	4
1342	VD	6	.016	75	AC	45S	.035	-1-2/3	+1/8	1/16	6-5/6	12.5	4
1342	VD	6	.016	75	AC	45S	.035	-1-2/3	+1/8	1/16	6-5/6	12.5	4
18436572	VD	5	.016	30	AC	45FFS	.035	-1-2/3	+1/8	1/16	6-5/6	12.5	4
153624	VD	3	.016	32	CH	H10	.035	+1/2M	0	1/8	8	12	4
153624	VD	8	.016	32	CH	H10	.035	+1/2M	0	1/8	8	11	4
153624	VD	8	.016	32	CH	H10	.035	+1/2M	0	1/8	8	11	4
18436572	VD	0	.016	30	CH	H10	.035	+1/2M	0	1/8	8	20	4
18436572	VD	0	.016	30	CH	H10	.035	+1/2M	0	1/8	8	19	4
18436572	VD	4	.016	30	CH	H14Y	.035	-1/2	+1/2	1/16	6	18	5

1962

	Wheelbase	No. of Cylinders Bore and Stroke	Displacement	Valve and Cylinder Arrangement	Compression Pressure	Maximum Brake Horsepower	Valve Tappet Clearance Intake	Exhaust	Cylinder Bolt Torque	Connecting Rod Bolt Torque
Buick Spe. 4000	112	6-3.625x3.20	198	VO		135@4600	hy	hy	70	150
Buick Spe. 4100	112	V8-3.50x2.80	215	VO		155@4600	hy	hy	55	150
Buick LaSabre	123	V8-4.1875x3.64	401	VO	180	280@4400	hy	hy	70	42
Buick Invicta	123	V8-4.1875x3.64	401	VO	180	280@4400	hy	hy	70	42
Buick Electra	126	V8-4.1875x3.64	401	VO	180	280@4400	hy	hy	70	42
Cadillac 62	129-1/2	V8-4.00x3.875	390	VO	175	325@4800	hy	hy	75	45
Cadillac 75	149-4/5	V8-4.00x3.875	390	VO	175	325@4800	hy	hy	75	45
Chevrolet Six	119	6-3.56x3.94	235.5	IO	130	135@4000	hy	hy	92	40
Chevrolet V8-283	119	V8-3.875x3.00	283	VO	150	170@4200	hy	hy	65	32
Chevrolet V8-327	119	V8-4.00x3.25	327	VO	160	250@4400	hy	hy	65	40
Chevrolet V8-409	119	V8-4.3125x3.50	409	VO	150	380@5800	.008H	.018H	-	-
Chevy II Four	110	4-3.876x3.25	153	IO	140	90@4000	hy	hy	92	32
Chevy II Six	110	6-3.5635x3.25	194	IO	140	120@4400	hy	hy	92	32
Chevrolet Corvair	108	6-3.4375x2.60	145	HA	130	80@4400	hy	hy	30	26
Chevrolet Corvette	102	V8-4.00x3.25	327	VO	160	250@4400	hy	hy	65	40
Chrysler Newport	122	V8-4.125x3.375	361	VO	150	265@4400	hy	hy	70	45
Chrysler N.Y.	126	V8-4.187x3.750	413	VO	165	340@4600	hy	hy	70	45
Chrysler 300	122	V8-4.25x3.375	383	VO	165	305@4600	hy	hy	70	45
Chrysler 300 H	122	V8-4.1875x3.750	413	VO	165	380@5000	.015H	.024H	70	45
Chrysler Imper.	129	V8-4.1875x3.750	413	VO	165	340@4600	hy	hy	70	45
Dodge Lancer SL1	106-1/2	6-3.40x3.125	170	IO	145	101@4400	.010H	.020H	65	45
Dodge Dart SD1	116	6-3.40x4.125	225	IO	145	145@4000	.010H	.020H	65	45
Dodge Dart SD2	116	V8-3.91x3.31	318	VO	150	230@4400	.010H	.018H	85	45
Dodge Dart SD2P	116	V8-4.12x3.38	361	VO	150	305@4800	hy	hy	70	45
Ford Fairlane	115-1/2	6-3.50x2.94	170	IO	170	101@4400	.016H	.016H	70	21
Ford Fairlane	115-1/2	V8-3.50x2.87	221	VO	150	145@4400	hy	hy	70	21
Ford Falcon	109-1/2	6-3.50x2.50	144	IO	170	85@4200	.016	.016	70	21
Ford Falcon	109-1/2	6-3.50x2.94	170	IO	170	101@4400	.016	.016	70	21
Ford Galaxie 223	119	6-3.62x3.60	223	IO	150	138@4200	hy	hy	70	42
Ford Galaxie 292	119	V8-3.75x3.30	292	VO	162	170@4200	.018H	.018H	70	42
Ford Galaxie 352	119	V8-4.00x3.50	352	VO	180	220@4300	hy	hy	85	42
Ford Galaxie 390	119	V8-4.05x3.78	390	VO	180	300@4600	hy	hy	85	42
Ford Thunderbird	113	V8-4.05x3.78	390	VO	180	300@4600	hy	ay	85	42
Lincoln Cont.	123	V8-4.2969x3.703	430	VO	160	315@4100	hy	hy	95	47
Mercury Meteor 6	116-1/2	6-3.50x2.937	170	IO	170	101@4400	.016	.016	70	21
Mercury Meteor 8	116-1/2	V8-3.50x2.875	221	VO	150	145@4400	hy	hy	70	21
Mercury Comet	114	6-3.50x2.50	144	IO	170	85@4200	.016	.016	70	21
Mercury Six	120	6-3.62x3.60	223	IO	150	138@4200	hy	hy	70	42
Mercury 292	120	V8-3.75x3.30	292	VO	162	170@4200	.018H	.018H	70	42
Mercury 352	120	V8-4.00x3.50	352	VO	180	220@4300	hy	hy	85	42
Mercury 390	120	V8-4.05x3.78	390	VO	180	300@4600	hy	hy	85	42
Oldsmobile F85	112	V8-3.50x2.80	215	VO	160	155@4800	hy	hy	50	32
Oldsmobile Dyn. 88	123	V8-4.13x3.68	394	VO	150	280@4400	hy	hy	70	43
Oldsmobile Sup. 88	123	V8-4.13x3.68	394	VO	155	330@4600	hy	hy	70	43
Oldsmobile 98	126	V8-4.13x3.68	394	VO	155	330@4600	hy	hy	70	43
Oldsmobile Starf.	123	V8-4.13x3.68	394	VO	160	345@4600	hy	hy	70	43
Plymouth Six	116	6-3.40x4.125	225	IO	145	145@4000	.010H	.010H	65	45
Plymouth 318	116	V8-3.91x3.31	318	VO	150	230@4400	.020H	.018H	85	45
Plymouth 361	116	V8-4.12x3.38	361	VO	150	305@4800	.010H	.018H	70	45
Plymouth Vali.	106-1/2	6-3.40x3.125	170	IO	145	101@4400	.010H	.020H	65	45
Pontiac Cat.	120	V8-4.06x3.75	389	VO	145	215@3600	hy	hy	95	45
Pontiac Star-Chief	123	V8-4.06x3.75	389	VO	145	215@3600	hy	hy	95	45
Pontiac Bonn.	123	V8-4.06x3.75	389	VO	145	235@3600	hy	hy	95	45
Pontiac Temp.	112	4-4.06x3.75	195	VO	140	110@3000	hy	hy	95	45
Rambler Del.	100	6-3.125x4.25	195.6	IL	140	90@3800	.016C	.018C	60	28
Rambler Amer.	100	6-3.125x4.25	195.6	IO	130	125@4200	.012H	.012H	60	28
Rambler Class.	108	6-3.125x4.25	195.6	IO	130	127@4200	hy	hy	60	28
Rambler Amb.	108	V8-4.00x3.25	327	VO	150	250@4700	hy	hy	60	28
Studebaker Lark 6	109	6-3.00x4.00	169.6	IL	140	112@4500	.024H	.026H	48	30
Studebaker Lark V8	113	V8-3.56x3.25	259.2	VO	140	180@4500	.024H	.026H	50	30
Studebaker Hawk	120-1/2	V8-3.562x3.63	289	VO	140	210@4500	.024H	.024H	50	53

Abbreviations

CP - Crankshaft Pulley
CC - Timing Case Cover
TC - Top Center
VO - V type engine, overhead valves

IO - In line engine, overhead valves
HA - Horizontal opposed engine
hy - Hydraulic valve lifters
H - Hot
C - Cold
VD - Vibration damper

f - Flywheel
AC - A C Spark Plug Co.
CH - Champion Spark Plug Co.
AL - Auto-Lite Spark Plugs
M - Manual shift transmission

Main Bearing Bolt Torque	Firing Order	Timing Mark Location	Breaker Point Opens B.T.D.C.	Breaker Point Gap	Cam Angle	Make	Model	Gap	Caster Man. Steer.	Camber Rt. Wheel	Toe-In	Steering Axis Inclination	Cooling System Capacity	Crankcase Capacity Qt.
							Spark Plugs							
55	165432	VD	5	.016	30	AC	44S	.035	-2	-5/8	1/8	7-1/2	12	4
110	18436572	VD	5	.016	30	AC	45FFS	.035	-2	-5/8	1/8	7-1/2	12	4
105	12784563	VD	12	.016	30	AC	44S	.035	-2	+1/3	3/16	9-5/6	18-1/2	4
105	12784563	VD	12	.016	30	AC	44S	.035	-2	+1/3	3/16	9-5/6	18-1/2	4
105	12784563	VD	12	.016	30	AC	44S	.035	-2	+1/3	3/16	9-5/6	18-1/2	4
95	18436572	VD	5	.016	30	AC	44	.035	-1/2	+3/8	3/16	6	19-1/4	4
95	18436572	VD	5	.016	30	AC	44	.035	-1/2	+3/8	3/16	6	20-3/4	4
105	165432	f	5	.016	30	AC	46	.035	0	+1/2	1/8	7-1/4	18	5
65	18436572	VD	4	.016	30	AC	46	.035	0	+1/2	1/8	7-1/4	18-3/4	4
100	18436572	VD	4	.016	30	AC	44	.035	0	+1/2	1/8	7-1/4	18-3/4	4
-	18436572	VD	12	.016	29	AC	43N	.035	0	+1/2	1/8	7-1/4	18-3/4	6
50	1342	VD	4	.016	30	AC	44N	.035	1	+1/2	1/4	-	9	4
50	153624	VD	8	.016	30	AC	44N	.035	1	+1/2	1/4	-	12	5
-	145236	VD	4	.016	33	AC	46FF	.035	2	+1/2	1/4	-	AIR	4
100	18436572	VD	4	.016	30	AC	44	.035	0	0	1/16	3-5/6	16-1/2	5
85	18436572	VD	10	.017	30	CH	J12Y	.035	-1/2M	+1/2	1/8	6-1/2	17	5
85	18436572	VD	10	.017	30	CH	J12Y	.035	-1/2M	+1/2	1/8	6-1/2	17	5
85	18436572	VD	10	.017	30	CH	J12Y	.035	-1/2M	+1/2	1/8	6-1/2	17	5
85	18436572	VD	10	.017	37	CH	J9Y	.035	-1/2M	+1/2	1/8	6-1/2	17	5
85	18436572	VD	10	.017	30	CH	J12Y	.035	-1/2M	+1/2	1/8	6-1/2	17	5
85	153624	VD	2	.020	42	CH	N16Y	.035	-1/2M	+1/2	1/8	7-1/2	12	4
85	153624	VD	2	.020	42	CH	N16Y	.035	-1/2M	+1/2	1/8	7-1/2	13	4
85	18436572	VD	5	.016	30	CH	J12Y	.035	-1/2M	+1/2	1/8	7-1/2	21	4
85	18436572	VD	10	.016	30	CH	J12Y	.035	-1/2M	+1/2	1/8	7-1/2	17	4
65	153624	CP	4	.025	36	AL	BF82	.034	0	+1/2	1/8	-	9-1/2	3-1/2
70	15426378	VD	6	.015	27	AL	BF92	.034	0	+1/2	1/8	-	14-1/2	4
65	153624	CP	6	.025	36	AL	BF82	.034	+1/2	+1/2	1/4	-	9-7/10	3-1/2
65	153624	CP	6	.025	36	AL	BF82	.034	+1/2	+1/2	1/4	-	9-7/10	3-1/2
100	153624	VD	6	.025	36	AL	BTF6	.034	0	+5/8	1/8	-	16	4
85	15486372	VD	5	.015	27	AL	BF82	.034	0	+5/8	1/8	-	20	5
100	15426378	VD	5	.015	27	AL	BF42	.034	0	+5/8	1/8	-	20	5
100	15426378	VD	5	.015	27	AL	BF42	.034	0	+5/8	1/8	-	20	5
100	15426378	VD	8	.015	27	AL	BF42	.034	-3/4	+3/8	1/8	-	20	5
100	15426378	VD	6	.015	27	CH	F11Y	.035	-3/4	+3/8	1/8	7	25	5
65	153624	CP	6	.025	36	AL	BF82	.035	-	-	-	-	9-7/10	3-1/2
70	15426378	VD	6	.015	27	AL	BF82	.035	-	-	-	-	14-1/2	4
65	153624	CP	6	.025	36	AL	BF82	.034	-	-	-	-	9-7/10	3-1/2
100	153624	VD	6	.025	36	AL	BTF6	.034	0	+5/8	1/8	-	16	4
85	15486372	VD	5	.015	27	AL	BF82	.034	0	+5/8	1/8	-	20	5
100	15426378	VD	5	.015	27	AL	BF42	.034	0	+5/8	1/8	-	20	5
100	15426378	VD	5	.015	27	AL	BF42	.034	0	+5/8	1/8	-	20	5
55	18436572	VD	5	.016	30	AC	46FF	.030	-1	+3/8	1/16	7-1/2	13-1/2	4
120	18736542	VD	5	.016	30	AC		.030	-1/2	+1/4	1/16	10	21-1/4	4
120	18736542	VD	5	.016	30	AC	46F	.030	-1/2	+1/4	1/16	10	21-1/4	4
120	18736542	VD	5	.016	30	AC	45	.030	-1/2	+1/4	1/16	10	21-1/4	4
120	18736542	VD	5	.016	30	AC	45	.030	-1/2	+1/4	1/16	10	21-1/4	4
85	153624	CC	2-1/2	.020	42	CH	N16Y	.035	-1/2	+1/2	1/8	7-1/2	13	4
85	18436572	CC	5	.016	30	CH	J12Y	.035	-1/2	+1/2	1/8	7-1/2	21	4
85	18436572	CC	10	.016	30	CH	J12Y	.035	-1/2	+1/2	1/8	7-1/2	21	4
85	153624	CC	2-1/2	.020	42	CH	N16Y	.035	-1/2	+1/2	1/8	7-1/2	12	4
95	18436572	VD	6	.016	30	AC	45S	.035	-1-1/2	+1/4	1/16	6-5/6	19-1/2	4
95	18436572	VD	6	.016	30	AC	45S	.035	-1-1/2	+1/4	1/16	6-5/6	19-1/2	4
95	18436572	VD	6	.016	30	AC	45S	.035	-1-1/2	+1/4	1/16	6-5/6	19-1/2	4
95	1342	VD	6	.016	30	AC	45S	.035	-1-2/3	+1/6	1/16	6-5/6	12-3/5	4
57	153624	VD	3	.020	39	CH	H10	.035	0	0	1/8	8	12	4
57	153624	VD	8	.016	31	CH	H18Y	.035	0	0	1/8	8	11	4
57	153624	VD	5	.016	31	CH	H18Y	.035	0	0	1/8	6-1/6	11	4
57	18436572	VD	TC	.016	34	CH	H18Y	.035	0	0	1/8	6-1/6	19	4
90	153624	VD	2	.020	39	CH	H14Y	.035	0	+1/2	3/16	6	12	5
90	18436572	VD	4	.016	29	CH	H14Y	.035	0	+1/2	3/16	6	18	5
90	18436572	VD	4	.016	29	CH	H14Y	.035	0	+1/2	3/16	6	18	5

1963

	Wheelbase	No. of Cylinders Bore and Stroke	Displacement (cu. in.)	Valve and Cylinder Arrangement	Compression Pressure (lbs.)	Maximum Brake Horsepower	Valve Tappet Clearance Intake	Valve Tappet Clearance Exhaust	Cylinder Bolt Torque (ft.-lbs.)	Connecting Rod Bolt Torque (ft.-lbs.)
Buick Skylark 4300	112	8-3.50x2.80	215	VO	170	200@5000	HY	HY	75	45
Special 4000	112	6-3.625x3.20	198	VO	180	135@4600	HY	HY	75	45
Special 4100	112	8-3.50x2.80	215	VO	170	155@4600	HY	HY	75	45
Le Sabre 4400	123	8-4.187x3.64	401	VO	170	280@4400	HY	HY	75	45
Invicta, Wildcat 4600	123	8-4.1875x3.64	401	VO	170	325@4400	HY	HY	75	45
Electra 225, 4800	126	8-4.1875x3.64	401	VO	170	325@4400	HY	HY	75	45
Riviera 4700	117	8-4.1875x3.64	401	VO	170	325@4400	HY	HY	75	45
Cadillac 60	129.5	8-4.00x3.875	390	VO	180	325@4800	HY	HY	80	45
Seventy Five	149.8	8-4.00x3.875	390	VO	180	325@4800	HY	HY	80	45
Chevy II, 100, 300	110	4-3.875x3.25	153	IO	130	90@4000	HY	HY	95	45
Chevy II, 200, Nova 400	110	6-3.563x3.25	194	IO	130	125@4400	HY	HY	95	35
Corvair 500, 700, Monza 900	108	6-3.4375x2.60	145	HO	140	80@4400	HY	HY	33	26
Chevrolet Bis., Bel Air, Imp.	119	6-3.875x3.250	230	IO	135	140@4400	HY	HY	95	45
Chevrolet Bis., Bel Air, Imp.	119	8-3.875x3.0	283	IO	150	195@4800	HY	HY	70	35
Corvette	98	8-4.00x3.25	327	VO	185	250@4400	HY	HY	70	35
Chrysler Newport	122	8-4.125x3.375	361	VO	160	305@4800	HY	HY	75	45
300	122	8-4.25x3.38	383	VO	165	325@4600	HY	HY	75	45
300J	122	8-4.19x3.750	413	VO	165	350@4600	.015	.025	75	45
New Yorker	122	8-4.19x3.750	413	VO	165	350@4600	HY	HY	75	45
Imperial	129	8-4.19x3.750	413	VO	165	350@4600	HY	HY	75	45
Dodge Dart, 170, 270, GT Models	111	6-3.40x3.125	170	IO	145	101@4400	.010	.020	65	45
Dart 170, 270 GT Models	111	6-3.40x4.125	225	IO	150	140@4000	.010	.020	65	45
330, 440 Polara	119	6-3.40x4.125	225	IO	150	145@4000	.010	.020	65	45
330, 440 Polara	119	8-3.91x3.31	312	VO	160	230@4400	.010	.020	75	45
330, 440 Polara	119	8-4.25x3.38	383	VO	160	325@4800	.016	.028	75	45
330, 440 Polara 500	119	8-4.25x3.75	426	VO	165	370@4600	.016	.028	75	45
800, Custom 880	119	8-4.25x3.375	361	VO	160	305@4800	HY	HY	75	45
880, Custom 880, Polara 500	119	8-4.25x3.38	383	VO	180	325@4800	HY	HY	75	45
Ford Fairlane	115.5	6-3.50x2.94	170	IO	150	101@4400	HY	HY	75	45
Fairlane	115.5	8-3.50x2.87	221	VO	150	145@4400	HY	HY	75	45
Fairlane	115.5	8-2.80x2.87	260	VO	150	101@4400		HY	70	45
Falcon	109.5	6-3.50x2.50	144	IO	170	85@4200	HY	HY	75	24
Falcon	109.5	6-3.50x2.94	170	IO	170	101@4400	HY	HY	75	24
Thunderbird	113	8-4.05x3.78	390	VO	180	300@4600	HY	HY	90	45
Galaxie	119	6-3.62x3.60	223	IO	150	138@4200	HY	HY	75	45
Galaxie	119	8-3.80x2.87	260	VO	150	164@4400	HY	HY	70	45
Galaxie	119	8-4.00x3.50	352	VO	180	220@4300	HY	HY	90	45
Galaxie	119	8-4.05x3.78	390	VO	180	300@4600	HY	HY	90	45
Lincoln Continental	123	8-4.30x3.70	430	VO	180	320@4600	HY	HY	105	50
Mercury Comet	114	6-3.50x2.50	144	IO	170	85@4200	HY	HY	75	24
Comet	114	6-3.50x2.94	170	IO	170	101@4400	HY	HY	75	24
Meteor	116.5	6-3.50x2.94	170	IO	170	101@4400	HY	HY	75	24
Meteor	116.5	8-3.50x2.87	221	VO	150	145@4400	HY	HY	75	45
Meteor	120	8-3.80x2.87	260	VO	150	164@4400	HY	HY	70	45
Monterey	120	8-4.05x3.78	390	VO	180	300@4600	HY	HY	90	50
Monterey	120	8-4.13x3.78	406	VO	180	385@5800	.027H	.027H	90	50
Oldsmobile F85	112	8-3.5x2.8	215	VO	140	155@4800	HY	HY	55	35
F85 Jetfire, Cutlass	112	8-3.5x2.8	215	VO	140	185@4800	HY	HY	55	35
88, Super 88	123	8-4.125x3.688	394	VO	185	280@4400	HY	HY	80	48
98, Starfire	123	8-4.125x3.688	394	VO	185	330@4600	HY	HY	80	48
Plymouth Valiant	106	6-3.40x3.125	170	IO	145	101@4400	.010H	.020H	65	45
Valiant	106	6-3.40x4.125	225	IO	145	145@4000	.010H	.020H	65	45
Plymouth	116	6-3.40x4.125	225	IO	145	145@4000	.010H	.020H	65	45
Plymouth	116	8-3.91x3.31	318	VO	155	230@4400	.010H	.018H	85	50
Plymouth	116	8-4.12x3.38	361	VO	165	265@4400	HY	HY	70	45
Pontiac Catalina	120	8-4.06x3.75	389	VO	180	215@3600	HY	HY	95	45
Star Chief, Bonneville	123	8-4.06x3.75	389	VO	180	235@3600	HY	HY	95	45
Grand Prix	120	8-4.06x3.75	389	VO	180	303@4600	HY	HY	95	45
Tempest, Le Mans	112	4-4.06x3.75	194.5	IO	145	115@4000	HY	HY	95	45
Tempest, Le Mans	112	8-3.72x3.75	326	VO	160	264@4800	HY	HY	55	35
Rambler American	100	6-3.125x4.25	195.6	IL	130	90@3800	.016H	.018H	60	30
American	100	6-3.125x4.25	195.6	IO	145	125@4200	.012H	.016H	60	30
Classic	112	6-3.125x4.25	195.6	IO	145	127@4200	.012H	.016H	60	30
Ambassador	112	8-4.0x3.25	327.0	VO	145	250@4700	HY	HY	60	50
Studebaker Lark	109	6-3.00x4.00	169.0	IO	150	112@4500	.024H	.024H	50	32
Lark	113	6-3.00x4.00	169.6	IO	150	112@4500	.024	.024	50	32
Cruiser/Lark	113	8-3.562x3.625	259.0	VO	140	180@4500	.026H	.026H	65	54
Cruiser	113	8-3.562x3.625	289.0	VO	140	210@4500	.026H	.026H	65	54
Hawk	120	8-3.562x3.625	289.0	VO	140	210@4500	.026H	.026H	65	54

ABBREVIATIONS:

AC - AC spark plugs
AL - Auto-Lite spark plugs
C - Cold engine

CC - Timing case cover
CP - Crankshaft pulley
H - Hot engine
HO - Horizontal opposed cylinders

Tuneup Specifications

Main Bearing Bolt Torque (ft.-lbs.)	Firing Order	Timing Mark Location	Breaker Point Opens B.T.D.C.	Breaker Point Gap	Cam Angle	Spark Plugs Make	Model	Gap	Caster Man. Steer. (deg.)	Camber Rt. Wheel (deg.)	Toe-In (ins.)	Steering Axle Inclination (deg.)	Cooling System Capacity (qts.)	Crankcase Capacity (qts.)
120	18436572	VD	7.5	.016	30	AC	44FFS	.033	1N	3/8P	3/16	9	13.5	4.0
120	165432	CP	7.5	.016	30	AC	44S	.033	1N	3/8P	3/16	9	12.0	4.0
120	18436572	VD	7.5	.016	30	AC	45FFS	.033	1N	3/8P	3/16	9	13.5	4.0
120	12784563	VD	12.0	.016	30	AC	44S	.033	1N	3/8P	3/16	9	18.5	4.0
120	12784563	VD	12.0	.016	30	AC	44S	.033	1N	3/8P	3/16	9	18.5	4.0
120	12784563	VD	12.0	.016	30	AC	44S	.033	1N	3/8P	3/16	9	18.5	4.0
120	12784563	VD	12.0	.016	30	AC	44S	.033	1N	3/8P	3/16	9	18.5	4.0
100	18726543	CP	5.0	.016	30	AC	44	.035	1N	3/8P	3/16	6	17.2	4.0
100	18726543	CP	5.0	.016	30	AC	44	.035	1N	3/8P	3/16	6	19.7	4.0
110	1342	CP	4.0	.019	32	AC	46N	.038	1/2P	1P	1/4	8	9.0	3.5
110	153624	VD	8.0	.019	32	AC	46N	.038	1/2P	1P	1/4	8	12.0	4.0
48	145236	CP	4.0	.019	32	AC	46FF	.038	1-1/2P	1P	(Front) 1/8-3/16	7	None	4.0
110	153624	VD	4.0	.019	32	AC	44N	.035	0	1/2P	1/16	7-1/4	12.0	4.0
70	18436572	CP	6.0	.019	30	AC	46	.035	0	1/2P	1/16	7-1/4	18.5	4.0
70	18436572	VD	4.0	.016	30	AC	44	.035	2P	0	1/4	4	16.5	4.0
85	18436572	CC	10.0	.016	30	CH	J12Y	.035	1/2N	0	1/8	6	17.0	5.0
85	18436572	CC	10.0	.016	30	CH	J12Y	.035	1/2N	0	1/8	6	17.0	5.0
85	18436572	CC	10.0	.016	34	CH	J9Y	.035	1/2N	0	1/8	6	17.0	5.0
85	18436572	CC	10.0	.016	30	CH	J12Y	.035	1/2N	0	1/8	6	17.0	5.0
85	18436572	CC	10.0	.016	30	CH	J12Y	.035	1/2N	0	1/8	6	17.0	5.0
85	153624	WP	2.5	.020	42	CH	N12Y	.035	1/2N	1/8P	1/8	7-1/2	12.0	4.0
85	153624	WP	2.5	.020	42	CH	N12Y	.035	1/2N	1/8P	1/8	7-1/2	12.0	4.0
85	153624	WP	2.5	.020	42	CH	N12Y	.035	1/2N	1/4P	1/8	7	12.0	4.0
85	18436572	CC	5.0	.017	30	CH	J12Y	.035	1/2N	1/4P	1/8	7	21.0	4.0
85	18436572	CC	10.0	.017	30	CH	J12Y	.035	1/2N	1/4P	1/8	7	17.0	4.0
85	18436572	CC	15.0	.017	34	CH	J9Y	.035	1/2N	1/4P	1/8	7	17.0	5.0
85	18436572	CC	10.0	.017	31	CH	J12Y	.035	1/2N	1/4P	1/8	7	17.0	4.0
85	18436572	CC	10.0	.017	30	CH	J12Y	.035	1/2N	1/4P	1/8	7	17.0	4.0
105	153624	CC	7.0	.025	37	AL	BF82	.034	0	1/2P	1/8	6-3/4	9.5	3.5
105	15426378	CC	4.0	.015	27	AL	BF82	.035	0	1/2P	1/8	6-3/4	14.5	4.0
75	15426378	CC	4.0	.015	27	AL	BF82	.035	0	1/2P	1/8	6-3/4	14.5	4.0
70	153624	CC	6.0	.025	35	AL	BF82	.035	1P	1/4P	3/16	7	10.5	3.5
70	153624	CC	6.0	.025	35	AL	BF82	.035	1P	1/4P	3/16	7	10.5	3.5
105	15426378	CC	7.0	.015	27	AL	BF42	.035	1/2P	1/2P	1/16	7-1/2	20.5	5.0
105	153624	CC	4.0	.025	37	AL	BF82	.035	0	1/2P	1/8	6-3/4	16.0	4.0
75	15426378	CC	7.0	.015	27	AL	BF82	.035	0	1/2P	1/8	6-3/4	14.5	4.0
105	15426378	CC	5.0	.015	27	AL	BF82	.035	0	1/2P	1/8	6-3/4	20.5	5.0
105	15426378	CC	5.0	.015	27	AL	BF42	.035	0	1/2P	1/8	6-3/4	20.5	5.0
105	15426378	CC	6.0	.015	27	AL	BF42	.035	3/4N	1/2P	1/16	7	25.0	5.0
70	153624	CC	6.0	.025	35	AL	BF82	.035	1P	1/4P	3/16	7	10.5	3.5
70	153624	CC	6.0	.025	35	AL	BF82	.035	1P	1/4P	3/16	7	10.5	3.5
70	153624	CC	6.0	.025	35	AL	BF82	.035	0	1/2P	1/8	7	10.5	3.5
105	15426378	CC	4.0	.015	27	AL	BF82	.035	0	1/2P	1/8	7	15.5	4.5
75	15426378	CC	7.0	.015	27	AL	BF82	.035	0	1/2P	1/8	7	14.5	3.5
105	15426378	CC	6.0	.015	27	AL	BF42	.034	0	1/2P	1/8	7	20.5	5.0
105	1542637	CC	10.0	.020	27	AL	BF82	.035	0	1/2P	1/8	7	21.0	5.0
60	18436572	CC	5.0	.016	30	AC	46FF	.035	1-3/4N	0	1/8	7-1/2	12.5	4.0
60	18436572	CC	5.0	.016	30	AC	45FF	.035	1-3/4N	0	1/8	7-1/2	12.5	4.0
120	18736542	VD	5.0	.016	30	AC	45	.030	1/2N	1/8P	1/8	10	20.25	4.0
120	18736542	VD	5.0	.016	30	AC	44	.030	1/2N	1/8P	1/8	10	20.25	4.0
85	153624	CC	2.5	.020	42	CH	N12Y	.035	1/2N	1/2P	1/8	7-1/2	12.0	4.0
85	153624	CC	2.5	.020	42	CH	N12Y	.035	1/2N	1/2P	1/8	7-1/2	13.0	4.0
85	153624	CC	2.5	.020	42	CH	N12Y	.035	3/8P	1/6	7	13.0	4.0
85	18436572	VD	10.0	.016	30	CH	J12Y	.035	1/2N	3/8P	1/16	7	21.0	4.0
85	18436572	CC	10.0	.016	30	CH	N12Y	.035	1/2N	3/8P	1/16	7	17.0	4.0
95	18436572	CP	6.0	.016	30	AC	45S	.035	1-1/2N	1/4P	0	4-1/2	19.5	4.0
95	18436572	CP	6.0	.016	30	AC	45S	.035	1-1/2N	1/4P	0	4-1/2	19.5	4.0
95	18436572	CP	6.0	.016	30	AC	45S	.035	1-1/2N	1/4P	0	4-1/2	19.5	4.0
95	1342	CP	6.0	.016	75	AC	45S	.035	1-1/4N	0	0	6-1/2	11.6	4.0
55	18436572	CP	5.0	.016	30	AC	45S	.032	1-1/4N	0	0	6-1/2	11.6	4.0
70	153624	VD	3	.020	39	CH	H10	.035	0	0	1/8	8	12	4
70	153624	VD	5	.016	32	CH	H18Y	.035	0	0	1/8	8	11	4
70	153624	VD	8	.020	32	CH	H10	.035	0	0	1/8	8	11	4
85	18436572	VD	5	.017	34	CH	H18Y	.035	1P	0	1/8	6-1/2	21	4
95	153624	VD	4	.020	39	CH	H14Y	.035	0	1/2P	1/16	6	12	5
95	153624	VD	4	.020	39	CH	H14Y	.035	0	1/2P	1/16	6	12	5
95	18436572	VD	5	.015	31	CH	H14Y	.035	0	1/2P	1/16	6	18	5
95	18436572	VD	4	.015	31	CH	H14Y	.035	0	1/2P	1/16	6	18	5
95	18436572	VD	5	.015	31	CH	H14Y	.035	0	1/2P	1/16	6	18	5

HY – Hydraulic valve lifters   P – Plus
IL – In-line L head   VD – Vibration Damper
IO – In-line engine, overhead valves   VO – V-type engine, overhead valves
N – Minus   WP – Water pump housing

1964

	Wheelbase	No. of Cylinders Bore and Stroke	Displacement (cu. in.)	Valve and Cylinder Arrangement	Compression Pressure (lbs.)	Maximum Brake Horsepower	Valve Tappet Clearance Intake	Valve Tappet Clearance Exhaust	Cylinder Bolt Torque (ft.-lbs.)	Connecting Rod Bolt Torque (ft.-lbs.)
Buick - Special	115	V-6-3.75x3.40	225	VO	160	155@1440	HY	HY	35	35
LeSabre	123	8-3.75x3.40	300	VO	170	210@4600	HY	HY	75	45
Skylark	115	8-3.75x3.40	300	VO	160	210@4600	HY	HY	35	35
Wildcat	123	8-4.1875x3.64	401	VO	170	325@4400	HY	HY	75	45
Electra 225	126	8-4.1875x3.64	401	VO	170	325@4400	HY	HY	75	45
Electra 225	126	8-4.3125x3.64	425	VO	170	340@4400	HY	HY	75	45
Riviera	117	8-4.3125x3.64	425	VO	170	340@4400	HY	HY	75	45
Cadillac - All	129.5	8-4.13x4.00	429	VO	170	340@4600	HY	HY	80	45
Chevrolet	119	6-3.875x3.25	230	IO	135	140@4400	HY	HY	95	45
Chevrolet	119	8-3.875x3.0	283	VO	150	140@4400	HY	HY	70	35
Chevrolet	119	8-4.0x3.25	327	VO	185	250@4400	HY	HY	70	35
Chevrolet	119	8-4.313x3.50	409	VO	190	340@5000	HY	HY	70	35
Chevy II	110	4-3.875x3.25	153	IO	140	90@4000	HY	HY	95	35
Chevy II	110	6-3.563x3.25	194	IO	140	120@4400	HY	HY	95	35
Chevelle	115	6-3.563x3.25	194	IO	140	120@4400	HY	HY	95	35
Chevelle	115	8-3.875x3.0	283	VO	150	195@4800	HY	HY	70	35
Corvair	108	6-3.4375x2.94	164	HO	130	95@3600	HY	HY	33	26
Corvette	98	8-4.0x3.25	327	VO	190	250@4400	HY	HY	70	35
Chrysler - Newport	122	8-4.12x3.38	361	VO	150	265@4400	HY	HY	85	50
300	122	8-4.25x3.38	383	VO	150	305@4600	HY	HY	75	45
New Yorker	122	8-4.19x3.75	413	VO	165	340@4600	HY	HY	75	45
Imperial	129	8-4.19x3.75	413	VO	165	340@4600	HY	HY	75	45
Dodge Dart	111	6-3.4x3.125	170	IO	150	101@4400	.010H	.020H	65	50
Dodge	119	6-3.4x4.125	225	IO	150	145@4000	.010H	.020H	65	50
Dodge	119	8-3.91x3.31	318	VO	160	230@4400	.013H	.021H	75	45
Dodge	119	8-4.25x3.38	383	VO	160	330@4600	HY	HY	75	45
880	122	8-4.12x3.38	361	VO	160	265@4400	HY	HY	85	50
880	122	8-4.25x3.38	383	VO	160	305@4600	HY	HY	85	50
Ford - Falcon	109.5	6-3.50x2.50	144	IO	170	85@4200	HY	HY	75	24
Falcon	109	6-3.50x2.94	170	IO	170	101@4400	HY	HY	75	24
Falcon	109	6-3.68x3.13	200	IO	170	116@4400	HY	HY	75	24
Falcon	109	8-3.80x2.87	260	VO	150	164@4400	HY	HY	70	24
Ford	119	6-3.62x3.60	223	IO	150	138@4200	.019H	.019H	115	45
Ford	119	8-4.0x2.87	289	VO	160	195@4400	HY	HY	70	24
Ford	119	8-4.0x3.50	352	VO	180	250@4400	HY	HY	90	45
Ford	119	8-4.05x3.78	390	VO	180	300@4600	HY	HY	90	45
Fairlane	115	6-3.50x2.94	170	IO	170	101@4400	HY	HY	75	24
Fairlane	115	6-3.68x3.13	200	IO	- - -	116@4400	HY	HY	75	24
Fairlane	115	8-3.68x3.13	260	VO	150	164@4400	HY	HY	70	24
Fairlane	115	8-4.0x2.87	289	VO	155	195@4400	HY	HY	70	24
Thunderbird	113	8-4.05x3.78	390	VO	180	300@4600	HY	HY	90	45
Lincoln Continental	126	8-4.30x3.70	430	VO	180	320@4600	HY	HY	105	50
Mercury	120	8-4.05x3.78	390	VO	180	250@4400	HY	HY	90	45
Mercury	120	8-4.23x3.78	427	VO	180	410@5600	.025H	.025H	110	58
Comet	114	6-3.50x2.94	170	IO	170	101@4400	HY	HY	75	24
Comet	114	8-3.80x2.87	260	VO	150	164@4400	HY	HY	70	24
Comet	114	8-4.0x2.87	289	IO	155	210@4400	HY	HY	70	24
Oldsmobile-F85	115	V-6-3.75x3.40	225	VO	160	155@4400	HY	HY	80	48
F85	115	8-3.9375x3.385	330	VO	180	230@4400	HY	HY	80	48
F85	115	8-3.9375x3.385	330	YO	180	290@4800	HY	HY	80	48
Jetstar 88	123	8-3.9375x3.385	330	VO	185	245@4600	HY	HY	80	48
Dynamic 88	123	8-4.125x3.688	394	VO	185	280@4400	HY	HY	80	48
Super 88-98, Starfire	126	8-4.125x3.688	394	VO	185	345@4800	HY	HY	80	48
Plymouth	116	6-3.40x4.125	225	IO	145	145@4000	.010	.020	65	45
Plymouth	116	8-3.91x3.31	318	VO	145	230@4400	.013	.021	65	45
Plymouth	116	8-4.12x3.38	361	VO	150	265@4400	HY	HY	65	45
Plymouth	116	8-4.25x3.375	383	VO	150	330@4600	HY	HY	70	45
Plymouth	116	8.425x3.75	426	VO	150	415@5600	HY	HY	70	45
Valiant	106	6-3.40x3.125	170	IO	145	101@4400	.010	.020	65	45
Valiant	106	6-3.40x4.125	225	IO	145	145@4000	.010	.020	65	45
Pontiac Tempest	115	6-3.75x3.25	215	IO	140	140@4200	HY	HY	95	45
Tempest	115	8-3.72x3.75	326	VO	160	250@4600	HY	HY	55	35
Catalina	120	8-4.06x3.75	389	VO	145	230@4000	HY	HY	95	45
Star Chief, Bonneville	123	8-4.06x3.75	389	VO	160	283@4400	HY	HY	95	45
Grand Prix	123	8-4.09x4.0	421	VO	160	350@4600	HY	HY	95	45
Rambler American L Head Eng	106	6-3.125x4.25	195.6	IL	130	90@3800	.016H	.018H	60	30
American	106	6-3.125x4.25	195.6	IO	145	125@4200	12H	16H	60	30
American Aluminum Engine	106	6-3.125x4.25	195.6	IO	145	138@4500	HY	HY	50	30
Classic	112	6-3.125x4.25	195.6	IO	145	127@4200	HY	HY	60	30
Classic	112	8-3.75x3.25	287	VO	145	198@4700	HY	HY	60	30
Ambassador	112	8-4.0x3.25	327	VO	145	250@4700	HY	HY	65	50
Studebaker Lark	109	6-3.0x4.0	170	IO	150	112@4500	.024H	.024H	50	32
Hawk	109	8-3.56x3.25	259.2	VO	150	180@4500	.024H	.024H	65	45
Hawk and Avanti	120	8-3.56x3.63	289	VO	185	210@4500	.026H	.026H	65	54

ABBREVIATIONS:

AC - AC spark plugs
AL - Auto-Lite Spark plugs
C - Cold engine

CC - Timing case cover
CP - Crankshaft pulley
H - Hot engine
HO - Horizontal opposed cylinders
HY - Hydraulic valve lifters

Main Bearing Bolt Torque (ft.-lbs.)	Firing Order	Timing Mark Location	Breaker Point Opens B.T.D.C.	Breaker Point Gap	Cam Angle	Spark Plugs Make	Spark Plugs Model	Spark Plugs Gap	Caster Man. Steer. (deg.)	Camber Rt. Wheel (deg.)	Toe-In (ins.)	Steering Axle Inclination (deg.)	Cooling System Capacity (qts.)	Crankcase Capacity (qts.)
120	165432	CP	5	.016	30	AC	44S	.035	1P	1P	5/16	8	10.7	4
120	18436572	VD	2.5	.016	30	AC	44FFS	.035	1P	1/3P	5/16	10	13.7	4
55	18436572	CP	5	.016	30	AC	45FFS	.035	1P	1P	5/16	8	10.5	4
120	18436572	VD	2.5	.016	30	AC	44S	.035	1P	1/3P	5/16	10	18.5	4
120	18436572	VD	2.5	.016	30	AC	44S	.035	1P	1/3P	5/16	10	18.5	4
120	18436572	VD	5	.016	30	AC	44S	.035	1P	1P	5/16	8	18.5	4
120	12784563	VD	2.5	.016	30	AC	44S	.035	1P	1/3P	5/16	10	18.5	4
100	18726543	VD	5	.016	30	AC	44	.035	1N	1/2P	1/4	6	17.25	4
110	153624	VD	4	.039	32	AC	46N*	.035	0	1/2P	3/32	7-1/4	12	4
70	18436572	CP	5	.019	30	AC	45	.035	0	1/2P	3/32	7-1/4	17	4
70	18436572	VD	6	.019	30	AC	44	.035	0	1/2P	3/32	7-1/4	21	4
70	18436572	VD	6	.019	30	AC	43N	.035	0	1/2P	3/32	7-1/4	22	4
110	1342	CP	4	.019	32	AC	46N*	.036	1P	1/2P	1/8	8	9	3.5
110	153624	VD	8	.019	32	AC	46N*	.035	1P	1/2P	1/8	8	11.5	4
110	153624	VD	8	.019	33	AC	46N*	.035	3/4P	1/2P	1/8	8	11.5	4
70	18436572	CP	5	.019	30	AC	45	.035	3/4P	1/2P	1/8	8	17	4
48	145236	CP	2**	.019	32	AC	46FF	.038	1P	0	11/16***	7	---	4
70	18436572	VD	4	.019	30	AC	44	.035	1-3/4P	3/4P	5/32	7	19	4
85	18436572	CC	10	.016	30	CH	J12Y	.035	1/2N	1/2P	3/32	7	17	5
85	18436572	VD	10	.016	30	CH	J12Y	.035	1/2N	1/2P	3/32	7	17	5
85	18436572	CC	10	.016	30	CH	J12Y	.035	1/2N	1/2P	3/32	7	17	5
85	18436572	CC	10	.016	30	CH	J12Y	.035	3/4P	1/2P	3/32	7	17	5
85	153624	CC	2.5	.020	42	CH	14Y	.035	1/2N	3/8P	1/8	7-1/2	12	4
85	153624	CC	2.5	.020	42	CH	N14Y	.035	1/2N	3/8P	3/32	7-1/2	13	4
85	18436572	CC	5	.016	30	CH	J12Y	.035	1/2N	3/8P	3/32	7-1/2	21	4
85	18436572	CC	10	.016	30	CH	J12Y	.035	1/2N	3/8P	3/32	7-1/2	17	5
85	18436572	CC	10	.016	30	CH	J12Y	.035	1/2N	3/8P	3/32	7-1/2	17	5
70	153624	CP	8	.025	36	AL	BF82	.034	1/2P	3/8P	5/16	7	9.5	3.5
70	153624	CP	6	.026	36	AL	BF82	.035	1/2P	3/8P	5/16	7	9.5	3.5
70	153624	CP	12	.025	36	AL	BF82	.034	1/2P	3/8P	5/16	7	9.5	3.5
70	15426378	CP	10	.015	27	AL	BF82	.034	1/2P	3/8P	5/16	7	14.5	4
105	153624	CC	4	.025	36	AL	BFT6	.034	1/4P	1/2P	1/4	6-3/4	16	4
70	15426378	CC	6	.015	27	AL	BF42	.034	1/4P	1/2P	1/4	6-3/4	15	4
105	15426378	CC	6	.015	27	AL	BF42	.034	1/4P	1/2P	1/4	6-3/4	20.5	5
105	15426378	CC	4	.015	27	AL	BF42	.034	1/4P	1/2P	1/4	6-3/4	20.5	5
70	153624	CC	6	.025	37	AL	BF82	.034	0	1/2P	3/16	7-1/4	9.5	4.5
70	153624	CC	6	.025	38	AL	BF82	.034	0	1/2P	3/16	7-1/4	9.5	3.5
75	15426378	CC	6	.015	27	AL	BF82	.034	0	1/2P	3/16	7-1/4	14.5	4
75	15426378	CC	6	.015	27	AL	BF82	.035	0	1/2P	3/16	7-1/4	15	5
105	15426378	CC	6	.015	27	AL	BF42	.034	1/2N	1/4P	1/4	6-3/4	20	5
105	15426378	VD	6	.015	27	AL	BF42	.034	1/2N	3/8P	3/16	7	25	5
105	15426378	CC	6	.015	27	AL	BF42	.034	0	5/8P	1/4	7	20.5	5
105	15426378	CC	8	.020	35	AL	BF32	.035	0	5/8P	1/4	7	19.5	5
70	153624	CC	6	.025	36	AL	BF82	.035	1/2P	3/8P	5/16	7	9.5	3.5
70	15426378	CC	6	.025	36	AL	BF82	.035	1/2P	3/8P	5/16	7	14.5	4
70	15426378	CC	6	.025	36	AL	BF82	.035	1/2P	3/8P	5/16	7	15	4
120	165432	CP	5	.016	30	AC	44S	.035	1-1/2N	0	1/8	7-1/2	10.7	4
120	18436572	CP	7.5	.016	30	AC	45S	.030	1-1/2N	0	1/8	7-1/2	17	4
120	18436572	CP	7.5	.016	30	AC	44S	.030	1-1/2N	0	1/8	7-1/2	17	4
120	18436572	CP	7.5	.016	30	AC	44S	.030	1/2N	1/8P	1/16	10	17	4
120	18736542	VD	2.5	.016	28-32	AC	44	.030	1/2N	1/8P	1/16	10	20.4	4
120	18736542	VD	2.5	.016	30	AC	44	.030	1/2N	1/8P	1/16	10	20.4	4
85	153624	CC	2.5	.020	42	CH	N14Y	.035	1/2N	3/8P	1/8	7-1/2	13	4
85	18436572	CC	5	.016	30	CH	J12Y	.035	1/2N	3/8P	5/32	6-1/2	21	4
85	18436572	CC	10	.016	30	CH	J12Y	.035	1/2N	3/8P	5/32	6-1/2	17	4
85	18436572	CC	10	.016	30	CH	J12Y	.035	1/2N	3/8P	5/32	6-1/2	16	5
85	18436572	CC	10	.016	30	CH	J9Y	.035	1/2N	3/8P	5/32	6-1/2	16	5
85	153624	CC	2.5	.020	42	CH	N14Y	.035	1/2N	3/8P	1/8	7-1/2	12	4
85	153624	CC	2.5	.020	42	CH	N14Y	.035	1/2N	3/8P	1/8	7-1/2	12	4
95	153624	CP	4	.016	32	AC	46N	.035	1-1/4N	1P	1/8	9	11.3	4
55	18436572	CP	6	.016	30	AC	45S	.035	1-1/4N	1P	1/8	9	20.5	4
95	18436572	CP	6	.016	30	AC	45S	.035	1-1/2N	1/4P	1/16	4-1/2	19.5	4
95	18436572	CP	6	.016	30	AC	45S	.035	1-1/2N	1/4P	1/16	4-1/2	19.5	4
95	18436572	CP	6	.016	30	AC	45S	.035	1-1/2N	1/4P	1/16	4-1/2	19.5	5
70	153624	VD	3	.019	32	CH	H18Y	.035	0	0	1/8	8	12	4
70	153624	VD	8	.020	32	CH	H18Y	.035	0	0	1/8	8	11	4
58	153624	VD	8	.020	32	CH	H18Y	.035	0	0	1/8	8	11	4
70	153624	VD	5	.019	32	CH	H18Y	.035	0	0	1/8	6-1/2	10.5	4
70	18436572	VD	5	.016	30	CH	H18Y	.035	0	0	1/8	6-1/2	19	4
85	18436572	CP	5	.016	30	CH	H18Y	.035	1P	0	1/8	6-1/2	19	4
95	153624	VD	2	.020	39	CH	H14Y	.035	3/4N	1/2P	1/8	6	12	5
95	18436572	VD	4	.016	30	CH	H14Y	.035	3/4N	1/2P	1/8	6	18	5
95	18436572	VD	4	.016	30	CH	H14Y	.035	3/4N	1/2P	1/8	6	18	5

IL - In-line L head	VO - V-type engine, overhead valves
IO - In-line engine, overhead valves	* - Long Reach
N - Minus	** - Auto. Trans. 10°
P - Plus	*** - Rear 3/8"
VD - Vibration Damper	

1965

	Wheelbase	No. of Cylinders Bore and Stroke	Displacement (cu. in.)	Valve and Cylinder Arrangement	Compression Pressure (lbs.)	Maximum Brake Horsepower	Valve Tappet Clearance Intake	Valve Tappet Clearance Exhaust	Cylinder Bolt Torque (ft.-lbs.)
Buick-Special, Skylark	115	V-6-3.75x3.40	225	VO	160	155@4400	HY	HY	80
LeSabre	123	8-3.75x3.40	300	VO	160	210@4600	HY	HY	80
Wildcat, Electra 225	126	8-4.1875x3.64	401	VO	175	325@4400	HY	HY	80
Riviera	117	8-4.3125x3.64	425	VO	175	340@4400	HY	HY	80
Cadillac	129.5[1]	8-4.13x4.0	429	VO	175	340@4600	HY	HY	60
Chevrolet, Chevelle, Chevy II	119[2]	6-3.875x3.25	230	IO	130	140@4400	HY	HY	100
Chevrolet, Chevelle, Chevy II	119[2]	8-3.875x3.0	283	VO	150	195@4800	HY	HY	70
Chevrolet	119	8-4.001x3.25	327	VO	160	250@4400	HY	HY	65
Chevrolet	119	8-4.313x3.5	409	VO	150	340@5000	HY	HY	70
Chevy II-100	110	4-3.875x3.25	153	IO	130	90@4000	HY	HY	100
Chevy II, Chevelle	110[2]	6-3.563x3.25	194	IO	130	120@4400	HY	HY	100
Chevy II, Chevelle	110[2]	8-4.001x3.25	327	VO	160	300@5000	HY	HY	70
Corvair	108	6-3.438x2.94	164	HO	130	95@3600	HY	HY	38
Corvair Corsa	108	6-3.438x2.94	164	HO	130	140@5200	HY	HY	38
Corvette	98	8-4.0x3.25	327	VO	160	250@4400	HY	HY	70
Corvette	98	8-4.0x3.25	327	VO	160	300@5000	HY	HY	70
Chrysler-Newport	124	8-4.25x3.38	383	VO	155	270@4400	HY	HY	70
300	124	8-4.25x3.38	383	VO	165	315@4400	HY	HY	70
New Yorker	124	8-4.19x3.75	413	VO	165	340@4600	HY	HY	70
300L	124	8-4.19x3.75	413	VO	165	360@4800	HY	HY	70
Imperial	129	8-4.19x3.75	413	VO	165	340@4600	HY	HY	70
Dodge-Dart	111	6-3.40x3.125	170	IO	140	101@4400	.010H	.020H	65
Dart, Coronet	111[7]	6-3.40x4.125	225	IO	140	145@4000	.010H	.020H	65
Dart, Coronet	111[7]	8-3.63x3.31	273	VO	150	180@4200	.013H	.021H	85
Coronet	117	8-3.91x3.31	318	VO	155	230@4400	.013H	.021H	85
Coronet	117	8-4.12x3.38	361	VO	155	265@4400	HY	HY	85
Coronet	117	8-4.25x3.38	383	VO	165	330@4600	HY	HY	70
Polara, Custom 880	121.5	8-4.25x3.38	383	VO	155	270@4400	HY	HY	70
Polara, Custom 880, Monaco	121.5	8-4.19x3.75	413	VO	165	340@4600	HY	HY	70
Ford-Falcon	109.5	6-3.50x2.94	170	IO	175	105@4400	HY	HY	75
Falcon	109.5	6-3.68x3.13	200	IO	175	120@4400	HY	HY	75
Falcon	109.5	8-4.0x2.87	289	VO	150	200@4400	HY	HY	70
Fairlane, Mustang	116[9]	6-3.68x3.13	200	IO	175	120@4400	HY	HY	75
Fairlane, Mustang	116[9]	8-4.0x2.87	289	VO	150	200@4400	HY	HY	70
Fairlane, Mustang-Exc. Sta. Wag.	116[9]	8-4.0x2.87	289	VO	150	271@6000	.020H	.020H	70
Ford-Except XL and LTD	119	6-4.0x3.18	240	IO	175	150@4000	HY	HY	75
Ford XL, LTD	119	8-4.0x2.87	289	VO	150	200@4400	HY	HY	75
Ford	119	8-4.0x3.5	352	VO	180	250@4400	HY	HY	90
Ford Thunderbird	113.2	8-4.05x3.78	390	VO	190	300@4600	HY	HY	90
Ford-Except Station Wagons	119	8-4.24x3.79	427	VO	180	425@6000	.025H	.025H	110
Lincoln Continental	126	8-4.30x3.70	430	VO	180	320@4000	HY	HY	135
Mercury-Comet	114	6-3.68x3.13	200	IO	175	120@4400	HY	HY	75
Comet	114	8-4.0x2.87	289	VO	150	225@4800	HY	HY	70
Mercury-Except Park Lane	123	8-4.05x3.78	390	VO	180	250@4400	HY	HY	90
Mercury-Park Lane	123	8-4.05x3.78	390	VO	190	300@4600	HY	HY	90
Mercury	123	8-4.05x3.78	390	VO	190	330@5000	.025H	.025H	90
Mercury-Except Station Wagons	123	8-4.23x3.78	427	VO	180	425@6000	.025H	.025H	110
Oldsmobile-F-85	115	V-6-3.75x3.4	225	VO	125	155@4400	HY	HY	70
F-85, Jetstar 88	115[12]	8-3.9375x3.385	330	VO	125	250@4800	HY	HY	80
Dynamic 88, Delta	123	8-4.125x3.975	425	VO	125	310@4400	HY	HY	80
98	126	8-4.125x3.975	425	VO	125	360@4800	HY	HY	80
Jetstar 1, Starfire	123	8-4.125x3.975	425	VO	125	370@4800	HY	HY	80
Plymouth-Valiant, Barracuda	106	6-3.4x3.125	170	IO	140	101@4400	.010H	.020H	65
Valiant, Barracuda	106	6-3.4x4.125	225	IO	140	145@4000	.010H	.020H	65
Valiant, Barracuda	106	8-3.63x3.31	273	VO	165	235@5200	.013H	.021H	85
Belvedere, Satellite, Fury	116[14]	6-3.4x4.125	225	IO	140	145@4000	.010H	.020H	65
Belvedere, Satellite	116	8-3.63x3.31	273	VO	150	180@4200	.013H	.021H	85
Fury	119	8-3.91x3.31	318	VO	155	230@4400	.013H	.021H	85
Belvedere, Satellite	116	8-4.12x3.38	361	VO	155	265@4400	HY	HY	70
Fury	119	8-4.25x3.38	383	VO	165	330@4600	HY	HY	70
Belvedere, Satellite, Fury	116[14]	8-4.25x3.75	426	VO	165	365@4800	HY	HY	70
Pontiac-Tempest, LeMans	115	6-3.75x3.25	215	IO	145	140@4200	HY	HY	95
Tempest-Except GTO	115	8-3.72x3.75	326	VO	160	250@4600	HY	HY	55
GTO	115	8-4.06x3.75	389	VO	160	335@5000	HY	HY	95
Catalina, Star Chief	121[16]	8-4.06x3.75	389	VO	160	290@4600	HY	HY	95
Grand Prix, Bonneville	121[16]	8-4.06x3.75	389	VO	160	333@5000	HY	HY	95
Pontiac	121[16]	8-4.09x4.0	421	VO	160	376@5000	HY	HY	95
Rambler-American 220, 330	106	6-3.125x4.25	195	IL	130	90@3800	.016C	.018C	60
American 440, 440H	106	6-3.125x4.25	195	IO	145	125@4200	.012H	.016H	60
Classic 550	112	6-3.75x3.0	199	IO	145	128@4400	HY	HY	60
Classic, Ambassador	112[17]	6-3.75x3.5	232	IO	145	155@4300	HY	HY	60
Classic	112	8-3.75x3.25	287	VO	145	198@4700	HY	HY	60
Ambassador	116	8-4.0x3.25	327	VO	145	270@4700	HY	HY	65
Studebaker-Commander, Cruiser	109[18]	6-3.563x3.25	194	IO	130	120@4400	HY	HY	100
Daytona	109[18]	8-3.875x3.0	283	VO	150	195@4800	HY	HY	70

ABBREVIATIONS - FOOTNOTES

AC	- AC spark plugs	CH	- Champion spark plugs	IO	- In-line engine, overhead valves
BF	- Autolite spark plugs	CP	- Crankshaft pulley	N	- Negative
BTF	- Autolite spark plugs	H	- Hot engine	P	- Positive
C	- Cold engine	HO	- Horizontal opposed cylinders	VD	- Vibration damper
CC	- Timing case cover	HY	- Hydraulic valve lifters	VO	- V-type engine, overhead valves
		IL	- In-line engine, L-head	WP	- Water pump housing

Tuneup Specifications

Connecting Rod Bolt Torque (ft.-lbs.)	Main Bearing Bolt Torque (ft.-lbs.)	Firing Order	Timing Mark Location	Breaker Point Opens B.T.D.C.	Breaker Point Gap	Cam Angle	Spark Plugs Make	Spark Plugs Model	Spark Plugs Gap	Caster Man. Steer. (deg.)	Camber Rt. Wheel (deg.)	Toe-In (inches)	Steering Axis Inclination (deg.)	Cooling System Capacity (qts.)	Crankcase Capacity (qts.)
40	120	165432	VD	5	.016	30	AC	44S	.035	1/2N	1/2P	3/16	8	10.7	4
40	120	18436572	VD	2.5	.016	30	AC	44S	.035	1P	1/4P	1/4	10-3/4	12.4	4
50	120	12784563	VD	2.5	.016	30	AC	44S	.035	1P	1/4P	1/4	10-3/4	17.7	4
50	120	12784563	VD	2.5	.016	30	AC	44S	.035	1P	1/2P	3/16	10	18.5	4
40	95	18726543	VD	5	.016	30	AC	44	.035	1N	1/4N	7/32	6	18.5	4
35	70	153624	VD	4	.019	32	AC	46N	.035	1/4P[3]	1/4P	3/16	7-1/2[4]	12	4
35	70	18436572	VD	4	.019	30	AC	45	.035	1/4P[3]	1/4P	3/16	7-1/2[4]	16	4
30	65	18436572	VD	8	.019	30	AC	44	.035	1/4P	1/4P	3/16	7-1/2	16	4
45	100	18436572	VD	6	.019	30	AC	43N	.035	1/4P	1/4P	3/16	7-1/2	22	4
35	70	1342	CP	4	.019	32	AC	46N	.035	1P	1/2P	1/4	7	9	3.5
35	70	153624	VD	8	.019	32	AC	46N	.035	1P[3]	1/2P	1/4	7[4]	11	4
35	70	18436572	VD	8	.019	30	AC	44	.035	1P[3]	1/2P	1/4	7[4]	17	4
26	55	145236	CP	6	.019	33	AC	46FF	.035	4P	1P	5/16[5]	6-1/2	---	4
26	55	145236	VD	18	.019	33	AC	44FF	.030	4P	1P	5/16[5]	6-1/2	---	4
35	70	18436572	VD	4	.019	30	AC	44	.035	1-1/2P	3/4P	9/32[6]	7	19	4
35	70	18436572	VD	8	.019	30	AC	44	.035	1-1/2P	3/4P	9/32[6]	7	19	4
45	85	18436572	WP	10	.016	30	CH	J-14Y	.035	1/2N	1/4P	1/8	9	17	4
45	85	18436572	WP	10	.016	30	CH	J-14Y	.035	1/2N	1/4P	1/8	9	17	4
45	85	18436572	WP	12.5	.016	30	CH	J-14Y	.035	1/2N	1/4P	1/8	9	17	4
45	85	18436572	WP	10	.016	30	CH	J-10Y	.035	1/2N	1/4P	1/8	9	17	4
45	85	18436572	WP	12.5	.016	30	CH	J-14Y	.035	1/2P	1/4P	1/8	6-1/2	17	4
45	85	153624	WP	2.5	.020	42	CH	N-14Y	.035	1/2N	1/4P	1/8	7-1/2	12	4
45	85	153624	CC	2.5	.020	42	CH	N-14Y	.035	1/2N	1/4P	1/8	7-1/2	13	4
45	85	18436572	WP	5	.016	30	CH	N-14Y	.035	1/2N	1/4P	1/8	7-1/2	18	4
45	85	18436572	WP	5	.016	30	CH	J-14Y	.035	1/2N	1/4P	1/8	7-1/2	21	4
45	85	18436572	WP	10	.016	30	CH	J-14Y	.035	1/2N	1/4P	1/8	7-1/2	17	4
45	85	18436572	WP	10	.016	28[8]	CH	J-10Y	.035	1/2N	1/4P	1/8	7-1/2	17	4
45	85	18436572	WP	10	.016	30	CH	J-14Y	.035	1/2N	1/4P	1/8	9	17	4
45	85	18436572	WP	12.5	.016	28[8]	CH	J-10Y	.035	1/2N	1/4P	1/8	9	17	4
24	70	153624	CC	6	.025	37	BF	82	.034	3/4P	1/2P	9/32	7-1/4	9.5	3.5
24	70	153624	CC	6	.025	37	BF	82	.034	3/4P	1/2P	9/32	7-1/4	9.5	3.5
24	70	15426378	CC	6	.015	27	BF	42	.035	1/4N	1/2P	9/32	7-1/4	14.5	4
24	70	153624	CC	6	.025	37	BF	82	.035	0[10]	1/4P	7/32	7-3/4[11]	9.5	3.5
24	70	15426378	CC	6	.015	27	BF	42	.035	0	1/4P	7/32	7-3/4[11]	15	4
45	70	15426378	CC	12	.020	33	BF	32	.035	0	1/4P	7/32	7-3/4[11]	15	4
45	70	153624	VD	6	.025	37	BTF	6	.035	1P	1/2P	5/32	7-1/4	15	4
45	70	15426378	VD	6	.015	27	BF	42	.035	1P	1/2P	5/32	7-1/4	20.5	4
45	105	15426378	VD	6	.015	27	BF	42	.035	1P	1/2P	5/32	7-1/4	20.5	5
45	105	15426378	CC	6	.015	27	BF	42	.035	1-1/2N	1/2P	5/32	7	20	5
58	105	15426378	VD	8	.020	34	BF	32	.035	1P	1/2P	5/32	7-1/4	20.5	5
45	105	15426378	VD	6	.015	27	BF	42	.035	1-1/2N	3/4P	5/32	7	25	5
24	70	153624	CC	6	.025	37	BF	82	.035	3/4P	1/2P	9/32	7-1/4	9.5	3.5
24	70	15426378	CC	6	.015	27	BF	42	.030	1/4N	1/2P	9/32	7-1/4	15	4
45	105	15426378	CC	6	.015	27	BF	42	.035	1P	1/2P	5/32	7-1/4	20.5	5
45	105	15426378	CC	4	.015	27	BF	42	.035	1P	1/2P	5/32	7-1/4	20.5	5
45	105	15426378	CC	4	.015	27	BF	42	.035	1P	1/2P	5/32	7-1/4	20.5	5
58	105	15426378	VD	8	.020	27	BF	32	.035	1P	1/2P	5/32	7-1/4	20.5	5
35	70	165432	VD	5	.016	30	AC	44S	.035	1-1/4N	1/4P	5/32	9	11	4
42	80[13]	18436572	VD	7.5	.016	30	AC	45S	.030	1-1/4N	1/4P	5/32	9	17	4
42	80[13]	18436572	VD	5	.016	30	AC	44S	.030	1N	1/4P	5/32	11	18	4
42	80[13]	18436572	VD	5	.016	30	AC	44S	.030	1N	1/4P	5/32	11	17.5	4
42	80[13]	18436572	VD	5	.016	30	AC	44S	.030	1N	1/4P	5/32	11	17.5	4
45	85	153624	WP	2.5	.020	42	CH	N-14Y	.035	1/2N	1/4P	1/8	6-1/2	12	4
45	85	153624	WP	2.5	.020	42	CH	N-14Y	.035	1/2N	1/4P	1/8	6-1/2	13	4
45	85	18436572	CC	10	.016	30[8]	CH	N-14Y	.035	1/2N	1/4P	1/8	6-1/2	18	4
45	85	153624	CC	2.5	.020	42	CH	N-14Y	.035	1/2N	1/4P	1/8	6-1/2[15]	13	4
45	85	18436572	WP	5	.016	30	CH	N-14Y	.035	1/2N	1/4P	1/8	6-1/2	18	4
45	85	18436572	WP	5	.016	30	CH	J-14Y	.035	1/2N	1/4P	1/8	9	21	4
45	85	18436572	WP	10	.016	30	CH	J-14Y	.035	1/2N	1/4P	1/8	6-1/2	17	4
45	85	18436572	WP	10	.016	30[8]	CH	J-14Y	.035	1/2N	1/4P	1/8	9	17	4
45	85	18436572	WP	10	.016	30[8]	CH	J-10Y	.035	1/2N	1/4P	1/8	6-1/2[15]	17	4
45	95	153624	CP	4	.016	32	AC	46N	.035	1-1/2N	1/4P	1/16	9	13.5	4
35	55	18436572	VD	6	.016	30	AC	45S	.035	1-1/2N	1/4P	1/16	9	20.5	5
45	95	18436572	VD	6	.016	30	AC	45S	.035	1-1/2N	1/4P	1/16	9	20.5	5
45	95	18436572	VD	6	.016	30	AC	45S	.035	1-1/2N	1/4P	1/16	8-1/2	20	5
45	95	18436572	VD	6	.016	30	AC	45S	.035	1-1/2N	1/4P	1/16	8-1/2	20	5
30	70	153624	VD	3	.019	32	CH	H-10	.035	1/4P	0	1/8	6-1/4	11	4
30	70	153624	VD	8	.019	32	CH	H-18Y	.035	1/4P	0	1/8	6-1/4	11	4
30	70	153624	VD	5	.019	32	CH	N-14Y	.035	1/4P	0	1/8	6-1/4	10.5	4
30	70	153624	VD	5	.019	32	CH	N-14Y	.035	1/4P	0	1/8	6-1/4	10.5	4
30	70	18436572	VD	5	.016	30	CH	H-14Y	.035	1/4P	0	1/8	6-1/4	19	4
50	85	18436572	VD	5	.016	30	CH	H-14Y	.035	1/4P	0	1/8	6-1/4	19	4
35	70	153624	VD	8	.019	32	AC	46N	.035	1/2N	1/2P	7/32	6	13.5	4
35	70	18436572	CP	4	.019	30	AC	45	.035	1/2N	1/2P	7/32	6	16	4

1 - Sixty Special 133 in., Seventy-Five 149.8 in.	7 - Coronet 117 in.	13 - #5 main 120 ft. lbs.
2 - Chevy II 110 in., Chevelle 115 in.	8 - Both sets 38 deg.	14 - Fury 119 in.
3 - Chevy II 1P, Chevelle 1N	9 - Mustang 108 in.	15 - Fury 9 deg.
4 - Chevy II 7, Chevelle 8-1/4	10 - Mustang 1P	16 - Star Chief, Bonneville 124 in.
5 - Rear 1/4 in.	11 - Mustang 7-1/4	17 - Ambassador 116 in.
6 - Rear 1/32 in.	12 - Jetstar 88 123 in.	18 - 4 dr. and station wagon 113 in.

1966

	Wheelbase	No. of Cylinders Bore and Stroke	Displacement (cu. in.)	Valve and Cylinder Arrangement	Compression Pressure (lbs.)	Maximum Brake Horsepower	Valve Tappet Clearance Intake	Exhaust	Cylinder Bolt Torque (ft. lbs.)
Buick – Special, Skylark	115	V6-3.75x3.40	225	VO	160	160@4200	HY	HY	80
Special	115	8-3.75x3.40	300	VO	175	210@4600	HY	HY	80
Skylark, Sportwagon	115 [1]	8-3.75x3.85	340	VO	175	220@4000	HY	HY	80
Skylark, Sportwagon	115 [1]	8-3.75x3.85	340	VO	175	260@4000	HY	HY	80
Skylark Gran Sport	115	8-4.1875x3.64	400	VO	175	325@4400	HY	HY	80
LeSabre	123	8-3.75x3.85	340	VO	175	260@4000	HY	HY	80
Wildcat, Electra	126	8-4.1875x3.64	401	VO	175	325@4400	HY	HY	80
Riviera	119	8-4.3125x3.64	425	VO	175	340@4400	HY	HY	80
Wildcat, Electra, Riviera	126 [2]	8-4.3125x3.64	425	VO	175	360@4400	HY	HY	80
Cadillac	129.5 [3]	8-4.13x4.00	429	VO	175	340@4600	HY	HY	60
Chevrolet	119	6-3.875x3.53	250	IO	130	155@4200	HY	HY	95
Chevrolet, Chevelle	119 [4]	8-3.875x3.00	283	VO	150	195@4800	HY	HY	65
Chevrolet, Chevelle	119 [4]	8-3.875x3.00	283	VO	150	220@4800	HY	HY	65
Chevrolet, Chevelle	119 [4]	8-4.00x3.25	327	VO	160	300@5000	HY	HY	65
Chevrolet, Chevelle	119 [4]	8-4.00x3.25	327	VO	160	275@4800	HY	HY	65
Corvette	98	8-4.00x3.25	327	VO	150	350@5800	HY	HY	65
Chevrolet, Chevelle	119 [4]	8-4.094x3.76	396	VO	160	325@4800	HY	HY	80
Chevelle	115	8-4.094x3.76	396	VO	160	360@5200	HY	HY	80
Chevelle	115	8-4.094x3.76	396	VO	160	375@5600	HY	HY	80
Chevrolet, Corvette	119 [4]	8-4.25x3.76	427	VO	160	390@5200	HY	HY	80
Chevrolet, Corvette	119 [4]	8-4.25x3.76	427	VO	150	425@5600	.024	.028	80
Chevelle, Chevy II	115 [4]	6-3.563x3.25	194	IO	130	120@4400	HY	HY	95
Chevelle, Chevy II	115 [4]	6-3.875x3.25	230	IO	130	140@4400	HY	HY	95
Chevy II	110	4-3.875x3.25	153	IO	130	90@4400	HY	HY	95
Corvair, Monza	108	6-3.4375x2.94	164	HO	130	95@3600	HY	HY	38
Corvair, Monza	108	6-3.4375x2.94	164	HO	130	110@4400	HY	HY	38
Corvair, Monza, Corsa	108	6-3.4375x2.94	164	HO	130	140@5200	HY	HY	38
Corsa	108	6-3.4375x2.94	164	HO	130	180@4000	HY	HY	38
Chrysler – Newport	124	8-4.25x3.38	383	VO	140	270@4400	HY	HY	70
Newport, 300	124	8-4.25x3.38	383	VO	140	325@4800	HY	HY	70
New Yorker	124	8-4.32x3.75	440	VO	150	350@4400	HY	HY	70
New Yorker, Newport, 300	124	8-4.32x3.75	440	VO	150	365@4600	HY	HY	70
Imperial	129	8-4.32x3.75	440	VO	150	350@4400	HY	HY	70
Dodge – Dart	111	6-3.40x3.125	170	IO	125	101@4400	.010H	.020H	65
Coronet, Dart	117 [14]	6-3.40x4.125	225	IO	125	145@4000	.010H	.020H	65
Coronet, Dart GT	117 [14]	8-3.63x3.31	273	VO	135	180@4200	.013H	.021H	85
Dart GT	111	8-3.63x3.31	273	VO	135	235@5200	.013H	.021H	85
Polara	121	8-3.91x3.31	318	VO	140	230@4400	.013H	.021H	85
Coronet	117	8-4.12x3.38	361	VO	140	265@4400	HY	HY	70
Polara, Monaco	121	8-4.25x3.38	383	VO	140	270@4400	HY	HY	70
Polara, Monaco	121	8-4.25x3.38	383	VO	140	325@4800	HY	HY	70
Coronet, Charger	117	8-4.25x3.75	426	VO	150	425@5000	.028C	.032C	70
Polara, Monaco	121	8-4.32x3.75	440	VO	150	350@4400	HY	HY	70
Ford – Falcon, Futura	110.9	6-3.50x2.94	170	IO	195	105@4400	HY	HY	75
Futura, Fairlane	110.9 [18]	6-3.684x3.13	200	IO	195	120@4400	HY	HY	75
Mustang	108	6-3.684x3.13	200	IO	195	120@4400	HY	HY	75
Ford	119	6-4.00x3.18	240	IO	175	150@4000	HY	HY	75
Falcon, Fairlane	110.9 [18]	8-4.005x2.87	289	VO	150	200@4400	HY	HY	70
Mustang	108	8-4.005x2.87	289	VO	150	225@4800	HY	HY	70
Mustang	108	8-4.005x2.87	289	VO	150	271@6000	.020H	.020H	70
Ford	119	8-4.00x3.50	352	VO	180	250@4400	HY	HY	90
Ford, Fairlane	119 [18]	8-4.05x3.78	390	VO	180	265@4400	HY	HY	90
Thunderbird	113	8-4.05x3.78	390	VO	180	315@4600	HY	HY	90
Fairlane GT, GTA	116	8-4.05x3.78	390	VO	180	335@4800	HY	HY	90
Ford	119	8-4.05x3.78	390	VO	180	275@4400	HY	HY	90

ABBREVIATIONS – FOOTNOTES:

AC – AC Spark Plugs
ATC – After Top Center
BF – Autolite Spark Plugs
BTF – Autolite Spark Plugs
C – Cold Engine
CC – Timing Case Cover
CH – Champion Spark Plugs
CP – Crankshaft Pulley
H – Hot Engine

HO – Horizontal Opposed Cylinders
HY – Hydraulic Valve Lifters
IO – In-line Engine, Overhead Valves
IOC – In-line Engine, Overhead Cam
N – Negative
NA – Not Applicable
P – Positive
TDC – Top Dead Center
VD – Vibration Damper
VO – V-Type Engine, Overhead Valves
WP – Water Pump Housing

1 – Sportwagon – 120 in.
2 – Riviera – 119 in.
3 – 60, Brougham – 133 in.; 75 – 149.8 in.
4 – Chevelle – 115 in.; Chevy II – 110 in.;
Corvette – 98 in.
5 – Chevelle – 1/2 N.
6 – Chevelle – 8-1/4 deg.
7 – 4-Bolt Cap – 115 ft. lbs.
8 – Corvette – 3/4 P.
9 – Corvette – 1/4 in.
10 – Corvette – 7 deg.

Tuneup Specifications

Connecting Rod Bolt Torque (ft.lbs.)	Main Bearing Bolt Torque (ft.lbs.)	Firing Order	Timing Mark Location	Breaker Point Opens BTDC	Breaker Point Gap	Cam Angle	Spark Plugs Make	Model	Gap	Caster Man. Steer. (deg.)	Camber Rt. Wheel (deg.)	Toe-in (in.)	Steering Axis Inclination (deg.)	Cooling System Capacity (qts.)	Crankcase Capacity (qts.)
40	120	165432	VD	5	.016	30	AC	44S	.035	1/2N	1/2P	3/16	8	10.7	4
40	120	18436572	VD	2.5	.016	30	AC	44S	.035	1/2N	1/2P	3/16	8	12.7	4
40	120	18436572	CP	2.5	.016	30	AC	44S	.035	1/2N	1/2P	3/16	8	12.7	4
40	120	18436572	CP	2.5	.016	30	AC	44S	.035	1/2N	1/2P	3/16	8	12.7	4
50	80	18436572	VD	2.5	.016	30	AC	44S	.035	1/2N	1/2P	3/16	8	12.7	4
40	120	18436572	VD	2.5	.016	30	AC	44TS	.035	1P	1/4P	1/4	10-1/2	14.5	4
50	80	12784563	VD	2.5	.016	30	AC	44S	.035	1P	1/4P	1/4	10-1/2	18	4
50	80	12784563	VD	2.5	.016	30	AC	44S	.035	1P	1/4P	1/4	10-1/2	18	4
50	80	12784563	VD	2.5	.016	30	AC	44S	.035	1P	1/4P	1/4	10-1/2	18	4
40	90	18726543	VD	5	.016	30	AC	44	.035	1/2N	1/4P	7/32	6	17.2	4
35	65	153624	VD	6	.019	32	AC	46N	.035	3/4P	1/4P	3/32	7-1/2	13	4
35	80	18436572	VD	4	.019	30	AC	45	.035	3/4P[5]	1/4P	3/32	7-1/2[6]	17	4
35	80	18436572	VD	6	.019	30	AC	45	.035	3/4P[5]	1/4P	3/32	7-1/2[6]	17	4
35	80	18436572	VD	6	.019	30	AC	44	.037	3/4P[5]	1/4P	3/32	7-1/2[6]	15	4
35	80	18436572	VD	8	.019	30	AC	44	.037	3/4P[5]	1/4P	3/32	7-1/2[6]	15	4
35	80	18436572	VD	10	.019	30	AC	44	.037	3/4P	3/4P	1/4	7	19	5
50	95[7]	18436572	VD	4	.019	30	AC	43N	.037	3/4P[5]	1/4P	3/32	7-1/2[6]	23	4
50	95[7]	18436572	VD	4	.019	30	AC	43N	.037	1/2N	1/4P	3/32	8-1/4	23	4
50	95[7]	18436572	VD	10	.019	30	AC	43N	.037	1/2N	1/4P	3/32	8-1/4	23	4
50	95[7]	18436572	VD	4	.019	30	AC	43N	.035	3/4P	1/4P[8]	3/32[9]	7-1/2[10]	22	4[11]
50	95[7]	18436572	VD	8	NA	NA	AC	43N	.035	3/4P	1/4P[8]	3/32[9]	7-1/2[10]	23	4[11]
35	65	153624	VD	8	.019	33	AC	46N	.035	1/2N[12]	1/4P	3/32	8-1/4[13]	12	4
35	65	153624	VD	4	.019	33	AC	46N	.035	1/2N[12]	1/4P	3/32	8-1/4[13]	12	4
35	65	1342	CP	4	.019	33	AC	46N	.035	1P	1/4P	5/32	7	9	4
26	55	145236	CP	6	.019	33	AC	46FF	.035	3P	1P	1/4	6-1/2	NA	4
26	55	145236	VD	14	.019	33	AC	44FF	.030	3P	1P	1/4	6-1/2	NA	4
26	55	145236	VD	18	.019	33	AC	44FF	.030	3P	1P	1/4	6-1/2	NA	4
26	55	145236	VD	24	.019	33	AC	44FF	.030	3P	1P	1/4	6-1/2	NA	4
45	85	18436572	WP	12.5	.016	30	CH	J-14Y	.035	1/2P	1/4P	1/8	9	17	4
45	85	18436572	WP	12.5	.016	30	CH	J-13Y	.035	1/2P	1/4P	1/8	9	17	4
45	70	18436572	WP	12.5	.016	30	CH	J-13Y	.035	1/2P	1/4P	1/8	9	17	4
45	70	18436572	WP	12.5	.016	30	CH	J-13Y	.035	1/2P	1/4P	1/8	9	17	4
45	70	18436572	WP	12.5	.016	30	CH	J-13Y	.035	3/4P	1/4P	1/8	6-1/2	18	5
45	85	153624	WP	5	.020	42	CH	N-14Y	.035	1/2N	1/4P	1/8	7-1/2	12	4
45	85	153624	WP	25	.020	42	CH	N-14Y	.035	1/2N	1/4P	1/8	7-1/2	13	4
45	85	18436572	CC	5[15]	.016	30	CH	N-14Y	.035	1/2N	1/4P	1/8	7-1/2	18	4
45	85	18436572	CC	10	.016	29[16]	CH	N-9Y	.035	1/2N	1/4P	1/8	7-1/2	18	4
45	85	18436572	WP	10	.016	30	CH	J-14Y	.035	1/2N	1/4P	1/8	9	21	4
45	85	18436572	WP	12.5	.016	30	CH	J-14Y	.035	1/2N	1/4P	1/8	7-1/2	17	4
45	85	18436572	WP	12.5	.016	30	CH	J-14Y	.035	1/2N	1/4P	1/8	9	17	4
45	85	18436572	WP	12.5	.016	30	CH	J-13Y	.035	1/2N	1/4P	1/8	9	17	4
45	85	18436572	WP	5A	.017	29[17]	CH	J-13Y	.035	1/2N	1/4P	1/8	7-1/2	17	5
45	85	18436572	WP	12.5	.016	30	CH	J-13Y	.035	1/2N	1/4P	1/8	9	17	4
24	70	153624	CC	6	.025	37	BF	82	.034	1/2P	1/4P	1/4	6-1/2	9.5	3.5
24	70	153624	CC	6	.025	37	BF	82	.034	1/2P	1/4P	1/4[19]	6-1/2[20]	9.5	3.5
24	70	153624	CC	6	.025	37	BF	82	.034	1/2P	1/2P	9/32	7	9.5	3.5
45	70	153624	VD	6	.025	37	BTF	6	.034	1P	1-1/2P	3/16	7	13	4
24	70	15426378	CC	6	.015	27	BF	42	.034	1/2P	1/4P	1/4[19]	6-1/2[20]	15	4
24	70	15426378	CC	6	.015	27	BF	42	.034	1/2N	1/2P	9/32	7	15	4
24	70	15426378	CC	12	.020	34	BF	32	.034	1/2N	1/2P	9/32	7	15	4
45	105	15426378	VD	6	.025	37	BTF	6	.034	1P	1-1/2P	3/16	7	17	4
45	105	15426378	VD	6	.015	26	BF	42	.034	1P[21]	1-1/2P[22]	3/16[19]	7	20.5	4
45	105	15426378	VD	10	.015	27	BF	42	.034	1-1/2N	1/2P	3/16	7-1/2	20.5	4
45	105	15426378	VD	10	.015	26	BF	32	.034	1/4P	1/4P	1/8	7	20.5	4
45	105	15426378	VD	10	.015	27	BF	42	.034	1P	1-1/2P	3/16	7-1/2	20.5	4

11 - Corvette - 5 qts.
12 - Chevy II - 1 P.
13 - Chevy II - 7 deg.
14 - Dart - 111 in.
15 - Auto. Trans. - 10 BTDC.
16 - Both Breakers - 36 to 40 deg.
17 - Both Breakers - 37 to 42 deg.
18 - Fairlane - 116 in.
19 - Fairlane - 1/8 in.
20 - Fairlane - 7 deg.
21 - Fairlane - 1/2 P.

22 - Fairlane - 1/4 P.
23 - Comet - 116 in.
24 - Comet - 0 deg.
25 - Comet - 1/4 in.
26 - Jetstar 88 - 123 in.
27 - Rear Main - 120 ft. lbs.
28 - Jetstar 88 - 44 S.
29 - Jetstar 88 - 16.5 qts.
30 - Dynamic 88, Delta 88 - 123 in.
31 - 98 - 126 in.
32 - Satellite - 116 in.

33 - Satellite - 7-1/2 deg.
34 - Both Breakers - 37 to 42 deg.
35 - Star Chief - 124 in.
36 - Grand Prix - 121 in.
37 - Bonneville - 124 in.
38 - Premium Fuel - 13 deg. BTDC.
39 - Premium Fuel - 3 deg. BTDC.
40 - Premium Fuel - 8 deg. BTDC.
41 - Classic, Marlin - 112 in.
42 - 4-Door Models - 113 in.
43 - 2-Door Models - 109 in.

1966

	Wheelbase	No. of Cylinders Bore and Stroke	Displacement (cu. in.)	Valve and Cylinder Arrangement	Compression Pressure (lbs.)	Maximum Brake Horsepower	Valve Tappet Clearance		Cylinder Bolt Torque (ft.-lbs.)
							Intake	Exhaust	
Thunderbird	113	8-4.13x3.98	428	VO	190	345@4600	HY	HY	110
Ford	119	8-4.13x3.98	428	VO	190	360@5400	HY	HY	110
Ford	119	8-4.23x3.78	427	VO	190	410@5600	.028H	.025	110
Ford	119	8-4.23x3.78	427	VO	190	425@6000	.028H	.025	110
Lincoln Continental	126	8-4.38x3.83	462	VO	180	340@4600	HY	HY	145
Mercury - Comet	116	6-3.68x3.13	200	IO	195	120@4400	HY	HY	75
Comet	116	8-4.00x2.87	289	VO	150	200@4400	HY	HY	70
Monterey, Montclair, Comet	123 23	8-4.054x3.78	390	VO	180	265@4400	HY	HY	90
Monterey, Montclair	123	8-4.054x3.78	390	VO	180	275@4400	HY	HY	90
Comet, Cyclone, GT, GTA	116	8-4.054x3.78	390	VO	180	335@4800	HY	HY	90
Parklane	123	8-4.054x3.98	410	VO	190	330@4600	HY	HY	90
S-55	123	8-4.13x3.98	428	VO	190	345@4600	HY	HY	110
Oldsmobile - F-85	115	6-3.875x3.53	250	IO	160	155@4200	HY	HY	95
F-85, Jetstar 88	115 26	8-3.9375x3.385	330	VO	175	250@4800	HY	HY	80
Cutlass	115	8-3.9375x3.385	330	VO	175	310@5200	HY	HY	80
Cutlass, Jetstar 88	115 26	8-3.93/5x3.385	330	VO	175	320@5200	HY	HY	80
Jetstar 88	123	8-3.9375x3.385	330	VO	175	260@4800	HY	HY	80
F-85, Cutlass, 4-4-2	115	8-4.00x3.975	400	VO	175	350@5000	HY	HY	80
Dynamic 88, Delta 88	123	8-4.125x3.975	425	VO	175	300@4400	HY	HY	80
Dynamic 88, Delta 88	123	8-4.125x3.975	425	VO	175	310@4400	HY	HY	80
98, Dynamic 88, Delta 88	126 30	8-4.125x3.975	425	VO	175	365@4800	HY	HY	80
Starfire, 98, Delta 88	123 31	8-4.125x3.975	425	VO	175	375@4800	HY	HY	80
Toronado	119	8-4.125x3.975	425	VO	175	385@4800	HY	HY	80
Plymouth - Valiant, Signet	106	6-3.40x3.125	170	IO	125	101@4400	.010H	.020H	65
Belvedere	116	6-3.40x4.125	225	IO	125	145@4000	.010H	.020H	65
Barracuda, Satellite	106 32	8-3.63x3.31	273	VO	135	180@4200	.013H	.021H	85
Barracuda	106	8-3.63x3.31	273	VO	135	235@5200	.013H	.021H	85
Fury, Satellite	119 32	8-3.91x3.31	318	VO	140	230@4400	.013H	.021H	85
Satellite	116	8-4.12x3.38	361	VO	140	265@4400	HY	HY	70
Sport Fury, VIP	119	8-4.25x3.38	383	VO	140	270@4400	HY	HY	70
Sport Fury VIP, Satellite	119 32	8-4.25x3.38	383	VO	140	325@4800	HY	HY	70
Belvedere, Satellite	116	8-4.25x3.75	426	VO	150	425@5000	.028C	.032C	70
Fury, Sport Fury, VIP	119	8-4.32x3.75	440	VO	150	365@4600	HY	HY	70
Pontiac - Tempest, LeMans	115	6-3.875x3.245	230	IOC	160	165@4700	HY	HY	93
Tempest, LeMans	115	6-3.875x3.245	230	IOC	195	207@5200	HY	HY	93
Tempest, LeMans	115	8-3.7187x3.746	326	VO	160	250@4600	HY	HY	95
Tempest, LeMans	115	8-3.7187x3.746	326	VO	160	285@5000	HY	HY	95
GTO	115	8-4.0625x3.746	389	VO	160	335@5000	HY	HY	95
Catalina, Star Chief	121 35	8-4.0625x3.746	389	VO	160	256@4600	HY	HY	95
Catalina, Star Chief	121 35	8-4.0625x3.746	389	VO	160	290@4600	HY	HY	95
Bonneville, Grand Prix	124 36	8-4.0625x3.746	389	VO	160	333@5000	HY	HY	95
GTO	115	8-4.0625x3.746	389	VO	160	360@5200	HY	HY	95
2 + 2	121	8-4.0937x3.996	421	VO	160	338@4600	HY	HY	95
2 + 2, Catalina, Star Chief	121 35	8-4.0937x3.996	421	VO	160	356@4800	HY	HY	95
2 + 2, Bonneville, Grand Prix	121 37	8-4.0937x3.996	421	VO	160	376@5000	HY	HY	95
Rambler - American	106	6-3.75x3.00	199	IO	145	128@4400	HY	HY	85
American (1966 1/2)	106	8-3.75x3.28	290	VO	145	200@4600	HY	HY	100
American (1966 1/2)	106	8-3.75x3.28	290	VO	145	225@4700	HY	HY	100
Classic, Marlin	112	6-3.75x3.50	232	IO	145	145@4300	HY	HY	85
Ambassador	116	6-3.75x3.50	232	IO	145	155@4300	HY	HY	85
Ambassador, Classic, Marlin	116 41	8-3.75x3.25	287	VO	145	198@4700	HY	HY	60
Ambassador, Classic, Marlin	116 41	8-4.00x3.25	327	VO	145	250@4700	HY	HY	60
Ambassador, Classic, Marlin	116 41	8-4.00x3.25	327	VO	145	270@4700	HY	HY	60
Studebaker - Daytona, Commander	109 42	6-3.563x3.25	194	IO	130	120@4400	HY	HY	95
Cruiser, Commander	113 43	6-3.875x3.25	230	IO	130	140@4400	HY	HY	95

ABBREVIATIONS - FOOTNOTES:

AC - AC Spark Plugs	HO - Horizontal Opposed Cylinders
ATC - After Top Center	HY - Hydraulic Valve Lifters
BF - Autolite Spark Plugs	IO - In-line Engine, Overhead Valves
BTF - Autolite Spark Plugs	IOC - In-line Engine, Overhead Cam
C - Cold Engine	N - Negative
CC - Timing Case Cover	NA - Not Applicable
CH - Champion Spark Plugs	P - Positive
CP - Crankshaft Pulley	TDC - Top Dead Center
H - Hot Engine	VD - Vibration Damper
	VO - V-Type Engine, Overhead Valves
	WP - Water Pump Housing

1 - Sportwagon - 120 in.
2 - Riviera - 119 in.
3 - 60, Brougham - 133 in.; 75 - 149.8 in.
4 - Chevelle - 115 in.; Chevy II - 110 in.; Corvette - 98 in.
5 - Chevelle - 1/2 N.
6 - Chevelle - 8-1/4 deg.
7 - 4-Bolt Cap - 115 ft. lbs.
8 - Corvette - 3/4 P.
9 - Corvette - 1/4 in.
10 - Corvette - 7 deg.

Tuneup Specifications

Connecting Rod Bolt Torque (ft.-lbs.)	Main Bearing Bolt Torque (ft.-lbs.)	Firing Order	Timing Mark Location	Breaker Point Opens B.T.D.C.	Breaker Point Gap	Cam Angle	Spark Plugs Make	Spark Plugs Model	Spark Plugs Gap	Caster Man. Steer. (deg.)	Camber Rt. Wheel (deg.)	Toe-In (inches)	Steering Axis Inclination (deg.)	Cooling System Capacity (qts.)	Crankcase Capacity (qts.)
45	105	15426378	VD	10	.015	27	BF	42	.034	1-1/2N	1/2P	3/16	7-1/2	20.5	4
45	105	15426378	VD	12	.015	27	BF	42	.034	1P	1-1/2P	3/16	7	20.5	4
58	105	15426378	VD	8	.020	23	BF	32	.034	1P	1-1/2P	3/16	7	20.5	4
58	105	15426378	VD	8	.020	23	BF	32	.034	1P	1-1/2P	3/16	7	20.5	4
45	105	15426378	VD	10	.017	29	BTF	42	.034	1-1/2N	1/2P	1/8	7-3/4	23	5
24	70	153624	VD	6	.025	32	BF	82	.034	0	1/4P	1/4	7-1/2	9.5	3.4
24	70	15426378	VD	6	.015	27	BF	42	.034	0	1/4P	1/4	15		4
45	105	15426378	VD	10	.015	26	BF	42	.034	1P[24]	1/4P	3/16[25]	7-1/2	20.5	4
45	105	15426378	VD	10	.015	26	BF	42	.034	1P	1/4P	3/16	7-1/2	20.5	4
45	105	15426378	VD	10	.015	26	BF	42	.034	0	1/4P	1/4	7-1/2	20.5	4
45	105	15426378	VD	10	.015	27	BF	42	.034	1P	1/4P	3/16	7-1/2	20.5	4
45	105	15426378	VD	10	.015	27	BF	42	.034	1P	1/4P	3/16	7-1/2	20.5	4
35	65	153624	VD	6	.020	34	AC	46N	.035	1-1/4N	0	1/8	8	17	4
42	80[27]	18436572	CP	7.5	.016	30	AC	45S[28]	.030	1-1/4N	0	1/8	8	17[29]	4
42	80[27]	18436572	CP	7.5	.016	30	AC	44S	.030	1-1/4N	0	1/8	8	17	4
42	80[27]	18436572	VD	7.5	.016	30	AC	44S	.030	1-1/4N	0	1/8	8	17	4
42	80[27]	18436572	CP	7.5	.016	30	AC	44S	.030	1-1/4N	0	1/8	8	16.5	4
42	120	18436572	CP	7.5	.016	30	AC	44S	.030	1-1/4N	0	1/8	8	16.9	4
42	120	18436572	CP	5	.016	30	AC	44S	.030	1-1/4N	1/4P	3/16	10	17.5	4
42	120	18436572	CP	5	.016	30	AC	44S	.030	1-1/4N	1/4P	3/16	10	17.5	4
42	120	18436572	CP	7.5	.016	30	AC	44S	.030	1-1/4N	1/4P	3/16	10	17.5	4
42	120	18436572	CP	7.5	.016	30	AC	44S	.030	2N	1/4P	1/16	11	17.5	5
45	85	153624	WP	5	.020	42	CH	N-14Y	.035	1/2N	1/4P	1/8	7-1/2	12	4
45	85	153624	WP	2.5	.020	42	CH	N-14Y	.035	1/2N	1/4P	1/8	7-1/2	13	4
45	85	18436572	CC	5	.016	30	CH	N-14Y	.035	1/2N	1/4P	1/8	7-1/2	18	4
45	85	18436572	CC	5	.016	30	CH	N-14Y	.035	1/2N	1/4P	1/8	7-1/2	18	4
45	85	18436572	WP	10	.016	30	CH	J-14Y	.035	1/2N	1/4P	1/8	9[33]	21	4
45	85	18436572	CC	12.5	.016	30	CH	J-14Y	.035	1/2N	1/4P	1/8	7-1/2	17	4
45	85	18436572	CC	12.5	.016	30	CH	J-14Y	.035	1/2N	1/4P	1/8	9	17	4
45	85	18436572	CC	12.5	.016	30	CH	J-14Y	.035	1/2N	1/4P	1/8	9[33]	17	4
45	85	18436572	CC	5A	.017	30[34]	CH	N-9Y	.035	1/2N	1/4P	1/8	7-1/2	18	5
45	85	18436572	WP	12.5	.016	30	CH	J-13Y	.035	1/2N	1/4P	1/8	9	17	4
33	100	153624	VD	5	.016	33	AC	44S	.035	1-1/2N	1/4P	1/16	9	13.5	5
33	100	153624	VD	5	.016	33	AC	44S	.035	1-1/2N	1/4P	1/16	9	13.5	5
43	100[27]	18436572	CP	6	.016	30	AC	44S	.035	1-1/2N	1/4P	1/16	9	20	6
43	100[27]	18436572	CP	6	.016	30	AC	44S	.035	1-1/2N	1/4P	1/16	9	20	6
43	100[27]	18436572	CP	6	.016	30	AC	45S	.035	1-1/2N	1/4P	1/16	9	20	6
43	100[27]	18436572	CP	6	.016	30	AC	45S	.035	1-1/2N	1/4P	1/16	8-1/2	20	6
43	100[27]	18436572	CP	6	.016	30	AC	45S	.035	1-1/2N	1/4P	1/16	8-1/2	20	6
43	100[27]	18436572	CP	6	.016	30	AC	45S	.035	1-1/2N	1/4P	1/16	9	20	6
43	100[27]	18436572	CP	6	.016	30	AC	44S	.035	1-1/2N	1/4P	1/16	8-1/2	19.5	6
43	100[27]	18436572	CP	6	.016	30	AC	44S	.035	1-1/2N	1/4P	1/16	8-1/2	19.5	6
30	85	153624	VD	10[38]	.016	33	CH	N-14Y	.035	1/4P	0	1/8	6-1/2	10.5	4
30	100	18436572	VD	TDC[39]	.016	30	CH	N-14Y	.035	1/4P	0	1/8	6-1/2	14	4
30	100	18436572	VD	TDC	.016	30	CH	N-9Y	.035	1/4P	0	1/8	6-1/2	14	4
30	85	153624	VD	5[40]	.016	33	CH	N-14Y	.035	1/4P	0	1/8	6-1/4	10.5	4
30	85	153624	VD	5[40]	.016	33	CH	N-14Y	.035	1/4P	0	1/8	6-1/4	10.5	4
50	85	18436572	VD	5[40]	.016	30	CH	H-14Y	.035	1/4P	0	1/8	6-1/4	19	4
50	85	18436572	VD	5[40]	.016	30	CH	H-14Y	.035	1/4P	0	1/8	6-1/4	19	4
50	85	18436572	VD	5	.016	30	CH	H-14Y	.035	1/4P	0	1/8	6-1/4	19	4
35	65	153624	VD	8	.016	33	AC	46N	.035	0	1/2P	7/32	6	13.5	4
35	65	153624	VD	4	.016	33	AC	46N	.035	0	1/2P	7/32	6	13.5	4

11 - Corvette - 5 qts.
12 - Chevy II - 1 P.
13 - Chevy II - 7 deg.
14 - Dart - 111 in.
15 - Auto. Trans. - 10 BTDC.
16 - Both Breakers - 36 to 40 deg.
17 - Both Breakers - 37 to 42 deg.
18 - Fairlane - 116 in.
19 - Fairlane - 1/8 in.
20 - Fairlane - 7 deg.
21 - Fairlane - 1/2 P.

22 - Fairlane - 1/4 P.
23 - Comet - 116 in.
24 - Comet - 0 deg.
25 - Comet - 1/4 in.
26 - Jetstar 88 - 123 in.
27 - Rear Main - 120 ft. lbs.
28 - Jetstar 88 - 44 S.
29 - Jetstar 88 - 16.5 qts.
30 - Dynamic 88, Delta 88 - 123 in.
31 - 98 - 126 in.
32 - Satellite - 116 in.

33 - Satellite - 7-1/2 deg.
34 - Both Breakers - 37 to 42 deg.
35 - Star Chief - 124 in.
36 - Grand Prix - 121 in.
37 - Bonneville - 124 in.
38 - Premium Fuel - 13 deg. BTDC.
39 - Premium Fuel - 3 deg. BTDC.
40 - Premium Fuel - 8 deg. BTDC.
41 - Classic, Marlin - 112 in.
42 - 4-Door Models - 113 in.
43 - 2-Door Models - 109 in.

1967

	Wheelbase	No. of Cylinders Bore and Stroke	Displacement (cu. in.)	Valve and Cylinder Arrangement	Compression Pressure (lbs.)	Maximum Brake Horsepower	Valve Tappet Clearance Intake	Exhaust	Cylinder Bolt Torque (ft. lbs.)
Buick – Special, Skylark	115	6-3.75x3.40	225	VO	160	160@4200	HY	HY	80
Skylark, Sportwagon	115[1]	8-3.75x3.85	340	VO	175	220@4200	HY	HY	80
Special, Skylark	115	8-3.75x3.85	340	VO	175	260@4200	HY	HY	80
GS 400	115	8-4.04x3.90	400	VO	175	340@5000	HY	HY	120
LeSabre	123	8-3.75x3.85	340	VO	175	220@4200	HY	HY	80
LeSabre	123	8-3.75x3.85	340	VO	175	260@4200	HY	HY	80
Wildcat, Electra	126	8-4.1875x3.90	430	VO	175	360@5000	HY	HY	120
Riviera, Riviera "GS"	119	8-4.1875x3.90	430	VO	175	360@5000	HY	HY	120
Special, Skylark	115	8-3.75x3.40	300	VO	175	210@4400	HY	HY	80
Cadillac	129.5[2]	8-4.13x4.00	429	VO	175	340@4600	HY	HY	60
Eldorado	120	8-4.13x4.00	429	VO	175	340@4600	HY	HY	60
Chevrolet, Chevelle	119[3]	6-3.875x3.53	250	IO	130	155@4200	HY	HY	95
Chevrolet, Chevelle	119[3]	8-3.875x3.00	283	VO	150	195@4800	HY	HY	65
Camaro	108	8-4.00x3.25	327	VO	160	210@4600	HY	HY	65
Chevrolet, Chevelle	119[3]	8-4.00x3.25	327	VO	160	275@4800	HY	HY	65
Chevelle	115	8-4.00x3.25	327	VO	160	325@5600	HY	HY	65
Corvette	98	8-4.00x3.25	327	VO	150	350@5800	HY	HY	65
Camaro	108	8-4.00x3.48	350	VO	150	295@4800	HY	HY	65
Chevrolet, Chevelle	119[3]	8-4.094x3.76	396	VO	160	325@4800	HY	HY	80
Chevelle	115	8-4.094x3.76	396	VO	160	350@5200	HY	HY	80
Chevrolet	119	8-4.251x3.76	427	VO	160	385@5200	HY	HY	80
Corvette	98	8-4.251x3.76	427	VO	160	390@5400	HY	HY	80
Corvette	98	8-4.251x3.76	427	VO	150	400@5400	HY	HY	80
Corvette	98	8-4.251x3.76	427	VO	150	435@5800	.024	.028	80
Corvette	98	8-4.00x3.25	327	VO	160	300@5000	HY	HY	65
Chevy II	110	4-3.875x3.25	153	IO	130	90@4000	HY	HY	95
Chevy II	110	6-3.563x3.25	194	IO	130	120@4400	HY	HY	95
Chevelle, Camaro	115[8]	6-3.875x3.25	230	IO	130	140@4400	HY	HY	95
Corvair	108	6-3.4375x2.94	164	HO	130	95@3600	HY	HY	40
Corvair	108	6-3.4375x2.94	164	HO	130	110@4400	HY	HY	40
Chrysler – Newport	124	8-4.25x3.38	383	VO	140	270@4400	HY	HY	70
Newport	124	8-4.25x3.38	383	VO	140	325@4800	HY	HY	70
300, New Yorker	124	8-4.32x3.75	440	VO	150	350@4400	HY	HY	70
Newport, 300, New Yorker	124	8-4.32x3.75	440	VO	150	375@4600	HY	HY	70
Imperial	127	8-4.32x3.75	440	VO	150	350@4400	HY	HY	70
Dodge – Dart, Dart GT	111	6-3.40x3.125	170	IO	125	115@4400	.010H	.013H	65
Dart, Dart GT, Coronet	111[13]	6-3.40x4.125	225	IO	125	145@4000	.010H	.020H	65
Dart, Dart GT, Coronet	111[13]	8-3.63x3.31	273	VO	140	180@4200	.013H	.021H	85
Dart, Dart GT	111	8-3.63x3.31	273	VO	140	235@5200	.013H	.021H	85
Dart GT	111	8-4.25x3.38	383	VO	140	280@4200	HY	HY	70
Charger, Polara	117[15]	8-3.91x3.31	318	VO	140	230@4400	HY	HY	85
Coronet, Polara, Monaco	117[15]	8-4.25x3.38	383	VO	140	270@4400	HY	HY	70
Coronet, Monaco 500	117[15]	8-4.25x3.38	383	VO	140	325@4800	HY	HY	70
Coronet R/T	117	8-4.25x3.75	426	VO	180	425@5000	.028C	.032C	75
Charger, Polara, Monaco	117[15]	8-4.32x3.75	440	VO	150	350@4400	HY	HY	70
Coronet R/T, Polara, Monaco	117[15]	8-4.32x3.75	440	VO	150	375@4600	HY	HY	70
Ford – Falcon	111	6-3.50x2.94	170	IO	195	105@4400	HY	HY	75
Falcon, Futura, Fairlane	111[18]	6-3.684x3.13	200	IO	195	120@4400	HY	HY	75
Mustang	108	6-3.684x3.13	200	IO	195	120@4400	HY	HY	75
Ford	119	6-4.00x3.18	240	IO	175	150@4000	HY	HY	75
Falcon, Futura, Fairlane GT	111[18]	8-4.005x2.87	289	VO	150	200@4400	HY	HY	72
Ford	119	8-4.005x2.87	289	VO	150	200@4400	HY	HY	72
Mustang	108	8-4.005x2.87	289	VO	150	225@4800	HY	HY	72
Mustang	108	8-4.005x2.87	289	VO	150	271@6000	.022H	.024H	72
Fairlane, Fairlane GT	116	8-4.05x3.78	390	VO	180	270@4000	HY	HY	90
Ford	119	8-4.05x3.78	390	VO	180	270@4000	HY	HY	90
Thunderbird, Ford	115[20]	8-4.05x3.78	390	VO	190	315@4600	HY	HY	90

ABBREVIATIONS - FOOTNOTES

	HO – Horizontal Opposed Cylinders	1 – Sportwagon – 120 in.
	HY – Hydraulic Valve Lifters	2 – 60 – 133 in.; 75 – 149.8 in.
AC – AC Spark Plugs	IO – In-line Engine, Overhead Valves	3 – Chevelle – 115 in.
ATC – After Top Center	IOC – In-line Engine, Overhead Cam	4 – Chevelle – 1 N.
BF – Autolite Spark Plugs	N – Negative	5 – Chevelle – 1/2 P.
BTF – Autolite Spark Plugs	NA – Not Applicable	6 – Chevelle – 8-1/4 deg.
C – Cold Engine	P – Positive	7 – 4-Bolt Cap – 115 ft. lbs.
CC – Timing Case Cover	TR – Transistorized	8 – Camaro – 108 in.
CH – Champion Spark Plugs	VD – Vibration Damper	9 – Camaro – 1/2 P.
CP – Crankshaft Pulley	VO – V-Type Engine, Overhead Valves	10 – Camaro – 1/4 P.
H – Hot Engine	WP – Water Pump Housing	11 – Camaro – 8-3/4 deg.

Tuneup Specifications

Connecting Rod Bolt Torque (ft.lbs.)	Main Bearing Bolt Torque (ft.lbs.)	Firing Order	Timing Mark Location	Breaker Point Opens BTDC	Breaker Point Gap	Cam Angle	Spark Plugs Make	Spark Plugs Model	Spark Plugs Gap	Caster Man. Steer. (deg.)	Camber Rt. Wheel (deg.)	Toe-in (in.)	Steering Axis Inclination (deg.)	Cooling System Capacity (qts.)	Crankcase Capacity (qts.)
40	120	165432	VD	5	.016	30	AC	44S	.035	1/2N	1/2P	3/16	8	10.7	4
40	120	18436572	VD	5	.016	30	AC	44S	.033	1/2N	1/2P	3/16	8	11.2	4
40	120	18436572	VD	5	.016	30	AC	44S	.033	1/2N	1/2P	3/16	8	11.2	4
50	115	18436572	VD	2.5	.016	30	AC	44TS	.033	1/2N	1/2P	3/16	8	16.6	4
40	120	18436572	VD	2.5	.016	30	AC	44S	.033	1P	1/4P	1/4	10-3/4	12.7	4
40	120	18436572	VD	2.5	.016	30	AC	44S	.033	1P	1/4P	1/4	10-3/4	12.7	4
50	115	18436572	VD	2.5	.016	30	AC	44TS	.033	1P	1/4P	1/4	10-3/4	16.7	4
50	115	18436572	VD	2.5	.016	30	AC	44TS	.033	1P	1/4P	1/4	10-3/4	16.7	4
40	120	18436572	VD	5	.016	30	AC	44S	.033	1/2N	1/2P	3/16	8	11.2	4
40	95	18726543	VD	5	.016	30	AC	44	.035	1-1/2N	1/8N	1/4	6	18.2	4
40	95	18726543	VD	5	.016	30	AC	44	.035	2N	0	1/4	6	18.2	4
35	65	153624	VD	4	.019	33	AC	46N	.035	3/4P[4]	1/4P[5]	3/16	7-1/2[6]	12	4
35	80	18436572	VD	4	.019	30	AC	45	.035	3/4P[4]	1/4P[5]	3/16	7-1/2[6]	17	4
35	80	18436572	VD	8	.019	30	AC	44	.035	1/2P	1/4P	3/16	8-3/4	16	4
35	80	18436572	VD	8	.019	30	AC	44	.035	3/4P[4]	1/4P[5]	3/16	7-1/2[6]	15	4
35	80	18436572	VD	10	.019	30	AC	44	.038	1N	1/2P	3/16	8-1/4	16	4
35	80	18436572	VD	10	.019	30	AC	44	.035	1P	3/4P	1/4	7	16	4
35	80	18436572	VD	4	.019	30	AC	44	.035	1/2P	1/4P	3/16	8-3/4	16	4
50	95	18436572	VD	4	.019	30	AC	43N	.035	3/4P[4]	1/4P[5]	3/16	7-1/2[6]	22	4
50	95	18436572	VD	4	.019	30	AC	43N	.038	1N	1/2P	3/16	8-1/4	23	4
50	95[7]	18436572	VD	4	.019	30	AC	43N	.035	3/4P	1/4P	3/16	7-1/2	22	4
50	95[7]	18436572	VD	5	.019	30	AC	43N	.035	1P	3/4P	1/4	7	23	5
50	95[7]	18436572	VD	4	.019	30	AC	43N	.035	1P	3/4P	1/4	7	23	5
50	95[7]	18436572	VD	8	TR	TR	AC	43N	.035	1P	3/4P	1/4	7	23	5
35	80	18436572	VD	6	.019	30	AC	44	.035	1P	3/4P	1/4	7	16	4
35	65	1342	CP	4	.019	33	AC	46N	.035	1P	1/2P	5/16	7	9	3.5
35	65	153624	VD	4	.019	33	AC	45N	.035	1P	1/2P	5/16	8	11	4
35	65	153624	VD	4	.019	33	AC	45N	.035	1N[9]	1P[10]	3/16	8-1/4[11]	11	4
25	55	145236	CP	6[12]	.019	33	AC	46FF	.035	2-1/4P	1P	1/4	6-1/2	NA	4
25	55	145236	VD	14	.019	33	AC	44FF	.031	2-1/4P	1P	1/4	6-1/2	NA	4
45	80	18436572	CC	12.5	.016	30	CH	J-14Y	.035	1/2N	1/4P	1/8	9	17	4
45	80	18436572	CC	12.5	.016	30	CH	J-13Y	.035	1/2N	1/4P	1/8	9	17	4
45	80	18436572	CC	12.5	.016	30	CH	J-13Y	.035	1/2N	1/4P	1/8	9	17	4
45	80	18436572	CC	12.5	.016	30	CH	J-13Y	.035	1/2N	1/4P	1/8	9	18	4
45	80	18436572	CC	12.5	.016	30	CH	J-13Y	.035	3/4P	1/4P	1/8	9	18	4
45	85	153624	WP	5	.020	43	CH	N-14Y	.035	1/2N	1/2P	1/8	7-1/2	12	4
45	85	153624	WP	5	.020	43	CH	N-14Y	.035	1/2N	1/2P	1/8	7-1/2	13	4
45	85	18436572	CC	10	.016	30	CH	N-14Y	.035	1/2N	1/2P	1/8	7-1/2	19	4
45	85	18436572	CC	10	.016	29[14]	CH	N-10Y	.035	1/2N	1/2P	1/8	7-1/2	19	4
45	80	18436572	CC	12.5	.016	30	CH	J-13Y	.035	1/2N	1/2P	1/8	7-1/2	17	4
45	85	18436572	CC	5	.016	30	CH	N-14Y	.035	1/2N	1/2P	1/8	7-1/2[16]	18	4
45	80	18436572	CC	12.5	.016	30	CH	J-14Y	.035	1/2N	1/2P	1/8	7-1/2[16]	17	4
45	80	18436572	CC	12.5	.016	30	CH	J-13Y	.035	1/2N	1/2P	1/8	7-1/2[16]	17	4
45	100	18436572	CC	12.5	.016	30[17]	CH	N-10Y	.035	1/2N	1/2P	1/8	7-1/2	18	5
45	80	18436572	CC	12.5	.016	30	CH	J-11Y	.035	1/2N	1/2P	1/8	7-1/2[16]	18	4
45	80	18436572	CC	12.5	.016	30	CH	J-11Y	.035	1/2N	1/2P	1/8	7-1/2[16]	18	4
24	70	153624	VD	6	.025	37	BF	82	.034	1/2N	1/4P	1/4	7	9.6	3.5
24	70	153624	VD	6	.025	37	BF	82	.034	1/2N	1/4P	1/4	7	9.5	3.5
24	70	153624	VD	6	.025	37	BF	82	.034	1P	1P	3/16	6-3/4	9.5	3.5
45	70	153624	VD	6[19]	.025	37	BTF	42	.034	1P	1/2P	3/16	7-1/2	13	4
24	70	15426378	VD	6	.015	27	BF	42	.034	1/2N	1/4P	1/4	7	15	4
24	70	15426378	VD	6	.015	27	BF	42	.034	1P	1/2P	3/16	7-1/2	15	4
24	70	15426378	VD	9	.015	27	BF	42	.034	1P	1P	3/16	6-3/4	15	4
45	70	15426378	VD	12	.020	34	BF	32	.034	1P	1P	3/16	6-3/4	15	4
45	105	15426378	VD	10	.015	26	BF	42	.034	1/2N	1/4P	1/4	7	20.5	4
45	105	15426378	VD	10	.017	29	BF	42	.034	1P	1/2P	3/16	7-1/2	20.5	4
45	105	15426378	VD	10	.017	29	BF	42	.034	1P	1/2P	3/16	7[21]	20.5	4

12 – With Auto. Trans. – 14 deg.
13 – Coronet – 117 in.
14 – Both Breakers – 36 to 40 deg.
15 – Polara, Monaco – 122 in.
16 – Polara, Monaco – 9 deg.
17 – Both Breakers – 37 to 42 deg.
18 – With Auto. Trans. – 10 deg.
19 – Fairlane, GT – 116 in.
20 – Ford – 119 in.
21 – Ford – 7-1/2 deg.
22 – T-Bird 4-Door Landau – 117 in.

23 – Thunderbird – 7 deg.
24 – Cougar – 111 in.
25 – Cougar – 1/4 P.
26 – Cougar – 1 P.
27 – Cougar – 6-3/4 deg.
28 – Cougar – 6-3/4 deg.
29 – Both Breakers – 36 to 40 deg.
30 – Rear Main Bearing – 120 ft. lbs.
31 – Fury – 119 in.
32 – Fury – 9 deg.
33 – Both Breakers – 37 to 42 deg.

34 – Belvedere GTX – 116 in.
35 – Belvedere GTX – 7-1/2 deg.
36 – Executive – 124 in.
37 – Grand Prix – 121 in.
38 – Premium Fuel – 13 deg.
39 – Premium Fuel – 8 deg.
40 – Premium Fuel – 3 deg.
41 – Rebel, Marlin, Ambassador – 6-1/8 deg.
42 – Rebel – 114 in.; Marlin, Ambassador – 118 in.

1967

	Wheelbase	No. of Cylinders Bore and Stroke	Displacement (cu. in.)	Valve and Cylinder Arrangement	Compression Pressure (lbs.)	Maximum Brake Horsepower	Valve Tappet Clearance Intake	Exhaust	Cylinder Bolt Torque (ft.-lbs.)
Fairlane, Fairlane GT	116	8-4.05x3.78	390	VO	190	320@4000	HY	HY	90
Mustang	108	8-4.05x3.78	390	VO	190	320@4000	HY	HY	90
Ford - Thunderbird	119[22]	8-4.13x3.98	428	VO	190	345@4600	HY	HY	110
Ford	119	8-4.13x3.98	428	VO	190	360@5400	HY	HY	110
Ford	119	8-4.23x3.78	427	VO	180	410@5600	.028	.025	110
Ford	119	8-4.23x3.78	427	VO	180	425@6000	.028	.025	110
Lincoln Continental	126	8-4.38x3.83	462	VO	180	340@4600	HY	HY	145
Mercury - Comet	116	6-3.684x3.13	200	IO	195	120@4400	HY	HY	75
Comet, Cyclone, Cougar	116[24]	8-4.00x2.87	289	VO	150	200@4400	HY	HY	72
Cougar	111	8-4.00x2.87	289	VO	150	225@4800	HY	HY	72
Comet, Cyclone	116	8-4.05x3.78	390	VO	150	270@4400	HY	HY	90
Cyclone GT, Cougar	116[24]	8-4.05x3.78	390	VO	190	320@4800	HY	HY	90
Monterey, Montclair	123	8-4.05x3.78	390	VO	180	270@4400	HY	HY	90
Park Lane, Brougham, Marquis	123	8-4.054x3.984	410	VO	190	330@4600	HY	HY	90
S-55	123	8-4.13x3.984	428	VO	190	345@4600	HY	HY	110
Oldsmobile - F-85	115	6-3.875x3.53	250	IO	160	155@4200	HY	HY	95
Cutlass	115	8-3.9375x3.385	330	VO	175	250@4800	HY	HY	80
Cutlass Supreme	115	8-3.9375x3.385	330	VO	175	320@5200	HY	HY	80
4-4-2	115	8-4.00x3.975	400	VO	175	350@5000	HY	HY	80
Delmont 88	123	8-3.9375x3.385	330	VO	175	250@4800	HY	HY	80
Delmont 88	123	8-4.125x3.975	425	VO	175	300@4400	HY	HY	80
Delta 88, Custom	123	8-4.125x3.975	425	VO	175	300@4400	HY	HY	80
98	126	8-4.125x3.975	425	VO	175	365@4800	HY	HY	80
Toronado	119	8-4.125x3.975	425	VO	175	385@4800	HY	HY	80
Plymouth - Valiant, Signet	108	6-3.40x3.125	170	IO	125	115@4400	.010H	.020H	65
Valiant, Signet, Barracuda	108	6-3.40x4.125	225	IO	125	145@4000	.010H	.020H	65
Valiant, Signet, Barracuda	108	8-3.63x3.31	273	VO	140	180@4200	.013H	.021H	85
Valiant, Signet, Barracuda	108	8-3.63x3.31	273	VO	140	235@5200	.013H	.021H	85
Barracuda	108	8-4.25x3.38	383	VO	140	280@4200	HY	HY	70
Belvedere, Fury	116[31]	6-3.40x4.125	225	IO	125	145@4000	.010H	.020H	65
Belvedere	116	8-3.63x3.31	273	VO	140	180@4200	.013H	.021H	85
Belvedere, Satellite, Fury	116[31]	8-3.91x3.31	318	VO	140	230@4400	HY	HY	85
Belvedere, Satellite, Fury	116[31]	8-4.25x3.38	383	VO	140	270@4400	HY	HY	70
Belvedere, Satellite, Fury	116[31]	8-4.25x3.38	383	VO	140	325@4800	HY	HY	70
Belvedere, Satellite	116	8-4.25x3.75	426	VO	180	425@5000	.028C	.032C	75
Fury	119	8-4.32x3.75	440	VO	150	350@4400	HY	HY	70
Fury, Belvedere GTX	119[34]	8-4.32x3.75	440	VO	150	375@4400	HY	HY	70
Pontiac - Tempest, LeMans	115	6-3.875x3.245	230	IOC	160	165@4700	HY	HY	95
Tempest, LeMans	115	6-3.875x3.245	230	IOC	195	215@5200	HY	HY	95
Tempest, LeMans	115	6-3.875x3.245	230	IOC	160	250@4600	HY	HY	95
Tempest, LeMans	115	8-3.7187x3.746	326	VO	160	285@5000	HY	HY	95
GTO	115	8-4.12x3.746	400	VO	160	335@5000	HY	HY	95
GTO Ram Air	115	8-4.12x3.746	400	VO	160	360@5400	HY	HY	95
Catalina, Executive	121[36]	8-4.12x3.746	400	VO	160	265@4600	HY	HY	95
Catalina, Executive	121[36]	8-4.12x3.746	400	VO	160	290@4600	HY	HY	95
Catalina, Executive	121[36]	8-4.12x3.746	400	VO	160	325@4800	HY	HY	95
Bonneville	124	8-4.12x3.746	400	VO	160	333@5000	HY	HY	95
Grand Prix	121	8-4.12x3.746	400	VO	160	350@5000	HY	HY	95
2 + 2, Catalina	121	8-4.12x3.996	428	VO	200	360@4600	HY	HY	95
Bonneville, Grand Prix	124[37]	8-4.12x3.996	428	VO	200	376@5100	HY	HY	95
Rambler - American	106	6-3.75x3.00	199	IO	145	128@4400	HY	HY	85
American, Marlin, Rebel	114[42]	6-3.75x3.50	232	IO	145	145@4300	HY	HY	85
American, Rebel, Ambassador	106[42]	6-3.75x3.50	232	IO	145	155@4400	HY	HY	85
American	106	8-3.75x3.28	290	VO	145	225@4700	HY	HY	100
Rebel, Ambassador	114[42]	8-3.75x3.28	290	VO	145	200@4600	HY	HY	100
Ambassador, Rebel	118[42]	8-4.08x3.28	343	VO	145	235@4400	HY	HY	100
Ambassador, Rebel	118[42]	8-4.08x3.28	343	VO	145	280@4800	HY	HY	100

ABBREVIATIONS - FOOTNOTES

AC - AC Spark Plugs
ATC - After Top Center
BF - Autolite Spark Plugs
BTF - Autolite Spark Plugs
C - Cold Engine
CC - Timing Case Cover
CH - Champion Spark Plugs
CP - Crankshaft Pulley
H - Hot Engine

HO - Horizontal Opposed Cylinders
HY - Hydraulic Valve Lifters
IO - In-line Engine, Overhead Valves
IOC - In-line Engine, Overhead Cam
N - Negative
NA - Not Applicable
P - Positive
TR - Transistorized
VD - Vibration Damper
VO - V-Type Engine, Overhead Valves
WP - Water Pump Housing

1 - Sportwagon - 120 in.
2 - 60 - 133 in.; 75 - 149.8 in.
3 - Chevelle - 115 in.
4 - Chevelle - 1 N.
5 - Chevelle - 1/2 P.
6 - Chevelle - 8-1/4 deg.
7 - 4-Bolt Cap - 115 ft. lbs.
8 - Camaro - 108 in.
9 - Camaro - 1/2 P.
10 - Camaro - 1/4 P.
11 - Camaro - 8-3/4 deg.

Tuneup Specifications

Connecting Rod Bolt Torque (ft.-lbs.)	Main Bearing Bolt Torque (ft.-lbs.)	Firing Order	Timing Mark Location	Breaker Point Opens B.T.D.C.	Breaker Point Gap	Cam Angle	Spark Plugs Make	Model	Gap	Caster Man. Steer. (deg.)	Camber Rt. Wheel (deg.)	Toe-In (inches)	Steering Axis Inclination (deg.)	Cooling System Capacity (qts.)	Crankcase Capacity (qts.)
45	105	15426378	VD	12	.015	26	BF	42	.034	1/2N	1/4P	1/4	7	20.5	4
45	105	15426378	VD	12	.015	27	BF	32	.034	1P	1P	3/16	6-3/4	20.5	4
45	105	15426378	VD	12	.020	32	BF	32	.030	1P	1/2P	3/16	7-1/2[23]	20.5	4
45	105	15426378	VD	12	.020	32	BF	32	.030	1P	1/2P	3/16	7-1/2	20.5	4
58	105	15426378	VD	8	.020	23	BF	32	.034	1P	1/2P	3/16	7-1/2	20.5	4
58	105	15426378	VD	8	.020	23	BF	32	.034	1P	1/2P	3/16	7-1/2	20.5	4
45	105	15426378	VD	10	.017	29	BTF	42	.034	1-1/2N	1/2P	1/8	7-3/4	23	5
24	70	153624	CC	6	.025	32	BF	82	.034	1/2N	1/4P	1/4	7-1/2	9.5	3.4
24	70	15426378	VD	6	.015	26	BF	42	.034	1/2N[25]	1/4P[26]	1/4[27]	7-1/2[28]	15	4
24	70	15426378	VD	6	.015	26	BF	42	.034	1/4P	1P	3/16	6-3/4	15	4
45	105	15426378	VD	10	.015	26	BF	42	.034	1/2N[25]	1/4P[26]	1/4[27]	7-1/2[28]	20.5	4
45	105	15426378	VD	12	.015	26	BF	42	.034	1P	1/4P	3/16	7-1/2	20.5	4
45	105	15426378	VD	10	.015	26	BF	42	.034	1P	1/4P	3/16	7-1/2	20.5	4
45	105	15426378	VD	10	.017	29	BF	42	.034	1P	1/4P	3/16	7-1/2	20.5	4
45	105	15426378	VD	10	.017	29	BF	42	.034	1P	1/4P	3/16	7-1/2	20.5	4
35	65	153624	VD	7.5	.016	34	AC	46N	.035	1-1/4N	0	1/8	8	12	4
42	80[30]	18436572	CP	7.5	.016	30	AC	45S	.030	1-1/4N	0	1/8	8	17	4
42	80[30]	18436572	VD	7.5	.016	30	AC	44S	.030	1-1/4N	0	1/8	8	17	4
42	120	18436572	CP	7.5	.016	30	AC	44S	.030	1-1/4N	0	1/8	8	17	4
42	80[30]	18436572	CP	7.5	.016	30	AC	44S	.030	1-1/4N	1/4P	3/16	10	16.5	4
42	120	18436572	CP	5	.016	30	AC	44S	.030	1-1/4N	1/4P	3/16	10	17.5	4
42	120	18436572	CP	5	.016	30	AC	44S	.030	1-1/4N	1/4P	3/16	10	17.5	4
42	120	18436572	CP	7.5	.016	30	AC	44S	.030	1-1/4N	1/4P	3/16	10	17.5	4
42	120	18436572	CP	7.5	.016	30	AC	44S	.030	2N	1/4P	1/16	11	17.5	4
45	85	153624	WP	5	.020	43	CH	N-14Y	.035	1/2N	1/4P	1/8	7-1/2	12	4
45	85	153624	WP	5	.020	43	CH	N-14Y	.035	1/2N	1/4P	1/8	7-1/2	13	4
45	85	18436572	CC	10	.016	30	CH	N-14Y	.035	1/2N	1/4P	1/8	7-1/2	19	4
45	85	18436572	CC	10	.016	29[29]	CH	N-10Y	.035	1/2N	1/4P	1/8	7-1/2	19	4
45	80	18436572	CC	12.5	.016	29	CH	N-13Y	.035	1/2N	1/4P	1/8	7-1/2	17	4
45	85	153624	WP	5	.019	43	CH	N-14Y	.035	1/2N	1/4P	1/8	7-1/2[32]	13	4
45	85	18436572	CC	10	.016	30	CH	N-14Y	.035	1/2N	1/4P	1/8	7-1/2	19	4
45	85	18436572	CC	10	.016	30	CH	N-14Y	.035	1/2N	1/4P	1/8	7-1/2[32]	18	4
45	80	18436572	CC	12.5	.016	30	CH	J-14Y	.035	1/2N	1/4P	1/8	7-1/2[32]	17	4
45	80	18436572	CC	12.5	.016	30	CH	J-11Y	.035	1/2N	1/4P	1/8	7-1/2[32]	17	4
45	100	18436572	CC	12.5	.016	30[33]	CH	N-10Y	.035	1/2N	1/4P	1/8	7-1/2	18	5
45	80	18436572	CC	12.5	.016	30	CH	J-11Y	.035	1/2N	1/4P	1/8	9	18	4
45	80	18436572	CC	12.5	.016	30	CH	J-11Y	.035	1/2N	1/4P	1/8	9[35]	18	4
33	100	153624	VD	5	.016	33	AC	44N	.035	1-1/2N	1/4P	1/16	9	12.1	5
33	100	153624	CP	5	.016	33	AC	44N	.035	1-1/2N	1/4P	1/16	9	12.1	5
43	100[30]	153624	CP	5	.016	33	AC	44N	.035	1-1/2N	1/4P	1/16	9	12.1	5
43	100[30]	18436572	CP	6	.016	30	AC	45S	.035	1-1/2N	1/4P	1/16	9	18.6	6
43	100[30]	18436572	CP	6	.016	30	AC	44S	.035	1-1/2N	1/4P	1/16	9	17.8	6
43	100[30]	18436572	CP	6	.016	30	AC	44S	.035	1-1/2N	1/4P	1/16	9	17.8	6
43	100[30]	18436572	CP	6	.016	30	AC	45S	.035	1-1/2N	1/4P	1/16	8-1/2	18	6
43	100[30]	18436572	CP	6	.016	30	AC	45S	.035	1-1/2N	1/4P	1/16	8-1/2	18	6
43	100[30]	18436572	CP	6	.016	30	AC	45S	.035	1-1/2N	1/4P	1/16	8-1/2	18	6
43	100[30]	18436572	CP	6	.016	30	AC	44S	.035	1-1/2N	1/4P	1/16	8-1/2	18.6	6
43	100[30]	18436572	CP	6	.016	30	AC	44S	.035	1-1/2N	1/4P	1/16	8-1/2	17.2	6
30	85	153624	VD	10[38]	.016	33	CH	N-14Y	.035	0	0	1/8	6-1/2	10.5	4
30	85	153624	VD	5[39]	.016	33	CH	N-14Y	.035	0	0	1/8	6-1/2[41]	10.5	4
30	85	153624	VD	5[39]	.016	33	CH	N-14Y	.035	0	0	1/8	6-1/2[41]	10.5	4
30	105	18436572	VD	TDC[40]	.016	30	CH	N-12Y	.035	0	0	1/8	6-1/2	13	4
30	105	18436572	VD	TDC[40]	.016	30	CH	N-12Y	.035	0	0	1/8	6-1/8	13	4
30	105	18436572	VD	TDC	.016	30	CH	N-12Y	.035	0	0	1/8	6-1/8	14	4
30	105	18436572	VD	TDC	.016	30	CH	N-12Y	.035	0	0	1/8	6-1/8	14	4

12 – With Auto. Trans. – 14 deg.
13 – Coronet – 117 in.
14 – Both Breakers – 36 to 40 deg.
15 – Polara, Monaco – 122 in.
16 – Polara, Monaco – 9 deg.
17 – Both Breakers – 37 to 42 deg.
18 – With Auto. Trans. – 10 deg.
19 – Fairlane, GT – 116 in.
20 – Ford – 119 in.
21 – Ford – 7-1/2 deg.
22 – T-Bird 4-Door Landau – 117 in.

23 – Thunderbird – 7 deg.
24 – Cougar – 111 in.
25 – Cougar – 1/4 P.
26 – Cougar – 1 P.
27 – Cougar – 6-3/4 deg.
28 – Cougar – 6-3/4 deg.
29 – Both Breakers – 36 to 40 deg.
30 – Rear Main Bearing – 120 ft. lbs.
31 – Fury – 119 in.
32 – Fury – 9 deg.
33 – Both Breakers – 37 to 42 deg.

34 – Belvedere GTX – 116 in.
35 – Belvedere GTX – 7-1/2 deg.
36 – Executive – 124 in.
37 – Grand Prix – 121 in.
38 – Premium Fuel – 13 deg.
39 – Premium Fuel – 8 deg.
40 – Premium Fuel – 3 deg.
41 – Rebel, Marlin, Ambassador – 6-1/8 deg.
42 – Rebel – 114 in.; Marlin, Ambassador – 118 in.

1968

	Wheelbase	No. of Cylinders Bore and Stroke	Displacement (cu. in.)	Valve and Cylinder Arrangement	Compression Pressure (lbs.)	Maximum Brake Horsepower	Valve Tappet Clearance Intake	Valve Tappet Clearance Exhaust	Cylinder Bolt Torque (ft. lbs.)
Buick – Special, Skylark	116	6-3.875x3.53	250	IO	165	155@4200	HY	HY	95
Special Deluxe, Skylark Custom	116	8-3.80x3.85	350	VO	175	230@4400	HY	HY	75
Sportwagon, GS "350"	121[1]	8-3.80x3.85	350	VO	175	280@4600	HY	HY	75
GS "400"	112	8-4.04x3.90	400	VO	175	340@5000	HY	HY	100
LeSabre	123	8-3.80x3.85	350	VO	175	230@4400	HY	HY	75
LeSabre	123	8-3.80x3.85	350	VO	175	280@4600	HY	HY	75
Wildcat, Electra, Riviera	126[4]	8-4.1875x3.90	430	VO	195	360@5000	HY	HY	100
Cadillac	129[5]	8-4.30x4.06	472	VO	175	375@4400	HY	HY	115
Eldorado	120	8-4.30x4.06	472	VO	175	375@4400	HY	HY	115
Chevrolet, Chevelle	119[7]	6-3.875x3.53	250	IO	130	155@4200	HY	HY	95
Chevrolet, Chevelle	119[7]	8-3.875x3.25	307	VO	150	200@4600	HY	HY	65
Chevrolet, Chevelle	119[7]	8-4.001x3.25	327	VO	160	250@4800	HY	HY	65
Chevrolet, Chevelle	119[7]	8-4.001x3.25	327	VO	160	275@4800	HY	HY	65
Corvette	98	8-4.001x3.25	327	VO	160	300@5000	HY	HY	65
Chevelle	112[7]	8-4.001x3.25	327	VO	150	325@5600	HY	HY	65
Corvette	98	8-4.001x3.25	327	VO	150	350@5800	HY	HY	65
Chevrolet, SS 396	119[7]	8-4.094x3.76	396	VO	160	325@4800	HY	HY	80
SS 396	112	8-4.094x3.76	396	VO	160	350@5200	HY	HY	80
Chevrolet	119	8-4.251x3.76	427	VO	160	385@5200	HY	HY	80
Corvette	98	8-4.251x3.76	427	VO	160	390@5400	HY	HY	80
Corvette	98	8-4.251x3.76	427	VO	150	400@5400	HY	HY	80
Corvette	98	8-4.251x3.76	427	VO	150	435@5400	.024	.028	80
Chevy II	111	4-3.875x3.25	153	IO	130	90@4000	HY	HY	95
Chevy II, Camaro	111[15]	6-3.875x3.25	230	IO	130	140@4400	HY	HY	95
Chevy II, Camaro	111[15]	6-3.875x3.53	250	IO	130	155@4200	HY	HY	95
Chevy II	111	8-3.875x3.25	307	VO	150	200@4600	HY	HY	65
Camaro	108	8-4.001x3.25	327	VO	160	210@4600	HY	HY	65
Chevy II, Camaro	111[15]	8-4.001x3.25	327	VO	160	275@4800	HY	HY	65
Chevy II, Camaro	111[15]	8-4.00x3.48	350	VO	160	295@4800	HY	HY	65
Camaro	108	8-4.094x3.76	396	VO	150	325@4800	HY	HY	80
Corvair, Monza	108	6-3.4375x2.94	164	HO	130	95@3600	HY	HY	40
Corvair, Monza	108	6-3.4375x2.94	164	HO	130	110@4400	HY	HY	40
Corvair, Monza	108	6-3.4375x2.94	164	HO	130	140@5200	HY	HY	40
Chrysler – Newport	124	8-4.25x3.38	383	VO	140	290@4400	HY	HY	70
Newport	124	8-4.25x3.38	383	VO	140	330@5000	HY	HY	70
New Yorker, 300	124	8-4.32x3.75	440	VO	150	350@4400	HY	HY	70
New Yorker, 300, Newport	124	8-4.32x3.75	440	VO	150	375@4600	HY	HY	70
Imperial	127	8-4.32x3.75	440	VO	150	350@4400	HY	HY	70
Dodge – Dart, Dart GT	111	6-3.40x3.125	170	IO	125	115@4400	.010H	.020H	65
Dart, Dart GT, Coronet	111[21]	6-3.40x4.125	225	IO	125	145@4000	.010H	.020H	65
Dart, Dart GT, Coronet	111[21]	8-3.63x3.31	273	VO	135	190@4400	HY	HY	85
Dart, Dart GT	111	8-3.91x3.31	318	VO	135	230@4400	HY	HY	85
Dart GTS	111	8-4.04x3.31	340	VO	140	275@5000	HY	HY	95
Dart GTS	111	8-4.25x3.38	383	VO	140	300@4400	HY	HY	70
Coronet, Charger	117	8-3.91x3.31	318	VO	135	230@4400	HY	HY	85
Coronet, Charger	117	8-4.25x3.38	383	VO	140	290@4400	HY	HY	70
Coronet, Charger	117	8-4.25x3.38	383	VO	140	330@5000	HY	HY	70
Coronet R/T, Charger R/T	117	8-4.32x3.75	440	VO	150	375@4600	HY	HY	70
Coronet R/T, Charger R/T	117	8-4.25x3.75	426	VO	150	425@5000	.028C	.032C	75
Polara	122	8-3.91x3.31	318	VO	135	230@4400	HY	HY	85
Polara, Monaco	122	8-4.25x3.38	383	VO	140	290@4400	HY	HY	70
Polara, Monaco	122	8-4.25x3.38	383	VO	140	330@5000	HY	HY	70
Polara, Monaco	122	8-4.32x3.75	440	VO	150	375@4600	HY	HY	70
Ford – Falcon	110.9	6-3.50x2.94	170	IO	175	100@4000	HY	HY	75
Falcon Deluxe, Fairlane	110.9[25]	6-3.68x3.13	200	IO	175	115@3800	HY	HY	75
Mustang	108	6-3.68x3.13	200	IO	175	115@3800	HY	HY	75
Ford	119	6-4.00x3.18	240	IO	175	150@4000	HY	HY	75
Mustang, Falcon, Deluxe	108[26]	8-4.00x2.87	289	VO	150	195@4600	HY	HY	72
Ford LTD, Torino GT	119[25]	8-4.00x3.00	302	VO	150	210@4600	HY	HY	72
Mustang GT, Falcon	108[26]	8-4.00x3.00	302	VO	150	230@4800	HY	HY	90
Ford, Fairlane	119[25]	8-4.05x3.78	390	VO	180	265@4400	HY	HY	90
Thunderbird, Ford	114.7[31]	8-4.05x3.78	390	VO	190	315@4600	HY	HY	90
Mustang GT	108	8-4.05x3.78	390	VO	190	325@4800	HY	HY	90
Torino GT	116	8-4.05x3.78	390	VO	190	335@4800	HY	HY	90
Ford	119	8-4.13x3.98	428	VO	190	340@4600	HY	HY	90

ABBREVIATIONS – FOOTNOTES

AC – AC Spark Plugs	IO – In-line Engine, Overhead Valves
ATC – After Top Center	IOC – In-line Engine, Overhead Cam
BF – Autolite Spark Plugs	MP – Magnetic Pulse Ignition
BTF – Autolite Spark Plugs	N – Negative
C – Cold Engine	NA – Not Applicable
CC – Timing Case Cover	P – Positive
CH – Champion Spark Plugs	VD – Vibration Damper
CP – Crankshaft Pulley	VO – V–Type Engine, Overhead Valves
H – Hot Engine	WP – Water Pump Housing
HO – Horizontal Opposed Cylinders	
HY – Hydraulic Valve Lifters	

1 – GS "350" – 112 in.
2 – GS "350" – CP
3 – GS "350" – 10 qts.

4 – Riviera – 119 in.
5 – 60 and Brougham – 133 in.; 75 – 149.8 in.
6 – 75 – 23.8 qts.
7 – Chevelle 4–Door Sedans – 116 in.;
  2–Door Sedans – 112 in.
8 – Auto. Trans. – 4 BTDC.
9 – Chevelle – 1 N.
10 – Chevelle – 1/2 P.
11 – Chevelle – 8-1/4 deg.
12 – Chevelle – 16 qts.
13 – 4–Bolt Cap – 105 ft. lbs.
14 – Chevelle SS 396 – 24 qts.
15 – Camaro – 108 in.

Tuneup Specifications

Connecting Rod Bolt Torque (ft. lbs.)	Main Bearing Bolt Torque (ft. lbs.)	Firing Order	Timing Mark Location	Breaker Point Opens BTDC	Breaker Point Gap	Cam Angle	Make	Model	Gap	Caster Man. Steer. (deg.)	Camber Kt. Wheel (deg.)	Toe-in (in.)	Steering Axis Inclination (deg.)	Cooling System Capacity (qts.)	Crankcase Capacity (qts.)
35	65	153624	VD	0	.019	33	AC	46N	.035	1/2N	1/2P	3/16	8	11.3	4
35	110	18436572	VD	0	.016	30	AC	45TS	.030	1/2N	1/2P	3/16	8	13.5	4
35	110	18436572	VD[2]	0	.016	30	AC	45TS	.030	1/2N	1/2P	3/16	8	13.5[2]	4
45	110	18436572	VD	0	.016	30	AC	44TS	.030	1/2N	1/2P	3/16	8	15	4
35	110	18436572	VD	0	.016	30	AC	45TS	.030	1P	1/4P	1/4	10-3/4	13.2	4
35	110	18436572	VD	0	.016	30	AC	45TS	.030	1P	1/4P	1/4	10-3/4	13.2	4
45	110	18436572	VD	0	.016	30	AC	44TS	.030	1P	1/4P	1/4	10-3/4	13.2	4
40	90	15634278	CP	5	.016	30	AC	44N	.035	1P	1/4P	1/4	6	20.8[6]	4
40	90	15634278	CP	5	.016	30	AC	44N	.035	2N	0	1/16	6	20.8	4
35	65	153624	VD	TDC[8]	.019	33	AC	46N	.035	3/4P[9]	1/4P[10]	3/16	7-1/2[11]	12	4
50	80	18436572	VD	2	.019	30	AC	45S	.035	3/4P[9]	1/4P[10]	3/16	7-1/2[11]	17	4
50	80	18436572	VD	4	.019	30	AC	44S	.035	3/4P[9]	1/4P[10]	3/16	7-1/2[11]	15[12]	4
50	80	18436572	VD	TDC[8]	.019	30	AC	44	.035	3/4P[9]	1/4P[10]	3/16	7-1/2[11]	15[12]	4
50	80	18436572	VD	4	.019	30	AC	44	.035	1P	3/4P	1/4	7	15	4
50	80	18436572	VD	4	.019	30	AC	44	.035	1P	3/4P	1/4	7	17	4
50	80	18436572	VD	4	.019	30	AC	44	.035	1P	3/4P	1/4	7	15	4
50	95[13]	18436572	VD	4	.019	30	AC	43N	.035	3/4P[9]	1/4P[10]	3/16	7-1/2[11]	22[14]	4
50	95[13]	18436572	VD	TDC	.019	30	AC	43N	.035	1N	1/2P	3/16	8-1/4	24	4
50	95[13]	18436572	VD	4	.019	30	AC	43N	.035	3/4P	1/4	3/16	7	22	4
50	95[13]	18436572	VD	4	.019	30	AC	43N	.035	1P	3/4P	1/4	7	22	5
50	95[13]	18436572	VD	4	.019	30	AC	43N	.035	1P	3/4P	1/4	7	22	5
50	95[13]	18436572	VD	4	MP	MP	AC	43N	.035	1P	3/4P	1/4	7	22	5
35	65	1342	VD	TDC[8]	.019	33	AC	46N	.035	1/2P	1/4P	3/16	8-3/4	9	4
35	65	153624	VD	TDC[8]	.019	33	AC	46N	.035	1/2P	1/4P	3/16	8-3/4	12	4
35	65	153624	VD	TDC[8]	.019	33	AC	46N	.035	1/2P	1/4P	3/16	8-3/4	12	4
50	80	18436572	VD	2	.019	30	AC	45S	.035	1/2P	1/4P	3/16	8-3/4	14	4
50	80	18436572	VD	2ATC[16]	.019	30	AC	44	.035	1/2P	1/4P	3/16	8-3/4	16	4
50	80	18436572	VD	TDC[8]	.019	30	AC	44	.035	1/2P	1/4P	3/16	8-3/4	16	4
50	80	18436572	VD	TDC[8]	.019	30	AC	44	.035	1/2P	1/4P	3/16	8-3/4	16	4
50	95[13]	18436572	VD	4	.019	30	AC	43N	.035	1/2P	1/4P	3/16	8-3/4	23	4
25	55	145236	CP	6[17]	.019	33	AC	46FF	.035	2-1/4P	1P	1/4	6-1/2	NA	4
25	55	145236	VD	4[18]	.019	33	AC	44FF	.031	2-1/4P	1P	1/4	6-1/2	NA	4
25	55	145236	VD	4	.019	33	AC	44FF	.031	1P	1P	1/4	6-1/2	NA	4
45	85	18436572	VD	TDC[19]	.016	30	CH	J-14Y	.035	1/2N	1/4P	1/8	9	17	4
45	85	18436572	VD	5	.016	30	CH	J-11Y	.035	1/2N	1/4P	1/8	9	17	4
45	85	18436572	VD	7.5	.016	30	CH	J-13Y	.035	1/2N	1/4P	1/8	9	18	4
45	85	18436572	VD	5	.016	30	CH	J-11Y	.035	1/2N	1/4P	1/8	9	18	4
45	85	18436572	VD	7.5	.016	30	CH	J-13Y	.035	3/4P	1/4P	1/8	9	17	5
45	85	153624	VD	5ATC[20]	.020	43	CH	N-14Y	.035	1/2N	1/4P	1/8	7-1/2	12	4
45	85	153624	VD	TDC	.020	43	CH	N-14Y	.035	1/2N	1/4P	1/8	7-1/2	13	4
45	85	18436572	VD	5ATC[20]	.016	31	CH	N-14Y	.035	1/2N	1/4P	1/8	7-1/2	19	4
45	85	18436572	VD	5ATC[20]	.016	31	CH	N-14Y	.035	1/2N	1/4P	1/8	7-1/2	18	4
45	85	18436572	VD	TDC[22]	.016	30[23]	CH	N-9Y	.035	1/2N	1/4P	1/8	7-1/2	18	4
45	85	18436572	VD	TDC[22]	.016	31	CH	J-11Y	.035	1/2N	1/4P	1/8	7-1/2	17	4
45	85	18436572	VD	5ATC[20]	.016	31	CH	N-14Y	.035	1/2N	1/4P	1/8	7-1/2	18	4
45	85	18436572	VD	TDC[19]	.016	31	CH	J-14Y	.035	1/2N	1/4P	1/8	7-1/2	17	4
45	85	18436572	VD	TDC[22]	.016	31	CH	J-11Y	.035	1/2N	1/4P	1/8	7-1/2	18	4
45	100	18436572	VD	TDC	.016	30[23]	CH	N-10Y	.035	1/2N	1/4P	1/8	7-1/2	18	5
45	85	18436572	VD	5ATC[20]	.016	31	CH	N-14Y	.035	1/2N	1/4P	1/8	9	18	4
45	85	18436572	VD	TDC[19]	.016	31	CH	J-14Y	.035	1/2N	1/4P	1/8	9	17	4
45	85	18436572	VD	TDC[22]	.016	31	CH	J-11Y	.035	1/2N	1/4P	1/8	9	17	4
45	85	18436572	VD	TDC[22]	.016	30[24]	CH	J-11Y	.035	1/2N	1/4P	1/8	9	17	4
24	70	153624	CC	6	.025	37	BF	82	.034	1/2P	1/4P	1/4	7	9.5	3.5
24	70	153624	VD	6	.025	37	BF	82	.034	1/2P	1/4P	1/4	7	9.5	3.5
24	70	153624	VD	6	.025	37	BF	82	.034	1/4P	1P	3/16	6-3/4	9.5	3.5
45	70	153624	CC	6	.025	37	BF	42	.034	1P	1/2P	3/16	7-3/4	13	4
24	70	15426378	VD	6	.017	27	BF	42	.034	1/4P[27]	1P[28]	3/16[29]	6-3/4[30]	15	4
24	70	15426378	VD	6	.017	29	BF	32	.034	1P[27]	1/2P[28]	3/16[29]	6-3/4[30]	15	4
24	70	15426378	VD	6	.017	29	BF	32	.034	1/4P[27]	1P[28]	3/16[29]	6-3/4[30]	15	4
45	105	15426378	VD	6	.017	29	BF	32	.034	1P[27]	1/2P[28]	3/16[29]	7-3/4[30]	20.5	4
45	105	15426378	VD	6	.017	29	BF	32	.034	1P	1/2P	3/16	7-3/4	20.5	4
45	105	15426378	VD	6	.020	29	BF	32	.034	1/4P	1P	3/16	6-3/4	20.5	4
45	105	15426378	VD	6	.015	27	BF	32	.034	1/2P	1/4P	1/4	7	20.5	4
45	105	15426378	VD	6	.017	29	BF	32	.034	1P	1/2P	3/16	7-3/4	20.5	4

16 – Auto. Trans. – 2 BTDC.
17 – Auto. Trans. – 14 BTDC.
18 – Auto. Trans. – 12 BTDC.
19 – Auto. Trans. – 7.5 BTDC.
20 – Auto. Trans. – 2.5 ATC.
21 – Coronet – 117 in.
22 – Auto. Trans. – 5 BTDC.
23 – Both Breakers – 37 to 42 deg.
24 – Man. Trans., Both Breakers – 37 to 42 deg.
25 – Fairlane, Torino – 116 in.
26 – Falcon – 110.9 in.
27 – Falcon, Fairlane – 1/2 P.
28 – Falcon, Fairlane – 1/4 P.

29 – Falcon, Fairlane – 1/4 in.
30 – Falcon, Fairlane – 7 deg.
31 – Ford – 119 in.
32 – Montego, Comet – 116 in.
33 – Montego, Comet – 1/2 P.
34 – Montego, Comet – 1/4 P.
35 – Montego, Comet – 1/4 in.
36 – Montego, Comet – 7 deg.
37 – Auto. Trans. – 6 BTDC.
38 – Rear Main – 120 ft. lbs.
39 – Auto. Trans. – 2.5 ATC.
40 – Belvedere – 116 in.
41 – Auto. Trans. – 5 BTDC.

42 – Fury – 119 in.
43 – Both Breakers – 37 to 42 deg.
44 – Fury – 9 deg.
45 – Man. Trans., Both Breakers – 37 to 42 deg.
46 – Firebird – 108.1 in.
47 – Firebird – 1/2 P.
48 – Firebird – 3/16 in.
49 – Firebird – 8-3/4 deg.
50 – Executive – 124 in.
51 – Grand Prix – 121 in.
52 – Javelin – 109 in.
53 – Ambassador – 118 in.

1968

Model	Wheelbase	No. of Cylinders Bore and Stroke	Displacement (cu. in.)	Valve and Cylinder Arrangement	Compression Pressure (lbs.)	Maximum Brake Horsepower	Valve Tappet Clearance Intake	Valve Tappet Clearance Exhaust	Cylinder Bolt Torque (ft.-lbs.)
Thunderbird	114.7	8-4.36x3.59	429	VO	190	360@4600	HY	HY	90
Mustang GT	108	8-4.23x3.78	427S	VO	180	390@5600	HY	HY	90
Ford	119	8-4.23x3.78	427S	VO	180	390@5600	HY	HY	90
Lincoln Continental	126	8-4.38x3.83	462	VO	180	340@4600	HY	HY	145
Mercury – Montego, Comet	116	6-3.68x3.13	200	IO	175	115@3800	HY	HY	75
Cougar, Montego, Comet	111[32]	8-4.00x3.00	302	VO	150	210@4600	HY	HY	72
Cougar, Montego, Comet	111[32]	8-4.00x3.00	302	VO	150	230@4800	HY	HY	72
Montego, Comet	116	8-4.05x3.78	390	VO	180	265@4400	HY	HY	90
Cougar	111	8-4.05x3.78	390	VO	180	280@4400	HY	HY	90
Cougar, Montego, Comet	111[32]	8-4.05x3.78	390	VO	190	325@4800	HY	HY	90
Cougar, Montego, Comet	111[32]	8-4.23x3.78	427	VO	180	390@5600	HY	HY	90
Monterey, Montclair	123	8-4.05x3.78	390	VO	180	265@4400	HY	HY	90
Monterey, Montclair	123	8-4.05x3.78	390	VO	180	280@4400	HY	HY	90
Park Lane, Brougham, Marquis	123	8-4.05x3.78	390	VO	190	315@4600	HY	HY	90
Park Lane, Brougham, Marquis	123	8-4.13x3.984	428	VO	190	340@4600	HY	HY	90
Oldsmobile – F-85, Cutlass	116	6-3.875x3.53	250	IO	160	155@4200	HY	HY	95
F-85, Cutlass, Supreme	116	8-4.057x3.385	350	VO	175	250@4400	HY	HY	80
F-85, Cutlass, Supreme	116	8-4.057x3.385	350	VO	175	310@4600	HY	HY	80
4-4-2	112	8-3.87x4.25	400	VO	175	325@4600	HY	HY	80
4-4-2	112	8-3.87x4.25	400	VO	175	350@4800	HY	HY	80
4-4-2	112	8-3.87x4.25	400	VO	175	360@5400	IIY	HY	80
Delmont	123	8-4.057x3.385	350	VO	175	250@4400	HY	HY	80
Delmont	123	8-4.057x3.385	350	VO	175	310@4600	HY	HY	80
Delmont, Delta	123	8-4.125x4.25	455	VO	175	310@4200	HY	HY	80
98, Delmont, Delta	126	8-4.125x4.25	455	VO	175	365@4600	HY	HY	80
Toronado	119	8-4.125x4.25	455	VO	175	375@4600	HY	HY	80
Toronado	119	8-4.125x4.25	455	VO	175	400@4800	HY	HY	80
Plymouth – Valiant, Signet	108	6-3.40x3.125	170	IO	125	115@4400	.010H	.020H	65
Valiant, Signet, Barracuda	108	6-3.40x4.125	225	IO	125	145@4000	.010H	.020H	65
Valiant, Signet, Belvedere	108[40]	8-3.63x3.31	273	VO	135	190@4400	HY	HY	85
Valiant, Barracuda, Belvedere	108[40]	8-3.91x3.31	318	VO	135	230@4400	HY	HY	85
Barracuda Formula S	108	8-4.04x3.31	340	VO	140	275@5000	HY	HY	95
Barracuda Formula S	108	8-4.25x3.38	383	VO	140	300@4400	HY	HY	85
Belvedere, Satellite, Fury	116[42]	8-4.25x3.38	383	VO	140	290@4400	HY	HY	85
Belvedere Road Runner	116	8-4.25x3.38	383	VO	140	335@5200	HY	HY	85
GTX	116	8-4.32x3.75	440	VO	150	375@4600	HY	HY	85
Belvedere, Satellite, GTX	116	8-4.25x3.75	426	VO	150	425@5000	.028C	.032C	100
Belvedere, Satellite, Fury	116[42]	6-3.40x4.125	225	IO	125	145@4000	.010H	.020H	85
Fury, VIP	119	8-3.91x3.31	318	VO	135	230@4000	HY	HY	85
Fury, Sport Fury, VIP	119	8-4.25x3.38	383	VO	140	330@5000	HY	HY	85
Fury, Sport Fury, VIP	119	8-4.32x3.75	440	VO	150	375@4600	HY	HY	85
Pontiac – Tempest, Firebird	116[46]	6-3.875x3.525	250	IOC	160	175@4800	HY	HY	95
Tempest, LeMans, Firebird	116[46]	6-3.875x3.525	250	IOC	195	215@5200	HY	HY	95
Tempest, LeMans, Firebird	116[46]	8-3.875x3.746	350	VO	160	265@4600	HY	HY	95
Tempest, LeMans, Firebird	116[46]	8-3.875x3.746	350	VO	160	320@5100	HY	HY	95
GTO	112	8-4.120x3.746	400	VO	160	265@4600	HY	HY	95
GTO Ram Air	112	8-4.120x3.746	400	VO	160	360@5400	HY	HY	95
Firebird 350	108.1	8-3.875x3.746	350	VO	160	265@4600	HY	HY	95
Firebird 350	108.1	8-3.875x3.746	350	VO	160	320@5100	HY	HY	95
Firebird 400	108.1	8-4.120x3.746	400	VO	160	330@4800	HY	HY	95
Firebird 400 Ram Air	108.1	8-4.120x3.746	400	VO	160	335@5300	HY	HY	95
Catalina, Executive	121[50]	8-4.120x3.746	400	VO	160	265@4600	HY	HY	95
Catalina, Executive	121[50]	8-4.120x3.746	400	VO	160	290@4600	HY	HY	95
Bonneville	124	8-4.120x3.746	400	VO	160	340@4800	HY	HY	95
Grand Prix	121	8-4.120x3.746	400	VO	160	350@5000	HY	HY	95
Catalina, Executive	121[50]	8-4.120x3.996	428	VO	200	375@4800	HY	HY	95
Bonneville, Grand Prix	124[51]	8-4.120x3.996	428	VO	200	390@5200	HY	HY	95
Rambler American	106	6-3.75x3.00	199	IO	145	128@4400	HY	HY	85
Rogue	106	6-3.75x3.50	232	IO	145	145@4300	HY	HY	85
American, Rogue, Javelin	106[52]	8-3.75x3.28	290	VO	145	225@4700	HY	HY	100
Rebel, Ambassador	114[53]	6-3.75x3.50	232	IO	145	145@4300	HY	HY	85
Rebel, Ambassador	114[53]	6-3.75x3.50	232	IO	145	155@4400	HY	HY	85
Rebel SST, Ambassador SST	114[53]	8-3.75x3.28	290	VO	145	200@4600	HY	HY	100
Rebel, Ambassador	114[53]	8-4.08x3.28	343	VO	145	235@4400	HY	HY	100
AMX	97	8-4.165x3.574	390	VO	145	315@4600	HY	HY	100

ABBREVIATIONS – FOOTNOTES

AC – AC Spark Plugs
ATC – After Top Center
BF – Autolite Spark Plugs
BTF – Autolite Spark Plugs
C – Cold Engine
CC – Timing Case Cover
CH – Champion Spark Plugs
CP – Crankshaft Pulley
H – Hot Engine
HO – Horizontal Opposed Cylinders
HY – Hydraulic Valve Lifters

IO – In-line Engine, Overhead Valves
IOC – In-line Engine, Overhead Cam
MP – Magnetic Pulse Ignition
N – Negative
NA – Not Applicable
P – Positive
VD – Vibration Damper
VO – V-Type Engine, Overhead Valves
WP – Water Pump Housing

1 – GS "350" – 112 in.
2 – GS "350" – CP
3 – GS "350" – 10 qts.

4 – Riviera – 119 in.
5 – 60 and Brougham – 133 in.; 75 – 149.8 in.
6 – 75 – 23.8 qts.
7 – Chevelle 4-Door Sedans – 116 in.;
    2-Door Sedans – 112 in.
8 – Auto. Trans. – 4 BTDC.
9 – Chevelle – 1 N.
10 – Chevelle – 1/2 P.
11 – Chevelle – 8-1/4 deg.
12 – Chevelle – 16 qts.
13 – 4-Bolt Cap – 105 ft. lbs.
14 – Chevelle SS 396 – 24 qts.
15 – Camaro – 108 in.

Tuneup Specifications

Connecting Rod Bolt Torque (ft.-lbs.)	Main Bearing Bolt Torque (ft.-lbs.)	Firing Order	Timing Mark Location	Breaker Point Opens B.T.D.C.	Breaker Point Gap	Cam Angle	Spark Plugs Make	Model	Gap	Caster Man. Steer. (deg.)	Camber Rt. Wheel (deg.)	Toe-In (inches)	Steering Axis Inclination (deg.)	Cooling System Capacity (qts.)	Crankcase Capacity (qts.)
45	105	15426378	VD	6	.015	27	BF	42	.034	1P	1/2P	3/16	7-3/4	20.5	4
45	105	15426378	VD	6	.017	29	BF	32	.034	1/4P	1P	3/16	6-3/4	20.5	4
45	105	15426378	VD	6	.017	29	BF	32	.034	1P	1P	3/16	7-3/4	20.5	4
45	105	15426378	VD	10	.017	29	BTF	42	.034	1-1/2N	1/2P	1/8	7-3/4	23	5
24	70	153624	VD	6	.025	37	BF	82	.034	1/2P	1/4P	1/4	7	9.5	3.5
24	70	15426378	VD	6	.021	27	BF	32	.034	1/4P[33]	1P[34]	3/16[35]	6-3/4[36]	15	4
24	70	15426378	VD	6	.021	27	BF	32	.034	1/4P[33]	1P[34]	3/16[35]	6-3/4[36]	15	4
45	105	15426378	VD	6	.021	27	BF	32	.034	1/2P	1P	1/4	7	20.5	4
45	105	15426378	VD	6	.021	27	BF	32	.034	1/4P	1P	3/16	6-3/4	20.5	4
45	105	15426378	VD	6	.021	27	BF	32	.034	1/4P[33]	1P[34]	3/16[35]	6-3/4[36]	20.5	4
45	105	15426378	VD	6	.017	29	BF	32	.034	1/4P[33]	1P[34]	3/16[35]	6-3/4[36]	20.5	4
45	105	15426378	VD	6	.021	27	BF	32	.034	1P	1/4P	3/16	7-1/2	20.5	4
45	105	15426378	VD	6	.017	29	BF	32	.034	1P	1/4P	3/16	7-1/2	20.5	4
45	105	15426378	VD	6	.017	29	BF	32	.034	1P	1/4P	3/16	7-1/2	20.5	4
45	105	15426378	VD	6	.017	29	BF	32	.034	1P	1/4P	3/16	7-1/2	20.5	4
35	65	153624	VD	4[37]	.016	33	AC	46N	.035	1-1/4N	1/8P	3/16	9	12.2	4
42	80[38]	18436572	VD	5	.016	30	AC	45S	.030	1-1/4N	1/8P	3/16	9	15.2	4
42	80[38]	18436572	VD	7.5	.016	30	AC	44S	.030	1-1/4N	1/8P	3/16	9	15.2	4
42	120	18436572	VD	0	.016	30	AC	44S	.030	1-1/4N	1/8P	3/16	9	16.2	4
42	120	18436572	VD	0	.016	30	AC	44S	.030	1-1/4N	1/8P	3/16	9	16.2	4
42	120	18436572	VD	0	.016	30	AC	44S	.030	1-1/4N	1/8P	3/16	9	16.2	4
42	120	18436572	VD	5	.016	30	AC	45S	.030	1N	1/8P	1/8	11	17.5	4
42	120	18436572	VD	5	.016	30	AC	45S	.030	1N	1/8P	1/8	11	17.5	4
42	120	18436572	VD	10	.016	30	AC	45S	.030	1N	1/8P	1/8	11	17.5	4
42	120	18436572	VD	10	.016	30	AC	45S	.030	1N	1/8P	1/8	11	17.5	4
42	120	18436572	VD	7.5	.016	30	AC	44S	.030	2N	1/8P	1/32	11	18	5
42	120	18436572	VD	7.5	.016	30	AC	44S	.030	2N	1/8P	1/32	11	18	5
45	85	153624	VD	5ATC[39]	.020	43	CH	N-14Y	.035	1/2N	1/4P	1/8	7-1/2	12	4
45	85	153624	VD	TDC	.020	43	CH	N-14Y	.035	1/2N	1/4P	1/8	7-1/2	13	4
45	85	18436572	VD	5ATC[39]	.016	30	CH	N-14Y	.035	1/2N	1/4P	1/8	7-1/2	19	4
45	85	18436572	VD	5ATC[39]	.016	30	CH	N-14Y	.035	1/2N	1/4P	1/8	7-1/2	17	4
45	85	18436572	VD	TDC[41]	.016	30[43]	CH	N-9Y	.035	1/2N	1/4P	1/8	7-1/2	18	4
45	85	18436572	VD	TDC[41]	.016	30	CH	J-11Y	.035	1/2N	1/4P	1/8	7-1/2	17	4
45	85	18436572	VD	TDC[41]	.016	30	CH	J-14Y	.035	1/2N	1/4P	1/8	7-1/2[44]	17	4
45	85	18436572	VD	TDC[41]	.016	30	CH	J-11Y	.035	1/2N	1/4P	1/8	7-1/2	17	4
45	85	18436572	VD	TDC[41]	.016	30[45]	CH	J-11Y	.035	1/2N	1/4P	1/8	7-1/2	17	4
45	85	18436572	VD	TDC	.016	30[43]	CH	N-10Y	.035	1/2N	1/4P	1/8	7-1/2	18	5
45	100	153624	VD	TDC	.020	43	CH	N-14Y	.035	1/2N	1/4P	1/8	7-1/2[44]	13	4
45	85	18436572	VD	5ATC[39]	.016	30	CH	N-14Y	.035	1/2N	1/4P	1/8	9	18	4
45	85	18436572	VD	TDC[41]	.016	30	CH	J-11Y	.035	1/2N	1/4P	1/8	9	17	4
45	85	18436572	VD	TDC[41]	.016	30[45]	CH	J-11Y	.035	1/2N	1/4P	1/8	9	18	4
33	100	153624	VD	TDC	.016	33	AC	44N	.035	1-1/2N[47]	1/4P	1/16[48]	9[49]	12.1	5
33	100	153624	VD	5	.016	33	AC	44N	.035	1-1/2N[47]	1/4P	1/16[48]	9[49]	12.1	5
43	100[38]	18436572	CP	9	.016	30	AC	45S	.035	1-1/2N[47]	1/4P	1/16[48]	9[49]	18.6	5
43	100[38]	18436572	CP	9	.016	30	AC	45S	.035	1-1/2N[47]	1/4P	1/16[48]	9[49]	18.6	5
43	100[38]	18436572	CP	9	.016	30	AC	44S	.035	1-1/2N	1/4P	1/16	9	17.8	5
43	100[38]	18436572	CP	9	.016	30	AC	44S	.035	1-1/2N	1/4P	1/16	9	17.8	5
43	100[38]	18436572	CP	9	.016	30	AC	45S	.035	1/2P	1/4P	3/16	8-3/4	18.6	5
43	100[38]	18436572	CP	9	.016	30	AC	45S	.035	1/2P	1/4P	3/16	8-3/4	18.6	5
43	100[38]	18436572	CP	9	.016	30	AC	44S	.035	1/2P	1/4P	3/16	8-3/4	17.8	5
43	100[38]	18436572	CP	9	.016	30	AC	44S	.035	1/2P	1/4P	3/16	8-3/4	17.8	5
43	100[38]	18436572	CP	9	.016	30	AC	45S	.034	1-1/2N	1/4P	1/16	8-1/2	18	5
43	100[38]	18436572	CP	9	.016	30	AC	45S	.034	1-1/2N	1/4P	1/16	8-1/2	18	5
43	100[38]	18436572	CP	9	.016	30	AC	45S	.034	1-1/2N	1/4P	1/16	8-1/2	18.6	5
43	100[38]	18436572	CP	9	.016	30	AC	44S	.034	1-1/2N	1/4P	1/16	8-1/2	17.2	5
43	100[38]	18436572	CP	9	.016	30	AC	44S	.034	1-1/2N	1/4P	1/16	8-1/2	17.2	5
30	85	153624	VD	TDC[41]	.016	33	CH	N-14Y	.035	0	0	1/8	6-1/2	10.5	4
30	85	153624	VD	TDC[41]	.016	33	CH	N-14Y	.035	0	0	1/8	6-1/2	10.5	4
30	105	18436572	VD	TDC	.016	30	CH	N-12Y	.035	0	0	1/8	6-1/2	13	4
30	85	153624	VD	TDC	.016	33	CH	N-14Y	.035	1/2N	0	1/8	6-1/4	10.5	4
30	85	153624	VD	TDC	.016	33	CH	N-14Y	.035	1/2N	0	1/8	6-1/4	10.5	4
30	105	18436572	VD	TDC	.016	30	CH	N-12Y	.035	1/2N	0	1/8	6-1/4	14	4
30	105	18436572	VD	TDC	.016	30	CH	N-12Y	.035	1/2N	0	1/8	6-1/4	13	4
30	105	18436572	VD	TDC	.016	30	CH	N-12Y	.035	0	0	1/8	6-1/2	13	4

16 – Auto. Trans. – 2 BTDC.
17 – Auto. Trans. – 14 BTDC.
18 – Auto. Trans. – 12 BTDC.
19 – Auto. Trans. – 7.5 BTDC.
20 – Auto. Trans. – 2.5 ATC.
21 – Coronet – 117 in.
22 – Auto. Trans. – 5 BTDC.
23 – Both Breakers – 37 to 42 deg.
24 – Man. Trans., Both Breakers – 37 to 42 deg.
25 – Fairlane, Torino – 116 in.
26 – Falcon – 110.9 in.
27 – Falcon, Fairlane – 1/2 P.
28 – Falcon, Fairlane – 1/4 P.

29 – Falcon, Fairlane – 1/4 in.
30 – Falcon, Fairlane – 7 deg.
31 – Ford – 119 in.
32 – Montego, Comet – 116 in.
33 – Montego, Comet – 1/2 P.
34 – Montego, Comet – 1/4 P.
35 – Montego, Comet – 1/4 in.
36 – Montego, Comet – 7 deg.
37 – Auto. Trans. – 6 BTDC.
38 – Rear Main – 120 ft. lbs.
39 – Auto. Trans. – 2.5 ATC.
40 – Belvedere – 116 in.
41 – Auto. Trans. – 5 BTDC.

42 – Fury – 119 in.
43 – Both Breakers – 37 to 42 deg.
44 – Fury – 9 deg.
45 – Man. Trans., Both Breakers – 37 to 42 deg.
46 – Firebird – 108.1 in.
47 – Firebird – 1/2 P.
48 – Firebird – 3/16 in.
49 – Firebird – 8-3/4 deg.
50 – Executive – 124 in.
51 – Grand Prix – 121 in.
52 – Javelin – 109 in.
53 – Ambassador – 118 in.

1969

	Wheelbase	No. of Cylinders Bore and Stroke	Displacement (cu. in.)	Valve and Cylinder Arrangement	Compression Pressure (lbs.)	Maximum Brake Horsepower	Valve Tappet Clearance Intake	Valve Tappet Clearance Exhaust	Cylinder Bolt Torque (ft. lbs.)
Buick – Special Deluxe, Skylark	116[1]	6–3.875x3.53	250	IO	165	155@4200	HY	HY	95
Special Deluxe Wagon, Skylark Custom	116[1]	8–3.80x3.85	350	VO	175	230@4400	HY	HY	75
Special Deluxe Wagon, Skylark Custom	116[1]	8–3.80x3.85	350	VO	175	280@4600	HY	HY	75
Sportwagon	121	8–3.80x3.85	350	VO	175	230@4400	HY	HY	75
Sportwagon, GS "350"	121[1]	8–3.80x3.85	350	VO	175	280@4600	HY	HY	75
Sportwagon "400", GS "400"	121[1]	8–4.040x3.90	400	VO	175	340@5000	HY	HY	100
LeSabre	123	8–3.80x3.85	350	VO	175	230@4400	HY	HY	75
Wildcat, Electra "225"	123[3]	8–4.1875x3.90	430	VO	195	360@5000	HY	HY	100
Riviera	119	8–4.1875x3.90	430	VO	195	360@5000	HY	HY	100
Cadillac	129.5[4]	8–4.3x4.06	472	VO	175	375@4400	HY	HY	115
Eldorado	120	8–4.3x4.06	472	VO	175	375@4400	HY	HY	115
Chevrolet, Chevelle	119[6]	6–3.875x3.53	250	IO	130	155@4200	HY	HY	95
Chevrolet	119	8–4.001x3.25	327	VO	160	235@4800	HY	HY	65
Chevrolet	119	8–4.00x3.48	350	VO	160	255@4800	HY	HY	95
Chevrolet, Chevelle	119[6]	8–4.00x3.48	350	VO	160	300@4800	HY	HY	95
Chevrolet	119	8–4.094x3.76	396	VO	160	265@4800	HY	HY	80
Chevrolet	119	8–4.251x3.76	427	VO	160	335@4800	HY	HY	80
Chevrolet	119	8–4.251x3.76	427	VO	160	390@5400	HY	HY	80
Chevelle	112[6]	6–3.875x3.25	230	IO	130	140@4400	HY	HY	95
Chevelle	112[6]	8–3.875x3.25	307	VO	150	200@4600	HY	HY	65
Chevelle	112[6]	8–4.00x3.48	350	VO	160	250@4800	HY	HY	95
Chevelle	112[6]	8–4.094x3.76	396	VO	160	325@4800	HY	HY	80
Chevelle	112[6]	8–4.094x3.76	396	VO	160	350@5200	HY	HY	80
Corvette, Camaro	98[13]	8–4.00x3.48	350	VO	160	300@4800	HY	HY	95
Corvette	98	8–4.00x3.48	350	VO	160	350@5600	HY	HY	95
Corvette	98	8–4.251x3.76	427	VO	160	390@5400 [19]	HY	HY	80
Corvette	98	8–4.251x3.76	427	VO	150	435@5400	.024	.028	80
Chevy Nova	111	4–3.875x3.25	153	IO	130	90@4000	HY	HY	95
Nova, Camaro	111[13]	6–3.875x3.25	230	IO	130	140@4400	HY	HY	95
Nova, Camaro	111[13]	6–3.875x3.53	250	IO	130	155@4200	HY	HY	95
Nova, Camaro	111[13]	8–3.875x3.25	307	VO	150	200@4600	HY	HY	65
Nova, Camaro	111[13]	8–4.00x3.48	350	VO	160	250@4800	HY	HY	95
Camaro	108	8–4.094x3.76	396	VO	160	325@4800	HY	HY	80
Corvair, Monza	108	6–3.4375x2.94	164	HO	130	95@3600	HY	HY	40
Corvair, Monza	108	6–3.4375x2.94	164	HO	130	110@4400 [21]	HY	HY	40
Chrysler – Newport	124	8–4.25x3.38	383	VO	140	290@4400	HY	HY	70
Newport	124	8–4.25x3.38	383	VO	140	330@5000	HY	HY	70
New Yorker, 300	124	8–4.32x3.75	440	VO	150	350@4400	HY	HY	70
New Yorker, 300, Newport	124	8–4.32x3.75	440	VO	150	375@4600	HY	HY	70
Imperial	127	8–4.32x3.75	440	VO	150	350@4400	HY	HY	70
Dodge – Dart, Dart GT	111	6–3.4x3.125	170	IO	125	115@4400	.010	.020	65
Dart, Dart GT, Coronet, Charger	111[27]	6–3.4x4.125	225	IO	125	145@4000	.010	.020	65
Dart, Dart GT	111	8–3.63x3.31	273	VO	135	190@4400	HY	HY	85
Dart, Dart GT, Coronet, Charger	111[27]	8–3.91x3.31	318	VO	135	230@4400	HY	HY	85
Dart, Dart GT, GTS, Swinger	111	8–4.04x3.31	340	VO	140	275@5000	HY	HY	95
Dart, Dart GT, GTS, Coronet, Charger	111[27]	8–4.25x3.38	383	VO	140	330@5200	HY	HY	70
Coronet, Charger	117	8–4.25x3.38	383	VO	140	290@4400	HY	HY	70
Coronet, Coronet R/T, Charger, Charger R/T	117	8–4.25x3.75	426	VO	150	425@5000	.028	.032	75
Coronet R/T, Charger R/T	117	8–4.32x3.75	440	VO	150	375@4000	HY	HY	70
Super Bee	117	8–4.25x3.38	383	VO	140	335@5000	HY	HY	70
Polara	122	8–3.91x3.31	318	VO	135	230@4400	HY	HY	85
Polara, Monaco	122	8–4.25x3.38	383	VO	140	290@4400	HY	HY	70
Polara, Monaco	122	8–4.25x3.38	383	VO	140	330@5000	HY	HY	70
Polara, Monaco	122	8–4.32x3.75	440	VO	150	350@4400	HY	HY	70
Polara, Monaco	122	8–4.32x3.75	440	VO	150	375@4600	HY	HY	70
Ford – Falcon	110.9	6–3.50x2.94	170	IO	175	100@4000	HY	HY	75
Falcon, Mustang	110.9[30]	6–3.682x3.126	200	IO	175	115@3800	HY	HY	75
Falcon, Mustang	110.9[30]	8–4.0x3.0	302	VO	150	220@4600	HY	HY	72
Fairlane, Torino, Mustang	116[30]	6–3.682x3.91	250	IO	175	155@4000	HY	HY	75
Fairlane, Torino, Mustang	116[30]	8–4.0x3.50	351	VO	180	250@4600	HY	HY	105
Fairlane, Torino, Mustang	116[30]	8–4.0x3.50	351	VO	180	290@4800	HY	HY	105
Fairlane, Torino, Mustang	116[30]	8–4.052x3.784	390	VO	190	320@4600	HY	HY	90
Fairlane, Torino, Mustang	116[30]	8–4.132x3.984	428	VO	190	335@5200 [38]	HY	HY	90
Fairlane, Torino, Ford	116[34]	8–4.0x3.0	302	VO	150	220@4600	HY	HY	72
Ford	121	6–4.0x3.18	240	IO	175	150@4000	HY	HY	75

ABBREVIATIONS – FOOTNOTES

AC – AC Spark Plugs
ATC – After Top Center
BF – Autolite Spark Plugs
BTDC – Before Top Dead Center
C – Cold Engine
CC – Timing Case Cover
CH – Champion Spark Plugs
CP – Crankshaft Pulley
H – Hot Engine

HO – Horizontal Opposed Cylinders
HY – Hydraulic Valve Lifters
IO – In-Line Engine, Overhead Valves
IOC – In-Line Engine, Overhead Cam
MP – Magnetic Pulse Ignition
N – Negative
NA – Not Applicable
P – Positive
TDC – Top Dead Center
VD – Vibration Damper
VO – V-Type Engine, Overhead Valves

1 – 2 Door – 112 in.
2 – Sportwagon – CP
3 – Electra "225" – 126.2 in.
4 – 60 and Brougham – 133 in.,
   75 – 149.8 in.
5 – 75 – 24.8 qts.
6 – Chevelle 2-Door – 112 in.,
   4-Door – 116 in.
7 – Auto. Trans. – 4 deg. BTDC
8 – Chevelle – Caster 1N., Camber 1/2P.
9 – Chevelle – 8-1/4 deg.

Tuneup Specifications

Connecting Rod Bolt Torque (ft. lbs.)	Main Bearing Bolt Torque (ft. lbs.)	Firing Order	Timing Mark Location	Breaker Point Opens BTDC	Breaker Point Gap	Cam Angle	Spark Plugs Make	Spark Plugs Model	Spark Plugs Gap	Caster Man. Steer. (deg.)	Camber Rt. Wheel (deg.)	Toe-in (in.)	Steering Axis Inclination (deg.)	Cooling System Capacity (qts.)	Crankcase Capacity (qts.)
35	65	153624	VD	TDC	.019	33	AC	R46N	.035	1/2N	1/2P	3/16	8	11.3	4
35	110	18436572	CP	TDC	.016	30	AC	R45TS	.030	1/2N	1/2P	3/16	8	13.5	4
35	110	18436572	CP	TDC	.016	30	AC	R45TS	.030	1/2N	1/2P	3/16	8	13.5	4
35	110	18436572	CP	TDC	.016	30	AC	R45TS	.030	1/2N	1/2P	3/16	8	13.5	4
45	110	18436572	VD[2]	TDC	.016	30	AC	R44TS	.030	1/2N	1/2P	3/16	8	16.2	4
35	110	18436572	VD	TDC	.016	30	AC	R45TS	.030	3/4P	0	1/4	10-3/4	13.2	4
45	110	18436572	VD	TDC	.016	30	AC	R44TS	.030	3/4P	0	1/4	10-3/4	16.7	4
45	110	18436572	VD	TDC	.016	30	AC	R44TS	.030	1P	1/4P	1/4	10-3/4	16.7	4
40	90	15634278	CP	7.5	.016	30	AC	R46N	.035	1N	0	1/16	6	21.3[5]	4
40	90	15634278	CP	7.5	.016	30	AC	R46N	.035	2N	0	1/16	6	21.3	5
35	65	153624	VD	TDC[7]	.019	33	AC	R46N	.035	3/4P[8]	1/4P[8]	3/16	7-1/2[9]	12[10]	4
50	80	18436572	VD	2ATC[11]	.019	30	AC	R45S	.035	3/4P	1/4P	3/16	7-1/2	17	4
50	80	18436572	VD	TDC[7]	.019	30	AC	R44S	.035	3/4P	1/4P	3/16	7-1/2	15	4
50	80	18436572	VD	TDC[7]	.019	30	AC	R44S	.035	3/4P[9]	1/4P[9]	3/16	7-1/2[9]	15[12]	4
50	95[18]	18436572	VD	TDC[7]	.019	30	AC	R44N	.035	3/4P	1/4P	3/16	7-1/2	23	4
50	95[18]	18436572	VD	4	.019	29	AC	R44N	.035	3/4P	1/4P	3/16	7-1/2	22	4
50	95[18]	18436572	VD	4	.019	29	AC	R43N	.035	3/4P	1/4P	3/16	7-1/2	22	4
35	65	153624	VD	TDC[7]	.019	33	AC	R46N	.035	1N	1/2P	3/16	8-1/4	13	4
50	80	18436572	VD	2	.019	30	AC	R45S	.035	1N	1/2P	3/16	8-1/4	17	4
50	80	18436572	VD	2	.019	30	AC	R45S	.035	1N	1/2P	3/16	8-1/4	16	4
50	95[18]	18436572	VD	4	.019	29	AC	R44N	.035	1N	1/2P	3/16	8-1/4	23	4
50	95[18]	18436572	VD	4	.019	29	AC	R43N	.035	1N	1/2P	3/16	8-1/4	23	4
50	80	18436572	VD	4	.019	30	AC	R44S	.035	1P[14]	3/4P[15]	1/8[16]	7[17]	15[12]	4
50	80	18436572	VD	8	.019	30	AC	R44	.035	1P[14]	3/4P	1/8	7	15	4
50	95[18]	18436572	VD	4	.019	29	AC	R43N	.035	1P[14]	3/4P	1/8	7	22	5
50	95[18]	18436572	VD	4	MP	30	AC	R43N	.035	1P[14]	3/4P	1/8	7	22	5
35	65	1342	VD	TDC[7]	.019	33	AC	R46N	.035	1/2P	1/4P	3/16	8-3/4	9	3.5
35	65	153624	VD	TDC[7]	.019	33	AC	R46N	.035	1/2P	1/4P	3/16	8-3/4	13	4
35	65	153624	VD	TDC[7]	.019	33	AC	R46N	.035	1/2P	1/4P	3/16	8-3/4	13	4
50	80	18436572	VD	2	.019	30	AC	R45S	.035	1/2P	1/4P	3/16	8-3/4	17	4
50	80	18436572	VD	TDC[7]	.019	30	AC	R44S	.035	1/2P	1/4P	3/16	8-3/4	16	4
50	95[18]	18436572	VD	4	.019	29	AC	R44N	.035	1/2P	1/4P	3/16	8-3/4	23	4
25	55	145236	CP	6[20]	.019	33	AC	R44FF	.031	2-1/4P	1P	1/4	6-1/2	NA	4
25	55	145236	VD	4[22]	.019	33	AC	R44FF	.031	2-1/4P	1P	1/4	6-1/2	NA	4
45	85	18436572	VD	TDC[23]	.016	33	CH	J-14Y	.035	1/2N	1/4P	1/8	9	16	4
45	85	18436572	VD	5	.016	33	CH	J-11Y	.035	1/2N	1/4P	1/8	9	16	4
45	85	18436572	VD	7.5	.016	33	CH	J-13Y	.035	1/2N	1/4P	1/8	9	17	4
45	85	18436572	VD	5	.016	33	CH	J-11Y	.035	1/2N	1/4P	1/8	9	17	4
45	85	18436572	VD	7.5	.016	33	CH	J-13Y	.035	3/4P	1/4P	1/8	9	19	4
45	85	153624	VD	2.5ATC[25]	.020	44	CH	N-14Y	.035	1/2N[26]	1/4P	1/8	7-1/2	12	4
45	85	153624	VD	TDC	.020	44	CH	N-14Y	.035	1/2N[26]	1/4P	1/8	7-1/2	13	4
45	85	18436572	VD	2ATC	.016	32	CH	N-14Y	.035	1/2N[26]	1/4P	1/8	7-1/2	17	4
45	85	18436572	VD	TDC[27]	.016	30[28]	CH	N-9Y	.035	1/2N[26]	1/4P	1/8	7-1/2	16	4
45	85	18436572	VD	TDC[27]	.016	30[28]	CH	J-11Y	.035	1/2N[26]	1/4P	1/8	7-1/2	16	4
45	85	18436572	VD	7.5	.016	32	CH	J-14Y	.035	1/2N[26]	1/4P	1/8	7-1/2	16	4
45	100	18436572	VD	TDC	.016	30[28]	CH	J-11Y	.035	1/2N[26]	1/4P	1/8	7-1/2	18	5
45	85	18436572	VD	TDC[27]	.016	30[29]	CH	N-10Y	.035	1/2N[26]	1/4P	1/8	7-1/2	18	4
45	85	18436572	VD	TDC[27]	.016	30[28]	CH	J-11Y	.035	1/2N[26]	1/4P	1/8	7-1/2	16	4
45	85	18436572	VD	TDC	.016	32	CH	N-14Y	.035	1/2N	1/4P	1/8	9	16	4
45	85	18436572	VD	TDC[23]	.016	32	CH	J-14Y	.035	1/2N	1/4P	1/8	9	16	4
45	85	18436572	VD	5	.016	32	CH	J-11Y	.035	1/2N	1/4P	1/8	9	16	4
45	85	18436572	VD	7.5	.016	32	CH	J-13Y	.035	1/2N	1/4P	1/8	9	17	4
45	85	18436572	VD	5	.016	32	CH	J-11Y	.035	1/2N	1/4P	1/8	9	17	4
24	70	153624	CC	6	.027	37	BF	82	.034	3/4N	1/4P	1/4	7	9.3	3.5
24	70	153624	CC	6	.027	37	BF	82	.034	3/4N[31]	1/4P[31]	1/4[32]	7[33]	9.1	3.5
24	70	15426378	VD	6	.021	27	BF	42	.034	3/4N[31]	1/4P[31]	1/4[32]	7[33]	13.5	4
26	70	153624	CC	6	.027	37	BF	82	.034	0[31]	1/4P[31]	1/4[32]	7[33]	9.9	4
45	70	13726548	VD	6	.017	28	BF	32	.034	0[31]	1/4P[31]	1/4[32]	7[33]	14.6	4
45	70	13726548	VD	6	.017	28	BF	32	.034	0[31]	1/4P[31]	1/4[32]	7[33]	14.6	4
45	105	15426378	VD	6	.017	28	BF	42	.034	0[31]	1/4P[31]	1/4[32]	7[33]	19.9	4
45	105	15426378	VD	6	.017	28	BF	32	.034	0[31]	1/4P[31]	1/4[32]	7[33]	19.6	4
24	70	15426378	VD	6	.021	27	BF	42	.034	0[35]	1/4P[35]	1/4[32]	7[36]	13.5[37]	4
45	70	153624	CC	6	.027	37	BF	42	.034	1P	1/2P	3/16	7-3/4	14.3	4

10 – Chevelle – 13 qts.
11 – Auto. Trans. – 6 deg. BTDC
12 – Chevelle, Camaro – 16 qts.
13 – Camaro – 108 in.
14 – Corvette Power Steering – 2-1/4P.
15 – Camaro – Caster 1/2P., Camber 1/4P.
16 – Camaro – 3/16 in.
17 – Camaro – 8-3/4 deg.
18 – 4-Bolt Cap – 105 ft. lbs.
19 – Also 400@5400
20 – Auto. Trans. – 14 deg. BTDC

21 – Also 140@5200
22 – Auto. Trans. – 12 deg. BTDC, 140 hp – 4 deg. BTDC
23 – Auto. Trans. – 7.5 deg. BTDC
24 – Coronet, Charger – 117 in.
25 – Auto. Trans. – TDC
26 – Power Steering – 3/4P.
27 – Auto Trans. – 5 deg. BTDC
28 – Both Breakers – 37 to 42 deg.
29 – Both Breakers – 37 to 42 deg., Auto. Trans. – 30 to 35 deg.

30 – Mustang – 108 in.
31 – Mustang – Caster 1/4P., Camber 1P.
32 – Mustang, Ford – 3/16 in.
33 – Mustang – 6-3/4 deg.
34 – Ford – 121 in.
35 – Ford – Caster 1P., Camber 1/2P.
36 – Ford – 7-3/4 deg.
37 – Ford – 15.4 qts.
38 – Also Ram Air

1969

	Wheelbase	No. of Cylinders Bore and Stroke	Displacement (cu. in.)	Valve and Cylinder Arrangement	Compression Pressure (lbs.)	Maximum Brake Horsepower	Valve Tappet Clearance		Cylinder Bolt Torque (ft. lbs.)
							Intake	Exhaust	
Ford	121	8-4.0x3.5	351	VO	180	250@4600	HY	HY	105
Ford	121	8-4.052x3.784	390	VO	190	265@4400	HY	HY	90
Ford	121	8-4.362x3.59	429	VO	190	320@4400	HY	HY	90
Ford, Thunderbird	121[1]	8-4.362x3.59	429	VO	190	360@4600	HY	HY	90
Lincoln Continental	126[2]	8-4.362x3.85	460	VO	180	365@4600	HY	HY	140
Mercury – Comet, Montego, Cyclone	116	6-3.682x3.91	250	IO	175	155@4000	HY	HY	75
Comet, Montego, Cyclone	116	8-4.00x3.00	302	VO	150	220@4600	HY	HY	72
Comet, Montego, Cyclone	116	8-4.002x3.50	351	VO	180	250@4600[6]	HY	HY	105
Comet, Montego, Cyclone	116	8-4.052x3.784	390	VO	190	320@4600	HY	HY	90
Comet, Montego, Cyclone	116	8-4.132x3.984	428	VO	190	335@5200[7]	HY[8]	HY[8]	90
Cougar, Cougar GT	111	8-4.002x3.50	351	VO	180	250@4600[6]	HY	HY	105
Cougar, Cougar GT	111	8-4.052x3.784	390	VO	190	320@4600	HY	HY	90
Cougar, Cougar GT	111	8-4.132x3.984	428	VO	190	335@5200[7]	HY	HY	90
Mercury (Except Brougham)	124	8-4.052x3.784	390	VO	190	265@4600[10]	HY	HY	90
Mercury (All)	124	8-4.362x3.59	429	VO	190	320@4400[11]	HY	HY	90
Oldsmobile – F-85, Cutlass	116[12]	6-3.875x3.53	250	IO	160	155@4200	HY	HY	95
F-85, Cutlass	116[12]	8-4.057x3.385	350	VO	175	250@4400[13]	HY	HY	80
F-85, Cutlass	116[12]	8-4.057x3.385	350	VO	175	325@5400	HY	HY	80
4-4-2	112	8-3.87x4.25	400	VO	175	350@4800	HY	HY	80
4-4-2	112	8-3.87x4.25	400	VO	175	325@4600[18]	HY	HY	80
Delta 88	124	8-4.057x3.305	350	VO	175	250@4400	HY	HY	80
Delta 88	124	8-4.125x4.25	455	VO	175	310@4200	HY	HY	80
Delta 88	124	8-4.125x4.25	455	VO	175	365@4600[20]	HY	HY	80
Ninety Eight	127	8-4.125x4.25	455	VO	175	365@4600	HY	HY	80
Toronado	119	8-4.126x4.25	455	VO	175	375@4600[22]	HY	HY	80
Plymouth – Valiant, Signet	108	6-3.40x3.125	170	IO	125	115@4400	.010H	.020H	65
Valiant, Signet, Belvedere, Barracuda	108[23]	6-3.40x4.125	225	IO	125	145@4000	.010H	.020H	65
Valiant, Signet	108	8-3.63x3.31	273	VO	135	190@4400	HY	HY	85
Valiant, Signet, Belvedere, Barracuda	108[23]	8-3.91x3.31	318	VO	135	230@4400	HY	HY	85
Barracuda	108	8-4.04x3.31	340	VO	140	275@5000	HY	HY	95
Belvedere	116	8-4.25x3.38	383	VO	140	290@4400	HY	HY	70
Belvedere Road Runner	116	8-4.25x3.38	383	VO	140	335@5200	HY	HY	70
Belvedere, Barracuda	116[27]	8-4.25x3.38	383	VO	140	330@5000	HY	HY	70
Belvedere	116	8-4.25x3:75	426	VO	150	425@4000	.028C	.032C	75
Belvedere, Fury, VIP	116[29]	8-4.32x3.75	440	VO	150	375@4600	HY	HY	70
Fury I, II, III	120	6-3.40x4.125	225	IO	125	145@4000	.010H	.020H	65
Fury, Sport Fury, VIP	120	8-3.91x3.31	318	VO	135	230@4400	HY	HY	85
Fury, Sport Fury, VIP	120	8-4.25x3.38	383	VO	140	290@4400	HY	HY	70
Fury, Sport Fury, VIP	120	8-4.25x3.38	383	VO	140	330@5000	HY	HY	70
Pontiac – Tempest, LeMans	116[32]	6-3.875x3.525	250	IOC	160[34]	175@4800[33]	HY	HY	95
Tempest, LeMans	116[32]	8-3.875x3.746	350	VO	160	265@4600[35]	HY	HY	95
GTO	112	8-4.12x3.746	400	VO	160	265@4600	HY	HY	95
GTO	112	8-4.12x3.746	400	VO	160	350@5000	HY	HY	95
GTO	112	8-4.12x3.746	400	VO	160	366@5100[36]	HY	HY	95
Firebird	112	6-3.875x3.525	250	IOC	160	175@4800	HY	HY	95
Firebird	112	8-3.875x3.746	350	VO	160	325@5100	HY	HY	95
Firebird	112	8-4.12x3.746	400	VO	160	330@4800[37]	HY	HY	95
Firebird	112	8-4.12x3.746	400	VO	160	345@5400	HY	HY	95
Grand Prix	118	8-4.12x3.746	400	VO	160	265@4600	HY	HY	95
Grand Prix	118	8-4.12x3.746	400	VO	160	350@5000	HY	HY	95
Grand Prix	118	8-4.12x3.996	428	VO	200	370@4800[38]	HY	HY	95
Catalina, Executive, Bonneville	122[39]	8-4.12x3.746	400	VO	160	265@4600	HY	HY	95
Catalina, Executive, Bonneville	122[39]	8-4.12x3.746	400	VO	160	290@4600	HY	HY	95
Catalina, Executive	122[39]	8-4.12x3.746	400	VO	160	340@4800	HY	HY	95
Catalina, Executive, Bonneville	122[39]	8-4.12x3.996	428	VO	200	360@4600	HY	HY	95
Catalina, Executive, Bonneville	122[39]	8-4.12x3.996	428	VO	200	390@5200	HY	HY	95
Rambler	106	6-3.75x3.0	199	IO	145	128@4400	HY	HY	85
Rambler, Javelin, AMX	106[42]	6-3.75x3.50	232	IO	145	145@4300	HY	HY	85
Rambler, Javelin, AMX	106[42]	8-3.75x3.28	290	VO	145	200@4600	HY	HY	100
Rambler, Javelin, AMX	106[42]	8-3.75x3.28	290	VO	145	225@4700	HY	HY	100
Rebel, Ambassador	114[43]	6-3.75x3.50	232	IO	145	145@4300[44]	HY	HY	85
Rebel, Ambassador	114[43]	8-3.75x3.28	290	VO	145	200@4600	HY	HY	100
Rebel, Ambassador	114[43]	8-4.08x3.28	343	VO	145	235@4400[45]	HY	HY	100
Ambassador	122	8-4.165x3.574	390	VO	145	315@4600	HY	HY	100
Javelin, AMX	109[42]	8-4.165x3.574	390	VO	145	315@4600	HY	HY	100

ABBREVIATIONS – FOOTNOTES

AC – AC Spark Plugs
ATC – After Top Center
BF – Autolite Spark Plug
BTDC – Before Top Dead Center
C – Cold Engine
CC – Timing Case Cover
CH – Champion Spark Plugs
CP – Crankshaft Pulley
H – Hot Engine
HO – Horizontal Opposed

HY – Hydraulic Valve Lifters
IO – In-Line Engine, Overhead Valves
IOC – In-Line Engine, Overhead Cam
MP – Magnetic Pulse Ignition
N – Negative
NA – Not Applicable
P – Positive
TDC – Top Dead Center
VD – Vibration Damper
VO – V-Type Engine – Overhead Valves
1 – T-Bird – 2-Door, 114.7 in., 4-Door, 117.2 in.

2 – Continental Mark III – 117.2 in.
3 – Continental Mark III – 1P
4 – Continental Mark III – 3/16 in.
5 – Continental Mark III – 7-3/4 deg.
6 – Also 290@4800
7 – Also Ram Air
8 – X-70 – .025 in. H.
9 – 290 hp – BF32
10 – Also 280@4400
11 – Also 360@4600
12 – Coupe, Convertible – 112 in.
13 – Also 310@4800

Tuneup Specifications

Connecting Rod Bolt Torque (ft. lbs.)	Main Bearing Bolt Torque (ft. lbs.)	Firing Order	Timing Mark Location	Breaker Point Opens BTDC	Breaker Point Gap	Cam Angle	Spark Plugs Make	Spark Plugs Model	Spark Plugs Gap	Caster Man. Steer. (deg.)	Camber Rt. Wheel (deg.)	Toe-in (in.)	Steering Axis Inclination (deg.)	Cooling System Capacity (qts.)	Crankcase Capacity (qts.)
45	70	13726548	VD	6	.017	28	BF	42	.034	1P	1/2P	3/16	7-3/4	15.4	4
45	105	15426378	VD	6	.017	28	BF	42	.034	1P	1/2P	3/16	7-3/4	20.1	4
45	105	15426378	VD	6	.016	28	BF	42	.034	1P	1/2P	3/16	7-3/4	18.6	4
45	105	15426378	VD	6	.016	28	BF	42	.034	1P	1/2P	3/16	7-3/4	18.6	4
45	105	15426378	VD	10	.017	28	BF	42	.034	1-1/2N[3]	1/2P	1/8[4]	7[5]	19.5	4
26	70	153624	CC	6	.027	37	BF	82	.034	0	1/4P	1/4	7	9.9	4
24	70	15426378	VD	6	.021	28	BF	42	.034	0	1/4P	1/4	7	13.5	4
45	70	13726548	VD	6	.021	28	BF	42	.034	0	1/4P	1/4	7	14.6	4
45	105	15426378	VD	6	.017	28	BF	42	.034	0	1/4P	1/4	7	19.9	4
45	105	15426378	VD	6	.016	28	BF	32	.034	0	1/4P	1/4	7	19.6	4
45	70	13726548	VD	6	.017	28	BF	42[9]	.034	1/4P	1P	3/16	6-3/4	14.6	4
45	105	15426378	VD	6	.017	28	BF	42	.034	1/4P	1P	3/16	6-3/4	20.1	4
45	105	15426378	VD	6	.017	28	BF	32	.034	1/4P	1P	3/16	6-3/4	19.3	4
45	105	15426378	VD	6	.017	28	BF	42	.034	1P	1/4P	3/16	7-1/2	20.1	4
45	105	15426378	VD	6	.018	28	BF	42	.034	1P	1/4P	3/16	7-1/2	19.7	4
35	65	153624	VD	TDC[15]	.016	33	AC	R46N	.035	1-1/4N	1/8P	3/16	9	10.1	4
42	80[14]	18436572	VD	6[16]	.016	30	AC	R45S	.030	1-1/4N	1/8P	3/16	9	22	4
42	80[14]	18436572	VD	12	.016	30	AC	R44S	.030	1-1/4N	1/8P	3/16	9	22	4
42	120	18436572	VD	2[17]	.016	30	AC	R44S	.030	1-1/4N	1/8P	3/16	9	16.2	4
42	120	18436572	VD	8[19]	.016	30	AC	R44S	.030	1-1/4N	1/8P	3/16	9	16.2	4
42	120	18436572	VD	6	.016	30	AC	R45S	.030	1N	3/8N	3/16	11	17.5	4
42	120	18436572	VD	6	.016	30	AC	R45S	.030	1N	3/8N	3/16	11	17.5	4
42	120	18436572	VD	6[21]	.016	30	AC	R43S	.030	1N	3/8N	3/16	11	17.5	4
42	120	18436572	VD	8	.016	30	AC	R44S	.030	1N	1/8P	3/16	11	17.5	4
42	120	18436572	VD	8	.016	30	AC	R44S	.030	2N	1/8P	0	18	18	5
45	85	153624	VD	2.5ATC[24]	.020	45	CH	N14Y	.035	1/2N	1/4P	1/8	7-1/2	12	4
45	85	153624	VD	TDC	.020	45	CH	N14Y	.035	1/2N	1/4P	1/8	7-1/2	13[32]	4
45	85	18436572	VD	2.5ATC	.017	33	CH	N14Y	.035	1/2N	1/4P	1/8	7-1/2	17[33]	4
45	85	18436572	VD	TDC	.017	33	CH	N14Y	.035	1/2N	1/4P	1/8	7-1/2	17[33]	4
45	85	18436572	VD	TDC[25]	.020	30[26]	CH	N9Y	.035	1/2N	1/4P	1/8	7-1/2	16	4
45	85	18436572	VD	TDC[25]	.017	33	CH	J14Y	.035	1/2N	1/4P	1/8	7-1/2	16	4
45	85	18436572	VD	TDC[25]	.017	30[26]	CH	J11Y	.035	1/2N	1/4P	1/8	7-1/2	16	4
45	85	18436572	VD	TDC[25]	.017	30[26]	CH	J11Y	.035	1/2N	1/4P	1/8	7-1/2	16	4
45	100	18436572	VD	TDC	.017	30[26]	CH	N10Y	.035	1/2N	1/4P	1/8	7-1/2[31]	18	5
45	85	18436572	VD	5	.017	30[28]	CH	J11Y	.035	1/2N	1/4P	1/8	18	18	4
45	85	153624	VD	TDC	.020	45	CH	N14Y	.035	1/2N	1/4P	1/8	9	13	4
45	85	18436572	VD	TDC	.017	33	CH	N14Y	.035	1/2N	1/4P	1/8	9	16	4
45	85	18436572	VD	TDC[30]	.017	33	CH	J14Y	.035	1/2N	1/4P	1/8	9	16	4
45	85	18436572	VD	TDC[25]	.017	33	CH	J11Y	.035	1/2N	1/4P	1/8	9	16	4
33	100	153624	VD	TDC[40]	.016	33	AC	R44NS	.035	1-1/2N	1/4P	1/16	9	11.9	4.5
43	100[14]	18436572	CP	9	.016	30	AC	R45S	.035	1-1/2N	1/4P	1/16	9	19.9	5
43	100[14]	18436572	CP	9	.016	30	AC	R46S	.035	1-1/2N	1/4P	1/16	9	18.3	5
43	100[14]	18436572	CP	9	.016	30	AC	R45S	.035	1-1/2N	1/4P	1/16	9	18.3	5
43	100[14]	18436572	CP	15	.016	30	AC	R44S	.035	1-1/2N	1/4P	1/16	9	18.3	5
33	100	153624	VD	TDC[40]	.016	33	AC	R44NS	.035	1/2P	1/4P	3/16	8-3/4	11.8	4.5
43	100[14]	18436572	VD	9	.016	30	AC	R45S	.035	1/2P	1/4P	3/16	8-3/4	19.4	5
43	100[14]	18436572	VD	9	.016	30	AC	R44S	.035	1/2P	1/4P	3/16	8-3/4	18.6	5
43	100[14]	18436572	VD	15	.016	30	AC	R44S	.035	1/2P	1/4P	3/16	8-3/4	18.6	5
43	100[14]	18436572	CP	9	.016	30	AC	R46S	.035	1-1/2N	1/4P	1/16	9	18.7	5
43	100[14]	18436572	CP	9	.016	30	AC	R45S	.035	1-1/2N	1/4P	1/16	9	18.7	5
43	100[14]	18436572	CP	9	.016	30	AC	R44S	.035	1-1/2N	1/4P	1/16	9	17.5	5
43	100[14]	18436572	CP	9	.016	30	AC	R46S	.035	1-1/2N	1/4P	1/16	8-1/2	18[41]	5
43	100[14]	18436572	CP	9	.016	30	AC	R46S	.035	1-1/2N	1/4P	1/16	8-1/2	18[41]	5
43	100[14]	18436572	CP	9	.016	30	AC	R46S	.035	1-1/2N	1/4P	1/16	8-1/2	18	5
43	100[14]	18436572	CP	9	.016	30	AC	R45S	.035	1-1/2N	1/4P	1/16	8-1/2	18[41]	5
43	100[14]	18436572	CP	9	.016	30	AC	R44S	.035	1-1/2N	1/4P	1/16	8-1/2	18[41]	5
30	85	153624	VD	TDC[25]	.016	33	CH	N14Y	.035	0	0	1/8	6-1/2	10.5	4
30	85	153624	VD	TDC[25]	.016	33	CH	N14Y	.035	0	0	1/8	6-1/2	10.5	4
30	105	18436572	VD	TDC	.016	30	CH	N12Y	.035	0	0	1/8	6-1/2	14	4
30	105	18436572	VD	TDC	.016	30	CH	N12Y	.035	0	0	1/8	6-1/2	14	4
30	85	153624	VD	TDC	.016	33	CH	N14Y	.035	1/2N	0	1/8	6-1/4	10.5	4
30	105	18436572	VD	TDC	.016	30	CH	N12Y	.035	1/2N	0	1/8	6-1/4	14	4
30	105	18436572	VD	TDC	.016	30	CH	N12Y	.035	1/2N	0	1/8	6-1/4	13	4
30	105	18436572	VD	TDC	.016	30	CH	N12Y	.035	0	0	1/8	6-1/2	13	4

14 - Rear Main - 120 ft. lbs.
15 - Auto. Trans. - 4 deg. BTDC
16 - 310 hp - 8 deg. BTDC
17 - Auto. Trans. - 8 deg. BTDC
18 - Also 360@5400
19 - 360 hp, W-30 - 14 deg. BTDC
20 - Also GT - 390@5000
21 - 390 hp GT - 10 deg. BTDC
22 - Also W-34 - 400@4800
23 - Belvedere - 116 in.
24 - Auto. Trans. - TDC
25 - Auto. Trans. - 5 BTDC

26 - Both Breakers - 37 to 42 deg.
27 - Barracuda - 108 in.
28 - Both Breakers - 37 to 42 deg., Auto. Trans. - 30 to 35 deg.
29 - Fury, VIP - 120 in.
30 - Auto. Trans. - 7.5 deg. BTDC
31 - Fury, VIP - 9 deg.
32 - 2-Door - 112 in.
33 - Also 215@5200, 230@5400
34 - 215 and 230 hp - 195 ft. lbs.
35 - Also 330@5100
36 - Also 370@5500, Ram Air

37 - Also 335@5000
38 - Also 390@5200
39 - Executive, Bonneville - 125 in.
40 - 215 and 230 hp - 5 deg. BTDC
41 - Bonneville - 17.2 qts.
42 - Javelin - 109 in., AMX - 97 in.
43 - Ambassador - 122 in.
44 - Also 155@4400
45 - Also 280@4800

1970

	Wheelbase	No. of Cylinders Bore and Stroke	Displacement (cu. in.)	Valve and Cylinder Arrangement	Compression Pressure (lbs.)	Maximum Brake Horsepower	Valve Tappet Clearance Intake	Exhaust	Cylinder Bolt Torque (ft. lbs.)
American Motors – Hornet	108	6-3.75x3.0	199	IO	145	128@4400	HY	HY	80
Hornet, Javelin, Rebel	108[2]	6-3.75x3.50	232	IO	145	145@4300	HY	HY	80
Hornet, Rebel, Ambassador	108[2]	6-3.75x3.50	232	IO	145	155@4400	HY	HY	80
Hornet, Javelin, Rebel, Ambassador	108[2]	8-3.75x3.44	304	VO	145	210@4400	HY	HY	110
Javelin, Rebel, Ambassador	109[2]	8-4.08x3.44	360	VO	145	245@4400	HY	HY	110
Javelin, Rebel, Ambassador	109[2]	8-4.08x3.44	360	VO	145	290@4800	HY	HY	110
AMX	97	8-4.08x3.44	360	VO	145	290@4800	HY	HY	110
AMX, Javelin, Rebel, Ambassador	97[2]	8-4.165x3.574	390	VO	145	325@5000	HY	HY	110
Rebel (Machine)	114	8-4.165x3.574	390	VO	145	340@5100	HY	HY	110
Buick – Skylark	112[4]	6-3.875x3.53	250	IO	165	155@4400	HY	HY	95
Skylark, Custom, "350", Sportwagon	112[4]	8-3.80x3.85	350	VO	175	260@4600[5]	HY	HY	75
GS	112	8-3.80x3.85	350	VO	175	315@4800	HY	HY	75
GS "455"	112	8-4.3125x3.90	455	VO	175	350@4600[7]	HY	HY	100
LeSabre	124	8-3.80x3.85	350	VO	175	260@4600[5]	HY	HY	75
LeSabre "455", Wildcat Custom	124	8-4.3125x3.90	455	VO	175	370@4600	HY	HY	100
Electra "225"	127	8-4.3125x3.90	455	VO	175	370@4600	HY	HY	100
Riviera	119	8-4.3125x3.90	455	VO	175	370@4600	HY	HY	100
Cadillac	129.5[9]	8-4.30x4.06	472	VO	175	375@4400	HY	HY	115
Eldorado	120	8-4.30x4.304	500[12]	VO	175	400@4400	HY	HY	115
Chevrolet, Chevelle	119[11]	6-3.875x3.53	250	IO	130	155@4200	HY	HY	95
Chevelle	112[11]	8-3.875x3.25	307	VO	150	200@4600	HY	HY	65
Chevelle, Monte Carlo	112[11]	8-4.0x3.48	350	VO	160	250@4800[17]	HY	HY	65
Chevrolet	119	8-4.0x3.48	350	VO	160	250@4800[17]	HY	HY	65
Chevrolet	119	8-4.125x3.75	400	VO	160	265@4400	HY	HY	65
Monte Carlo	116	8-4.125x3.75	400	VO	160	265@4400	HY	HY	65
Monte Carlo, Chevelle	116[11]	8-4.126x3.76	402	VO	160	330@4800	HY	HY	80[18]
Chevelle SS 396	112	8-4.126x3.76	402	VO	160	350@5200	HY	HY	80[18]
Chevrolet	119	8-4.251x4.0	454	VO	160	345@4400	HY	HY	80[18]
Monte Carlo	116	8-4.251x4.0	454	VO	160	360@4400	HY	HY	80[18]
Chevrolet	119	8-4.251x4.0	454	VO	160	390@4800	HY	HY	80[18]
Chevy Nova	111	4-3.875x3.25	153	IO	130	90@4000	HY	HY	95
Nova, Camaro	111[19]	6-3.875x3.25	230	IO	130	140@4400	HY	HY	95
Nova, Camaro	111[19]	6-3.875x3.53	250	IO	130	155@4200	HY	HY	95
Nova, Camaro	111[19]	8-3.875x3.25	307	VO	150	200@4600	HY	HY	65
Nova, Camaro	111[19]	8-4.0x3.48	350	VO	160	250@4800[17]	HY	HY	65
Camaro SS	108	8-4.126x3.76	402	VO	160	325@4800	HY	HY	80[18]
Corvette	98	8-4.0x3.48	350	VO	160	300@4800	HY	HY	65
Corvette	98	8-4.0x3.48	350	VO	160	350@5600	HY	HY	65
Corvette	98	8-4.251x3.76	427	VO	160	390@5400[21]	HY	HY	80[18]
Corvette	98	8-4.251x3.76	427	VO	150	435@5800	.024H	.028H	80[18]
Chrysler – Newport, Custom	124	8-4.25x3.38	383	VO	140	290@4400[22]	HY	HY	70
New Yorker, 300	124	8-4.32x3.75	440	VO	150	350@4400	HY	HY	70
Newport, Custom, New Yorker, 300	124	8-4.32x3.75	440	VO	150	375@4600	HY	HY	70
Dodge – Dart, Swinger	111	6-3.4x3.64	198	IO	125	125@4400	.010H	.020H	65
Dart, Swinger, Coronet, Charger	111[27]	6-3.4x4.12	225	IO	125	145@4000	.010H	.020H	65
Dart, Swinger, Coronet, Charger	111[27]	8-3.91x3.31	318	VO	140	230@4400	HY	HY	85
Swinger 340, Challenger	111[28]	8-4.04x3.31	340	VO	150	275@5000	HY	HY	95
Coronet, Charger, Challenger	117[28]	8-4.25x3.38	383	VO	140	290@4400	HY	HY	70
Coronet, Challenger	117[28]	8-4.25x3.38	383	VO	150	330@5000	HY	HY	70
Coronet, Charger, Super Bee	117	8-4.25x3.38	383	VO	150	335@5200	HY	HY	70
Coronet R/T, Charger R/T, Super Bee	117	8-4.25x3.75	426	VO	150	425@5000	HY	HY	75
Coronet R/T, Charger R/T, Challenger R/T	117[28]	8-4.32x3.75	440	VO	150	375@4600	HY	HY	70
Coronet R/T, Charger R/T, Super Bee	117	8-4.32x3.75	440	VO	150	290@4700	HY	HY	70
Polara	122	8-3.91x3.31	318	VO	140	230@4400	HY	HY	85
Polara, Monaco	122	8-4.25x3.38	383	VO	140	290@4400	HY	HY	70
Polara, Monaco	122	8-4.32x3.75	440	VO	150	350@4700	HY	HY	70
Challenger	110	6-3.4x4.12	225	IO	125	145@4000	.010H	.020H	65
Challenger	110	8-3.91x3.31	318	VO	140	230@4400	HY	HY	85
Challenger, Challenger R/T	110	8-4.25x3.38	383	VO	150	335@5200	HY	HY	70
Challenger R/T	110	8-4.25x3.75	426	VO	150	425@5000	HY	HY	75
Challenger R/T	110	8-4.32x3.75	440	VO	150	390@4700	HY	HY	70
Ford – Falcon, Futura	110.9	6-3.682x3.126	200	IO	175	120@4000	HY	HY	75
Falcon, Futura	110.9	8-4.002x3.0	302	VO	150	220@4400	HY	HY	75
Maverick	103	6-3.502x2.94	170	IO	175	105@4200	HY	HY	75
Maverick	103	6-3.682x3.126	200	IO	175	120@4000	HY	HY	75

ABBREVIATIONS – FOOTNOTES

AC – AC Spark Plugs
BF – Autolite Spark Plugs
BTDC – Before Top Dead Center
C – Cold Engine
CF – Crankshaft Flange
CH – Champion Spark Plugs
CP – Crankshaft Pulley

H – Hot Engine
HY – Hydraulic Lifters
IO – In-Line Engine – Overhead Valves
MP – Magnetic Pulse Ignition
N – Negative
P – Positive
TDC – Top Dead Center
VD – Vibration Damper
VO – V-Type Engine – Overhead Valves

1 – Power Steering – 1P
2 – Javelin – 108 in., Rebel – 114 in., Ambassador – 122 in.
3 – Effective with Engine Code 209x26, 5 deg. BTDC on Earlier Engines
4 – Custom and 4-Door Sedans – 116 in.
5 – Also 285 and 315 hp
6 – Auto. Trans. – 4 deg. BTDC
7 – Also 360 hp

Tuneup Specifications

Connecting Rod Bolt Torque (ft. lbs.)	Main Bearing Bolt Torque (ft. lbs.)	Firing Order	Timing Mark Location	Breaker Point Opens BTDC	Breaker Point Gap	Cam Angle	Spark Plugs Make	Spark Plugs Model	Spark Plugs Gap	Caster Man. Steer. (deg.)	Camber Rt. Wheel (deg.)	Toe-in (in.)	Steering Axis Inclination (deg.)	Cooling System Capacity (qts.)	Crankcase Capacity (qts.)
28	80	153624	VD	3	.016	33	CH	N14Y	.035	0[1]	1P	1/8	7-3/4	10.5	4
28	80	153624	VD	3	.016	33	CH	N14Y	.035	0[1]	1P	1/8	7-3/4	10.5	4
28	80	153624	VD	3	.016	33	CH	N12Y	.035	0[1]	1P	1/8	7-3/4	10.5	4
28	100	18436572	VD	5	.016	30	CH	N12Y	.035	0[1]	1P	1/8	7-3/4	14	4
28	100	18436572	VD	5	.016	30	CH	N12Y	.035	0[1]	1P	1/8	7-3/4	13	4
28	100	18436572	VD	5	.016	30	CH	N12Y	.035	0[1]	1P	1/8	7-3/4	13	4
33	100	18436572	VD	TDC[3]	.016	30	CH	N12Y	.035	0[1]	1P	1/8	7-3/4	13	4
33	100	18436572	VD	TDC[3]	.016	30	CH	N10Y	.035	0[1]	1P	1/8	7-3/4	13	4
35	65	153624	VD	TDC[6]	.019	32	AC	R46N	.035	1/2N	1/2P	3/16	8	16	4
35	95	18436572	CF	6	.016	30	AC	R45TS	.030	1/2N	1/2P	3/16	8	16.5	4
35	95	18436572	VD	6	.016	30	AC	R45TS	.030	1/2N	1/2P	3/16	8	16.5	4
45	110	18436572	VD	6[8]	.016	30	AC	R44TS	.030	1/2N	1/2P	3/16	8	19	4
35	95	18436572	VD	6	.016	30	AC	R45TS	.030	3/4P	0	1/4	10-3/4	16	4
45	110	18436572	VD	6	.016	30	AC	R44TS	.030	3/4P	0	1/4	10-3/4	19.7	4
45	110	18436572	VD	6	.016	30	AC	R44TS	.030	3/4P	0	1/4	10-3/4	19.7	4
45	110	18436572	VD	6	.016	30	AC	R44TS	.030	1P	0	3/16	10-3/4	19.7	4
40	90	15634278	CP	7.5	.016	30	AC	R46N	.035	1N	0	3/16	6	21.3[10]	4
40	90	15634278	CP	7.5	.016	30	AC	R46N	.035	2N	0	1/16	11	21.3	5
35	65	153624	VD	TDC[6]	.019	33	AC	R46T	.035	3/4P[13]	1/4P[14]	3/16	7-1/2[15]	12	4
45	75[16]	18436572	VD	2	.019	30	AC	R45	.035	1N	1/2P	3/16	8	15	4
45	75[16]	18436572	VD	TDC	.019	30	AC	R44	.035	1N	1/2P	3/16	8	16	4
45	75[16]	18436572	VD	4	.019	30	AC	R44	.035	3/4P	1/4P	3/16	7-1/2	16	4
45	75[16]	18436572	VD	8	.019	30	AC	R44	.035	3/4P	1/4P	3/16	7-1/2	16	4
45	75[16]	18436572	VD	8	.019	30	AC	R44	.035	1N	1/2P	3/16	8	16	4
50	105	18436572	VD	4	.019	29	AC	R44T	.035	1N	1/2P	3/16	8	23	4
50	105	18436572	VD	TDC	.019	29	AC	R44T	.035	1N	1/2P	3/16	8	23	4
50	105	18436572	VD	6	.019	29	AC	R44T	.035	3/4P	1/4P	3/16	7-1/2	22	4
50	105	18436572	VD	4	.019	29	AC	R43T	.035	1N	1/2P	3/16	8	22	4
50	105	18436572	VD	6	.019	29	AC	R43T	.035	3/4P	1/4P	3/16	7-1/2	22	4
35	65	1342	VD	TDC	.019	33	AC	R46N	.035	1/2P	1/4P	3/16	8-3/4	9	3.5
35	65	153624	VD	TDC	.019	33	AC	R46N	.035	1/2P	1/4P	3/16	8-3/4	13	4
35	65	153624	VD	TDC	.019	33	AC	R46N	.035	1/2P	1/4P	3/16	8-3/4	13	4
45	75[16]	18436572	VD	2	.019	30	AC	R45S	.035	1/2P	1/4P	3/16	8-3/4	17	4
45	75[16]	18436572	VD	TDC	.019	30	AC	R44S	.035	1/2P	1/4P	3/16	8-3/4	16	4
50	105	18436572	VD	4	.019	29	AC	R44N	.035	1/2P	1/4P	3/16	8-3/4	23	4
45	75[16]	18436572	VD	4	.019	30	AC	R44S	.035	1P[20]	3/4P	1/8	7	15	4
45	75[16]	18436572	VD	8	.019	30	AC	R44	.035	1P[20]	3/4P	1/8	7	15	4
50	105	18436572	VD	4	.019	30	AC	43N	.035	1P[20]	3/4P	1/8	7	22	5
50	105	18436572	VD	4	MP	MP	AC	43N	.035	1P[20]	3/4P	1/8	7	22	5
45	85	18436572	VD	2.5[23]	.019	30.5	CH	J14Y[24]	.035	1/2N	1/4P	1/8	9	14.5[25]	4
45	85	18436572	VD	5	.019	30.5	CH	J13Y	.035	1/2N	1/4P	1/8	9	15.5	4
45	85	18436572	VD	TDC	.019	30.5	CH	J11Y	.035	1/2N	1/4P	1/8	9	15.5	6
45	85	153624	VD	TDC	.020	44	CH	N14Y	.035	1/2N[26]	1/4P	1/8	7-1/2	13	4
45	85	153624	VD	TDC	.020	44	CH	N14Y	.035	1/2N[26]	1/4P	1/8	7-1/2	13	4
45	85	18436572	VD	TDC	.017	32	CH	N14Y	.035	1/2N[26]	1/4P	1/8	7-1/2	16	4
45	85	18436572	VD	5	.017	32	CH	N9Y	.035	1/2N[26]	1/4P	1/8	7-1/2	15	4
45	85	18436572	VD	TDC[29]	.019	30.5	CH	J14Y	.035	1/2N[26]	1/4P	1/8	7-1/2	14.5	4
45	85	18436572	VD	TDC[29]	.019	30.5	CH	J11Y	.035	1/2N[26]	1/4P	1/8	7-1/2	14.5	4
75	100	18436572	VD	TDC[30]	.017	30[31]	CH	N10Y	.035	1/2N[26]	1/4P	1/8	7-1/2	17	5
45	85	18436572	VD	TDC[29]	.019	30.5	CH	J11Y	.035	1/2N[26]	1/4P	1/8	7-1/2	17	4
45	85	18436572	VD	5	.017	30[31]	CH	J11Y	.035	1/2N[26]	1/4P	1/8	7-1/2	17	4
45	85	18436572	VD	TDC	.017	32	CH	N14Y	.035	1/2N	1/4P	1/8	9	17	4
45	85	18436572	VD	TDC[29]	.019	30.5	CH	J14Y	.035	1/2N	1/4P	1/8	9	14.5	4
45	85	18436572	VD	5	.019	30.5	CH	J13Y	.035	1/2N	1/4P	1/8	9	15.5	4
45	85	153624	VD	TDC	.020	44	CH	N14Y	.035	1/2N[26]	1/4P	1/8	7-1/2	13	4
45	85	18436572	VD	TDC	.017	32	CH	N14Y	.035	1/2N[26]	1/4P	1/8	7-1/2	16	4
45	85	18436572	VD	TDC[29]	.019	30.5	CH	J14Y	.035	1/2N[26]	1/4P	1/8	7-1/2	14.5	4
75	100	18436572	VD	TDC[30]	.017	30[31]	CH	N10Y	.035	1/2N[26]	1/4P	1/8	7-1/2	17	5
45	85	18436572	VD	5	.017	30[31]	CH	J11Y	.035	1/2N[26]	1/4P	1/8	7-1/2	17	4
24	70	153624	VD	6	.027	38	BF	82	.034	3/4N	1/4P	1/4	6-3/4	8.7	3.5
24	70	15426378	VD	6	.021	27	BF	42	.034	3/4N	1/4P	1/4	6-3/4	13.7	4
24	70	153624	VD	6	.027	38	BF	82	.034	1/4P	1/4P	3/16	6-3/4	8.9	3.5
24	70	153624	VD	6	.027	38	BF	82	.034	1/4P	1/4P	3/16	6-3/4	8.7	3.5

8 – 360 hp – 10 deg. BTDC
9 – 60 and Brougham – 133 in., 75 – 149.8 in.
10 – 75 – 24.8 qts.
11 – Chevelle 2-Door Sedans – 112 in., 4-Door – 116 in., Monte Carlo – 116 in.
12 – 8.2 Litre Engine
13 – Chevelle – 1N
14 – Chevelle – 1/2P
15 – Chevelle – 8 deg.
16 – Outer Bolts on 4-Bolt Cap – 65 ft. lbs.
17 – Also 300 hp @ 4800
18 – Alum. Head Short Bolts – 65 ft. lbs., Long Bolts – 75 ft. lbs.
19 – Camaro – 108 in.
20 – Power Steering – 2-1/4P
21 – Also 400 hp @ 5400
22 – Also 330 hp @ 5000
23 – Man. Trans. – TDC
24 – 330 hp – J11Y
25 – 330 hp – 15.5 qts.
26 – Power Steering 3/4P
27 – Coronet, Charger – 117 in.
28 – Challenger – 110 in.
29 – Auto. Trans. – 2.5 BTDC
30 – Auto. Trans. – 5 BTDC
31 – Both Breakers – 37 to 42 deg.

1970

Model	Wheelbase	No. of Cylinders Bore and Stroke	Displacement (cu. in.)	Valve and Cylinder Arrangement	Compression Pressure (lbs.)	Maximum Brake Horsepower	Valve Tappet Clearance Intake	Valve Tappet Clearance Exhaust	Cylinder Bolt Torque (ft. lbs.)
Mustang, Deluxe, Grande	108	6-3.682x3.126	200	IO	175	120@4000	HY	HY	75
Mustang, Deluxe, Grande	108	6-3.682x3.910	250	IO	175	155@4000	HY	HY	75
Mustang, Deluxe, Grande	108	8-4.002x3.0	302	VO	150	220@4600	HY	HY	72
Mustang, Deluxe, Grande	108	8-4.002x3.50	351	VO	170	250@4600 [1]	HY	HY	100
Mustang, Deluxe, Grande	108	8-4.002x3.50	351	VO	170	300@5400 [1]	HY	HY	100
Mustang, Deluxe, Grande, Mach 1	108	8-4.132x3.984	428	VO	190	335@5200 [5]	HY	HY	90
Fairlane, Torino	117	6-3.682x3.91	250	IO	175	155@4000	HY	HY	75
Fairlane, Torino, GT	117	8-4.002x3.0	302	VO	150	220@4600	HY	HY	72
Fairlane, Torino, GT	117	8-4.002x3.50	351	VO	160	250@4600 [2]	HY	HY	100
Fairlane, Torino, GT, Cobra	117	8-4.362x3.59	429	VO	190	360@4600	HY	HY	140
Fairlane, Torino, GT, Cobra	117	8-4.362x3.59	429	VO	190	370@4700 [5]	HY	HY	140
Fairlane, Torino, GT, Cobra	117	8-4.362x3.59	429	VO	190	375@5600	.020H	.020H	140
Ford Custom, 500, Galaxie 500	121	6-4.0x3.18	240	IO	175	150@4000	HY	HY	75
Ford Custom, 500, Galaxie 500	121	8-4.0x3.0	302	VO	150	220@4600	HY	HY	72
Ford (All)	121	8-4.0x3.50	351	VO	160	250@4600	HY	HY	100
Ford (All)	121	8-4.052x3.784	390	VO	180	265@4400	HY	HY	90
Ford (All)	121	8-4.362x3.59	429	VO	190	320@4400	HY	HY	140
Ford (All), Thunderbird	121 [8]	8-4.362x3.59	429	VO	190	360@4600	HY	HY	140
Imperial	127	8-4.32x3.75	440	VO	150	350@4400	HY	HY	70
Lincoln Continental	127 [10]	8-4.362x3.85	460	VO	180	365@4600	HY	HY	140
Mercury - Cougar, XR-7	111.1	8-4.002x3.0	302	VO	150	220@4600	HY	HY	72
Cougar, XR-7	111.1	8-4.002x3.50	351	VO	170	250@4600 [2]	HY	HY	100
Cougar, XR-7, Eliminator	111.1	8-4.132x3.984	428	VO	190	335@5200 [5]	HY	HY	90
Montego, MX, MX Brougham	117	6-3.682x3.91	250	IO	175	155@4000 [13]	HY	HY	75
Montego, MX, MX Brougham	117	8-4.002x3.0	302	VO	150	220@4600 [13]	HY	HY	72
Montego, Cyclone GT	117	8-4.002x3.50	351	VO	160	250@4600 [14]	HY	HY	100
Montego, Cyclone, Spoiler, GT	117	8-4.362x3.590	429	VO	190	360@4600 [15]	HY	HY	140
Cyclone, Spoiler, GT	117	8-4.362x3.590	429	VO	190	375@3600	.020H	.020H	140
Mercury	124	8-4.052x3.784	390	VO	180	265@4400 [19]	HY	HY	90
Mercury (All)	124	8-4.362x3.59	429	VO	190	320@4400 [20]	HY	HY	140
Oldsmobile - F-85, Cutlass	116	6-3.875x3.53	250	IO	160	155@4200	HY	HY	95
F-85, Cutlass, Supreme	116	8-4.057x3.385	350	VO	175	250@4400 [22]	HY	HY	80
F-85, Cutlass, Supreme	116	8-4.057x3.385	350	VO	175	325@5400	HY	HY	80
Delta 88	124	8-4.057x3.385	350	VO	175	250@4400	HY	HY	80
Delta 88, Custom, Royale	124	8-4.125x4.250	455	VO	175	310@4200	HY	HY	80
Delta 88, Custom, Royale, 98	124 [24]	8-4.125x4.250	455	VO	175	365@4600	HY	HY	80
4-4-2	112	8-4.125x4.250	455	VO	175	365@4600 [25]	HY	HY	80
Toronado	119	8-4.125x4.250	455	VO	175	375@4600	HY	HY	80
Toronado	119	8-4.125x4.250	455	VO	175	400@3200	HY	HY	80
Plymouth - Valiant, Duster	108	6-3.40x3.64	198	IO	125	125@4400	.010H	.020H	65
Valiant, Duster, Belvedere, Satellite	108 [27]	6-3.40x4.12	225	IO	125	145@4000	.010H	.020H	65
Valiant, Duster, Belvedere, Satellite	108 [27]	8-3.91x3.31	318	VO	140	230@4400	HY	HY	85
Valiant, Duster, 'Cuda	108	8-4.04x3.31	340	VO	150	275@5000	HY	HY	95
Belvedere, Satellite, Barracuda	116 [28]	8-4.25x3.38	383	VO	140	290@4400	HY	HY	70
Belvedere, Satellite, Road Runner	116	8-4.25x3.38	383	VO	150	330@5000 [31]	HY	HY	70
Road Runner, GTX, 'Cuda	116 [28]	8-4.25x3.75	426	VO	150	425@5000	HY	HY	75
GTX, 'Cuda, Fury I, II, III, Sport Fury	116 [28]	8-4.32x3.75	440	VO	150	375@4600	HY	HY	70
Fury I, II, III, Sport Fury, Barracuda	120 [28]	8-3.40x4.12	225	IO	125	145@4000	.010H	.020H	65
Fury I, II, III, Barracuda	120 [28]	8-3.91x3.31	318	VO	140	230@4400	HY	HY	85
Fury I, II, III, Sport Fury, Barracuda	120 [28]	8-4.25x3.38	383	VO	140	290@4400	HY	HY	70
Fury I, II, III, Sport Fury, Barracuda	120 [28]	8-4.25x3.38	383	VO	150	330@5000 [31]	HY	HY	70
Road Runner, GTX, 'Cuda, Sport Fury GT	116 [28]	8-4.32x3.75	440	VO	150	390@4700 [36]	HY	HY	70
Pontiac-Tempest, LeMans, LeMans Sport	112 [39]	6-3.875x3.525	250	IO	160	155@4200	HY	HY	95
Tempest, LeMans, LeMans Sport	112 [39]	8-3.875x3.746	350	VO	160	255@4600	HY	HY	95
Tempest, LeMans, Lemans Sport, Grand Prix	112 [39]	8-4.12x3.746	400	VO	160	265@4600	HY	HY	95
Tempest, LeMans, LeMans Sport	112 [39]	8-4.12x3.746	400	VO	160	330@4800	HY	HY	95
GTO, Grand Prix	112 [39]	8-4.12x3.746	400	VO	160	350@5000	HY	HY	95
GTO	112	8-4.12x3.746	400	VO	160	366@5100 [40]	HY	HY	95
Catalina	122	8-3.875x3.746	350	VO	160	255@4600	HY	HY	95
Catalina, Executive, Bonneville	122 [41]	8-4.12x3.746	400	VO	160	265@4600	HY	HY	95
Catalina, Executive	122 [41]	8-4.12x3.746	400	VO	160	290@4600	HY	HY	95
Catalina, Executive	122 [41]	8-4.12x3.746	400	VO	160	330@4800	HY	HY	95
GTO	112	8-4.151x4.206	455	VO	160	360@4300 [41]	HY	HY	95
Catalina, Executive, Bonneville	122 [40]	8-4.151x4.206	455	VO	160	360@4300	HY	HY	95

ABBREVIATIONS - FOOTNOTES

AC - AC Spark Plugs
AF, BF - Autolite Spark Plugs
BA - Balancer Assembly
BTDC - Before Top Dead Center
C - Cold Engine
CH - Champion Spark Plugs
CP - Crankshaft Pulley
H - Hot Engine
HY - Hydraulic Lifters

IO - In-Line Engine - Overhead Valves
N - Negative
P - Positive
TDC - Top Dead Center
VD - Vibration Damper
VO - V-Type Engine - Overhead Valves
1 - Mach 1 Only - Ram Air
2 - Also 300 hp @ 5400
3 - Auto. Trans. - .017 in.
4 - 300 hp - AF - 32
5 - Also Ram Air

6 - Auto. Trans. - .020 in.
7 - Auto. Trans. - 28.5 deg.
8 - T-Bird 2-Door - 114.7 in., 4-Door - 117.1 in.
9 - T-Bird - 19.4 qts.
10 - Continental Mark III - 117.2 in.
11 - Continental Mark III - 1P
12 - Continental Mark III - 3/16 in.
13 - Except 2-Door Hardtops
14 - Also Eliminator - 300 hp @ 5400
15 - Also Cyclone - 370 hp @ 5400 and Ram Air

Tuneup Specifications

Connecting Rod Bolt Torque (ft. lbs.)	Main Bearing Bolt Torque (ft. lbs.)	Firing Order	Timing Mark Location	Breaker Point Opens BTDC	Breaker Point Gap	Cam Angle	Spark Plugs Make	Spark Plugs Model	Spark Plugs Gap	Caster Man. Steer. (deg.)	Camber Rt. Wheel (deg.)	Toe-in (in.)	Steering Axis Inclination (deg.)	Cooling System Capacity (qts.)	Crankcase Capacity (qts.)
24	70	153624	VD	6	.027	38	BF	82	.034	0	1P	3/16	6-3/4	9	4
26	70	153624	VD	6	.027	38	BF	82	.034	0	1P	3/16	6-3/4	9.8	4
24	70	15426378	VD	6	.021	27	BF	42	.034	0	1P	3/16	6-3/4	13.5	4
45	70	13726548	VD	6	.021	27	AF	42	.034	0	1P	3/16	6-3/4	13.6	4
45	70	13726548	VD	6	.021	27	AF	32	.034	0	1P	3/16	6-3/4	13.6	4
58	105	15426378	VD	6	.021	27	BF	32	.034	0	1P	3/16		19.3	4
26	70	153624	VD	6	.027	38	BF	82	.034	3/4N	1/4P	1/4	7-3/4	11.4	4
24	70	15426378	VD	6	.021	27	BF	42	.034	3/4N	1/4P	1/4	7-3/4	15.2	4
45	105	13726548	VD	6	.021[3]	27	AF	42[4]	.034	3/4N	1/4P	1/4	7-3/4	15.4	4
45	105	15426378	VD	6	.021	27	BF	42	.034	3/4N	1/4P	1/4		19	4
45	105	15426378	VD	10	.021[6]	24.5[7]	AF	32	.034	3/4N	1/4P	1/4	7-3/4	19.6	6
45	105	15426378	VD	10	.021[6]	24.5[7]	AF	32	.034	3/4N	1/4P	1/4	7-3/4	19.6	6
45	70	153624	VD	6	.027	38	BF	42	.034	1P	1/2P	3/16	7-3/4	14.4	4
24	70	15426378	VD	6	.021	27	BF	42	.034	1P	1/2P	3/16	7-3/4	15.4	4
45	105	13726548	VD	6	.021	27	AF	42	.034	1P	1/2P	3/16	7-3/4	16.5	4
45	105	15426378	VD	6	.017	28	BF	42	.034	1P	1/2P	3/16	7-3/4	20.1	4
45	105	15426378	VD	6	.021	27	BF	42	.034	1P	1/2P	3/16	7-3/4	18.6	4
45	105	15426378	VD	6	.021	27	BF	42	.034	1P	1/2P	3/16	7-3/4	18.6[9]	4
45	85	18436572	VD	5	.019	30.5	CH	J13Y	.035	1/2P	1/4P	1/8	9	16.5	4
45	105	15426378	VD	10	.017	29	BF	42	.034	1-1/2P[11]	1/2P	0[12]	7-3/4	19.6	4
24	70	15426378	VD	6	.021	27	BF	42	.034	0	1P	3/16		13.5	4
45	70	13726548	VD	6	.021[3]	27	AF	42[4]	.034	0	1P	3/16	6-3/4	14.6	4
58	105	15426378	VD	6	.021[3]	27	BF	32	.034	0	1P	3/16		19.3	4
26	70	153624	VD	6	.027	38	BF	82	.034	3/4N	1/4P	1/4	7-3/4	11.4	4
24	70	15426378	VD	6	.021	27	BF	42	.034	3/4N	1/4P	1/4	7-3/4	15.2	4
45	105	13726548	VD	6	.021[3]	27	AF	42[4]	.034	3/4N	1/4P	1/4	7-3/4	15.4	4
45	105	15426378	VD	6[16]	.021[3]	27	BF	42	.034	3/4N	1/4P	1/4	7-3/4	19[17]	4[18]
45	105	15426378	VD	10	.021	27	AF	32	.034	3/4N	1/4P	1/4	7-3/4	19.6	6
45	105	15426378	VD	6	.021	27	BF	42	.034	1P	1/2P	3/16	7-1/2	20.1	4
45	105	15426378	VD	6	.021	27	BF	42	.034	1P	1/2P	3/16		18.6	4
35	65[23]	153624	VD	TDC[21]	.016	33	AC	R46T	.035	1-1/4N	1/8P	3/16	9	12.2	4
42	80[23]	18436572	BA	10	.016	30	AC	R46S	.030	1-1/4N	1/8P	3/16	9	15.2	4
42	80[23]	18436572	BA	14	.016	30	AC	R43S	.030	1-1/4N	1/8P	3/16	9	15.2	4
42	80	18436572	BA	10	.016	30	AC	R46S	.030	1N	1/8P	3/16	11	17.5	4
42	120	18436572	BA	8	.016	30	AC	R46S	.030	1N	1/8P	3/16	11	17.5	4
42	120	18436572	BA	8	.016	30	AC	R45S	.030	1N	1/8P	3/16	11	17.5	4
42	120	18436572	BA	12	.016	30	AC	R44S	.030	1-1/4N	1/8P	3/16	9	16.2	4
42	120	18436572	BA	8	.016	30	AC	R45S	.030	2-1/4N	1/8P	0	11	18	5
42	120	18436572	BA	12	.016	30	AC	R44S	.030	2-1/4N	1/8P	0	11	18	5
45	85	153624	VD	TDC	.020	44	CH	N14Y	.035	1/2N[26]	1/4P	1/8	7-1/2	13	4
45	85	153624	VD	TDC	.020	44	CH	N14Y	.035	1/2N[26]	1/4P	1/8	7-1/2	13	4
45	85	18436572	VD	TDC	.017	32	CH	N14Y	.035	1/2N[26]	1/4P	1/8	7-1/2	16	4
45	85	18436572	VD	5	.017	30[29]	CH	N9Y	.035	1/2N[26]	1/4P	1/8	7-1/2	15	4
45	85	18436572	VD	2.5	.019	30.5	CH	N14Y	.035	1/2N[26]	1/4P	1/8	7-1/2	14.5[33]	4
45	85	18436572	VD	TDC[30]	.019	30.5	CH	J11Y	.035	1/2N[26]	1/4P	1/8	7-1/2	14.5	4
75	100	18436572	VD	TDC[32]	.017	30[29]	CH	N10Y	.035	1/2N[26]	1/4P	1/8	7-1/2	17[34]	6[36]
45	85	18436572	VD	TDC[30]	.019	30.5	CH	J11Y	.035	1/2N[26]	1/4P	1/8	7-1/2[38]	17[34]	4
45	85	153624	VD	TDC	.020	44	CH	N14Y	.035	1/2N[26]	1/4P	1/8	9	17[35]	4
45	85	18436572	VD	TDC	.017	32	CH	N14Y	.035	1/2N[26]	1/4P	1/8	9	16	4
45	85	18436572	VD	2.5	.019	30.5	CH	N14Y	.035	1/2N[26]	1/4P	1/8	9	16	4
45	85	18436572	VD	TDC[30]	.019	30.5	CH	J11Y	.035	1/2N[26]	1/4P	1/8	9	16	4
45	85	18436572	VD	5	.017	30[29]	CH	J11Y	.035	1/2N[26]	1/4P	1/8	7-1/2[38]	17[34]	6[37]
35	65	153624	VD	TDC[21]	.019	33	AC	R46T	.035	1-1/2N	1/4P	1/16	9	13	4
43	100[23]	18436572	CP	9	.016	30	AC	R46S	.035	1-1/2N	1/4P	1/16	9	19.9	5
43	100[23]	18436572	CP	9	.016	30	AC	R45S	.035	1-1/2N	1/4P	1/16	9	18.3	5
43	100[23]	18436572	CP	9	.016	30	AC	R45S	.035	1-1/2N	1/4P	1/16	9	18.3	5
43	100[23]	18436572	CP	15	.016	30	AC	R44S	.035	1-1/2N	1/4P	1/16	9	18.3	5
43	100[23]	18436572	CP	9	.016	30	AC	R46S	.035	1-1/2N	1/4P	1/16	8-1/2	19.6	5
43	100[23]	18436572	CP	9	.016	30	AC	R46S	.035	1-1/2N	1/4P	1/16	8-1/2	18[43]	5
43	100[23]	18436572	CP	9	.016	30	AC	R45S	.035	1-1/2N	1/4P	1/16	8-1/2	18	5
43	100[23]	18436572	CP	9	.016	30	AC	R44S	.035	1-1/2N	1/4P	1/16	9	18.3	5
43	100[23]	18436572	CP	9	.016	30	AC	R44S	.035	1-1/2N	1/4P	1/16	8-1/2	18[43]	5

16 – 370 hp – 10 deg. BTDC	27 – Belvedere, Satellite – 116 in.	38 – Fury, Sport Fury – 9 deg.
17 – 370 hp – 19.6 qts.	28 – Barracuda – 108 in., Fury – 120 in.	39 – 2-Door – 112 in., 4-Door – 116 in., Grand Prix – 118 in.
18 – 370 hp – '6 qts.	29 – Both Breakers – 37 to 42 deg.	40 – Ram Air – Also 370 hp @ 5500
19 – All Except Brougham	30 – Auto. Trans. – 2.5 deg. BTDC	41 – Executive, Bonneville – 125 in.
20 – Also 360 hp @ 4600	31 – Also 335 hp @ 5200	42 – Also 370 hp @ 4600 on Catalina, Executive, Bonneville and Grand Prix
21 – Auto. Trans. – 4 deg. BTDC	32 – Auto. Trans. – 5 deg. BTDC	43 – Bonneville – 17.2 qts.
22 – Also 310 hp @ 4800	33 – Barracuda	
23 – Rear Main – 120 ft. lbs.	34 – Barracuda – 15.5 qts.	
24 – Ninety Eight – 127 in.	35 – Barracuda – 13 qts.	
25 – Also 370 hp @ 5200	36 – Also GT – 350 hp @ 4400	
26 – Power Steering – 3/4P	37 – Road Runner, GTX – 4 qts.	

1971

Model	Wheelbase (in.)	No. of Cylinders Bore and Stroke (in.)	Displacement (cu. in.)	Valve and Cylinder Arrangement	Compression Pressure (lbs.)	Maximum Brake Horsepower @ rpm	Valve Tappet Clearance Intake	Valve Tappet Clearance Exhaust	Cylinder Bolt Torque (ft. lbs.)
American Motors – Gremlin, Hornet	96 [1]	6-3.75x3.50	232	IO	185	135@4000	HY	HY	85
Sportabout, Javelin, SST, Matador	108 [3]	6-3.75x3.50	232	IO	185	135@4000	HY	HY	85
Gremlin, Hornet, SST, Sportabout	96 [1]	6-3.75x3.90	258	IO	185	150@3800	HY	HY	85
Javelin, SST, Matador, Ambassador DPL	110 [3]	6-3.75x3.90	258	IO	185	150@3800	HY	HY	85
Hornet SST, Sportabout, Javelin, SST	108 [3]	8-3.75x3.44	304	VO	185	210@4400	HY	HY	110
Matador SST, Ambassador, SST, Brougham	118 [3]	8-3.75x3.44	304	VO	185	210@4400	HY	HY	110
Hornet SC/360, Javelin, SST, AMX	108 [3]	8-4.08x3.44	360	VO	185	245@4400 [6]	HY	HY	110
Matador SST, Ambassador SST, Brougham	118 [3]	8-4.08x3.44	360	VO	185	245@4400 [6]	HY	HY	110
Javelin, SST, AMX	110	8-4.165x3.68	401	VO	200	330@5000	HY	HY	110
Matador SST, Ambassador SST, Brougham	118 [3]	8-4.165x3.68	401	VO	200	330@5000	HY	HY	110
Buick – Skylark	112 [7]	6-3.874x3.53	250	IO	165 [8]	145@4000	HY	HY	95
Skylark, Custom, Sportwagon	112 [7]	8-3.80x3.85	350	VO	175 [8]	230@4400 [9]	HY	HY	75
LeSabre, LeSabre Custom	124	8-3.80x3.85	350	VO	175 [8]	230@4400 [9]	HY	HY	75
LeSabre, Custom, Estate Wagon	124 [12]	8-4.125x3.90	455	VO	175 [8]	315@4400	HY	HY	100
GS	112	8-4.125x3.90	455	VO	175 [8]	315@4400 [15]	HY	HY	100
Centurion, Electra 225, Custom	124 [16]	8-4.125x3.90	455	VO	175 [8]	315@4400 [17]	HY	HY	100
Riviera	122	8-4.125x3.90	455	VO	175 [8]	315@4400 [18]	HY	HY	100
Cadillac – All Except Eldorado	130 [19]	8-4.30x4.06	472	VO	175	345@4400	HY	HY	115
Eldorado	126.3	8-4.30x4.304	500	VO	175	365@4400	HY	HY	115
Chevrolet – Vega 2300	97	4-3.501x3.625	140	IOC	140	90@4600	.015C [22]	.030C [22]	60
Vega 2300 (L11)	97	4-3.501x3.625	140	IOC	140	110@4800	.015C [22]	.030C [22]	60
Camaro	108	6-3.875x3.53	250	IO	130	145@4200	HY	HY	95
Nova	111	6-3.875x3.53	250	IO	130	145@4200	HY	HY	95
Chevelle	112 [7]	6-3.875x3.53	250	IO	130	145@4200	HY	HY	95
Chevrolet (All Except Caprice)	121.5	6-3.875x3.53	250	IO	130	145@4200	HY	HY	95
Camaro, Nova, Chevelle	108 [25]	8-3.875x3.25	307	VO	150	200@4600	HY	HY	65
Camaro, Nova, Chevelle, Monte Carlo	108 [25]	8-4.0x3.48	350	VO	160	245@4800	HY	HY	65
Chevrolet (All Except Caprice)	121.5	8-4.0x3.48	350	VO	160	245@4800	HY	HY	65
Chevrolet (All)	121.5	8-4.0x3.48	350	VO	160	270@4800	HY	HY	65
Corvette	98	8-4.0x3.48	350	VO	160	270@4800	HY	HY	65
Camaro, Nova, Chevelle, Monte Carlo	108 [25]	8-4.0x3.48	350	VO	160	270@4800	HY	HY	65
Camaro (Z28)	108	8-4.0x3.48	350	VO	150	330@5600	.020	.025	65
Corvette	98	8-4.0x3.48	350	VO	150	330@5600	.020	.025	65
Chevrolet (All)	121.5	8-4.125x3.75	400	VO	160	255@4400	HY	HY	80
Chevrolet (All)	121.5	8-4.126x3.76	402	VO	160	300@4800	HY	HY	65
Camaro, Chevelle, Monte Carlo	108 [25]	8-4.126x3.76	402	VO	160	300@4800	HY	HY	65
Chevelle, Monte Carlo	112 [25]	8-4.251x4.0	454	VO	160	365@4800 [33]	HY	HY	80
Chevrolet (All)	121.5	8-4.251x4.0	454	VO	160	365@4800	HY	HY	80
Corvette	98	8-4.251x4.0	454	VO	160	365@4800	HY	HY	80
Corvette	98	8-4.251x4.0	454	VO	160	425@5600	.024	.028	80
Chrysler – Newport Royal	124	8-4.0x3.58	360	VO	100	255@4000	HY	HY	95
Newport, Custom, Royal	124	8-4.25x3.38	383	VO	100	275@4400 [35]	HY	HY	70
300, New Yorker	124	8-4.32x3.75	440	VO	110	335@4400	HY	HY	70
Newport, Custom, Royal, 300, New Yorker	124	8-4.32x3.75	440	VO	110	370@4600	HY	HY	70
Imperial	127	8-4.32x3.75	440	VO	110	335@4400	HY	HY	70
Dodge – Dart, Dart Demon, Swinger Special	111 [37]	6-3.40x3.64	198	IO	100	125@4400	.010H	.020H	70
Challenger Coupe	111	6-3.40x3.84	198	IO	100	125@4400	.010H	.020H	70
Dart, Demon, Custom, Swinger Special	111 [37]	6-3.40x4.12	225	IO	100	145@4400	.010H	.020H	70
Challenger, Charger Coupe, Coronet, Custom	111 [38]	6-3.40x4.12	225	IO	100	145@4400	.010H	.020H	70
Polara	122	6-3.40x4.12	225	IO	100	145@4400	.010H	.020H	70
Dart, Demon, Custom, Swinger, Special	111 [37]	8-3.91x3.31	318	VO	100	230@4400	HY	HY	95
Challenger, Coupe, Charger, Coupe, 500, SE	111 [38]	8-3.91x3.31	318	VO	100	230@4400	HY	HY	95
Coronet, Custom, Brougham	118	8-3.91x3.31	318	VO	100	230@4400	HY	HY	95
Polara, Custom	122	8-3.91x3.31	318	VO	100	230@4400	HY	HY	95
Challenger, R/T, Demon 340	111 [37]	8-4.04x3.31	340	VO	110	275@5000	HY	HY	95
Charger, Super Bee	115	8-4.04x3.31	340	VO	110	275@5000	HY	HY	95
Polara, Custom	122	8-4.0x3.58	360	VO	100	255@4400	HY	HY	95
Challenger, Coupe, Charger, Coupe, 500, SE	111 [38]	8-4.25x3.38	383	VO	100	275@4400 [41]	HY	HY	70
Coronet, Custom, Brougham, Super Bee	118 [42]	8-4.25x3.38	383	VO	100	300@4800	HY	HY	70
Polara, Custom, Brougham, Monaco	122	8-4.25x3.38	383	VO	100	275@4400 [44]	HY	HY	70
Challenger R/T, Charger R/T, Super Bee	111 [38]	8-4.25x3.75	426	VO	110	425@5000	HY	HY	75
Charger R/T, Super Bee, SE	111 [38]	8-4.32x3.75	440	VO	110	370@4600	HY	HY	70
Challenger R/T, Charger R/T, Super Bee	111 [38]	8-4.32x3.75	440	VO	110	385@4700	HY	HY	70
Polara, Custom, Brougham, Monaco	122	8-4.32x3.75	440	VO	70 [48]	335@4400	HY	HY	70
Ford – Pinto	94	4-3.188x3.056	97.6	IO	70 [48]	75@5000	.010C	.017C	70
Pinto	94	4-3.575x3.029	122	IOC	80 [48]	100@5600	.008C	.010C	80
Maverick, GT	103 [50]	6-3.502x2.94	170	IO	175 [48]	100@4200	HY	HY	75
Maverick, GT	103 [50]	6-3.682x3.126	200	IO	175 [48]	115@4000	HY	HY	75
Ford Custom, 500, Galaxie 500	121	6-4.0x3.18	240	IO	175 [48]	140@4000	HY	HY	75
Maverick, GT, Mustang, Grande	103 [52]	6-3.682x3.91	250	IO	175 [48]	145@4000	HY	HY	75
Torino, 500, GT	117	6-3.682x3.91	250	IO	175 [48]	145@4000	HY	HY	75
Maverick, GT, Mustang, Grande, Mach 1	103 [52]	8-4.002x3.0	302	VO	150 [48]	210@4600	HY	HY	72
Torino, 500, GT, Brougham	117	8-4.002x3.0	302	VO	150 [48]	210@4600	HY	HY	72

ABBREVIATIONS - FOOTNOTES:

AC – AC Spark Plugs
AU – Autolite Spark Plugs
B – Before Top Dead Center
C – Cold Engine
CH – Champion Spark Plugs
CP – Crankshaft Pulley
EL – Electronic Ignition
H – Hot Engine
HY – Hydraulic Lifters
IO – In-Line Engine, Overhead Valves
IOC – In-Line Engine, Overhead Cam

N – Negative
P – Positive
TDC – Top Dead Center
VD – Vibration Damper
VO – V-Type Engine, Overhead Valves
1 – Hornet, Sportabout – 108
2 – Manual Trans. – 3B@700
3 – Javelin – 110, Matador – 118,
   Ambassador – 122
4 – Manual Trans. – 5B@700
5 – Manual Trans. – 2.5B@750
6 – Also 285@4800
7 – 4-Door – 116, Sportwagon – 116

8 – Lowest Cylinder Must Be At
   Least 70 Percent of Highest
9 – Also 260@4600, Incl. GS
10 – Manual Trans. – 6B@600
11 – Sportwagon – 1/2N
12 – Estate Wagon – 127
13 – Estate Wagon – 10-3/4
14 – Estate Wagon – 18.7
15 – Also GS Stage 1 – 345@5000
16 – Electra 225, Custom – 127
17 – Also Centurion – 330@4600
18 – Also Riviera GS – 330@4600
19 – Fleetwood Brougham – 133, 75 - 151.5

Firing Order	Timing Mark Location	Initial Ignition Timing @ rpm	Breaker Point Gap (in.)	Cam Angle (deg.)	Make	Model	Gap (in.)	Caster Manual Steering (deg.)	Camber Right Wheel (deg.)	Toe-In (in.)	Steering Axis Inclination (deg.)	Cooling System Capacity (qts.)	Crankcase Capacity (qts.)
153624	VD	5B@600 [2]	.016	32	CH	N12Y	.035	1P	0	1/8	7-3/4	10.5	4
153624	VD	5B@600 [2]	.016	32	CH	N12Y	.035	1P	0	1/8	7-3/4	10.5	4
153624	VD	5B@600 [4]	.016	32	CH	N12Y	.035	1P	0	1/8	7-3/4	10.5	4
153624	VD	5B@600	.016	32	CH	N12Y	.035	1P	0	1/8	7-3/4	10.5	4
18436572	VD	2.5B@650 [5]	.016	30	CH	N12Y	.035	1P	0	1/8	7-3/4	14	4
18436572	VD	2.5B@650	.016	30	CH	N12Y	.035	1P	0	1/8	7-3/4	14	4
18436572	VD	2.5B@650 [5]	.016	30	CH	N12Y	.035	1P	0	1/8	7-3/4	13	4
18436572	VD	2.5B@650	.016	30	CH	N12Y	.035	1P	0	1/8	7-3/4	13	4
18436572	VD	2.5B@650 [5]	.016	30	CH	N12Y	.035	1P	0	1/8	7-3/4	13	4
18436572	VD	2.5B@650	.016	30	CH	N12Y	.035	1P	0	1/8	7-3/4	13	4
153624	VD	4B@600	.019	32	AC	R46T	.035	1/2P	1/2P	3/16	8	16	4
18436572	VD	10B@600 [10]	.016	30	AC	R45TS	.030	1/2P[11]	1/2P	3/16	8	16.45	4
18436572	VD	4B@600 [10]	.016	30	AC	R45TS	.030	1P	1/4P	3/16	9-5/8	16.45	4
18436572	VD	4B@600 [10]	.016	30	AC	R45TS	.030	1P	1/4P	3/16	9-5/8[13]	16.45[14]	4
18436572	VD	4B@600 [10]	.016	30	AC	R45TS	.030	1/2P	1/2P	3/16	8	16.45	4
18436572	VD	4B@600 [10]	.016	30	AC	R44TS	.030	1P	1/4P	3/16	9-5/8	18.7	4
18436572	VD	4B@600	.016	30	AC	R44TS	.030	1P	1/4P	3/16	9-5/8	18.7	4
15634278	VD	8B@600	.016	30	AC	R46N	.035	1-1/2N[20]	0	3/16	6	21.3[21]	4
15634278	VD	8B@600	.015	30	AC	R46N	.035	1N	0	0	11	21.8	5
1342	CP	6B@550 [23]	.019	32	AC	R42TS	.035	3/4N	1/4P	1/4	8-1/2	6.5	3
1342	CP	10B@550 [23]	.019	32	AC	R42TS	.035	3/4N	1/4P	1/4	8-1/2	6.5	3
153624	VD	4B@500 [24]	.019	32	AC	R46TS	.035	0	1P	3/16	9-1/2	12	4
153624	VD	4B@500 [24]	.019	32	AC	R46TS	.035	1/2P	1/4P	3/16	8-3/4	12	4
153624	VD	4B@500 [24]	.019	32	AC	R46TS	.035	1N	3/4P	3/16	8-1/4	12	4
153624	VD	4B@500 [24]	.019	32	AC	R46TS	.035	1N	1/2P	3/16	10	12	4
18436572	VD	8B@550 [26]	.019	30	AC	R45TS	.035	0[27]	1P[28]	3/16	9-1/2[29]	15	4
18436572	VD	6B@550 [30]	.019	30	AC	R45TS	.035	0[27]	1P[28]	3/16	9-1/2[29]	16	4
18436572	VD	6B@550 [30]	.019	30	AC	R45TS	.035	1/2P	1/2P	3/16	10	16	4
18436572	VD	8B@600	.019	30	AC	R44TS	.035	1N	1/2P	3/16	10	16	4
18436572	VD	8B@550 [31]	.019	30	AC	R44TS	.035	1P	3/4P	3/16	7	15	4
18436572	VD	8B@550 [26]	.019	30	AC	R44TS	.035	0[27]	1P[28]	3/16	9-1/2[29]	16	4
18436572	VD	12B@700 [32]	.019	30	AC	R43TS	.035	1N	3/4P	3/16	9-3/4	16	4
18436572	VD	8B@700	EL	EL	AC	R43TS	.035	1P	3/4P	3/16	7	18	4
18436572	VD	8B@550 [26]	EL	30	AC	R44TS	.035	1N	1/2P	3/16	10	16	4
18436572	VD	8B@600	.019	29	AC	R44TS	.035	1N	1/2P	3/16	10	23	4
18436572	VD	8B@600	.019	29	AC	R44TS	.035	0[27]	1P[28]	3/16	9-1/2[29]	24	4
18436572	VD	8B@600 [34]	.019	29	AC	R43TS	.035	1N	3/4P	1/4	8-1/4	22	4
18436572	VD	8B@600	.019	29	AC	R43TS	.035	1N	1/2P	3/16	10	22	4
18436572	VD	8B@600	.019	29	AC	R43TS	.035	3/4P		1/4	7	22	5
18436572	VD	12B@600	EL	EL	AC	R44XL	.035	1P	3/4P	1/4	7	20	5
18436572	VD	2.5B@700 [5]	.016	32	CH	N10Y	.035	1/2N	1/4P	1/8	9	15.5	4
18436572	VD	12.5B@800 [36]	.018	30.5	CH	J14Y	.035	1/2N	1/4P	1/8	9	14.5	4
18436572	VD	12.5B@750	.018	30.5	CH	J13Y	.035	1/2N	1/4P	1/8	9	15.5	4
18436572	VD	12.5B@900	.018	30.5	CH	J11Y	.035	1/2N	1/4P	1/8	9	15.5	4
18436572	VD	5B@650	.018	30.5	CH	J13Y	.035	3/4P	1/4P	1/8	9	17.5	4
153624	VD	2.5B@800	.020	43	CH	N14Y	.035	1/2N	1/4P	1/8	7-1/2	13	4
153624	VD	2.5B@800	.020	43	CH	N14Y	.035	1/2N	1/4P	1/8	7-1/2	13	4
153624	VD	TDC@750	.020	43	CH	N14Y	.035	1/2N	1/4P	1/8	7-1/2	13	4
153624	VD	TDC@750	.020	43	CH	N14Y	.035	1/2N	1/4P	1/8	7-1/2	13	4
153624	VD	TDC@750	.020	43	CH	N14Y	.035	1/2N	1/4P	1/8	9	13	4
18436572	VD	TDC@700 [39]	.016	32	CH	N14Y	.035	1/2N	1/4P	1/8	7-1/2	16	4
18436572	VD	TDC@700 [39]	.016	32	CH	N14Y	.035	1/2N	1/4P	1/8	7-1/2	16	4
18436572	VD	TDC@700 [39]	.016	32	CH	N14Y	.035	1/2N	1/4P	1/8	9	16	4
18436572	VD	5B@900	.016	32	CH	N9Y	.035	1/2N	1/4P	1/8	7-1/2	15.5	4
18436572	VD	5B@700 [40]	.016	32	CH	N9Y	.035	1/2N	1/4P	1/8	7-1/2	15	4
18436572	VD	2.5B@700 [39]	.016	32	CH	N13Y	.035	1/2N	1/4P	1/8	9	15.5	4
18436572	VD	12.5B@700	.018	30.5	CH	J14Y	.035	1/2N	1/4P	1/8	9	14.5	4
18436572	VD	12.5B@800 [43]	.018	30.5	CH	J11Y	.035	1/2N	1/4P	1/8	7-1/2	14.5	4
18436572	VD	12.5B@700 [36]	.018	30.5	CH	J14Y	.035	1/2N	1/4P	1/8	9	14.5	4
18436572	VD	2.5B@900	.016	30	CH	N10Y	.035	1/2N	1/4P	1/8	7-1/2	17	6
18436572	VD	12.5B@800 [45]	.016	30.5	CH	J11Y	.035	1/2N	1/4P	1/8	7-1/2	15.5[46]	6
18436572	VD	12.5B@900	.016	30	CH	J11Y	.035	1/2N	1/4P	1/8	7-1/2	15.5[46]	6
18436572	VD	12.5B@750	.016	30.5	CH	J13Y	.035	1/2N	1/4P	1/8	9	15.5	4
1243	CP	12B@900	.025	40	AU	AGS22	.025	1-1/2P	3/4P	3/16	9	6.8	3
1342	VD	6B@650 [49]	.025	40	AU	BRF32	.034	1-1/2P	3/4P	3/16	9	7.5	4
153624	VD	6B@750	.027	35	AU	BRF82	.034	0	3/4P	3/16	6-3/4	9.2	4
153624	VD	6B@550 [49]	.027	35	AU	BRF82	.034	0	3/4P	3/16	6-3/4	14.1	4
153624	VD	6B@500 [51]	.027	35	AU	BRF42	.034	1P	1/2P	3/16	7-3/16	14.1	4
153624	VD	6B@600 [49]	.027	35	AU	BRF82	.034	0	3/4P	3/16	6-3/4	9.7[53]	4
153624	VD	6B@600 [49]	.027	35	AU	BRF82	.034	3/4N	1/4P	1/4	7-3/4	11.2	4
15426378	VD	6B@575 [51]	.021	27	AU	BRF42	.034	0	3/4P	3/16	6-3/4	13.5[54]	4
15426378	VD	6B@575 [51]	.017	28	AU	BRF42	.034	3/4N	1/4P	1/4	7-3/4	15.1	4

20 – Fleetwood Brougham – 1N, 75 – 2-1/2N
21 – 75 – 24.8
22 – Running – Intake .015, Exhaust .016
23 – Manual Trans. – 6B@700
24 – Manual Trans. – 4B@550
25 – Nova – 111, Chevelle – 112/116, Monte Carlo – 116
26 – Manual Trans. – 4B@600
27 – Chevelle – 1N, Nova – 1/2P
28 – Chevelle – 3/4P, Nova – 1/4P
29 – Nova – 8-3/4, Chevelle/Monte Carlo – 8-1/4
30 – Manual Trans. – 2B@600
31 – Manual Trans. – 8B@600
32 – Manual Trans. – 8B@700
33 – Also 425@5600
34 – Monte Carlo 425 – 12B@700, Manual Trans. – 8B@700
35 – Also 300@4800
36 – Manual Trans. – 10B@750
37 – Demon – 108, Swinger – 111
38 – Charger – 115, Coronet – 118
39 – Manual Trans. – TDC@750
40 – Manual Trans. – 5B@750
41 – Also Challenger R/T – 300@4800
42 – Super Bee – 115
43 – Manual Trans. – 10B@900
44 – Also 300@4800
45 – Manual Trans. – 10B@800
46 – Manual Trans. – 17
47 – Both Sets of Points – 39
48 – Lowest Cylinder Must Be At Least 75 Percent of Highest
49 – Manual Trans. – 6B@750
50 – 4-Door – 110
51 – Manual Trans. – 6B@800
52 – Mustang – 109
53 – Mustang – 11.2
54 – Mustang – 15.1

1971

	Wheelbase (in.)	No. of Cylinders Bore and Stroke (in.)	Displacement (cu. in.)	Valve and Cylinder Arrangement	Compression Pressure (lbs.)	Maximum Brake Horsepower @ rpm	Valve Tappet Clearance Intake	Valve Tappet Clearance Exhaust	Cylinder Bolt Torque (ft. lbs.)
Ford, Custom, 500, Galaxie 500	121	8-4.002x3.0	302	VO	150 [1]	210@4600	HY	HY	72
Ford LTD, Brougham	121	8-4.0x3.50	351W	VO	160 [1]	240@4600	HY	HY	112
Torino, 500, GT, Brougham	117	8-4.002x3.50	351C	VO	170 [1]	240@4600 [14]	HY	HY	100
Mustang, Grande, Mach 1	109	8-4.002x3.50	351C	VO	170 [1]	240@4600 [3]	HY	HY	100
Mustang, Grande, Mach 1	109	8-4.002x3.50	351C	VO	170 [1]	280@5800 [5]	HY	HY	100
Ford (All)	121	8-4.052x3.784	390	VO	180 [1]	255@4400	HY	HY	90
Ford (All)	121	8-4.0x4.0	400	VO	180 [1]	260@4400	HY	HY	100
Ford (All)	121	8-4.362x3.59	429	VO	190 [1]	320@4400 [7]	HY	HY	140
Thunderbird	114.7 [8]	8-4.362x3.59	429	VO	190 [1]	360@4600	HY	HY	140
Torino, 500, GT, Brougham	117	8-4.362x3.59	429	VO	190 [1]	370@5400	HY	HY	140
Mustang, Grande, Mach 1	109	8-4.362x3.59	429	VO	190 [1]	370@5400 [11]	HY	HY	140
Lincoln	127	8-4.362x3.85	460	VO	180 [1]	365@4600	HY	HY	140
Mark III	117.2	8-4.362x3.85	460	VO	180 [1]	365@4600	HY	HY	140
Mercury - Comet, GT	103 [12]	6-3.502x2.94	170	IO	175 [1]	100@4200	HY	HY	75
Comet, GT	103 [12]	6-3.682x3.126	200	IO	175 [1]	115@4000	HY	HY	75
Comet, GT	103 [12]	6-3.682x3.910	250	IO	175 [1]	145@4000	HY	HY	75
Montego, "MX", Brougham	117	6-3.682x3.910	250	IO	175 [1]	145@4000	HY	HY	75
Comet, GT	103 [12]	8-4.002x3.0	302	VO	150 [1]	210@4600	HY	HY	72
Montego, "MX", Brougham	117	8-4.002x3.0	302	VO	150 [1]	210@4600	HY	HY	72
Montego, "MX", Brougham, Cyclone GT	117	8-4.002x3.50	351C	VO	170 [1]	240@4600 [14]	HY	HY	100
Monterey, Custom	124	8-4.0x3.50	351W	VO	160 [1]	240@4600	HY	HY	112
Cougar, XR-7, GT	112.1	8-4.002x3.50	351C	VO	170 [1]	240@4600 [14]	HY	HY	100
Cougar, XR-7, GT	112.1	8-4.002x3.50	351C	VO	170 [1]	280@5800	HY	HY	100
Monterey, Custom	124	8-4.0x4.0	400	VO	100 [1]	260@4400	HY	HY	100
Monterey, Custom, Marquis, Brougham	124	8-4.362x3.59	429	VO	190 [1]	320@4400 [7]	HY	HY	140
Cyclone, GT, Spoiler	117	8-4.362x3.59	429	VO	190 [1]	370@5400	HY	HY	140
Cougar, XR-7, GT	112.1	8-4.362x3.59	429	VO	190 [1]	370@5400 [5]	HY	HY	140
Oldsmobile - F-85, Cutlass	112 [15]	6-3.875x3.53	250	IO	100 [16]	145@4200	HY	HY	85
F-85, Cutlass, Supreme	112 [15]	8-4.057x3.385	350	VO	100 [16]	240@4200 [18]	HY	HY	85
Delta 88	124	8-4.057x3.385	350	VO	100 [16]	240@4200	HY	HY	85
Delta 88, Custom, Royale	124	8-4.125x4.250	455	VO	100 [16]	280@4000	HY	HY	85
Delta 88, Custom, Royale, 98	124 [20]	8-4.125x4.250	455	VO	100 [16]	320@4400	HY	HY	85
Cutlass Supreme	112	8-4.125x4.250	455	VO	100 [16]	320@4400	HY	HY	85
4-4-2	112	8-4.125x4.250	455	VO	100 [16]	340@4600 [21]	HY	HY	85
Toronado	122.3	8-4.125x4.250	455	VO	100 [16]	350@4400	HY	HY	85
Plymouth - Valiant, Scamp	108 [22]	6-3.40x3.64	198	IO	100	125@4400	.010H	.020H	70
Barracuda, Coupe	108	6-3.40x3.64	198	IO	100	125@4400	.010H	.020H	70
Barracuda, Coupe	108	6-3.40x4.12	225	IO	100	145@4000	.010H	.020H	70
Valiant, Scamp	108 [22]	6-3.40x4.12	225	IO	100	145@4000	.010H	.020H	70
Satellite, Coupe, Custom, Sebring	115 [23]	6-3.40x4.12	225	IO	100	145@4000	.010H	.020H	70
Fury I, II, III	120	6-3.40x4.12	225	IO	100	145@4000	.010H	.020H	70
Valiant, Scamp, Barracuda, Coupe, Gran Coupe	108 [22]	8-3.91x3.31	318	VO	100	230@4400	HY	HY	95
Satellite, Coupe, Custom, Sebring, Road Runner	115 [23]	8-3.91x3.31	318	VO	110	230@4400	HY	HY	95
Fury I, II, III, Sport Fury	120	8-3.91x3.31	318	VO	110	230@4400	HY	HY	95
Duster 340, 'Cuda	108	8-4.04x3.31	340	VO	110	275@5000	HY	HY	95
Satellite Sebring, Road Runner	115	8-4.04x3.31	340	VO	110	275@5000	HY	HY	95
Fury I, II, III, Sport Fury	120	8-4.0x3.58	360	VO	100	255@4000	HY	HY	95
Barracuda, Coupe, Gran Coupe	108	8-4.25x3.38	383	VO	100	275@4400 [29]	HY	HY	70
Satellite, Coupe, Custom, Sebring, Brougham	115 [23]	8-4.25x3.38	383	VO	100	275@4400 [29]	HY	HY	70
Fury, I, II, III, Sport Fury	120	8-4.25x3.38	383	VO	100	275@4400 [29]	HY	HY	70
Road Runner, GTX, 'Cuda	115 [30]	8-4.25x3.75	426	VO	110	425@5000	HY	HY	75
Fury I, II, III, Sport Fury	120	8-4.32x3.75	440	VO	110	335@4400	HY	HY	70
Sport Fury GT	120	8-4.32x3.75	440	VO	110	370@4600	HY	HY	70
GTX	115	8-4.32x3.75	440	VO	110	370@4600	HY	HY	70
GTX, Road Runner, 'Cuda	115 [30]	8-4.32x3.75	440	VO	110	385@4700	HY	HY	70
Pontiac - Ventura II, Firebird	111 [33]	6-3.875x3.53	250	IO	130 [34]	145@4200	HY	HY	95
LeMans, T-37, Sport	112 [15]	6-3.875x3.53	250	IO	140 [34]	145@4200	HY	HY	95
Ventura II	111	8-3.875x3.25	307	VO	150 [34]	200@4400	HY	HY	65
Ventura II, Firebird, Esprit, Formula 350	111 [33]	8-3.875x3.75	350	VO	140 [34]	250@4400	HY	HY	95
LeMans, T-37, Sport	112 [15]	8-3.875x3.75	350	VO	140 [34]	250@4400	HY	HY	95
Catalina	123.5	8-3.875x3.75	350	VO	140 [34]	250@4400	HY	HY	95
Firebird Esprit	108	8-4.120x3.75	400	VO	140 [34]	265@4400 [40]	HY	HY	95
LeMans, T-37, Sport	112 [15]	8-4.120x3.75	400	VO	140 [34]	265@4400 [42]	HY	HY	95
Catalina, Brougham	123.5	8-4.120x3.75	400	VO	140 [34]	265@4400 [43]	HY	HY	95
Grand Prix	118	8-4.120x3.75	400	VO	140 [34]	300@4800	HY	HY	95
Grand Prix, Firebird Formula 455	118 [33]	8-4.152x4.21	455	VO	140 [34]	325@4400	HY	HY	95
Catalina, Brougham	123.5	8-4.152x4.21	455	VO	140 [34]	280@4400 [47]	HY	HY	95
Bonneville	126	8-4.152x4.21	455	VO	140 [34]	280@4400 [47]	HY	HY	95
Grand Ville	126	8-4.152x4.21	455	VO	140 [34]	325@4400	HY	HY	95
LeMans, T-37, Sport, GTO	112 [15]	8-4.152x4.21	455	VO	140 [34]	325@4400	HY	HY	95
LeMans, T-37, Sport, GTO	112	8-4.152x4.21	455	VO	140 [34]	335@4800	HY	HY	95
Firebird Formula 455, Trans AM	108	8-4.152x4.21	455	VO	140 [34]	335@4800	HY	HY	95

ABBREVIATIONS - FOOTNOTES:

AC - AC Spark Plugs
AU - Autolite Spark Plugs
B - Before Top Dead Center
CH - Champion Spark Plugs
H - Hot Engine
HY - Hydraulic Lifters
IO - In-Line Engine, Overhead Valves
N - Negative
P - Positive

TDC - Top Dead Center
VD - Vibration Damper
VO - V-Type Engine, Overhead Valves
1 - Lowest Cylinder Must Be At Least 75 Percent of Highest
2 - Manual Trans. - 6B@775
3 - Also Ram Air and 285@5400
4 - Manual Trans. - 6B@750
5 - Also Ram Air
6 - Manual Trans. - 10B@750
7 - Also 360@4600

8 - 4-Door - 117.2
9 - Manual Trans. - 10B@700
10 - Manual Trans. - Both Sets of Points - 33
11 - Also Ram Air and 375@5600
12 - 4-Door - 110
13 - Manual Trans. - 6B@800
14 - Also 285@5400
15 - 4-Door - 116
16 - Lowest Cylinder Must Be At Least 80 Percent of Highest

Firing Order	Timing Mark Location	Initial Ignition Timing @ rpm	Breaker Point Gap (in.)	Cam Angle (deg.)	Spark Plugs Make	Model	Gap	Caster Manual Steering (deg.)	Camber Right Wheel (deg.)	Toe-In (in.)	Steering Axis Inclination (deg.)	Cooling System Capacity (qts.)	Crankcase Capacity (qts.)
15426378	VD	6B@575 [13]	.021	27	AU	BRF42	.034	1P	1/2P	3/16	7-3/16	15.2	4
13726548	VD	6B@575 [2]	.021	27	AU	BRF6	.034	1P	1/2P	3/16	7-3/16	16.3	4
13726548	VD	6B@625 [4]	.017	29	AU	ARF42	.034	3/4N	1/4P	1/4	7-3/4	15.3	4
13726548	VD	6B@625 [4]	.017	29	AU	ARF42	.034	0	3/4P	3/16	6-3/4	15.7	4
13726548	VD	10B@600 [6]	.021	27	AU	ARF32	.034	0	3/4P	3/16	6-3/4	16.3	4
15426378	VD	6B@600	.021	27	AU	BRF6	.034	1P	1/2P	3/16	7-3/16	20.3	4
13726548	VD	6B@625	.017	29	AU	ARF42	.034	1P	1/2P	3/16	7-3/16	17.6	4
15426378	VD	4B@600	.021	27	AU	BRF42	.034	1P	1/2P	3/16	7-3/4	18.8	6
15426378	VD	4B@600	.017	29	AU	BRF42	.034	1P	1/2P	3/16	7-3/4	19.4	4
15426378	VD	10B@650 [9]	.020	28.5 [10]	AU	ARF32	.034	3/4N	1/4P	1/4	7-3/4	19.4	6
15426378	VD	10B@650 [9]	.020	28.5 [10]	AU	ARF32	.034	3/4N	1/4P	1/4	7-3/4	19.4	6
15426378	VD	4B@590	.017	29	AU	BRF42	.034	1-1/2P	1/2P	1/8	7-7/8	19.6	4
15426378	VD	4B@600	.017	29	AU	BRF42	.034	1P	1/2P	3/16	7-3/4	19.4	4
153624	VD	6B@750	.027	35	AU	BRF82	.034	0	3/4P	3/16	6-3/4	9.2	4
153624	VD	6B@550 [4]	.027	35	AU	BRF82	.034	0	3/4P	3/16	6-3/4	9	4
153624	VD	6B@600	.027	35	AU	BRF82	.034	0	3/4P	3/16	6-3/4	9.7	4
153624	VD	6B@600	.027	35	AU	BRF82	.034	3/4N	1/4P	1/4	7-3/4	11.2	4
15426378	VD	6B@575 [13]	.021	27	AU	BRF42	.034	0	3/4P	3/16	7-3/4	13.5	4
15426378	VD	6B@575 [13]	.017	29	AU	BRF42	.034	3/4N	1/4P	1/4	7-3/4	15.1	4
13726548	VD	6B@625 [4]	.017	29	AU	BRF42	.034	3/4N	1/4P	1/4	7-3/4	15.3	4
13726548	VD	6B@575 [2]	.021	27	AU	BRF42	.034	1P	1/2P	3/16	7-3/4	16.3	4
13726548	VD	6B@625 [4]	.017	29	AU	ARF42	.034	0	3/4P	3/16	6-3/4	15.7	4
13726548	VD	10B@600 [6]	.021	27	AU	ARF32	.034	0	3/4P	3/16	6-3/4	15.7	4
13726548	VD	6B@625	.017	29	AU	ARF42	.034	1P	1/2P	3/16	7-3/4	17.6	4
15426378	VD	4B@600	.021	27	AU	BRF42	.034	1P	1/2P	3/16	7-3/4	18.8	6
15426378	VD	10B@650 [9]	.020	28.5 [10]	AU	ARF32	.034	3/4N	1/4P	1/4	7-3/4	19.4	6
15426378	VD	10B@650 [9]	.020	28.5 [10]	AU	ARF32	.034	0	3/4P	3/16	6-3/4	19.4	6
153624	VD	4B@500 [17]	.016	32	AC	R46TS	.035	1-1/4N	1/8P	1/8	8	12.2	4
18436572	VD	10B@1100 [19]	.016	30	AC	R46S	.040	1-1/4N	1/8P	1/8	8	15.2	4
18436572	VD	10B@1100	.016	30	AC	R46S	.040	1P	1/8P	1/8	10-1/2	17.5	4
18436572	VD	8B@1100	.016	30	AC	R46S	.040	1P	1/8P	1/8	10-1/2	17.5	4
18436572	VD	8B@1100	.016	30	AC	R46S	.040	1P	1/8P	1/8	10-1/2	17.5	4
18436572	VD	8B@1100	.016	30	AC	R46S	.040	1-1/4N	1/8P	1/8	8	17.5	4
18436572	VD	10B@1100	.016	30	AC	R45S	.040	1-1/4N	1/8P	1/8	8	16.2	4
18436572	VD	10B@1100	.016	30	AC	R46S	.040	2-1/4P	1/8P	1/16	11	18	5
153624	VD	2.5B@800	.020	43	CH	N14Y	.035	1/2N	1/4P	1/8	7-1/2	13	4
153624	VD	2.5B@800	.020	43	CH	N14Y	.035	1/2N	1/4P	1/8	7-1/2	13	4
153624	VD	TDC@750	.020	43	CH	N14Y	.035	1/2N	1/4P	1/8	7-1/2	13	4
153624	VD	TDC@750	.020	43	CH	N14Y	.035	1/2N	1/4P	1/8	7-1/2	13	4
153624	VD	TDC@750	.020	43	CH	N14Y	.035	1/2N	1/4P	1/8	7-1/2	13	4
153624	VD	TDC@750	.020	43	CH	N14Y	.035	1/2N	1/4P	1/8	9	13	4
18436572	VD	TDC@700 [24]	.016	32	CH	N14Y	.035	1/2N	1/4P	1/8	7-1/2	16	4
18436572	VD	TDC@700 [24]	.016	32	CH	N14Y	.035	1/2N	1/4P	1/8	7-1/2	16	4
18436572	VD	TDC@700 [24]	.016	32	CH	N14Y	.035	1/2N	1/4P	1/8	9	16	4
18436572	VD	5B@900	.016	32 [27]	CH	N9Y	.035	1/2N	1/4P	1/8	7-1/2	15 [25]	4
18436572	VD	5B@700 [26]	.016	32	CH	N9Y	.035	1/2N	1/4P	1/8	7-1/2	15	4
18436572	VD	2.5B@700 [28]	.016	32	CH	N13Y	.035	1/2N	1/4P	1/8	9	15.5	4
18436572	VD	12.5B@700	.018	30.5	CH	J14Y	.035	1/2N	1/4P	1/8	7-1/2	14.5	4
18436572	VD	12.5B@700	.018	30.5	CH	J14Y	.035	1/2N	1/4P	1/8	7-1/2	14.5	4
18436572	VD	12.5B@700 [6]	.018	30.5	CH	J14Y	.035	1/2N	1/4P	1/8	9	14.5	4
18436572	VD	2.5B@900	.016	32	CH	N10Y	.035	1/2N	1/4P	1/8	7-1/2	15.5	6
18436572	VD	12.5B@750	.018	30.5	CH	J13Y	.035	1/2N	1/4P	1/8	9	15.5	4
18436572	VD	12.5B@900	.018	30.5	CH	J11Y	.035	1/2N	1/4P	1/8	9	15.5	6
18436572	VD	12.5B@800 [31]	.018	30.5	CH	J11Y	.035	1/2N	1/4P	1/8	7-1/2	15.5	6
18436572	VD	12.5B@900	.016	29 [32]	CH	J11Y	.035	1/2N	1/4P	1/8	7-1/2	15.5	6
153624	VD	4B@550 [35]	.019	32	AC	R46T	.035	1/2P [36]	1/4P [37]	3/16	8-3/4	12.1	4
153624	VD	4B@550 [35]	.019	32	AC	R45T	.035	1-1/2N	1/4P	1/16	9	13	4
18436572	VD	8B@550 [38]	.019	30	AC	R45TS	.035	1/2P	1/4P	3/16	8-3/4	15	4
18436572	VD	9B@600 [39]	.016	30	AC	R47S	.035	1/2P [36]	1/4P [37]	3/16	8-3/4	19.4	5
18436572	VD	9B@600 [39]	.016	30	AC	R47S	.035	1/2N	1/4P	1/16	9	20.2	5
18436572	VD	9B@600 [39]	.016	30	AC	R46S	.035	1-1/2N	1/4P	1/16	9	20.2	5
18436572	VD	9B@700 [41]	.016	30	AC	R46S	.035	1N	3/4P	3/16	8-3/4	18.6	5
18436572	VD	9B@700 [41]	.016	30	AC	R46S	.035	1-1/2N	1/4P	1/16	9	18.6	5
18436572	VD	9B@700 [41]	.016	30	AC	R46S	.035	1-1/2N	1/4P	1/16	8-1/2	18.6	5
18436572	VD	9B@700	.016	30	AC	R46S	.035	1-1/2N	1/4P	1/16	9	18.7	5
18436572	VD	9B@700 [41]	.016	30	AC	R46S	.035	1-1/2N [36]	1/4P [37]	1/16 [44]	9 [45]	18.1 [46]	5
18436572	VD	9B@700 [41]	.016	30	AC	R46S	.035	1-1/2N	1/4P	1/16	8-1/2	17.9	5
18436572	VD	9B@700 [41]	.016	30	AC	R46S	.035	1-1/2N	1/4P	1/16	8-1/2	17.9	5
18436572	VD	9B@700	.016	30	AC	R46S	.035	1-1/2N	1/4P	1/16	9	17.9	5
18436572	VD	9B@700 [41]	.016	30	AC	R46S	.035	1-1/2N	1/4P	1/16	9	17.9	5
18436572	VD	9B@700 [41]	.016	30	AC	R46S	.035	1N	3/4P	3/16	8-3/4	17.9	5

17 – Manual Trans. – 4B@550
18 – Also 260@4600
19 – Manual Trans. – 260 hp – 10B@1100
20 – 98 – 127
21 – Also 350@4700
22 – Scamp – 111
23 – 4-Door – 117
24 – Manual Trans. – TDC@750
25 – 'Cuda – 15.5
26 – Manual Trans. – 5B@750
27 – Manual Trans. – Both Sets of Points – 33

28 – Manual Trans. – 2.5B@750
29 – Also 300@4800
30 – 'Cuda – 108
31 – Manual Trans. – 10B@900
32 – Both Sets of Points – 39
33 – Firebird – 108
34 – Lowest Cylinder Must Be More Than 80 Percent of Highest
35 – Manual Trans. – 5B@700
36 – Firebird – 1N
37 – Firebird – 3/4P

38 – Manual Trans. – 8B@700
39 – Manual Trans. – 9B@800
40 – Also Formula 400 – 300@4800
41 – Manual Trans. – 9B@600
42 – Also GTO – 300@4800
43 – Also 300@4800
44 – Firebird – 3/16
45 – Firebird – 8-3/4
46 – Firebird – 17.9
47 – Also 325@4400

1972

Model	Wheelbase (in.)	No. of Cylinders Bore and Stroke (in.)	Displacement (cu. in.)	Valve and Cylinder Arrangement	Compression Pressure (lbs.)	Net Brake Horsepower @ rpm	Intake	Exhaust	Cylinder Bolt Torque (ft. lbs.)
American Motors – Gremlin, Hornet SST	96 [1]	6–3.75x3.50	232	IO	185 [2]	100@3600	HY	HY	85
Sportabout, Javelin SST, Matador	108 [3]	6–3.75x3.50	232	IO	185 [2]	100@3600	HY	HY	85
Gremlin, Hornet SST, Sportabout	96 [1]	6–3.75x3.90	258	IO	185 [2]	110@3500	HY	HY	85
Javelin SST, Matador	110 [3]	6–3.75x3.90	258	IO	185 [2]	110@3500	HY	HY	85
Gremlin, Hornet SST, Sportabout	96 [1]	8–3.75x3.44	304	VO	185 [2]	150@4200	HY	HY	110
Javelin, Matador, Ambassador	110 [3]	8–3.75x3.44	304	VO	185 [2]	150@4200	HY	HY	110
Hornet SST, Sportabout, Javelin	108 [3]	8–4.08x3.44	360	VO	185 [2]	175@4000	HY	HY	110
Matador, Ambassador	118 [3]	8–4.08x3.44	360	VO	185 [2]	175@4000	HY	HY	110
Javelin, Matador, Ambassador	110 [3]	8–4.08x3.44	360	VO	185 [2]	195@4400	HY	HY	110
Javelin, Matador, Ambassador	110 [3]	8–4.165x3.68	401	VO	200 [2]	255@4600	HY	HY	110
Buick – Skylark, Skylark Custom, Sportwagon	112 [4]	8–3.80x3.85	350	VO	175 [5]	155@3800	HY	HY	75
LeSabre, LeSabre Custom	124	8–3.80x3.85	350	VO	175 [5]	155@3800	HY	HY	75
Skylark, Skylark Custom, GS, Sportwagon	112 [4]	8–3.80x3.85	350	VO	175 [5]	180@3800 [7]	HY	HY	75
LeSabre, LeSabre Custom, GS, Riviera	124 [8]	8–4.3125x3.90	455	VO	175 [5]	225@4000 [9]	HY	HY	100
Centurion, Electra 225, Electra 225 Custom	124 [14]	8–4.3125x3.90	455	VO	175 [5]	225@4000 [15]	HY	HY	100
Estate Wagon	127	8–4.3125x3.90	455	VO	175 [5]	225@4000	HY	HY	100
GS (Stage 1)	112	8–4.3125x3.90	455	VO	175 [5]	270@4400	HY	HY	100
Riviera, Centurion (GS Riviera Option)	122 [8]	8–4.3125x3.90	455	VO	175 [5]	260@4400	HY	HY	100
Cadillac – All Except Eldorado	130 [17]	8–4.30x4.06	472	VO	175	220@4000	HY	HY	115
Eldorado	126.3	8–4.30x4.304	500	VO	175	235@3800	HY	HY	115
Chevrolet – Vega 2300	97	4–3.501x3.625	140	IOC	140	80@4400	.015C [19]	.030C [19]	60
Vega 2300 (L11)	97	4–3.501x3.625	140	IOC	140	90@4800	.015C [19]	.030C [19]	60
Camaro	108	6–3.875x3.53	250	IO	130	110@3800	HY	HY	95
Nova	111	6–3.875x3.53	250	IO	130	110@3800	HY	HY	95
Chevelle	112 [21]	6–3.875x3.53	250	IO	130	110@3800	HY	HY	95
Chevrolet	121.5	6–3.875x3.53	250	IO	130	110@3800	HY	HY	95
Camaro, Nova, Chevelle	108 [22]	8–3.875x3.25	307	VO	150	130@4000	HY	HY	65
Camaro, Nova, Chevelle, Monte Carlo	108 [22]	8–4.0x3.48	350	VO	160	165@4000 [27]	HY	HY	65
Chevrolet	121.5	8–4.0x3.48	350	VO	160	165@4000	HY	HY	65
Camaro (Z27), Nova	108 [22]	8–4.0x3.48	350	VO	160	200@4400	HY	HY	65
Corvette	98	8–4.0x3.48	350	VO	160	200@4400	HY	HY	65
Camaro (Z28)	108	8–4.0x3.48	350	VO	150	255@5600	.020	.025	65
Corvette	98	8–4.0x3.48	350	VO	150	255@5600	.020	.025	65
Chevrolet	121.5	8–4.126x3.75	400	VO	160	170@3400	HY	HY	80
Chevrolet	121.5	8–4.126x3.76	402	VO	160	210@4400	HY	HY	65
Camaro, Chevelle, Monte Carlo	108 [22]	8–4.126x3.76	402	VO	160	240@4400	HY	HY	65
Chevelle, Monte Carlo	112 [21]	8–4.251x4.0	454	VO	160	270@4000	HY	HY	80
Chevrolet	121.5	8–4.251x4.0	454	VO	160	270@4000	HY	HY	80
Corvette	98	8–4.251x4.0	454	VO	160	270@4000	HY	HY	80
Chrysler – Newport Royal	124	8–4.0x3.58	360	VO	100	175@4000	HY	HY	95
Newport Royal, Custom	124	8–4.34x3.38	400	VO	100	190@4400	HY	HY	95
Newport Royal, Custom	124	8–4.32x3.75	440	VO	110	225@4400	HY	HY	70
New Yorker, Brougham	124	8–4.32x3.75	440	VO	110	225@4400	HY	HY	70
Imperial	127	8–4.32x3.75	440	VO	110	225@4400	HY	HY	70
Dodge – Dart, Dart Demon, Swinger Special	111 [30]	6–3.4x3.64	198	IO	100	100@4400	.010H	.020H	70
Dart Custom, Swinger	111	6–3.4x3.64	198	IO	100	100@4400	.010H	.020H	70
Dart, Demon, Custom, Swinger Special	111 [30]	6–3.4x4.12	225	IO	100	110@4000	.010H	.020H	70
Challenger, Charger, Coronet, Custom	110 [31]	6–3.4x4.12	225	IO	100	110@4000	.010H	.020H	70
Dart, Demon, Custom, Swinger Special	111 [30]	8–3.91x3.31	318	VO	100	150@4000	HY	HY	95
Challenger, Coronet, Charger, SE	110 [31]	8–3.91x3.31	318	VO	100	150@4000	HY	HY	95
Polara, Polara Custom	122	8–3.91x3.31	318	VO	100	150@4000	HY	HY	95
Dart Demon 340, Swinger	108 [30]	8–4.04x3.31	340	VO	100	240@4800	HY	HY	95
Challenger, Charger Coupe	110 [31]	8–4.04x3.31	340	VO	100	240@4800	HY	HY	95
Polara, Custom, Monaco	122	8–4.0x3.58	360	VO	100	175@4000	HY	HY	95
Charger, SE, Coronet, Custom	115 [31]	8–4.34x3.38	400	VO	100	190@4400	HY	HY	70
Charger, SE, Coronet, Custom	115 [31]	8–4.34x3.38	400	VO	100	255@4800	HY	HY	70
Polara, Custom, Monaco	122	8–4.34x3.38	400	VO	100	190@4400	HY	HY	70
Charger, SE, Coronet, Custom	115 [31]	8–4.32x3.75	440	VO	110	280@4800	HY	HY	70
Charger, SE, Coronet, Custom	115 [31]	8–4.32x3.75	440	VO	110	330@4800	HY	HY	70
Polara, Custom, Monaco	122	8–4.32x3.75	440	VO	110	225@4400	HY	HY	70
Ford – Pinto	94.2	4–3.188x3.056	97.6	IO	70 [2]	54@4600	.010H	.017H	70
Pinto	94.2	4–3.575x3.029	122	IOC	80 [2]	86@5400	.008C	.010C	80
Maverick	103 [34]	6–3.502x2.94	170	IO	175 [2]	82@4400	HY	HY	75
Maverick, GT	103 [34]	6–3.682x3.126	200	IO	175 [2]	91@4000	HY	HY	75
Ford Custom, 500, Galaxie 500	121	6–4.0x3.18	240	IO	175 [2]	103@3800	HY	HY	75
Maverick, GT, Mustang, Grande	103 [34]	6–3.682x3.91	250	IO	175 [2]	98@3600	HY	HY	75

ABBREVIATIONS – FOOTNOTES:

AC – AC Spark Plugs
AU – Autolite Spark Plugs
B – Before Top Dead Center
C – Cold Engine
CH – Champion Spark Plugs
CP – Crankshaft Pulley
EL – Electronic Ignition
H – Hot Engine
HY – Hydraulic Lifters

IO – In-Line Engine, Overhead Valves
IOC – In-Line Engine, Overhead Cam
N – Negative
P – Positive
TDC – Top Dead Center
VD – Vibration Damper
VO – V-Type Engine, Overhead Valves
1 – Hornet, Sportabout – 108
2 – Lowest Cylinder Must Be At Least 75 Percent of Highest

3 – Javelin – 110, Matador – 118, Ambassador – 122
4 – 4-Door and Sportwagon – 116
5 – Lowest Cylinder Must Be At Least 70 Percent of Highest
6 – Manual Trans. – 4B@800
7 – GS W/Dual Exh. – 195@4000
8 – GS – 112, Riviera – 122, Centurion – 124
9 – Riviera or Dual Exh., Except GS – 250@4000

| Firing Order | Timing Mark Location | Initial Ignition Timing @ rpm | Breaker Point Gap (in.) | Cam Angle (deg.) | Spark Plugs | | | Caster Manual Steering (deg.) | Camber Right Wheel (deg.) | Toe-In | Steering Axis Inclination (deg.) | Cooling System Capacity (qts.) | Crankcase Capacity (qts.) |
					Make	Model	Gap (in.)						
153624	VD	5B@550	.016	32	CH	N12Y	.035	1P	1/8P	1/8	7-3/4	10.5	4
153624	VD	5B@550	.016	32	CH	N12Y	.035	1P	1/8P	1/8	7-3/4	10.5	4
153624	VD	3B@550	.016	32	CH	N12Y	.035	1P	1/8P	1/8	7-3/4	10.5	4
153624	VD	3B@550	.016	32	CH	N12Y	.035	1P	1/8P	1/8	7-3/4	10.5	4
18436572	VD	5B@650	.016	30	CH	N12Y	.035	1P	1/8P	1/8	7-3/4	14.0	4
18436572	VD	5B@650	.016	30	CH	N12Y	.035	1P	1/8P	1/8	7-3/4	14.0	4
18436572	VD	5B@700	.016	30	CH	N12Y	.035	1P	1/8P	1/8	7-3/4	13.0	4
18436572	VD	5B@700	.016	30	CH	N12Y	.035	1P	1/8P	1/8	7-3/4	13.0	4
18436572	VD	5B@700	.016	30	CH	N12Y	.035	1P	1/8P	1/8	7-3/4	13.0	4
18436572	VD	4B@650[6]	.016	30	AC	R45TS	.040	1/2P	1/2P	3/16[11]	8	16.45	4
18436572	VD	4B@650	.016	30	AC	R45TS	.040	1P	1/4P	3/16[11]	9-5/8	18.9	4
18436572	VD	4B@650[6]	.016	30	AC	R45TS	.040	1/2P	1/2P	3/16[11]	8	16.45	4
18436572	VD	4B@650[6]	.016	30	AC	R45TS	.040	1P[10]	1/4P[10]	3/16[11]	9-5/8[12]	18.9[13]	4
18436572	VD	4B@650	.016	30	AC	R45TS	.040	1P	1/4P	3/16[11]	9-5/8	18.7	4
18436572	VD	4B@650	.016	30	AC	R45TS	.040	1P	1/4P	3/16[11]	10-3/8	18.7	4
18436572	VD	10B@650[16]	.016	30	AC	R45TS	.040	1/2P	1/2P	3/16[11]	8	21.8	4
18436572	VD	4B@650	.016	30	AC	R45TS	.040	1P	1/4P	3/16[11]	9-5/8	18.7	4
15634278	VD	8B@600	.016	30	AC	R46N	.035	1N	0	3/16[11]	6	21.8[18]	4
15634278	VD	8B@600	.016	30	AC	R46N	.035	1N	0	0	11	21.3	5
1342	CP	6B@700	.019	32	AC	R42TS	.035	3/4N	1/4P	1/4	8-1/2	6.5	3
1342	CP	8B@700	.019	32	AC	R42TS	.035	3/4N	1/4P	1/4	8-1/2	6.5	3
153624	VD	4B@600[20]	.019	32	AC	R46T	.035	0	1P	3/16	9-1/2	12	4
153624	VD	4B@600[20]	.019	32	AC	R46T	.035	1/2P	1/4P	3/16	8-3/4	12	4
153624	VD	4B@600[20]	.019	32	AC	R46T	.035	1N	3/4P	3/16	8-1/4	12	4
153624	VD	4B@600[20]	.019	32	AC	R46T	.035	1N	1/2P	3/16	10	12	4
18436572	VD	8B@600[23]	.019	30	AC	R44T	.035	0[24]	1P[25]	3/16	9-1/2[26]	15	4
18436572	VD	6B@600[28]	.019	30	AC	R44T	.035	0[24]	1P[25]	3/16	9-1/2[26]	16	4
18436572	VD	6B@600	.019	30	AC	R44T	.035	1N	1/2P	3/16	10	16	4
18436572	VD	8B@600[28]	.019	30	AC	R44T	.035	0[24]	1P[25]	3/16	9-1/2[26]	16	4
18436572	VD	8B@600[29]	.019	30	AC	R44T	.035	1P	3/4P	1/4	7	15	4
18436572	VD	12B@700[6]	.019	30	AC	R44T	.035	0	1P	3/16	9-3/4	16	4
18436572	VD	4B@900	.019	30	AC	R44T	.035	1P	3/4P	1/4	7	18	4
18436572	VD	6B@600	.019	30	AC	R44T	.035	1N	1/2P	3/16	10	16	4
18436572	VD	6B@600	.019	29	AC	R44T	.035	1N	1/2P	3/16	10	23	4
18436572	VD	8B@600	.019	29	AC	R44T	.035	0	1P	3/16	9-1/2	24	4
18436572	VD	8B@600[29]	.019	29	AC	R44T	.035	1N	3/4P	3/16	8-1/4	22	4
18436572	VD	8B@600	.019	29	AC	R44T	.035	1N	1/2P	3/16	10	22	4
18436572	VD	8B@600[29]	.019	29	AC	R44T	.035	1P	3/4P	1/4	7	22	5
18436572	VD	TDC@750	.017	32	CH	N13Y	.035	5/8P	1/4P	1/8	9	15.5	4
18436572	VD	5B@700	.018	30.5	CH	J13Y	.035	5/8P	1/4P	1/8	9	14.5	4
18436572	VD	10B@750	.018	30.5	CH	J11Y	.035	5/8P	1/4P	1/8	9	15.5	4
18436572	VD	10B@750	.018	30.5	CH	J11Y	.035	5/8P	1/4P	1/8	9	15.5	4
18436572	VD	10B@750	EL	EL	CH	J11Y	.035	5/8P	1/4P	1/8	9	17.5	4
153624	VD	2.5B@800	.020	43	CH	N14Y	.035	5/8N	1/4P	1/8	7-1/2	13	4
153624	VD	2.5B@800	.020	43	CH	N14Y	.035	5/8N	1/4P	1/8	7-1/2	13	4
153624	VD	TDC@750	.020	43	CH	N14Y	.035	5/8N	1/4P	1/8	7-1/2	13	4
153624	VD	TDC@750	.020	43	CH	N14Y	.035	5/8N	1/4P	1/8	7-1/2	13	4
18436572	VD	TDC@750	.016	32	CH	N13Y	.035	5/8N	1/4P	1/8	7-1/2	16	4
18436572	VD	TDC@750	.016	32	CH	N13Y	.035	5/8P	1/4P	1/8	9	16	4
18436572	VD	2.5B@750[32]	EL	EL	CH	N9Y	.035	5/8N	1/4P	1/8	7-1/2	15	4
18436572	VD	2.5B@750[32]	EL	EL	CH	N9Y	.035	5/8N	1/4P	1/8	7-1/2	15	4
18436572	VD	TDC@750	.016	32	CH	N13Y	.035	5/8P	1/4P	1/8	9	15.5	4
18436572	VD	5B@700	.018	30.5	CH	J13Y	.035	5/8N	1/4P	1/8	7-1/2	14.5	4
18436572	VD	10B@750[32]	EL	EL	CH	J11Y	.035	5/8N	1/4P	1/8	7-1/2	15	4
18436572	VD	5B@750	.018	30.5	CH	J13Y	.035	5/8P	1/4P	1/8	9	14.5	4
18436572	VD	10B@900[32]	EL	EL	CH	J11Y	.035	5/8N	1/4P	1/8	7-1/2	15	4
18436572	VD	2.5B@900	EL	EL	CH	J11Y	.035	5/8N	1/4P	1/8	7-1/2	15	6
18436572	VD	10B@750	.018	30.5	CH	J11Y	.035	5/8P	1/4P	1/8	9	15.5	4
1243	CP	12B@900	.025	40	AU	AGR22	.030	1-1/2P	3/4P	3/16	9	7.8	3
1342	CP	6B@650[33]	.025	40	AU	BRF32	.034	1-1/2P	3/4P	3/16	9	8.5	4
153624	VD	6B@750	.027	35	AU	BRF82	.034	1/2N	1/4P	3/16	6-3/4	9.2	4
153624	VD	6B@550	.027	35	AU	BRF82	.034	1/2N	1/4P	3/16	6-3/4	9	4
153624	VD	6B@500	.027	37	AU	BRF42	.034	1P	1/4P	3/16	7-1/4	14.1	4
153624	VD	6B@600[33]	.027	35	AU	BRF82	.034	1/2N[35]	1/4P[36]	3/16	6-3/4	9.2[37]	4

10 – GS – 1/2P
11 – + or – 1/8 in.
12 – GS – 8
13 – GS – 16.2, Riviera – 18.7
14 – Electra 225, Custom – 127
15 – Dual Exhaust – 250@4000
16 – Manual Trans. – 8B@900
17 – Brougham – 133, 75 – 151.5
18 – 75 – 24.8
19 – Running – Intake .015, Exh. .016

20 – Manual Trans. – 4B@700
21 – Chevelle 4-Door, Monte Carlo – 116
22 – Nova – 111, Chevelle – 112/116, Monte Carlo – 116
23 – Manual Trans. – 4B@900
24 – Nova – 1/2P, Chevelle/Monte Carlo – 1N
25 – Nova – 1/4P, Chevelle/Monte Carlo – 3/4P
26 – Nova – 8-3/4, Chevelle/Monte Carlo – 8-1/4
27 – Chevelle/Monte Carlo – Also 175@4000
28 – Manual Trans. – 6B@900

29 – Manual Trans. – 8B@800
30 – Demon – 108, Swinger 111
31 – Charger – 115, Coronet 118
32 – Manual Trans. – 2.5B@900
33 – Manual Trans. – 6B@750
34 – 4-Door – 110, Mustang – 109
35 – Mustang – 0
36 – Mustang – 3/4P
37 – Mustang – 11.2

1972

	Wheelbase (in.)	No. of Cylinders Bore and Stroke (in.)	Displacement (cu. in.)	Valve and Cylinder Arrangement	Compression Pressure (lbs.)	Net Brake Horsepower @ rpm	Valve Tappet Clearance Intake	Exhaust	Cylinder Bolt Torque (ft. lbs.)
Torino, Gran Torino, Sport	114[1]	6-3.682x3.91	250	IO	175[2]	95@3600	HY	HY	75
Maverick, GT, Mustang, Grande, Mach 1	103[4]	8-4.002x3.0	302	VO	150[2]	143@4200	HY	HY	72
Torino, Gran Torino, Sport	114[1]	8-4.002x3.0	302	VO	150[2]	140@4000	HY	HY	72
Ford Custom, 500	121	8-4.002x3.0	302	VO	150[2]	140@4000	HY	HY	72
Ford LTD, Brougham	121	8-4.0x3.50	351W	VO	160[2]	153@3800	HY	HY	112
Ford (All)	121	8-4.0x3.50	351C	VO	170[2]	163@3800	HY	HY	100
Torino, Gran Torino, Sport	114[1]	8-4.0x3.50	351C	VO	170[2]	161@4000	HY	HY	100
Mustang, Grande, Mach 1	109	8-4.0x3.50	351C	VO	170[2]	177@4000	HY	HY	100
Torino, Gran Torino, Sport	114[1]	8-4.0x3.50	351C	VO	170[2]	248@5400	HY	HY	100
Mustang, Grande, Mach 1	109	8-4.0x3.50	351C	VO	170[2]	266@5400	HY	HY	100
Torino, Gran Torino, Sport	114[1]	8-4.0x4.0	400	VO	180[2]	168@4200	HY	HY	100
Ford (All)	121	8-4.0x4.0	400	VO	180[2]	172@4000	HY	HY	100
Torino, Gran Torino, Sport	114[1]	8-4.362x3.59	429	VO	190[2]	205@4400	HY	HY	140
Ford (All)	121	8-4.362x3.59	429	VO	190[2]	208@4400	HY	HY	140
Thunderbird	120.4	8-4.362x3.59	429	VO	190[2]	212@4400	HY	HY	140
Thunderbird	120.4	8-4.362x3.85	460	VO	180[2]	212@4400	HY	HY	140
Lincoln	127	8-4.362x3.85	460	VO	180[2]	224@4400	HY	HY	140
Mark IV	120.4	8-4.362x3.85	460	VO	180[2]	212@4400	HY	HY	140
Mercury - Comet (All)	103[4]	6-3.502x2.94	170	IO	175[2]	82@4400	HY	HY	75
Comet (All)	103[4]	6-3.682x3.126	200	IO	175[2]	91@4000	HY	HY	75
Comet (All)	103[4]	6-3.682x3.91	250	IO	175[2]	98@3600	HY	HY	75
Montego	114[1]	6-3.682x3.91	250	IO	175[2]	95@3600	HY	HY	75
Comet (All)	103[4]	8-4.002x3.0	302	VO	150[2]	143@4200	HY	HY	72
Montego	114[1]	8-4.002x3.0	302	VO	150[2]	140@4000	HY	HY	72
Montego, GT	114[1]	8-4.002x3.0	351W	VO	160[2]	161@4000	HY	HY	112
Cougar (All), Monterey	112.1[11]	8-4.002x3.50	351C	VO	170[2]	164@4000	HY	HY	100
Cougar (All)	112.1	8-4.002x3.50	351C	VO	170[2]	262@5400[14]	HY	HY	100
Montego, GT	112.1[11]	8-4.002x3.50	351C	VO	170[2]	248@5400	HY	HY	100
Montego, GT	112.1[11]	8-4.0x4.0	400	VO	180[2]	168@4200	HY	HY	100
Monterey, Custom	124	8-4.0x4.0	400	VO	180[2]	172@4000	HY	HY	100
Monterey, Custom, Marquis, Brougham	124	8-4.362x3.59	429	VO	190[2]	208@4400	HY	HY	140
Montego, GT	114	8-4.362x3.59	429	VO	190[2]	205@4400	HY	HY	140
Monterey, Custom, Marquis, Brougham	124	8-4.362x3.85	460	VO	180[2]	200@4400	HY	HY	140
Oldsmobile - F-85, Cutlass, Supreme	112[17]	8-4.057x3.385	350	VO	160[18]	160@4000[19]	HY	HY	85
Delta 88, Royale	124	8-4.057x3.385	350	VO	160[18]	160@4000	HY	HY	85
F-85, Cutlass, Supreme	112[17]	8-4.057x3.385	350	VO	160[18]	180@4000[20]	HY	HY	85
Delta 88, Royale	124	8-4.057x3.385	350	VO	160[18]	180@4000	HY	HY	85
Delta 88, Royale, 98	124[22]	8-4.126x4.250	455	VO	160[18]	225@3600[23]	HY	HY	85
F-85, Cutlass, Supreme	112[17]	8-4.126x4.250	455	VO	160[18]	250@4200[24]	HY	HY	85
Toronado	122	8-4.126x4.250	455	VO	160[18]	265@4200	HY	HY	85
F-85, Cutlass, Supreme	112[17]	8-4.126x4.250	455	VO	160[18]	300@4700	HY	HY	85
Plymouth - Valiant, Duster, Scamp	108[26]	6-3.40x3.64	198	IO	100	100@4400	.010H	.020H	70
Valiant, Duster, Scamp, Barracuda	108[26]	6-3.40x4.12	225	IO	100	110@4000	.010H	.020H	70
Satellite, Custom, Sebring	115[27]	6-3.40x4.12	225	IO	100	110@4000	.010H	.020H	70
Valiant, Duster, Scamp, Barracuda, 'Cuda	108[26]	8-3.91x3.31	318	VO	100	150@4000	HY	HY	95
Satellite, Custom, Sebring, Sebring Plus	115[27]	8-3.91x3.31	318	VO	100	150@4000	HY	HY	95
Fury I, II, III, Gran Coupe, Sedan	120	8-3.91x3.31	318	VO	100	150@4000	HY	HY	95
Duster 340, Barracuda, 'Cuda	108	8-4.04x3.31	340	VO	100	240@4800	HY	HY	95
Road Runner	115	8-4.04x3.31	340	VO	100	240@4800	HY	HY	95
Fury I, II, III, Gran Coupe, Sedan	120	8-4.0x3.58	360	VO	100	175@4000	HY	HY	95
Satellite, Custom, Sebring, Sebring Plus	115[27]	8-4.34x3.38	400	VO	100	190@4400[29]	HY	HY	70
Fury I, II, III, Gran Coupe, Sedan	120	8-4.34x3.38	400	VO	100	190@4400	HY	HY	70
Fury I, II, III, Gran Coupe, Sedan	120	8-4.32x3.75	440	VO	110	225@4400	HY	HY	70
Road Runner	115	8-4.32x3.75	440	VO	110	280@4800[31]	HY	HY	70
Pontiac - Ventura II, Firebird	111[32]	6-3.875x3.53	250	IO	140[33]	110@3800	HY	HY	95
LeMans, Sport	112[17]	6-3.875x3.53	250	IO	140[33]	110@3800	HY	HY	95
Ventura II	111	8-3.875x3.25	307	VO	150[33]	130@4400	HY	HY	65
Ventura II, Firebird, Esprit, Formula 350	111[32]	8-3.875x3.75	350	VO	140[33]	160@4400[39]	HY	HY	95
LeMans, Sport, Luxury	112[17]	8-3.875x3.75	350	VO	140[33]	160@4400[39]	HY	HY	95
LeMans, Sport, Luxury, GTO	112[17]	8-4.120x3.75	400	VO	140[33]	175@4000[40]	HY	HY	95
Grand Prix, Firebird, Formula 400	118[32]	8-4.120x3.75	400	VO	140[33]	250@3600[39]	HY	HY	95
Catalina, Brougham	123.5	8-4.120x3.75	400	VO	140[33]	175@4000	HY	HY	95
Catalina, Brougham, Bonneville	123.5[44]	8-4.152x4.21	455	VO	140[33]	185@4000[40]	HY	HY	95
Catalina, Brougham, Bonneville, Grand Ville	123.5[44]	8-4.152x4.21	455	VO	140[33]	220@3600[45]	HY	HY	95
LeMans, Sport, Luxury, Grand Prix	112[47]	8-4.152x4.21	455	VO	140[33]	250@3600[48]	HY	HY	95
LeMans, Sport, Firebird, Formula, Trans AM	112	8-4.152x4.21	455	VO	140[33]	300@4000	HY	HY	95

ABBREVIATIONS - FOOTNOTES:

AC - AC Spark Plugs
AU - Autolite Spark Plugs
B - Before Top Dead Center
C - Cold Engine
CH - Champion Spark Plugs
EL - Electronic Ignition
H - Hot Engine
HY - Hydraulic Lifters
IO - In-Line Engine, Overhead Valves
N - Negative

P - Positive
TDC - Top Dead Center
VD - Vibration Damper
VO - V-Type Engine, Overhead Valves
1 - 4-Door - 118
2 - Lowest Cylinder Must Be At Least 75 Percent of Highest
3 - Manual Trans. - 6B@750
4 - 4-Door - 110, Mustang - 109
5 - Mustang - 6B@625, Manual Trans. - 6B@800
6 - Mustang - 0

7 - Mustang - 3/4P
8 - Mustang - 15.2
9 - Manual Trans. - 6B@850
10 - Manual Trans. - 10B@900
11 - Monterey - 124
12 - Monterey - 1P
13 - Monterey - 7-1/4
14 - Also CJ - 266@5400
15 - Manual Trans. - 6B@825
16 - CJ - 16.3
17 - 4-Door - 116

Tuneup Specifications

Firing Order	Timing Mark Location	Initial Ignition Timing @ rpm	Breaker Point Gap (in.)	Cam Angle (deg.)	Make	Model	Gap (in.)	Caster Manual Steering (deg.)	Camber Right Wheel (deg.)	Toe-In (in.)	Steering Axis Inclination (deg.)	Cooling System Capacity (qts.)	Crankcase Capacity (qts.)
153624	VD	6B@600[3]	.027	37	AU	BRF82	.034	1-1/4P	3/4P	3/16	7-3/4	11.5	4
15426378	VD	6B@550[5]	.021	27	AU	BRF42	.034	1/2N[6]	1/4P[7]	3/16	6-3/4	13.4[8]	4
15426378	VD	6B@575[9]	.021	27	AU	BRF42	.034	1-1/4P	3/4P	3/16	7-3/4	15.2	4
15426378	VD	6B@600	.017	28	AU	BRF42	.034	1P	1/2P	3/16	7-1/4	15.2	4
13726548	VD	6B@600	.017	28	AU	BRF42	.034	1P	1/2P	3/16	7-1/4	15.8	4
13726548	VD	6B@600	.017	28	AU	ARF42	.034	1P	1/2P	3/16	7-1/4	16.3	4
13726548	VD	6B@625	.017	28	AU	ARF42	.034	1-1/4P	3/4P	3/16	7-3/4	15.5	4
13726548	VD	6B@625[3]	.021	27	AU	ARF42	.034	0	3/4P	3/16	6-3/4	15.8	4
13726548	VD	16B@700[10]	.017	28	AU	ARF42	.034	1-1/4P	3/4P	3/16	7-3/4	15.5	4
13726548	VD	16B@700[10]	.017	28	AU	ARF42	.034	0	3/4P	3/16	6-3/4	16.3	4
13726548	VD	6B@625	.017	28	AU	ARF42	.034	1-1/4P	3/4P	3/16	7-3/4	17.7	4
13726548	VD	6B@625	.017	28	AU	ARF42	.034	1P	1/2P	3/16	7-1/4	17.7	4
15426378	VD	10B@600	.017	28	AU	BRF42	.034	1-1/4P	3/4P	3/16	7-3/4	18.8	4
15426378	VD	10B@600	.017	28	AU	BRF42	.034	1P	1/2P	3/16	7-1/4	18.8	6
15426378	VD	10B@600	.020	28	AU	BRF42	.034	1-1/4P	3/4P	3/16	7-3/4	18.8	4
15426378	VD	10B@600	.020	28	AU	BRF42	.034	1-1/4P	3/4P	3/16	7-3/4	20	4
15425378	VD	10B@600	.017	28	AU	BRF42	.034	1-1/2P	1/2P	1/8	7-7/8	19.5	4
15426378	VD	10B@600	.017	28	AU	BRF42	.034	1-1/2P	3/4P	3/16	7-3/4	19.5	4
153624	VD	6B@750	.027	35	AU	BRF82	.034	1/2N	1/4P	3/16	6-3/4	9.2	4
153624	VD	6B@550[3]	.027	35	AU	BRF82	.034	1/2N	1/4P	3/16	6-3/4	9	4
153624	VD	6B@600	.027	35	AU	BRF82	.034	1/2N	1/4P	3/16	6-3/4	9.7	4
153624	VD	6B@625[3]	.027	37	AU	BRF82	.034	3/4P	3/4P	3/16	7-3/4	11.5	4
15426378	VD	6B@500[5]	.021	27	AU	BRF42	.034	1/2N	1/4P	3/16	6-3/4	13.4	4
15426378	VD	6B@625[9]	.021	27	AU	BRF42	.034	3/4P	3/4P	3/16	7-3/4	15.2	4
13726548	VD	6B@625	.017	28	AU	BRF42	.034	3/4P	3/4P	3/16	7-3/4	15.8	4
13726548	VD	6B@625[3]	.021	27	AU	ARF42	.034	0[12]	1/2P	3/16	6-3/4[13]	15.8	4
13726548	VD	6B@650[15]	.021	27	AU	ARF42	.034	0	1/2P	3/16	6-3/4	15.8[16]	4
13726548	VD	16B@700[10]	.017	28	AU	ARF42	.034	3/4P	3/4P	3/16	7-3/4	15.5	4
13726548	VD	6B@625	.017	28	AU	ARF42	.034	3/4P	3/4P	3/16	7-3/4	17.7	4
13726548	VD	6B@625	.017	28	AU	ARF42	.034	1P	1/2P	3/16	7-1/4	17.7	4
15426378	VD	10B@600	.017	28	AU	BRF42	.034	1P	1/2P	3/16	7-1/4	18.8	6
15426378	VD	10B@600	.017	28	AU	BRF42	.034	3/4P	3/4P	3/16	7-3/4	18.8	4
15426378	VD	10B@600	.017	28	AU	BRF42	.034	1P	1/2P	3/16	7-1/4	19.5	4
18436572	VD	8B@1100	.016	30	AC	R46S	.040	1-1/4N	1/4N	0	8	15.2	4
18436572	VD	8B@1100	.016	30	AC	R46S	.040	1P	1/4N	0	9-5/8	16.2	4
18436572	VD	12B@1100[21]	.016	30	AC	R46S	.040	1-1/4N	1/4N	0	8	15.2	4
18436572	VD	12B@1100	.016	30	AC	R46S	.040	1P	1/4N	0	9-5/8	16.2	4
18436572	VD	8B@1100	.016	30	AC	R46S	.040	1P	1/4N	0	9-5/8	17	4
18436572	VD	8B@1100[25]	.016	30	AC	R46S	.040	1-1/4N	1/4N	0	8	17	4
18436572	VD	8B@1100	.016	30	AC	R46S	.040	2N	1/4N	0	11	19.5	5
18436572	VD	10B@850[25]	.016	30	AC	R45S	.040	1-1/4N	1/4N	0	8	17	4
153624	VD	2.5B@800	.020	43	CH	N14Y	.035	5/8N	1/4P	1/8	7-1/2	13	4
153624	VD	TDC@750	.020	43	CH	N14Y	.035	5/8N	1/4P	1/8	7-1/2	13	4
153624	VD	TDC@750	.020	43	CH	N14Y	.035	5/8N	1/4P	1/8	7-1/2	13	4
18436572	VD	TDC@750	.016	32	CH	N13Y	.035	5/8N	1/4P	1/8	7-1/2	16	4
18436572	VD	TDC@750	.016	32	CH	N13Y	.035	5/8N	1/4P	1/8	9	16	4
18436572	VD	TDC@750	.016	32	CH	N13Y	.035	5/8P	1/4P	1/8	9	16	4
18436572	VD	2.5B@750[28]	EL	EL	CH	N9Y	.035	5/8N	1/4P	1/8	7-1/2	15	4
18436572	VD	2.5B@750[28]	EL	EL	CH	N9Y	.035	5/8N	1/4P	1/8	7-1/2	15	4
18436572	VD	TDC@750	.016	32	CH	N13Y	.035	5/8P	1/4P	1/8	9	15.5	4
18436572	VD	5B@700[30]	.018	30.5	CH	J13Y	.035	5/8N	1/4P	1/8	7-1/2	14.5	4
18436572	VD	5B@700	.018	30.5	CH	J13Y	.035	5/8P	1/4P	1/8	9	14.5	4
18436572	VD	10B@750	.018	30.5	CH	J11Y	.035	5/8P	1/4P	1/8	9	15.5	4
18436572	VD	10B@900	EL	EL	CH	J11Y	.035	5/8N	1/4P	1/8	7-1/4	15	4
153624	VD	4B@550[34]	.019	32	AC	R46TS	.035	1/2P[35]	1/4P[36]	3/16	8-3/4[37]	12	4
153624	VD	4B@550[34]	.019	32	AC	R46T	.035	1-1/2N	1/4P	1/16	9	13	4
18436572	VD	8B@550[38]	.019	30	AC	R45TS	.035	1/2P	1/4P	3/16	8-3/4	15	4
18436572	VD	10B@625	.016	30	AC	R46TS	.035	1/2P[35]	1/4P[36]	3/16	8-3/4[37]	19.4	5
18436572	VD	10B@550[38]	.016	30	AC	R46TS	.035	1-1/2N	1/4P	1/16	9	20.2	5
18436572	VD	10B@625[41]	.016	30	AC	R46TS	.035	1-1/2N	1/4P	1/16	9	18.6	5
18436572	VD	10B@500[42]	.016	30	AC	R45TS	.035	1-1/2N[35]	1/4P[36]	1/16[43]	9[37]	18.7	5
18436572	VD	10B@625	.016	30	AC	R45TS	.035	1-1/2N	1/4P	1/16	8-1/2	18.6	5
18436572	VD	10B@625	.016	30	AC	R45TS	.035	1-1/2N	1/4P	1/16	8-1/2	17.9	5
18436572	VD	10B@625	.016[46]	30[46]	AC	R45TS	.035	1-1/2N	1/4P	1/16	8-1/2	17.9	5
18436572	VD	10B@500	.016	30	AC	R45TS	.035	1-1/2N	1/4P	1/16	9	17.9	5
18436572	VD	10B@500	.016[46]	30[46]	AC	R45TS	.035	1-1/2N[35]	1/4P[36]	1/16[43]	9[37]	17.9	5

18 – Lowest Cylinder Must Be At Least 70 Percent of Highest
19 – Dual Exh. – 175@4000
20 – Dual Exh. – 200@4400
21 – Manual Trans. – 8B@1100
22 – 98-127
23 – Dual Exhaust – 250@4400
24 – Also 270@4400
25 – Manual Trans. – 10B@1100
26 – Scamp – 111
27 – 4-Door – 117
28 – Manual Trans. – 2.5B@900
29 – Also Road Runner – 255 and 265@4800
30 – 4 Bbl. with Auto. Trans. – 10B@750, Manual Trans. – 10B@900
31 – Also 290@4800
32 – Firebird – 108
33 – Lowest Cylinder Must Be At Least 80 Percent of Highest
34 – Manual Trans. – 4B@550
35 – Firebird – 1N
36 – Firebird – 3/4P
37 – Firebird – 8-1/2
38 – Manual Trans. – 8B@700
39 – Also Firebird, Esprit, LeMans – 175@4400
40 – Also 200@4000, GTO – 250@4400
41 – 4 Bbl. – 10B@500
42 – Manual Trans. – 8B@600
43 – Firebird – 3/16
44 – Bonneville, Grande Ville – 126
45 – Also 250@3600
46 – Grande Ville, HO, SJ – EL
47 – Grand Prix – 118
48 – Also 230@4400

FOREIGN MAKE	Year	Model	Nationality	No. of Cylinders and Piston Displacement	Firing Order	Valve Tappet Clearance Intake (In.)	Exhaust (In.)	Ignition Breaker Timing (Deg.)	Breaker Gap (In.)	Dwell (Deg.)	Timing Mark Location	Spark Plugs Make	Model	Gap (In.)
Alfa Romeo	1963-67	Giulia 1600 T1	Ita.	4-97	1342	.019C	.021C	3B	.015	60	CP	LO	ZHL	.022
Alfa Romeo	1966-67	Giulia Super, Sprint GTV	Ita.	4-78	1342	.019C	.021C	3B	.015	60	CP	LO	ZHL	.022
Alfa Romeo	1967-68	Giulia 1300 T1	Ita.	4-78	1342	.019C	.021C	3B	.015	60	CP	LO	HLN	.022
Alfa Romeo	1969-70	1750 Berlina, Veloce	Ita.	4-109	1342	.019C	.021C	2ATC	.018	60	CP	LO	HL	.022
Aston-Martin	1966-68	DB6	Eng.	6-244	153624	.010C	.012C	11B	.015	36	VD	CH	N-9Y	.025
Aston-Martin	1969-70	DB5	Eng.	6-244	153624	.010C	.012C	4B	.015	36	VD	CH	N-9Y	.025
Austin	1960-67	Mini	Eng.	4-51.5	1342	.012C	.012C	TDC	.015	60	FW	CH	N-5	.025
Austin	1962-68	Mini-Cooper	Eng.	4-60	1342	.012C	.012C	5B	.015	60	FW	CH	N-5	.025
Austin	1962-67	1100	Eng.	4-67	1342	.012C	.012C	3B[1]	.015	60	FW	CH	N-5	.025
Austin	1967	1300	Eng.	4-78	1342	.012C	.012C	TDC[1]	.015	60	FW	CH	N-9Y	.025
Austin	1968-70	America	Eng.	4-78	1342	.012C	.012C	TDC[1]	.015	60	FW	CH	N-9Y	.025
Austin-Healey	1961-63	Sprite Mark II	Eng.	4-60	1342	.012C	.012C	4B[1]	.015	60	CP	CH	N-5	.025
Austin-Healey	1963-66	Sprite Mark III	Eng.	4-67	1342	.012C	.012C	5B[1]	.015	60	CP	CH	N-5	.025
Austin-Healey	1967	Sprite Mark IV	Eng.	4-78	1342	.012C	.012C	7B[1]	.015	60	CP	CH	N-5	.025
Austin-Healey	1968-69	Sprite Mark IV	Eng.	4-78	1342	.012C	.012C	4B[1]	.015	60	CP	CH	N-9Y	.025
Austin-Healey	1966-67	3000	Eng.	6-180	153624	.012C	.012C	10B	.015	35	CP	CH	UN-12Y	.025
Bentley	1969-70	Bentley T	Eng.	V8-381	15486372	HYD	HYD	TDC	.014	34	VD	CH	N-14Y	.026
BMW	1965-70	1600	Ger.	4-96	1342	.006H	.008H	23B	.016	60	FP	BO	W200T30	.028
BMW	1966-70	2002	Ger.	4-121	1342	.006H	.008H	23B	.016	60	FP	BO	W200T30	.028
BMW	1969-70	2500	Ger.	6-152	153624	.006H	.008H	3B	.014	35	FP	BO	W175T2	.028
BMW	1969-70	2800	Ger.	6-170	153624	.006H	.008H	3B	.014	35	FP	BO	W175T2	.028
Citroen	1960-65	ID19	Fre.	4-121	1342	.008H	.010H	TDC	.016	59	FW	BO	W225T1	.025
Citroen	1966-68	DS19	Fre.	4-121	1342	.008H	.010H	TDC	.015	59	FW	BO	W225T1	.025
Citroen	1969-70	DS21, Pallas	Fre.	4-133	1342	.008H	.010H	TDC	.015	59	FW	BO	W225T1	.025
Datsun	1961-64	1200	Jap.	4-72.5	1342	.014H	.014H	15B	.020	52	CP	NGK	B-6E	.030
Datsun	1961-67	SP 310, 311, 312	Jap.	4-72.5	1342	.014H	.014H	15B	.020	52	CP	NGK	B-6E	.030
Datsun	1961-67	1300 Deluxe	Jap.	4-79.1	1342	.014H	.014H	15B	.020	52	CP	NGK	B-6E	.030
Datsun	1968-70	510 Sedan, Wagon	Jap.	4-97.3	1342	.010H	.012H	5B	.020	52	CP	NGK	BP7E[2]	.025
Datsun	1968-70	SRL 311	Jap.	4-120.9	1342	.017H[3]	.017H[4]	5B	.020	52	CP	NGK	B-6E[2]	.030
Fiat	1964-67	1500	Ita.	4-90.9	1342	.008C	.010C[5]	10B[1]	.017	60	CP	CH	N-9Y	.022
Fiat	1967	124 Sedan, Wagon	Ita.	4-73	1342	.006C	.006C	10B[1]	.017	60	CP	CH	N-4	.022
Fiat	1968-70	124 Sedan, Wagon	Ita.	4-73	1342	.008C	.008C	TDC	.017	60	CP	CH	N-4	.022
Fiat	1968-70	124 Coupe, Spider	Ita.	4-88	1342	.018C	.020C	10B	.017	60	CP	CH	N-6Y	.022
Ford	1960-66	Anglia	Eng.	4-73	1243	.010H	.017H	10B	.015	60	CP	AU	AG32	.025
Ford	1967	Anglia Super 1200	Eng.	4-73	1243	.010H	.017H	6B	.016	60	CP	AU	AG32	.025
Ford	1967	1300 Cortina	Eng.	4-79	1243	.010H	.017H	10B	.016	60	CP	AU	AG32	.025
Ford	1967	1500 Cortina "C"	Eng.	4-91.4	1243	.010H	.017H	6B	.025	39	CP	AU	AG32	.023
Ford	1967	1500 GT Cortina "C"	Eng.	4-91.4	1243	.012H	.022H	10B	.025	39	CP	AU	AG22	.023
Ford	1968-70	1600 Cortina "C"	Eng.	4-98	1243	.010H	.020H	12B	.025	40	CP	AU	AG22	.023
Ford	1968-70	1600 GT Cortina "C"	Eng.	4-98	1243	.012H	.022H	TDC	.025	40	CP	AU	AG22	.025
Honda	1969-70	N600	Jap.	2-36.5	12	.004C	.004C	TDC	.014	100	CP	CH	N-4	.025
Honda	1970	1300	Jap.	4-79.2	1342	.014H	.014H	5B	.020	52	CP	CH	N-4	.025
Jaguar	1969-70	XKE Roadster, Coupe	Eng.	6-258.5	153624	.004H	.006H	10B	.015	35	VD	CH	N-11Y	.025
Jaguar	1969-70	XKE 2 + 2	Eng.	6-258.5	153624	.004H	.006H	10B	.015	35	VD	CH	N-11Y	.025
Jaguar	1969-70	XJ Sedan	Eng.	6-258.5	153624	.004H	.006H	10B	.015	35	VD	CH	N-11Y	.025
Lancia	1964-67	Flavia 1.8	Ita.	4-130	1342	.004H	.008H	14B	.017	60	CP	CH	N-5	.022
Lancia	1966-68	Fulvia Sport	Ita.	4-80	1342	.006H	.010H	14B	.017	60	CP	CH	N-4	.022
Lancia	1970	Flavia Coupe	Ita.	4-122	1342	.004H	.008H	5B	.017	60	CP	CH	N-6Y	.025
Land Rover	1968	Land Rover	Eng.	6-158	153624	.006H	.010H	2B[6]	.016	36	FW	CH	N-4	.030
Land Rover	1969-70	Land Rover	Eng.	4-140	1342	.010C	.010C	3A	.015	52	FW	CH	UN-12Y	.030
Lotus	1969-70	Elan, +2	Eng.	4-95.2	1243	.010H	.017H	10B	.025	39	CP	AU	AG22	.023
Lotus	1969-70	Europa	Eng.	4-90.5	1342	.008C	.010C	TDC	.018	56	CP	CH	N-4	.025
MG	1963-67	Sports Sedan	Eng.	4-67	1342	.012C	.012C	5B[1]	.015	60	FW	CH	N-5	.025
MG	1963-67	Sports Sedan	Eng.	4-78	1342	.012C	.012C	5B[1]	.015	60	FW	CH	N-5	.025
MG	1963-67	MGB	Eng.	4-110	1342	.015H	.015H	10B[1]	.015	60	CP	CH	N-9Y	.025
MG	1968-70	MGB, GT	Eng.	4-110	1342	.015C	.015C	20B	.015	60	CP	CH	N-9Y	.025
MG	1963-66	Midget Mark II	Eng.	4-67	1342	.012C	.012C	5B[1]	.015	60	CP	CH	N-5	.025
MG	1967-70	Midget Mark IV	Eng.	4-78	1342	.012C	.012C	7B[7]	.015	60	CP	CH	N-9Y	.025
Mercedes-Benz	1965-70	200	Ger.	4-121.3	1342	.003C	.007C	2B	.018	50	VD	BO	W200T27	.029
Mercedes-Benz	1965-67	220	Ger.	4-134	1342	.003C	.007C	3B	.014	36	VD	BO	W215T28	.029
Mercedes-Benz	1968-70	220/8	Ger.	4-134	1342	.003C	.008C	43B[8]	.018	50	VD	BO	W215T28	.029
Mercedes-Benz	1966-68	230, 230S, 230SL	Ger.	6-139.9	153624	.003C	.007C	1B[9]	.014	38[10]	VD	BO	W215T28	.029
Mercedes-Benz	1968-69	230/8	Ger.	6-139.9	153624	.003C	.007C	37B[8]	.014	38[11]	VD	BO	W215T28	.029
Mercedes-Benz	1966-68	250, 250S, 250SE, 250SL	Ger.	6-152.4	153624	.003C	.007C	37B[12]	.014	38	VD	BO	W215T28	.029
Mercedes-Benz	1968-69	250/8	Ger.	6-152.4	153624	.003C	.007C	37B	.014	38	VD	BO	W215T28	.029
Mercedes-Benz	1968-69	280S/8,-SE/8,-SL/8	Ger.	6-169.5	153624	.003C	.007C	37B[12]	.014	38	VD	BO	W215T28	.029
Mercedes-Benz	1969-70	300SEL 2.8	Ger.	6-169.5	153624	.003C	.007C	37B	.014	38	VD	BO	WG215T28	.018

ABBREVIATIONS - FOOTNOTES:

A — After Top Center
AC — AC Spark Plug Div., GMC
AU — Autolite Div., Ford

B — Before Top Dead Center
BO — Robert Bosch Corp.
C — Cold
CH — Champion Spark Plug Co.
CP — Crankshaft Pulley

Eng. — English
FP — Fan Pulley
Fre. — French
FW — Flywheel
Ger. — German

H — Hot
HYD — Hydraulic Lifters
Ita. — Italian
Jap. — Japanese
LO — Lodge

and Tuneup Specifications

FOREIGN MAKE	Year	Model	Nationality	No. of Cylinders and Piston Displacement	Firing Order	Intake (In.)	Exhaust (In.)	Breaker Timing (Deg.)	Breaker Gap (In.)	Dwell (Deg.)	Timing Mark Location	Make	Model	Gap (In.)
NSU	1963-67	Sport Prinz	Ger.	2-37	12	.004C	.004C	TDC	.014	100	CP	BO	W200T30	.028
NSU	1967-70	1000C	Ger.	4-72	1342	.007C	.007C	4B	.014	60	CP	BO	W200T30	.028
NSU	1967-70	1200C, 1200TT	Ger.	4-72	1342	.007C	.007C	4B	.014	60	CP	BO	W200T30	.028
NSU	1968-70	RO 80 Wankel	Ger.	2-60	12	NA	NA	7B	NA	NA	FW	BO	MAG310T2SP	.024
Opel	1966-67	Kadett	Ger.	4-66	1342	.006H	.010H	10A	.018	52	CP	AC	44F	.030
Opel	1967	Rallye Kadett	Ger.	4-66	1342	.006H	.010H	10A	.018	50	CP	AC	44F	.030
Opel	1968-70	Kadett	Ger.	4-66	1342	.006H	.010H	10A	.018	50	CP	AC	43FFS	.030
Opel	1968	Rallye Kadett	Ger.	4-91	1342	.012H	.012H	TDC	.018	50	FW	AC	44XLD	.030
Opel	1969-70	Rallye Kadett, GT	Ger.	4-66	1342	.006H	.010H	10A	.018	50	CP	AC	43FFS	.030
Opel	1969-70	GT 1-9	Ger.	4-116	1342	.012H	.012H	TDC	.018	50	FW	AC	42FS	.030
Peugeot	1963-67	403	Fre.	4-99	1342	.004C	.010C	TDC	.020	48	FW	AC	42F	.024
Peugeot	1964-70	404	Fre.	4-99	1342	.006C	.010C	TDC	.020	57	FW	AC	44XL	.025
Peugeot	1969-70	504	Fre.	4-110	1342	.006C	.010C	TDC	.020	57	FW	BO	44XL	.025
Porsche	1966-69	911	Ger.	6-121.5	162435	.004C	.004C	TDC	.016	38	CP	BO	W230T30	.020
Porsche	1966-69	912	Ger.	4-102	1432	.004C	.006C	3B	.016	50	CP	BO	W200T35	.028
Porsche	1970	911T	Ger.	6-134	162435	.004C	.004C	TDC	.016	38	CP	BO	W230T30	.020
Porsche	1970	914	Ger.	4-102	1432	.004C	.006C	3B	.016	50	CP	BO	W200T35	.028
Porsche	1970	914/6	Ger.	6-121	162435	.004C	.004C	TDC	.016	38	CP	BO	W230T30	.020
Renault	1964-69	Caravelle 1133	Fre.	4-68	1342	.006C	.008C	TDC[13]	.018	56	CP	CH	L-87Y	.025
Renault	1967-69	R8 1130	Fre.	4-68	1342	.006C	.008C	TDC[13]	.018	56	CP	CH	L-87Y	.025
Renault	1967-69	R10 1190	Fre.	4-68	1342	.006C	.008C	TDC[13]	.018	56	CP	CH	L-87Y	.032
Renault	1969	R16 1152	Fre.	4-95	1342	.008C	.010C	TDC	.018	56	CP	CH	N-5	.025
Rolls-Royce	1967-70	Silver Shadow	Eng.	8-381	15486372	HYD	HYD	TDC	.014	34	VD	CH	N-14Y	.026
Rover	1967-70	2000 SC	Eng.	4-121	1342	.010C	.015C	4B	.015	52	FW	CH	N-9Y	.025
Rover	1967-70	2000 TC	Eng.	4-121	1342	.010C	.015C	6B	.015	52	FW	CH	N-6Y	.025
Saab	1966-68	96	Swe.	3-45	123	NA	NA	10B	.016	79	FP	BO	M175T1	.028
Saab	1966-67	850 Monte Carlo	Swe.	3-45	123	NA	NA	10B	.018	79	FP	BO	MV340P1	.015
Saab	1967-69	95, 96, Sonnet II	Swe.	4-91.4	1432	.017H	.017H	6B	.018	50	FP	BO	M225T35	.032
Saab	1969	99	Swe.	4-104.3	1432	.017H	.017H	6B	.018	50	FP	BO	W200T30	.028
Simca	1967	1301	Fre.	4-57.6	1342	.004H	.006H	12B	.020	56	CP	CH	H-88	.024
Simca	1967	1501	Fre.	4-57.6	1342	.008H	.014H	12B	.020	56	CP	CH	N-9Y	.024
Simca	1962-67	1000	Fre.	4-57.6	1342	.014H	.014H	12B	.020	56	CP	CH	N-9Y	.024
Simca	1968	1000	Fre.	4-57.6	1342	.012H	.014H	8A	.020	56	CP	CH	N-9Y	.024
Simca	1969	1118	Fre.	4-68.2	1342	.012C	.014C	4A	.012	56	CP	CH	N-9Y	.024
Simca	1970	1118	Fre.	4-68.2	1342	.012C	.014C	4A	.012	56	CP	CH	N-9Y	.024
Simca	1969-70	1204	Fre.	4-73.4	1342	.012C	.014C	4A	.012	56	CP	CH	N-9Y	.024
Subaru	1969-70	360 Sedan	Jap.	2-21.7	12	NA	NA	13B	.014	100	CP	NGK	B7H	.027
Subaru	1969-70	FF-1 Sedan, Wagon	Jap.	4-66.4	1324	.009C	.011C	TDC	.018	52	CP	NTT	BP-6E	.035
Sunbeam	1964-66	Alpine IV	Eng.	4-105	1342	.012H	.014H	10B	.016	60	CP	CH	N-5	.025
Sunbeam	1967	Alpine V	Eng.	4-105	1342	.012H	.014H	8B	.016	60	CP	CH	N-9Y	.025
Sunbeam	1966-67	Rapier V	Eng.	4-105	1342	.012H	.014H	6B	.015	60	CP	CH	N-9Y	.025
Sunbeam	1965-67	Tiger	Eng.	8-289	15426378	HYD	HYD	6B	.015	27	CP	AU	BF42	.034
Sunbeam	1968-70	Arrow	Eng.	4-105	1342	.019H	.020H	8B	.015	60	CP	CH	N-9Y	.025
Sunbeam	1968-70	Alpine Coupe, GT	Eng.	4-105	1342	.012H	.014H	8B	.016	60	CP	CH	N-9Y	.025
Toyota	1965-67	Corona	Jap.	4-113	1243	.008H	.014H	12B	.018	52	CP	CH	N-9Y	.032
Toyota	1968-70	Corona	Jap.	4-113	1243	.008H	.014H	5B	.018	52	CP	CH	N-9Y	.032
Toyota	1969-70	Corolla	Jap.	4-66	1243	.008H	.012H	5A	.018	52	CP	CH	N-9Y	.032
Toyota	1967-70	Crown	Jap.	6-137.5	153624	.007H	.010H	15B	.018	41	CP	CH	N-9Y	.032
Triumph	1965-68	TR4A	Eng.	4-130.5	1342	.010C	.010C	TDC[14]	.015	60	VD	CH	UN-12Y	.025
Triumph	1967	GT6	Eng.	6-122	153624	.010C	.010C	13B	.015	41	VD	CH	UN-12Y	.025
Triumph	1968-70	GT6+	Eng.	6-122	153624	.010C	.010C	4A	.015	41	VD	CH	UN-12Y	.025
Triumph	1968	TR250	Eng.	6-152	153624	.010C	.010C	4A	.015	35	VD	CH	UN-12Y	.025
Triumph	1969-70	TR6	Eng.	6-152	153624	.010C	.010C	4A	.015	35	VD	CH	UN-12Y	.025
Volkswagen	1961-65	1200	Ger.	4-72.74	1432	.008C	.012C	10B	.016	42	CP	BO	W175T1	.026
Volkswagen	1966	1300	Ger.	4-78.42	1432	.004C[15]	.004C[15]	7-1/2B	.016	48	CP	BO	W175T1	.026
Volkswagen	1967	Sedan	Ger.	4-91.1	1432	.004C	.004C	7-1/2B	.016	50	CP	BO	W175T1	.028
Volkswagen	1968-69	Sedan	Ger.	4-91.1	1432	.004C	.004C	TDC	.016	50	CP	BO	W145T1	.028
Volkswagen	1966	Squareback, Fastback	Ger.	4-96.6	1432	.004C	.004C	10B	.016	53	CP	BO	W145T1	.026
Volkswagen	1967	Squareback, Fastback	Ger.	4-96.6	1432	.004C	.004C	7-1/2B	.016	53	CP	BO	W145T1	.028
Volkswagen	1968-70	Squareback, Fastback	Ger.	4-96.6	1432	.004C	.004C	TDC	.016	50	CP	BO	W145T1	.028
Volkswagen	1970	Deluxe Sedan	Ger.	4-96.6	1432	.004C	.004C	TDC	.016	50	CP	BO	W145T1	.028
Volvo	1962-67	122S	Swe.	4-108	1342	.020H	.020H	18B	.018	60	CP	BO	W175T35	.028
Volvo	1968	122S	Swe.	4-108	1342	.020H	.020H	5B	.018	60	CP	BO	W200T35	.028
Volvo	1966-67	1800	Swe.	4-108	1342	.020H	.020H	18B	.018	60	CP	BO	W200T35	.028
Volvo	1968	1800	Swe.	4-108	1342	.020H	.020H	5B	.018	60	CP	BO	W200T35	.028
Volvo	1969	1800	Swe.	4-121	1342	.021H	.021H	10B	.018	60	CP	BO	W200T35	.028
Volvo	1969	140	Swe.	4-121	1342	.021H	.021H	10B	.018	60	CP	BO	W200T35	.028

NA – Not Applicable
NGK – NGK Spark Plug Co.
NTT – Nippon Tokushu Togyo
TDC – Top Dead Center
VD – Vibration Damper

1 – Static Setting Method
2 – City Driving – BP6E
3 – W/Solex Carb. – .008 in.
4 – W/Solex Carb. – .012 in.
5 – 1964-65 W/4-Sp. Trans. – .008 in.

6 – W/Premium Fuel – 6 Deg. BTDC
7 – W/Thermactor – 10 Deg. BTDC
8 – @ 4500 RPM
9 – 230 SL – 4 Deg. BTDC
10 – 230 SL – 36 Deg.

11 – Early 68 – 37 Deg.
12 – SE, SL – 30 Deg. BTDC @ 4500 RPM
13 – 1968 Models – 6 Deg. ATDC
14 – 1965-67 Models – 4 Deg. BTDC
15 – Untagged Engines – Inlet .008, Exhaust .012

FOREIGN MAKE	Year	Model	Nationality	No. of Cylinders and Piston Displacement	Firing Order	Valve Tappet Clearance Intake (in.)	Exhaust (in.)	Ignition Breaker Timing (deg.)	Breaker Gap (in.)	Dwell (deg.)	Timing Mark Location	Spark Plugs Make	Model	Gap (in.)
Aston-Martin	1967-70	DB6	Eng.	6-244	153624	.010C	.012C	11B[1]	.015	36	VD	CH	N-9Y	.025
Aston-Martin	1967-70	DBS	Eng.	6-244	153624	.010C	.012C	4B[1]	.015	36	VD	CH	N-9Y	.025
Aston-Martin	1967-72	DB6, DBS	Eng.	6-244	153624	.010C	.012C	11B[1]	.015	36	VD	CH	N-9Y	.025
Audi	1972	S 90	Ger.	4-107.4	1342	.008	.016	9A	.016	50	CP	BO	W200T30	.028
Audi	1972	100 LS	Ger.	4-114.2	1342	.008	.016	8B[2]	.016	50	CP	BO	W200T30	.024
Austin	1968-70	1000	Eng.	4-61	1342	.012C	.012C	5B	.015	60	FW	CH	N-5	.025
Austin	1967-70	1100	Eng.	4-67	1342	.012C	.012C	3B	.015	60	FW	CH	N-5	.025
Austin	1971	1100	Eng.	4-67	1342	.012C	.012C	3B[3]	.015	60	FW	CH	N-9Y	.025
Austin	1968-72	1300, GT	Eng.	4-78	1342	.012C	.012C	8B[4]	.015	60	FW	CH	N-9Y	.025
Austin	1970-72	Maxi 1500	Eng.	4-90	1342	.018H	.022H	12B	.015	60	FW	CH	N-9Y	.025
Austin	1971	Maxi 1750	Eng.	4-106	1342	.018H	.022H	12B	.015	60	FW	CH	N-9Y	.025
Austin	1969-72	1800	Eng.	4-109.6	1342	.015C	.015C	12B	.015	60	FW	CH	N-9Y	.025
Austin	1969-72	3-Litre	Eng.	6-177.7	153624	.012C	.012C	4B[5]	.015	35	CP	CH	N-9Y	.025
Austin-Healey	1967-72	Sprite Mark IV	Eng.	4-78	1342	.012C	.012C	7B	.015	60	CP	CH	UN-12Y[6]	.025
Bentley	1970-71	Bentley T	Eng.	8-380	15486372	HY	HY	2B[7]	.015	34	VD	CH	N-14Y	.025
Capri	1972	1600	Ger.	4-97.5	1243	.010H	.017H	12B	.025	38	CP	AU	AGR-22	.030
Capri	1972	2000	Ger.	4-122	1342	.008C	.010C	6B[8]	.025	38	CP	AU	BF-32D	.034
Citroen	1971-72	SM	Fre.	6-162.9	162534	.013	.021	27B[9]	.016	88	FW	CH	N-6Y	.025
Citroen	1971-72	DS-21	Fre.	4-132.7[10]	1342	.008H	.010H	10B[11]	.016	57	FW[12]	CH	L-92Y	.025
Datsun	1970-72	L16	Jap.	4-97.3	1342	.010H	.012H	10B[13]	.020	52	CP	NGK	BP5-ES	.034
Datsun	1971-72	A12	Jap.	4-71.5	1342	.014H	.014H	5B	.020	52	CP	NGK	BP5-ES	.034
Datsun	1972	L24	Jap.	6-146	153624	.010H	.012H	5B[14]	.020	37	CP	NGK	BP6-ES	.034
Dodge	1971-72	Colt	Jap.	4-97.5	1342	.006H	.010H	TDC	.020	52	CP	CH	N-9Y	.030
Fiat	1967-69	850 Series	Ita.	4-51.4	1342	.006C	.008C	10B	.018	60	VD	CH	N-6Y	.022
Fiat	1970-72	850 Sedan	Ita.	4-54.4	1342	.006C	.008C	10B	.018	60	VD	CH	N-9Y	.022
Fiat	1967-69	850 Sport Coupe, Spider	Ita.	4-51.4	1342	.006C	.008C	10B	.018	60	VD	CH	N-6Y	.022
Fiat	1970-71	850 Sport Coupe, Spider	Ita.	4-54.4	1342	.006C	.008C	TDC	.016	55	VD	CH	N-7Y	.022
Fiat	1972	850 Sport Spider	Ita.	4-54.4	1342	.006C	.008C	TDC	.016	55	VD	CH	N-7Y	.022
Fiat	1972	128	Ita.	4-68	1342	.012C	.016C	TDC	.016	55	VD	CH	N-9Y	.022
Fiat	1968-69	124 Sedan, Wagon	Ita.	4-87.7	1342	.008C	.008C	TDC	.018	55	VD	CH	N-4	.022
Fiat	1970	124 Sedan, Wagon	Ita.	4-87.7	1342	.008C	.008C	TDC	.018	55	VD	CH	N-9Y	.022
Fiat	1971-72	124 Sedan, Wagon	Ita.	4-98	1342	.008C	.008C	TDC	.018	60	VD	CH	N-9Y	.022
Fiat	1968-69	124 Sport Coupe, Spider	Ita.	4-87.7	1342	.018C	.020C	10B	.018	60	VD	CH	N-6Y	.022
Fiat	1970	124 Sport Coupe, Spider	Ita.	4-87.7	1342	.018C	.020C	5B	.016	56	VD	CH	N-6Y	.022
Fiat	1971-72	124 Sport Coupe, Spider	Ita.	4-98	1342	.018C	.020C	5B[15]	.016	55	VD	CH	N-6Y	.022
Ford	1967-68	Anglia Super 1200	Eng.	4-73	1243	.010H	.017H	2B	.015	60	CP	AU	AG-32	.022
Ford	1968-70	Cortina Lotus	Eng.	4-95	1243	.007H	.008H	12B	.015	40	CP	AU	AG-22	.025
Ford	1969-70	Cortina GT, 1600E	Eng.	4-97.5	1243	.012H	.022H	8B	.025	40	CP	AU	AG-22	.025
Ford	1971	Cortina GT, GXL	Eng.	4-97.1	1243	.008H	.010H	6B	.025	40	CP	AU	BF-32	.025
Ford	1971	Cortina 2000, GT, GXL	Eng.	4-121.6	1243	.008H	.010H	4B	.025	40	CP	AU	BF-32	.025
Ford	1968-70	Zephyr 6	Eng.	V6-152.2	142536	.012H	.022H	12B	.015	36	CP	AU	AG-22	.025
Ford	1971	Zephyr 6	Eng.	V6-152.2	142536	.010H	.018H	12B	.015	36	CP	AU	AG-32A	.025
Ford	1968-70	Zodiac, Executive 6	Eng.	V6-182.5	142536	.012H	.022H	12B	.015	36	VD	AU	AG-22	.025
Ford	1971	Zodiac, Executive 6	Eng.	V6-182.5	142536	.010H	.018H	12B	.025	36	VD	AU	AG-32A	.025
Jaguar	1969-70	XJ6 2.8 Litre	Eng.	6-170	153624	.004H	.006H	12B	.015	35	VD	CH	N-9Y	.025
Jaguar	1971	XJ6 2.8 Litre	Eng.	6-170	153624	.014C	.014C	22B[16]	.015	35	VD	CH	N-7Y	.025
Jaguar	1969-70	XJ6 4.2 Litre	Eng.	6-258.2	153624	.004H	.006H	8B	.015	35	VD	CH	N-11Y	.025
Jaguar	1971	XJ6 4.2 Litre	Eng.	6-258.2	153624	.014C	.014C	22B[17]	.015	35	VD	CH	N-11Y	.025
Jaguar	1969-70	"E" Type Series II, 4.2 Litre	Eng.	6-258.2	153624	.004H	.006H	10B	.015	35	VD	CH	N-11Y	.025
Jaguar	1971	"E" Type Series II, 4.2 Litre	Eng.	6-258.2	153624	.014C	.014C	10B	.015	35	VD	CH	N-11Y	.025
M.G.	1968-72	Midget Mark III	Eng.	4-78	1342	.012C	.012C	7B	.015	60	CP	CH	N-9Y	.025
M.G.	1969-72	1300 Mark II	Eng.	4-78	1342	.012C	.012C	5B	.015	60	CP	CH	N-9Y	.025
M.G.	1968-70	M.G.B., GT	Eng.	4-109.6	1342	.015C	.015C	20B	.015	60	CP	CH	N-9Y	.025
M.G.	1971	M.G.B., GT	Eng.	4-109.6	1342	.015C	.015C	15B	.015	60	CP	CH	N-9Y	.025
M.G.	1972	M.G.B., GT	Eng.	4-109.6	1342	.015C	.015C	16B	.015	60	CP	CH	N-9Y	.025
Mazda	1969-72	R-100	Jap.	30x2[18]	12	NA	NA	0[19]	.018	58	FP	CH	N-80B	.033
Mazda	1971-72	RX-2	Jap.	35x2[18]	12	NA	NA	0[19]	.018	58	FP	CH	N-80B	.033
Mazda	1970-72	616	Jap.	4-96.8	1342	.014H	.016H	8B	.020	52	FP	CH	N-9Y	.031
Mercedes-Benz	1965-70	200	Ger.	4-121.3	1342	.003C	.007C	2B	.018	50	VD	BO	W200T27	.028
Mercedes-Benz	1965-67	220	Ger.	4-134	1342	.003C	.007C	3B	.014	36	VD	BO	W215T28	.028
Mercedes-Benz	1968-71	220/8	Ger.	4-134	1342	.003C	.008C	5A[20]	.018	50	VD	BO	W215T30	.028
Mercedes-Benz	1972	220/8	Ger.	4-134	1342	.003C	.008C	5A[20]	.018	50	VD	BO	W175T30	.024
Mercedes-Benz	1966-68	230, 230 S, 230 SL	Ger.	6-139.9	153624	.003C	.007C	1B[21]	.014	38[22]	VD	BO	W215T30	.028
Mercedes-Benz	1968-69	230/8	Ger.	6-139.9	153624	.003C	.007C	TDC[20]	.014	38	VD	BO	W215T30	.028
Mercedes-Benz	1966-68	250, 250 S, 250 SE, 250 SL	Ger.	6-152.4	153624	.003C	.007C	4B[23]	.014	38	VD	BO	W215T30	.028[24]
Mercedes-Benz	1969-70	250/8	Ger.	6-152.4	153624	.003C	.007C	TDC[25]	.014	38	VD	BO	W215T30	.028

ABBREVIATIONS – FOOTNOTES:

A – After Top Center
AC – AC Spark Plugs
AU – Autolite Spark Plugs
B – Before Top Center
BO – Bosch Spark Plugs
C – Cold Engine

CH – Champion Spark Plugs
CP – Crankshaft Pulley
FP – Fan Pulley
FW – Flywheel
H – Hot Engine
HY – Hydraulic Lifters
NA – Not Applicable
NGK – NGK Spark Plugs

TDC – Top Dead Center
VD – Vibration Damper
1 – Static Method
2 – Auto. Trans. - 8A@950
3 – Auto. Trans. - 5B
4 – Auto. Trans., GT - 3B
5 – 1971-72 - 12B@600
6 – 1971-72 - N-9Y

7 – 1971 - TDC
8 – Auto. Trans. - 10B
9 – @2000
10 – DV Model - 121.1
11 – DV Model - 12B@2000
12 – 1972 - FP
13 – 1972 - 7A@700
14 – Auto. Trans. - TDC@600

FOREIGN MAKE	Year	Model	Nationality	No. of Cylinders and Piston Displacement	Firing Order	Valve Tappet Clearance Intake (in.)	Exhaust (in.)	Breaker Timing (deg.)	Ignition Breaker Gap (in.)	Dwell (deg.)	Timing Mark Location	Spark Plugs Make	Model	Gap (in.)
Mercedes-Benz	1971–72	250/8	Ger.	6–169.5	153624	.003C	.008C	4A[20]	.014	36	VD	BO	W215T30[26]	.028
Mercedes-Benz	1968–69	280 S/8, – SE/8, – SL/8	Ger.	6–169.5	153624	.003C	.007C	4A	.014	36	VD	BO	W215T30	.028
Mercedes-Benz	1970–71	280 S/8, – SE/8, – SL/8	Ger.	6–169.5	153624	.003C	.008C	8A	.014	36	VD	BO	W215T30	.024
Mercedes-Benz	1971	280 SE 3.5, 280 SEL 3.5	Ger.	8–213.5	15486372	.003C	.008C	6A	.016	33	VD	BO	W175T30	.024
Mercedes-Benz	1972	280 SE 4.5, 280 SEL 4.5	Ger.	8–276	15486372	.003C	.008C	5A[20]	.016	32	VD	BO	W175T30	.024
Mercedes-Benz	1972	350 SEL 4.5, 350 SEL	Ger.	8–276	15486372	.003C	.008C	5A[20]	.016	32	VD	BO	W175T30	.024
Mercedes-Benz	1972	600	Ger.	8–386.3	15486372	.003C	.008C	5A	.016	32	VD	BO	W175T30	.024
Opel	1968–70	Kadett	Ger.	4–66	1342	.006H	.010H	10A	.018	50	CP	AC	43FFS	.030
Opel	1968	Rallye Kadett	Ger.	4–91	1342	.012H	.012H	TDC	.018	50	FW	AC	44XLD	.030
Opel	1969–70	Rallye Kadett, GT	Ger.	4–66	1342	.006H	.010H	10A	.018	50	CP	AC	43FFS	.030
Opel	1969–70	GT 1-9	Ger.	4–115.8	1342	.012H	.012H	TDC	.018	50	FW	AC	42FS	.030
Opel	1971	1.1R US	Ger.	4–66	1342	HY	HY	TDC	.018	50	CP	AC	42FS	.030
Opel	1971–72	1.9 US, GT, 1900, Rallye	Ger.	4–115.8	1342	HY	HY	TDC	.018	50	FW	AC	42FS	.030
Peugeot	1969–70	504	Fre.	4–110	1342	.006C	.010C	TDC	.020	57	FW	CH	N-9Y	.025
Peugeot	1971–72	304	Fre.	4–78.6	1342	.004C	.010C	5A	.016	60	CP	CH	N-7Y	.024
Peugeot	1971	504	Fre.	4–120.3	1342	.004C	.010C	TDC	.016	60	CP	CH	N-7Y	.024
Peugeot	1972	504	Fre.	4–120.3	1342	.004C	.010C	5A	.016	60	CP	CH	N-7Y	.024
Plymouth	1971–72	Cricket	Eng.	4–91.4	1342	.008	.016	30B[27]	.015	62	CP	CH	N-9Y	.025
Porsche	1966–69	911	Ger.	6–121.5	162435	.004C	.004C	TDC	.016	38	CP	BO	W230T30	.020
Porsche	1966–69	912	Ger.	4–102.5	1432	.004C	.006C	3B	.016	50	CP	BO	W200T35	.028
Porsche	1970	911T	Ger.	6–135	162435	.004C	.004C	TDC	.016	38	CP	BO	W230T30	.020
Porsche	1970	914	Ger.	4–102.5	1432	.004C	.006C	3B	.016	50	CP	BO	W200T35	.028
Porsche	1971	911T	Ger.	6–121.5	162435	.004C	.004C	TDC	.016	38	CP	BO	W230T30	.020
Porsche	1971	914	Ger.	4–102.5	1432	.004C	.004C	27B[28]	.016	50	CP	BO	W175T2	.028
Porsche	1972	911T, E, S	Ger.	6–142.8	162435	.004C	.004C	5A[29]	.014	38	CP	BO	W265P21[30]	.028
Porsche	1972	914	Ger.	4–102.5	1432	.004C	.004C	27B[28]	.016	50	CP	BO	W175T2	.028
Renault	1968–70	R10	Fre.	4–67.6	1342	.006C	.008C	TDC[31]	.018	56	CP	CH	L-88Y[32]	.024
Renault	1971	R10	Fre.	4–67.6	1342	.006C	.008C	3A	.018	56	CP	CH	L-88Y	.032
Renault	1971–72	R12	Fre.	4–78.6[33]	1342	.008C	.010C	TDC[34]	.018	57	FW	CH	N-5	.027
Renault	1969–72	R16	Fre.	4–95.5	1342	.008C	.010C	TDC[35]	.018	57	FW	CH	N-5	.027
Rolls Royce	1967–70	Silver Shadow	Eng.	8–381	15486372	HY	HY	TDC	.014	34	VD	CH	N-14Y	.024
Rolls Royce	1971–72	Silver Shadow	Eng.	8–412	15486372	HY	HY	TDC	.015	27	VD	CH	N-14Y	.025
Rover	1967–72	2000 SC	Eng.	4–121	1342	.010C	.015C	4B	.015	52	FW	CH	N-9Y	.025
Rover	1967–72	2000 TC	Eng.	4–121	1342	.010C	.015C	6B	.015	52	FW	CH	N-6Y[36]	.025
Saab	1969–70	95/96, Sonnet II	Swe.	V4–91.4	1342	.014H	.016H	6B[37]	.016	50	FP	BO	W200T30	.026
Saab	1971–72	95/96, Sonnet III	Swe.	V4–104	1342	.014H	.016H	3B[37]	.016	50	FP	BO	W145T30	.026
Saab	1969–71	99	Swe.	4–104.2	1342	.009	.017	9B[38]	.018	40[39]	FW	BO	W175T30	.026
Saab	1971–72	99, 99E	Swe.	4–113.1	1342	.009	.017	9B[38]	.018	40[39]	FW	BO	W175T30	.026
Simca	1969–71	1204	Fre.	4–73.5	1342	.012C	.014C	TDC[40]	.020	56	CP	CH	N-6Y	.024
Subaru	1970–71	A32, Phase 2	Jap.	4–66.4	1324	.010C	.011C	TDC	.019	53	FW	NGK	BP-6ES	.030
Subaru	1971–72	"G"	Jap.	4–77.3	1324	.011C	.013C	TDC[41]	.019	53	FW	NGK	BP-6ES	.030
Sunbeam	1968–72	Alpine, Rapier	Eng.	4–105	1342	.012H	.014H	8B	.015	60	CP	CH	N-9Y	.025
Toyota	1968–71	Corona	Jap.	4–113.4	1342	.008H	.014H	TDC[42]	.018	52	CP	NGK	BP-6ES	.032
Toyota	1972	Corona	Jap.	4–120	1342	.008H	.014H	7B	.018	52	CP	NGK	BP-6ES	.030
Toyota	1970–72	Corolla 1200	Jap.	4–71.2	1342	.008H	.012H	5A[43]	.018	52	CP	NGK	BP-6ES	.030
Toyota	1971–72	Corolla 1600	Jap.	4–96.9	1342	.008H	.013H	5B	.018	52	CP	NGK	BP-6ES	.030
Toyota	1972	Crown	Jap.	6–156.4	153624	.007H	.010H	5B	.018	41	CP	NGK	BP-6ES	.030
Triumph	1968–72	GT6	Eng.	6–122	153624	.010C	.010C	4A	.015	39	VD	CH	N-12Y	.025
Triumph	1968–72	TR6	Eng.	6–152	153624	.010C	.010C	4A	.015	35	VD	CH	N-12Y	.025
Volkswagen	1961–65	1200	Ger.	4–72.74	1432	.008C	.012C	10B	.016	42	CP	BO	W175T1	.026
Volkswagen	1966	1300	Ger.	4–78.42	1432	.004C[43]	.004C[43]	7.5B	.016	48	CP	BO	W175T1	.026
Volkswagen	1967	Sedan	Ger.	4–91.1	1432	.004C	.004C	7.5B	.016	50	CP	BO	W175T1	.028
Volkswagen	1968–69	Sedan	Ger.	4–91.1	1432	.004C	.004C	TDC	.016	50	CP	BO	W145T1	.028
Volkswagen	1970	Deluxe Sedan	Ger.	4–96.6	1432	.004C	.004C	TDC	.016	50	CP	BO	W145T1	.028
Volkswagen	1966	Squareback, Fastback	Ger.	4–96.6	1432	.004C	.004C	10B	.016	53	CP	BO	W145T1	.026
Volkswagen	1967	Squareback, Fastback	Ger.	4–96.6	1432	.004C	.004C	7.5B	.016	53	CP	BO	W145T1	.028
Volkswagen	1968–70	Squareback, Fastback	Ger.	4–96.6	1432	.004C	.004C	TDC	.016	50	CP	BO	W145T1	.028
Volkswagen	1971–72	Squareback, Type 3	Ger.	4–96.6	1432	.004C	.004C	TDC	.016	50	CP	BO	W145T1	.028
Volkswagen	19/1–72	Sedan 111, Sedan 113	Ger.	4–96.6	1432	.006C	.006C	5A[45]	.016	50	CP	BO	W145T1	.028
Volkswagen	1971–72	411 – Type 4	Ger.	4–102.5	1432	.006C	.006C	27B[28]	.016	50	FP	BO	W175T2	.028
Volvo	1969–72	B20B	Swe.	4–121	1342	.021C	.021C	10B	.016	62	CP	BO	W200T35	.030
Volvo	1970–71	B20E	Swe.	4–121	1342	.017C	.017C	10B	.016	62	CP	BO	W225T35	.030
Volvo	1972	B20F	Swe.	4–121	1342	.017C	.017C	10B	.016	62	CP	BO	W200T35	.030
Volvo	1969–72	B30A	Swe.	6–181.6	153624	.021C	.021C	10B	.016	40	CP	BO	W200T35	.030
Volvo	1972	B30F	Swe.	6–181.6	153624	.021C	.021C	10B	.016	40	CP	BO	W200T35	.030

15 – 1972 – TDC
16 – @1000
17 – @1700
18 – 2-Rotor Rotary Engine
19 – Trailing Distributor – 10A
20 – 1968–69 – @850, 1970–72 – @800 with Vacuum Connected
21 – 230SL – 4B
22 – 230SL – 36

23 – SE and SL – 3B
24 – SE and SL – .024
25 – 1970 – 4A
26 – 1972 – W175T30@.024
27 – @3000
28 – @3500
29 – @950
30 – 911T – W235P21

31 – 1968 – 6A
32 – 1968 – L-87Y@.032
33 – Auto. Trans. – 67.6
34 – Auto. Trans. – 6B
35 – Auto. Trans., 1970 – 6B
36 – 1971–72 – N-7Y
37 – @900 with Vacuum Disconnected
38 – Fuel Inj. – 5B@800

39 – Fuel Inj. – 50
40 – Auto. Trans. – 4B
41 – 1972 – 8B@750
42 – 1971 – 10B@650
43 – 1972 – 5B@650
44 – Untagged Eng. – Intake .008, Exhaust .012
45 – @800 with Vacuum Connected

Above. Mark Donohue, winner of the 1972 Indianapolis 500, averaged a record of 162.962 miles per hour in his Sunoco McLaren car. Below. Al Unser, winner of both the 1970 and 1971 Indianapolis 500, pictured with his 1971 car, the Johnny Lightning Special, which averaged 157.735 miles per hour.

INDIANAPOLIS RACE RESULTS

YEAR	DRIVER	CAR	TIME	MPH	
1911	Ray Harroun	Marmon Wasp	6:42:08	74.59	
1912	Joe Dawson	National	6:21:06	78.72	
1913	Jules Goux	Peugeot	6:35:05:00	75.933	
1914	Rene Thomas	Delage	6:03:45	82.47	
1915	Ralph DePalma	Mercedes	5:33:55.51	89.84	
1916	Dario Resta	Peugeot	3:34:17	84.00	(300 mi.)
1919	Howard Wilcox	Peugeot	5:40:42.87	88.05	
1920	Gaston Chevrolet	Monroe	5:38:32.00	88.62	
1921	Tommy Milton	Frontenac	5:34:44.65	89.62	
1922	James A. Murphy	Murphy Special	5:17:30.79	94.48	
1923	Tommy Milton	H. C. S. Special	5:29:50.17	90.95	
1924	L. L. Corum and Joe Boyer	Duesenberg Special	5:05:23.51	98.23	
1925	Peter DePaolo	Duesenberg Special	4:56:39.46	101.13	
1926	Frank Lockhart	Miller Special	4:10:14.95	95.904	(400 mi.) *
1927	George Souders	Duesenberg	5:07:33.08	97.545	
1928	Louis Meyer	Miller Special	5:01:33.75	99.482	
1929	Ray Keech	Simplex Piston Ring	5:07:25.42	97.585	
1930	Billy Arnold	Miller Hartz Special	4:58:39.72	100.448	
1931	L. Schneider	Bowes Seal Fast Spl.	5:10:27.93	96.629	
1932	Fred Frame	Miller Hartz Special	4:48:03.79	104.144	
1933	Louis Meyer	Tydol Special	4:48:00.75	104.162	
1934	Wm. Cummings	Boyle Products Spl.	4:46:05.20	104.863	
1935	Kelly Petillo	Gilmore Speedway Spl.	4:42:22.71	106.240	
1936	Louis Meyer	Ring Free Special	4:35:03.39	109.069	
1937	Wilbur Shaw	Shaw Gilmore Spl.	4:24:07.80	113.580	
1938	Floyd Roberts	Burd Piston Ring Spl.	4:15:58.40	117.200	
1939	Wilbur Shaw	Boyle Special	4:20:47.39	115.035	
1940	Wilbur Shaw	Boyle Special	4:22:31.17	114.277	
1941	Mauri Rose and Floyd Davis	Noc-Out Hose Clamp Sp.	4:20:36.24	115.117	
1946	George Robson	Thorne Engineer. Spl.	4:21:26.70	114.820	
1947	Mauri Rose	Blue Crown Spk. Plg. Sp.	4:17:52.17	116.338	
1948	Mauri Rose	Blue Crown Spk. Plg. Sp.	4:10:23.33	119.814	
1949	Bill Holland	Blue Crown Spk. Plg. Sp.	4:07:15.97	121.327	
1950	Johnny Parsons	Kurtis-Kraft	2:46:55.97	124.002	(345 mi.) *
1951	Lee Wallard	Belanger Special	3:57:38.05	126.244	
1952	Troy Ruttman	Agajanian Special	3:52:41.88	128.922	
1953	Bill Vukovich	Fuel Injection Spl.	3:53:01.69	128.740	
1954	Bill Vukovich	Fuel Injection Spl.	3:49:17.27	130.840	
1955	Bob Sweikert	John Zink Special	3:53:59.13	128.209	
1956	Pat Flaherty	John Zink Special	3:53:28.84	128.490	
1957	Sam Hanks	Belond Exhaust Spl.	3:41:14.25	135.601	
1958	Jimmy Bryan	Belond AP Special	3:44:13.80	133.791	
1959	Rodger Ward	Leader Card 500 Rdstr.	3:40:49.20	135.857	
1960	Jim Rathmann	Ken-Paul Special	3:36:11.36	138.767	
1961	A. J. Foyt	Bowes Seal Fast Spl.	3:35:37.49	139.130	
1962	Roger Ward	Leader Card Spl.	3:33:50.38	140.292	
1963	Parnelli Jones	Agajanian-Williard Battery Special	3:29:35.40	143.137	
1964	A. J. Foyt	Sheraton Thompson Sp.	3:23:35.83	147.350	
1965	Jim Clark	Lotus Ford	3:19:05.34	150.686	
1966	Graham Hill	American Red Ball Sp.	3:27:52.53	144.317	
1967	A. J. Foyt	Coyote Ford	3:18:04.02	151.207	
1968	Bobby Unser	Eagle Offenhauser	3:16:20.30	152.882	
1969	Mario Andretti	Brawner-McGee Hawk	3:11:14.71	156.867	
1970	Al Unser	Johnny Lightning Special	3:12:37.04	155.749	
1971	Al Unser	Johnny Lightning Special	3:10:11.56	157.735	
1972	Mark Donohue	Sunoco McLaren	3:04:05.54	162.962	

* Race called because of rain.

ACKNOWLEDGMENTS

In the preparation of this encyclopedia, almost every manufacturer in the automotive industry was consulted. Without exception they extended to us the utmost in cooperation. Information, records and illustrations have been available to us. As a result, we have herein a complete library of automotive service knowledge.

A list of every source of such assistance would result in a directory of the industry. The editors and publishers therefore wish to thank the industry and the individual companies for their valued assistance. It is our hope that this encyclopedia will be helpful to the industry as a whole as well as students, teachers and automotive enthusiasts.

Some of the manufacturers who have been particularly cooperative are as follows:

AC Spark Plug Div., G.M.C.; AP Parts Corp.; Abex Corp.; Airtex Automotive; Allen Testproducts; American Bosch-Ambac Industries, Inc.; American Hammered Div., Sealed Power Corp.; American Motors Corp.; AMMCO Tools, Inc.; The Anderson Co.; Autolite-Ford Parts Div., Ford Marketing Corp.; John Bean Div., FMC Corp.; Bear Mfg. Corp.; Bee-Line Co.; Behr-Manning Corp.; Belden Corp.; The Bendix Corp.; Binks Mfg. Co.; Blackhawk Mfg. Co.; Bonney Hand Tool Div., Utica Tool Co., Inc.; Borg-Warner Corp.; Robert Bosch Corp.; Briggs and Stratton Corp.; Buda Co.; Buick Motor Div., G.M.C.; Cadillac Motor Car Div., G.M.C.; Carborundum Co.; Carter Carburetor Div., ACF Industries, Inc.; Central Tool Co., Inc.; Champion Spark Plug Co.; Chevrolet Motor Div., G.M.C.; Chicago Pneumatic Tool Co.; Chrysler-Plymouth Div., Chrysler Motors Corp.; Clayton Mfg. Co.; Columbus Parts, A Questor Co.; Cummins Engine Co.; Curtiss-Wright Corp., Dana Corp.; Deere and Co.; Delco Products Div., G.M.C.; Delco-Remy Div., G.M.C.; Deluxe Products Div., Walker Mfg. Co.; Detroit Diesel Div., G.M.C.; The Devilbiss Co.; Ditzler Automotive Finishes, PPG Industries, Inc.; Dodge Div., Chrysler Motors Corp.; Dow Chemical U.S.A.; Draf Tool Co., Inc.; E. I. du Pont de Nemours and Co.; ESB Brands, Inc.; Eaton Corp.; E. Edelmann and Co.; Electric Autopulse Div., Walbro Corp.; Evinrude Motors; Federal-Mogul Corp.; Ford Motor Co.; Fox Products Co.; Fram Corp.; Gabriel Div., Maremont Corp.; The Gates Rubber Co.; General Electric Co.; Globe Hoist; The Goodyear Tire and Rubber Co.; Grant Div., Royal Industries; Grizzly Div., Maremont Corp.; Grey-Rock Div., Raybestos-Manhattan, Inc.; Gumout Div., Pennsylvania Refining Co.; Harley Davidson; Hastings Mfg. Co.; Hein-Werner Corp.; Heli-Coil Corp.; Holley Carburetor; Hunter Engineering Co.; Imperial-Eastman Corp.; International Harvester Corp.; Johns-Manville Sales Corp.; Kelsey-Hayes Co.; King Electronics Co.; Kwik-Way; Leece Neville Co.; Lempco Industries Inc.; Lincoln Electric Co.; Lincoln St. Louis; Lincoln-Mercury Div., Ford Motor Co.; Linde Air Products; Lisle Corp.; Lucas Electric Services, Inc.; Mallory Electric Corp.; Marquette Mfg. Co.; McCord Replacement Products Div., McCord Corp.; McCulloch Motors Corp.; Milwaukee Electric Tool Corp.; Monroe Auto Equipment Co.; Moog Industries, Inc.; Mystik Adhesive Products; Nicholson File Co.; C. E. Niehoff and Co.; Oldsmobile Div., G.M.C.; Perfect Circle Products; Pontiac Motor Div., G.M.C.; H. K. Porter, Inc.; Pratt and Whitney Aircraft; Purolator, Inc.; Ramsey Corp.; Raybestos Div., Raybestos-Manhattan, Inc.; Reo Motors Inc.; Rochester Products Div., G.M.C.; Russell Mfg. Co.; Sealed Power Corp.; Sherwin-Williams Co.; Simplex Piston Ring Mfg. Co.; Sioux Tools; Skil Corp.; A. O. Smith Co.; Snap-on Tools Corp.; Society of Automotive Engineers; L. S. Starrett Mfg. Co.; Stewart-Warner Corp.; Sun Electric Corp.; Sunnen Products Co.; TRW Replacement Products Div., TRW Inc.; 3 M Co.; Trico Products Corp.; Union Carbide Corp.; United Motors Service Div., G.M.C.; Van Norman Machine Co.; Wagner Electric Corp.; Walker Mfg. Co.; Warner Electric Brake Mfg. Co.; Waukesha Motor Co.; Weaver Div., Dura Corp.; Westinghouse Air Brake Co.; Westinghouse Electric Corp.; Winona Tool Mfg. Co.; Wix Corp.; Zenith Carburetor Div., Bendix Corp.

We also are indebted to our friends who represent manufacturers of imported cars for fine cooperation in furnishing technical information and specifications. We hope that their efforts and ours will help bring about a better understanding of their products in the U. S. A. with resultant better service and improved customer satisfaction.

The Associated Octel Co., LTD.; British Leyland Motors, Inc.; Capri Service, Lincoln-Mercury Div., Ford Marketing Corp.; Citroen Cars Corp.; Fiat-Roosevelt Motors, Inc.; Mazda Motors of Texas, Inc.; Mercedes-Benz of North America, Inc.; Nissan Motor Corp. in U.S.A.; Opel, Buick Motor Div., G.M.C.; Peugeot, Inc.; Porsche-Audi Div., Volkswagen of America, Inc.; Renault, Inc.; Rolls-Royce, Inc.; Saab Motors, Inc.; Subaru of America, Inc.; Toyota Motor Sales, U.S.A., Inc.; Volkswagen of America, Inc.

INDEX

Index

Index

Index

Index